Fourth Edition

Understanding Basic Statistics

with Student Solutions Manual

Charles Henry Brase
Regis University

Corrinne Pellillo Brase
Arapahoe Community College

Houghton Mifflin Company
Boston   New York

UNDERSTANDING BASIC STATISTICS: FOURTH EDITION
by Charles Henry Brase and Corrinne Pellillo Brase
Copyright © 2007 by Houghton Mifflin Company. All rights reserved.

Vice President, Publisher: Jack Shira
Sponsoring Editor: Leonid Tunik
Development Editor: Karie Mergen
Editorial Assistant: Caitlin Lynch
Senior Project Editor: Nancy Blodget
Editorial Assistants: Sean McGann, Sarah Driver
Compositin Buyer: Chuck Dutton
Art and Design Manager: Gary Crespo
Manufacturing Manager: Ben Rivera
Marketing Associate: Lisa Lawler

STUDENT SOLUTIONS MANUAL TO ACCOMPANY UNDERSTANDING BASIC STATISTICS:
FOURTH EDITION
by Charles Henry Brase and Corrinne Pellillo Brase
Copyright © 2007 by Houghton Mifflin Company. All rights reserved.

Publisher: Richard Stratton
Sponsoring Editor: Leonid Tunik
Assistant Editor: Carl Chudyk
Editorial Associate: Allison Lewis
Senior Project Editor: Nancy Blodget
Editorial Assistants: Sean McGann, Sarah Driver
Manufacturing Coordinator: Brian Pieragostini
Senior Marketing Manager: Katherine Greig
Marketing Assistant: Naveen Hariprasad

Custom Publishing Editor: Dan Luciano
Custom Publishing Production Manager: Tina Kozik
Project Coordinator: Jennifer Feltri

Cover Art: Image Archive
Cover Design: Christina Goodwin

This book contains select works from existing Houghton Mifflin Company resources and
was produced by Houghton Mifflin Custom Publishing for collegiate use. As such, those
adopting and/or contributing to this work are responsible for editorial content, accuracy,
continuity and completeness.

Printed in the United States of America.

ISBN-13: 978-0-618-77470-8
ISBN-10: 0-618-77470-X
N-06362

6 7 8 9 – CCI – 08

 Houghton Mifflin
Custom Publishing
222 Berkeley Street • Boston, MA 02116

Address all correspondence and order information to the above address.

Contents

7 Normal Curves and Sampling Distributions 246

8 Estimation 314

9 Hypothesis Testing 358

10 Inferences About Differences 414

11 Additional Topics Using Inference 468

Welcome to the exciting world of statistics! We have written this text to make statistics accessible to everyone, including those with a limited mathematics background. Statistics affects all aspects of our lives. Whether we are testing new medical devices or determining what will entertain us, applications of statistics are so numerous that, in a sense, we are limited only by our own imagination in discovering new uses for statistics.

Overview

The fourth edition of *Understanding Basic Statistics* continues to emphasize concepts of statistics. Statistical methods are carefully presented with a focus on understanding both the *suitability of the method* and the *meaning of the result*. Statistical methods and measurements are developed in the context of applications.

We have retained and expanded features that made the first three editions of the text very readable. New definition boxes highlight important terms. New procedure displays summarize steps for analyzing data. Examples, exercises, and problems touch on applications appropriate to a broad range of interests.

Technology-based components give both students and professors additional resources. The HM statSpace™ CD-ROM contains data sets (in Microsoft Excel, Minitab, SPSS, and TI-84Plus/TI-83Plus and ASCII file formats), as well as interactive tutorial exercises and quizzes for each chapter section. The web site for the text provides a wealth of material including digital lessons, a glossary, statistical tables, and links to other relevant web sites. In addition, a new component, Eduspace®, provides students with interactive lessons including audio, streaming video, animation, and computer simulations along with interactive tutorial activities. Instructional videos and DVDs covering every section of the text provide even more learning support.

Major Content Changes in the Fourth Edition

With each new edition, the authors reevaluate the scope, appropriateness, and effectiveness of the text's presentation and reflect on extensive user feedback. Revisions have been made throughout the text to clarify explanations of important concepts and to update problems.

Introduction of Hypothesis Testing Using *P*-Values

Chapter 9, Hypothesis Testing, has been reorganized. In keeping with the use of computer technology and standard practice in research, hypothesis testing is now introduced using *P*-values. The critical region method is still supported, but not given primary emphasis.

Use of Student's *t* Distribution in Confidence Intervals and Testing of Means

If the normal distribution is used in confidence intervals and testing of means, then the *population standard deviation must be known.* If the population standard deviation is not known, then under conditions described in the text, the Student's *t* distribution is used. This is the most commonly used procedure in statistical research. It is also used in statistical software packages such as Microsoft Excel, Minitab, SPSS, and TI-84Plus/TI-83Plus calculators.

Confidence Intervals and Hypothesis Tests of Difference of Means

If the normal distribution is used, then both population standard deviations must be known. When this is not the case, the Student's *t* distribution incorporates an approximation for *t*, with a commonly used conservative choice for the degrees of freedom. Satterthwaite's approximation for the degrees of freedom as used in computer software is also discussed. The pooled standard deviation is presented for appropriate applications ($\sigma_1 \approx \sigma_2$).

Organization of Other Sections and Chapters

In Chapter 2, Organizing Data, frequency distributions and histograms are now presented in Section 2.1 while other graphs such as bar graphs, circle graphs, and time-series graphs are presented in Section 2.2.

In Chapter 4, Correlation and Regression, scatter diagrams and the sample correlation coefficient are presented in Section 4.1. The equation of the least-squares line is presented in Section 4.2. In both sections, the computation formulas have been streamlined.

All inferences regarding correlation and regression are included in Section 11.4, Inferences for Correlation and Regression. This section is carefully divided into subsections so that some or all of the inferential topics may be included, depending on a particular syllabus.

The third edition's Chapter 7, Normal Distributions, and Chapter 8, Introduction to Sampling Distributions, have been combined into a single chapter, Chapter 7, Normal Curves and Sampling Distributions. Material in this new chapter has been streamlined, allowing more rapid progress through the normal distribution and sampling distributions.

Features in the Fourth Edition

Chapter and Section Lead-ins

- *Preview Questions* at the beginning of each chapter are keyed to the sections.
- *Focus Problems* at the beginning of each chapter demonstrate types of questions students can answer once they master the concepts and skills presented in the chapter.
- *Focus Points* at the beginning of each section describe the primary learning objectives of the section.

Carefully Developed Pedagogy

- *Examples* show students how to select and use appropriate procedures.
- *Guided Exercises* within the sections give students an opportunity to work with a new concept. Completely worked-out solutions appear beside each exercise to give immediate reinforcement.

- New! *Definition boxes* highlight important definitions throughout the text.
- New! *Procedure displays* summarize key strategies for carrying out statistical procedures and methods.
- *Labels* for each example or guided exercise highlight the technique, concept, or process illustrated by the example or guided exercise. In addition, labels for section and chapter problems describe the field of application and show the wide variety of subjects in which statistics is used.
- *Section and chapter problems* require the student to use all the new concepts mastered in the section or chapter. Problem sets include a variety of real-world applications with data or settings from identifiable sources. Key steps and solutions to odd-numbered problems appear at the end of the book.

- New! *Expand Your Knowledge problems* present enrichment topics for applications of probability and statistics.

- New! *Problems incorporating real-world data available on a CD-ROM or text web site* alert students to data available electronically.
- New! *Cumulative review problem sets* occur after every third chapter and include key topics from previous chapters. Answers to *all* cumulative review problems are given at the end of the book.
- *Data Highlights and Linking Concepts* provide group projects and writing projects.
- *Viewpoints* are brief essays presenting diverse situations in which statistics is used.
- *Design and photos* are appealing and enhance readability.

Technology within the Text

- *Tech Notes* within sections provide brief point-of-use instructions for the TI-84Plus and TI-83Plus calculators, Microsoft Excel, and Minitab.
- *Using Technology* sections have been revised to show the use of SPSS as well as the TI-84Plus and TI-83Plus calculators, Microsoft Excel, and Minitab.

Supplements for Students

- *Student Solutions Manual.* This manual provides solutions to the odd-numbered section and chapter exercises and to all the Cumulative Review exercises in the student textbook.
- *Technology Guide.* This guide contains information and examples for the TI-84Plus and TI-83Plus graphing calculators, Minitab software, Microsoft Excel, and SPSS software.
- *Eduspace®.* Powerful, customizable, and interactive, Eduspace, powered by Blackboard®, is Houghton Mifflin's online learning tool for instructors and students. Eduspace is a text-specific, web-based learning environment that your instructor can use to offer students a combination of practice exercises, multimedia tutorials, video explanations, online algorithmic homework, and more. Specific content is available 24 hours a day to help students succeed in the course.
- *HM statSpace™ Student Tutorial CD-ROM.* For students who prefer the portability of a CD-ROM, this tutorial provides opportunities for self-paced review

and practice with algorithmically generated exercises and step-by-step solutions. The CD-ROM also includes:

— Data sets for additional experimentation with Minitab, Microsoft Excel, SPSS, and the TI-84Plus/TI-83Plus calculators.

— Links to online resources, including additional data sets and an online graphing calculator.

- *Houghton Mifflin Instructional DVDs*. Hosted by Dana Mosely and professionally produced, these text-specific DVDs are ideal for promoting individual study and review. These comprehensive DVDs also support students in online courses and students who have missed a lecture.

- *SMARTHINKING®*. Houghton Mifflin's unique partnership with SMARTHINKING brings students real-time, online tutorial support when they need it most. This partnership offers students a range of tutorial services exclusively for students using Houghton Mifflin texts. Using state-of-the-art whiteboard technology and feedback tools, students interact and communicate with "e-structors." These specially trained tutors guide students through the learning and problem-solving process without providing answers or rewriting students' work. SMARTHINKING offers three levels of service:*

— *Live Tutorial Help* provides real-time, one-on-one instruction.

— *Questions Any Time* allows students to e-mail questions to a tutor outside of the scheduled tutorial sessions and receive a reply, usually within 24 hours.

— *Independent Study Resources* connects students around-the-clock to additional educational resources, ranging from interactive web sites to Frequently Asked Questions.

Visit **smarthinking.com** for more information.

- *Online Study Center*. Access the Online Study Center for this text by visiting **college.hmco.com/pic/braseUBS4e**. Resources include flashcards, glossary, data sets, ACE quizzes with step-by-step tutorial help, technology guide, statistical tables, frequently used formulas, digital lessons, digital art, and web links.

- *Student Version of MINITAB or SPSS*. These statistical software packages manipulate and interpret data to produce textual, graphical, and tabular results. MINITAB and/or SPSS may be packaged with the textbook. Please visit the Houghton Mifflin web site or contact your Houghton Mifflin sales representative.

Supplements for Instructors

- Online *Instructor Solutions*. This supplement provides complete solutions to all exercises in the text.

- *Eduspace®*. Powerful, customizable, and interactive, Eduspace, powered by Blackboard®, is Houghton Mifflin's online learning tool. Eduspace provides instructors with online courses and content. By pairing the widely recognized tools of Blackboard with quality, text-specific content from Houghton Mifflin Company (HMCo), Eduspace makes it easy for instructors to create all or part of a course online. Homework exercises, quizzes, tests, tutorials, and supplemental study materials all come ready-to-use. Instructors can choose to use the content as is

*Limits apply; terms and hours of SMARTHINKING service are subject to change.

or modify it, and they can even add their own content. Visit **www.eduspace.com** for more information.

- *HM ClassPrep™ with HM Testing (powered by Diploma™). HM Class Prep* offers a combination of two class-management tools including supplements and text-specific resources for the instructor. *HM Testing* (powered by *Diploma*) offers instructors a flexible and powerful tool for test generation and test management. Now supported by the Brownstone Research Group's market-leading *Diploma* software, this new version of *HM Testing* significantly improves on functionality and ease-of-use by offering all the tools needed to create, author, deliver, and customize multiple types of tests—including authoring and editing algorithmic questions. *Diploma* is currently in use at thousands of college and university campuses throughout the United States and Canada.

- *Online Teaching Center.* Access the Online Teaching Center for this text by visiting **college.hmco.com/pic/braseUBS4e.** In addition to the student resources (see previous description for Online Study Center), online *Instructor Solutions* are also available.

Alternate Routes Through the Text

Understanding Basic Statistics, Fourth Edition, is designed to be flexible. It offers the professor a choice of teaching possibilities. In most one-semester courses, it is not practical to cover all the material in depth. However, depending on the emphasis of the course, the professor may choose to cover various topics. For help in topic selection, refer to the *Table of Prerequisite Material* on page 1.

- *Linear Regression.* Chapter 4, Correlation and Regression, may be delayed until after Chapter 9. The descriptive topics of linear regression may then be followed immediately by the inferential topics of linear regression presented in Chapter 11.

- *Probability.* For courses requiring minimal probability, Section 5.1, What Is Probability? and the first part of Section 5.2, Some Probability Rules—Compound Events, will be sufficient.

Acknowledgments

It is our pleasure to acknowledge the prepublication reviewers of this text. All of their insights and comments have been very valuable to us. Reviewers of this text include:

Paul Ache, Kutztown University
Delores Anderson, Truett-McConnell College
Robert J. Astalos, Feather River College
Lynda L. Ballou, Kansas State University
Larry Bernett, Benedictine University
Kristy E. Bland, Valdosta State University
John Bray, Broward Community College
Bill Burgin, Gaston College
Toni Carroll, Siena Heights University
Pinyuen Chen, Syracuse University
Jennifer M. Dollar, Grand Rapids Community College
Larry E. Dunham, Wor-Wic Community College

Andrew Ellett, Indiana University
Mary Fine, Moberly Area Community College
Rene Garcia, Miami-Dade Community College
Larry Green, Lake Tahoe Community College
Jane Keller, Metropolitan Community College
Raja Khoury, Collin County Community College
Charles G. Laws, Cleveland State Community College
Michael R. Lloyd, Henderson State University
Beth Long, Pellissippi State Technical and Community College
Lewis Lum, University of Portland
Darcy P. Mays, Virginia Commonwealth University
Charles C. Okeke, College of Southern Nevada, Las Vegas
Peg Pankowski, Community College of Allegheny County
Michael L. Russo, Suffolk County Community College
Janel Schultz, Saint Mary's University of Minnesota
Winson Taam, Oakland University
Jennifer L. Taggart, Rockford College
William Truman, University of North Carolina at Pembroke
Jim Wienckowski, State University of New York at Buffalo
Stephen M. Wilkerson, Susquehanna University
Hongkai Zhang, East Central University
Shunpu Zhang, University of Alaska, Fairbanks

We would especially like to thank George Pasles for his careful accuracy review of this text, and Lauren Arnest for her creative illustrations that accompany the Viewpoint essays. We are especially appreciative of the excellent work by the editorial and production professionals at Houghton Mifflin. In particular, we thank Lauren Schultz, Kasey McGarrigle, Sean McGann, Sarah Driver, David George, Katie Mergen, and Nancy Blodget. Without their creative insight and attention to detail, a project of this quality and magnitude would not be possible. Finally, we acknowledge the cooperation of Minitab, Inc., SPSS, Texas Instruments, and Microsoft Excel.

Charles Henry Brase

Corrinne Pellillo Brase

Table of Prerequisite Material

Chapter	Prerequisite Sections
1 Getting Started	None
2 Organizing Data	1.1, 1.2
3 Averages and Variation	1.1, 1.2, 2.1
4 Correlation and Regression	1.1, 1.2, 3.1, 3.2
5 Elementary Probability Theory	1.1, 1.2, 2.1
6 The Binomial Probability Distribution and Related Topics	1.1, 1.2, 2.1, 3.1, 3.2, 5.1, 5.2 5.3 useful but not essential
7 Normal Curves and Sampling Distributions (omit 7.6) (include 7.6)	1.1, 1.2, 2.1, 3.1, 3.2, 5.1, 5.2, 6.1 also 6.2, 6.3
8 Estimation (omit 8.3) (include 8.3)	1.1, 1.2, 2.1, 3.1, 3.2, 5.1, 5.2, 6.1, 7.1, 7.2, 7.3, 7.4, 7.5 also 6.2, 6.3, 7.6
9 Hypothesis Testing (omit 9.3) (include 9.3)	1.1, 1.2, 2.1, 3.1, 3.2, 5.1, 5.2, 6.1, 7.1, 7.2, 7.3, 7.4, 7.5 also 6.2, 6.3, 7.6
10 Inferences About Differences (omit 10.3) (include 10.3)	1.1, 1.2, 2.1, 3.1, 3.2, 5.1, 5.2, 6.1, 7.1, 7.2, 7.3, 7.4, 7.5, 8.1, 8.2, 9.1, 9.2 also 6.2, 6.3, 7.6, 9.3
11 Additional Topics Using Inference (Part I: 11.1, 11.2, 11.3) (Part II: 11.4)	1.1, 1.2, 2.1, 3.1, 3.2, 5.1, 5.2, 6.1, 7.1, 7.2, 7.3, 7.4, 7.5, 9.1 Chapter 4, 8.1, 8.2 also

1

Getting Started

To guess is cheap,
To guess wrongly is expensive.

Tell me, I'll forget.
Show me, I may remember.
But involve me and I'll understand.

—Old Chinese Proverbs

Most of the important decisions in life involve incomplete information. Such decisions often involve so many complicated factors that a complete analysis is not practical or even possible. We are often forced into the position of making a guess based on limited information. However, as the first proverb implies, a blind guess is not the best solution. Statistical methods, such as those you will learn in this book, can help you make the best "educated guess."

The authors of this book want you to understand and enjoy statistics. The reading material will *tell you* about the subject. The examples will *show you* how it works. To understand, however, the second proverb says you must *get involved*. Guided exercises, calculator and computer applications, section and chapter problems, and writing exercises are all designed to get you involved in the subject. As you grow in your understanding of statistics, we believe you will enjoy learning a subject that has a world full of interesting applications.

Dragon Gate, Chinatown, San Francisco

Dragon Gate is one of the many landmarks in San Francisco that exemplifies the city's ethnic diversity.

PREVIEW QUESTIONS

◇ Why is statistics important?   (SECTION 1.1)

◇ What is the nature of data?   (SECTION 1.1)

◇ How can you draw a random sample?   (SECTION 1.2)

◇ What are other sampling techniques?   (SECTION 1.2)

◇ How can you design ways to collect data?   (SECTION 1.3)

 For on-line student resources, visit **math.college.hmco.com/students** and follow the Statistics links to the Brase/Brase, *Understanding Basic Statistics,* 4th edition web site.

Where Have All the Fireflies Gone?

A feature article in *The Wall Street Journal* discusses the disappearance of fireflies. In the article, Professor Sara Lewis of Tufts University and other scholars express concern about the decline in the worldwide population of fireflies.

There are a number of possible explanations for the decline, including habitat reduction of woodlands, wetlands, and open fields; pesticides; and pollution. Artificial nighttime lighting might interfere with the Morse-code-like mating ritual of the fireflies. Some chemical companies pay a bounty for fireflies because the insects contain two rare chemicals used in medical research and electronic detection systems used in spacecraft.

What does any of this have to do with statistics?

The truth, at this time, is that no one really knows (a) how much the world firefly population has declined or (b) how to explain the decline. The population of all fireflies is simply too large to study in its entirety.

In any study of fireflies, we must rely on incomplete information from samples. Furthermore, from these samples we must draw realistic conclusions that have statistical integrity. This is the kind of work that uses statistical methods to determine ways to collect, analyze, and investigate data.

Adapted from Ohio State University Firefly Files logo

3

Suppose you are conducting a study to compare firefly populations exposed to normal daylight/darkness conditions with firefly populations exposed to continuous light (24 hours a day). You set up two firefly colonies in a laboratory environment. The two colonies are identical except that one colony is exposed to normal daylight/darkness conditions and the other is exposed to continuous light. Each colony is populated with the same number of mature fireflies. After 72 hours, you count the number of living fireflies in each colony.

After completing this chapter, you will be able to answer the following questions.

(a) Is this an experiment or an observation study? Explain.
(b) Is there a control group? Is there a treatment group?
(c) What is the variable in this study?
(d) What is the level of measurement (nominal, interval, ordinal, or ratio) of the variable?

(See Problem 9 of the Chapter 1 Review Problems.)

1.1
What Is Statistics?

FOCUS POINTS

✓ Identify variables in a statistical study.
✓ Distinguish between quantitative and qualitative variables.
✓ Identify populations and samples.
✓ Determine the level of measurement.
✓ Compare descriptive and inferential statistics.

Introduction

Decision making is an important aspect of our lives. We make decisions based on the information we have, our attitudes, and our values. Statistical methods help us examine information. Moreover, statistics can be used for making decisions when we are faced with uncertainties. For instance, if we wish to estimate the proportion of people who will have a severe reaction to a flu shot without giving the shot to everyone who wants it, statistics provides appropriate methods. Statistical methods enable us to look at information from a small collection of people or items and make inferences about a larger collection of people or items.

Procedures for analyzing data, together with rules of inference, are central topics in the study of statistics.

Statistics

> **Statistics** is the study of how to collect, organize, analyze, and interpret numerical information from data.

The statistical procedures you will learn in this book should supplement your built-in system of inference—that is, the results from statistical procedures and good sense should dovetail. Of course, statistical methods themselves have no power to work miracles. These methods can help us make some decisions, but not all conceivable decisions. Remember, a properly applied statistical procedure is no more accurate than the data, or facts, on which it is based. Finally, statistical results should be interpreted by one who understands not only the methods, but also the subject matter to which they have been applied.

The general prerequisite for statistical decision making is the gathering of data. First, we need to identify the individuals or objects to be included in the study and the characteristics or features of the individuals that are of interest.

Individuals
Variable

> **Individuals** are the people or objects included in the study.
> A **variable** is the characteristic of the individual to be measured or observed.

For instance, if we want to do a study about the people who have climbed Mt. Everest, then the individuals in the study are all people who have actually made it to the summit. One variable might be the height of such individuals. Other variables might be age, weight, gender, nationality, income, and so on. Regardless of the variables we use, we would not include measurements or observations from people who have not climbed the mountain.

The variables in a study may be *quantitative* or *qualitative* in nature.

Quantitative variable
Qualitative variable

> A **quantitative variable** has a value or numerical measurement for which operations such as addition or averaging make sense. A **qualitative variable** describes an individual by placing the individual into a category or group, such as male or female.

For the Mt. Everest climbers, variables such as height, weight, age, or income are *quantitative* variables. *Qualitative variables* involve nonnumerical observations such as gender or nationality. Sometimes qualitative variables are referred to as *categorical*.

Another important issue regarding data is their source. Do the data comprise information from *all* individuals of interest, or from just *some* of the individuals?

Population data
Sample data

> In **population data,** the data are from *every* individual of interest.
> In **sample data,** the data are from *only some* of the individuals of interest.

For instance, if we have data from *all* the individuals who have climbed Mt. Everest, then we have population data. On the other hand, if our data come from just some of the climbers, we have sample data.

EXAMPLE 1
Using basic terminology

The Hawaii Department of Tropical Agriculture is conducting a study of ready-to-harvest pineapples in an experimental field.

(a) The pineapples are the *objects* (individuals) of the study. If the researchers are interested in the individual weights of pineapples in the field, then the *variable* consists of weights. At this point, it is important to specify units of measurement

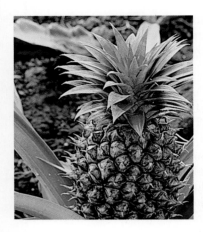

and degree of accuracy of measurement. The weights could be to the nearest ounce or gram. Weight is a *quantitative* variable because it is a numerical measure. If weights of *all* the ready-to-harvest pineapples in the field are included in the data, then we have a *population*.

(b) Suppose the researchers also want data on taste. A panel of tasters rates the pineapples according to the categories poor, acceptable, and good. Only some of the pineapples are included in the taste test. In this case, the *variable* is taste. This is a *qualitative* or *categorical* variable. Because only some of the pineapples in the field are included in the study, we have a *sample*.   ◇

Throughout this text, you will encounter *guided exercises* embedded in the reading material. These exercises are included to give you an opportunity to work immediately with new ideas. The questions guide you through appropriate analysis. Cover the answers on the right side (an index card will fit this purpose). After you have thought about or written down *your own response*, check the answers. If there are several parts to an exercise, check each part before you continue. You should be able to answer most of these exercise questions, but don't skip them—they are important.

GUIDED EXERCISE **1**

Using basic terminology

Television station QUE wants to know the proportion of TV owners in Virginia who watch the station's new program at least once a week. The station asked a group of 1000 TV owners in Virginia if they watch the program at least once a week.

(a) Identify the individuals of the study and the variable.

⟹ The individuals are the 1000 TV owners surveyed. The variable is the response does, or does not, watch the new program at least once a week.

(b) Do the data comprise a sample? If so, what is the underlying population?

⟹ The data comprise a sample of the population of responses from all TV owners in Virginia.

(c) Is the variable qualitative or quantitative?

⟹ Qualitative—the categories are the two possible responses, does or does not watch the program.

(d) Identify a quantitative variable that might be of interest.

⟹ Age or income might be of interest.

Levels of Measurement: Nominal, Ordinal, Interval, Ratio

We have categorized data as either qualitative or quantitative. Another way to classify data is according to one of the four *levels of measurement*. These levels indicate the type of arithmetic that is appropriate for the data, such as ordering, taking differences, or taking ratios.

Nominal level

Ordinal level

Interval level

Ratio level

> **Levels of measurement**
>
> The **nominal level of measurement** applies to data that consist of names, labels, or categories. There are no implied criteria by which the data can be ordered from smallest to largest.
>
> The **ordinal level of measurement** applies to data that can be arranged in order. However, differences between data values either cannot be determined or are meaningless.
>
> The **interval level of measurement** applies to data that can be arranged in order. In addition, differences between data values are meaningful.
>
> The **ratio level of measurement** applies to data that can be arranged in order. In addition, both differences between data values and ratios of data values are meaningful. Data at the ratio level have a true zero.

EXAMPLE 2

Levels of Measurement

Identify the type of data.

(a) Taos, Acoma, Zuni, and Cochiti are the names of four Native American pueblos from the population of names of all Native American pueblos in Arizona and New Mexico.

SOLUTION: These data are at the *nominal* level. Notice that these data values are simply names. By looking at the name alone, we cannot determine if one name is "greater than or less than" another. Any ordering of the names would be numerically meaningless.

(b) In a high school graduating class of 319 students, Jim ranked 25th, June ranked 19th, Walter ranked 10th, and Julia ranked 4th, where 1 is the highest rank.

SOLUTION: These data are at the *ordinal* level. Ordering the data clearly makes sense. Walter ranked higher than June. Jim had the lowest rank, and Julia the highest. However, numerical differences in ranks do not have meaning. The difference between June's and Jim's rank is 6, and this is the same difference that exists between Walter's and Julia's rank. However, this difference doesn't really mean anything significant. For instance, if you looked at grade point average, Walter and Julia may have had a large gap between their grade point averages, whereas June and Jim may have had closer grade point averages. In any ranking system, it is only the relative standing that matters. Differences between ranks are meaningless.

(c) Body temperatures (in degrees Celsius) of trout in the Yellowstone River.

SOLUTION: These data are at the *interval* level. We can certainly order the data, and we can compute meaningful differences. However, for Celsius-scale temperatures, there is not an inherent starting point. The value 0°C may seem to be a starting point, but this value does not indicate the state of "no heat." Furthermore, it is not correct to say 20°C is twice as hot as 10°C.

(d) Length of trout swimming in the Yellowstone River.

SOLUTION: These data are at the *ratio* level. An 18-inch trout is three times as long as a 6-inch trout. Observe that we can divide 6 into 18 to determine a meaningful *ratio* of trout lengths.   ◇

In summary, there are four levels of measurement. The nominal is considered the lowest, and in ascending order we have the ordinal, interval, and ratio levels. In general, calculations based on a particular level of measurement may not be appropriate for a lower level.

PROCEDURE

How to determine the level of measurement

The levels of measurement, listed from lowest to highest, are nominal, ordinal, interval, and ratio. To determine the level of measurement of data, state the *highest level* that can be justified for the entire collection of data. Consider which calculations are suitable for the data.

Level of Measurement	Suitable Calculation
Nominal	We can put the data into categories.
Ordinal	We can order the data from smallest to largest or "worst" to "best." Each data value can be *compared* with another data value.
Interval	We can order the data and also take the differences between data values. At this level, it makes sense to compare the differences between data values. For instance, we can say that one data value is 5 more than or 12 less than another data value.
Ratio	We can order the data, take differences, and also find the ratio between data values. For instance, it makes sense to say that one data value is twice as large as another.

GUIDED EXERCISE 2

Levels of measurement

The following describes different data associated with a state senator. For each data entry, indicate the corresponding *level of measurement*.

(a) The senator's name is Sam Wilson.

⟹ Nominal level

(b) The senator is 58 years old.

⟹ Ratio level. Notice that age has a meaningful zero. It makes sense to give age ratios. For instance, Sam is twice as old as someone who is 29.

(c) The years in which the senator was elected to the Senate are 1992, 1998, and 2004.

⟹ Interval level. Dates can be ordered, and the difference between dates has meaning. For instance, 2004 is six years later than the year 1998. However, ratios do not make sense. The year 2000 is not twice as large as the year 1000. In addition, the year 0 does not mean "no time."

Continued

GUIDED EXERCISE 2 continued

(d) The senator's total taxable income last year was $878,314.

⟹ Ratio level. It makes sense to say that the senator's income is 10 times that of someone earning $87,831.40.

(e) The senator surveyed his constituents regarding his proposed water protection bill. The choices for response were strong support, support, neutral, against, or strongly against.

⟹ Ordinal level. The choices can be ordered, but there is no meaningful numerical difference between two choices.

(f) The senator's marital status is "married."

⟹ Nominal level

(g) A leading news magazine claims the senator is ranked seventh for his voting record on bills regarding public education.

⟹ Ordinal level. Ranks can be ordered, but differences between ranks may vary in their meaning.

Looking Ahead

The purpose of collecting and analyzing data is to obtain information. Statistical methods provide us tools to obtain information from data. These methods break into two branches.

Descriptive statistics

Inferential statistics

> **Descriptive statistics** involves methods of organizing, picturing, and summarizing information from samples or populations.
> **Inferential statistics** involves methods of using information from a sample to draw conclusions regarding the population.

We will look at methods of descriptive statistics in the next three chapters. These methods may be applied to data from samples or populations.

Sometimes we do not have access to an entire population. At other times, the difficulties or expense of working with the entire population are prohibitive. In such cases, we will use inferential statistics together with probability. These are the topics of Chapters 5 through 11.

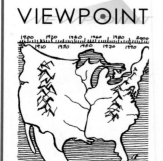

VIEWPOINT

The First Measured Century

The 20th century saw measurements of aspects of American life that had never been systematically studied before. Social conditions involving crime, sex, food, fun, religion, and work were numerically investigated. The measurements and survey responses taken over the entire century reveal unsuspected statistical trends. *The First Measured Century* is a book by Caplow, Hicks, and Wattenberg. It is also a PBS documentary available on video. For more information, visit the Brase/Brase statistics site at **http://math.college.hmco.com/students** and find the link to the PBS *First Measured Century* documentary.

1. *Marketing: Fast Food USA Today* reported that 44.9% of those surveyed (1261 adults) ate in fast-food restaurants from one to three times each week.
   (a) Identify the variable.
   (b) Is the variable quantitative or qualitative?
   (c) What is the implied population?

2. *Advertising: Auto Mileage* What is the average miles per gallon (mpg) for all new cars? Using *Consumer Reports,* a random sample of 35 new cars gave an average of 21.1 mpg.
   (a) Identify the variable.
   (b) Is the variable quantitative or qualitative?
   (c) What is the implied population?

3. *Academic: Student/Faculty Ratio* The students at Eastmore College are concerned about the ratio of number of students to number of faculty at their school. Using *Barron's Profiles of American Colleges,* they took a random sample of 45 colleges in the nation and obtained the student/faculty ratios at these institutions. From this information, they concluded that their student/faculty ratio is higher than those of most colleges in the nation.
   (a) Identify the variable.
   (b) Is the variable quantitative or qualitative?
   (c) What is the implied population?

4. *Archaeology: Ireland* The archaeological site of Tara is more than 4000 years old. Tradition states that Tara was the seat of the high kings of Ireland. Because of its archaeological importance, Tara has received extensive study (Reference: *Tara: An Archaeological Survey* by Conor Newman, Royal Irish Academy, Dublin). Suppose an archaeologist wants to estimate the density of ferromagnetic artifacts in the Tara region. For this purpose, a random sample of 55 plots, each of size 100 square meters, is used. The number of ferromagnetic artifacts for each plot is determined.
   (a) Identify the variable.
   (b) Is the variable quantitative or qualitative?
   (c) What is the implied population?

5. *Ecology: Wetlands* Government agencies carefully monitor water quality and its effect on wetlands (Reference: *Environmental Protection Agency Wetland Report* EPA 832-R-93-005). Of particular concern is the concentration of nitrogen in water draining from fertilized lands. Too much nitrogen can kill fish and wildlife. Twenty-eight samples of water were taken at random from a lake. The nitrogen concentration (milligrams of nitrogen per liter of water) was determined for each sample.
   (a) Identify the variable.
   (b) Is the variable quantitative or qualitative?
   (c) What is the implied population?

6. *Education: Teacher Evaluation* If you were going to apply *statistical methods* to analyze teacher evaluations, which question form, A or B, would be better?
   Form A: In your own words, tell how this teacher compares with other teachers you have had.
   Form B: Use the following scale to rank your teacher as compared with other teachers you have had.

1	2	3	4	5
worst	below average	average	above average	best

7. *Student Life: Levels of Measurement* Categorize these measurements associated with student life according to level: nominal, ordinal, interval, or ratio.
   (a) Length of time to complete an exam
   (b) Time of first class
   (c) Major field of study
   (d) Course evaluation scale: poor, acceptable, good
   (e) Score on last exam (based on 100 possible points)
   (f) Age of student

8. *Business: Levels of Measurement* Categorize these measurements associated with a robotics company according to level: nominal, ordinal, interval, or ratio.
   (a) Salesperson's performance: below average, average, above average
   (b) Price of company's stock
   (c) Names of new products
   (d) Temperature (°F) in CEO's private office
   (e) Gross income for each of the past 5 years
   (f) Color of product packaging

9. *Fishing: Levels of Measurement* Categorize these measurements associated with fishing according to level: nominal, ordinal, interval, or ratio.
   (a) Species of fish caught: perch, bass, pike, trout
   (b) Cost of rod and reel
   (c) Time of return home
   (d) Guidebook rating of fishing area: poor, fair, good
   (e) Number of fish caught
   (f) Temperature of water

1.2
Random Samples

Simple Random Samples

FOCUS POINTS

✓ Explain the importance of random samples.
✓ Construct a simple random sample using random numbers.
✓ Simulate a random process.
✓ Describe stratified sampling, cluster sampling, systematic sampling, and convenience sampling.

Eat lamb—20,000 coyotes can't be wrong!

This slogan is sometimes found on bumper stickers in the western United States. The slogan indicates the trouble that ranchers have experienced in protecting their flocks from predators. Based on their experience with this sample of the coyote population, the ranchers concluded that *all* coyotes are dangerous to their flocks and should be eliminated! The ranchers used a special poison bait to get rid of the coyotes. Not only was this poison distributed on ranch land, but with government cooperation it also was distributed widely on public lands.

The ranchers found that the results of the widespread poisoning were not very beneficial. The sheep-eating coyotes continued to thrive while the general population of coyotes and other predators declined. What was the problem? The sheep-eating coyotes the ranchers had observed were not a representative sample of all coyotes. Modern methods of predator control target the sheep-eating coyotes. To a certain extent, the new methods have come about through a closer examination of the sampling techniques used.

Simple random sample

In this section, we will examine several widely used sampling techniques. One of the most important sampling techniques is a *simple random sample.*

> A **simple random sample** of n measurements from a population is a subset of the population selected in a manner such that
>
> (a) every sample of size n from the population has an equal chance of being selected and
>
> (b) every member of the population has an equal chance of being included in the sample.

Notice that two criteria are necessary for a simple random sample of a specified size. Not only must every member of the population have an equal chance of being included, but every sample of the specified size must have an equal chance of being selected as well.

GUIDED EXERCISE 3

Simple random sample

Is open space around metropolitan areas important? Players of the Colorado Lottery might think so, because some of the proceeds of the game go to fund open space and outdoor recreational space. To play the game, you pay one dollar and choose any six different numbers from the group of numbers 1 through 42. If your group of six numbers matches the winning group of six numbers selected by simple random sampling, then you are a winner of a grand prize of at least 1.5 million dollars.

(a) Is the number 25 as likely to be selected in the winning group of six numbers as the number 5?

$\implies$ Yes. Because the winning numbers constitute a simple random sample, each number from 1 through 42 has an equal chance of being selected.

(b) Could all the winning numbers be even?

$\implies$ Yes, since six even numbers is one of the possible groups of six numbers.

(c) Your friend always plays the numbers

   1 2 3 4 5 6

Could she ever win?

$\implies$ Yes. In a simple random sample, the listed group of six numbers is *as likely as any* of the 5,245,786 groups of six numbers to be selected as the winner. (See Section 5.3 to learn how to compute the number of possible groups of six numbers that can be selected from 42 numbers.)

How do we get random samples? Suppose you need to know if the emission systems of the latest shipment of Toyotas satisfy pollution-control standards. You want to pick a random sample of 30 cars from this shipment of 500 cars and test them. One way to pick a random sample is to number the cars 1 through 500. Write these numbers on cards, mix up the cards, and then draw 30 numbers. The sample will consist of the cars with the chosen numbers. If you mix the cards sufficiently, this procedure produces a random sample.

Random-number table

An easier way to select the numbers is to use a *random-number table*. You can make one yourself by writing the digits 0 through 9 on separate cards and mixing up these cards in a hat. Then draw a card, record the digit, return the card, and mix up the cards again. Draw another card, record the digit, and so on. Table 1 in the Appendix is a ready-made random-number table (adapted from Rand Corporation, *A Million Random Digits with 100,000 Normal Deviates*). Let's see how to pick our random sample of 30 Toyotas by using this random-number table.

EXAMPLE 3

Random-number table

Use a random-number table to pick a random sample of 30 cars from a population of 500 cars.

SOLUTION: Again, we assign each car a different number between 1 and 500, inclusive. Then we use the random-number table to choose the sample. Table 1 in the Appendix has 35 rows and 10 blocks of five digits each; it can be thought of as a solid mass of digits that has been broken up into rows and blocks for user convenience.

You read the digits by beginning anywhere in the table. We dropped a pin on the table, and the head of the pin landed in row 15, block 5. We'll begin there and list all the digits in that row. If we need more digits, we'll move on to row 16, and so on. The digits we begin with are

    99281   59640   15221   96079   09961   05371

Since the highest number assigned to a car is 500, and this number has three digits, we regroup our digits into blocks of 3:

    992   815   964   015   221   960   790   996   105   371

To construct our random sample, we use the first 30 car numbers we encounter in the random-number table when we start at row 15, block 5. We skip the first three groups—992, 815, and 964—because these numbers are all too large. The next group of three digits is 015, which corresponds to 15. Car number 15 is the first car included in our sample, and the next is car number 221. We skip the next three groups and then include car numbers 105 and 371. To get the rest of the cars in the sample, we continue to the next line and use the random-number table in the same fashion. If we encounter a number we've used before, we'll skip it. ◇

◇ **COMMENT** When we use the term *(simple) random sample,* we have very specific criteria in mind for selecting the sample. One proper method for selecting a simple random sample is to use a computer-based or calculator-based random-number generator or to use a table of random numbers as we have done in the example. The term *random* should not be confused with *haphazard!* ◇

> **PROCEDURE**
>
> **How to draw a random sample**
>
> 1. Number all members of the population sequentially.
> 2. Use a table, calculator, or computer to select random numbers from the numbers assigned to the population members.
> 3. Create the sample by using population members with numbers corresponding to those randomly selected.

Simulation

Another important use of random-number tables is in *simulation*. We use the word *simulation* to refer to the process of providing arithmetic imitations of "real" phenomena. Simulation methods have been productive in studying a diverse array of subjects such as nuclear reactors, cloud formation, cardiology (and medical science in general), highway design, production control, shipbuilding, airplane design, war games, economics, and electronics. A complete list would probably include something from every aspect of modern life. In Guided Exercise 4 we'll perform a brief simulation.

> A **simulation** is a numerical facsimile or representation of a real-world phenomenon.

GUIDED EXERCISE 4

Simulation

Use a random-number table to simulate the outcomes of tossing a balanced (that is, fair) penny 10 times.

(a) How many outcomes are possible when you toss a coin once?

⟹ Two; heads or tails

(b) There are several ways to assign numbers to the two outcomes. Because we assume a fair coin, assign an even digit to the outcome heads and an odd digit to the outcome tails. Then, starting at block 3 of row 2 of Table 1 in the Appendix, list the first 10 single digits.

⟹ 7 1 5 4 9 4 4 8 4 3

(c) What are the outcomes associated with the 10 digits?

⟹ T T T H T H H H H T

(d) If you start in a different block and row of Table 1 in the Appendix, will you get the same sequence of outcomes?

⟹ It is possible, but not very likely. (In Section 5.3 you will learn how to determine that there are 1024 possible sequences of outcomes for 10 tosses of a coin.)

TECH NOTE Most statistical software packages, spreadsheet programs, and statistical calculators generate random numbers. In general, these devices sample with replacement. *Sampling with replacement* means that although a number is selected for the sample, it is *not removed* from the population. Therefore, the same number may be selected for the sample more than once. If you need to sample without replacement, generate more items than you need for the sample. Then sort the sample and remove duplicate values. Specific procedures for generating random samples using the TI-84Plus/TI-83Plus calculator, Excel, Minitab, and ComputerStat are shown in Using Technology at the end of this chapter. More details are given in the separate Technology Guides for each of these technologies.

Other Sampling Techniques

Although we will assume throughout this text that (simple) random samples are used, other methods of sampling are also widely used. Appropriate statistical techniques exist for these sampling methods, but they are beyond the scope of this text.

Stratified sampling

One of these sampling methods is called *stratified sampling*. Groups or classes inside a population that share a common characteristic are called *strata* (plural of *stratum*). For example, in the population of all undergraduate college students, some strata might be freshmen, sophomores, juniors, or seniors. Other strata might be men or women, or in-state students or out-of-state students, and so on. In the method of stratified sampling, the population is divided into at least two distinct strata. Then a (simple) random sample of a certain size is drawn from each stratum, and the information obtained is carefully adjusted or weighted in all resulting calculations.

The groups or strata are often sampled in proportion to their actual percentages of occurrence in the overall population. However, other (more sophisticated) ways to determine the optimal sample size in each stratum may give the best results. In general, statistical analysis and tests based on data obtained from stratified samples are somewhat different from techniques discussed in an introductory course in statistics. Such methods for stratified sampling will not be discussed in this text.

Systematic sampling

Another popular method of sampling is called *systematic sampling*. In this method, it is assumed that the elements of the population are arranged in some natural sequential order. Then we select a (random) starting point and select every kth element for our sample. For example, people lining up to buy rock concert tickets are "in order." To generate a systematic sample of these people (and ask questions regarding topics such as age, smoking habits, income level, etc.), we could include every 5th person in line. The "starting" person could be selected at random from the first five.

The advantage of a systematic sample is that it is easy to get. However, there are dangers in using systematic sampling. When the population is repetitive or cyclic in nature, systematic sampling should not be used. For example, consider a fabric mill that produces dress material. Suppose the loom that produces the material makes a mistake every 17th yard, but we check only every 16th yard with an automated electronic scanner. In this case, a random starting point may or may not result in detection of fabric flaws before a large amount of fabric is produced.

Cluster sampling

Cluster sampling is a method used extensively by government agencies and certain private research organizations. In cluster sampling, we begin by dividing the demographic area into sections. Then we randomly select sections or clusters. Every member of the cluster is included in the sample. For example, in conducting a survey

Convenience sampling

of school children in a large city, we could first randomly select five schools and then include all the children from each selected school.

Convenience sampling simply uses results or data that are conveniently and readily obtained. In some cases, this may be all that is available, and in many cases, it is better than no information at all. However, convenience sampling does run the risk of being severely biased. For instance, consider a newsperson who wishes to get the "opinions of the people" about a proposed seat tax to be imposed on tickets to all sporting events. The revenues from the seat tax will then be used to support the local symphony. The newsperson stands in front of a classical music store at noon and surveys the first five people coming out of the store who will cooperate. This method of choosing a sample will produce some opinions, and perhaps some human interest stories, but it certainly has bias. It is hoped that the city council will not use these opinions as the sole basis for a decision about the proposed tax. It is good advice to be very cautious indeed when the data come from the method of convenience sampling.

> **Sampling techniques**
> **Random sampling:** Use a simple random sample from the entire population.
> **Stratified sampling:** Divide the entire population into distinct subgroups called strata. The strata are based on a specific characteristic such as age, income, education level, and so on. All members of a stratum share the specific characteristic. Draw random samples from each stratum.
> **Systematic sampling:** Number all members of the population sequentially. Then, from a starting point selected at random, include every kth member of the population in the sample.
> **Cluster sampling:** Divide the entire population into pre-existing segments or clusters. The clusters are often geographic. Make a random selection of clusters. Include every member of each selected cluster in the sample.
> **Convenience sampling:** Create a sample by using data from population members that are readily available.

Our discussion of sampling methods is intended to be brief and general. This is not the place for an extensive treatment of the theory and practice of sampling. However, the interested reader is referred to the book *A Sampler on Sampling*, by Bill Williams, John Wiley and Sons, Inc.

VIEWPOINT   *Extraterrestrial Life?*

Do you believe intelligent life exists on other planets? Using methods of random sampling, a Fox News opinion poll found that about 54% of all U.S. men do believe in intelligent life on other planets, whereas only 47% of women believe there is such life. How could you conduct a random survey of students on your campus regarding belief in extraterrestrial life?

SECTION 1.2   PROBLEMS

1. *Sampling: Random*
   (a) In your own words, explain the meanings of the terms *random numbers* and *random samples*.
   (b) Why are random samples so important in statistics?

2. *Sampling: Random* Use a random-number table to get a list of eight random numbers from 1 to 976. Explain your work.

3. *Sampling: Random* Use a random-number table to get a list of six random numbers from 1 to 8615. Explain your work.

4. *Simulation: Coin Toss* Use a random-number table to simulate the outcomes of tossing a quarter 25 times. Assume that the quarter is balanced (i.e., fair).

5. *Computer Simulation: Roll of a Die* A die is a cube with dots on each face. The faces have 1, 2, 3, 4, 5, or 6 dots. The table below is a computer simulation (from the software package Minitab) of the results of rolling a fair die 20 times.

   DATA DISPLAY

ROW	C1	C2	C3	C4	C5	C6	C7	C8	C9	C10
1	5	2	2	2	5	3	2	3	1	4
2	3	2	4	5	4	5	3	5	3	4

   (a) Assume that each number in the table corresponds to the number of dots on the upward face of the die. Is it appropriate that the same number appears more than once? Why? What is the outcome of the 4th roll?
   (b) If we simulate more "rolls of the die," do you expect to get the same sequence of outcomes? Why or why not?

6. *Simulation: Birthday Problem* Suppose there are 30 people at a party. Do you think any two share the same birthday? Let's use the random-number table to simulate the birthdays of the 30 people at the party. Ignoring leap year, let's assume that the year has 365 days. Number the days, with 1 representing January 1, 2 representing January 2, and so forth, with 365 representing December 31. Draw a random sample of 30 days (with replacement). These days represent the birthdays of the people at the party. Were any two of the birthdays the same? Compare your results with those obtained by other students in the class. Would you expect the results to be the same or different?

7. *Sampling: Students in Class* Suppose you are assigned the number 1, and each of the other students in your statistics class calls out consecutive numbers until each person in class has his or her own number. Explain how you could get a random sample of four students from your statistics class.
   (a) Explain why the first four students walking into the classroom would not necessarily form a random sample.
   (b) Explain why four students coming in late would not necessarily form a random sample.
   (c) Explain why four students sitting in the back row would not necessarily form a random sample.
   (d) Explain why the four tallest students would not necessarily form a random sample.

8. *Education: Test Construction* Professor Gill uses true–false questions. She wishes to place 20 such questions on the next test. To decide whether to place a true statement or a false statement in each of the 20 questions, she uses a random-number

table. She selects 20 digits from the table. An even digit tells her to use a true statement. An odd digit tells her to use a false statement. Use a random-number table to pick a sequence of 20 digits, and describe the corresponding sequence of 20 true–false questions. What would the test key for your sequence look like?

9. *Education: Test Construction* Professor Gill is designing a multiple-choice test. There are to be 10 questions. Each question is to have five choices for answers. The choices are to be designated by the letters *a, b, c, d,* and *e.* Professor Gill wishes to use a random-number table to determine which letter choice should correspond to the correct answer for a question. Using the number correspondence 1 for *a,* 2 for *b,* 3 for *c,* 4 for *d,* and 5 for *e,* use a random-number table to determine the letter choice for the correct answer for each of the 10 questions.

10. *Sampling Methods: Health Care* Modern Managed Hospitals (MMH) is a national for-profit chain of hospitals. Management wants to survey patients discharged this past year to obtain patient satisfaction profiles. They wish to use a sample of such patients. Several sampling techniques are described below. Categorize each technique as *simple random sample, stratified sample, systematic sample, cluster sample,* or *convenience sample.*
    (a) Obtain a list of patients discharged from all MMH facilities. Divide the patients according to length of hospital stay (2 days or less, 3–7 days, 8–14 days, more than 14 days). Draw simple random samples from each group.
    (b) Obtain lists of patients discharged from all MMH facilities. Number these patients, and then use a random-number table to obtain the sample.
    (c) Randomly select some MMH facilities from each of five geographic regions, and then include all the patients on the discharge lists of the selected hospitals.
    (d) At the beginning of the year, instruct each MMH facility to survey every 500th patient discharged.
    (e) Instruct each MMH facility to survey 10 discharged patients this week and send in the results.

11. *Sampling Methods: Benefits Package* An important part of employee compensation is a benefits package that might include health insurance, life insurance, child care, vacation days, retirement plan, parental leave, bonuses, etc. Suppose you want to conduct a survey of benefits packages available in private businesses in Hawaii. You want a sample size of 100. Some sampling techniques are described below. Categorize each technique as *simple random sample, stratified sample, systematic sample, cluster sample,* or *convenience sample.*
    (a) Assign each business in the Island Business Directory a number, and then use a random-number table to select the businesses to be included in the sample.
    (b) Use the postal ZIP Codes to divide the state into regions. Pick a random sample of 10 ZIP Code areas and then include all the businesses in each selected ZIP Code area.
    (c) Send a team of five research assistants to Bishop Street in downtown Honolulu. Let each assistant select a block or building and interview an employee from each business found. Each researcher can have the rest of the day off after getting responses from 20 different businesses.
    (d) Use the Island Business Directory. Number all the businesses. Select a starting place at random, and then use every 50th business listed until you have 100 businesses.
    (e) Group the businesses according to type: medical, shipping, retail, manufacturing, financial, construction, restaurant, hotel, tourism, other. Then select a random sample of 10 businesses from each business type.

1.3
Introduction to Experimental Design

Planning a Statistical Study

FOCUS POINTS

✓ Discuss what it means to take a census.

✓ Describe simulations, observational studies, and experiments.

✓ Identify control groups, placebo effects, and randomized two-treatment design.

✓ Discuss potential pitfalls that might make your data unreliable.

Planning a statistical study and gathering data are essential components for obtaining reliable information. Depending on the nature of the statistical study, a great deal of expertise and resources may be required during the planning stage. In this section, we look at some of the basics of planning a statistical study.

> **PROCEDURE**
>
> **Basic guidelines for planning a statistical study**
>
> 1. First, identify the individuals or objects of interest.
> 2. Specify the variables as well as protocols for taking measurements or making observations.
> 3. Determine if you will use an entire population or a representative sample. If using a sample, decide on a viable sampling method.
> 4. In your data collection plan, address issues of ethics, subject confidentiality, and privacy. If you are collecting data at a business, store, college, or other institution, be sure to be courteous and to obtain permission as necessary.
> 5. Collect the data.
> 6. Use appropriate descriptive statistics methods (Chapters 2, 3, 4) and make decisions using appropriate inferential statistics methods (Chapters 8–11).
> 7. Finally, note any concerns you might have about your data collection methods and list any recommendations for future studies.

One issue to consider is whether to use the entire population in a study or a representative sample. If we use data from the entire population, we have a *census*.

Census

> In a **census,** measurements or observations from the *entire* population are used.

When the population is small and easily accessible, a census is very useful because it gives complete information about the population. However, obtaining a census can be both expensive and difficult. Every 10 years, the U.S. Department of Commerce Census Bureau is required to conduct a census of the United States. However, contacting some members of the population—such as the homeless—is almost impossible. Sometimes members of the population will not respond. In such cases, statistical estimates for the missing responses are often supplied.

If we use data from only part of the population of interest, we have a *sample*.

Sample

> In a **sample,** measurements or observations from *part* of the population are used.

In the previous section, we examined several sampling strategies: simple random sampling, stratified sampling, cluster sampling, systematic sampling, and convenience sampling. In this text, we will study methods of inferential statistics based on simple random samples.

Simulation

As discussed in Section 1.2, *simulation* is a numerical facsimile of real-world phenomena. Sometimes simulation is called a "dry lab" approach, in the sense that it is a mathematical imitation of a real situation. Advantages of simulation are that arithmetic and statistical simulations can fit real-world problems extremely well. The researcher can explore procedures in simulation that might be very dangerous in real life.

Experiments and Observation

When gathering data for a statistical study, we want to distinguish between observational studies and experiments.

> In an **observational study,** observations and measurements of individuals are conducted in a way that doesn't change the response or the variable being measured.
>
> In an **experiment,** a *treatment* is deliberately imposed on the individuals in order to observe a possible change in the response or variable being measured.

EXAMPLE 4

Experiment

In 1778, Captain James Cook landed in what we now call the Hawaiian Islands. He gave the islanders a present of several goats, and over the years these animals multiplied into wild herds totaling several thousand. They eat almost anything, including the famous silver sword plant, which was once unique to Hawaii. At one time, the silver sword grew abundantly on the island of Maui (in Haleakala, a national park on that island, the silver sword can still be found), but each year there seemed to be fewer and fewer plants. Biologists suspected that the goats were partially responsible for the decline in the number of plants and conducted a statistical study that verified their theory.

(a) To test the theory, park biologists set up stations in remote areas of Haleakala. At each station two plots of land similar in soil conditions, climate, and plant count were selected. One plot was fenced to keep out the goats, while the other was not. At regular intervals a plant count was made in each plot. This study involves an *experiment* because a *treatment* (the fence) was imposed on one plot.

(b) The experiment involved two plots at each station. The plot that was not fenced represents the *control* plot. This is the plot on which a treatment was specifically not imposed, but it was similar to the fenced plot in every other way.   ◇

Silver sword plant, Haleakala National Park

Placebo effect

Statistical experiments are commonly used to determine the effect of a treatment. However, the design of the experiment needs to *control* for other possible causes of the effect. For instance, in medical experiments, the *placebo effect* is the improvement or change that is the result of patients just believing in the treatment, whether or not the treatment itself is effective.

> The **placebo effect** occurs when a subject receives no treatment, but (incorrectly) believes he or she is in fact receiving treatment and responds favorably.

To account for the placebo effect, patients are divided into two groups. One group receives the prescribed treatment. The other group, called the *control group,* receives a dummy or placebo treatment that is disguised to look like the real treatment. Finally, after the treatment cycle, the medical condition of the patients in the *treatment group* is compared to that of the patients in the control group.

It is difficult to account for all variables that might influence a patient's response to a treatment. Sometimes patients assigned to a treatment group and a control group are carefully matched by age, gender, level of medical condition, smoker, etc. However, a more common way to assign patients to the treatment and control groups is by using a random process. This is the essence of a *randomized two-treatment experiment.*

Randomized two-treatment experiment

EXAMPLE 5

Randomized two-treatment experiment

Can chest pain be relieved by drilling holes in the heart? For more than a decade, surgeons have been using a laser procedure to drill holes in the heart. Many patients report a lasting and dramatic decrease in angina (chest pain) symptoms. Is the relief due to the procedure, or is it a placebo effect? A recent research project at Lenox Hill Hospital in New York City provided some information about this issue by using a randomized two-treatment experiment. The laser treatment was applied through a less invasive (catheter laser) process. A group of 298 volunteers with severe, untreatable chest pain were randomly assigned to get the laser or not. The patients were sedated but awake. They could hear the doctors discuss the laser process. Each patient thought he or she was receiving the treatment.

The experimental design can be pictured as

The laser patients did well. But shockingly, the placebo group showed more improvement in pain relief. The medical impacts of this study are still being investigated. ◈

The study cited in Example 5 has many features of good experimental design.

> There is a **control group.** This group received a dummy treatment, enabling the researchers to control for the placebo effect. In general, a control group is used to account for the influence of other known or unknown variables that might be an underlying cause of a change in response in the experimental group. Such variables are called **lurking** or **confounding variables.**
>
> **Randomization** is used to assign individuals to the two treatment groups. This helps prevent bias in selecting members for each group.
>
> **Replication** of the experiment on many patients reduces the possibility that the differences in pain relief for the two groups occurred by chance alone.

Double-blind experiment

Many experiments are also *double-blind.* This means that neither the individuals in the study nor the observers know which subjects are receiving the treatment. Double-blind experiments help control for subtle biases that a doctor might pass on to a patient.

GUIDED EXERCISE 5

Collecting data

Which technique for gathering data (sampling, experiment, simulation, or census) do you think might be the most appropriate for the following studies?

(a) Study of the effect of stopping the cooling process of a nuclear reactor.

⟹ Simulation, since you probably do not want to risk a nuclear meltdown.

(b) Study of the amount of time college students taking a full course load spend watching television.

⟹ Sampling and using an observational study would work well. Notice that obtaining the information from a student will probably not change the amount of time the student spends watching television.

(c) Study of the effect of a calcium supplement given to young girls on bone mass.

⟹ Experimentation. A study by Tom Lloyd reported in the *Journal of the American Medical Association* utilized 94 young girls. Half were randomly selected and given a placebo. The other half were given calcium supplements to bring their daily calcium intake up to about 1400 milligrams per day. The group getting the experimental treatment of calcium gained 1.3% more bone mass in a year than the girls getting the placebo.

(d) Study of the credit hours load of *each* student enrolled at your college at the end of the drop/add period this semester.

⟹ Census. The registrar can obtain records for *every* student.

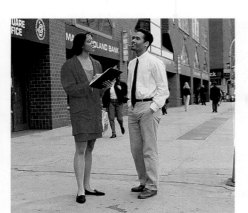

Surveys

Once you decide whether you are going to use sampling, census, observation, or experiments, a common means to gather data about people is to ask them questions. This process is the essence of *surveying*. Sometimes the possible responses are simply yes or no. Other times the respondents choose a number on a scale that represents their feelings from, say, strongly disagree to strongly agree. Such a scale is called a *Likert scale*. In the case of an open-ended, discussion-type response, the researcher must determine a way to convert the response to a category or number.

A number of issues can arise when using a survey. Are the questions asked in a neutral way, or is conscious or unconscious bias built into the wording? In the case of an interviewer, is he or she giving the respondents subtle feedback that might influence the responses? How can you be sure the respondents are answering truthfully? Is your sample representative of the population? For instance, when conducting election polls, some studies use only registered voters because these are the only people eligible to vote. Other polls use only "likely" voters. They first inquire if the respondent is planning to vote.

Other problems arise if the selected respondent cannot be contacted or refuses to respond. This is known as *nonresponse*. If the nonresponse is sufficiently high, the study may be biased and some sort of adjustment may need to be made.

Voluntary response samples often overrepresent people with strong opinions. Data from voluntary responses can be useful and interesting. However, the information given is anecdotal in nature. It would be questionable to generalize the results to the entire population of interest. Surveys must be designed and administered carefully for the results to generalize.

Whenever you gather data, whether by sampling a population, by experiment, or by simulation, you should view the data with a critical eye. The way the data are gathered may produce a *hidden bias*. This means that in reality you are not actually measuring what you hoped to measure. For instance, asking students if parking lots are large enough and safe before asking if they would approve an increase in parking fees might bias responses. Care must be taken to deal with all units or subjects in the same way so that no (conscious or unconscious) preferential treatment or selection can occur.

Sometimes our goal is to understand the cause-and-effect relationships between two variables (as might occur in regression and correlation of two variables, presented in Chapter 4). However, the effect of one variable on another can be hidden by other variables for which no data have been obtained. These variables are called *lurking* or *confounding* variables. For instance, a study of ticket price and attendance at a sporting event might show that higher ticket prices and higher attendance are related, since events with higher ticket prices seem to have greater attendance. You might be led to conclude that if you want to increase attendance at an event, you should raise the price of the tickets. What is missing from this analysis is the lurking variable of *event popularity*.

The problem of other variables that influence one or both of the original variables often can be overcome if the researcher not only is familiar with statistics but also is well versed in the field of investigation.

Some researchers want to generalize their findings to a situation of wider scope than that of the actual data setting. The true scope of a new discovery must be determined by repeated studies in various real-world settings. Statistical experiments showing that a drug had a certain effect on a collection of laboratory rats do not

Potential pitfalls

Nonresponse

Voluntary response

Hidden bias

Other variables

Generalizing results

guarantee that the drug will have a similar effect on a herd of wild horses in Montana.

GUIDED EXERCISE 6

Cautions about data

Comment on the usefulness of the data collected as described.

(a) A uniformed police officer interviews a group of 20 college freshmen. She asks each one his or her name and then if he or she has used an illegal drug in the last month.

⟹ Respondents may not answer truthfully. Some may refuse to participate.

(b) Jessica saw some data that show that cities with more low-income housing have more homeless people. Does building low-income housing cause homelessness?

⟹ There may be some other confounding or lurking variables, such as the size of the city. Larger cities may have more low-income housing and more homeless.

(c) A survey about food in the student cafeteria was conducted by having forms available for customers to pick up at the cash register. A drop box for completed forms was available outside the cafeteria.

⟹ The voluntary response will likely produce more negative comments.

(d) Extensive studies on coronary problems were conducted using men over age 50 as the subjects.

⟹ Conclusions for men over age 50 may or may not generalize to other age and gender groups. These results may be useful for women or younger people, but studies specifically involving these groups may need to be performed.

VIEWPOINT   Is the Placebo Effect a Myth?

Henry Beecher, former Chief of Anesthesiology at Massachusetts General Hospital, published a paper in the *Journal of the American Medical Association* (1955) in which he claimed that the placebo effect is so powerful that about 35% of patients would improve simply if they believed a dummy treatment (placebo) was real. However, two Danish medical researchers refute this widely accepted claim in the *New England Journal of Medicine*. They say the placebo effect is nothing more than a "regression effect," referring to a well-known statistical observation that patients who feel especially bad one day will almost always feel better the next day, no matter what is done for them. However, other respected statisticians question the findings of the Danish researchers. Regardless of the new controversy surrounding the placebo effect, medical researchers agree that placebos are still needed in clinical research. Double-blind research using placebos prevents the researchers from inadvertently biasing results.

1. *Ecology: Gathering Data* Which technique for gathering data (observational study or experiment) do you think was used in the following studies?
   (a) The Colorado Division of Wildlife netted and released 774 fish at Quincy Reservoir. There were 219 perch, 315 blue gill, 83 pike, and 157 rainbow trout.
   (b) The Colorado Division of Wildlife caught 41 bighorn sheep on Mt. Evans and gave each one an injection to prevent heartworm. A year later, 38 of these sheep did not have heartworm, while the other three did.
   (c) The Colorado Division of Wildlife imposed special fishing regulations on the Deckers section of the South Platte River. All trout under 15 inches had to be released. A study of trout before and after the regulation went into effect showed that the average length of a trout increased by 4.2 inches after the new regulation.
   (d) An ecology class used binoculars to watch 23 turtles at Lowell Ponds. It was found that 18 were box turtles, and five were snapping turtles.

2. *General: Gathering Data* Which technique for gathering data (sampling, experiment, simulation, or census) do you think was used in the following studies?
   (a) An analysis of a sample of 31,000 patients from New York hospitals suggests that the poor and the elderly sue for malpractice at one-fifth the rate of wealthier patients (*Journal of the American Medical Association*).
   (b) The effects of wind shear on airplanes during both landing and takeoff are studied by using complex computer programs that mimic actual flight.
   (c) A study of all league football scores attained through touchdowns and field goals was conducted by the National Football League to determine whether field goals account for more scoring events than touchdowns (*USA Today*).
   (d) An Australian study included 588 men and women who already had some precancerous skin lesions. Half got a skin cream containing a sunscreen with a sun protection factor of 17; half got an inactive cream. After 7 months, those using the sunscreen with the sun protection had fewer new precancerous skin lesions (*New England Journal of Medicine*).

3. *General: Randomized Two-Treatment Experiment* How would you use a randomized two-treatment experiment in each of the following settings? Is a placebo being used or not? Be specific and give details.
   (a) A veterinarian wants to test a strain of antibiotic on calves to determine their resistance to common infection. In a pasture are 22 newborn calves. There is enough vaccine for 10 calves. However, blood tests to determine resistance to infection can be done on all calves.
   (b) The Denver Police Department wants to improve its image with teenagers. A uniformed officer is sent to a school one day a week for 10 weeks. Each day the officer visits with students, eats lunch with students, attends pep rallies, and so on. There are 18 schools, but the police department can visit only half of these schools this semester. A survey regarding how teenagers view police is sent to all 18 schools at the end of the semester.
   (c) A skin patch contains a new drug to help people quit smoking. A group of 75 cigarette smokers have volunteered as subjects to test the new skin patch. For one month 40 of the volunteers receive skin patches with the new drug. The other volunteers receive skin patches with no drugs. At the end of two months, each subject is surveyed regarding his or her current smoking habits.

4. *Surveys: Manipulation* The *New York Times* did a special report on polling that was carried in papers across the nation. The article pointed out how readily the results of a survey can be manipulated. Some features that can influence the results of a poll include the following: the number of possible responses, the phrasing of the question, the sampling techniques used (voluntary response or sample designed to

be representative), the fact that words may mean different things to different people, the questions that precede the question of interest, and finally, the fact that respondents can offer opinions on issues that they know nothing about.

(a) Consider the expression "over the last few years." Do you think that this expression means the same time span to everyone? What would be a more precise phrase?

(b) Consider this question: "Do you think fines for running stop signs should be doubled?" Do you think the response would be different if the question "Have you ever run a stop sign?" preceded the question about fines?

(c) Consider this question: "Do you watch too much television?" What do you think the responses would be if the only responses possible were yes or no? What do you think the responses would be if the possible responses were rarely, sometimes, or frequently?

SUMMARY

In this chapter, you've seen that statistics is the study of how to collect, organize, analyze, and interpret numerical information from populations or samples. First, you looked at classifying data as quantitative or qualitative. Next, you examined levels of measurement. The technique of drawing a simple random sample was discussed along with other sampling methods. Finally, you looked at methods of collecting data and some of the issues involved in experimental design and surveys.

IMPORTANT WORDS & SYMBOLS

Section 1.1*
Statistics
Individual
Variable
Quantitative variable
Qualitative variable
Population data
Sample data
Levels of measurement
    Nominal
    Ordinal
    Interval
    Ratio
Descriptive statistics
Inferential statistics

Section 1.2
Simple random sample
Random-number table
Simulation
Sampling with replacement
Stratified sample

Systematic sample
Cluster sample
Convenience sample

Section 1.3
Census
Observational study
Experiment
Placebo effect
Randomized two-treatment experiment
Double-blind experiment
Control group
Treatment group
Confounding variable
Lurking variable
Randomization
Replication
Survey
Nonresponse
Voluntary response
Hidden bias

*Indicates section of first appearance.

VIEWPOINT

Is Chocolate Good for Your Heart?

A study of 7,841 Harvard alumni showed that the death rate was 30% lower in those who ate candy compared with those who abstained. It turns out that candy, especially chocolate, contains antioxidants that help slow the aging process. Also, chocolate, like aspirin, reduces the activity of blood platelets that contribute to plaque and blood clotting. Furthermore, chocolate seems to raise high-density lipoprotein (HDL), the good cholesterol. However, these results are all preliminary. The investigation is far from complete. A wealth of information on this topic was published in the August 2000 issue of the *Journal of Nutrition*. Statistical studies and reliable experimental design are indispensable in this type of research.

CHAPTER REVIEW PROBLEMS

1. *General: Samples and Variables* Find a newspaper or web site article that uses statistics. Are the data from an entire population or from just a sample? What are the variables?

2. *Radio Talk Show: Sample Bias* A radio talk show host asked listeners to respond either yes or no to the question, Is the candidate who spends the most on a campaign the most likely to win? Fifteen people called in and nine said yes. What is the implied population? What is the variable? Can you detect any bias in the selection of the sample?

3. *Colorado Lotto: Simulation* Lotto is the name of the Colorado lottery. The Lotto boards consist of 42 numbers (from 1 to 42). To play, you select six distinct numbers. Every week a drawing machine randomly selects six numbered Ping-Pong balls. If one of your boards contains all six winning numbers, in any order, you've hit the jackpot! You can pick your numbers any way you wish. However, suppose you want to use a random-number table to pick your six numbers. Describe how you would do so, and list your selected numbers. (To play, you must pay $1 to have your selections entered into a computer for a specified week's drawing.)

4. *General: Type of Sampling* Categorize the type of sampling (simple random, stratified, systematic, cluster, or convenience) used in each of the following situations.
   (a) To conduct a preelection opinion poll on a proposed amendment to the state constitution, a random sample of 10 telephone prefixes (first three digits of the phone number) was selected, and all households from the phone prefixes selected were called.
   (b) To conduct a study on depression among the elderly, a sample of 30 patients in one nursing home was used.
   (c) To maintain quality control in a brewery, every 20th bottle of beer coming off the production line was opened and tested.
   (d) Subscribers to the magazine *Sound Alive* were assigned numbers. Then a sample of 30 subscribers was selected by using a random-number table. The subscribers in the sample were invited to rate new compact disc players for a "What the Subscribers Think" column.

(e) To judge the appeal of a proposed television sitcom, a random sample of 10 people from each of three different age categories was selected and those chosen were asked to rate a pilot show.

5. *General: Gathering Data* Which technique for gathering data (observational study or experiment) do you think was used in the following studies? Explain your answer.
   (a) The U.S. Census Bureau tracks population age. In 1900, the percentage of the population that was 19 years old or younger was 44.4%. In 1930, the percentage was 38.8%; in 1970, the percentage was 37.9%; and in 2000, the percentage in the age group was down to 28.5% (*The First Measured Century*, T. Caplow, L. Hicks, B. J. Wattenberg).
   (b) After receiving the same lessons, a class of 100 students was randomly divided into two groups of 50 each. One group was given a multiple-choice exam covering the material in the lessons. The other group was given an essay exam. The average test scores for the two groups were then compared.

6. *General: Randomized Two-Treatment Experiment* How would you use a randomized two-treatment experiment in each of the following settings? Is a placebo being used or not? Be specific and give details.
   (a) A charitable nonprofit organization wants to test two methods of fund raising. From a list of 1,000 past donors, half will be sent literature about the successful activities of the charity and asked to make another donation. The other 500 donors will be contacted by phone and asked to make another donation. The percentage of people from each group who make a new donation will be compared.
   (b) A tooth-whitening gel is to be tested for effectiveness. A group of 85 adults have volunteered to participate in the study. Of these, 43 are to be given a gel that contains the tooth-whitening chemicals. The remaining 42 are to be given a similar-looking package of gel that does not contain the tooth-whitening chemicals. A standard method will be used to evaluate the whiteness of teeth for all participants. Then the results for the two groups will be compared. How could this experiment be designed to be double-blind?

7. *Student Life: Data Collection Project* Make a statistical profile of your own statistics class. Items of interest might be
   (a) Height, age, gender, pulse, number of siblings, marital status
   (b) Number of college credit hours completed (as of beginning of term); grade point average
   (c) Major; number of credit hours enrolled in this term
   (d) Number of scheduled hours working per week
   (e) Distance from residence to first class; time it takes to travel from residence to first class
   (f) Year, make, and color of car usually driven

   What directions would you give to people answering these questions? For instance, how accurate should the measurements be? Should age be recorded as of last birthday?

8. *Census: Web Site Census and You,* a publication of the Census Bureau, indicates that "Wherever your Web journey ends up, it should start at the Census Bureau's site." Visit the Brase/Brase statistics site at **http://math.college.hmco.com/students** and find a link to the Census Bureau's site, as well as to Fedstats, another extensive site offering links to federal data. The Census Bureau site touts itself as the source of "official statistics." But it is willing to share the spotlight. The web site now has links to other "official" sources: other federal agencies, foreign statistical agencies, and state data centers. If you have access to the Internet, try the Census Bureau's site.

9. *Focus Problem: Fireflies* Suppose you are conducting a study to compare firefly populations exposed to normal daylight/darkness conditions with firefly populations exposed to continuous light (24 hours a day). You set up two firefly colonies in a laboratory environment. The two colonies are identical except that one colony is exposed to normal daylight/darkness conditions and the other is exposed to continuous light. Each colony is populated with the same number of mature fireflies. After 72 hours, you count the number of living fireflies in each colony.
   (a) Is this an experiment or an observation study? Explain.
   (b) Is there a control group? Is there a treatment group?
   (c) What is the variable in this study?
   (d) What is the level of measurement (nominal, interval, ordinal, or ratio) of the variable?

DATA HIGHLIGHTS: GROUP PROJECTS

1. Use a random-number table or random-number generator to simulate tossing a fair coin 10 times. Generate 20 such simulations of 10 coin tosses. Compare the simulations. Are there any strings of 10 heads? of 4 heads? Does it seem that in most of the simulations half the outcomes are heads? half are tails? In Chapter 6, we will study the probability of getting from 0 to 10 heads in such a simulation.

2. Use a random-number table or random-number generator to generate a random sample of 30 distinct values from the set of integers from 1 to 100. Instructions for doing this using the TI-84Plus/TI-83Plus, Excel, Minitab, or SPSS are given in Using Technology at the end of this chapter. Generate five such samples. How many of the samples include the number 1? the number 100? Comment about the differences among the samples. How well do the samples seem to represent the numbers between 1 and 100?

LINKING CONCEPTS: WRITING PROJECTS

Discuss each of the following topics in class or review the topics on your own. Then write a brief but complete essay in which you summarize the main points. Please include formulas and graphs as appropriate.

1. What does it mean to say that we are going to use a sample to draw an inference about a population? Why is a random sample so important for this process? If we wanted a random sample of students in the cafeteria, why couldn't we just take the students who order Diet Pepsi with their lunch? Comment on the statement, "A random sample is like a miniature population, whereas samples that are not random are likely to be biased." Why would the students who order Diet Pepsi with lunch not be a random sample of students in the cafeteria?

2. In your own words, explain the differences among the following sampling techniques: simple random sample, stratified sample, systematic sample, cluster sample, and convenience sample. Describe situations in which each type might be useful.

General spreadsheet programs such as Microsoft's Excel, specific statistical software packages such as Minitab or SPSS, and graphing calculators such as the TI-84Plus and TI-83Plus all offer computing support for statistical methods. Applications in this section may be completed using software or calculators with statistical functions. Select keystroke or menu choices are shown for the TI-84Plus and TI-83Plus calculators, Minitab, Excel, and SPSS in the Technology Hints portion of this section. More details can be found in the software-specific Technology Guide that accompanies this text.

APPLICATIONS

Most software packages sample *with replacement*. That is, the same number may be used more than once in the sample. If your applications require sampling without replacement, draw more items than you need. Then use sort commands in the software to put the data in order, and delete repeated data.

1. Simulate the results of tossing a fair die 18 times. Repeat the simulation. Are the results the same? Do you expect them to be the same? Why or why not? Do there appear to be equal numbers of outcomes 1 through 6 in each simulation? In Chapter 5, we will encounter the law of large numbers, which tells us that we would expect equal numbers of outcomes only when the simulation is very large.

2. A college has 5,000 students, and the registrar wishes to use a random sample of 50 students to examine credit hour enrollment for this semester. Write a brief description of how a random sample can be drawn. Draw a random sample of 50 students. Are you sampling with or without replacement?

Technology Hints: Random Numbers

TI-84Plus/TI-83Plus

To select a random set of integers between two specified values, press the **MATH** key and highlight **PRB** with **5:randInt** (low value, high value, sample size). Press Enter and fill in the low value, high value, and sample size. To store the sample in list L1, press the **STO➡** key and then L1. The screen display shows two random samples of size 5 drawn from the integers between 1 and 100.

```
randInt(1,100,5)
{63 89 13 46 47}
randInt(1,100,5)
{29 82 99 50 41}
```

Excel

To select a random number between two specified values, type the command **=Randbetween(low value, high value)** in the formula bar. Alternatively, access a dialogue box for the command by clicking on the **paste function** [fₓ] key on the menu bar. Then choose **All** in the left drop-down menu and **RANDBETWEEN** in the right menu. Fill in the dialogue box.

A5	▼		=	=RANDBETWEEN(1,100)	
	A	B	C	D	E
1	99				
2	58				
3	69				
4	86				
5	13				

Minitab

To generate random integers between specified values, use the menu selection **Calc ➤ Random Data ➤ Integer**. Fill in the dialogue box to get five random numbers between 1 and 100.

	Worksheet 2 ***
	C1
↓		
1	8
2	35
3	33
4	9
5	15

SPSS

SPSS is a research statistical package for the social sciences. Data are entered in the data editor, which has a spreadsheet format. In the data editor window, you have a choice of data view (default) or variable view. In the variable view, you name variables, declare type (numeric for measurements, string for category), determine format, and declare measurement type. The choices for measurement type are scale (for ratio or interval data), ordinal, or nominal. Once you have entered data, you can use the menu bar at the top of the screen to select activities, graphs, or analysis appropriate to the data.

SPSS supports several random sample activities. In particular, you can select a random sample from an existing data set or from a variety of probability distributions.

Selecting a random integer between two specified values involves several steps. First, in the data editor, enter the sample numbers in the first column. For instance, to generate five random numbers, list the values 1 through 5 in the first column. Notice that the label for the first column is now var00001. SPSS does not have a direct function for selecting a random sample of integers. However, there is a function for sampling values from the uniform distribution of all real numbers between two specified values. We will use that function and then truncate the values to obtain a random sample of integers between two specified values.

Use the menu options **Transform ➤ Compute**. In the dialog box, type in var00002 as the target variable.

Then, in the function box, select the function **RV.UNIFORM(min, max)**. Use 1 as the minimum and 101 as the maximum. The maximum is 101 because numbers between 100 and 101 truncate to 100.

The random numbers from the uniform distribution now appear in the second column under var00002. You can visually truncate the values to obtain random integers. However, if you want SPSS to truncate the values for you, you can again use the menu choices **Transform ➤ Compute**. In the dialogue box, enter var00003 for the target variable. From the functions box, select **TRUNC(numexpr)**. Use var00002 in place of numexpr. The random integers between 1 and 100 appear in the third column under var00003.

Output 1 - SPSS Viewer

File Edit View Data Transform Analyze Graphs

6: var00003

	var00001	var00002	var00003
1	1.00	14.96	14
2	2.00	44.13	44
3	3.00	62.22	62
4	4.00	30.08	30
5	5.00	16.57	16

2

Organizing Data

In dwelling upon the vital importance of sound observation, it must never be lost sight of what observation is for. It is not for the sake of piling up miscellaneous information or curious facts, but for the sake of saving life and increasing health and comfort.

—Florence Nightingale, *Notes on Nursing*

Florence Nightingale (1820–1910)

Florence Nightingale has been described as a "passionate statistician" and a "relevant statistician." She viewed statistics as a science that allowed one to transcend his or her narrow individual experience and aspire to the broader service of humanity. She was one of the first nurses to use graphic representation of statistics, illustrating with charts and diagrams how improved sanitation decreased the rate of mortality. Her statistical reports about the appalling sanitary conditions at Scutari (the main British hospital during the Crimean War) were taken very seriously by the English Secretary at War, Sidney Herbert. When sanitary reforms recommended by Nightingale were instituted in military hospitals, the mortality rate dropped from an incredible 42.7% to only 2.2%.

PREVIEW QUESTIONS

◇ What are histograms? When are they used?   (SECTION 2.1)

◇ What are common distribution shapes?   (SECTION 2.1)

◇ How can you select graphs appropriate for given data sets?   (SECTION 2.2)

◇ How can you quickly order data and, at the same time, reveal the distribution shape?   (SECTION 2.3)

For on-line student resources, visit **math.college.hmco.com/students** and follow the Statistics links to the Brase/Brase, *Understanding Basic Statistics*, 4th edition web site.

FOCUS PROBLEM

Say It with Pictures

Edward R. Tufte, in his book *The Visual Display of Quantitative Information*, presents a number of guidelines for producing good graphics. According to the criteria, a graphical display should

- show the data;
- induce the viewer to think about the substance of the graphic rather than about the methodology, the design, the technology, or other production devices;
- avoid distorting what the data have to say.

As an example of a graph that violates some of the criteria, Tufte includes a graphic that appeared in a well-known newspaper. Figure 2-1(a) shows a facsimile of the problem graphic, whereas part (b) of the figure shows a better rendition of the data display.

After completing this chapter, you will be able to answer the following questions.

(a) Look at the graph in Figure 2-1(a). Is it essentially a bar graph? Explain. What are some of the flaws of Figure 2-1(a) as a bar graph?

(b) Examine Figure 2-1(b), which shows the same information. Is it essentially a time-series graph? Explain. In what ways does the second graph seem to display the information in a clearer manner?

(See Problem 1 of the Chapter 2 Review Problems.)

FIGURE 2-1

Fuel Economy Standards for Autos

(a)

Fuel Economy Standards for Autos

Set by Congress and supplemented by the Transportation Department. In miles per gallon.

Source: Copyright © 1978 by The New York Times Company. Reprinted by permission.

(b)   REQUIRED FUEL ECONOMY STANDARDS: NEW CARS BUILT FROM 1978 TO 1985

19.1 mpg, expected average for all cars, 1985

13.7 mpg, average for all cars, 1978

Source: The Visual Display of Quantitative Information by Edward R. Tufte, p. 57. Copyright © 1983. Reprinted by permission of Graphics Press.

2.1
Frequency Distributions, Histograms, and Related Topics

FOCUS POINTS

✓ Organize raw data using a frequency table.

✓ Construct histograms and relative-frequency histograms.

✓ Recognize basic distribution shapes: uniform, symmetric, skewed, and bimodal.

✓ Interpret graphs in the context of the data setting.

Frequency Tables

When we have a large set of quantitative data, it's useful to organize it into smaller intervals or *classes* and count how many data values fall into each class. A frequency table does just that.

> A **frequency table** partitions data into classes or intervals and shows how many data values are in each class. The classes or intervals are constructed so that each data value falls into exactly one class.

Constructing a frequency table involves a number of steps. Example 1 demonstrates the steps.

EXAMPLE 1

Frequency table

A task force to encourage car pooling did a study of one-way commuting distances of workers in the downtown Dallas area. A random sample of 60 of these workers was taken. The commuting distances of the workers in the sample are given in Table 2-1. Make a frequency table for these data.

SOLUTION:

(a) First decide how many classes you want. Five to 15 classes are usually used. If you use fewer than five classes, you risk losing too much information. If you use more

TABLE 2-1   One-Way Commuting Distances (in Miles) for 60 Workers in Downtown Dallas

13	47	10	3	16	20	17	40	4	2
7	25	8	21	19	15	3	17	14	6
12	45	1	8	4	16	11	18	23	12
6	2	14	13	7	15	46	12	9	18
34	13	41	28	36	17	24	27	29	9
14	26	10	24	37	31	8	16	12	16

than 15 classes, the data may not be sufficiently summarized. Let the spread of the data and the purpose of the frequency table be your guide when selecting the number of classes. In the case of the commuting data, let's use *six* classes.

(b) Next, find the *class width* for the six classes.

Class width

> **PROCEDURE**
>
> **How to find the class width**
>
> 1. Compute $\dfrac{\text{Largest data value} - \text{smallest data value}}{\text{Desired number of classes}}$
>
> 2. Increase the value computed to the next highest whole number.

Note: To ensure that all the classes taken together cover the data, we need to increase the result of step 1 to the *next whole number,* even if step 1 produced a whole number. For instance, if the calculation in step 1 produces the value 4, we make the class width 5.

To find the class width for the commuting data, we observe that the largest distance commuted is 47 miles and the smallest is 1 mile. Using six classes, the class width is 8, since

$$\text{Class width} = \frac{47 - 1}{6} \approx 7.7 \quad \text{(increase to 8)}$$

(c) Now we determine the data range for each class.

Class limits

> The **lower class limit** is the lowest data value that can fit in a class. The **upper class limit** is the highest data value that can fit in a class. The **class width** is the difference between the *lower* class limit of one class and the *lower* class limit of the next class.

The smallest commuting distance in our sample is 1 mile. We use this *smallest* data value as the lower class limit of the *first* class. Since the class width is 8, we add 8 to 1 to find that the lower class limit for the *second* class is 9. Following this pattern, we establish *all* the *lower class limits*. Then we fill in the

TABLE 2-2 **Frequency Table of One-Way Commuting Distances for 60 Downtown Dallas Workers** (data in miles)

Class Limits	Class Boundaries	Tally	Frequency	Class Midpoint
Lower–Upper	Lower–Upper			
1–8	0.5–8.5	|||| |||| ||||	14	4.5
9–16	8.5–16.5	|||| |||| |||| ||||		21	12.5
17–24	16.5–24.5	|||| ||||		11	20.5
25–32	24.5–32.5	||||		6	28.5
33–40	32.5–40.5	||||	4	36.5
41–48	40.5–48.5	||||	4	44.5

upper class limits so that the classes span the entire range of data. Table 2-2 shows the upper and lower class limits for the commuting distance data.

(d) Now we are ready to tally the commuting distance data into the six classes and find the frequency for each class.

PROCEDURE

How to tally data

Tallying data is a method of counting data values that fall into a particular class or category.

To tally data into classes of a frequency table, examine each data value. Determine which class contains the data value and make a tally mark or vertical stroke (|) beside that class. For ease of counting, each fifth tally mark of a class is placed diagonally across the prior four marks (||||).

Class frequency

The *class frequency* for a class is the number of tally marks corresponding to that class.

Table 2-2 shows the tally and frequency of each class.

Class midpoint or class mark

(e) The center of each class is called the *midpoint* (or *class mark*). The midpoint is often used as a representative value of the entire class. The midpoint is found by adding the lower and upper class limits of one class and dividing by 2.

$$\textbf{Midpoint} = \frac{\text{Lower class limit} + \text{upper class limit}}{2}$$

Table 2-2 shows the class midpoints.

Class boundaries

(f) There is a space between the upper limit of one class and the lower limit of the next class. The halfway points of these intervals are called *class boundaries*. These are shown in Table 2-2.

> **PROCEDURE**
>
> **How to find class boundaries (integer data)**
>
> To find **upper class boundaries**, add 0.5 unit to the upper class limits. To find **lower class boundaries**, subtract 0.5 unit from the lower class limits.

Relative frequency

Basic frequency tables show how many data values fall into each class. It's also useful to know the *relative frequency* of a class. The relative frequency of a class is the proportion of all data values that fall into that class. To find the relative frequency of a particular class, divide the class frequency f by the total of all frequencies n (sample size).

$$\text{Relative frequency} = \frac{f}{n} = \frac{\text{Class frequency}}{\text{Total of all frequencies}}$$

Table 2-3 shows the relative frequencies for the commuter data of Table 2-1. Since we already have the frequency table (Table 2-2), the relative-frequency table is obtained easily. The sample size is $n = 60$. Notice that the sample size is the total of all the frequencies. Therefore, the relative frequency for the first class (the class from 1 to 8) is

$$\text{Relative frequency} = \frac{f}{n} = \frac{14}{60} \approx 0.23$$

The symbol $\approx$ means "approximately equal to." We use the symbol because we rounded the relative frequency. Relative frequencies for the other classes are computed in a similar way.

The total of the relative frequencies should be 1. However, rounded results may make the total slightly higher or lower than 1.

TABLE 2-3   Relative Frequencies of One-Way Commuting Distances

Class	Frequency f	Relative Frequency f/n
1–8	14	$14/60 \approx 0.23$
9–16	21	$21/60 \approx 0.35$
17–24	11	$11/60 \approx 0.18$
25–32	6	$6/60 \approx 0.10$
33–40	4	$4/60 \approx 0.07$
41–48	4	$4/60 \approx 0.07$

Let's summarize the procedure for making a frequency table that includes relative frequencies.

PROCEDURE

How to make a frequency table

1. Determine the number of classes and the corresponding class width.
2. Create the distinct classes. We use the convention that the *lower class limit* of the first class is the smallest data value. Add the class width to this number to get the *lower class limit* of the next class.
3. Fill in *upper class limits* to create distinct classes that accommodate all possible data values from the data set.
4. Tally the data into classes. Each data value should fall into exactly one class. Total the tallies to obtain each *class frequency*.
5. Compute the *midpoint* (class mark) for each class.
6. Determine the *class boundaries*.

PROCEDURE

How to make a relative-frequency table

First make a frequency table. Then, for each class, compute the *relative frequency f/n*, where *f* is the class frequency and *n* is the total sample size.

Histograms and Relative-Frequency Histograms

Histograms and relative-frequency histograms provide effective visual displays of data organized into frequency tables. In these graphs, we use bars to represent each class, where the width of the bar is the class width. For histograms, the height of the bar is the class frequency, whereas for relative-frequency histograms, the height of the bar is the relative frequency of that class.

PROCEDURE

How to make a histogram or a relative-frequency histogram

1. Make a frequency table (including relative frequencies) with the designated number of classes.
2. Place class boundaries on the horizontal axis and frequencies or relative frequencies on the vertical axis.
3. For each class of the frequency table, draw a bar whose width extends between corresponding class boundaries. For histograms, the height of each bar is the corresponding class frequency. For relative-frequency histograms, the height of each bar is the corresponding class relative frequency.

EXAMPLE 2

Histogram and relative-frequency histogram

Make a histogram and a relative-frequency histogram with six bars for the data in Table 2-1 showing one-way commuting distances.

SOLUTION: The first step is to make a frequency table and a relative-frequency table with six classes. We'll use Table 2-2 and Table 2-3. Figures 2-2 and 2-3 show the histogram and relative-frequency histogram. In both graphs, class boundaries are marked on the horizontal axis. For each class of the frequency table, make a corresponding bar with horizontal width extending from the lower boundary to the upper boundary of the respective class. For a histogram, the height of each bar is the corresponding class frequency. For a relative-frequency histogram, the height of each bar is the corresponding relative frequency. Notice that the basic shapes of the graphs are the same. The only difference involves the vertical axis. The vertical axis of the histogram shows frequencies, whereas that of the relative-frequency histogram shows relative frequencies.

FIGURE 2-2

Histogram for Dallas Commuters: One-Way Commuting Distances

FIGURE 2-3

Relative-Frequency Histogram for Dallas Commuters: One-Way Commuting Distances

◇ **COMMENT** The use of class boundaries in histograms assures us that the bars of the histogram touch and that no data fall on the boundaries. Both of these features are important. But a histogram displaying class boundaries may look awkward. For instance, the mileage range of 8.5 to 16.5 miles shown in Figure 2-2 isn't as natural a choice as a mileage range of 8 to 16 miles. For this reason, many magazines and newspapers do not use class boundaries as labels on a histogram. Instead, some use lower class limits as labels, with the convention that *a data value falling on the class limit is included in the next higher class (class to the right of the limit)*. Another convention is to label midpoints instead of class boundaries. Determine the convention being used before creating frequency tables and histograms on a computer. ◇

GUIDED EXERCISE 1

Histogram and relative-frequency histogram

One irate customer called Dollar Day Mail Order Company 40 times during the last two weeks to see why his order had not arrived. Each time he called, he recorded the length of time he was put "on hold" before being allowed to talk to a customer service representative.

TABLE 2-4 Length of Time on Hold, in Minutes

1	5	5	6	7	4	8	7	6	5
5	6	7	6	6	5	8	9	9	10
7	8	11	2	4	6	5	12	13	6
3	7	8	8	9	9	10	9	8	9

(a) What are the largest and smallest values in Table 2-4? If we want five classes in a frequency table, what should the class width be?

➡ The largest value is 13; the smallest value is 1. The class width is

$$\frac{13 - 1}{5} = 2.4 \approx 3 \quad \text{Note: } \textit{Increase} \text{ the value to 3.}$$

(b) Complete the following frequency table.

TABLE 2-5 Time on Hold

Class Limits				
Lower–Upper		Tally	Frequency	Midpoint
1	– 3	____	____	____
4	– ___	____	____	____
___	– 9	____	____	____
___	– ___	____	____	____
___	– ___	____	____	____

➡ **TABLE 2-6 Completion of Table 2-5**

Class Limits	Tally	Frequency	Midpoint
1–3	III	3	2
4–6	ﬀﬀ ﬀﬀ ﬀﬀ	15	5
7–9	ﬀﬀ ﬀﬀ ﬀﬀ II	17	8
10–12	IIII	4	11
13–15	I	1	14

(c) Recall that the class boundary is halfway between the upper limit of one class and the lower limit of the next. Use this fact to find the class boundaries in Table 2-7 and to complete the partial histogram in Figure 2-4.

TABLE 2-7 Class Boundaries

Class Limits	Class Boundaries
1–3	0.5–3.5
4–6	3.5–6.5
7–9	6.5–_____
10–12	_____–_____
13–15	_____–_____

➡ **TABLE 2-8 Completion of Table 2-7**

Class Limits	Class Boundaries
1–3	0.5–3.5
4–6	3.5–6.5
7–9	6.5–9.5
10–12	9.5–12.5
13–15	12.5–15.5

Continued

GUIDED EXERCISE 1 continued

FIGURE 2-4

FIGURE 2-5 Completion of Figure 2-4

(d) Compute the relative class frequency *f/n* for each class in Table 2-9 and complete the partial relative-frequency histogram in Figure 2-6.

TABLE 2-9 Relative Class Frequency

Class	f/n
1–3	3/40 = 0.075
4–6	15/40 = 0.375
7–9	———
10–12	———
13–15	———

TABLE 2-10 Completion of Table 2-9

Class	f/n
1–3	0.075
4–6	0.375
7–9	0.425
10–12	0.100
13–15	0.025

FIGURE 2-6

FIGURE 2-7 Completion of Figure 2-6

We will see relative-frequency distributions again when we study probability in Chapter 5. There we will see that if a random sample is large enough, then we can estimate the probability of an event by the relative frequency of the event. The relative-frequency distribution then can be interpreted as a *probability distribution*. Such distributions will form the basis of our work in inferential statistics.

Distribution Shapes

Histograms are valuable and useful tools. If the raw data came from a random sample of population values, the histogram constructed from the sample values should have a distribution shape that is reasonably similar to that of the population.

Several terms are commonly used to describe histograms and their associated population distributions.

(a) **Symmetrical:** This term refers to a histogram in which both sides are (more or less) the same when the graph is folded vertically down the middle. Figure 2-8(a) shows a typical histogram with a symmetrical shape.

(b) **Uniform or rectangular:** These terms refer to a histogram in which every class has equal frequency. From one point of view, a uniform distribution is symmetrical with the added property that the bars are of the same height. Figure 2-8(b) illustrates a typical histogram with a uniform shape.

(c) **Skewed left or skewed right:** These terms refer to a histogram in which one tail is stretched out longer than the other. The direction of skewness is on the side of the *longer* tail. So if the longer tail is on the left, we say the histogram is skewed to the left. Figure 2-8(c) shows a typical histogram skewed to the left and another skewed to the right.

(d) **Bimodal:** This term refers to a histogram in which the two classes with the largest frequencies are separated by at least one class. The top two frequencies of these classes may have slightly different values. This type of situation sometimes indicates that we are sampling from two different populations. Figure 2-8(d) illustrates a typical histogram with a bimodal shape.

FIGURE 2-8

Types of Histograms

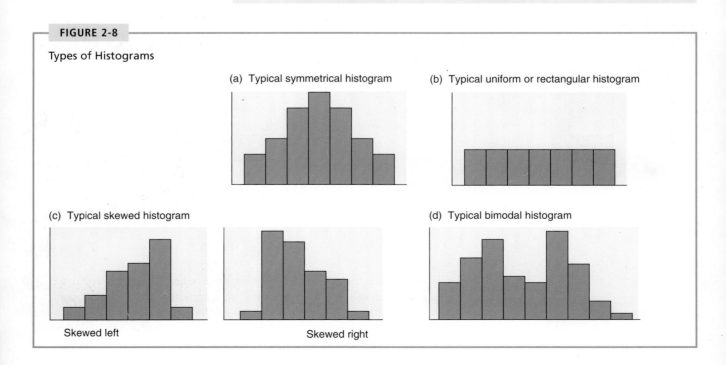

(a) Typical symmetrical histogram

(b) Typical uniform or rectangular histogram

(c) Typical skewed histogram

(d) Typical bimodal histogram

Skewed left

Skewed right

TECH NOTE The TI-84Plus/TI-83Plus calculators, Excel, and Minitab all create histograms. However, each technology automatically selects the number of classes to use. In Using Technology at the end of this chapter, you will see instructions for specifying the number of classes yourself and for generating histograms such as those we create "by hand."

VIEWPOINT

Mush, You Huskies!

In 1925, the village of Nome, Alaska, had a terrible diphtheria epidemic. Serum was available in Anchorage but had to be brought to Nome by dogsled over the 1161-mile Iditarod Trail. Since 1973, the Iditarod Dog Sled Race from Anchorage to Nome has been an annual sporting event with a current purse of more than $600,000. Winning times range from more than 20 days to a little over 9 days.

To collect data on winning times, visit the Brase/Brase statistics site at **http://math.college.hmco.com/students** and find the link to the Iditarod. Make a frequency distribution for these times.

SECTION 2.1	PROBLEMS

For Problems 1–6, use the specified number of classes to do the following:
(a) Find the class width.
(b) Make a frequency table showing class limits, class boundaries, midpoints, frequencies, and relative frequencies.
(c) Draw a histogram.
(d) Draw a relative-frequency histogram.

1. *Sports: Dog Sled Racing* How long does it take to finish the 1161-mile Iditarod Dog Sled Race from Anchorage to Nome, Alaska (*see* Viewpoint)? Finish times (to the nearest hour) for 57 dogsled teams are shown below.

261	271	236	244	279	296	284	299	288	288	247	256
338	360	341	333	261	266	287	296	313	311	307	307
299	303	277	283	304	305	288	290	288	289	297	299
332	330	309	328	307	328	285	291	295	298	306	315
310	318	318	320	333	321	323	324	327			

Use five classes.

2. *Medical: Glucose Testing* The following data represent glucose blood levels (mg/100 ml) after a 12-hour fast for a random sample of 70 women (Reference:

American Journal of Clinical Nutrition, Vol. 19, pp. 345–351). *Note:* These data are also available with other software on the statSpace CD-ROM.

45	66	83	71	76	64	59	59
76	82	80	81	85	77	82	90
87	72	79	69	83	71	87	69
81	76	96	83	67	94	101	94
89	94	73	99	93	85	83	80
78	80	85	83	84	74	81	70
65	89	70	80	84	77	65	46
80	70	75	45	101	71	109	73
73	80	72	81	63	74		

Use six classes.

3. *Medical: Tumor Recurrence* Certain kinds of tumors tend to recur. The following data represent the lengths of time, in months, for a tumor to recur after chemotherapy (Reference: D. P. Byar, *Journal of Urology,* Vol. 10, pp. 556–561). *Note:* These data are also available with other software on the statSpace CD-ROM.

19	18	17	1	21	22	54	46	25	49
50	1	59	39	43	39	5	9	38	18
14	45	54	59	46	50	29	12	19	36
38	40	43	41	10	50	41	25	19	39
27	20								

Use five classes.

4. *Archaeology: New Mexico* The Wind Mountain excavation site in New Mexico is an important archaeological location of the ancient Native American Anasazi culture. The following data represent depths (in cm) below surface grade at which significant artifacts were discovered at this site (Reference: Woosley, A. I. and McIntyre, A. J. *Mimbres Mogollon Archaeology,* University of New Mexico Press). *Note:* These data are also available with other software on the statSpace CD-ROM.

85	45	75	60	90	90	115	30	55	58
78	120	80	65	65	140	65	50	30	125
75	137	80	120	15	45	70	65	50	45
95	70	70	28	40	125	105	75	80	70
90	68	73	75	55	70	95	65	200	75
15	90	46	33	100	65	60	55	85	50
10	68	99	145	45	75	45	95	85	65
65	52	82							

Use seven classes.

5. *Environment: Gasoline Consumption* The following data represent highway fuel consumption in miles per gallon (mpg) for a random sample of 55 models of passenger cars (Source: Environmental Protection Agency). *Note:* These data are also available with other software on the statSpace CD-ROM.

30	27	22	25	24	25	24	15
35	35	33	52	49	10	27	18
20	23	24	25	30	24	24	24
18	20	25	27	24	32	29	27
24	27	26	25	24	28	33	30
13	13	21	28	37	35	32	33
29	31	28	28	25	29	31	

Use five classes.

6. *Advertising: Readability* "Readability Levels of Magazine Ads," by F. K. Shuptrine and D. D. McVicker, is an article in the *Journal of Advertising Research*. (For more information, visit the Brase/Brase statistics site at **http://math.college.hmco.com/students** and find the link to DASL, the Carnegie Mellon University Data and Story Library. Look in Data Subjects under Consumer and then Magazine Ads Readability file.) The following is a list of the number of three-syllable (or longer) words in advertising copy of randomly selected magazine advertisements.

34	21	37	31	10	24	39	10	17	18	32
17	3	10	6	5	6	6	13	22	25	3
5	2	9	3	0	4	29	26	5	5	24
15	3	8	16	9	10	3	12	10	10	10
11	12	13	1	9	43	13	14	32	24	15

Use eight classes.

7. *Education: Testing* Professor Silva teaches anatomy and physiology. He has developed five different versions of a test on the same material. On giving each version to a different sample of 60 students, he discovered that the test score distributions looked like those shown in Figure 2-9.

FIGURE 2-9

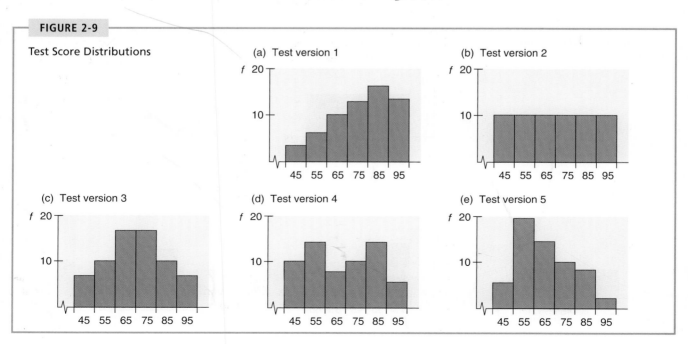

Test Score Distributions

(a) Test version 1

(b) Test version 2

(c) Test version 3

(d) Test version 4

(e) Test version 5

(a) Categorize the distribution shapes as uniform, symmetric, bimodal, skewed left, or skewed right.

(b) Comment on some advantages or problems with each test version. As a student, which version might you prefer? Which version would you like the least?

8. *Consumer: Warranty Cards* Many products come with owner registration or warranty cards. Usually, the consumer is asked a few questions about his or her family and household income. Random samples of warranty or registration cards for the indicated product revealed the household income distributions shown in Figure 2-10 below.

(a) Categorize the distribution shapes as uniform, symmetric, bimodal, skewed left, or skewed right.

(b) If you were in charge of advertising, how would you use income-distribution information of present customers to target ads for the indicated product?

(c) How valid do you think income information is on warranty cards?

 9. *Expand Your Knowledge: Decimal Data* The following data represent tonnes of wheat harvested each year (1894–1925) from Plot 19 at the Rothamsted Agricultural Experiment Stations, England.

2.71	1.62	2.60	1.64	2.20	2.02	1.67	1.99	2.34	1.26	1.31
1.80	2.82	2.15	2.07	1.62	1.47	2.19	0.59	1.48	0.77	2.04
1.32	0.89	1.35	0.95	0.94	1.39	1.19	1.18	0.46	0.70	

(a) Multiply each data value by 100 to "clear" the decimals.

(b) Use the standard procedures of this section to make a frequency table and histogram with your whole-number data. Use six classes.

(c) Divide class limits, class boundaries, and class midpoints by 100 to get back to your original data values.

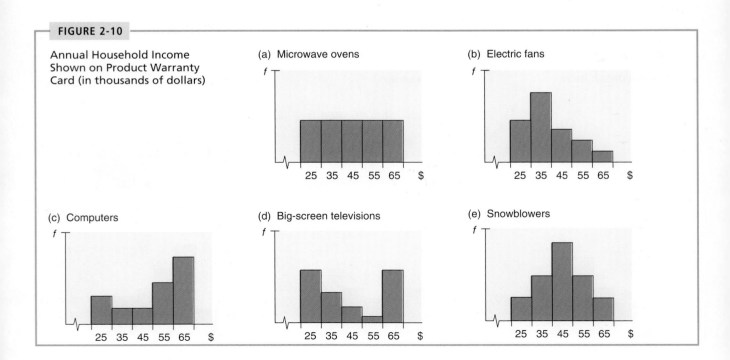

FIGURE 2-10

Annual Household Income Shown on Product Warranty Card (in thousands of dollars)

(a) Microwave ovens

(b) Electric fans

(c) Computers

(d) Big-screen televisions

(e) Snowblowers

10. *Decimal Data: Batting Averages* The following data represent baseball batting averages for a random sample of National League players near the end of the baseball season. The data are from the baseball statistics section of *The Denver Post*.

0.194	0.258	0.190	0.291	0.158	0.295	0.261	0.250	0.181
0.125	0.107	0.260	0.309	0.309	0.276	0.287	0.317	0.252
0.215	0.250	0.246	0.260	0.265	0.182	0.113	0.200	

(a) Multiply each data value by 1000 to "clear" the decimals.
(b) Use the standard procedures of this section to make a frequency table and histogram with your whole-number data. Use five classes.
(c) Divide class limits, class boundaries, and class midpoints by 1000 to get back to your original data.

 11. *Expand Your Knowledge: Dotplot* Another display technique that is somewhat similar to a histogram is a *dotplot*. In a dotplot, the data values are displayed along the horizontal axis. A dot is then plotted over each data value in the data set.

> **PROCEDURE**
>
> **How to make a dotplot**
>
> Display the data along a horizontal axis. Then plot each data value with a dot or point above the corresponding value on the horizontal axis. For repeated data values, stack the dots.

The next display shows a dotplot generated by Minitab (➤**Graph** ➤**Dotplot**) for the number of licensed drivers per 1000 residents by state, including the District of Columbia (Source: U.S. Department of Transportation).

Dotplot for Licensed Drivers per 1000 Residents

Licensed drivers

(a) From the dotplot, how many states have 600 or fewer licensed drivers per 1000 residents?
(b) About what percentage of the states (out of 51) seem to have close to 800 licensed drivers per 1000 residents?
(c) Consider the intervals 550 to 650, 650 to 750, and 750 to 850 licensed drivers per 1000 residents. In which interval do most of the states fall?

 12. *Dotplot: Dog Sled Racing* Make a dotplot for the data in Problem 1 regarding the finish time (number of hours) for the Iditarod Dog Sled Race. Compare the dotplot to the histogram of Problem 1.

 13. *Dotplot: Tumor Recurrence* Make a dotplot for the data in Problem 3 regarding the recurrence of tumors after chemotherapy. Compare the dotplot to the histogram of Problem 3.

2.2
Bar Graphs, Circle Graphs, and Time-Series Graphs

FOCUS POINTS

✓ Determine types of graphs appropriate for specific data.

✓ Construct bar graphs, Pareto charts, circle graphs, and time-series graphs.

✓ Interpret information displayed in graphs.

Histograms provide a useful visual display of the distribution of data. However, the data must be quantitative. In this section, we examine other types of graphs, some of which are suitable for qualitative or category data as well.

Let's start with *bar graphs*. These are graphs that can be used to display quantitative or qualitative data.

Bar graphs

Features of a bar graph

1. Bars can be vertical or horizontal.

2. Bars are of uniform width and uniformly spaced.

3. The lengths of the bars represent values of the variable being displayed, the frequency of occurrence, or the percentage of occurrence. The same measurement scale is used for the length of each bar.

4. The graph is well annotated with title, labels for each bar, and vertical scale or actual value for the length of each bar.

EXAMPLE 3

Bar graph

Figure 2-11 shows two bar graphs depicting the life expectancies for men and women born in the designated year. Let's analyze the features of these graphs.

SOLUTION: The graphs are called *clustered bar graphs* because there are two bars for each year of birth. One bar represents the life expectancy for men, and the other represents the life expectancy for women. The height of each bar represents the life expectancy (in years).   ◇

FIGURE 2-11

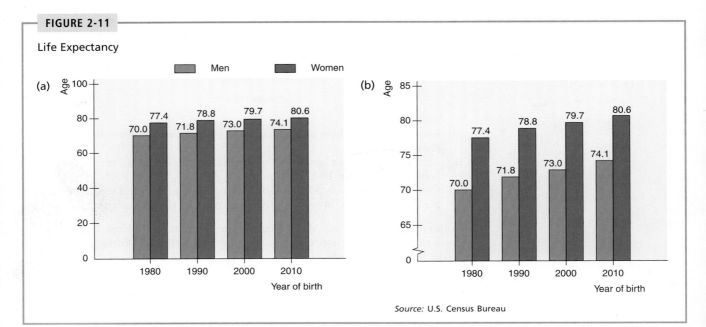

Life Expectancy

Source: U.S. Census Bureau

Changing scales

An important feature illustrated in Figure 2-11(b) is that of a *changing scale*. Notice that the scale between 0 and 65 is compressed. The changing scale amplifies the apparent difference between life spans for men and women, as well as the increase in life spans from those born in 1980 to the projected span of those born in 2010.

Changing Scale

Whenever you use a change in scale in a graphic, warn the viewer by using a squiggle ∿ on the changed axis. Sometimes, if a single bar is unusually long, the bar length is compressed with a squiggle in the bar itself.

Pareto charts

Quality control is an important aspect of today's production and service industries. Dr. W. Edwards Deming was one of the developers of total quality management (TQM). In his book *Out of Crisis*, he outlines many strategies for monitoring and improving service and production industries. In particular, Dr. Deming recommends the use of some statistical methods to organize and analyze data from industries so that sources of problems can be identified and then corrected. *Pareto* (pronounced "Pah-rāy-tō) *charts* are among the many techniques used in quality-control programs.

A **Pareto chart** is a bar graph in which the bar height represents frequency of an event. In addition, the bars are arranged from left to right according to decreasing height.

GUIDED EXERCISE 2

Pareto charts

This exercise is adapted from *The Deming Management Method* by Mary Walton. Suppose you want to arrive at college 15 minutes before your first class so that you can feel relaxed when you walk into class. An early arrival time also allows room for unexpected delays. However, you always find yourself arriving "just in time" or slightly late. What causes you to be late? Charlotte made a list of possible causes and then kept a checklist for 2 months (Table 2-11). On some days more than one item was checked because several events occurred that caused her to be late.

Continued

GUIDED EXERCISE 2 continued

TABLE 2-11   Causes for Lateness
             (September–October)

Cause	Frequency
Snoozing after alarm goes off	15
Car trouble	5
Too long over breakfast	13
Last-minute studying	20
Finding something to wear	8
Talking too long with roommate	9
Other	3

(a) Make a Pareto chart showing the causes for lateness. Be sure to label the causes, and draw the bars using the same vertical scale.

FIGURE 2-12 Pareto Chart: Conditions That Might Cause Lateness

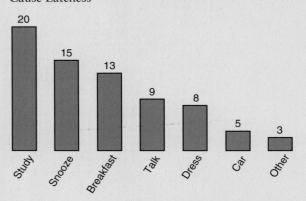

(b) Looking at the Pareto chart, what recommendations do you have for Charlotte?

According to the chart, rearranging study time, or getting up earlier to allow for studying, would cure her most frequent cause for lateness. Repairing the car might be important, but for getting to campus early, it would not be as effective as adjusting study time.

Circle graphs or pie charts

Another popular pictorial representation of data is the *circle graph* or *pie chart*. It is relatively safe from misinterpretation and is especially useful for showing the division of a total quantity into its component parts. The total quantity, or 100%, is represented by the entire circle. Each wedge of the circle represents a component part of the total. These proportional segments are usually labeled with corresponding percentages of the total. Guided Exercise 3 shows how to make a circle graph.

In a **circle graph** or **pie chart,** wedges of a circle visually display proportional parts of the total population that share a common characteristic.

GUIDED EXERCISE 3

Circle graph

How long do we spend talking on the telephone after hours (at home after 5 P.M.)? The results from a recent survey of 500 people (as reported in *USA Today*) are shown in Table 2-12. We'll make a circle graph to display these data.

TABLE 2-12   Time Spent on Home Telephone After 5 P.M.

Time	Number	Fractional Part	Percentage	Number of Degrees
Less than ½ hour	296	296/500	59.2	59.2% × 360° ≈ 213°
½ hour to 1 hour	83	83/500	16.6	16.6% × 360° ≈ 60°
More than 1 hour	121	——	——	——————
Total	——		——	——

(a) Fill in the missing parts in Table 2-12 for "More than 1 hour." Remember that the central angle of a circle is 360°. Round to the nearest degree.

⇒ For "More than 1 hour," Fractional Part = 121/500; Percentage = 24.2%; Number of Degrees = 24.2% × 360° ≈ 87°. The symbol ≈ means approximately equal.

(b) Fill in the totals. What is the total number of responses? Do the percentages total 100% (within rounding error)? Do the numbers of degrees total 360° (within rounding error)?

⇒ The total number of responses is 500. The percentages total 100%. You must have such a total in order to create a circle graph. The numbers of degrees total 360°.

(c) Draw a circle graph. Divide the circle into pieces with the designated numbers of degrees. Label each piece, and show the percentage corresponding to each piece. The numbers of degrees are usually omitted from pie charts shown in newspapers, magazines, journals, and reports.

⇒ **FIGURE 2-13** Hours on Home Telephone After 5 P.M.

Suppose you begin an exercise program that involves walking or jogging for 30 minutes. You exercise several times a week but monitor yourself by logging the distance you cover in 30 minutes each Saturday. How do you display these data in a meaningful way? Making a bar chart showing the frequency of distances you cover might be interesting, but it does not really show how the distance you cover in 30 minutes has changed over time. A graph showing the distance covered on each date will let you track your performance over time.

Time-series graph

We will use a *time-series graph*. A time-series graph is a graph showing data measurements in chronological order. To make a time-series graph, we put time on the horizontal scale and the variable being measured on the vertical scale. In a basic time-series graph, we connect the data points by lines.

> In a **time-series graph,** data are plotted in order of occurrence at regular intervals over a period of time.

EXAMPLE 4

Time-series graph

Suppose you have been in the walking/jogging exercise program for 20 weeks, and for each week you have recorded the distance you covered in 30 minutes. Your data log is shown in Table 2-13.

TABLE 2-13   Distance (in Miles) Walked/Jogged in 30 Minutes

Week	1	2	3	4	5	6	7	8	9	10
Distance	1.5	1.4	1.7	1.6	1.9	2.0	1.8	2.0	1.9	2.0
Week	11	12	13	14	15	16	17	18	19	20
Distance	2.1	2.1	2.3	2.3	2.2	2.4	2.5	2.6	2.4	2.7

(a) Make a time-series graph.

SOLUTION: The data are appropriate for a time-series graph because they represent the same measurement (distance covered in a 30-minute period) taken at different times. The measurements are also recorded at equal time intervals (every week). To make our time-series graph, we list the weeks in order on the horizontal scale. Above each week, plot the distance covered that week on the vertical scale. Then connect the dots. Figure 2-14 shows the time-series graph. Be sure the scales are labeled.

FIGURE 2-14

Time-Series Graph of Distance (in miles) Jogged in 30 Minutes

(b) From looking at Figure 2-14, can you detect any patterns?

> **SOLUTION:** There seems to be an upward trend in distance covered. The distances covered in the last few weeks are about a mile farther than those for the first few weeks. However, we cannot conclude that this trend will continue. Perhaps you have reached your goal for this training activity and now wish to maintain a distance of about 2.5 miles in 30 minutes. ◊

Time series

Data sets composed of similar measurements taken at regular intervals over time are called *time series*. Time series are often used in economics, finance, sociology, medicine, and any situation in which we want to study or monitor a similar measure over a period of time. A time-series graph can reveal some of the main features of time series.

> **Time-series data** consist of measurements of the same variable for the same subject taken at regular intervals over a period of time.

We've seen several styles of graphs. Which kinds are suitable for a specific data collection?

PROCEDURE

How to decide which type of graph to use

Bar graphs are useful for quantitative or qualitative data. With qualitative data, the frequency or percentage of occurrence can be displayed. With quantitative data, the measurement itself can be displayed, as was done in the bar graph showing life expectancy. Watch that the measurement scale is consistent or that a jump scale squiggle is used.

Pareto charts identify the frequency of events or categories in decreasing order of frequency of occurrence.

Circle graphs display how a *total* is dispersed into several categories. The circle graph is very appropriate for qualitative data, or any data for which percentage of occurrence makes sense. Circle graphs are most effective when the number of wedges is 10 or fewer.

Time-series graphs display how data change over time. It is best if the units of time are consistent in a given graph. For instance, measurements taken every day should not be mixed on the same graph with data taken every week.

For any graph: Provide a title, label the axes, and identify units of measure. As Edward Tufte suggests in his book *The Visual Display of Quantitative Information*, don't let artwork or skewed perspective cloud the clarity of the information displayed.

TECH NOTES *Bar graphs, circle graphs, and time-series graphs*

TI-84Plus/TI-83Plus Only time-series. Place consecutive values 1 through the number of time segments in list L1 and corresponding data in L2. Press **Stat Plot** and highlight an *xy* line plot.

Excel Use the chart wizard on the toolbar . Select the desired option and follow the instructions in the dialogue boxes.

Minitab Use the menu selection **Graph.** Select the desired option and follow the instructions in the dialogue boxes.

VIEWPOINT

Do Ethical Standards Vary by the Situation?

The Lutheran Brotherhood did a national survey and found that nearly 60% of all U.S. adults claim that ethics vary by the situation; 33% claim that there is only one ethical standard; and 7% were not sure. How could you draw a circle graph to make a visual impression of Americans' views on ethical standards?

SECTION 2.2   PROBLEMS

1. *Education: Does College Pay Off?* It is costly in both time and money to go to college. Does it pay off? According to the Bureau of Census, the answer is yes. The average annual income (in thousands of dollars) of a *household* headed by a person with the stated education level is as follows: 16.1 if ninth grade is the highest level achieved, 34.3 for high school graduates, 48.6 for those holding associate degrees, 62.1 for those with bachelor's degrees, 71.0 for those with master's degrees, and 84.1 for those with doctoral degrees. Make a bar graph showing household income for each education level.

2. *Accidents: Child Deaths* How safe is the world for kids? Unfortunately, some children between the ages of 1 and 14 die of injuries every year. United Nations data show that by nation, the annual numbers of deaths from injuries per 100,000 children are as follows: Australia, 9.5; Canada, 9.7; Denmark, 8.1; France, 9.1; Germany, 8.3; Hungary, 10.8; Ireland, 8.3; Italy, 6.1; Japan, 8.4; Korea, 25.6; Mexico, 19.8; New Zealand, 13.7; Netherlands, 6.6; Poland, 13.4; Portugal, 17.8; Spain, 8.1; Sweden, 5.2; Switzerland, 9.6; U.K., 6.1; United States, 14.1. Display these data in a Pareto chart.

3. *Commercial Fishing: Gulf of Alaska* It's not an easy life, but it's a good life! Suppose you decide to take the summer off and sign on as a deck hand for a commercial fishing boat in Alaska that specializes in deep-water fishing for groundfish.

What kind of fish can you expect to catch? One way to answer this question is to examine government reports on groundfish caught in the Gulf of Alaska. The following list indicates the types of fish caught annually in thousands of metric tons (Source: *Report on the Status of U.S. Living Marine Resources*, National Oceanic and Atmospheric Administration): flatfish, 36.3; Pacific cod, 68.6; sablefish, 16.0; Walleye pollock, 71.2; rockfish, 18.9. Make a Pareto chart showing the annual harvest for commercial fishing in the Gulf of Alaska.

4. *Archaeology: Ireland* Commercial dredging operations in ancient rivers occasionally uncover archaeological artifacts of great importance. One such artifact is Bronze Age spearheads recovered from ancient rivers in Ireland. A recent study gave the following information regarding discoveries of ancient bronze spearheads in Irish rivers.

River	Bann	Blackwater	Erne	Shannon	Barrow
No. of spearheads	19	8	15	33	14

(Based on information from *Crossing the Rubicon, Bronze Age Studies 5*, Lorraine Bourke, Department of Archaeology, National University of Ireland, Galway.)
(a) Make a Pareto chart for these data.
(b) Make a circle graph for these data.

5. *Lifestyle: Hide the Mess!* A survey of 1000 adults (reported in *USA Today*) uncovered some interesting housekeeping secrets. When unexpected company comes, where do we hide the mess? The survey showed that 68% of the respondents toss their mess in the closet, 23% shove things under the bed, 6% put things in the bathtub, and 3% put the mess in the freezer. Make a circle graph to display this information.

6. *Education: College Professors' Time* How do college professors spend their time? *The National Education Association Almanac of Higher Education* gives the following average distribution of professional time allocation: teaching, 51%; research, 16%; professional growth, 5%; community service, 11%; service to the college, 11%; and consulting outside the college, 6%. Make a pie chart showing the allocation of professional time for college professors.

7. *FBI Report: Hawaii* In the Aloha state, you are very unlikely to be murdered! However, it is considerably more likely that your house might be burgled, your car might be stolen, or you might be punched in the nose. That said, Hawaii is still a great place for a vacation or, if you are very lucky, to live. The following numbers represent the crime rates per 100,000 population in Hawaii: murder, 2.6; rape, 33.4; robbery, 93.3; house burglary, 911.6; motor vehicle theft, 550.7; assault, 125.3 (Source: *Crime in the United States*, U.S. Department of Justice, Federal Bureau of Investigation).
(a) Display this information in a Pareto chart, showing the crime rate for each category.
(b) Could the information as reported be displayed as a circle graph? Explain. *Hint:* Other forms of crime, such as arson, are not included in the information. In addition, some crimes might occur together.

8. *Driving: Bad Habits* Driving would be more pleasant if we didn't have to put up with the bad habits of other drivers. *USA Today* reported the results of a Valvoline Oil Company survey of 500 drivers in which the drivers marked their complaints about other drivers. The top complaints turned out to be tailgating, marked by 22% of the respondents; not using turn signals, marked by 19%; 16% marked being cut off; 11% complained about other drivers driving too slowly; and 8% complained

about other drivers being inconsiderate. Make a Pareto chart showing percentage of drivers listing each stated complaint. Could this information as reported be put in a circle graph? Why or why not?

9. *Ecology: Lakes* Pyramid Lake, Nevada, is described as the pride of the Paiute Indian Nation. It is a beautiful desert lake famous for very large trout. The elevation of the lake surface (feet above sea level) varies according to the annual flow of the Truckee River from Lake Tahoe. The U.S. Geological Survey provided the following data:

Year	Elevation		Year	Elevation		Year	Elevation
1986	3817		1992	3798		1998	3811
1987	3815		1993	3797		1999	3816
1988	3810		1994	3795		2000	3817
1989	3812		1995	3797			
1990	3808		1996	3802			
1991	3803		1997	3807			

Make a time-series graph displaying the data. For more information, visit the Brase/Brase statistics site at **http://math.college.hmco.com/students** and find the link to the Pyramid Lake Fisheries.

10. *Vital Statistics: Height* How does average height for boys change as boys get older? According to *Physician's Handbook,* the average heights at different ages are as follows:

Age (years)	0.5	1	2	3	4	5	6	7
Height (inches)	26	29	33	36	39	42	45	47

Age (years)	8	9	10	11	12	13	14
Height (inches)	50	52	54	56	58	60	62

Make a time-series graph for average height for ages 0.5 through 14 years.

2.3
Stem-and-Leaf Displays

Exploratory Data Analysis

Together with histograms and other graphics techniques, the stem-and-leaf display is one of many useful ways of studying data in a field called *exploratory data analysis* (often abbreviated as *EDA*). John W. Tukey wrote one of the definitive books on the subject, *Exploratory Data Analysis* (Addison-Wesley). Another very useful reference for EDA techniques is the book *Applications, Basics, and Computing of Exploratory Data Analysis* by Paul F. Velleman and David C. Hoaglin

(Duxbury Press). Exploratory data analysis techniques are particularly useful for detecting patterns and extreme data values. They are designed to help us explore a data set, to ask questions we had not thought of before, or to pursue leads in many directions.

EDA techniques are similar to those of an explorer. An explorer has a general idea of destination but is always alert to the unexpected. An explorer needs to assess situations quickly and often simplify and clarify them. An explorer makes pictures—that is, maps showing the relationships of landscape features. The aspects of rapid implementation, visual displays such as graphs and charts, data simplification, and robustness (that is, analysis that is not influenced much by extreme data values) are key ingredients of EDA techniques. In addition, these techniques are good for exploration because they require very few prior assumptions about the data.

EDA methods are especially useful when our data have been gathered for general interest and observation of subjects. For example, we may have data regarding the ages of applicants to graduate programs. We don't have a specific question in mind. We want to see what the data reveal. Are the ages fairly uniform or spread out? Are there exceptionally young or old applicants? If there are, we might look at other characteristics of these applicants, such as field of study. EDA methods help us quickly absorb some aspects of the data and then may lead us to ask specific questions to which we might apply methods of traditional statistics.

In contrast, when we design an experiment to produce data to answer a specific question, we focus on particular aspects of the data that are useful to us. If we want to determine the average highway gas mileage of a specific sports car, we use that model car in well-designed tests. We don't need to worry about unexpected road conditions, poorly trained drivers, different fuel grades, sudden stops and starts, etc. Our experiment is designed to control outside factors. Consequently, we do not need to "explore" our data as much. We can often make valid assumptions about the data. Methods of traditional statistics will be very useful to analyze such data and answer our specific questions.

Stem-and-Leaf Display

In this text, we will introduce two EDA techniques: stem-and-leaf displays and, in Section 3.3, box-and-whisker plots. Let's first look at a stem-and-leaf display.

> A **stem-and-leaf display** is a method of exploratory data analysis that is used to rank-order and arrange data into groups.

We know that frequency distributions and histograms provide a useful organization and summary of data. However, in a histogram, we lose most of the specific data values. A stem-and-leaf display is a device that organizes and groups data but allows us to recover the original data if desired. In the next example, we will make a stem-and-leaf display.

EXAMPLE 5
Stem-and-leaf display

Many airline passengers seem weighted down with their carry-on luggage. Just how much weight are they carrying? The carry-on luggage weights in pounds for a random sample of 40 passengers returning from a vacation to Hawaii were recorded (see Table 2-14).

TABLE 2-14   Weights of Carry-On Luggage in Pounds

30	27	12	42	35	47	38	36	27	35
22	17	29	3	21	0	38	32	41	33
26	45	18	43	18	32	31	32	19	21
33	31	28	29	51	12	32	18	21	26

To make a stem-and-leaf display, we break the digits of each data value into *two* parts. The left group of digits is called a *stem,* and the remaining group of digits on the right is called a *leaf.* We are free to choose the number of digits to be included in the stem.

The weights in our example consist of two-digit numbers. For a two-digit number, the stem selection is obviously the left digit. In our case, the tens digits will form the stems, and the units digits will form the leaves. For example, for the weight 12, the stem is 1, and the leaf is 2. For the weight 18, the stem is again 1, but the leaf is 8. In the stem-and-leaf display, we list each possible stem once on the left and all its leaves in the same row on the right, as in Figure 2-15(a). Finally, we order the leaves as shown in Figure 2-15(b).

Figure 2-15 shows a stem-and-leaf display for the weights of carry-on luggage. From the stem-and-leaf display in Figure 2-15, we see that two bags weighed 27 lb, one weighed 3 lb, one weighed 51 lb, and so on. We see that most of the weights were in the 30-lb range, only two were less than 10 lb, and six were over 40 lb. Note that the lengths of the lines containing the leaves give the visual impression that a sideways histogram would present.

As a final step, we need to indicate the scale. This is usually done by indicating the value represented by the stem and one leaf.   ◈

There are no firm rules for selecting the group of digits for the stem. But whichever group you select, you must list all the possible stems from smallest to largest in the data collection.

FIGURE 2-15

Stem-and-Leaf Displays of Airline Carry-On Luggage Weights

(a) Leaves Not Ordered

```
  3 | 2   represents 32 lb
Stem | Leaves
   0 | 3 0
   1 | 2 7 8 8 9 2 8
   2 | 7 7 2 9 1 6 1 8 9 1 6
   3 | 0 5 8 6 5 8 2 3 2 1 2 3 1 2
   4 | 2 7 1 5 3
   5 | 1
```

(b) Final Display with Leaves Ordered

```
  3 | 2   represents 32 lb
Stem | Leaves
   0 | 0 3
   1 | 2 2 7 8 8 8 9
   2 | 1 1 1 2 6 6 7 7 8 9 9
   3 | 0 1 1 2 2 2 2 3 3 5 5 6 8 8
   4 | 1 2 3 5 7
   5 | 1
```

PROCEDURE

How to make a stem-and-leaf display

1. Divide the digits of each data value into two parts. The leftmost part is called the *stem* and the rightmost part is called the *leaf*.

2. Align all the stems in a vertical column from smallest to largest. Draw a vertical line to the right of all the stems.

3. Place all the leaves with the same stem in the same row as the stem, and arrange the leaves in increasing order.

4. Use a label to indicate the magnitude of the numbers in the display. We include the decimal position in the label rather than with the stems or leaves.

GUIDED EXERCISE 4

Stem-and-leaf display

What does it take to win at sports? If you're talking about basketball, one sports writer gave the answer. He listed the winning scores of the conference championship games over the last 35 years. The scores for those games follow below.

132	118	124	109	104	101	125	83	99
131	98	125	97	106	112	92	120	103
111	117	135	143	112	112	116	106	117
119	110	105	128	112	126	105	102	

To make a stem-and-leaf display, we'll use the first *two* digits as the stems (see Figure 2-16). Notice that the distribution of scores is fairly symmetrical.

(a) Use the first *two* digits as the stem. Then order the leaves. Provide a label that shows the meaning and units of the first stem and first leaf.

    FIGURE 2-16 Winning Scores

```
08 | 3  represents 083 or 83 points
08 | 3
09 | 2 7 8 9
10 | 1 2 3 4 5 5 6 6 9
11 | 0 1 2 2 2 2 6 7 7 8 9
12 | 0 4 5 5 6 8
13 | 1 2 5
14 | 3
```

(b) Looking at the distribution, would you say that it is fairly symmetrical?

    Yes. Notice that stem 11 has the most data.

◇ **COMMENT** Stem-and-leaf displays organize the data, let the data analyst spot extreme values, and are easy to create. In fact, they can be used to organize data so that frequency tables are easier to make. However, at this time, histograms are used more often in formal data presentations, whereas stem-and-leaf displays are used by data analysts to gain initial insights about the data. ◇

TECH NOTE *Stem-and-Leaf Display*

TI-84Plus/TI-83Plus Does not support stem-and-leaf displays. You can sort the data by using keys **Stat ➤ Edit ➤ 2:SortA.**

Excel Does not support stem-and-leaf displays. You can sort the data by using menu choices **Data ➤ Sort.**

Minitab Use the menu selections **Graph ➤ Stem-and-Leaf** and fill in the dialogue box.

Minitab Release 14 Stem-and-Leaf Display (for Data in Guided Exercise 4)

```
Stem-and-Leaf of Scores     N=35
Leaf Unit=1.0

   1                       8    3
   5                       9    2789
  14                      10    123455669
 (11)                     11    01222267789
  10                      12    045568
   4                      13    125
   1                      14    3
```

The values shown in the left column represent depth. Numbers above the value in parentheses show the cumulative number of values from the top to the stem of the middle value. Numbers below the value in parentheses show the cumulative number of values from the bottom to the stem of the middle value. The number in parentheses shows how many values are on the same line as the middle value.

VIEWP◉INT   *What Does It Take to Win?*

Scores for NFL Super Bowl games can be found at the NFL web site. Visit the Brase/Brase statistics site at **http://math.college.hmco.com/students** and find the link to the NFL. Once at the NFL web site, follow the links to the Super Bowl. Of special interest in football statistics is the spread, or difference, between scores of the winning and losing teams. If the spread is too large, the game can appear to be lopsided, and TV viewers become less interested in the game (and accompanying commercial ads). Make a stem-and-leaf display of the spread for the NFL Super Bowl games and analyze the results.

SECTION 2.3   PROBLEMS

1. *Cowboys: Longevity* How long did *real* cowboys live? One answer may be found in the book *The Last Cowboys* by Connie Brooks (University of New Mexico Press). This delightful book presents a thoughtful sociological study of cowboys in West Texas and Southeastern New Mexico around the year 1890. A sample of 32 cowboys gave the following years of longevity:

58	52	68	86	72	66	97	89	84	91	91
92	66	68	87	86	73	61	70	75	72	73
85	84	90	57	77	76	84	93	58	47	

(a) Make a stem-and-leaf display for these data.

(b) Consider the following quote from Baron von Richthofen in his *Cattle Raising on the Plains of North America:* "Cowboys are to be found among the sons of the best families. The truth is probably that most were not a drunken, gambling lot, quick to draw and fire their pistols." Does the data distribution of longevity lend credence to this quote?

2. *Ecology: Habitat* Wetlands offer a diversity of benefits. They provide habitat for wildlife, spawning grounds for U.S. commercial fish, and renewable timber resources. In the last 200 years the United States has lost more than half its wetlands. *Environmental Almanac* gives the percentage of wetlands lost in each state in the last 200 years. For the lower 48 states, the percentage loss of wetlands per state is as follows:

46	37	36	42	81	20	73	59	35	50
87	52	24	27	38	56	39	74	56	31
27	91	46	9	54	52	30	33	28	35
35	23	90	72	85	42	59	50	49	
48	38	60	46	87	50	89	49	67	

Make a stem-and-leaf display of these data. Be sure to indicate the scale. How are the percentages distributed? Is the distribution skewed? Are there any gaps?

3. *Health Care: Hospitals* The American Medical Association Center for Health Policy Research included data, by state, on the number of community hospitals and the average patient stay (in days) in its publication *State Health Care Data: Utilization, Spending, and Characteristics.* The data (by state) are shown in the table. Make a stem-and-leaf display of the data for the average length of stay in days. Comment about the general shape of the distribution.

State	No. of Hospitals	Average Length of Stay	State	No. of Hospitals	Average Length of Stay	State	No. of Hospitals	Average Length of Stay
Alabama	119	7.0	Colorado	71	6.8	Georgia	162	7.2
Alaska	16	5.7	Connecticut	35	7.4	Hawaii	19	9.4
Arizona	61	5.5	Delaware	8	6.8	Idaho	41	7.1
Arkansas	88	7.0	Dist. of Columbia	11	7.5	Illinois	209	7.3
California	440	6.0	Florida	227	7.0	Indiana	113	6.6

Continued

State	No. of Hospitals	Average Length of Stay	State	No. of Hospitals	Average Length of Stay	State	No. of Hospitals	Average Length of Stay
Iowa	123	8.4	Nebraska	90	9.6	Rhode Island	12	6.9
Kansas	133	7.8	Nevada	21	6.4	S. Carolina	68	7.1
Kentucky	107	6.9	New Hampshire	27	7.0	S. Dakota	52	10.3
Louisiana	136	6.7	New Jersey	96	7.6	Tennessee	122	6.8
Maine	38	7.2	New Mexico	37	5.5	Texas	421	6.2
Maryland	51	6.8	New York	231	9.9	Utah	42	5.2
Massachusetts	101	7.0	N. Carolina	117	7.3	Vermont	15	7.6
Michigan	175	7.3	N. Dakota	47	11.1	Virginia	98	7.0
Minnesota	148	8.7	Ohio	193	6.6	Washington	92	5.6
Mississippi	102	7.2	Oklahoma	113	6.7	W. Virginia	59	7.1
Missouri	133	7.4	Oregon	66	5.3	Wisconsin	129	7.3
Montana	53	10.0	Pennsylvania	236	7.5	Wyoming	27	8.5

4. *Health Care: Hospitals* Using the number of hospitals per state listed in the table in Problem 3, make a stem-and-leaf display for the number of community hospitals per state. Which states have an unusually high number of hospitals?

5. *Expand Your Knowledge: Split Stem* The Boston Marathon is the oldest and best known U.S. marathon. It covers a route from Hopkinton, Massachusetts, to downtown Boston. The distance is approximately 26 miles. Visit the Brase/Brase statistics site at **http://math.college.hmco.com/students** and find the link to the Boston Marathon. Search the marathon site to find a wealth of information about the history of the race. In particular, the site gives the winning times for the Boston Marathon. They are all over 2 hours. The following data are the minutes over 2 hours for the winning male runners:

1961–1980

23	23	18	19	16	17	15	22	13	10
18	15	16	13	9	20	14	10	9	12

1981–2000

9	8	9	10	14	7	11	8	9	8
11	8	9	7	9	9	10	7	9	9

(a) Make a stem-and-leaf display for the minutes over 2 hours of the winning times for the years 1961 to 1980. Use two lines per stem.

PROCEDURE

How to split a stem

When a stem has many leaves, it is useful to split the stem into two lines or more. For two lines per stem, place leaves 0 to 4 on the first line and leaves 5 to 9 on the next line.

(b) Make a stem-and-leaf display for the minutes over 2 hours of the winning times for the years 1981 to 2000. Use two lines per stem.

(c) Compare the two distributions. How many times under 15 minutes are in each distribution?

6. *Split Stem: Golf* The U.S. Open Golf Tournament was played at Congressional Country Club, Bethesda, Maryland, with prizes ranging from $465,000 for first place to $5000. Par for the course is 70. The tournament consists of four rounds played on different days. The scores for each round of the 32 players who placed in the money (more than $17,000) were given on a web site. For more information, visit the Brase/Brase statistics site at **http://math.college.hmco.com/students** and find the link to golf. The scores for the first round were as follows:

71	65	67	73	74	73	71	71	74	73	71
70	75	71	72	71	75	75	71	71	74	75
66	75	75	75	71	72	72	73	71	67	

The scores for the fourth round for these players were as follows:

69	69	73	74	72	72	70	71	71	70	72
73	73	72	71	71	71	69	70	71	72	73
74	72	71	68	69	70	69	71	73	74	

(a) Make a stem-and-leaf display for the first-round scores. Use two lines per stem. (See Problem 5.)

(b) Make a stem-and-leaf display for the fourth-round scores. Use two lines per stem.

(c) Compare the two distributions. How do the highest scores compare? How do the lowest scores compare?

Are cigarettes bad for people? Cigarette smoking involves tar, carbon monoxide, and nicotine. The first two are definitely not good for a person's health, and the last ingredient can cause addiction. Problems 7, 8, and 9 refer to Table 2-15, which was taken from the web site maintained by the *Journal of Statistics Education*. For more information, visit the Brase/Brase statistics site at **http://math.college.hmco.com/students** and find the link to the *Journal of Statistics Education*. Follow the links to the cigarette data.

TABLE 2-15   Milligrams of Tar, Nicotine, and Carbon Monoxide (CO) per One Cigarette

Brand	Tar	Nicotine	CO	Brand	Tar	Nicotine	CO
Alpine	14.1	0.86	13.6	MultiFilter	11.4	0.78	10.2
Benson & Hedges	16.0	1.06	16.6	Newport Lights	9.0	0.74	9.5
Bull Durham	29.8	2.03	23.5	Now	1.0	0.13	1.5
Camel Lights	8.0	0.67	10.2	Old Gold	17.0	1.26	18.5
Carlton	4.1	0.40	5.4	Pall Mall Lights	12.8	1.08	12.6
Chesterfield	15.0	1.04	15.0	Raleigh	15.8	0.96	17.5
Golden Lights	8.8	0.76	9.0	Salem Ultra	4.5	0.42	4.9
Kent	12.4	0.95	12.3	Tareyton	14.5	1.01	15.9
Kool	16.6	1.12	16.3	True	7.3	0.61	8.5
L&M	14.9	1.02	15.4	Viceroy Rich Light	8.6	0.69	10.6
Lark Lights	13.7	1.01	13.0	Virginia Slim	15.2	1.02	13.9
Marlboro	15.1	0.90	14.4	Winston Lights	12.0	0.82	14.9
Merit	7.8	0.57	10.0				

Source: Journal of Statistics Education web site at http://www.amstat.org/publications/jse. Reprinted with permission.

7. *Health: Cigarette Smoke* Use the data in Table 2-15 to make a stem-and-leaf display for milligrams of tar per cigarette smoked.

8. *Health: Cigarette Smoke* Use the data in Table 2-15 to make a stem-and-leaf display for milligrams of carbon monoxide per cigarette smoked.

9. *Health: Cigarette Smoke* Use the data in Table 2-15 to make a stem-and-leaf display for milligrams of nicotine per cigarette smoked. In this case, truncate the measurements at the tenths position and use two lines per stem (see Problem 5, part a).

10. *Expand Your Knowledge: Back-to-Back Stem Plot* In archaeology, the depth (below surface grade) at which artifacts are found is very important. Greater depths sometimes indicate older artifacts, perhaps from a different archaeological period. Figure 2-17 is a *back-to-back stem plot* showing the depths of artifact locations at two different archaeological sites. These sites are from similar geographic locations. Notice that the stems are in the center of the diagram. The leaves for Site I artifact depths are shown to the left of the stem, while the leaves for Site II are to the right of the stem (see *Mimbres Mogollon Archaeology* by A. I. Woosley and A. J. McIntyre, University of New Mexico Press).

(a) What are the least and greatest depths of artifact finds at Site I? at Site II?

(b) Describe the data distribution of depths of artifact finds at Site I and at Site II.

(c) At Site II, there is a gap in the depths at which artifacts were found. Does the Site II data distribution suggest that there might have been a period of no occupation?

FIGURE 2-17

Depth (in cm) of Artifact Location

```
                    5 | 2 | 0   = 25 cm at Site I and 20 cm at Site II
            Site I                Site II
                    5 | 2 | 0  5  5
                  5 0 | 3 | 0  0  0  0  5  5
              5 5 5 5 | 4 | 0  0  0  5
                  5 0 | 5 | 0  0  5  5
          5 5 5 5 5 0 | 6 | 0  0  0  5  5  5
    5 5 5 5 5 5 0 0 | 7 |
          5 5 0 0 0 | 8 |
          5 5 0 0 | 9 |
              5 5 | 10 |
                0 | 11 | 0  0  5  5  5  5
                  | 12 | 0  0  0  0  5
```

SUMMARY

Organizing and presenting data are the main purposes of the branch of statistics called descriptive statistics. In this chapter, we have studied histograms, relative-frequency histograms, bar graphs, Pareto charts, circle graphs, time-series graphs, and stem-and-leaf displays. From the viewpoint of future applications, histograms are the most important because the area under a bar can represent the likelihood of data values falling into that class. Histograms and stem-and-leaf displays both reveal distribution properties such as uniformity, symmetry, or skewness.

IMPORTANT WORDS & SYMBOLS

Section 2.1
Frequency
Frequency distribution
Class width
Class, lower limit, upper limit
Class frequency
Class midpoint
Class mark
Frequency table
Class boundaries
Histogram
Relative-frequency table
Relative-frequency histogram
Symmetric distribution
Uniform distribution
Skewed left
Skewed right

Bimodal distribution
Dotplot

Section 2.2
Bar graph
Pareto chart
Pie chart or circle graph
Time-series graph
Time series

Section 2.3
EDA
Stem
Leaf
Stem-and-leaf display
Back-to-back stem plot

VIEWPOINT

*"This land is your land, This land is my land"**
—Woody Guthrie

But who actually owns the forest? On many maps, forest land (including national forests) is colored green. Such maps give the impression that vast areas of the western United States are public land. This is not the case! *USA Today* gave the following information about ownership of U.S. timber lands: state/local, 17%; federal, 10%; forest industry, 14%; and private nonindustry, 59%. Organize these data for better visual presentation using a Pareto chart and a circle graph.

*Words and music by Woody Guthrie TRO © Copyright 1956 (Renewed) 1958 (Renewed) Ludlow Music, Inc., New York, New York. Used by permission.

CHAPTER REVIEW PROBLEMS

1. *Focus Problem: Fuel Economy* Solve the focus problem at the beginning of this chapter.

2. *Criminal Justice: Prisoners* The time plot in Figure 2-18 on the next page gives the number of state and federal prisoners per 100,000 population (Source: *Statistical Abstract of the United States*, 120th Edition).
   (a) Estimate the number of prisoners per 100,000 people for 1980 and for 1997.
   (b) During the time period shown there was increased prosecution of drug offenses, longer sentences for common crimes, and reduced access to parole. What does

FIGURE 2-18

Number of State and
Federal Prisoners per
100,000 Population

the time-series graph say about the prison population change per 100,000
people?

(c) In 1997, the U.S. population was approximately 266,574,000 people. At the rate
of 444 prisoners per 100,000 population, about how many prisoners were in the
system? The projected U.S. population for the year 2020 is 323,724,000. If the
rate of prisoners per 100,000 stays the same as in 1997, about how many prisoners do you expect will be in the system in 2020? To obtain the most recent
information, visit the Brase/Brase statistics site at **http://math.college.hmco.com/
students** and find the link to the Census Bureau.

3. *IRS: Tax Returns* Almost everyone files (or will sometime file) a federal income
tax return. A research poll for Turbo Tax (a computer software package to aid
in tax-return preparation) asked what aspect of filing a return people thought to
be the most difficult. The results showed that 43% of the respondents said understanding the IRS jargon, 28% said knowing deductions, 10% said getting the
right form, 8% said calculating the numbers, and 10% didn't know. Make a circle graph to display this information. *Note:* Percentages will not total 100%
because of rounding.

4. *Law Enforcement: DUI* Driving under the influence of alcohol (DUI) is a serious
offense. The following data give the ages of a random sample of 50 drivers arrested
while driving under the influence of alcohol. This distribution is based on the age
distribution of DUI arrests given in the *Statistical Abstract of the United States*
(112th Edition).

46	16	41	26	22	33	30	22	36	34
63	21	26	18	27	24	31	38	26	55
31	47	27	43	35	22	64	40	58	20
49	37	53	25	29	32	23	49	39	40
24	56	30	51	21	45	27	34	47	35

(a) Make a stem-and-leaf display of the age distribution.
(b) Make a frequency table using seven classes.
(c) Make a histogram showing class boundaries.

5. *Agriculture: Apple Trees* The following data represent trunk circumferences (in mm) for a random sample of 60 four-year-old apple trees at East Malling Agriculture Research Station in England (Reference: S. C. Pearce, University of Kent at Canterbury). *Note:* These data are also available with other software on the statSpace CD-ROM.

108	99	106	102	115	120	120	117	122	142
106	111	119	109	125	108	116	105	117	123
103	114	101	99	112	120	108	91	115	109
114	105	99	122	106	113	114	75	96	124
91	102	108	110	83	90	69	117	84	142
122	113	105	112	117	122	129	100	138	117

(a) Make a frequency table with seven classes showing class limits, class boundaries, midpoints, frequencies, and relative frequencies.
(b) Draw a histogram.
(c) Draw a relative-frequency histogram.

6. *Law: Corporation Lawsuits* Many people say the civil justice system is overburdened. Many cases center on suits involving businesses. The following data are based on a *Wall Street Journal* report. Researchers conducted a study of lawsuits involving 1908 businesses ranked in the Fortune 1000 over a 20-year period. They found the following distribution of civil justice caseloads brought before the federal courts involving the businesses:

Case Type	Number of Filings (in thousands)
Contracts	107
General torts (personal injury)	191
Asbestos liability	49
Other product liability	38
All other	21

Note: Contracts cases involve disputes over contracts between businesses.
(a) Make a Pareto chart of the caseloads. Which type of cases occur most frequently?
(b) Make a circle chart showing the percentage of cases of each type.

7. *Archaeology: Tree-Ring Data* The Sand Canyon Archaeological Project, edited by W. D. Lipe and published by Crow Canyon Archaeological Center, contains the stem-and-leaf diagram in Figure 2-19 on the next page. The study uses tree rings to accurately determine the year in which a tree was cut. The figure gives the tree-ring-cutting dates for samples of timbers found in the architectural units at Sand Canyon Pueblo. The text referring to the figure says, "The three-digit numbers in the left column represent centuries and decades A.D. The numbers to the right represent individual years, with each number derived from an individual sample. Thus, **124 2 2 2** represents three samples dated to A.D. 1242." Use Figure 2-19 and the verbal description to answer the following questions.
(a) Which decade contained the most samples?
(b) How many samples had a tree-ring-cutting date between 1200 A.D. and 1239 A.D., inclusive?

FIGURE 2-19

Tree-Ring-Cutting Dates from Architectural Units at Sand Canyon Pueblo: *The Sand Canyon Archaeological Project*

119	5 6
120	0 0 1 2 3 3 3 3 3 3 3 3 3 3 3 3 3 3 3 3 3 3 3 3 3 3 3 3 3 3 3 3
120	
121	2
121	5 5
122	0 0 1 1 1 1 2 2 3 4 4 4 4 4 4 4
122	5 8 9
123	0 1 2 3 3 4
123	5 5 5 5 5 5 5 5 5 5 5 5 5 5 6 8 8 9
124	1 2 2 2 2 2 2 2 2 2 2 2 2 2 2 2 2 2 2 2 2 3 4 4
124	5 6 8 9 9 9 9 9 9 9 9 9
125	0 0 0 0 0 0 0 0 0 0 0 0 0 0 0 1 1 1 1 1 1 1 2 2 2
125	
126	0 0 0 1 2 2 2 2 2 2 2 2 2 2 2 2 2 4 4 4 4 4 4 4
126	5 5 5 6 6 7
127	0 1 1 1 1 4 4

(c) What are the dates of the longest interval during which no tree-cutting samples occurred? What might this indicate about new construction or renovation of the pueblo structures during this period?

DATA HIGHLIGHTS: GROUP PROJECTS

Break into small groups and discuss the following topics. Organize a brief outline in which you summarize the main points of your group discussion.

1. Examine Figure 2-20, "Everyone Agrees: Slobs Make Worst Roommates." This is a double bar graph because two percentages are given for each response category: responses from men and responses from women. Comment about how the artistic rendition has slightly changed the format of a bar graph. Do the bars seem to have lengths that accurately reflect the relative percentages of the responses? In your own opinion, does the artistic rendition enhance or confuse the information? Explain. Which characteristic of "worst roommates" does the graphic seem to illustrate? Can this graph be considered a Pareto chart for men? for women? Why or why not? From the information given in the figure, do you think the survey just listed the four given annoying characteristics? Do you think a respondent could choose more than one characteristic? Explain your answer in terms of the percentages given and in terms of the explanation given in the graphic. Could this information also be displayed in one circle graph for men and another for women? Explain.

2. Examine Figure 2-21, "Global Teen Worries." How many countries were contained in the sample? The graph contains bars and a circle. Which bar is the longest? Which bar represents the greatest percentage? Is this a bar graph or not? If not, what changes would need to be made to put the information into a bar graph? Could the graph be made into a Pareto chart? Could it be made into a circle graph? Explain.

FIGURE 2-20

Everyone Agrees: Slobs Make Worst Roommates When asked what bothers them most about living with another person, men and women responded:

- Sloppiness — 35% / 41%
- Uneven sharing of chores — 32%
- Irritating personal habits — 15%
- Invasions of privacy — 24% / 22%
- 9% / 22%

■ Men □ Women

Source: Advantage Business Research for Mattel *Compatibility*

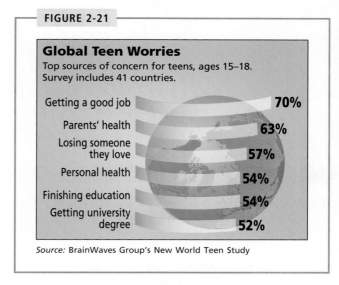

FIGURE 2-21

Global Teen Worries Top sources of concern for teens, ages 15–18. Survey includes 41 countries.

- Getting a good job — **70%**
- Parents' health — **63%**
- Losing someone they love — **57%**
- Personal health — **54%**
- Finishing education — **54%**
- Getting university degree — **52%**

Source: BrainWaves Group's New World Teen Study

LINKING CONCEPTS: WRITING PROJECTS

Discuss each of the following topics in class or review the topics on your own. Then write a brief but complete essay in which you summarize the main points. Please include formulas and graphs as appropriate.

1. In your own words, explain the differences among histograms, relative-frequency histograms, bar graphs, circle graphs, time-series graphs, Pareto charts, and stem-and-leaf displays. If you have nominal data, which graphic displays might be useful? What if you have ordinal, interval, or ratio data?

2. What do we mean when we say a histogram is skewed to the left? to the right? What is a bimodal histogram? Discuss the following statement: "A bimodal histogram usually results if we draw a sample from two populations at once." Suppose you took a sample of weights of college football players and with this sample you included weights of cheerleaders. Do you think a histogram made from the combined weights would be bimodal? Explain.

3. Discuss the statement that stem-and-leaf displays are quick and easy to construct. How can we use a stem-and-leaf display to make the construction of a frequency table easier? How does a stem-and-leaf display help you spot extreme values quickly?

4. Go to the library and pick up a current issue of *The Wall Street Journal, Newsweek, Time, USA Today,* or other news media. Examine each newspaper or magazine for graphs of the type discussed in this chapter. List the variables used, method of data collection, and general type of conclusion drawn from the graphs. Another source for information is the Internet. Explore several web sites, and categorize the graphs you find as you did for the print media. For interesting web sites, visit the Brase/Brase statistics site at **http://math.college.hmco.com/students** and find links to the Social Statistics Briefing Room, to law enforcement, and to golf.

Using Technology

APPLICATIONS

The following tables show the first-round winning scores of the NCAA men's and women's basketball teams.

TABLE 2-16   Men's Winning First-Round NCAA Tournament Scores

95	70	79	99	83	72	79	101
69	82	86	70	79	69	69	70
95	70	77	61	69	68	69	72
89	66	84	77	50	83	63	58

TABLE 2-17   Women's Winning First-Round NCAA Tournament Scores

80	68	51	80	83	75	77	100
96	68	89	80	67	84	76	70
98	81	79	89	98	83	72	100
101	83	66	76	77	84	71	77

1. Use the software or method of your choice to construct separate histograms for the men's and women's winning scores. Try 5, 7, and 10 classes for each. Which number of classes seems to be the best choice? Why?

2. Use the same class boundaries for histograms of men's and of women's scores. How do the scores for the two groups compare? What general shape do the histograms follow?

3. Use the software or method of your choice to make stem-and-leaf displays for each set of scores. If your software does not make stem-and-leaf displays, sort the data first and then make a back-to-back display by hand. Do there seem to be any extreme values in either set? How do the data sets compare?

Technology Hints: Creating Histograms

The default histograms produced by the TI-84Plus/TI-83Plus calculators, Minitab, and Excel all determine automatically the number of classes to use. To control the number of classes the technology uses, follow the key steps as indicated. The display screens are generated for data found in Table 2-1—Commuting Distances of Dallas Workers.

TI-84Plus/TI-83Plus

Determine the class width for the number of classes you want and the lower class boundary for the first class. Enter the data in list L1.

Press **STATPLOT** and highlight On and the histogram plot.

Press **WINDOW** and set Xmin = lowest class boundary, Xscl = class width. Use appropriate values for the other settings.

Press **GRAPH. TRACE** gives boundaries and frequency.

Excel

Determine the upper class boundaries for the five classes. Enter the data. In a separate column, enter the upper class boundaries. Use the menu selection **Tools ➤ Data Analysis ➤ Histogram**.

Put the data range in the Input Range. Put the upper class boundaries range in the Bin Range.

To make bars touch, right click on a bar and select **Format Data Series ➤ Options tab.** Set the **gap width** to 0.

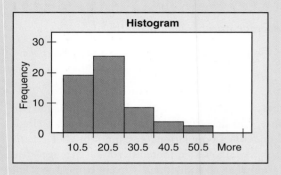

Minitab

Determine the class boundaries. Enter the data. Use the menu selection **Graph ➤ Histogram.**

In the Dialogue Box, press **Options.** Then select cutpoints and enter the class boundaries as cutpoint positions.

Select **Frame** to adjust scales. Otherwise, press **OK.**

SPSS

The SPSS screenshot shows the default histogram created by the menu choices **Analyze ➤ Descriptive Statistics ➤ Frequencies.** In the dialogue box, move the variable containing the data into the variables window. Click **Charts** and select **Histograms.** Click the Continue button and then the OK button. In SPSS version 12, there are procedures to control the boundaries (cutpoints) of the histogram.

Specific instructions for setting class boundaries (cut points) of a histogram are provided in the Technology Guide that accompanies this text.

3

Averages and Variation

While the individual man is an insolvable puzzle,
in the aggregate he becomes
a mathematical certainty. You can,
for example, never foretell what any one man
will do, but you can say
with precision what an average number will be up to.

—Arthur Conan Doyle, *The Sign of Four*

Sherlock Holmes

Sherlock Holmes spoke these words to his colleague Dr. Watson as the two were unraveling a mystery. The detective was implying that if a single member is drawn at random from a population, we cannot predict *exactly* what that member will look like. However, there are some "average" features of the entire population that an individual is likely to possess. The degree of certainty with which we would expect to observe such average features in any individual depends on our knowledge of the variation among individuals in the population. Sherlock Holmes has led us to two of the most important statistical concepts: average and variation.

PREVIEW QUESTIONS

◇ What are commonly used measures of central tendency? What do they tell you?   (SECTION 3.1)

◇ How do variance and standard deviation measure data spread? Why is this important?   (SECTION 3.2)

◇ How do you make a box-and-whisker plot, and what does it tell about the spread of the data?   (SECTION 3.3)

For on-line student resources, visit **math.college.hmco.com/students** and follow the Statistics links to the Brase/Brase, *Understanding Basic Statistics,* 4th edition web site.

FOCUS PROBLEM

The Educational Advantage

Is it really worth all the effort to get a college degree? From a philosophical point of view, the love of learning is sufficient reason to get a college degree. However, the U.S. Census Bureau also makes another relevant point. Annually, college graduates (bachelor's degree) earn on average $17,583 more than high school graduates. This means college graduates earn about 77% more than high school graduates, and according to "Education Pays" on the next page, the gap in earnings is increasing. Furthermore, as the College Board indicates, for most Americans college remains relatively affordable.

After completing this chapter, you will be able to answer the following questions.

(a) Does a college degree *guarantee* someone a 77% increase in earnings over a high school degree? Remember, we are using only *averages* from census data.

(b) Using census data (not shown in "Education Pays"), it is estimated that the standard deviation of college-graduate earnings is about $8,500. Compute a 75% Chebyshev confidence interval centered on the mean ($40,478) for bachelor's degree earnings.

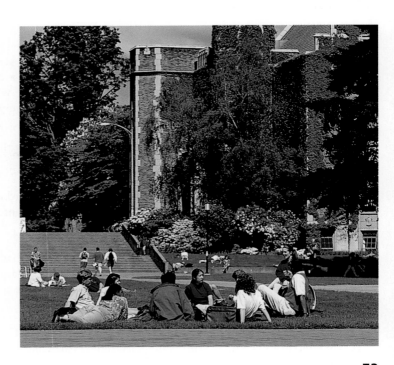

(c) How much does college tuition cost? That depends, of course, on where you go to college. Construct a weighted average. Using the data from "College Afford-able for Most," estimate midpoints for the cost intervals. Say 51% of tuitions cost about $3,500; 21% cost about $6,000; 6% cost about $10,000; 8% cost about $14,000; 7% cost about $18,000; and 7% cost about $25,000. Compute the weighted average of college tuition charged at all colleges. (See Problem 7 in the Chapter Review Problems.)

Education Pays
Average annual salary gap increases by education level

Advanced degree **$63,229**
Bachelor's degree **$40,478**
High school diploma **$22,895**
No diploma **$16,124**

Source: Census Bureau

College Affordable for Most
Annual tuition and fees at four-year colleges

$20,000 and over
$16,000 to $19,999 — 7%
$12,000 to $15,999 — 7%
— 8%
$8,000 to $11,999 — 6%
Under $4,000 **51%**
$4,000 to $7,999 — 21%

Source: The College Board

3.1   Measures of Central Tendency: Mode, Median, and Mean

FOCUS POINTS

✓ Compute mean, median, and mode from raw data.

✓ Interpret what mean, median, and mode tell you.

✓ Explain how mean, median, and mode can be affected by extreme data values.

✓ What is a trimmed mean? How do you compute it?

✓ Compute a weighted average.

The average price of an ounce of gold is $420. The Zippy car averages 39 miles per gallon on the highway. A survey showed the average shoe size for women is size 8.

In each of the preceding statements, *one* number is used to describe the entire sample or population. Such a number is called an *average*. There are many ways to compute averages, but we will study only three of the major ones.

The easiest average to compute is the *mode*.

> The **mode** of a data set is the value that occurs most frequently.

EXAMPLE 1

Mode

Count the letters in each word of this sentence and give the mode. The numbers of letters in the words of the sentence are

5   3   7   2   4   4   2   4   8   3   4   3   4

Scanning the data, we see that 4 is the mode because more words have 4 letters than any other number. For larger data sets, it is useful to order—or sort—the data before scanning them for the mode.   ◊

Not every data set has a mode. For example, if Professor Fair gives equal numbers of A's, B's, C's, D's, and F's, then there is no modal grade. In addition, the mode is not very stable. Changing just one number in a data set can change the mode dramatically. However, the mode is a useful average when we want to know the most frequently occurring data value, such as the most frequently requested shoe size.

Median

Another average that is useful is the *median*, or central value, of an ordered distribution. When you are given the median, you know there are an equal number of data values in the ordered distribution that are above it and below it.

> **PROCEDURE**
>
> **How to find the median**
>
> The **median** is the central value of an ordered distribution. To find it,
>
> 1. Order the data from smallest to largest.
> 2. For an *odd* number of data values in the distribution,
>
> $$\text{Median} = \text{Middle data value}$$
>
> 3. For an *even* number of data values in the distribution,
>
> $$\text{Median} = \frac{\text{Sum of middle two values}}{2}$$

EXAMPLE 2

Median

What do barbecue-flavored potato chips cost? According to *Consumer Reports*, Volume 66, No. 5, the prices per ounce in cents of the rated chips are

19   19   27   28   18   35

(a) To find the median, we first order the data, and then note that there are an even number of entries. So the median is constructed using the two middle values.

18   19   19   27   28   35

middle values

$$\text{Median} = \frac{19 + 27}{2} = 23 \text{ cents}$$

(b) According to *Consumer Reports*, the brand with the lowest overall taste rating costs 35 cents per ounce. Eliminate that brand, and find the median price per ounce for the remaining barbecue-flavored chips. Again order the data. Note that there are an odd number of entries, so the median is simply the middle value.

18   19   19   27   28

↑

middle value

$$\text{Median} = \text{middle value} = 19 \text{ cents}$$

(c) One ounce of potato chips is considered a small serving. Is it reasonable to budget about $10.45 to serve the barbecue-flavored chips to 55 people?

Yes, since the median price of the chips is 19 cents per small serving. This budget for chips assumes that there is plenty of other food! ◇

The median uses the *position* rather than the specific value of each data entry. If the extreme values of a data set change, the median usually does not change. This is why the median is often used as the average for house prices. If one mansion costing several million dollars sells in a community of much-lower-priced homes, the median selling price for houses in the community would be affected very little, if at all.

GUIDED EXERCISE 1

Median and mode

Belleview College must make a report to the budget committee about the average credit hour load a full-time student carries. (A 12-credit-hour load is the minimum requirement for full-time status. For the same tuition, students may take up to 20 credit hours.) A random sample of 40 students yielded the following information (in credit hours):

17	12	14	17	13	16	18	20	13	12
12	17	16	15	14	12	12	13	17	14
15	12	15	16	12	18	20	19	12	15
18	14	16	17	15	19	12	13	12	15

(a) Organize the data from smallest to largest number of credit hours.

⟹   12 12 12 12 12 12 12 12 12 12
13 13 13 13 14 14 14 14 15 ⑮
⑮ 15 15 15 16 16 16 16 17 17
17 17 17 18 18 18 19 19 20 20

(b) Since there are an _____ (odd, even) number of values, we add the two middle values and divide by 2 to get the median. What is the median credit hour load?

⟹   There are an even number of entries. The two middle values are circled in part (a).

$$\text{Median} = \frac{15 + 15}{2} = 15$$

(c) What is the mode of this distribution? Is it different from the median? If the budget committee is going to fund the school according to the average student credit hour load (more money for higher loads), which of these two averages do you think the college will use?

⟹   The mode is 12. It is different from the median. Since the median is higher, the school will probably use it and indicate that the average being used is the median.

Note: For small ordered data sets, we can easily scan the set to find the *location* of the median. However, for large ordered data sets of size n, it is convenient to have a formula to find the middle of the data set.

For an ordered data set of size n,

$$\textbf{Position of the middle value} = \frac{n + 1}{2}$$

For instance, if $n = 99$, then the middle value is the $(99 + 1)/2$ or 50th data value in the ordered data. If $n = 100$, then $(100 + 1)/2 = 50.5$ tells us that the two middle values are in the 50th and 51st positions.

Mean

An average that uses the exact value of each entry is the *mean* (sometimes called the *arithmetic mean*). To compute the mean, we add the values of all the entries and then divide by the number of entries.

$$\text{Mean} = \frac{\text{Sum of all the entries}}{\text{Number of entries}}$$

The mean is the average usually used to compute a test average.

EXAMPLE 3

Mean

To graduate, Linda needs at least a B in biology. She did not do very well on her first three tests; however, she did well on the last four. Here are her scores:

58	67	60	84	93	98	100

Compute the mean and determine if Linda's grade will be a B (80 to 89 average) or a C (70 to 79 average).

SOLUTION:

$$\text{Mean} = \frac{\text{Sum of scores}}{\text{Number of scores}} = \frac{58 + 67 + 60 + 84 + 93 + 98 + 100}{7}$$

$$= \frac{560}{7} = 80$$

Since the average is 80, Linda will get the needed B.

◇ **COMMENT** When we compute the mean, we sum the given data. There is a convenient notation to indicate the sum. Let x represent any value in the data set. Then the notation

Σx (read "the sum of all given x values")

means that we are to sum all the data values. In other words, we are to sum all the entries in the distribution. The *summation symbol* Σ means *sum the following* and is capital sigma, the *S* of the Greek alphabet. ◇

Formulas for the mean

The symbol for the mean of a *sample* distribution of x values is denoted by $\bar{x}$ (read "x bar"). If your data comprise the entire *population*, we use the symbol μ (lowercase Greek letter mu, pronounced "mew") to represent the mean. The procedure to compute the mean is the same regardless of whether we have population or sample data. If we let n represent the number of entries in a *sample* data set and N represent the number of entries in a *population* data set, the formulas are

$$\text{Sample mean} = \bar{x} = \frac{\Sigma x}{n} \qquad\qquad \text{Population mean} = \mu = \frac{\Sigma x}{N}$$

● **CALCULATOR NOTE** It is very easy to compute the mean on *any* calculator: Simply add the data values and divide the total by the number of data. However, on calculators with a statistics mode, you place the calculator in that mode, *enter* the data, and then press the key for the mean. The key is usually designated $\bar{x}$. Because the formula for the population mean is the same as that for the sample mean, the same key gives the value for μ.

We have seen three averages: the mode, the median, and the mean. For later work, the mean is the most important. A disadvantage of the mean, however, is that it can be affected by exceptional values.

Resistant measure

A *resistant measure* is one that is not influenced by extremely high or low data values. The mean is not a resistant measure of center because we can make the mean as large as we want by changing the size of only one data value. The median, on the other hand, is more resistant. However, a disadvantage of the median is that it is not sensitive to the specific size of a data value.

Trimmed mean

A measure of center that is more resistant than the mean but still sensitive to specific data values is the *trimmed mean*. A trimmed mean is the mean of the data values left after "trimming" a specified percentage of the smallest and largest data values from the data set. Usually a 5% trimmed mean is used. This implies that we trim the lowest 5% of the data as well as the highest 5% of the data. A similar procedure is used for a 10% trimmed mean.

PROCEDURE

How to compute a 5% trimmed mean

1. Order the data from smallest to largest.
2. Delete the bottom 5% of the data and the top 5% of the data. *Note:* If the calculation of 5% of the number of data values does not produce a whole number, *round* to the nearest integer.
3. Compute the mean of the remaining 90% of the data.

GUIDED EXERCISE 2

Mean and trimmed mean

Barron's Profiles of American Colleges, 19th Edition, lists average class size for introductory lecture courses at each of the profiled institutions. A sample of 20 colleges and universities in California showed class size for introductory lecture courses to be

⑭	20	20	20	20	23	25	30	30	30
35	35	35	40	40	42	50	50	80	⑧⓪

(a) Compute the mean for the entire sample.

⟹ Add all the values and divide by 20:

$$\bar{x} = \frac{\Sigma x}{n} = \frac{719}{20} \approx 36.0$$

(b) Compute a 5% trimmed mean for the sample.

⟹ The data are already ordered. Since 5% of 20 is 1, we eliminate one data value from the bottom of the list and one from the top. These values are circled in the data set. Then take the mean of the remaining 18 entries.

$$5\% \text{ trimmed mean} = \frac{\Sigma x}{n} = \frac{625}{18} \approx 34.7$$

Continued

GUIDED EXERCISE 2 continued

(c) Find the median for the original data set.   ⟹   Note that the data are already ordered.

$$\text{Median} = \frac{30 + 35}{2} = 32.5$$

(d) Find the median of the 5% trimmed data set. Does the median change when you trim the data?   ⟹   The median is still 32.5. Notice that trimming the same number of entries from both ends leaves the middle position of the data set unchanged.

(e) Is the trimmed mean or the original mean closer to the median?   ⟹   The trimmed mean is closer to the median.

TECH NOTE Minitab, Excel, and TI-84Plus/TI-83Plus calculators all provide the mean and median of a data set. Minitab and Excel also provide the mode. The TI-84Plus/TI-83Plus calculators sort data, so you can easily scan the sorted data for the mode. Minitab provides the 5% trimmed mean, as does Excel.

All this technology is a wonderful aid for analyzing data. However, *a measurement has no meaning if you do not know what it represents or how a change in data values might affect the measurement.* The defining formulas and procedures for computing the measures tell you a great deal about the measures. Even if you use a calculator to evaluate all the statistical measures, pay attention to the information the formulas and procedures give you about the components or features of the measurement.

◇ **COMMENT** In Chapter 1, we examined four levels of data: nominal, ordinal, interval, and ratio. The mode (if it exists) can be used with all four levels, including nominal. For instance, the modal color of all passenger cars sold last year might be blue. The median may be used with data at the ordinal level or above. If we ranked the passenger cars in order of customer satisfaction level, we could identify the median satisfaction level. For the mean, our data need to be at the interval or ratio level (although there are exceptions in which the mean of ordinal-level data is computed). We can certainly find the mean model year of used passenger cars sold or the mean price of new passenger cars. ◇

Weighted Average

Sometimes we wish to average numbers, but we want to assign more importance or weight to some of the numbers. For instance, suppose your professor tells you that your grade will be based on a midterm and a final exam, each of which has 100 possible points. However, the final exam will be worth 60% of the grade and the midterm only 40%. How could you determine your average score to reflect these different weights? The average you need is the *weighted average*.

Weighted average

$$\textbf{Weighted average} = \frac{\Sigma x w}{\Sigma w}$$

where x is a data value and w is the weight assigned to that data value. The sum is taken over all data values.

EXAMPLE 4

Weighted average

Suppose your midterm test score is 83 and your final exam score is 95. Using weights of 40% for the midterm and 60% for the final exam, compute the weighted average of your scores. If the minimum average for an A is 90, will you earn an A?

SOLUTION: By the formula, we multiply each score by its weight and add the results together. Then we divide by the sum of all the weights. Converting the percentages to decimal notation, we get

$$\text{Weighted average} = \frac{83(0.40) + 95(0.60)}{0.40 + 0.60}$$

$$= \frac{33.2 + 57}{1} = 90.2$$

Your average is high enough to earn an A.   ◇

 TECH NOTE The TI-84Plus/TI-83Plus calculators directly support weighted averages. Both Excel and Minitab can be programmed to provide the averages.

TI-84Plus/TI-83Plus   Enter the data into one list, such as L1, and the corresponding weights into another list, such as L2. Then press **Stat ➤ Calc ➤ 1: 1-Var Stats.** Enter the list containing the data, followed by a comma and the list containing the weights.

VIEWPOINT

What's Wrong with Pitching Today?

One way to answer this question is to look at *averages*. Batting averages and average hits per game are shown for selected years from 1901 to 2000 (Source: *The Wall Street Journal*).

Year	1901	1920	1930	1941	1951	1961	1968	1976	1986	2000
B.A.	0.277	0.284	0.288	0.267	0.263	0.256	0.231	0.256	0.262	0.276
Hits	19.2	19.2	20.0	18.4	17.9	17.3	15.2	17.3	17.8	19.1

A quick scan of the averages shows that batting averages and average hits per game are virtually the same as almost 100 years ago. It seems there is *nothing* wrong with today's pitching! So what's changed? For one thing, the rules have changed! The strike zone is considerably smaller than it once was, and the pitching mound is lower. Both give the hitter an advantage over the pitcher. Even so, pitchers don't give up hits with any greater frequency than they did a century ago (look at the averages). However, modern hits go much farther, which is something a pitcher can't control.

SECTION 3.1   PROBLEMS

1. *Environmental Studies: Death Valley* How hot does it get in Death Valley? The following data are taken from a study conducted by the National Park System, of which Death Valley is a unit. The ground temperatures (°F) were taken from May to November in the vicinity of Furnace Creek.

146	152	168	174	180	178	179
180	178	178	168	165	152	144

Compute the mean, median, and mode for these ground temperatures.

2. *Ecology: Wolf Packs* How large is a wolf pack? The following information is from a random sample of winter wolf packs in regions of Alaska, Minnesota, Michigan, Wisconsin, Canada, and Finland (Source: *The Wolf,* by L. D. Mech, University of Minnesota Press). Winter pack size:

13	10	7	5	7	7	2	4	3
2	3	15	4	4	2	8	7	8

Compute the mean, median, and mode for the size of winter wolf packs.

3. *Medical: Injuries* The Grand Canyon and the Colorado River are beautiful, rugged, and sometimes dangerous. Thomas Myers is a physician at the park clinic in Grand Canyon Village. Dr. Myers has recorded (for a 5-year period) the number of visitor injuries at different landing points for commercial boat trips down the Colorado River in both the Upper and Lower Grand Canyon (Source: *Fateful Journey* by Myers, Becker, Stevens).

Upper Canyon: Number of Injuries per Landing Point Between North Canyon and Phantom Ranch

2	3	1	1	3	4	6	9	3	1	3

Lower Canyon: Number of Injuries per Landing Point Between Bright Angel and Lava Falls

8	1	1	0	6	7	2	14	3	0	1	13	2	1

(a) Compute the mean, median, and mode for injuries per landing point in the Upper Canyon.
(b) Compute the mean, median, and mode for injuries per landing point in the Lower Canyon.
(c) Compare the results of parts (a) and (b).
(d) The Lower Canyon stretch had some extreme data values. Compute a 5% trimmed mean for this region, and compare this result to the mean for the Upper Canyon computed in part (a).

4. *Football: Age of Professional Players* How old are professional football players? The 11th Edition of *The Pro Football Encyclopedia* gave the following information. Random sample of pro football player ages in years:

24	23	25	23	30	29	28	26	33	29
24	37	25	23	22	27	28	25	31	29
25	22	31	29	22	28	27	26	23	21
25	21	25	24	22	26	25	32	26	29

(a) Compute the mean, median, and mode of the ages.
(b) Compare the averages. Does one seem to represent the age of the pro football players most accurately? Explain.

5. *Leisure: Maui Vacation* How expensive is Maui? If you want a vacation rental condominium (up to four people), visit the Brase/Brase statistics site at **http://math.college.hmco.com/students,** find the link to Maui, and then search for accommodations. *The Maui News* gave the following costs in dollars per day for a random sample of condominiums located throughout the island of Maui.

89	50	68	60	375	55	500	71	40	350
60	50	250	45	45	125	235	65	60	130

(a) Compute the mean, median, and mode for the data.

(b) Compute a 5% trimmed mean for the data, and compare it with the mean computed in part (a). Does the trimmed mean more accurately reflect the general level of the daily rental costs?

(c) If you were a travel agent, and a client asked about the daily cost of renting a condominium on Maui, what average would you use? Explain. Is there any other information about the costs that you think might be useful, such as the spread of the costs?

6. *Financial: Credit Cards* Consider the following types of data that were obtained from a random sample of 49 credit card accounts. Identify all the averages (mean, median, or mode) that can be used to summarize the data.

(a) Outstanding balance on each account

(b) Name of credit card (e.g., MasterCard, Visa, American Express, etc.)

(c) Dollar amount due on next payment

7. *General: Mean and Median* Consider a data set of 15 distinct measurements with mean A and median B.

(a) If the highest number were increased, what would be the effect on the median and mean? Explain.

(b) If the highest number were decreased to a value that is still larger than B, what would be the effect on the median and mean?

(c) If the highest number were decreased to a value smaller than B, what would be the effect on the median and mean?

8. *Grades: Weighted Average* In your biology class, your final grade is based on several things: a lab score, scores on two major tests, and your score on the final exam. There are 100 points available for each score. However, the lab score is worth 25% of your total grade, each major test is worth 22.5%, and the final exam is worth 30%. Compute the weighted average for the following scores: 92 on the lab, 81 on the first major test, 93 on the second major test, and 85 on the final exam.

9. *Merit Pay Scale: Weighted Average* At General Hospital, nurses are given performance evaluations to determine eligibility for merit pay raises. The supervisor rates the nurses on a scale of 1 to 10 (10 being the highest rating) for several activities: promptness, record keeping, appearance, and bedside manner with patients. Then an average is determined by giving a weight of 2 for promptness, 3 for record keeping, 1 for appearance, and 4 for bedside manner with patients. What is the average rating for a nurse with ratings of 9 for promptness, 7 for record keeping, 6 for appearance, and 10 for bedside manner?

10. *EPA: Wetlands* Where does all the water go? According to the Environmental Protection Agency (EPA), in a typical wetland environment, 38% of the water is outflow; 47% is seepage; 7% evaporates; and 8% remains as water volume in the ecosystem (Reference: United States Environmental Protection Agency Case Studies Report 832-R-93-005). Chloride compounds as residuals from residential areas are a problem for wetlands. Suppose that in a particular wetland environment the following concentrations (mg/l) of chloride compounds were found: outflow, 64.1; seepage, 75.8; remaining due to evaporation, 23.9; in the water volume, 68.2.

(a) Compute the weighted average of chlorine compound concentration (mg/l) for this ecological system.

(b) Suppose the EPA has established an average chlorine compound concentration target of no more than 58 mg/l. Comment on whether this wetlands system meets the target standard for chlorine compound concentration.

3.2
Measures of Variation

FOCUS POINTS

✓ Find the range, variance, and standard deviation.

✓ Compute the coefficient of variation from raw data. Why is the coefficient of variation important?

✓ Apply Chebyshev's theorem to raw data. What does a Chebyshev interval tell us?

An average is an attempt to summarize a set of data in just one number. As some of our examples have shown, an average taken by itself may not always be very meaningful. We need a statistical cross-reference that measures the spread of the data.

The range is one such measure of variation.

> The **range** is the difference between the largest and smallest values of a data distribution.

EXAMPLE 5

Range

A large bakery regularly orders cartons of Maine blueberries. The average weight of a carton is supposed to be 22 ounces. Random samples of cartons from two suppliers were weighed. The weights in ounces of the cartons were

Supplier I:	17	22	22	22	27
Supplier II:	17	19	20	27	27

(a) Compute the range of carton weights from each supplier.

$$\text{Range} = \text{Largest value} - \text{smallest value}$$
$$\text{Supplier I range} = 27 - 17 = 10 \text{ ounces}$$
$$\text{Supplier II range} = 27 - 17 = 10 \text{ ounces}$$

(b) Compute the mean weight of cartons from each supplier. In both cases the mean is 22 ounces.

(c) Look at the two samples again. The samples have the same range and mean. How do they differ? The bakery uses one carton of blueberries in each blueberry muffin recipe. It is important that the cartons be of consistent weight so that the muffins turn out right.

Supplier I provides more cartons that have weights closer to the mean. Or put another way, the weights of cartons from Supplier I are more clustered around the mean. The bakery might find Supplier I more satisfactory.   ◇

Blueberry patch

As we see in Example 5, although the range tells the difference between the largest and smallest values in a distribution, it does not tell us how much other values vary from one another or from the mean.

Variance and Standard Deviation

Variance and standard deviation

We need a measure of the distribution or spread of data around an expected value (either $\bar{x}$ or μ). The *variance* and *standard deviation* provide such measures. Formulas and rationale for these measures are described in the next Procedure display. Then examples and guided exercises show how to compute and interpret these measures.

As we will see later, the formulas for variance and standard deviation differ slightly depending on whether we are using a sample or the entire population.

PROCEDURE

How to compute the sample variance and sample standard deviation

Quantity	Description
x	The variable x represents a **data value** or outcome.
Mean $$\bar{x} = \frac{\Sigma x}{n}$$	This is the **average of the data values,** or what you "expect" to happen the next time you conduct the statistical experiment. Note that n is the sample size.
$x - \bar{x}$	This is the **difference** between what happened and what you expected to happen. This represents a "deviation" away from what you "expect" and is a measure of risk.
$\Sigma(x - \bar{x})^2$	The expression $\Sigma(x - \bar{x})^2$ is called the **sum of squares**. The $(x - \bar{x})$ quantity is squared to make it nonnegative. The sum is over all the data. If you don't square $(x - \bar{x})$, then the sum $\Sigma(x - \bar{x}) = 0$ because the negative values cancel the positive values. This occurs even if some $(x - \bar{x})$ values are large, indicating a large deviation or risk.
Sum of squares $$\Sigma(x - \bar{x})^2$$ or $$\Sigma x^2 - \frac{(\Sigma x)^2}{n}$$	This is an **algebraic simplification of the sum of squares** that is easier to compute. The **defining formula** for the sum of squares is the upper one. The **computation formula** for the sum of squares is the lower one. Both formulas give the same result.
Sample variance $$s^2 = \frac{\Sigma(x - \bar{x})^2}{n - 1}$$ or $$s^2 = \frac{\Sigma x^2 - (\Sigma x)^2/n}{n - 1}$$	The **sample variance** is s^2. The variance can be thought of as a kind of average of the $(x - \bar{x})^2$ values. However, for technical reasons, we divide the sum by the quantity $n - 1$ rather than n. This gives us the best mathematical estimate for the sample variance. The **defining formula** for the variance is the upper one. The **computation formula** for the variance is the lower one. Both formulas give the same result.
Sample standard deviation $$s = \sqrt{\frac{\Sigma(x - \bar{x})^2}{n - 1}}$$ or $$s = \sqrt{\frac{\Sigma x^2 - (\Sigma x)^2/n}{n - 1}}$$	This is **sample standard deviation, s.** Why do we take the square root? Well, if the original x units were, say, days or dollars, then the s^2 units would be days squared or dollars squared (wow, what's that?). We take the square root to return to the original units of the data measurements. The standard deviation can be thought of as a measure of variability or risk. Larger values of s imply greater variability in the data. The **defining formula** for the standard deviation is the upper one. The **computation formula** for the standard deviation is the lower one. Both formulas give the same result.

◇ **COMMENT** Why is *s* called a *sample standard* deviation? First, it is computed from sample data. Then why do we use the word *standard* in the name? We know *s* is a measure of deviation or risk. You should be aware that there are other statistical measures of risk that we have not yet mentioned. However, *s* is the one that everyone uses, so it is called the "standard" (like standard time). ◇

In statistics, the sample standard deviation and sample variance are used to describe the spread of data about the mean $\bar{x}$. The next example shows how to find these quantities by using the defining formulas. Guided Exercise 3 shows how to use the computation formulas.

As you will discover, for "hand" calculations, the computation formulas for s^2 and *s* are much easier to use. However, the defining formulas for s^2 and *s* emphasize the fact that the variance and standard deviation are based on the differences between each data value and the mean.

Defining formulas (sample data)

$$\text{Sample variance} = s^2 = \frac{\Sigma(x - \bar{x})^2}{n - 1} \tag{1}$$

$$\text{Sample standard deviation} = s = \sqrt{\frac{\Sigma(x - \bar{x})^2}{n - 1}} \tag{2}$$

where *x* is a member of the data set, $\bar{x}$ is the mean, and *n* is the number of data values. The sum is taken over all data values.

Computation formulas (sample data)

$$\text{Sample variance} = s^2 = \frac{\Sigma x^2 - (\Sigma x)^2/n}{n - 1} \tag{3}$$

$$\text{Sample standard deviation} = s = \sqrt{\frac{\Sigma x^2 - (\Sigma x)^2/n}{n - 1}} \tag{4}$$

where *x* is a member of the data set, $\bar{x}$ is the mean, and *n* is the number of data values. The sum is taken over all data values.

EXAMPLE 6

Sample standard deviation (defining formula)

Big Blossom Greenhouse was commissioned to develop an extra large rose for the Rose Bowl Parade. A random sample of blossoms from Hybrid A bushes yielded the following diameters (in inches) for mature peak blooms.

> 2   3   3   8   10   10

Find the sample variance and standard deviation.

SOLUTION: Several steps are involved in computing the variance and standard deviation. A table will be helpful (see Table 3-1 on the next page). Since *n* = 6, we take the sum of the entries in the first column of Table 3-1 and divide by 6 to find the mean $\bar{x}$.

$$\bar{x} = \frac{\Sigma x}{n} = \frac{36}{6} = 6.0 \text{ inches}$$

TABLE 3-1   Diameter of Rose Blossoms (in inches)

Column I x	Column II $x - \bar{x}$	Column III $(x - \bar{x})^2$
2	$2 - 6 = -4$	$(-4)^2 = 16$
3	$3 - 6 = -3$	$(-3)^2 = 9$
3	$3 - 6 = -3$	$(-3)^2 = 9$
8	$8 - 6 = 2$	$(2)^2 = 4$
10	$10 - 6 = 4$	$(4)^2 = 16$
10	$10 - 6 = 4$	$(4)^2 = 16$
$\Sigma x = 36$		$\Sigma(x - \bar{x})^2 = 70$

Using this value for $\bar{x}$, we obtain Column II. Square each value in the second column to obtain Column III, and then add the values in Column III. To get the sample variance, divide the sum of Column III by $n - 1$. Since $n = 6$, $n - 1 = 5$.

$$s^2 = \frac{\Sigma(x - \bar{x})^2}{n - 1} = \frac{70}{5} = 14$$

Now obtain the sample standard deviation by taking the square root of the variance.

$$s = \sqrt{s^2} = \sqrt{14} \approx 3.74$$

(Use a calculator to compute the square root. Because of rounding, we use the approximately equal symbol, $\approx$.)   ◊

GUIDED EXERCISE 3

Sample standard deviation (computation formula)

Big Blossom Greenhouse gathered another random sample of mature peak blooms from Hybrid B. The six blossoms had these widths (in inches):

    5   5   5   6   7   8

(a) Again, we will construct a table so we can find the mean, variance, and standard deviation more easily. In this case, what is the value of n? Find the sum of Column I in Table 3-2, and compute the mean.

 $n = 6$. The sum of Column I is $\Sigma x = 36$, so the mean is

$$\bar{x} = \frac{36}{6} = 6 \text{ in.}$$

Continued

GUIDED EXERCISE 3 continued

TABLE 3-2   Complete Columns I and II

I x	II x^2
5	_____
5	_____
5	_____
6	_____
7	_____
8	_____
$\Sigma x =$ _____	$\Sigma x^2 =$ _____

TABLE 3-3   Completion of Table 3-2

I x	II x^2
5	25
5	25
5	25
6	36
7	49
8	64
$\Sigma x = 36$	$\Sigma x^2 = 224$

(b) What is the value of n? of $n - 1$? Use the computation formula to find the sample variance s^2. *Note:* Be sure to distinguish between Σx^2 and $(\Sigma x)^2$. For Σx^2 you square the x values first, and then sum them. For $(\Sigma x)^2$, you sum the x values first and then square the result.

⟹ $n = 6;\ n - 1 = 5.$

$$s^2 = \frac{\Sigma x^2 - (\Sigma x)^2/n}{n - 1}$$

$$= \frac{224 - (36)^2/6}{5} = \frac{8}{5} = 1.6$$

(c) Use a calculator to find the square root of the variance. Is this the standard deviation?

⟹ $s = \sqrt{s^2} = \sqrt{1.6} \approx 1.26$

Yes.

Let's summarize and compare the results of Guided Exercise 3 and Example 6. The greenhouse found the following blossom diameters for Hybrid A and Hybrid B:

> *Hybrid A:*   mean, 6.0 in.; standard deviation, 3.74 in.
>
> *Hybrid B:*   mean, 6.0 in.; standard deviation, 1.26 in.

In both cases, the means are the same: 6 in. But the first hybrid has a larger standard deviation. This means that the blossoms of Hybrid A are less consistent than those of Hybrid B. If you want a rosebush that occasionally has 10-in. blooms and 2-in. blooms, use the first hybrid. But if you want a bush that consistently produces roses close to 6 in. across, use Hybrid B.

● **ROUNDING NOTE**   Rounding errors cannot be completely eliminated, even if a computer or calculator does all the computations. However, software and calculator routines are designed to minimize the error. If the mean is rounded, the value of the standard deviation will change slightly depending on how much the mean is rounded. If you do your calculations "by hand" or reenter intermediate values into a calculator, try to carry one or two more digits than occur in the original data. If your resulting answers vary slightly from those in this text, do not be overly concerned. The text answers are computer- or calculator-generated.

Population mean variance and
standard deviation

In most applications of statistics, we work with a random sample of data rather than the entire population of *all* possible data values. However, if we have data for the entire population, we can compute the *population mean* μ (lowercase Greek letter mu, pronounced "mew"), *population variance* σ^2, and *population standard deviation* σ (lowercase Greek letter sigma) using the following formulas:

$$\text{Population mean} = \mu = \frac{\Sigma x}{N}$$

$$\text{Population variance} = \sigma^2 = \frac{\Sigma(x - \mu)^2}{N}$$

$$\text{Population standard deviation} = \sigma = \sqrt{\frac{\Sigma(x - \mu)^2}{N}}$$

where N is the number of data values in the population, and x represents the individual data values of the population.

We note that the formula for μ is the same as the formula for $\bar{x}$ (the sample mean) and the formulas for σ^2 and σ are the same as those for s^2 and s (sample variance and sample standard deviation), except that the population size N is used instead of $n - 1$. Also, μ is used instead of $\bar{x}$ in the formulas for σ^2 and σ.

In the formulas for s and σ we use $n - 1$ to compute s, and N to compute σ. Why? The reason is that N (capital letter) represents the *population size*, while n (lowercase letter) represents the sample size. Since a random sample usually will not contain extreme data values (large or small), we divide by $n - 1$ in the formula for s to make s a little larger than it would have been had we divided by n. Courses in advanced theoretical statistics show that this procedure will give us the best possible estimate for the standard deviation σ. In fact, s is called the *unbiased estimate* for σ. If we have the population of all data values, then extreme data values are, of course, present, so we divide by N instead of $N - 1$.

◇ **COMMENT** The computation formula for the population standard deviation is

$$\sigma = \sqrt{\frac{\Sigma x^2 - (\Sigma x)^2/N}{N}} \quad ◇$$

We've seen that the standard deviation (sample or population) is a measure of data spread. We will use the standard deviation extensively in later chapters.

TECH NOTE   Most scientific or business calculators have a statistics mode and provide the mean and sample standard deviation directly. The TI-84Plus/TI-83Plus calculators, Excel, and Minitab provide the median and several other measures as well.

Many technologies display only the sample standard deviation s. You can quickly compute σ if you know s by using the formula

$$\sigma = s\sqrt{\frac{n - 1}{n}}$$

The mean given in displays can be interpreted as the sample mean $\bar{x}$ or the population mean μ as appropriate.

The following three displays show output for the hybrid rose data of Guided Exercise 3.

TI-84Plus/TI-83Plus Display
Press **STAT ➤ CALC ➤ 1:1-Var Stats.** S_x is the sample standard deviation. σ_x is the population standard deviation.

```
1-Var Stats
 x̄=6
 Σx=36
 Σx²=224
 Sx=1.264911064
 σx=1.154700538
↓n=6
■
```

Excel Display
Menu choices: **Tools ➤ Data Analysis ➤ Descriptive Statistics.** Check the summary statistics box. The standard deviation is the sample standard deviation.

Column 1	
Mean	6
Standard Error	0.516398
Median	5.5
Mode	5
Standard Deviation	1.264911
Sample Variance	1.6
Kurtosis	−0.78125
Skewness	0.889391
Range	3
Minimum	5
Maximum	8
Sum	36
Count	6

Minitab Display
Menu choices: **Stat ➤ Basic Statistics ➤ Display Descriptive Statistics.** StDev is the sample standard deviation. TrMean is a 5% trimmed mean.

N	Mean	Median	TrMean	StDev	SE Mean
6	6.000	5.500	6.000	1.265	0.516

Minimum	Maximum	Q1	Q3	
5.000	8.000	5.000	7.250	

Now let's look at two immediate applications of the standard deviation. The first is the coefficient of variation, and the second is Chebyshev's theorem.

Coefficient of Variation

Coefficient of variation

A disadvantage of the standard deviation as a comparative measure of variation is that it depends on the units of measurement. This means that it is difficult to use the standard deviation to compare measurements from different populations. For this reason, statisticians have defined the *coefficient of variation*, which expresses the standard deviation as a percentage of the sample or population mean.

If $\bar{x}$ and s represent the sample mean and sample standard deviation, respectively, then the sample **coefficient of variation** CV is defined to be

$$CV = \frac{s}{\bar{x}} \cdot 100$$

If μ and σ represent the population mean and standard deviation, respectively, then the population coefficient of variation CV is defined to be

$$CV = \frac{\sigma}{\mu} \cdot 100$$

Notice that the numerator and denominator in the definition of CV have the same units, so CV itself has no units of measurement. This gives us the advantage of being able to directly compare the variability of two different populations using the coefficient of variation.

In the next example and guided exercise, we will compute the CV of a population and of a sample and then compare the results.

EXAMPLE 7

Coefficient of variation

The Trading Post on Grand Mesa is a small, family-run store in a remote part of Colorado. The Grand Mesa region contains many good fishing lakes, so the Trading Post sells spinners (a type of fishing lure). The store has a very limited selection of spinners. In fact, the Trading Post has only eight different types of spinners for sale. The prices (in dollars) are

2.10   1.95   2.60   2.00   1.85   2.25   2.15   2.25

Since the Trading Post has only eight different kinds of spinners for sale, we consider the eight data values to be the *population*.

(a) Use a calculator with appropriate statistics keys to verify that for the Trading Post data, $\mu \approx \$2.14$ and $\sigma \approx \$0.22$.

SOLUTION: Since the computation formulas for $\bar{x}$ and μ are identical, most calculators provide the value of $\bar{x}$ only. Use the output of this key for μ. The computation formulas for the sample standard deviation s and the population standard deviation σ are slightly different. Be sure that you use the key for σ (sometimes designated as σ_n or σ_x).

(b) Compute the CV of prices for the Trading Post and comment on the meaning of the result.

SOLUTION:

$$CV = \frac{\sigma}{\mu} \times 100 = \frac{0.22}{2.14} \times 100 = 10.28\%$$

The coefficient of variation can be thought of as a measure of the spread of the data relative to the average of the data. Since the Trading Post is very small, it carries a small selection of spinners that are all priced similarly. The CV tells us that the standard deviation of the spinner prices is only 10.28% of the mean.   ◇

GUIDED EXERCISE 4

Coefficient of variation

Cabela's in Sidney, Nebraska, is a very large outfitter that carries a broad selection of fishing tackle. It markets its products nationwide through a catalog service. A random sample of 10 spinners from Cabela's extensive spring catalog gave the following prices (in dollars):

| 1.69 | 1.49 | 3.09 | 1.79 | 1.39 | 2.89 | 1.49 | 1.39 | 1.49 | 1.99 |

(a) Use a calculator with sample mean and sample standard deviation keys to compute $\bar{x}$ and s.

⟹ $\bar{x} = \$1.87$ and $s \approx \$0.62$.

(b) Compute the CV for the spinner prices at Cabela's.

⟹ $CV = \dfrac{s}{\bar{x}} \times 100 = \dfrac{0.62}{1.87} \times 100 = 33.16\%$

(c) Compare the mean, standard deviation, and CV for the spinner prices at the Grand Mesa Trading Post (Example 7) and Cabela's. Comment on the differences.

⟹ The CV for Cabela's is more than three times the CV for the Trading Post. Why? First, because of the remote location, the Trading Post tends to have somewhat higher prices (larger μ). Second, the Trading Post is very small, so it has a rather limited selection of spinners with a smaller variation in price.

Chebyshev's Theorem

From our earlier discussion about standard deviation, we recall that the spread or dispersion of a set of data about the mean will be small if the standard deviation is small, and it will be large if the standard deviation is large. If we are dealing with a symmetrical bell-shaped distribution, then we can make very definite statements about the proportion of the data that must lie within a certain number of standard deviations on either side of the mean. This will be discussed in detail in Chapter 7 when we talk about normal distributions.

However, the concept of data spread about the mean can be expressed quite generally for *all data distributions* (skewed, symmetric, or other shape) by using the remarkable theorem of Chebyshev.

Chebyshev's theorem

For *any* set of data (either population or sample) and for any constant k greater than 1, the proportion of the data that must lie within k standard deviations on either side of the mean is *at least*

$$1 - \frac{1}{k^2}$$

Results of Chebyshev's theorem

For *any* set of data:

- at *least* 75% of the data fall in the interval from $\mu - 2\sigma$ to $\mu + 2\sigma$.
- at *least* 88.9% of the data fall in the interval from $\mu - 3\sigma$ to $\mu + 3\sigma$.
- at *least* 93.8% of the data fall in the interval from $\mu - 4\sigma$ to $\mu + 4\sigma$.

The results of Chebyshev's theorem can be derived by using the theorem and a little arithmetic. For instance, if we create an interval $k = 2$ standard deviations on either side of the mean, Chebyshev's theorem tells us that

$$1 - \frac{1}{2^2} = 1 - \frac{1}{4} = \frac{3}{4} \text{ or } 75\%$$

is the minimum percentage of data in the $\mu - 2\sigma$ to $\mu + 2\sigma$ interval.

Notice that Chebyshev's theorem refers to the *minimum* percentage of data that must fall within the specified number of standard deviations of the mean. If the distribution is mound-shaped, an even *greater* percentage of data will fall into the specified intervals (see the Empirical Rule in Section 7.1).

EXAMPLE 8

Chebyshev's theorem

Students Who Care is a student volunteer program in which college students donate work time to various community projects such as planting trees. Professor Gill is the faculty sponsor for this student volunteer program. For several years, Dr. Gill has kept a careful record of x = total number of work hours volunteered by a student in the program each semester. For a random sample of students in the program, the mean number of hours was $\bar{x} = 29.1$ hours each semester, with a standard deviation of $s = 1.7$ hours each semester. Find an interval A to B for the number of hours volunteered into which at least 75% of the students in this program would fit.

SOLUTION: According to results of Chebyshev's theorem, at least 75% of the data must fall within 2 standard deviations of the mean. Because the mean $\bar{x} = 29.1$ and the standard deviation $s = 1.7$, the interval is

$$\bar{x} - 2s \text{ to } \bar{x} + 2s$$
$$29.1 - 2(1.7) \text{ to } 29.1 + 2(1.7)$$
$$25.7 \text{ to } 32.5$$

At least 75% of the students would fit into the group that volunteered from 25.7 to 32.5 hours each semester.   ◇

GUIDED EXERCISE 5

Chebyshev interval

The *East Coast Independent News* periodically runs ads in its own classified section offering a month's free subscription to those who respond. In this way, management can get a sense about the number of subscribers who read the classified section each day. Over a period of 2 years, careful records have been kept. The mean number of responses per ad is $\bar{x} = 525$ with standard deviation $s = 30$.

Determine a Chebyshev interval about the mean in which at least 88.9% of the data fall.

$\Longrightarrow$ By Chebyshev's theorem, at least 88.9% of the data fall into the interval

$$\bar{x} - 3s \text{ to } \bar{x} + 3s$$

Because $\bar{x} = 525$ and $s = 30$, the interval is

$$525 - 3(30) \text{ to } 525 + 3(30)$$

or from 435 to 615 responses per ad.

VIEWPOINT   *Socially Responsible Investing*

Make a difference *and* make money! Socially responsible mutual funds tend to screen out corporations that sell tobacco, weapons, and alcohol, as well as companies that are environmentally unfriendly. In addition, these funds screen out companies that use child labor in sweatshops. There are 68 socially responsible funds tracked by the Social Investment Forum. For more information, visit the Brase/Brase statistics site at **http://math.college.hmco.com/students** and find the link to social investing.

How do these funds rate compared to other funds? One way to answer this question is to study the annual percent returns of the funds using both the *mean* and *standard deviation*. (See Problem 6 of this section.)

SECTION 3.2   PROBLEMS

$$\frac{\Sigma x(x - \bar{x})^2}{n-1} = s^2$$

$$\sqrt{\frac{\Sigma(x - \bar{x})^2}{n-1}} = s$$

1. *General Concepts: Variance, Standard Deviation* Given the sample data

   x: 23   17   15   30   25

   (a) Find the range.
   (b) Verify that $\Sigma x = 110$ and $\Sigma x^2 = 2568$.
   (c) Use the results of part (b) and appropriate computation formulas to compute the sample variance s^2 and sample standard deviation s.
   (d) Use the defining formulas to compute the sample variance s^2 and sample standard deviation s.

(e) Suppose the given data comprise the entire population of all x values. Compute the population variance σ^2 and population standard deviation σ.

2. *Investing: Stocks and Bonds* Do bonds reduce the overall risk of an investment portfolio? Let x be a random variable representing annual percent return for Vanguard Total Stock Index (all stocks). Let y be a random variable representing annual return for Vanguard Balanced Index (60% stock and 40% bond). For the past several years, we have the following data (Reference: Morningstar Research Group, Chicago).

$x:$	11	0	36	21	31	23	24	−11	−11	−21
$y:$	10	−2	29	14	22	18	14	−2	−3	−10

(a) Compute Σx, Σx^2, Σy, and Σy^2.
(b) Use the results of part (a) to compute the sample mean, variance, and standard deviation for x and for y.
(c) Compute a 75% Chebyshev interval around the mean for x values and also for y values. Use the intervals to compare the two funds.
(d) Compute the coefficient of variation for each fund. Use the coefficients of variation to compare the two funds. If s represents risks and $\bar{x}$ represents expected return, then $s/\bar{x}$ can be thought of as a measure of risk per unit of expected return. In this case, why is a smaller CV better? Explain.

3. *Space Shuttle: Epoxy* Kevlar epoxy is a material used on the NASA Space Shuttle. Strands of this epoxy were tested at the 90% breaking strength. The following data represent time to failure (in hours) for a random sample of 50 epoxy strands (Reference: R. E. Barlow, University of California, Berkeley). Let x be a random variable representing time to failure (in hours) at 90% breaking strength. *Note:* These data are also available with other software on the statSpace CD-ROM.

0.54	1.80	1.52	2.05	1.03	1.18	0.80	1.33	1.29	1.11
3.34	1.54	0.08	0.12	0.60	0.72	0.92	1.05	1.43	3.03
1.81	2.17	0.63	0.56	0.03	0.09	0.18	0.34	1.51	1.45
1.52	0.19	1.55	0.02	0.07	0.65	0.40	0.24	1.51	1.45
1.60	1.80	4.69	0.08	7.89	1.58	1.64	0.03	0.23	0.72

(a) Find the range.
(b) Use a calculator to verify that $\Sigma x = 62.11$ and $\Sigma x^2 \approx 164.23$.
(c) Use the results of part (b) to compute the sample mean, variance, and standard deviation for the time to failure.
(d) Use the results of part (c) to compute the coefficient of variation. What does this number say about time to failure? Why does a small CV indicate more consistent data, whereas a larger CV indicates less consistent data? Explain.

4. *Archaeology: Ireland* The Hill of Tara in Ireland is a place of great archaeological importance. This region has been occupied by people for more than 4,000 years. Geomagnetic surveys detect subsurface anomalies in the earth's magnetic field. These surveys have led to many significant archaeological discoveries. After collecting data, the next step is to begin a statistical study. The following data measure magnetic susceptibility (centimeter-gram-second $\times 10^{-6}$) on two of the main grids of the Hill of Tara (Reference: *Tara: An Archaeological Survey* by Conor Newman, Royal Irish Academy, Dublin).

Grid E: x variable

13.20	5.60	19.80	15.05	21.40	17.25	27.45
16.95	23.90	32.40	40.75	5.10	17.75	28.35

Grid H: *y* variable

11.85	15.25	21.30	17.30	27.50	10.35	14.90
48.70	25.40	25.95	57.60	34.35	38.80	41.00
31.25						

(a) Compute Σx, Σx^2, Σy, and Σy^2.

(b) Use the results of part (a) to compute the sample mean, variance, and standard deviation for *x* and for *y*.

(c) Compute a 75% Chebyshev interval around the mean for *x* values and also for *y* values. Use the intervals to compare the magnetic susceptibility on the two grids. Higher numbers indicate higher magnetic susceptibility. However, extreme values, high or low, could mean an anomaly and possible archaeological treasure.

(d) Compute the sample coefficient of variation for each grid. Use the *CV*'s to compare the two grids. If *s* represents variability in the signal (magnetic susceptibility) and $\bar{x}$ represents the expected level of the signal, then $s/\bar{x}$ can be thought of as a measure of the variability per unit of expected signal. Remember, a considerable variability in the signal (above or below average) might indicate buried artifacts. Why, in this case, would a large *CV* be better, or at least more exciting? Explain.

5. *Wildlife: Mallard Ducks and Canada Geese* For mallard ducks and Canada geese, what percent of nests are successful (at least one offspring survives)? Studies in Montana, Illinois, Wyoming, Utah, and California gave the following percentages of successful nests (Reference: *The Wildlife Society Press*, Washington, D.C.).

x: **Percentage success for mallard duck nests**

    56   85   52   13   39   100

y: **Percentage success for Canada goose nests**

    24   53   60   69   18

(a) Use a calculator to verify that $\Sigma x = 245$; $\Sigma x^2 = 14,755$; $\Sigma y = 224$; and $\Sigma y^2 = 12,070$.

(b) Use the results of part (a) to compute the sample mean, variance, and standard deviation for *x*, the percent of successful mallard nests.

(c) Use the results of part (a) to compute the sample mean, variance, and standard deviation for *y*, the percent of successful Canada goose nests.

(d) Use the results of parts (b) and (c) to compute the coefficient of variation for successful mallard nests and Canada goose nests. Write a brief explanation of the meaning of these numbers. What do these results say about the nesting success rates for mallards compared to Canada geese? Would you say one group of data is more or less consistent than the other? Explain.

6. *Investing: Socially Responsible Mutual Funds* Pax World Balanced is a highly respected, socially responsible mutual fund of stocks and bonds (see Viewpoint). Vanguard Balanced Index is another highly regarded fund that represents the entire U.S. stock and bond market (an index fund). The mean and standard deviation of annualized percent returns are shown below. The annualized mean and standard deviation are based on the years 1993 through 2002 (Source: Morningstar).

Pax World Balanced: $\bar{x} = 9.58\%$; $s = 14.05\%$

Vanguard Balanced Index: $\bar{x} = 9.02\%$; $s = 12.50\%$

(a) Compute the coefficient of variation for each fund. If $\bar{x}$ represents return and s represents risk, then explain why the coefficient of variation can be taken to represent risk per unit of return. From this point of view, which fund appears to be better? Explain.

(b) Compute a 75% Chebyshev interval around the mean for each fund. Use the intervals to compare the two funds. As usual, past performance does not guarantee future performance.

7. *Medical: Physician Visits* In some reports, the mean and coefficient of variation are given. For instance, in *Statistical Abstract of the United States*, 116th Edition, one report gives the average number of physician visits by males per year. The average reported is 2.2, and the reported coefficient of variation is 1.5%. Use this information to determine the standard deviation of the annual number of visits to physicians made by males.

8. *Lifestyle: Gathering Data* For the next 2 weeks, record how long it takes you to go from your residence (or job) to your first class. Record the values to the nearest minute. Compute the range, mean, sample standard deviation, and coefficient of variation. Use Chebyshev's theorem to compute an interval in which at least 88.9% of the travel times fall. Were there any unusual data values in your data set? How would you explain them?

Grouped data

Approximating $\bar{x}$ and s from grouped data

Expand Your Knowledge: Grouped data

When data are grouped, such as in a frequency table or histogram, we can estimate the mean and standard deviation by using the following formulas. Notice that all data values in a given class are treated as though each of them equals the midpoint x of the class.

Sample mean for a frequency distribution

$$\bar{x} = \frac{\Sigma xf}{n} \tag{5}$$

Sample standard deviation for a frequency distribution

$$s = \sqrt{\frac{\Sigma(x - \bar{x})^2 f}{n - 1}} \tag{6}$$

Computation formula for the sample standard deviation

$$s = \sqrt{\frac{\Sigma x^2 f - (\Sigma xf)^2/n}{n - 1}} \tag{7}$$

where

x is the midpoint of a class,
f is the number of entries in that class,
n is the total number of entries in the distribution, and $n = \Sigma f$.
The summation Σ is over all classes in the distribution.

Use formulas (5) and (6) or (5) and (7) to solve Problems 9–12. To use formulas (5) and (6) to evaluate the sample mean and standard deviation, use the following column heads:

Midpoint x	Frequency f	xf	$(x - \bar{x})$	$(x - \bar{x})^2$	$(x - \bar{x})^2 f$

For formulas (5) and (7), use these column heads:

Midpoint x	Frequency f	xf	x^2	$x^2 f$

Note: On the TI-83 calculator, enter the midpoints in column L_1 and the frequencies in column L_2. Then use **1-VarStats L_1, L_2.**

9. *Crime: Shoplifting* What is the age distribution of adult shoplifters (21 years of age or older) in supermarkets? The following is based on information taken from the National Retail Federation. A random sample of 895 incidents of shoplifting gave the following age distribution:

Age range (years)	21–30	31–40	41 and over
Number of shoplifters	260	348	287

Estimate the mean age, sample variance, and sample standard deviation for the shoplifters. For the class 41 and over, use 45.5 as the class midpoint.

10. *Anthropology: Navajo Reservation* What was the age distribution of prehistoric Native Americans? Extensive anthropologic studies in the southwestern United States gave the following information about a prehistoric extended family group of 80 members on what is now the Navajo Reservation in northwestern New Mexico. (*Source:* Based on information taken from *Prehistory in the Navajo Reservation District,* by F. W. Eddy, Museum of New Mexico Press.)

Age range (years)	1–10*	11–20	21–30	31 and over
Number of individuals	34	18	17	11

*Includes infants.

Estimate the mean age expressed in years for this community, the sample variance, and the sample standard deviation. For the class 31 and over, use 35.5 as the class midpoint.

11. *Business Administration: Profits/Assets* What are the big corporations doing with their wealth? One way to answer this question is to examine profits as percentage of assets. A random sample of 50 *Fortune 500* companies gave the following information. (*Source:* Based on information from *Fortune 500,* Vol. 135, No. 8.)

Profit as percentage of assets	8.6–12.5	12.6–16.5	16.6–20.5	20.6–24.5	24.6–28.5
Number of companies	15	20	5	7	3

Estimate the sample mean, sample variance, and sample standard deviation for profit as percentage of assets.

12. *Medical: Hours of Sleep per Day* Alexander Borbely is a professor at the University of Zurich Medical School, where he is director of the sleep laboratory. The histogram

in Figure 3-1 is based on information in his book *Secrets of Sleep*. The histogram displays hours of sleep per day for a random sample of 200 subjects. Estimate the mean hours of sleep, standard deviation of hours of sleep, and coefficient of variation.

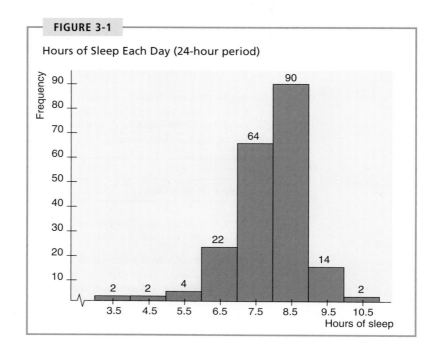

FIGURE 3-1

Hours of Sleep Each Day (24-hour period)

3.3
Percentiles and Box-and-Whisker Plots

We've seen measures of central tendency and spread for a set of data. The arithmetic mean $\bar{x}$ and the standard deviation s will be very useful in later work. However, because they each utilize every data value, they can be heavily influenced by one or two extreme data values. In cases where our data distributions are heavily skewed or even bimodal, we often get a better summary of the distribution by utilizing relative position of data rather than exact values.

Recall that the median is an average computed by using relative position of the data. If we are told that 81 is the median score on a biology test, we know that after the data have been ordered, 50% of the data fall at or below the median value of 81. The median is an example of a *percentile*; in fact, it is the 50th percentile. The general definition of the Pth percentile follows.

Percentile

For whole numbers P (where $1 \leq P \leq 99$), the Pth **percentile** of a distribution is a value such that P% of the data fall at or below it and $(100 - P)$% of the data fall at or above it.

In Figure 3-2, we see the 60th percentile marked on a histogram. We see that 60% of the data lie below the mark and 40% lie above it.

FIGURE 3-2

A Histogram with the 60th Percentile Shown

GUIDED EXERCISE 6

Percentiles

You took the English achievement test to obtain college credit in freshman English by examination.

(a) If your score is at the 89th percentile, what percentage of scores are at or below yours?

→ The percentile means that 89% of the scores are at or below yours.

(b) If the scores ranged from 1 to 100 and your raw score is 95, does this necessarily mean that your score is at the 95th percentile?

→ No, the percentile gives an indication of relative position of the scores. The determination of your percentile has to do with the number of scores at or below yours. If everyone did very well and only 80% of the scores fell at or below yours, you would be at the 80th percentile even though you got 95 out of 100 points on the exam.

There are 99 percentiles, and in an ideal situation, the 99 percentiles divide the data set into 100 equal parts. (See Figure 3-3.) However, if the number of data

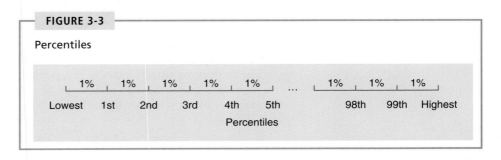

FIGURE 3-3

Percentiles

elements is not exactly divisible by 100, the percentiles will not divide the data into equal parts.

There are several widely used conventions for finding percentiles. They lead to slightly different values for different situations, but these values are close together. For all conventions, the data are first *ranked* or ordered from smallest to largest. A natural way to find the *P*th percentile is to then find a value such that *P*% of the data fall at or below it. This will not always be possible, so we take the nearest value satisfying the criterion. It is at this point that there are a variety of processes to determine the exact value of the percentile.

We will not be very concerned about exact procedures for evaluating percentiles in general. However, *quartiles* are special percentiles used so frequently that we want to adopt a specific procedure for their computation.

Quartiles are those percentiles that divide the data into fourths. The *first quartile* Q_1 is the 25th percentile, the *second quartile* Q_2 is the median, and the *third quartile* Q_3 is the 75th percentile. (See Figure 3-4.)

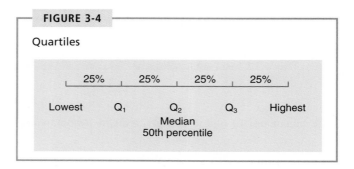

FIGURE 3-4

Quartiles

Again, several conventions are used for computing quartiles, but the following one utilizes the median and is widely adopted.

PROCEDURE

How to compute quartiles

1. Order the data from smallest to largest,

2. Find the median. This is the second quartile.

3. The first quartile Q_1 is then the median of the lower half of the data; that is, it is the median of the data falling *below* the Q_2 position (and not including Q_2).

4. The third quartile Q_3 is the median of the upper half of the data; that is, it is the median of the data falling *above* the Q_2 position (and not including Q_2).

In short, all we do to find the quartiles is to find three medians.

The median, or second quartile, is a popular measure of the center utilizing relative position. A useful measure of data spread utilizing relative position is the *interquartile range (IQR)*. It is simply the difference between the third and first quartiles.

$$\text{Interquartile range} = Q_3 - Q_1$$

The interquartile range tells us the spread of the middle half of the data. Now let's look at an example to see how to compute all these quantities.

EXAMPLE 9

Quartiles

In a hurry? On the run? Hungry as well? How about an ice cream bar as a snack? Ice cream bars are popular among all age groups. *Consumer Reports* did a study of ice cream bars. Twenty-seven bars with taste ratings of at least "fair" were listed, and cost per bar was included in the report. Just how much will an ice cream bar cost? The data, expressed in dollars, appear in Table 3-4. As you can see, the cost varies quite a bit, partly because the bars are not of uniform size.

(a) Find the quartiles.

SOLUTION: We first order the data from smallest to largest. Table 3-5 shows the data in order. Next, we find the median. Since the number of data values is 27, there are an odd number of data, and the median is simply the center or 14th value. The value is shown boxed in Table 3-5.

$$\text{Median} = Q_2 = 0.50$$

There are 13 values below the median position, and Q_1 is the median of these values. It is the middle or seventh value and is shaded in Table 3-5.

$$\text{First quartile} = Q_1 = 0.33$$

There are also 13 values above the median position. The median of these is the seventh value from the right end. This value is also shaded in Table 3-5.

$$\text{Third quartile} = Q_3 = 1.00$$

TABLE 3-4   Cost of Ice Cream Bars (in dollars)

0.99	1.07	1.00	0.50	0.37	1.03	1.07	1.07
0.97	0.63	0.33	0.50	0.97	1.08	0.47	0.84
1.23	0.25	0.50	0.40	0.33	0.35	0.17	0.38
0.20	0.18	0.16					

TABLE 3-5   Ordered Cost of Ice Cream Bars (in dollars)

0.16	0.17	0.18	0.20	0.25	0.33	0.33	0.35
0.37	0.38	0.40	0.47	0.50	0.50	0.50	0.63
0.84	0.97	0.97	0.99	1.00	1.03	1.07	1.07
1.07	1.08	1.23					

(b) Find the interquartile range.

SOLUTION:

$$\begin{aligned} IQR &= Q_3 - Q_1 \\ &= 1.00 - 0.33 \\ &= 0.67 \end{aligned}$$

This means that the middle half of the data has a cost spread of 67¢.

GUIDED EXERCISE 7

Quartiles

Many people consider the number of calories in an ice cream bar as important as, if not more important than, the cost. The *Consumer Reports* article also included the calorie count of the rated ice cream bars (Table 3-6). There were 22 vanilla-flavored bars rated. Again, the bars varied in size, and some of the smaller bars had fewer calories. The calorie counts for the vanilla bars follow.

TABLE 3-6   Calories in Vanilla-Flavored Ice Cream Bars

342	377	319	353	295
234	294	286	377	182
310	439	111	201	182
197	209	147	190	151
131	151			

(a) Our first step is to order the data. Do so.

⇨ **TABLE 3-7   Ordered Data**

111	131	147	151	151	182
182	190	197	201	209	234
286	294	295	310	319	342
353	377	377	439		

(b) There are 22 data values. Find the median.

⇨ Average the 11th and 12th data values boxed together in Table 3-7.

$$\text{Median} = \frac{209 + 234}{2}$$
$$= 221.5$$

(c) How many values are below the median position? Find Q_1.

⇨ Since the median lies halfway between the 11th and 12th values, there are 11 values below the median position. Q_1 is the median of these values.

$Q_1 = 182$

(d) There are the same number of data above as below the median. Use this fact to find Q_3.

⇨ Q_3 is the median of the upper half of the data. There are 11 values in the upper portion.

$Q_3 = 319$

(e) Find the interquartile range and comment on its meaning.

⇨ $IQR = Q_3 - Q_1$
$= 319 - 182$
$= 137$

The middle portion of the data has a spread of 137 calories.

Box-and-Whisker Plots

Five-number summary

The quartiles together with the low and high data values give us a very useful *five-number summary* of the data and their spread.

> **Five-number summary**
>
> Lowest value, Q_1, median, Q_3, highest value

Box-and-whisker plot

We will use these five numbers to create a graphic sketch of the data called a *box-and-whisker plot*. Box-and-whisker plots provide another useful technique from exploratory data analysis (EDA) for describing data.

PROCEDURE

How to make a box-and-whisker plot

1. Draw a vertical scale to include the lowest and highest data values.
2. To the right of the scale, draw a box from Q_1 to Q_3.
3. Include a solid line through the box at the median level.
4. Draw vertical lines, called *whiskers*, from Q_1 to the lowest value and from Q_3 to the highest value.

FIGURE 3-5

Box-and-Whisker Plot

The next example demonstrates the process of making a box-and-whisker plot.

EXAMPLE 10

Box-and-whisker plot

Using the data from Guided Exercise 7, make a box-and-whisker plot showing the calories in vanilla-flavored ice cream bars. Use the plot to make observations about the distribution of calories.

(a) In Guided Exercise 7, we ordered the data (see Table 3-7) and found the values of the median, Q_1, and Q_3. From this previous work we have the five-number summary:

low value = 111; Q_1 = 182; median = 221.5; Q_3 = 319; high value = 439

(b) We select an appropriate vertical scale and make the plot (Figure 3-6).

(c) A quick glance at the box-and-whisker plot reveals the following:

  (i) The box tells us where the middle half of the data lies, so we see that half of the ice cream bars have between 182 and 319 calories, with an interquartile range of 137 calories.

  (ii) The median is slightly closer to the lower part of the box. This means that the lower calorie counts are more concentrated. The calorie counts above the median are more spread out, indicating that the distribution is slightly skewed toward the higher values.

  (iii) The upper whisker is longer than the lower, which again emphasizes skewness toward the higher values.

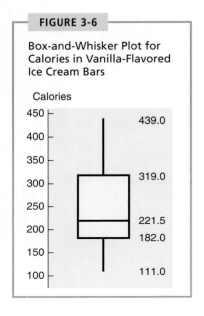

FIGURE 3-6

Box-and-Whisker Plot for Calories in Vanilla-Flavored Ice Cream Bars

◇ **COMMENT** In exploratory data analysis, *hinges* rather than quartiles are used to create the box. Hinges are computed in a manner similar to the method used to compute quartiles. However, in the case of an odd number of data values, include the median itself in both the lower and upper halves of the data (see *Applications, Basics, and Computing of Exploratory Data Analysis*, by Paul Velleman and David Hoaglin, Duxbury Press). This has the effect of shrinking the box and moving the ends of the box slightly toward the median. For an even number of data, the quartiles as we computed them equal the hinges.   ◇

GUIDED EXERCISE 8

Box-and-whisker plot

The Renata College Development Office sent salary surveys to alumni who graduated 2 and 5 years ago. The voluntary responses received are summarized in the box-and-whisker plots shown in Figure 3-7.

(a) From Figure 3-7, estimate the median and extreme values of salaries of alumni graduating 2 years ago. In what range are the middle half of the salaries?

⇒ The median seems to be about $44,000. The extremes are about $33,000 and $54,000. The middle half of the salaries fall between $40,000 and $47,000.

FIGURE 3-7 Box-and-Whisker Plots for Alumni Salaries (in thousands of dollars)

(b) From Figure 3-7, estimate the median and the extreme values of salaries of alumni graduating 5 years ago. What is the location of the middle half of the salaries?

⇒ The median seems to be $47,000. The extremes are $34,000 and $58,000. The middle half of the data are enclosed by the box with low side at $41,000 and high side at $50,000.

(c) Compare the two box plots and make comments about the salaries of alumni graduating 2 and 5 years ago.

⇒ The salaries of the alumni graduating 5 years ago have a larger range. They begin slightly higher than and extend to levels about $4,000 above the salaries of those graduating 2 years ago. The middle half of the data are also more spread out, with higher boundaries and a higher median.

We have developed the skeletal box-and-whisker plot. Other variations may include *fences,* which are marks placed on either side of the box to represent various portions of the data. Values that lie outside the fences are called *outliers* (see Problem 10 of this section). These values seem to stand by themselves, away from most of the data. They might be exceptional values and deserve closer study. Or they may be the result of data entry error. For a more complete discussion of outliers and variations of box plots, see *Applications, Basics, and Computing of Exploratory Data Analysis,* by Velleman and Hoaglin.

 TECH NOTE   *Box-and-Whisker Plot* Both Minitab and the TI-84Plus/ TI-83Plus calculators support box-and-whisker plots. On the TI-84Plus/ TI-83Plus, the quartiles Q_1 and Q_3 are calculated as we calculate them in this text. In Minitab and Excel, they are calculated using a slightly different process.

TI-84Plus/TI-83Plus
Press **STATPLOT** ➤ **On.** Highlight box plot. Use **Trace** and the arrow keys to display the values of the five-number summary. The display shows the plot for calories in ice cream bars.

Med=221.5

Excel
Does not produce plot. **Paste Function** (f_x) ➤ **Statistics** ➤ **Quartiles** gives the five-number summary.

Minitab
Press **Graph** ➤ **Boxplot.** In the dialogue box, set Display to IQRange Box.

VIEWPOINT   *Is Shorter Higher?*

Can you estimate a person's *height* from the *pitch* of his or her voice? Is a soprano shorter than an alto? Is a bass taller than a tenor? A statistical study of singers in the New York Choral Society provided information. For more information, visit the Brase/Brase statistics site at **http://math.college.hmco.com/ students** and find the link to DASL, the Carnegie Mellon University Data and Story Library. From the Data Subjects, select music and then singers. Methods of this chapter can be used with new methods we will learn in Chapters 8 and 9 to examine such questions from a statistical point of view.

SECTION 3.3   PROBLEMS

1. *Education: Aptitude Test* Angela took a general aptitude test and scored in the 82nd percentile for aptitude in accounting. What percentage of the scores were at or below her score? What percentage were above?

2. *Education: College Admission* One standard for admission to Redfield College is that the student must rank in the upper quartile of his or her graduating high school class. What is the minimal percentile rank of a successful applicant?

3. *Education: Competency Exam* The town of Butler, Nebraska, decided to give a teacher-competency exam and defined the passing scores to be those in the 70th percentile or higher. The raw test scores ranged from 0 to 100. Was a raw score of 82 necessarily a passing score? Explain.

4. *Education: Test Scores* Clayton and Timothy took different sections of Introduction to Economics. Each section had a different final exam. Timothy scored 83 out of 100 and had a percentile rank in his class of 72. Clayton scored 85 out of 100 but his percentile rank in his class was 70. Who performed better with respect to the rest of the students in the class, Clayton or Timothy? Explain your answer.

5. *Health Care: Nurses* At Center Hospital there is some concern about the high turnover of nurses. A survey was done to determine how long (in months) nurses had been in their current positions. The responses (in months) of 20 nurses were

23	2	5	14	25	36	27	42	12	8
7	23	29	26	28	11	20	31	8	36

Make a box-and-whisker plot of the data. Find the interquartile range.

6. *Health Care: Staff* Another survey was done at Center Hospital to determine how long (in months) clerical staff had been in their current positions. The responses (in months) of 20 clerical staff members were

25	22	7	24	26	31	18	14	17	20
31	42	6	25	22	3	29	32	15	72

(a) Make a box-and-whisker plot. Find the interquartile range.
(b) Compare this plot with the one in Problem 5. Discuss the location of the medians, the location of the middle half of the data banks, and the distance from Q_1 and Q_3 to the extreme values.

7. *Sociology: College Graduates* What percentage of the general U.S. population have bachelor's degrees? The *Statistical Abstract of the United States*, 120th Edition, gives the percentage of bachelor's degrees by state. For convenience, the data are sorted in increasing order.

17	18	18	18	19	20	20	20	21	21
21	21	22	22	22	22	22	22	23	23
24	24	24	24	24	24	24	24	25	26
26	26	26	26	26	27	27	27	27	27
28	28	29	31	31	32	32	34	35	38

(a) Make a box-and-whisker plot and find the interquartile range.
(b) Illinois has a bachelor's degree percentage rate of about 26%. Into what quartile does this rate fall?

8. *Sociology: High-school Dropouts* What percentage of the general U.S. population are high-school dropouts? The *Statistical Abstract of the United States,* 120th Edition, gives the percentage of high-school dropouts by state. For convenience, the data are sorted in increasing order.

5	6	7	7	7	7	8	8	8	8
8	9	9	9	9	9	9	9	10	10
10	10	10	10	10	10	11	11	11	11
11	11	11	11	12	12	12	12	13	13
13	13	13	13	14	14	14	14	14	15

(a) Make a box-and-whisker plot and find the interquartile range.
(b) Wyoming has a dropout rate of about 7%. Into what quartile does this rate fall?

9. *Auto Insurance: Interpret Graphs Consumer Reports* rated automobile insurance companies and gave annual premiums for top-rated companies in several states. Figure 3-8 shows box plots for annual premiums for urban customers (married couple with one 17-year-old son) in three states. The box plots in Figure 3-8 were all drawn using the same scale on a TI-84Plus/TI-83Plus calculator.

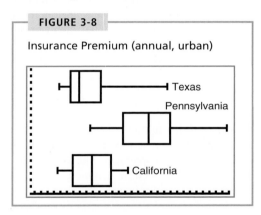

FIGURE 3-8

Insurance Premium (annual, urban)

(a) Which state has the lowest premium? the highest?
(b) Which state has the highest median premium?
(c) Which state has the smallest range of premiums? the smallest interquartile range?
(d) Figure 3-9 gives the five-number summaries generated on the TI-84Plus/TI-83Plus calculators for the box plots of Figure 3-8. Match the five-number summaries to the appropriate box plots.

FIGURE 3-9

Five-Number Summaries for Insurance Premiums

(a)
```
1-Var Stats
↑n=10
  minX=2382
  Q1=2758
  Med=2991
  Q3=3652
  maxX=5715
```

(b)
```
1-Var Stats
↑n=10
  minX=3314
  Q1=4326
  Med=5116.5
  Q3=5801
  maxX=7527
```

(c)
```
1-Var Stats
↑n=10
  minX=2323
  Q1=2801
  Med=3377.5
  Q3=3966
  maxX=4482
```

10. *Expand Your Knowledge: Outliers* Some data sets include values so high or so low that they seem to stand apart from the rest of the data. These data are called *outliers*. Outliers may represent data collection errors, data entry errors, or simply valid but unusual data values. It is important to identify outliers in the data set and examine the outliers carefully to determine if they are in error. One way to detect outliers is to use a box-and-whisker plot. Data values that fall beyond the limits

Lower limit: $Q_1 - 1.5 \times (IQR)$

Upper limit: $Q_3 + 1.5 \times (IQR)$

where *IQR* is the interquartile range, are suspected outliers. In the computer software package Minitab, values beyond these limits are plotted with asterisks (*).

Students from a statistics class were asked to record their heights in inches. The heights (as recorded) were

65	72	68	64	60	55	73	71	52	63	61	74
69	67	74	50	4	75	67	62	66	80	64	65

(a) Make a box-and-whisker plot of the data.
(b) Find the value of the interquartile range (*IQR*).
(c) Multiply the *IQR* by 1.5 and find the lower and upper limits.
(d) Are there any data values below the lower limit? above the upper limit? List any suspected outliers. What might be some explanations for the outliers?

SUMMARY

To characterize numerical data, we use both measures of center and of variation. An average is an attempt to summarize the data into just one number. We studied several important averages: the mode, the median, the mean, and weighted averages. We also looked at trimmed means, which are more resistant to the effects of extreme values. However, an average alone can be misleading; we really need another statistical cross-reference. The measure of data spread, or variation, satisfies the purpose. The variations that we looked at most carefully were the range, the variance, the standard deviation, and the interquartile range. Chebyshev's theorem enables us to estimate the data spread. The coefficient of variation lets us compare relative spread from different data sets. A box-and-whisker plot gives a good visual impression of the range of the data and the location of the middle half of the data.

In later work the average we will use most is the mean; the measure of variation we will use most is the standard deviation. Because the mean and standard deviation are so important, we learned how to estimate these values from data already organized in a frequency distribution.

IMPORTANT WORDS & SYMBOLS

Section 3.1
Average
Mode
Median
Mean
Sample mean, $\bar{x}$
Population mean, μ
Summation symbol, Σ
Resistant measure
Trimmed mean
Weighted average

Section 3.2
Range
Sum of squares, $\Sigma(x - \bar{x})^2$
Sample standard deviation, s

Sample variance, s^2
Population standard deviation, σ
Population size, N
Coefficient of variation, CV
Chebyshev's theorem
Mean of grouped data
Standard deviation of grouped data

Section 3.3
Percentile
Quartile
Interquartile range, IQR
Five-number summary
Box-and-whisker plot
Whisker
Outlier

VIEWPOINT

The Fujita Scale

How do you measure a tornado? Professor Fujita and Allen Pearson (Director of the National Severe Storm Forecast Center) developed a measure based on wind speed and type of damage done by a tornado. The result is an excellent example of both descriptive and inferential statistical methods. For more information, visit the Brase/Brase statistics site at **http://math.college.hmco.com/students** and find the link to the tornado project. Then look up Fujita scale. If we group the data a little, the scale becomes

FS	WS	%
F0 & F1	40–112	67
F2 & F3	113–206	29
F4 & F5	207–318	4

where *FS* represents Fujita scale; *WS*, wind speed in miles per hour; and %, percentage of all tornadoes. Out of 100 tornadoes, what would you estimate for the mean and standard deviation of wind speed?

CHAPTER REVIEW PROBLEMS

1. *Consumer: Power Surge Protector* June purchased a new home computer and has been having trouble with voltage spikes on the power line. Such voltage jumps can be caused by the operation of appliances, such as clothes dryers and electric irons, or just by a power surge on the outside power line. Her friend Jim is an electronics technician and has obtained the following data about voltages when certain electric appliances are turned on and off. Remember, the normal line voltage is 110 volts. All measurements are taken from the line and measured in volts.

   | 73 | 140 | 78 | 142 | 80 | 140 | 90 | 133 |

   (a) Compute the sample mean, sample standard deviation, coefficient of variation, and range.

   Jim advised June to buy a device called a *power surge protector* that protects the computer from strong voltage spikes. Using the power surge protector, Jim again measured voltages to the computer when the same appliances were turned on and off. The results in volts were

   | 100 | 120 | 108 | 114 | 105 | 117 | 103 | 114 |

   (b) Compute the sample mean, sample standard deviation, coefficient of variation, and range of the voltages using the power surge protector.
   (c) Compare your answers for parts (a) and (b). Were the means about the same? Were the voltage distributions different with and without the power surge protector? How did the standard deviation, coefficient of variation, and range reflect this when the mean did not? Explain your answer.

2. *Consumer: Radon Gas* "Radon: The Problem No One Wants to Face" is the title of an article appearing in *Consumer Reports*. Radon is a gas emitted from the ground that can collect in houses and buildings. At certain levels it can cause lung cancer. Radon concentrations are measured in picocuries per liter (pCi/L). A radon level of 4 pCi/L is considered "acceptable." Radon levels in a house vary from week to week. In one house, a sample of 8 weeks had the following readings for radon level (in pCi/L):

   | 1.9 | 2.8 | 5.7 | 4.2 | 1.9 | 8.6 | 3.9 | 7.2 |

   (a) Find the mean, median, and mode.
   (b) Find the sample standard deviation, coefficient of variation, and range.

3. *Political Science: Georgia Democrats* How Democratic is Georgia? County-by-county results are shown for a recent election. For your convenience, the data have been sorted in increasing order (Source: *County and City Data Book,* 12th edition, U.S. Census Bureau).

   ### Percentage of Democratic Vote by Counties in Georgia

31	33	34	34	35	35	35	36	38	38	38	39	40	40	40	40
41	41	41	41	41	41	41	42	42	43	44	44	44	45	45	46
46	46	46	47	48	49	49	49	49	50	51	52	52	53	53	53
53	53	55	56	56	57	57	59	62	66	66	68				

(a) Make a box-and-whisker plot of the data. Find the interquartile range.

(b) *Grouped Data* Make a frequency table using five classes. Then estimate the mean and sample standard deviation using the frequency table. Compute a 75% Chebyshev interval centered about the mean.

(c) If you have a statistical calculator or computer, use it to find the actual sample mean and sample standard deviation. Otherwise, use the values $\Sigma x = 2769$ and $\Sigma x^2 = 132,179$ to compute the sample mean and sample standard deviation.

4. *Grades: Weighted Average* Professor Cramer determines a final grade based on attendance, two papers, three major tests, and a final exam. Each of these activities has a total of 100 possible points. However, the activities carry different weights. Attendance is worth 5%, each paper is worth 8%, each test is worth 15%, and the final is worth 34%.

(a) What is the average for a student with 92 on attendance, 73 on the first paper, 81 on the second paper, 85 on test 1, 87 on test 2, 83 on test 3, and 90 on the final exam?

(b) Compute the average for a student with the above scores on the papers, tests, and final exam, but with a score of only 20 on attendance.

5. *General: Average Weight* An elevator is loaded with 16 people and is at its load limit of 2500 lb. What is the mean weight of these people?

6. *Agriculture: Harvest Weight of Maize* The following data represent weights in kilograms of maize harvest from a random sample of 72 experimental plots on St. Vincent, an island in the Caribbean (Reference: B. G. F. Springer, *Proceedings, Caribbean Food Corps. Soc.*, Vol. 10, pp. 147–152). *Note:* These data are also available with other software on the statSpace CD-ROM. For convenience, the data are presented in increasing order.

7.8	9.1	9.5	10.0	10.2	10.5	11.1	11.5	11.7	11.8
12.2	12.2	12.5	13.1	13.5	13.7	13.7	14.0	14.4	14.5
14.6	15.2	15.5	16.0	16.0	16.1	16.5	17.2	17.8	18.2
19.0	19.1	19.3	19.8	20.0	20.2	20.3	20.5	20.9	21.1
21.4	21.8	22.0	22.0	22.4	22.5	22.5	22.8	22.8	23.1
23.1	23.2	23.7	23.8	23.8	23.8	23.8	24.0	24.1	24.1
24.5	24.5	24.9	25.1	25.2	25.5	26.1	26.4	26.5	26.7
27.1	29.5								

(a) Compute the five-number summary.

(b) Compute the interquartile range.

(c) Make a box-and-whisker plot.

(d) Discuss the distribution. Does the lower half of the distribution show more data spread than the upper half?

7. *Focus Problem: The Educational Advantage* Solve the focus problem at the beginning of this chapter.

8. *Agriculture: Bell Peppers* The pathogen *Phytophthora capsici* causes bell pepper plants to wilt and die. A research project was designed to study the effect of soil water content and the spread of the disease in fields of bell peppers (Source: *Journal of Agricultural, Biological, and Environmental Statistics*, Vol. 2, No. 2). It is thought that too much water helps spread the disease. The fields were divided into rows and quadrants. The soil water content (percent of water by volume of soil) was determined for each plot. An important first step in such a research project is to give a statistical description of the data.

Soil Water Content for Bell Pepper Study

15	14	14	14	13	12	11	11	11	11	10	11	13	16	10
9	15	12	9	10	7	14	13	14	8	9	8	11	13	13
15	12	9	10	9	9	16	16	12	10	11	11	12	15	6
10	10	10	11	9										

(a) Make a box-and-whisker plot of the data. Find the interquartile range.

(b) *Grouped Data* Make a frequency table using four classes. Then estimate the mean and sample standard deviation using the frequency table. Compute a 75% Chebyshev interval centered about the mean.

(c) If you have a statistical calculator or computer, use it to find the actual sample mean and sample standard deviation.

9. *Performance Rating: Weighted Average* A performance evaluation for new sales representatives at Office Automation Incorporated involves several ratings done on a scale of 1 to 10, with 10 the highest rating. The activities rated include new contacts, successful contacts, total contacts, dollar volume of sales, and reports. Then an overall rating is determined by using a weighted average. The weights are 2 for new contacts, 3 for successful contacts, 3 for total contacts, 5 for dollar value of sales, and 3 for reports. What would the overall rating be for a sales representative with ratings of 5 for new contacts, 8 for successful contacts, 7 for total contacts, 9 for dollar volume of sales, and 7 for reports?

DATA HIGHLIGHTS: GROUP PROJECTS

Break into small groups and discuss the following topics. Organize a brief outline in which you summarize the main points of your group discussion.

Old Faithful Geyser, Yellowstone National Park

1. *The Story of Old Faithful* is a short book written by George Marler and published by the Yellowstone Association. Chapter 7 of this interesting book talks about the effect of the 1959 earthquake on eruption intervals for Old Faithful Geyser. Dr. John Rinehart (a senior research scientist with the National Oceanic and Atmospheric Administration) has done extensive studies of the eruption intervals before and after the 1959 earthquake. Examine Figure 3-10. Notice the general shape. Is the graph more or less symmetrical? Does it have a single mode frequency? The mean interval between eruptions has remained steady at about 65 minutes for the past 100 years. Therefore, the 1959 earthquake did not significantly change the mean, but it did change the distribution of eruption intervals. Examine Figure 3-11. Would you say there are really two frequency modes, one shorter and the other longer? Explain. The overall mean is about the same for both graphs, but one graph has a much larger standard deviation (for eruption intervals) than the other. Do no calculations, just look at both graphs, and then explain which graph has the smaller and which has the larger standard deviation. Which distribution will have the larger coefficient of variation? In everyday terms, what would this mean if you were actually at Yellowstone waiting to see the next eruption of Old Faithful? Explain your answer.

2. Most academic advisors tell students to major in a field the student really loves. After all, it is true that money cannot buy happiness! Nevertheless, it is interesting to at least look at some of the higher-paying fields of study. After all, a field like mathematics can be a lot of fun, once you get into it. We see that women's salaries tend to be less than men's salaries. However, women's salaries are rapidly catching

FIGURE 3-10

Typical Behavior of Old Faithful Geyser Before 1959 Quake

Winter 1952–53

FIGURE 3-11

Typical Behavior of Old Faithful Geyser After 1959 Quake

1–30 June 1967

up, and this benefits the entire work force in different ways. Figure 3-12 shows the median incomes for college graduates with different majors. The employees in the sample are all at least 30 years old. Does it seem reasonable to assume that many of the employees are in jobs beyond the entry level? Explain. Compare the median incomes shown for all women aged 30 or older holding bachelor's degrees with the median incomes for men of similar age holding bachelor's degrees. Look at the particular majors listed. What percentage of men holding bachelor's degrees in mathematics make $52,316 or more? What percentage of women holding computer/ information science degrees make $41,559 or more? How do median incomes for men and women holding engineering degrees compare? What about pharmacy degrees?

FIGURE 3-12

Lucrative Majors for Bachelor's Degrees

The U.S. median income for women and men (age 30 or older) with bachelor's degrees

Women
Median salary: $31,848

Major	Median income
Pharmacy	$47,567
Engineering	$46,389
Computer/ Infomation Sciences	$41,559
Physical Therapy/ related services	$40,491
Nursing	$40,096

Men
Median salary: $43,856

Major	Median income
Engineering	$52,998
Mathematics	$52,316
Physics	$51,819
Pharmacy	$50,805
Economics	$50,360

Source: Bureau of Labor Statistics

LINKING CONCEPTS: WRITING PROJECTS

Discuss each of the following topics in class or review the topics on your own. Then write a brief but complete essay in which you summarize the main points. Please include formulas and graphs as appropriate.

1. An average is an attempt to summarize a collection of data into just *one* number. Discuss how the mean, median, and mode all represent averages in this context. Also discuss the differences among these averages. Why is the mean a balance point? Why is the median a midway point? Why is the mode the most common data point? List three areas of daily life in which you think either the mean, median, or mode would be the best choice to describe an "average."

2. Why do we need to study the variation of a collection of data? Why isn't the average by itself adequate? We have studied three ways to measure variation. The range, standard deviation, and, to a large extent, a box-and-whisker plot all indicate the variation within a data collection. Discuss similarities and differences among these ways to measure data variation. Why would it seem reasonable to pair the median with a box-and-whisker plot and to pair the mean with the standard deviation? What are the advantages and disadvantages of each method of describing data spread? Comment on statements such as the following: (a) The range is easy to compute, but it doesn't give much information; (b) although the standard deviation is more complicated to compute, it has some significant applications; (c) the box-and-whisker plot is fairly easy to construct, and it gives a lot of information at a glance.

3. Why is the coefficient of variation important? What do we mean when we say that the coefficient of variation has no units? What advantage can there be in having no units? Why is *relative size* important?

   Consider robin eggs; the mean weight of a collection of robin eggs is 0.72 ounce and the standard deviation is 0.12 ounce. Now consider elephants; the mean weight of elephants in the zoo is 6.42 tons, with a standard deviation 1.07 tons. The units of measurement are different and there is a great deal of difference between the size of an elephant and that of a robin's egg. Yet the coefficient of variation is about the same for both. Comment on this from the viewpoint of the size of the standard deviation relative to the mean.

4. What is Chebyshev's theorem? Suppose you have a friend who knows very little about statistics. Write a paragraph or two in which you describe Chebyshev's theorem for your friend. Keep the discussion as simple as possible, but be sure to get the main ideas across to your friend. Suppose he or she asks, "What is this stuff good for?" and suppose you respond (a little sarcastically) that Chebyshev's theorem applies to everything from butterflies to the orbits of the planets! Would you be correct? Explain.

Using Technology

Raw Data

APPLICATION 1

Using the software or calculator available to you, do the following.

1. Trade winds are one of the beautiful features of island life in Hawaii. The following data represent total air movement in miles per day over a weather station in Hawaii as determined by a continuous anemometer recorder. The period of observation is January 1 to February 15, 1971.

26	14	18	14	113	50	13	22
27	57	28	50	72	52	105	138
16	33	18	16	32	26	11	16
17	14	57	100	35	20	21	34
18	13	18	28	21	13	25	19
11	19	22	19	15	20		

Source: United States Department of Commerce, National Oceanic and Atmospheric Administration, Environmental Data Service. *Climatological Data, Annual Summary, Hawaii,* Vol. 67, No. 13. Asheville: National Climatic Center, 1971, pp. 11, 24.

(a) Use the computer to find the sample mean, median, and (if it exists) mode. Also, find the range, sample variance, and sample standard deviation.

(b) Use the five-number summary provided by the computer to make a box-and-whisker plot of total air movement over the weather station.

(c) Four data values are exceptionally high: 113, 105, 138, and 100. The strong winds of January 5 (113 reading) brought in a cold front that dropped snow on Haleakala National Park (at the 8000 ft elevation). The residents were so excited that they drove up to see the snow and caused such a massive traffic jam that the Park Service had to close the road. The winds of January 15, 16, and 28 (readings 105, 138, and 100) accompanied a storm with funnel clouds that did much damage. Eliminate these values (i.e., 100, 105, 113, and 138) from the data bank and redo parts (a) and (b). Compare your results with those previously obtained. Which average is most affected? What happens to the standard deviation? How do the two box-and-whisker plots compare?

Technology Hints: Raw Data

TI-84Plus/TI-83Plus, Excel, Minitab

The Tech Note of Section 3.2 gives brief instructions for finding summary statistics for raw data using the TI-84Plus/TI-83Plus calculators, Excel, and Minitab. The Tech Note of Section 3.3 gives brief instructions for constructing box plots using the TI-84Plus/TI-83Plus calculators and Minitab.

SPSS

Many commands in SPSS provide an option to display various summary statistics. A direct way to display summary statistics is to use the menu choices **Analyze ➤ Descriptive Statistics ➤ Descriptives.** In the dialogue box, move the variable containing your data into the variables box. Click **Options...** and then check the summary statistics you wish to display. Click Continue and then OK. Notice that the median is not available. A more complete list of summary statistics is available with the menu choices **Analyze ➤ Descriptive Statistics ➤ Frequencies.** Click the **Statistics** button and check the summary statistics you wish to display.

For box-and-whisker plots, use the menu options **Graphs ➤ Interactive ➤ Boxplot.** In the dialogue box, place the variable containing your data in the box along the vertical axis. After selecting the options you want, click OK.

Cumulative Review Problems

CHAPTERS 1–3

In West Texas, water is extremely important. The following data represent pH levels in ground water for a random sample of 102 West Texas wells. A pH less than 7 is acidic and a pH above 7 is alkaline. Scanning the data, you can see that water in this region tends to be hard (alkaline). Too high a pH means the water is unusable or needs expensive treatment to make it useable (Reference: C. E. Nichols and V. E. Kane, Union Carbide Technical Report K/UR-1). These data are also available with other software on the statSpace CD-ROM. For convenience, the data are presented in increasing order. Note: The pH for distilled water is 0, which is neutral.

x: pH of Ground Water in 102 West Texas Wells

7.0	7.0	7.0	7.0	7.0	7.0	7.0	7.0	7.1	7.1	7.1	7.1
7.1	7.1	7.1	7.1	7.1	7.1	7.2	7.2	7.2	7.2	7.2	7.2
7.2	7.2	7.2	7.2	7.3	7.3	7.3	7.3	7.3	7.3	7.3	7.3
7.3	7.3	7.3	7.4	7.4	7.4	7.4	7.4	7.4	7.4	7.4	7.4
7.5	7.5	7.5	7.5	7.5	7.5	7.5	7.5	7.6	7.6	7.6	7.6
7.6	7.6	7.6	7.6	7.6	7.7	7.7	7.7	7.7	7.7	7.7	7.8
7.8	7.8	7.8	7.8	7.9	7.9	7.9	7.9	7.9	8.0	8.1	8.1
8.1	8.1	8.1	8.1	8.1	8.2	8.2	8.2	8.2	8.2	8.2	8.2
8.4	8.5	8.6	8.7	8.8	8.8						

1. Write a brief description in which you outline how you would obtain a random sample of 102 West Texas water wells. Explain how random numbers would be used in the selection process.

2. Is the given data nominal, ordinal, interval, or ratio? Explain.

3. Make a stem-and-leaf display. Use five lines per stem so that leaf values 0 and 1 are on one line, 2 and 3 are on the next line, 4 and 5 are on the next, 6 and 7 are on the next, and 8 and 9 are on the last line of the stem.

4. Make a frequency table, histogram, and relative-frequency histogram. Recall that for decimal data, we "clear the decimal" to determine classes for whole number data and then reinsert the decimal to obtain the classes for the frequency table of the original data.

5. Compute the range, mean, median, and mode for the given data.

6. (a) Verify that $\Sigma x = 772.9$ and $\Sigma x^2 = 5876.6$.
   (b) Compute the sample variance, sample standard deviation, and coefficient of variation for the given data. Is the sample standard deviation small relative to the mean pH?

7. Compute a 75% Chebyshev interval centered on the mean.

8. Make a box-and-whisker plot. Find the interquartile range.

Summary

Wow! In Problems 1–8 you constructed a lot of information regarding the pH of West Texas ground water based on sample data. Let's continue the investigation.

9. Look at the histogram. Is the pH distribution for these wells symmetric or skewed? Are lower or higher values more common?

10. Look at the stem-and-leaf plot. Are there any unusually high or low pH levels in this sample of wells? How many wells are neutral (pH of 7)?

11. Use the box-and-whisker plot to describe how the data are spread around the median. Are the pH values above the median more spread out than those below? Is this observation consistent with the skew of the histogram?

12. Suppose you are working for the regional water commissioner. You have been asked to submit a brief report about the pH level in ground water in the West Texas region. Write such a report and include appropriate graphs.

Correlation and Regression

When it is not in our power to determine what is true, we ought to follow what is most probable.

—René Descartes

**René Descartes
(1596–1650)**

French mathematician and philosopher.

It is important to realize that statistics and probability do not deal in the realm of certainty. If there is any realm of human knowledge in which genuine certainty exists, you may be sure that our statistical methods are not needed there. In most human endeavors, and in almost all of the natural world around us, the element of chance happenings cannot be avoided. When we cannot expect something with true certainty, we must rely on probability to be our guide. In this chapter we will study regression, correlation, and forecasting. One of the tools we use is a scatter plot. René Descartes was the first mathematician to systematically use rectangular coordinate plots. For this reason, such a coordinate axis is called a Cartesian axis.

PREVIEW QUESTIONS

◇ How can you use a scatter diagram to visually estimate the degree of linear correlation of two random variables? (SECTION 4.1)

◇ How do you compute the correlation coefficient and what does it tell you about the strength of the linear relationship between two random variables? (SECTION 4.1)

◇ What is the least-squares criterion? How do you find the equation of the least-squares line? (SECTION 4.2)

◇ What is the coefficient of determination and what does it tell you about explained variation of y in a random sample of data pairs (x, y)? (SECTION 4.2)

For on-line student resources, visit **math.college.hmco.com/students** and follow the Statistics links to the Brase/Brase, *Understanding Basic Statistics*, 4th edition web site.

Changing Populations and Crime Rate

Is the crime rate higher in neighborhoods where people might not know each other very well? Is there a relationship between crime rate and population change? If so, can we make predictions based on such a relationship? Is the relationship statistically significant? Is it possible to predict crime rate from population changes?

Denver is a city that has had a lot of growth and consequently a lot of population change in recent years. Sociologists studying population changes and crime rate could find a wealth of information in Denver statistics. Let x be a random variable representing percentage change in neighborhood population in the past few years, and let y be a random variable representing crime rate (crimes per 1,000 population). A random sample of six Denver neighborhoods gave the following information (Source: *Neighborhood Facts,* The Piton Foundation). To find out more about the Piton Foundation, visit the Brase/Brase statistics site at **http://math.college.hmco.com/students** and find the link to the Piton Foundation.

119

x	29	2	11	17	7	6
y	173	35	132	127	69	53

Using information presented in this chapter, you will be able to analyze the relationship between the variables x and y using the following tools.

- Scatter diagram

- Sample correlation coefficient and coefficient of determination

- Least-squares line equation

- Predictions for y using the least-squares line

(See Problem 6 in the Chapter Review Problems.)

4.1
Scatter Diagrams and Linear Correlation

FOCUS POINTS

✓ Make a scatter diagram.
✓ Visually estimate the location of the "best-fitting" line for a scatter diagram.
✓ Use sample data to compute the sample correlation coefficient r.
✓ Investigate the meaning of the correlation coefficient r.

Scatter diagram

Studies of correlation and regression of two variables usually begin with a graph of *paired data values* (x, y). We call such a graph a *scatter diagram*.

> A **scatter diagram** is a graph in which data pairs (x, y) are plotted as individual points on a grid with horizontal axis x and vertical axis y. We call x the **explanatory** variable and y the **response** variable.

By looking at a scatter diagram of data pairs, you can observe if there seems to be a linear relationship between the x and y values.

EXAMPLE 1

Scatter diagram

Phosphorous is a chemical used in many household and industrial cleaning compounds. Unfortunately, phosphorous tends to find its way into surface water, where it can kill fish, plants, and other wetland creatures. Phosphorous reduction programs are required by law and are monitored by the Environmental Protection Agency (EPA). (Reference: *EPA Case Study 832-R-93-005.*)

A random sample of eight sites in a California wetlands study gave the following information about phosphorous reduction in drainage water. In this study, x is a random variable that represents phosphorous concentration (in 100 mg/l) at the inlet of a passive biotreatment facility, and y is a random variable that represents total phosphorous concentration (in 100 mg/l) at the outlet of the passive biotreatment facility.

x	5.2	7.3	6.7	5.9	6.1	8.3	5.5	7.0
y	3.3	5.9	4.8	4.5	4.0	7.1	3.6	6.1

FIGURE 4-1

Phosphorous Reduction (100 mg/l)

(a) Make a scatter diagram for these data.

> **SOLUTION:** Figure 4-1 shows points corresponding to the given data pairs. These plotted points constitute the scatter diagram. To make the diagram, first scan the data and decide on an appropriate scale for each axis. Figure 4-1 shows the scatter diagram (points) along with a line segment showing the basic trend. Notice a "jump scale" on both axes.

(b) Comment on the relationship between x and y shown in Figure 4-1.

> **SOLUTION:** By inspecting the figure, we see that smaller values of x are associated with smaller values of y and larger values of x tend to be associated with larger values of y. Roughly speaking, the general trend seems to be reasonably well represented by an upward-sloping line segment, as shown in the diagram.   ◇

Of course, it is possible to draw many curves close to the points in Figure 4-1, but a straight line is the simplest and most widely used for elementary studies of paired data. We can draw many lines in Figure 4-1, but in some sense, the "best" line should be the one that comes closest to each of the points of the scatter diagram. To single out one line as the "best-fitting line," we must find a mathematical criterion for this line and a formula representing the line. This will be done in Section 4.2 using the *method of least squares*.

Introduction to linear correlation

Another problem precedes that of finding the "best-fitting line." That is the problem of determining how well the points of the scatter diagram are suited for

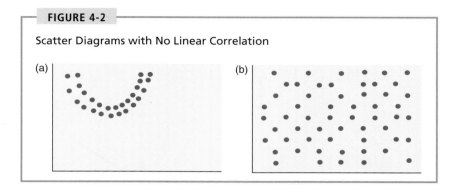

FIGURE 4-2

Scatter Diagrams with No Linear Correlation

(a)   (b)

fitting *any* line. Certainly, if the points are a very poor fit to *any* line, there is little use in trying to find the "best" line.

If the points of a scatter diagram are located so that *no* line is realistically a "good" fit, we then say that the points possess *no linear correlation*. We see some examples of scatter diagrams for which there is no linear correlation in Figure 4-2.

GUIDED EXERCISE 1

Scatter diagram

A large industrial plant has seven divisions that do the same type of work. A safety inspector visits each division of 20 workers quarterly. The number *x* of work-hours devoted to safety training and the number *y* of work-hours lost due to industry-related accidents are recorded for each separate division in Table 4-1.

TABLE 4-1   Safety Report

Division	x	y
1	10.0	80
2	19.5	65
3	30.0	68
4	45.0	55
5	50.0	35
6	65.0	10
7	80.0	12

(a) Make a scatter diagram for these pairs. Represent the *x* values on the horizontal axis and the *y* values on the vertical axis.

FIGURE 4-3   Scatter Diagram for Safety Report

Hours in safety training

Continued

GUIDED EXERCISE 1 continued

(b) As the number of hours spent on safety training increases, what happens to the number of hours lost due to industry-related accidents?

⟹ In general, as the number of hours in safety training goes up, the number of hours lost due to accidents goes down.

(c) Does a line fit the data reasonably well?

⟹ A line fits reasonably well.

(d) Draw a line that you think "fits best."

⟹ Use a downward-sloping line that lies close to the points. Later, you will find the equation of the line that is a "best fit."

TECH NOTE   The TI-84Plus and TI-83Plus calculators, Excel, and Minitab all produce scatter plots. For each technology, enter the x values in one column and the corresponding y values in another column. The displays show the data from Guided Exercise 1 regarding safety training and hours lost because of accidents. Notice that the scatter plots do not necessarily show the origin.

TI-84Plus/TI-83Plus Enter the data into two columns. Use **Stat Plot** and choose the first type. Use option **9: ZoomStat** under **Zoom**. To check the scale, look at the settings displayed under **Window**.

Excel Enter the data into two columns. Use the menu choices **Chart wizard ➤ Scatter Diagram.** Dialogue box choices permit you to label the axes and title the chart. Changing the size of the diagram box changes the scale on the axes.

Minitab Enter the data into two columns. Use the menu selections **Stat ➤ Regression ➤ Fitted Line Plot.** The best-fit line is automatically plotted on the scatter diagram.

TI-84Plus/TI-83Plus Display

Excel Display

Minitab Display

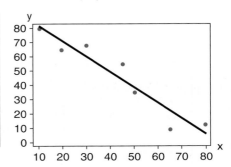

Sample Correlation Coefficient *r*

Looking at a scatter diagram to see whether a line best describes the relationship between the values of data pairs is useful. In fact, whenever you are looking for a relationship between two variables, making a scatter diagram is a good first step.

There is a mathematical measurement that describes the strength of the linear association between two variables. This measure is the *sample correlation coefficient r.*

The full name for *r* is the *Pearson product-moment correlation coefficient,* named in honor of the English statistician Karl Pearson (1857–1936), who is credited with formulating *r*.

> The **correlation coefficient *r*** is a numerical measurement that assesses the strength of a *linear* relationship between two variables *x* and *y*.
>
> 1. *r* is a unitless measurement between −1 and 1. In symbols, $-1 \leq r \leq 1$. If $r = 1$, there is perfect positive linear correlation. If $r = -1$, there is perfect negative linear correlation. If $r = 0$, there is no linear correlation. The closer *r* is to 1 or −1, the better a line describes the relationship between the two variables *x* and *y*.
>
> 2. Positive values of *r* imply that as *x* increases, *y* tends to increase. Negative values of *r* imply that as *x* increases, *y* tends to decrease.
>
> 3. The value of *r* is the same regardless of which variable is the explanatory variable and which is the response variable. In other words, the value of *r* is the same for the pairs (*x*, *y*) and the corresponding pairs (*y*, *x*).
>
> 4. The value of *r* does not change when either variable is converted to different units.

We'll develop the defining formula for *r* and then give a more convenient computation formula.

Development of Formula for *r*

If there is a *positive* linear relation between the variables *x* and *y*, then high values of *x* are paired with high values of *y*, and low values of *x* are paired with low values of *y*. [See Figure 4-4(a).] In the case of *negative* linear correlation, high values

---

FIGURE 4-4

Patterns for Linear Correlation

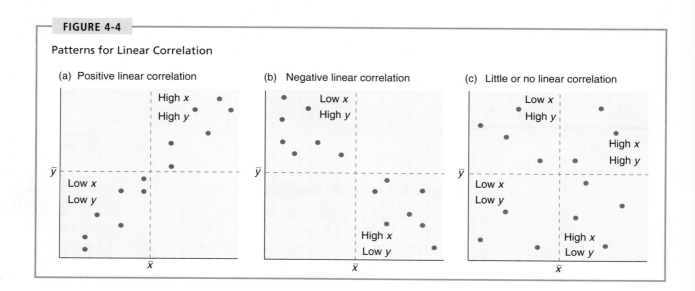

of x are paired with low values of y, and low values of x are paired with high values of y. This relation is pictured in Figure 4-4(b). If there is *little or no linear correlation* between x and y, however, then we will find both high and low x values sometimes paired with high y values and sometimes paired with low y values. This relation is shown in Figure 4-4(c).

These observations lead us to the development of the formula for the correlation coefficient r. Taking *high* to mean "above the mean," we can express the relationships pictured in Figure 4-4 by considering the products

$$(x - \bar{x})(y - \bar{y})$$

If both x and y are high, both factors will be positive, and the product will be positive as well. The sign of this product will depend on the relative values of x and y compared with their respective means.

$$(x - \bar{x})(y - \bar{y}) \begin{cases} \text{is positive if } x \text{ and } y \text{ are both "high"} \\ \text{is positive if } x \text{ and } y \text{ are both "low"} \\ \\ \text{is negative if } x \text{ is "low," but } y \text{ is "high"} \\ \text{is negative if } x \text{ is "high," but } y \text{ is "low"} \end{cases}$$

In the case of positive linear correlation, most of the products $(x - \bar{x})(y - \bar{y})$ will be positive and so will the sum over all the data pairs

$$\Sigma(x - \bar{x})(y - \bar{y})$$

For negative linear correlation, the products will tend to be negative, so the sum also will be negative. On the other hand, in the case of little, if any, linear correlation, the sum will tend to be zero.

One trouble with the preceding sum is that it will be larger or smaller, depending on the units of x and y. Because we want r to be unitless, we standardize both x and y of a data pair by dividing each factor $(x - \bar{x})$ by the sample standard deviation s_x and each factor $(y - \bar{y})$ by s_y. Finally, we take an average of all the products. For technical reasons, we take the average by dividing by $n - 1$ instead of by n. This process leads us to the desired measurement, r.

$$r = \frac{1}{n - 1} \Sigma \left(\frac{(y - \bar{y})}{s_y} \cdot \frac{(x - \bar{x})}{s_x} \right) \tag{1}$$

Computation Formula for r

The defining formula for r shows how the mean and standard deviation of each variable in the data pair enter into the formulation of r. However, the defining formula is technically difficult to work with because of all the subtractions and products. A computation formula for r uses the raw data values of x and y directly.

PROCEDURE

How to compute the sample correlation coefficient *r*

Obtain a random sample of *n* data pairs (x, y).

1. Using the data pairs, compute Σx, Σy, Σx^2, Σy^2, and Σxy.

2. With n = sample size, Σx, Σy, Σx^2, Σy^2, and Σxy, you are ready to compute the sample correlation coefficient *r* using the computation formula

$$r = \frac{n\Sigma xy - (\Sigma x)(\Sigma y)}{\sqrt{n\Sigma x^2 - (\Sigma x)^2}\ \sqrt{n\Sigma y^2 - (\Sigma y)^2}} \qquad (2)$$

Be careful! The notation Σx^2 means first square *x* and then calculate the sum, whereas $(\Sigma x)^2$ means first sum the *x* values, then square the result.

Note: Inferences for the population correlation coefficient (Section 11.4) require the data pairs to have a *bivariate normal distribution*. That is, for a fixed value of *x*, the *y* values should have a normal distribution (or at least a mound-shaped and symmetric distribution), and for a fixed value of *y*, the *x* values should have their own (approximately) normal distribution. Chapter 6 discusses normal distributions.

It can be shown mathematically that *r* is always a number between +1 and −1 ($-1 \leq r \leq +1$). Table 4-2 on the next page gives a quick summary of some basic facts about *r*.

For most applications you will use a calculator or computer software to compute *r* directly. However, to build some familiarity with the structure of the correlation coefficient, it is useful to do some calculations for yourself. Example 2 and Guided Exercise 2 show how to use the computation formula to compute *r*.

EXAMPLE 2

Computing r

Sand driven by wind creates large beautiful dunes at the Great Sand Dunes National Monument, Colorado. Of course, the same natural forces also create large dunes in the Great Sahara and Arabia. Is there a linear correlation between wind velocity and sand drift rate? Let *x* be a random variable representing wind velocity (in 10 cm/sec) and let *y* be a random variable representing drift rate of sand (in 100 g/cm/sec). A test site at the Great Sand Dunes National Monument gave the following information about *x* and *y* (Reference: *Hydrologic, Geologic, and Biologic Research at Great Sand Dunes National Monument*, Proceedings of the National Park Service Research Symposium).

x	70	115	105	82	93	125	88
y	3	45	21	7	16	62	12

(a) Construct a scatter diagram. Do you expect *r* to be positive?

SOLUTION: Figure 4-5 displays the scatter diagram. From the scatter diagram it appears that as *x* values increase, *y* values also tend to increase. Therefore, *r* should be positive.

TABLE 4-2   Some Facts About the Correlation Coefficient

If r Is	Then	The Scatter Diagram Might Look Something Like
0	There is no linear relation among the points of the scatter diagram.	
1 or −1	There is a perfect linear relation between x and y values; all points lie on the least-squares line.	$r = -1$ $r = 1$
Between 0 and 1 $(0 < r < 1)$	The x and y values have a *positive correlation*. By this, we mean that *large x* values are associated with *large y* values, and *small x* values are associated with *small y* values.	As we go from left to right, the least-squares line goes *up*.
Between −1 and 0 $(-1 < r < 0)$	The x and y values have a *negative correlation*. By this, we mean *large x* values are associated with *small y* values, and *small x* values are associated with *large y* values.	As we go from left to right, the least-squares line goes *down*.

FIGURE 4-5

Wind Velocity (10 cm/sec) and Drift Rate of Sand (100 g/cm/sec)

(b) Compute r using the computation formula (formula 2).

SOLUTION: To find r, we need to compute Σx, Σx^2, Σy, Σy^2, and Σxy. It is convenient to organize the data in a table of five columns (Table 4-3) and then sum the entries in each column. Of course, many calculators give these sums directly.

TABLE 4-3   Computation Table

x	y	x^2	y^2	xy
70	3	4900	9	210
115	45	13,225	2025	5175
105	21	11,025	441	2205
82	7	6724	49	574
93	16	8649	256	1488
125	62	15,625	3844	7750
88	12	7744	144	1056
$\Sigma x = 678$	$\Sigma y = 166$	$\Sigma x^2 = 67{,}892$	$\Sigma y^2 = 6768$	$\Sigma xy = 18{,}458$

Using the computation formula for r, the sums from Table 4-3, and $n = 7$, we have

$$r = \frac{n\Sigma xy - (\Sigma x)(\Sigma y)}{\sqrt{n\Sigma x^2 - (\Sigma x)^2}\ \sqrt{n\Sigma y^2 - (\Sigma y)^2}} \tag{2}$$

$$= \frac{7(18{,}458) - (678)(166)}{\sqrt{7(67{,}892) - (678)^2}\ \sqrt{7(6768) - (166)^2}} \approx \frac{16{,}658}{(124.74)(140.78)} \approx 0.949$$

Note: Using a calculator to compute r directly gives 0.949, to three places after the decimal.

(c) What does the value of r tell you?

SOLUTION: Since r is very close to 1, we have an indication of a strong positive linear correlation between wind velocity and drift rate of sand. In other words, we expect that higher wind speeds tend to mean greater drift rates. Because r is so close to 1, the association between the variables appears to be linear.   ◇

It is quite a task to compute r for even seven data pairs. The use of columns as in Example 2 is extremely helpful. Your value for r should always be between -1 and 1, inclusive. Use a scatter diagram to get a rough idea of the value of r. If your computed value of r is outside the allowable range, or if it disagrees quite a bit with the scatter diagram, recheck your calculations. Be sure you distinguish between expressions such as (Σx^2) and $(\Sigma x)^2$. Negligible rounding errors may occur, depending on how you (or your calculator) round.

GUIDED EXERCISE 2

Computing r

In one of the Boston city parks, there has been a problem with muggings in the summer months. A police cadet took a random sample of 10 days (out of the 90-day summer) and compiled the following data. For each day, x represents the number of police officers on duty in the park and y represents the number of reported muggings on that day.

x	10	15	16	1	4	6	18	12	14	7
y	5	2	1	9	7	8	1	5	3	6

(a) Construct a scatter diagram of x and y values.

⟹   Figure 4-6 shows the scatter diagram.

FIGURE 4-6 Scatter Diagram for Number of Police Officers versus Number of Muggings

(b) From the scatter diagram, do you think the computed value of r will be positive, negative, or zero? Explain.

⟹ r will be negative. The general trend is that large x values are associated with small y values and vice versa. From left to right, the least-squares line goes down.

(c) Verify that $\Sigma x = 103$, $\Sigma y = 47$, $\Sigma x^2 = 1347$, $\Sigma y^2 = 295$, and $\Sigma xy = 343$.

⟹   Use a calculator.

(d) Compute r. Alternatively, find the value of r directly by using a calculator or computer software.

⟹
$$r = \frac{n\Sigma xy - (\Sigma x)(\Sigma y)}{\sqrt{n\Sigma x^2 - (\Sigma x)^2}\ \sqrt{n\Sigma y^2 - (\Sigma y)^2}}$$

$$= \frac{10(343) - (103)(47)}{\sqrt{10(1347) - (103)^2}\ \sqrt{10(295) - (47)^2}}$$

$$\approx \frac{-1411}{(53.49)(27.22)} \approx -0.969$$

TECH NOTE   Most calculators that support two-variable statistics provide the value of the correlation coefficient *r* directly. Statistical software provides *r*, r^2, or both.

TI-84Plus/TI-83Plus First use **CATALOG**, scroll to **DiagnosticOn,** and press **Enter** twice. Then, when you use **STAT, CALC,** option **8:LinReg(a+bx)**, the value of *r* will be given (data from Example 2). In the next section we will discuss the line $y = a + bx$ and the meaning of r^2.

Excel Use the menu selection **Paste function** ⬚ ➤ **Statistical** ➤ **Correl.**

Minitab Use the menu selection **Stat** ➤ **Basic Statistics** ➤ **Correlation.**

```
LinReg
  y=a+bx
  a=-79.97763496
  b=1.070565553
  r²=.8997719968
  r=.9485631222
  ■
```

Cautions about Correlation

Sample compared to population correlation

The correlation coefficient can be thought of as a measure of how well a linear model fits the data points on a scatter diagram. The closer *r* is to +1 or −1, the better a line "fits" the data. Values of *r* close to 0 indicate a poor fit to any line.

Usually a scatter diagram does not contain *all* possible data points that could be gathered. Most scatter diagrams represent only a *random sample* of data pairs taken from a very large population of all possible pairs. Because *r* is computed on the basis of a random sample of (x, y) pairs, we expect the values of *r* to vary from one sample to the next (much as the sample mean $\bar{x}$ varies from sample to sample). This brings up the question of the *significance* of *r*. Or, put another way, what are the chances that our random sample of data pairs indicates a high correlation when, in fact, the population *x* and *y* values are not so strongly correlated. Right now let's just say that the significance of *r* is a separate issue that will be treated in Section 11.4, where we test the *population correlation coefficient* ρ (Greek letter *rho,* pronounced "row").

> $r = $ **sample** correlation coefficient computed from a random sample of (x, y) data pairs.
>
> $\rho = $ **population** correlation coefficient computed from all population data pairs (x, y).

Causation

There is a less formal way to address the significance of *r* using a table of "critical values" or "cut-off values" based on the *r* distribution and the number of data pairs. Problem 15 at the end of this section discusses this method.

The correlation coefficient is a mathematical tool for measuring the strength of a linear relationship between two variables. As such, it makes no implication about cause or effect. The fact that two variables tend to increase or decrease together does not mean that a change in one is *causing* a change in the other. A strong correlation between *x* and *y* is sometimes due to other (either known or unknown) variables. Such variables are called *lurking variables.*

In ordered pairs (x, y), x is called the **explanatory** variable and y is called the **response** variable. When r indicates a linear correlation between x and y, changes in values of y tend to respond to changes in values of x according to a linear model. A **lurking variable** is a variable that is neither an explanatory nor a response variable. Yet, a lurking variable may be responsible for changes in both x and y.

EXAMPLE 3

Causation and lurking variables

Over a period of years, the population of a certain town increased. It was observed that during this period the correlation between x, the number of people attending church, and y, the number of people in the city jail, was $r = 0.90$. Does going to church *cause* people to go to jail? Is there a *lurking variable* that might cause both variables x and y to increase?

SOLUTION: We hope church attendance does not cause people to go to jail! During this period, there was an increase in population. Therefore, it is not too surprising that both the number of people attending church and the number of people in jail increased. The high correlation between x and y is likely due to the lurking variable of population increase. ◇

Correlation between averages

The correlation between two variables consisting of averages is usually higher than the correlation between two variables representing corresponding raw data. One reason is that the use of averages reduces the variation existing between individual measurements (see Section 7.5 and the central limit theorem). A high correlation based on two variables consisting of averages does not necessarily imply a high correlation between two variables consisting of individual measurements.

VIEWPOINT

Low on Credit, High on Cost!!!

How do you measure automobile insurance risk? One way is to use a little statistics and customer credit ratings. Insurers say statistics show that drivers who have a history of bad credit are more likely to be in serious car accidents. According to a high-level executive at Allstate Insurance Company, financial instability is an extremely powerful predictor of future insurance losses. In short, there seems to be a strong correlation between bad credit ratings and auto insurance claims. Consequently, insurance companies want to charge higher premiums to customers with bad credit ratings. Consumer advocates object strongly because they say bad credit *does not cause* automobile accidents. More than 20 states prohibit or restrict the use of credit ratings to determine auto insurance premiums. Insurance companies respond by saying that your best defense is to pay your bills on time!

SECTION 4.1   PROBLEMS

Note: Answers may vary due to rounding.

1. *Scatter Diagrams: Linear Correlation* Look at the diagrams at the top of the next page. Does each diagram show high linear correlation, moderate or low linear correlation, or no linear correlation?

(a)   (b)   (c)

2. *Scatter Diagrams: Linear Correlation* Look at the following diagrams. Does each diagram show high linear correlation, moderate or low linear correlation, or no linear correlation?

(a)   (b)   (c)

3. *Causation: Lurking Variables* Over the past few years, there has been a strong positive correlation between the annual consumption of diet soda drinks and the number of traffic accidents.
   (a) Do you think increasing consumption of diet soda drinks causes traffic accidents? Explain.
   (b) What lurking variables might be causing the increase in one or both of the variables? Explain.

4. *Causation: Lurking Variables* Over the past decade, there has been a strong positive correlation between teacher salaries and prescription drug costs.
   (a) Do you think paying teachers more causes prescription drugs to cost more? Explain.
   (b) What lurking variables might be causing the increase in one or both of the variables? Explain.

5. *Causation: Lurking Variables* Over the past 50 years, there has been a strong negative correlation between average annual income and the record time to run 1 mile. In other words, average annual incomes have been rising while the record time to run 1 mile has been decreasing.
   (a) Do you think increasing incomes cause decreasing times to run the mile? Explain.
   (b) What lurking variables might be causing the increase or decrease in either of the variables? Explain.

6. *Causation: Lurking Variables* Over the past 30 years in the United States, there has been a strong negative correlation between the number of infant deaths at birth and the number of people over age 65.
   (a) Is the fact that people are living longer causing a decrease in infant mortalities at birth?
   (b) What lurking variables might be causing the increase or decrease in either of the variables? Explain.

7. *Veterinary Science: Shetland Ponies* How much should a healthy Shetland pony weigh? Let x be the age of the pony (in months), and let y be the average weight of the pony (in kilograms). The following information is based on data taken from *The Merck Veterinary Manual* (a reference used in most veterinary colleges).

x	3	6	12	18	24
y	60	95	140	170	185

(a) Make a scatter diagram and draw the line you think best fits the data.
(b) Would you say the correlation is low, moderate, or strong? positive or negative?
(c) Use a calculator to verify that $\Sigma x = 63$, $\Sigma x^2 = 1089$, $\Sigma y = 650$, $\Sigma y^2 = 95,350$, and $\Sigma xy = 9930$. Compute r. As x increases, does the value of r imply that y should tend to increase or decrease? Explain.

8. *Health Insurance: Administrative Cost* The following data are based on information from *Domestic Affairs*. Let x be the average number of employees in a group health insurance plan, and let y be the average administrative cost as a percentage of claims.

x	3	7	15	35	75
y	40	35	30	25	18

(a) Make a scatter diagram and draw the line you think best fits the data.
(b) Would you say the correlation is low, moderate, or strong? positive or negative?
(c) Use a calculator to verify that $\Sigma x = 135$, $\Sigma x^2 = 7133$, $\Sigma y = 148$, $\Sigma y^2 = 4674$, and $\Sigma xy = 3040$. Compute r. As x increases, does the value of r imply that y should tend to increase or decrease? Explain.

9. *Meteorology: Cyclones* Can a low barometer reading be used to predict maximum wind speed of an approaching tropical cyclone? Data for this problem are based on information taken from *Weatherwise* (vol. 46, no. 1), a publication of the American Meteorological Society. For a random sample of tropical cyclones, let x be the lowest pressure (in millibars) as a cyclone approaches, and let y be the maximum wind speed (in miles per hour) of the cyclone.

x	1004	975	992	935	985	932
y	40	100	65	145	80	150

(a) Make a scatter diagram and draw the line you think best fits the data.
(b) Would you say the correlation is low, moderate, or strong? positive or negative?
(c) Use a calculator to verify that $\Sigma x = 5823$, $\Sigma x^2 = 5,655,779$, $\Sigma y = 580$, $\Sigma y^2 = 65,750$, and $\Sigma xy = 556,315$. Compute r. As x increases, does the value of r imply that y should tend to increase or decrease? Explain.

10. *Geology: Earthquakes* Is the magnitude of an earthquake related to the depth below the surface at which the quake occurs? Let x be the magnitude of an earthquake (on the Richter scale), and let y be the depth (in kilometers) of the quake below the surface at the epicenter. The following is based on information taken from the National Earthquake Information Service of the U.S. Geological Survey. Additional data may be found by visiting the Brase/Brase statistics site at **http://math.college.hmco.com/students** and finding the link to earthquakes.

x	2.9	4.2	3.3	4.5	2.6	3.2	3.4
y	5.0	10.0	11.2	10.0	7.9	3.9	5.5

(a) Make a scatter diagram and draw the line you think best fits the data.
(b) Would you say the correlation is low, moderate, or strong? positive or negative?
(c) Use a calculator to verify that $\Sigma x = 24.1$, $\Sigma x^2 = 85.75$, $\Sigma y = 53.5$, $\Sigma y^2 = 458.31$, and $\Sigma xy = 190.18$. Compute r. As x increases, does the value of r imply that y should tend to increase or decrease? Explain.

11. *Archaeology: Pottery* Wind Mountain archaeological site is located in southwest New Mexico. Ancient, prehistoric pottery vessels are usually found as sherds (broken

pieces) and carefully reconstructed if enough sherds can be found. For reconstructed (or even rare unbroken) pottery vessels, let x be the body diameter (in centimeters), and let y be the height (in centimeters) of the vessel. The following data are based on information taken from *Mimbres Mogollon Archaeology,* by A. I. Woosley and A. J. McIntyre (University of New Mexico Press).

x	7.3	31.0	18.4	6.5	4.9	2.6	19.5	9.2	23.7
y	5.5	28.5	19.7	5.0	5.7	2.1	11.5	5.0	11.6

(a) Make a scatter diagram and draw the line you think best fits the data.
(b) Would you say the correlation is low, moderate, or high? positive or negative?
(c) Using a calculator, verify that $\Sigma x = 123.1$, $\Sigma x^2 = 2452.45$, $\Sigma y = 94.6$, $\Sigma y^2 = 1584.3$, and $\Sigma xy = 1897.19$. Compute r. As x increases, does the value of r imply that y should tend to increase or decrease? Explain.

12. *University Crime: FBI Report* Do larger universities tend to have more property crime? University crime statistics are affected by a variety of factors. The surrounding community, accessibility given to outside visitors, and many other factors influence crime rate. Let x be a variable that represents student enrollment (in thousands) on a university campus. Let y be a variable that represents the number of burglaries in a year on a university campus. A random sample of $n = 8$ universities in California gave the following information about enrollments and annual burglary incidents. (Reference: *Crime in the United States,* Federal Bureau of Investigation.)

x	12.5	30.0	24.5	14.3	7.5	27.7	16.2	20.1
y	26	73	39	23	15	30	15	25

(a) Make a scatter diagram and draw the line you think best fits the data.
(b) Would you say the correlation is low, moderate, or high? positive or negative?
(c) Using a calculator, verify that $\Sigma x = 152.8$, $\Sigma x^2 = 3350.98$, $\Sigma y = 246$, $\Sigma y^2 = 10{,}030$, and $\Sigma xy = 5488.4$. Compute r. As x increases, does the value of r imply that y should tend to increase or decrease? Explain.

13. *Expand Your Knowledge: Effect of Scale on Scatter Diagram* The initial visual impact of a scatter diagram depends on the scales used on the x and y axes. Consider the following data:

x	1	2	3	4	5	6
y	1	4	6	3	6	7

(a) Make a scatter diagram using the same scale on both the x and y axes (i.e., make sure the unit lengths on the two axes are equal).
(b) Make a scatter diagram using a scale on the y axis that is twice as long as that on the x axis.
(c) Make a scatter diagram using a scale on the y axis that is half as long as that on the x axis.
(d) On each of the three graphs, draw the straight line that you think best fits the data points. How do the slopes (or directions) of the three lines appear to change? (*Note:* The actual slopes will be the same; they just appear different because of the choice of scale factors.)

14. *Expand Your Knowledge: Effect on r of Exchanging x and y Values* Examine the computation formula for r, the sample correlation coefficient [formulas (1) and (2) of this section].

(a) In the formula for r, if we exchange the symbols x and y, do we get a different result or do we get the same (equivalent) result? Explain.

(b) If we have a set of x and y data values, and we exchange each corresponding x and y value to get a new data set, should the sample correlation coefficient be the same for both sets of data? Explain.

(c) Compute the sample correlation coefficient r for each of the following data sets and show that r is the same for both.

x	1	3	4
y	2	1	6

x	2	1	6
y	1	3	4

 15. *Expand Your Knowledge: Using a Table to Test* ρ The correlation coefficient r is a *sample* statistic. What does it tell us about the value of the population correlation coefficient ρ (Greek letter rho)? We will build the formal structure of hypothesis tests of ρ in Section 11.4. However, there is a quick way to determine if the sample evidence based on r is strong enough to conclude that there is some population correlation between the variables. In other words, we can use the value of r to determine if $\rho \neq 0$. We do this by comparing the value $|r|$ to an entry in Table 4-4. The value of α in the table gives us the probability of concluding that $\rho \neq 0$ when in fact $\rho = 0$ and there is no population correlation. We have two choices for α: $\alpha = 0.05$ or $\alpha = 0.01$.

PROCEDURE

How to use Table 4-4 to test ρ

1. First compute r from a random sample of n data pairs (x, y).

2. Find the table entry in the row headed by n and the column headed by your choice of α. Your choice of α is the risk you are willing to take of mistakenly concluding that $\rho \neq 0$ when in fact $\rho = 0$.

3. Compare $|r|$ to the table entry.
   (a) If $|r| \geq$ table entry, then there is sufficient evidence to conclude that $\rho \neq 0$, and we say that r is **significant**. In other words, we conclude that there is some population correlation between the two variables x and y.

   (b) If $|r| <$ table entry, then the evidence is insufficient to conclude that $\rho \neq 0$, and we say that r is **not significant**. We do not have enough evidence to conclude that there is any correlation between the two variables x and y.

TABLE 4-4   Critical Values for Correlation Coefficient r

n	$\alpha = 0.05$	$\alpha = 0.01$	n	$\alpha = 0.05$	$\alpha = 0.01$	n	$\alpha = 0.05$	$\alpha = 0.01$
3	1.00	1.00	13	0.53	0.68	23	0.41	0.53
4	0.95	0.99	14	0.53	0.66	24	0.40	0.52
5	0.88	0.96	15	0.51	0.64	25	0.40	0.51
6	0.81	0.92	16	0.50	0.61	26	0.39	0.50
7	0.75	0.87	17	0.48	0.61	27	0.38	0.49
8	0.71	0.83	18	0.47	0.59	28	0.37	0.48
9	0.67	0.80	19	0.46	0.58	29	0.37	0.47
10	0.63	0.76	20	0.44	0.56	30	0.36	0.46
11	0.60	0.73	21	0.43	0.55			
12	0.58	0.71	22	0.42	0.54			

(a) Look at Problem 7 regarding the variables x = age of a Shetland pony and y = weight of that pony. Is the value of $|r|$ large enough to conclude that weight and age of Shetland ponies are correlated? Use $\alpha = 0.05$.

(b) Look at Problem 9 regarding the variables x = lowest barometric pressure as a cyclone approaches and y = maximum wind speed of the cyclone. Is the value of $|r|$ large enough to conclude that lowest barometric pressure and wind speed of a cyclone are correlated? Use $\alpha = 0.01$.

16. *Expand Your Knowledge: Sample Size and Significance of Correlation* In this problem we use Table 4-4 to explore the significance of r based on different sample sizes. See Problem 15.

(a) Is a sample correlation coefficient $r = 0.820$ significant at the $\alpha = 0.01$ level based on a sample size of $n = 7$ data pairs? What about $n = 9$ data pairs?

(b) Is a sample correlation coefficient $r = 0.40$ significant at the $\alpha = 0.05$ level based on a sample size of $n = 20$ data pairs? What about $n = 27$ data pairs?

(c) Is it true that in order to be significant, an r value must be larger than 0.90? larger than 0.70? larger than 0.50? What does sample size have to do with the significance of r? Explain.

4.2 Linear Regression and the Coefficient of Determination

FOCUS POINTS

✓ State the least-squares criterion.

✓ Use sample data to find the equation of the least-squares line. Graph the least-squares line.

✓ Use the least-squares line to predict a value of the response variable y for a specified value of the explanatory variable x.

✓ Explain the difference between interpolation and extrapolation.

✓ Explain why extrapolation beyond the sample data range might give results that are misleading or meaningless.

✓ Use r^2 to determine *explained* and *unexplained* variation of the response variable y.

In Denali National Park, Alaska, the wolf population is dependent on a large, strong caribou population. In this wild setting caribou are found in very large herds. The well-being of an entire caribou herd is not threatened by wolves. In fact, it is thought that wolves keep caribou herds strong by helping prevent overpopulation. Can the caribou population be used to predict the size of the wolf population?

Let x be a random variable that represents the fall caribou population (in hundreds) in Denali National Park. Let y be a random variable that represents the late-winter wolf population in the park. A random sample of recent years gave the following information (Reference: U.S. Department of the Interior, National Biological Service).

x	30	34	27	25	17	23	20
y	66	79	70	60	48	55	60

Looking at the scatter diagram in Figure 4-7 on the next page, we can ask some questions.

1. Do the data indicate a linear relationship between x and y?

2. Can you find an equation for the best-fitting line relating x and y? Can you use this relationship to predict the size of the wolf population when you know the size of the caribou population?

3. What fractional part of the variability in y can be associated with the variability in x? What fractional part of the variability in y is not associated with a corresponding variability in x?

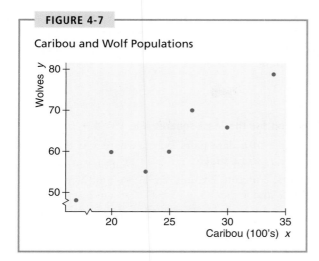

FIGURE 4-7

Caribou and Wolf Populations

FIGURE 4-8

Least-Squares Criterion

The first step in answering these questions is to try to express the relationship between x and y as a mathematical equation. There are many possible equations, but the simplest and most widely used is the linear equation, or the equation of a straight line. Because we will be using this line to predict the y values from the x values, we call x the *explanatory variable* and y the *response variable*.

Our job is to find the "best" linear equation representing the points of the scatter diagram. For our criterion of best-fitting line, we use the *least-squares criterion*, which states that the line we fit to the data points must be such that *the sum of the squares of the vertical distances from the points to the line is as small as possible*. The least-squares criterion is illustrated in Figure 4-8.

Least-squares criterion

The sum of the squares of the vertical distances from the data points (x, y) to the line is made as small as possible.

In Figure 4-8, d represents the difference between the y coordinate of the data point and the corresponding y coordinate on the line. Thus, if the data point lies above the line, d is positive, but if the data point lies below the line, d is negative. As a result, the sum of the d values can be small even if the points are widely spread in the scatter diagram. However, the squares d^2 cannot be negative. By minimizing the sum of the squares, we are, in effect, not allowing positive and negative d values to "cancel out" one another in the sum. It is in this way that we can meet the least-squares criterion of minimizing the sum of the squares of the vertical distances between the points and the line over *all* points in the scatter diagram.

We use the notation $\hat{y} = a + bx$ for the least-squares line. A little algebra tells us that b is the slope and a is the intercept of the line. In this context $\hat{y}$ (read

Explanatory variable
Response variable
Least-squares criterion

Least-squares line

"y hat") represents the value of the response variable y estimated using the least squares line and a given value of the explanatory variable x.

Techniques of calculus can be applied to show that a and b may be computed using the following procedure.

PROCEDURE

How to find the equation for the least-squares line $\hat{y} = a + bx$

Obtain a random sample of n data pairs (x, y), where x is the *explanatory variable* and y is the *response variable*.

1. Using the data pairs, compute Σx, Σy, Σx^2, Σy^2, and Σxy. Then compute the sample means $\bar{x}$ and $\bar{y}$.

2. With n = sample size, Σx, Σy, Σx^2, Σy^2, Σxy, $\bar{x}$, and $\bar{y}$, you are ready to compute the slope b and intercept a using the computation formulas

$$\text{Slope:} \qquad b = \frac{n\Sigma xy - (\Sigma x)(\Sigma y)}{n\Sigma x^2 - (\Sigma x)^2} \qquad\qquad (3)$$

$$\text{Intercept:} \quad a = \bar{y} - b\bar{x} \qquad\qquad (4)$$

Be careful! The notation Σx^2 means first square x and then calculate the sum, whereas $(\Sigma x)^2$ means first sum the x values, then square the result.

3. The equation of the least-squares line computed from your sample data is

$$\hat{y} = a + bx \qquad\qquad (5)$$

Note: Inferences for the population slope (Section 11.4) require the data pairs to have a *bivariate normal distribution*. That is, for a fixed value of x, the y values should have a normal distribution (or at least a mound-shaped and symmetric distribution), and for a fixed value of y, the x values should have their own (approximately) normal distribution. Chapter 6 discusses normal distributions.

◇ **COMMENT:** The computation formulas for the slope of the least-squares line, the correlation coefficient r, and the standard deviations s_x and s_y use many of the same sums. There is, in fact, a relationship between the correlation coefficient r and the slope of the least-squares line b. In instances where we know r, s_x, and s_y, we can use the following formula to compute b.

$$b = r\left(\frac{s_y}{s_x}\right) \qquad\qquad (6) ◇$$

◇ **COMMENT:** In other mathematics courses, the slope-intercept form of the equation of a line is usually given as $y = mx + b$, where m refers to the slope of the line and b to the y-coordinate of the y-intercept. In statistics, when there is only one explanatory variable, it is common practice to use the letter b to designate the slope of the least-squares line and the letter a to designate the y-coordinate of the intercept. For example, these are the symbols used on the TI-84Plus and TI-83Plus calculators as well as many other calculators. ◇

Using the formulas to find the
values of a and b

For most applications, you can use a calculator or computer software to compute a and b directly. However, to build some familiarity with the structure of the computation formulas, it is useful to do some calculations for yourself. Example 4 shows how to use the computation formulas to find the values of a and b and the equation of the least-squares line $\hat{y} = a + bx$.

Note: If you are using your calculator to find the values of a and b directly, then you may omit the discussion regarding use of the formulas. Go to the margin header "Using the values of a and b to construct the equation of the least-squares line."

EXAMPLE 4

Least-squares line

Let's find the least-squares equation relating the variables x = size of caribou population (in hundreds) and y = size of wolf population in Denali National Park. Use x as the explanatory variable and y as the response variable.

(a) Use the computation formulas to find the slope of the least-squares line b and the y-intercept a.

SOLUTION: Table 4-5 gives the data values x and y, along with the values x^2, y^2, and xy. First compute the sample means.

$$\bar{x} = \frac{\Sigma x}{n} = \frac{176}{7} \approx 25.14 \quad \text{and} \quad \bar{y} = \frac{\Sigma y}{n} = \frac{438}{7} \approx 62.57$$

Next compute the slope b.

$$b = \frac{n\Sigma xy - (\Sigma x)(\Sigma y)}{n\Sigma x^2 - (\Sigma x)^2} = \frac{7(11{,}337) - (176)(438)}{7(4628) - (176)^2} = \frac{2271}{1420} \approx 1.60$$

Use the values of b, $\bar{x}$, and $\bar{y}$ to compute the y-intercept a.

$$a = \bar{y} - b\bar{x} \approx 62.57 - 1.60(25.14) \approx 22.35$$

TABLE 4-5 Sums for Computing b, $\bar{x}$, and $\bar{y}$

x	y	x^2	y^2	xy
30	66	900	4356	1980
34	79	1156	6241	2686
27	70	729	4900	1890
25	60	625	3600	1500
17	48	289	2304	816
23	55	529	3025	1265
20	60	400	3600	1200
$\Sigma x = 176$	$\Sigma y = 438$	$\Sigma x^2 = 4628$	$\Sigma y^2 = 28{,}026$	$\Sigma xy = 11{,}337$

Using the values of a and b to
construct the equation of the
least-squares line

Note that calculators give the values $b \approx 1.599$ and $a \approx 22.36$. These values differ slightly from those you computed using the formulas because of rounding.

(b) Use the values of a and b (either computed or obtained from a calculator) to find the equation of the least-squares line.

SOLUTION:

$$\hat{y} = a + bx$$
$$\hat{y} \approx 22.35 + 1.60x \quad \text{since} \quad a \approx 22.35 \quad \text{and} \quad b \approx 1.60$$

Graphing the least squares line

(c) Graph the equation of the least-squares line on a scatter diagram.

SOLUTION: To graph the least-squares line, we have several options available. The slope-intercept method of algebra is probably the quickest, but may not always be convenient if the intercept is not within the range of the sample data values. It is just as easy to select two x values in the range of the x data values and then use the least-squares line to compute two corresponding $\hat{y}$ values.

In fact, we already have the coordinates of one point on the least squares line. By the formula for the intercept [Equation (4)], the point $(\bar{x}, \bar{y})$ is always on the least-squares line. For our example, $(\bar{x}, \bar{y}) = (25.14, 62.57)$.

The point $(\bar{x}, \bar{y})$ is always on the least-squares line.

Another x value within the data range is $x = 34$. Using the least-squares line to compute the corresponding $\hat{y}$ value gives

$$\hat{y} \approx 22.35 + 1.60(34) \approx 76.75$$

We place the two points (25.14, 62.57) and (34, 76.75) on the scatter diagram (using a different symbol than that used for the sample data points) and connect the points with a line segment (Figure 4-9). ◇

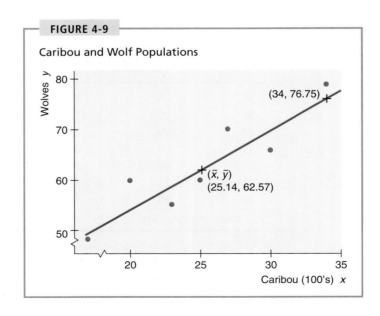

FIGURE 4-9

Caribou and Wolf Populations

Meaning of slope

In the equation $\hat{y} = a + bx$, the slope b tells us how many units $\hat{y}$ changes for each unit change in x. In Example 4 regarding size of wolf and caribou populations,

$$\hat{y} \approx 22.35 + 1.60x$$

The slope 1.60 tells us that if the number of caribou (in hundreds) changes by 1 (hundred), then we expect the sustainable wolf population to change by 1.60. In other words, our model says that an increase of 100 caribou will increase the predicted wolf population by 1.60. If the caribou population decreases by 400, we predict the sustainable wolf population will decrease by 6.4.

> The slope of the least-squares line tells how many units the response variable is expected to change for each unit change in the explanatory variable. The number of units change in the response variable for each unit change in the explanatory variable is called the **marginal change** of the response variable.

Predicting *y* for a specified *x*

Making predictions is one of the main applications of linear regression. In other words, you use the equation of the least-squares line to predict the $\hat{y}$ value for a specified x value. Of course, the accuracy of the prediction depends on how well the least-squares line fits the original raw data points. It is a good idea to check that the correlation coefficient indicates a strong linear correlation.

Interpolation, extrapolation

Another issue that affects the validity of predictions is whether you are *interpolating* or *extrapolating*.

> Predicting $\hat{y}$ values for x values that are **between** observed x values in the data set is called **interpolation.**

> Predicting $\hat{y}$ values for x values that are **beyond** observed x values in the data set is called **extrapolation.**

The least-squares line is developed from sample data pairs (x, y). The least-squares line may not reflect the relationship between x and y for values of x outside the data range. For example, there is a fairly high correlation between height and age for boys ages 1 year to 10 years. In general, the older the boy, the taller the boy. A least-squares line based on such data would give good predictions of height for ages between 1 and 10. However, it would be fairly meaningless to use the same linear regression line to predict the height of a 20-year-old or 50-year-old man.

Another consideration when working with predictions is the fact that the least-squares line is based on sample data. Each different sample will produce a slightly different equation for the least-squares line.

One more important fact about predictions. The least-squares line is developed with x as the explanatory variable and y as the response variable. This model can be used only to predict y values from specified x values. If you wish to begin with y values and predict corresponding x values, you must start all over and compute a new equation. Such an equation would be developed using a model with x as the response variable and y as the explanatory variable. See Problem 11 at the end of this section. Note that the equation for predicting x values *cannot* be derived from the least-squares line predicting y simply by solving the equation for x.

> The least-squares line developed with x as the explanatory variable and y as the response variable can be used only to predict y values from specified x values.

The next example shows how to use the least-squares line for predictions.

EXAMPLE 5

Predictions

We continue with Example 4 regarding size of the wolf population as it relates to size of the caribou population. Suppose you want to predict the size of the wolf population when the size of the caribou population is 21 (hundred).

(a) In the least-squares model developed in Example 4, which is the explanatory variable and which is the response variable? Can you use the equation to predict the size of the wolf population for a specified size of caribou population?

SOLUTION: The least-squares line $\hat{y} \approx 22.35 + 1.60x$ was developed using x = size of caribou population in hundreds as the explanatory variable and y = size of wolf population as the response variable. We can use the equation to predict the y value for a specified x value.

(b) The sample data pairs have x values ranging from 17 (hundred) to 34 (hundred) for the size of the caribou population. To predict the size of the wolf population when the size of the caribou population is 21 (hundred), will you be interpolating or extrapolating?

SOLUTION: Interpolating, since 21 (hundred) falls within the range of sample x values.

(c) Predict the size of the wolf population when the caribou population is 21 (hundred).

SOLUTION: Using the least-squares line from Example 4 and the value 21 in place of x gives

$$\hat{y} \approx 22.35 + 1.60x \approx 22.35 + 1.60(21) \approx 55.95$$

Rounding up to a whole number gives a prediction of 56 for the size of the wolf population. ◇

GUIDED EXERCISE 3

Least-squares line

The Quick Sell car dealership has been using 1-minute spot ads on a local TV station. The ads always occur during the evening hours and advertise the different models and price ranges of cars on the lot that week. During a 10-week period, the Quick Sell dealer kept a weekly record of the number x of TV ads versus the number y of cars sold. The results are given in Table 4-6.

The manager decided that Quick Sell can afford only 12 ads per week. At that level of advertisement, how many cars can Quick Sell expect to sell each week? We'll answer this question in several steps.

TABLE 4-6

x	y
6	15
20	31
0	10
14	16
25	28
16	20
28	40
18	25
10	12
8	15

(a) Draw a scatter diagram for the data.

The scatter diagram is shown in Figure 4-10. The plain red dots in Figure 4-10 are the points of the scatter diagram. Notice that the least-squares line is also shown with two extra points used to position the line.

FIGURE 4-10 Scatter Diagram and Least-Squares Line for Table 4-6

(b) Verify that $\Sigma x = 145$, $\Sigma y = 212$, $\Sigma x^2 = 2785$, and $\Sigma xy = 3764$.

Use a calculator.

(c) Compute the sample means $\bar{x}$ and $\bar{y}$.

$\bar{x} = \dfrac{\Sigma x}{n} = \dfrac{145}{10} = 14.5$; $\bar{y} = \dfrac{\Sigma y}{n} = \dfrac{212}{10} = 21.2$

Continued

GUIDED EXERCISE 3 continued

(d) Compute a and b for the equation $\hat{y} = a + bx$ of the least-squares line.

$\Longrightarrow$

$$b = \frac{n\Sigma xy - (\Sigma x)(\Sigma y)}{n\Sigma x^2 - (\Sigma x)^2}$$

$$= \frac{10(3764) - (145)(212)}{10(2785) - (145)^2} = \frac{6900}{6825} \approx 1.01$$

$$a = \bar{y} - b\bar{x}$$

$$\approx 21.2 - 1.01(14.5) \approx 6.56$$

(e) What is the equation of the least-squares line $\hat{y} = a + bx$?

$\Longrightarrow$

Using the values of a and b computed in part (d) or values of a and b obtained directly from a calculator,

$$\hat{y} \approx 6.56 + 1.01x$$

(f) Plot the least-squares line on your scatter diagram.

$\Longrightarrow$

The least-squares line goes through the point $(\bar{x}, \bar{y}) = (14.5, 21.2)$. To get another point on the line, select a value for x and compute the corresponding y value using the equation $y = 6.56 + 1.01x$. For $x = 20$, we get $y = 6.56 + 1.01(20) = 26.8$, so the point $(20, 26.8)$ is also on the line. The least-squares line is shown in Figure 4-10.

(g) Read the y value for $x = 12$ from your graph. Then use the equation of the least-squares line to calculate y when $x = 12$. How many cars can the manager expect to sell if 12 ads per week are aired on TV?

$\Longrightarrow$

The graph gives $y \approx 19$. From the equation we get

$$y = 6.56 + 1.01x$$

$$= 6.56 + 1.01(12) \quad \text{using 12 in place of } x$$

$$= 18.68$$

To the nearest whole number, the manager can expect to sell 19 cars when 12 ads are aired on TV each week.

TECH NOTE When we have more data pairs, it is convenient to use a technology tool such as the TI-84Plus and TI-83Plus calculators, Excel, or Minitab to find the equation of the least-squares line. The displays show results for the data of Guided Exercise 3 regarding car sales and ads.

TI-84Plus/TI-83Plus Press **STAT**, choose **Calculate**, and use option **8:LinReg(a+bx)**. For a graph showing the scatter plot and the least-squares line, press the **STAT PLOT** key, turn on a plot, and highlight the first type. Then press the **Y=** key. To enter the equation of the least-squares line, press **VARS**, select **5:Statistics**, highlight **EQ**, and then select **1:RegEQ**. Press **ENTER**. Finally, press **ZOOM** and choose **9:ZoomStat**.

Excel There are several ways to find the equation of the least-squares line in Excel. One way is to make a scatter plot using the menu choices **Chart wizard ➤ Scatter Diagram**. When the diagram is complete, **right click** on one of the points on the diagram, select **trendline**, and under options check to display the equation of the line.

TI-84Plus/TI-83Plus Display   Excel Display

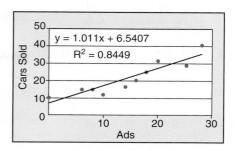

```
LinReg
 y=a+bx
 a=6.5407
 b=1.0110
 r²=.8449
 r=.9192
```

Minitab There are a number of ways to generate the least-squares line. One way is to use the menu selection **Stat ➤ Regression ➤ Fitted Line Plot.** The least-squares equation is shown with the diagram.

Coefficient of Determination

There is another way to answer the question, How good is the least-squares line as an instrument of regression? The *coefficient of determination* r^2 is the square of the sample correlation coefficient r.

Coefficient of determination r^2

1. Compute the sample correlation coefficient r using the procedure of Section 4.1. Then simply compute r^2, the sample coefficient of determination.

2. The value r^2 is the ratio of explained variation over total variation. That is, r^2 is the fractional amount of total variation in y that can be explained by using the linear model $\hat{y} = a + bx$.

3. Furthermore, $1 - r^2$ is the fractional amount of total variation in y that is due to random chance or to the possibility of lurking variables that influence y.

In other words, the coefficient of determination r^2 is a measure of the proportion of variation in y that is explained by the regression line, using x as the explanatory variable. If $r = 0.90$, then $r^2 = 0.81$ is the coefficient of determination. We can say that about 81% of the (variation) behavior of the y variable can be explained by the corresponding (variation) behavior of the x variable if we use the equation of the least-squares line. The remaining 19% of the (variation) behavior of the y variable is due to random chance or to the possibility of lurking variables that influence y.

GUIDED EXERCISE 4

Coefficient of determination r^2

In Guided Exercise 3 we looked at the relationship between x = number of 1-minute spot ads on TV advertising different models of cars and y = number of cars sold each week by the sponsoring car dealership.

(a) Using the sums found in Guided Exercise 3, compute the correlation coefficient r. $n = 10$, $\Sigma x = 145$, $\Sigma y = 212$, $\Sigma x^2 = 2785$, and $\Sigma xy = 3764$. You also need $\Sigma y^2 = 5320$.

$$r = \frac{n\Sigma xy - (\Sigma x)(\Sigma y)}{\sqrt{n\Sigma x^2 - (\Sigma x)^2}\sqrt{n\Sigma y^2 - (\Sigma y)^2}}$$

$\Rightarrow$
$$r = \frac{10(3764) - (145)(212)}{\sqrt{10(2785) - (145)^2}\sqrt{10(5320) - (212)^2}}$$

$$\approx \frac{6900}{(82.61)(90.86)}$$

$$\approx 0.919$$

(b) Compute the coefficient of determination r^2.

$\Rightarrow$ $r^2 \approx 0.845$

(c) What percentage of the variation in the number of car sales can be explained by the ads and the least-squares line?

$\Rightarrow$ 84.5%

(d) What percentage of the variation in the number of car sales is not explained by the ads and the least-squares line?

$\Rightarrow$ 100% − 84.5%, or 15.5%

VIEWPOINT   *It's Freezing!*

Can you use average temperatures in January to predict how bad the rest of the winter will be? Can you predict the number of days with freezing temperatures for the entire calendar year using conditions in January? How good would such a forecast be for predicting growing season or number of frost-free days? Methods of this section can help you answer such questions. For more information, visit the Brase/Brase statistics site at **http://math.college.hmco.com/students** and find the link to temperatures.

SECTION 4.2   PROBLEMS

For Problems 1–8, please do the following.
(a) Draw a scatter diagram displaying the data.
(b) Verify the given sums Σx, Σy, Σx^2, Σy^2, and Σxy and the value of the sample correlation coefficient r.
(c) Find $\bar{x}, \bar{y}$, a, and b. Then find the equation of the least squares line $\hat{y} = a + bx$.
(d) Graph the least-squares line on your scatter diagram. Be sure to use the point $(\bar{x}, \bar{y})$ as one of the points on the line.

(e) Find the value of the coefficient of determination r^2. What percentage of the variation in y can be *explained* by the corresponding variation in x and the least-squares line? What percentage is *unexplained*?

Answers may vary slightly due to rounding.

1. *Economics: Entry-Level Jobs* An economist is studying the job market in Denver area neighborhoods. Let x represent the total number of jobs in a given neighborhood, and let y represent the number of entry-level jobs in the same neighborhood. A sample of six Denver neighborhoods gave the following information (units in 100s of jobs).

x	16	33	50	28	50	25
y	2	3	6	5	9	3

Source: Neighborhood Facts, The Piton Foundation. To find out more, visit the Brase/Brase statistics site at **http://math.college.hmco.com/students** and find the link to the Piton Foundation.

Complete parts (a) through (e), given $\Sigma x = 202$, $\Sigma y = 28$, $\Sigma x^2 = 7754$, $\Sigma y^2 = 164$, $\Sigma xy = 1096$, and $r \approx 0.860$.
(f) For a neighborhood with $x = 40$ jobs, how many are predicted to be entry-level jobs?

2. *Ranching: Cattle* You are the foreman of the Bar-S cattle ranch in Colorado. A neighboring ranch has calves for sale, and you are going to buy some calves to add to the Bar-S herd. How much should a healthy calf weigh? Let x be the age of the calf (in weeks), and let y be the weight of the calf (in kilograms). The following information is based on data taken from *The Merck Veterinary Manual* (a reference used by many ranchers).

x	1	3	10	16	26	36
y	42	50	75	100	150	200

Complete parts (a) through (e), given $\Sigma x = 92$, $\Sigma y = 617$, $\Sigma x^2 = 2338$, $\Sigma y^2 = 82{,}389$, $\Sigma xy = 13{,}642$, and $r \approx 0.998$.
(f) The calves you want to buy are 12 weeks old. What does the least-squares line predict for a healthy weight?

3. *Weight of Car: Miles per Gallon* Do heavier cars really use more gasoline? Suppose that a car is chosen at random. Let x be the weight of the car (in hundreds of pounds), and let y be the miles per gallon (mpg). The following information is based on data taken from *Consumer Reports* (vol. 62, no. 4).

x	27	44	32	47	23	40	34	52
y	30	19	24	13	29	17	21	14

Complete parts (a) through (e), given $\Sigma x = 299$, $\Sigma y = 167$, $\Sigma x^2 = 11{,}887$, $\Sigma y^2 = 3773$, $\Sigma xy = 5814$, and $r \approx -0.946$.
(f) Suppose that a car weighs $x = 38$ (hundred pounds). What does the least-squares line forecast for $y =$ miles per gallon?

4. *Basketball: Fouls* Data for this problem are based on information from *STATS Basketball Scoreboard*. It is thought that basketball teams that make too many fouls in

a game tend to lose the game even if they otherwise play well. Let x be the number of fouls more than (i.e., over and above) the opposing team. Let y be the percentage of times the team with the larger number of fouls wins the game.

x	0	2	5	6
y	50	45	33	26

Complete parts (a) through (e), given $\Sigma x = 13$, $\Sigma y = 154$, $\Sigma x^2 = 65$, $\Sigma y^2 = 6290$, $\Sigma xy = 411$, and $r \approx -0.988$.
(f) If a team had $x = 4$ fouls over and above the opposing team, what does the least-squares equation forecast for y?

5. *Auto Accidents: Age* Data for this problem are based on information taken from *The Wall Street Journal*. Let x be the age in years of a licensed automobile driver. Let y be the percentage of all fatal accidents (for a given age) due to speeding. For example, the first data pair indicates that 36% of all fatal accidents involving 17-year-olds are due to speeding.

x	17	27	37	47	57	67	77
y	36	25	20	12	10	7	5

Complete parts (a) through (e), given $\Sigma x = 329$, $\Sigma y = 115$, $\Sigma x^2 = 18,263$, $\Sigma y^2 = 2639$, $\Sigma xy = 4015$, and $r \approx -0.959$.
(f) Predict the percentage of all fatal accidents due to speeding for 25-year-olds.

6. *Auto Accidents: Age* Let x be the age of a licensed driver in years. Let y be the percentage of all fatal accidents (for a given age) due to failure to yield the right of way. For example, the first data pair says that 5% of all fatal accidents involving 37-year-olds are due to failure to yield the right of way. *The Wall Street Journal* article referenced in Problem 5 reported the following data:

x	37	47	57	67	77	87
y	5	8	10	16	30	43

Complete parts (a) through (e), given $\Sigma x = 372$, $\Sigma y = 112$, $\Sigma x^2 = 24,814$, $\Sigma y^2 = 3194$, $\Sigma xy = 8254$, and $r \approx 0.943$.
(f) Predict the percentage of all fatal accidents due to failing to yield the right of way for 70-year-olds.

7. *Archaeology: Artifacts* Data for this problem are based on information taken from *Prehistoric New Mexico: Background for Survey* (by D. E. Stuart and R. P. Gauthier, University of New Mexico Press). It is thought that prehistoric Indians did not take their best tools, pottery, and household items when they visited higher elevations for their summer camps. It is hypothesized that archaeological sites tend to lose their cultural identity and specific cultural affiliation as the elevation of the site increases. Let x be the elevation (in thousands of feet) for an archaeological site in the southwestern United States. Let y be the percentage of unidentified artifacts (no

specific cultural affiliation) at a given elevation. The following data were obtained for a collection of archaeological sites in New Mexico:

x	5.25	5.75	6.25	6.75	7.25
y	19	13	33	37	62

Complete parts (a) through (e), given $\Sigma x = 31.25$, $\Sigma y = 164$, $\Sigma x^2 \approx 197.813$, $\Sigma y^2 = 6832$, $\Sigma xy = 1080$, and $r \approx 0.913$.

(f) At an archaeological site with elevation 6.5 (thousand feet), what does the least-squares equation forecast for y = percentage of culturally unidentified artifacts?

8. *Cricket Chirps: Temperature* Anyone who has been outdoors on a summer evening has probably heard crickets. Did you know that it is possible to use the cricket as a thermometer? Crickets tend to chirp more frequently as temperatures increase. This phenomenon was studied in detail by George W. Pierce, a physics professor at Harvard. In the following data, x is a random variable representing chirps per second and y is a random variable representing temperature (°F). These data are on the statSpace CD-ROM.

x	20.0	16.0	19.8	18.4	17.1	15.5	14.7	17.1
y	88.6	71.6	93.3	84.3	80.6	75.2	69.7	82.0

x	15.4	16.2	15.0	17.2	16.0	17.0	14.4
y	69.4	83.3	79.6	82.6	80.6	83.5	76.3

Source: Reprinted by permission of the publisher from *The Songs of Insects* by George W. Pierce, Cambridge, Mass.: Harvard University Press, Copyright © 1948 by the President and Fellows of Harvard College.

Complete parts (a) through (e), given $\Sigma x = 249.8$, $\Sigma y = 1200.6$, $\Sigma x^2 = 4200.56$, $\Sigma y^2 = 96{,}725.86$, $\Sigma xy = 20{,}127.47$, and $r \approx 0.835$.

(f) What is the predicted temperature when $x = 19$ chirps per second?

9. *Expand Your Knowledge: Residual Plot* The least-squares line usually does not go through all the sample data points (x, y). In fact, for a specified x value from a data pair (x, y), there is usually a difference between the predicted value $\hat{y}$ and the y value paired with x. This difference is called the *residual*.

> The **residual** is the difference between the y value in a specified data pair (x, y) and the value $\hat{y} = a + bx$ predicted by the least-squares line for the same x.
>
> $y - \hat{y}$ is the **residual.**

One way to assess how well a least-squares line serves as a model for the data is a **residual plot**. To make a residual plot, we put the x values in order on the horizontal axis and plot the corresponding residuals $y - \hat{y}$ in the vertical direction. Because for a least-squares model the mean of the residuals is always zero, we dash in a horizontal line at zero. The figure on the next page shows a residual plot for the data of Guided Exercise 3, in which the relationship between the number of ads run per week and the number of cars sold that week was explored. To make the residual plot, first compute all the residuals. Remember that x and y are the given data values, and $\hat{y}$ is computed from the least-squares line $\hat{y} \approx 6.56 + 1.01x$.

x	y	$\hat{y}$	Residual $y - \hat{y}$	x	y	$\hat{y}$	Residual $y - \hat{y}$
6	15	12.6	2.4	16	20	22.7	−2.7
20	31	26.8	4.2	28	40	34.8	5.2
0	10	6.6	3.4	18	25	24.7	0.3
14	16	20.7	−4.7	10	12	16.7	−4.7
25	28	31.8	−3.8	8	15	14.6	0.4

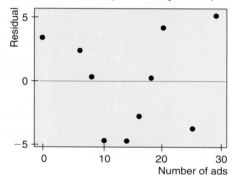

Residual Plot (Produced by Minitab)

(a) If the least-squares line provides a reasonable model for the data, the pattern of points in the plot will seem random and unstructured around the horizontal line at 0. Is this the case for the residual plot?

(b) If a point on the residual plot seems far outside the pattern of other points, it might reflect an unusual data point (x, y), called an *outlier*. Such points may have quite an influence on the least-squares model. Do there appear to be any outliers in the data for the residual plot?

 10. *Residual Plot: Miles per Gallon* Consider the data of Problem 3.
   (a) Make a residual plot for the least-squares model.
   (b) Use the residual plot to comment about the appropriateness of the least-squares model for these data. See Problem 9.

11. *Least-Squares Equation: Exchange x and y*
   (a) Suppose that you are given the following x, y data pairs:

x	1	3	4
y	2	1	6

   Show that the least-squares equation for these data is $y = 1.071x + 0.143$ (rounded to three digits after the decimal).
   (b) Now suppose that you are given these x, y data pairs:

x	2	1	6
y	1	3	4

Show that the least-squares equation for these data is $y = 0.357x + 1.595$ (rounded to three digits after the decimal).

(c) In the data for parts (a) and (b), did we simply exchange the x and y values of each data pair?

(d) Solve $y = 0.143 + 1.071x$ for x. Do you get the least-squares equation of part (b) with the symbols x and y exchanged?

(e) In general, suppose that we have the least-squares equation $y = a + bx$ for a set of data pairs x and y. If we solve this equation for x, will we *necessarily* get the least-squares equation for the set of data pairs y, x (with x and y exchanged)? Explain using parts (a) through (d).

SUMMARY

Scatter diagrams of data pairs (x, y) are useful in helping us determine visually if there is any relation between x and y values and, if so, how strong the relation might be. We call x the explanatory variable and y the response variable.

The Pearson product-moment correlation coefficient r gives a numerical measurement assessing the strength of a *linear* relationship between x and y based on a random sample of data pairs (x, y). The value of r ranges from -1 to 1, with 1 indicating perfect positive linear correlation, -1 indicating perfect negative linear correlation, and 0 indicating no linear correlation. The closer the sample statistic r is to 1 or -1, the stronger the linear correlation.

If the scatter diagram and correlation coefficient r indicate a linear relationship, then we use the least-squares criterion to develop the equation of the least-squares line between the explanatory variable x and the response variable y

$$\hat{y} = a + bx$$

where $\hat{y}$ is the value of y predicted by the least-squares line, a is the y-intercept, and b is the slope.

The coefficient of determination r^2 is a value that measures the proportion of variation in y explained by the least-squares line.

IMPORTANT WORDS & SYMBOLS

Section 4.1
Paired data values
Explanatory variable
Response variable
Scatter diagram
Sample correlation coefficient r
Perfect linear correlation
No linear correlation
Lurking variable

Section 4.2
Least-squares criterion
Least-squares line $\hat{y} = a + bx$

Meaning of slope
Interpolation
Extrapolation
Explained variation
Unexplained variation
Coefficient of determination r^2
Residual
Residual plot

VIEWPOINT

Living Arrangements

Male, female, married, single, living alone, living with friends or relatives—all these categories are of interest to the U.S. Census Bureau. In addition to these categories, there are others, such as age, income, and health needs. How strongly correlated are these variables? Can we use one or more of these variables to predict the others? How good is such a prediction? Methods of this chapter can help you answer such questions. For more information regarding such data, visit the Brase/Brase statistics site at **http://math.college.hmco.com/students** and find the link to Census Bureau.

CHAPTER REVIEW PROBLEMS

For Problems 1–6, please do the following.
  (a) Draw a scatter diagram.
  (b) Find the equation of the least-squares line, and plot the line on the scatter diagram of part (a).
  (c) Find the correlation coefficient r. Find the coefficient of determination r^2. What percentage of variation in y is explained by the variation in x and the least-squares model?

1. *Desert Ecology: Wildlife* Bighorn sheep are beautiful wild animals found throughout the western United States. Data for this problem are based on information taken from *The Desert Bighorn*, edited by Monson and Sumner (University of Arizona Press). Let x be the age of a bighorn sheep (in years), and let y be the mortality rate (percent that die) for this age group. For example, $x = 1$, $y = 14$ means that 14% of the bighorn sheep between 1 and 2 years old died. A random sample of Arizona bighorn sheep gave the following information:

x	1	2	3	4	5
y	14	18.9	14.4	19.6	20.0

$\Sigma x = 15$; $\Sigma y = 86.9$; $\Sigma x^2 = 55$; $\Sigma y^2 = 1544.73$; $\Sigma xy = 273.4$

2. *Sociology: Job Changes* A sociologist is interested in the relation between $x =$ number of job changes and $y =$ annual salary (in thousands of dollars) for people living in the Nashville area. A random sample of 10 people employed in Nashville provided the following information:

x (Number of job changes)	4	7	5	6	1	5	9	10	10	3
y (Salary in $1000)	33	37	34	32	32	38	43	37	40	33

$\Sigma x = 60$; $\Sigma y = 359$; $\Sigma x^2 = 442$; $\Sigma y^2 = 13,013$; $\Sigma xy = 2231$
  (d) If someone had $x = 2$ job changes, what does the least-squares line predict for y, the annual salary?

3. *Medical: Fat Babies* Modern medical practice tells us not to encourage babies to become too fat. Is there a positive correlation between the weight x of a 1-year-old baby and the weight y of the mature adult (30 years old)? A random sample of medical files produced the following information for 14 females:

x (lb)	21	25	23	24	20	15	25	21	17	24	26	22	18	19
y (lb)	125	125	120	125	130	120	145	130	130	130	130	140	110	115

$\Sigma x = 300$; $\Sigma y = 1775$; $\Sigma x^2 = 6572$; $\Sigma y^2 = 226,125$; $\Sigma xy = 38,220$

(d) If a female baby weighs 20 lb at 1 year, what do you predict she will weigh at 30 years of age?

4. *Sales: Insurance* Dorothy Kelly sells life insurance for the Prudence Insurance Company. She sells insurance by making visits to her clients' homes. Dorothy believes that the number of sales should depend, to some degree, on the number of visits made. For the past several years, she has kept careful records of the number of visits (x) she made each week and the number of people (y) who bought insurance that week. For a random sample of 15 such weeks, the x and y values follow:

x	11	19	16	13	28	5	20	14	22	7	15	29	8	25	16
y	3	11	8	5	8	2	5	6	8	3	5	10	6	10	7

$\Sigma x = 248$; $\Sigma y = 97$; $\Sigma x^2 = 4856$; $\Sigma y^2 = 731$; $\Sigma xy = 1825$

(d) During a week in which Dorothy makes 18 visits, how many people do you predict will buy insurance from her?

5. *Marketing: Coupons* Each box of Healthy Crunch breakfast cereal contains a coupon entitling you to a free package of garden seeds. At the Healthy Crunch home office, they use the weight of incoming mail to determine how many of their employees are to be assigned to collecting coupons and mailing out seed packages on a given day. (Healthy Crunch has a policy of answering all its mail on the day it is received.)

Let x = weight of incoming mail and y = number of employees required to process the mail in one working day. A random sample of 8 days gave the following data:

x (lb)	11	20	16	6	12	18	23	25
y (Number of employees)	6	10	9	5	8	14	13	16

$\Sigma x = 131$; $\Sigma y = 81$; $\Sigma x^2 = 2435$; $\Sigma y^2 = 927$; $\Sigma xy = 1487$

(d) If Healthy Crunch receives 15 lb of mail, how many employees should be assigned mail duty?

6. *Focus Problem: Changing Population and Crime Rate* Let x be a random variable representing percentage change in neighborhood population in the past few years, and let y be a random variable representing crime rate (crimes per 1000 population). A random sample of six Denver neighborhoods gave the following information (Source: *Neighborhood Facts*, The Piton Foundation).

x	29	2	11	17	7	6
y	173	35	132	127	69	53

$\Sigma x = 72; \Sigma y = 589; \Sigma x^2 = 1340; \Sigma y^2 = 72,277; \Sigma xy = 9499$

(d) For a neighborhood with $x = 12\%$ change in population in the past few years, predict the change in the crime rate (per 1000 residents).

DATA HIGHLIGHTS: GROUP PROJECTS

Break into small groups and discuss the following topics. Organize a brief outline in which you summarize the main points of your group discussion.

Scatter diagrams! Are they really useful? Scatter diagrams give a first impression of a data relationship and help us assess whether a linear relation provides a reasonable model for the data. In addition, we can spot *influential points*. A data point with an extreme x value can heavily influence the position of the least-squares line. In this project, we look at data sets with an influential point.

x	1	4	5	9	10	15
y	3	7	6	10	12	4

(a) Compute r and b, the slope of the least-squares line. Find the equation of the least-squares line, and sketch the line on the scatter diagram.

(b) Notice the point boxed in blue in Figure 4-11. Does it seem to lie away from the linear pattern determined by the other points? The coordinates of that point are (15, 4). Is it an influential point? Remove that point from the model and recompute r, b, and the equation of the least-squares line. Sketch this least-squares line on the diagram. How does the removal of the influential point affect the values of r and b and the position of the least-squares line?

(c) Consider the scatter diagram of Figure 4-12. Is there an influential point? If you remove the influential point, will the slope of the new least-squares line be larger or smaller than the slope of the line from the original data? Will the correlation coefficient be larger or smaller?

FIGURE 4-11

Scatter Diagram

FIGURE 4-12

Scatter Diagram

LINKING CONCEPTS: WRITING PROJECTS

Discuss each of the following topics in class or review the topics on your own. Then write a brief but complete essay in which you summarize the main points. Please include formulas and graphs as appropriate.

1. What do we mean when we say that two variables have a strong positive (or negative) linear correlation? What would a scatter diagram for these variables look like? Is it possible that two variables could be strongly related somehow, but have a low *linear* correlation? Explain and draw a scatter diagram to demonstrate your point.

2. What do we mean by the least-squares criterion? Give a very general description of how the least-squares criterion is involved in the construction of the least-squares line. Why do we say the least-squares line is the "best-fitting" line for the data set?

3. Use the Internet or go to the library and find a magazine or journal article in your field of major interest to which the content of this chapter could be applied. List the variables used, method of data collection, and general type of information and conclusions drawn.

Using Technology

Simple Linear Regression (one explanatory variable)

APPLICATION

The data in this section are taken from this reference:

King, Cuchlaine A. M. *Physical Geography.* Oxford: Basil Blackwell, 1980, 77–86, 196–206. Reprinted with permission of Basil Blackwell Limited, Oxford, England.

Throughout the world, natural ocean beaches are beautiful sights to see. If you have visited natural beaches, you may have noticed that when the gradient or dropoff is steep, the grains of sand tend to be larger. In fact, a manmade beach with the "wrong" size granules of sand tends to be washed away and eventually replaced when the proper size grain is selected by the action of the ocean and the gradient of the bottom. Since manmade beaches are expensive, grain size is an important consideration.

In the data that follow, x = median diameter (in millimeters) of granules of sand, and y = gradient of beach slope in degrees on natural ocean beaches.

x	y
0.17	0.63
0.19	0.70
0.22	0.82
0.235	0.88
0.235	1.15
0.30	1.50
0.35	4.40
0.42	7.30
0.85	11.30

1. Find the sample mean and standard deviation for and y.

2. Make a scatter plot. Would you expect a moderat high correlation and a good fit for the least-square line?

3. Find the equation of the least-squares line, and graph the line on the scatter plot.

4. Find the correlation coefficient r and the coefficien of determination r^2.

5. Suppose that you have a truckload of sifted sand which the median size of granules is 0.38 mm. If y want to put this sand on a beach and you don't want the sand to wash away, then what does the least-squares line predict for the angle of the beac *Note:* Heavy storms that produce abnormal wave may also wash out the sand. However, in the long run, the size of sand granules that remain on the beach or that are brought back to the beach by lo term wave action are determined to a large extent the angle at which the beach drops off.

6. Suppose you now have a truckload of sifted sand which the median size of the granules is 0.45 mm. Repeat Problem 5.

Technology Hints

TI-84Plus/TI-83Plus

Be sure to set **DiagnosticOn** (under **Catalog**).
   (a) Scatter diagram: Use **STAT PLOT**, select the fi type, and use **ZOOM** option 9:**ZoomStat**.
   (b) Least-squares line and r: Use **STAT, CALC,** op tion 8:**LinReg(a + bx)**.

(c) Graph least-squares line and predict: Press **Y=**. Then, under **VARS**, select **5:Statistics,** then select **EQ,** and finally select item **1:RegEQ.** Press **Enter.** This sequence of steps will automatically set $Y_1 =$ your regression equation. Press **GRAPH.** To find a predicted value when the graph is showing, press the **CALC** key and select item **1:Value.** Enter the x value and the corresponding y value will appear.

cel

(a) Scatter plot, least-squares line, r^2: Use **Chart wizard.** Select **scatter plot.** Once the plot is displayed, *right* click on any data point. Select **trend line.** Under options, check display line and display r^2.

(b) Prediction: Use the paste function $\boxed{f_x}$ ➤ **Statistical** ➤ **Forecast.**

(c) Coefficient r: Use $\boxed{f_x}$ ➤ **Statistical** ➤ **Correl.**

Minitab

Scatter plot, least-squares line, r^2: Use the menu selection **Stat** ➤ **Regression** ➤ **Fitted line plot.**

SPSS

SPSS offers several options for finding the correlation coefficient r and the equation of the least-squares line. First enter the data in the data editor and label the variables appropriately in the variable view window. Use the menu choices **Analyze** ➤ **Regression** ➤ **Linear** and select dependent and independent variables. The output includes the correlation coefficient, the constant (y=intercept), and the coefficient of the dependent variable.

5

Elementary Probability Theory

We see that the theory of probabilities is at bottom only common sense reduced to calculation; it makes us appreciate with exactitude what reasonable minds feel by a sort of instinct, often without being able to account for it.

—Pierre-Simon Laplace

Pierre-Simon Laplace (1749–1827)

This renowned French astronomer and mathematician wrote *The Analytical Theory of Probability.*

This is how the great mathematician Laplace described the theory of mathematical probability. The discovery of the mathematical theory of probability was shared by two Frenchmen: Blaise Pascal and Pierre Fermat. These seventeenth-century scholars were attracted to the subject by the inquiries of the Chevalier de Méré, a gentleman gambler.

Although the first applications of probability were to games of chance and gambling, today the subject seems to pervade almost every aspect of modern life. Everything from the orbits of spacecraft to the social behavior of woodchucks is described in terms of probabilities.

PREVIEW QUESTIONS

◇ Why would anyone study probability? *Hint:* Most big issues in life involve uncertainty.   (SECTION 5.1)

◇ What are the basic definitions and rules of probability? (SECTION 5.2)

◇ What are counting techniques, trees, permutations, and combinations?   (SECTION 5.3)

For on-line student resources, visit **math.college.hmco.com/students** and follow the Statistics links to the Brase/Brase, *Understanding Basic Statistics*, 4th edition web site.

How Often Do Lie Detectors Lie?

James Burke is an educator who is known for his interesting science-related radio and television shows aired by the British Broadcasting Corporation. His book *Chances: Risk and Odds in Everyday Life* (Virginia Books, London) contains a great wealth of fascinating information about probabilities. The following quote is from Professor Burke's book:

If I take a polygraph test and lie, what is the risk I will be detected? According to some studies, there's about a 72 percent chance you will be caught by the machine.

What is the risk that if I take a polygraph test it will incorrectly say that I lied? At least 1 in 15 will be thus falsely accused.

Both of these statements contain conditional probabilities, which we will study in Section 5.2. Information from that section will enable us to answer the following:

159

Suppose a person answers 10% of a long battery of questions with lies. Assume that the remaining 90% of the questions are answered truthfully.

1. Estimate the percentage of answers the polygraph will *wrongly* indicate as lies.

2. Estimate the percentage of answers the polygraph will *correctly* indicate as lies.

(See Problem 15 in Section 5.2.)

5.1
What Is Probability?

FOCUS POINTS

✓ Assign probabilities to events.
✓ Explain how the law of large numbers relates to relative frequencies.
✓ Apply basic rules of probability in everyday life.
✓ Explain the relationship between statistics and probability.

Basic concepts

We encounter statements given in terms of probability all the time. An excited sports announcer claims that Sheila has a 90% chance of breaking the world record in the upcoming 100-yard dash. Henry figures that if he guesses on a true–false question, the probability of getting it right is 1/2. The Right to Health Lobby claims the probability is 0.40 of getting an erroneous report from a medical laboratory in one low-cost health center. It is consequently lobbying for a federal agency to license and monitor all medical laboratories.

When we use probability in a statement, we're using a *number between 0 and 1* to indicate the likelihood of an event.

> **Probability** is a numerical measure between 0 and 1 that describes the likelihood that an event will occur. Probabilities closer to 1 indicate that the event is more likely to occur. Probabilities closer to 0 indicate that the event is less likely to occur.

> $P(A)$, read "P of A," denotes the **probability of event A.**
> If $P(A) = 1$, the event A is certain to occur.
> If $P(A) = 0$, the event A is certain not to occur.

It is important to know what probability statements mean and how to determine probabilities of events, because probability is the language of inferential statistics.

Probability assignments

1. A probability assignment based on **intuition** incorporates past experience, judgment, or opinion to estimate the likelihood of an event.

2. A probability assignment based on **relative frequency** uses the formula

$$\text{Probability of event} = \text{relative frequency} = \frac{f}{n} \tag{1}$$

where f is the frequency of the event occurrence in a sample of n observations.

3. A probability assignment based on **equally likely outcomes** uses the formula

$$\text{Probability of an event} = \frac{\text{Number of outcomes favorable to event}}{\text{Total number of outcomes}} \tag{2}$$

EXAMPLE 1

Probability assignment

Consider each of the following events, and determine how the probability is assigned.

(a) A sports announcer claims that Sheila has a 90% chance of breaking the world record in the 100-yard dash.

SOLUTION: It is likely the sports announcer used intuition based on Sheila's past performance.

(b) Henry figures that if he guesses on a true–false question, the probability of getting it right is 0.50.

SOLUTION: In this case there are two outcomes: Henry's answer is either correct or incorrect. Since Henry is guessing, we assume the outcomes are equally likely. There are $n = 2$ equally likely outcomes, and only one is correct. By formula (2),

$$P(\text{correct answer}) = \frac{\text{Number of favorable outcomes}}{\text{Total number of outcomes}} = \frac{1}{2}$$

(c) The Right to Health Lobby claims that the probability of getting an erroneous medical laboratory report is 0.40, based on a random sample of 200 laboratory reports, of which 80 were erroneous.

SOLUTION: Formula (1) for relative frequency gives the probability, with sample size $n = 200$ and number of errors $f = 80$.

$$P(\text{error}) = \text{relative frequency} = \frac{f}{n} = \frac{80}{200} = 0.40 \qquad \diamond$$

We've seen three ways to assign probabilities: intuition, relative frequency, and—when outcomes are equally likely—a formula. Which do we use? Most of the time it depends on the information that is at hand or that can be feasibly obtained. Our choice of methods also depends on the particular problem. In Guided Exercise 1, you will see three different situations, and you will decide which way to assign the probabilities. *Remember, probabilities are numbers between 0 and 1, so don't assign probabilities outside this range.*

GUIDED EXERCISE 1

Determine a probability

Assign a probability to the indicated event on the basis of the information provided. Indicate the technique you used: intuition, relative frequency, or the formula for equally likely outcomes.

(a) A random sample of 500 students at Hudson College were surveyed and it was determined that 375 wore glasses or contact lenses. Estimate the probability that a Hudson College student selected at random wears corrective lenses.

⟹ In this case we are given a sample size of 500, and we are told that 375 of these students wear corrective lenses. It is appropriate to use a relative frequency for the desired probability:

$$P(\text{student needs glasses}) = \frac{f}{n} = \frac{375}{500} = 0.75$$

Continued

(b) The Friends of the Library host a fund-raising barbecue. George is on the cleanup committee. There are four members on this committee, and they draw lots to see who will clean the grills. Assuming that each member is equally likely to be drawn, what is the probability that George will be assigned the grill-cleaning job?

⟹ There are four people on the committee, and each is equally likely to be drawn. It is appropriate to use the formula for equally likely events. George can be drawn in only one way, so there is only one outcome favorable to the event.

$$P(\text{George}) = \frac{\text{No. of favorable outcomes}}{\text{Total no. of outcomes}} = \frac{1}{4} = 0.25$$

(c) Joanna photographs whales for Sea Life Adventure Films. On her next expedition, she is to film blue whales feeding. Based on her knowledge of the habits of blue whales, she is almost certain she will be successful. What specific number do you suppose she estimates for the probability of success?

⟹ Since Joanna is almost certain of success, she should make the probability close to 1. We could say $P(\text{success})$ is above 0.90 but less than 1. This probability assignment is based on intuition.

The technique of using the relative frequency of an event as the probability of that event is a common way of assigning probabilities and will be used a great deal in later chapters. The underlying assumption we make is that if events occurred a certain percentage of times in the past, they will occur about the same percentage of times in the future. In fact, this assumption can be strengthened to a very general statement called the *law of large numbers*.

Law of large numbers

Law of large numbers

In the long run, as the sample size increases and increases, the relative frequencies of outcomes get closer and closer to the theoretical (or actual) probability value.

The law of large numbers is the reason such businesses as health insurance, automobile insurance, and gambling casinos can exist and make a profit.

No matter how we compute probabilities, it is useful to know what outcomes are possible in a given setting. For instance, if you are going to decide the probability that Hardscrabble will win the Kentucky Derby, you need to know which other horses will be running.

Statistical experiment

To determine the possible outcomes for a given setting, we need to define a *statistical experiment*.

Event

A **statistical experiment** or **statistical observation** can be thought of as any random activity that results in a definite outcome.

An **event** is a collection of one or more outcomes of a statistical experiment or observation.

Simple event

A **simple event** is an outcome of a statistical experiment that consists of one and only one of the outcomes of the experiment.

Sample space

The set of all simple events constitutes the **sample space** of an experiment.

EXAMPLE 2

Using a sample space

Human eye color is controlled by a single pair of genes (one from the father and one from the mother) called a *genotype*. Brown eye color, B, is dominant over blue eye color, ℓ. Therefore, in the genotype Bℓ, consisting of one brown gene B and one blue gene ℓ, the brown gene dominates. A person with a Bℓ genotype has brown eyes.

If both parents have brown eyes and have genotype Bℓ, what is the probability that their child will have blue eyes? What is the probability the child will have brown eyes?

SOLUTION: To answer these questions, we need to look at the sample space of all possible eye-color genotypes for the child. They are given in Table 5-1.

TABLE 5-1   Eye Color Genotypes for Child

Father	Mother	
	B	ℓ
B	BB	Bℓ
ℓ	ℓB	ℓℓ

According to genetics theory, the four possible genotypes for the child are equally likely. Therefore, we can use Formula (2) to compute probabilities. Blue eyes can occur only with the ℓℓ genotype, so there is only one outcome favorable to blue eyes. By Formula (2),

$$P(\text{blue eyes}) = \frac{\text{Number of favorable outcomes}}{\text{Total number of outcomes}} = \frac{1}{4}$$

Brown eyes occur with the three remaining genotypes: BB, Bℓ, and ℓB. By Formula (2),

$$P(\text{brown eyes}) = \frac{\text{Number of favorable outcomes}}{\text{Total number of outcomes}} = \frac{3}{4} \qquad \diamond$$

GUIDED EXERCISE 2

Using a sample space

Professor Gutierrez is making up a final exam for a course in literature of the Southwest. He wants the last three questions to be of the true–false type. To guarantee that the answers do not follow his favorite pattern, he lists all possible true–false combinations for three questions on slips of paper and then picks one at random from a hat.

(a) Finish listing the outcomes in the given sample space.

⟹   The missing outcomes are FFT and FFF.

TTT	FTT	TFT	_____
TTF	FTF	TFF	_____

Continued

GUIDED EXERCISE 2 continued

(b) What is the probability that all three items will be false? Use the formula

$$P(\text{all F}) = \frac{\text{No. of favorable outcomes}}{\text{Total no. of outcomes}}$$

⟹ There is only one outcome, FFF, favorable to all false, so

$$P(\text{all F}) = \frac{1}{8}$$

(c) What is the probability that exactly two items will be true?

⟹ There are three outcomes that have exactly two true items: TTF, TFT, and FTT. Thus,

$$P(\text{two T}) = \frac{\text{No. of favorable outcomes}}{\text{Total no. of outcomes}} = \frac{3}{8}$$

There is another important point about probability assignments of simple events.

> The **sum** of the probabilities of all simple events in a sample space must equal 1.

We can use this fact to determine the probability that an event will not occur. For instance, if you think the probability is 0.65 that you will win a tennis match, you assume the probability is 0.35 that your opponent will win.

Complement of an event

The *complement* of an event A is the event that A *does not occur.* We use the notation A^c to designate the complement of event A. Figure 5-1 shows the event A and its complement A^c.

Notice that the two distinct events A and A^c make up the entire sample space. Therefore, the sum of their probabilities is 1.

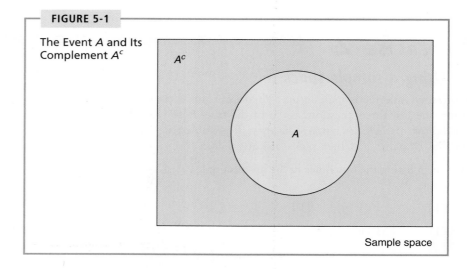

FIGURE 5-1

The Event A and Its Complement A^c

A^c

A

Sample space

The **complement of event** A is the event that A *does not occur.* A^c designates the complement of event A. Furthermore,

1. $P(A) + P(A^c) = 1$

2. $P(\text{event } A \text{ does } not \text{ occur}) = P(A^c) = 1 - P(A)$ (3)

EXAMPLE 3

Complement of an event

The probability that a college student without a flu shot will get the flu is 0.45. What is the probability that a college student will *not* get the flu if the student has not had the flu shot?

SOLUTION: In this case, we have

$P(\text{will get flu}) = 0.45$

$P(\text{will } not \text{ get flu}) = 1 - P(\text{will get flu}) = 1 - 0.45 = 0.55$ ◇

GUIDED EXERCISE 3

Complement of an event

A veterinarian tells you that if you breed two cream-colored guinea pigs, the probability that an offspring will be pure white is 0.25. What is the probability that an offspring will not be pure white?

(a) $P(\text{pure white}) + P(not \text{ pure white}) = $ _____   ⟹   1

(b) $P(not \text{ pure white}) = $ _____   ⟹ $1 - 0.25$, or 0.75

Summary: Some important facts about probability

1. A **statistical experiment** or **statistical observation** is any random activity that results in a definite outcome. A **simple event** consists of one and only one outcome of the experiment. The **sample space** is the set of all simple events. An **event** A is any subset of the sample space.

2. The probability of an event A is denoted by $P(A)$.

3. The probability of an event is a number between 0 and 1. The closer to 1 the probability is, the more likely it is the event will occur. The closer to 0 the probability is, the less likely it is the event will occur.

4. The sum of the probabilities of all simple events in a sample space is 1.

5. Probabilities can be assigned by using intuition, relative frequencies, or the formula for equally likely outcomes. Additional ways to assign probabilities will be introduced in later chapters.

6. The **complement** of an event A is denoted by A^c. So, A^c is the event that A does not occur.

7. $P(A) + P(A^c) = 1$

Probability Related to Statistics

We conclude this section with a few comments on the nature of statistics versus probability. Although statistics and probability are closely related fields of mathematics, they are nevertheless separate fields. It can be said that probability is the medium through which statistical work is done. In fact, if it were not for probability theory, inferential statistics would not be possible.

Put very briefly, probability is the field of study that makes statements about what will occur when samples are drawn from a *known population*. Statistics is the field of study that describes how samples are to be obtained and how inferences are to be made about *unknown populations*.

A simple but effective illustration of the difference between these two subjects can be made by considering how we treat the following examples:

Example of a probability application

Condition: We *know* the exact makeup of the *entire* population.
Example: Given 3 green marbles, 5 red marbles, and 4 white marbles in a bag, draw 6 marbles at random from the bag. What is the probability that none of the marbles is red?

Example of a statistical application

Condition: We have only *samples* from an otherwise *unknown* population.
Example: Draw a random sample of 6 marbles from the (unknown) population of all marbles in a bag and observe the colors. Based on the sample results, make a conjecture about the colors and numbers of marbles in the entire population of all marbles in the bag.

In another sense, probability and statistics are like flip sides of the same coin. On the probability side, you know the overall description of the population. The central problem is to compute the likelihood that a specific outcome will happen. On the statistics side, you know only the results of a sample drawn from the population. The central problem is to describe the sample (descriptive statistic) and to draw conclusions about the population based on the sample results (inferential statistics).

In statistical work, the inferences we draw about an unknown population are not claimed to be absolutely correct. Since the population remains unknown (in a theoretical sense), we must accept a "best guess" for our conclusions and act using the most probable answer rather than absolute certainty.

Probability is the topic of this chapter. However, we will not study probability just for its own sake. Probability is a wonderful field of mathematics, but we will study mainly the ideas from probability that are needed for a proper understanding of statistics.

VIEWPOINT *What Makes a Good Teacher?*

A survey of 735 students at nine colleges in the United States was taken to determine instructor behaviors that help students succeed. Data from this survey can be found by visiting the Brase/Brase statistics site at **http://math.college .hmco.com/students** and finding the link to DASL, the Carnegie Mellon University Data and Story Library. Once at the DASL site, select Data Subjects, then Psychology, and then Instructor Behavior. You can estimate the probability of how a student would respond (very positive, neutral, very negative) to different instructor behaviors. For example, more than 90% of the students responded "very positive" to the instructor's use of real-world examples in the classroom.

SECTION 5.1   PROBLEMS

1. *General: Concepts* In your own words, carefully answer the question: What is probability? List three methods of assigning probabilities.

2. *General: Provide Examples* List examples of how probability might be applied in business, medicine, social science, and natural science. Identify some ways that probability will be useful in the study of statistics.

3. *General: Valid Probabilities* Which of the following numbers cannot be the probability of some event?

   (a) 0.71   (b) 4.1   (c) $\frac{1}{8}$ (d) -0.5

   (e) 0.5   (f) 0   (g) 1   (h) 150%

4. *General: Valid Probabilities*
   (a) Explain why -0.41 cannot be the probability of some event.
   (b) Explain why 1.21 cannot be the probability of some event.
   (c) Explain why 120% cannot be the probability of some event.
   (d) Can the number 0.56 be the probability of an event? Explain.

5. *Probability Estimate: Wiggle Your Ears* Can you wiggle your ears? Use the students in your statistics class (or a group of friends) to estimate the percentage of people who can wiggle their ears. How can your result be thought of as an estimate for the probability that a person chosen at random can wiggle his or her ears? *Comment:* National statistics indicate that about 13% of Americans can wiggle their ears (Source: Bernice Kanner, *Are You Normal?*, St. Martin's Press, New York).

6. *Probability Estimate: Raise One Eyebrow* Can you raise one eyebrow at a time? Use the students in your statistics class (or a group of friends) to estimate the percentage of people who can raise one eyebrow at a time. How can your result be thought of as an estimate for the probability that a person chosen at random can raise one eyebrow at a time? *Comment:* National statistics indicate that about 30% of Americans can raise one eyebrow at a time (see source in Problem 5).

7. *Myers–Briggs: Personality Types* Isabel Briggs Myers was a pioneer in the study of personality types. The personality types are broadly defined according to four main preferences. Do married couples choose similar or different personality types in

their mates? The following data give an indication (Source: I. B. Myers and M. H. McCaulley, *A Guide to the Development and Use of the Myers–Briggs Type Indicators*).

Similarities and Differences in a Random Sample of 375 Married Couples

Number of Similar Preferences	Number of Married Couples
All four	34
Three	131
Two	124
One	71
None	15

Suppose that a married couple is selected at random.
(a) Use the data to estimate the probability that the couple will have 0, 1, 2, 3, or 4 personality preferences in common.
(b) Do the probabilities add up to 1? Why should they? What is the sample space in this problem?

8. *General: Roll a Die*
   (a) If you roll a single fair die and count the number of dots on top, what is the sample space of all possible outcomes? Are the outcomes equally likely?
   (b) Assign probabilities to the outcomes of the sample space of part (a). Do the probabilities add up to 1? Should they add up to 1? Explain.
   (c) What is the probability of getting a number less than 5 on a single throw?
   (d) What is the probability of getting 5 or 6 on a single throw?

9. *Psychology: Creativity* When do creative people get their *best* ideas? *USA Today* did a survey of 966 inventors (who hold U.S. patents) and obtained the following information:

Time of Day When Best Ideas Occur

Time	Number of Inventors
6 A.M.–12 noon	290
12 noon–6 P.M.	135
6 P.M.–12 midnight	319
12 midnight–6 A.M.	222

(a) Assuming that the time interval includes the left value and all the times up to but not including the right value, estimate the probability that an inventor has a best idea during each time interval: from 6 A.M. to 12 noon, from 12 noon to 6 P.M., from 6 P.M. to 12 midnight, and from 12 midnight to 6 A.M.
(b) Do the probabilities of part (a) add up to 1? Why should they? What is the sample space in this problem?

10. *Agriculture: Cotton* A botanist has developed a new hybrid cotton plant that can withstand insects better than other cotton plants. However, there is some concern about the germination of seeds from the new plant. To estimate the probability that a seed from the new plant will germinate, a random sample of 3000 seeds was planted in warm, moist soil. Of these seeds, 2430 germinated.
(a) Use relative frequencies to estimate the probability that a seed will germinate. What is your estimate?

(b) Use relative frequencies to estimate the probability that a seed will *not* germinate. What is your estimate?

(c) Either a seed germinates, or it does not. What is the sample space in this problem? Do the probabilities assigned to the sample space add up to 1? Should they add up to 1? Explain.

(d) Are the outcomes in the sample space of part (c) equally likely?

11. *Business: Customers* John runs a computer software store. Yesterday he counted 127 people who walked by his store, 58 of whom came into the store. Of the 58, only 25 bought something in the store.

(a) Estimate the probability that a person who walks by the store will enter the store.

(b) Estimate the probability that a person who walks into the store will buy something.

(c) Estimate the probability that a person who walks by the store will come in *and* buy something.

(d) Estimate the probability that a person who comes into the store will buy nothing.

5.2
Some Probability Rules—Compound Events

Conditional Probability and Multiplication Rules

FOCUS POINTS

✓ Compute probabilities of general compound events.
✓ Compute probabilities involving independent events or mutually exclusive events.
✓ Use survey results to compute conditional probabilities.

You roll two dice. What is the probability that you will get a 5 on each die? You draw two cards from a well-shuffled, standard deck without replacing the first card before drawing the second. What is the probability that they will both be aces?

It seems that these two problems are nearly alike. They are alike in the sense that in each case you are to find the probability of two events occurring *together*. In the first problem, you are to find

$P(5$ on 1st die *and* 5 on 2nd die$)$

In the second, you want

$P($ace on 1st card *and* ace on 2nd card$)$

The two problems differ in one important aspect, however. In the dice problem, the outcome of a 5 on the first die does not have any effect on the probability of getting a 5 on the second die. Because of this, the events are *independent*.

Independent events

> Two events are **independent** if the occurrence or nonoccurrence of one does *not* change the probability that the other will occur.

In the card problem, the probability of an ace on the first card is 4/52, since there are 52 cards in the deck and 4 of them are aces. If you get an ace on the first card, then the probability of an ace on the second is changed to 3/51, because one ace has already been drawn and only 51 cards remain in the deck. Therefore, the two events in the card-draw problem are *not* independent. They are, in fact, *dependent,* since the outcome of the first draw changes the probability of getting an ace on the second draw.

Probability of A and B

Why does the *independence* or *dependence* of two events matter? The type of events determines the way we compute the probability of the two events happening together. If two events A and B are *independent,* then we use Formula (4), shown on the next page, to compute the probability of the event A *and* B.

Multiplication rule for independent events

$$P(A \text{ and } B) = P(A) \cdot P(B) \tag{4}$$

Conditional probability

If the events are *dependent,* then we must take into account the changes in the probability of one event caused by the occurrence of the other event. The notation $P(A, given\ B)$ denotes the probability that event A will occur, *given* that event B has occurred. This is called a *conditional probability.* We read $P(A, given\ B)$ as "probability of A given B." If A and B are dependent events, then $P(A) \neq P(A, given\ B)$ because the occurrence of event B has changed the probability that event A will occur. A standard notation for $P(A, given\ B)$ is $P(A \mid B)$. However, we will use the more expanded notation $P(A, given\ B)$ to remind you that we assume that event B has already occurred. We use either Formula (5) or Formula (6) to compute the probability of A and B when the events A and B are dependent.

General multiplication rule for any events

$$P(A \text{ and } B) = P(A) \cdot P(B, given\ \text{that } A \text{ has occurred}) \tag{5}$$

$$P(A \text{ and } B) = P(B) \cdot P(A, given\ \text{that } B \text{ has occurred}) \tag{6}$$

We will use either Formula (5) or Formula (6) according to the information available.

Formulas (4), (5), and (6) constitute the *multiplication rules* of probability. They help us compute the probability of events happening together when the sample space is too large for convenient reference or when it is not completely known.

Let's use the multiplication rules to complete the dice and card problems. We'll compare the results with those obtained by using the sample space directly.

EXAMPLE 4

Multiplication rule

Suppose you are going to throw two fair dice. What is the probability of getting a 5 on each die?

SOLUTION USING THE MULTIPLICATION RULE: The two events are independent, so we should use Formula (4). $P(5 \text{ on 1st die } and\ 5 \text{ on 2nd die}) = P(5 \text{ on 1st}) \cdot P(5 \text{ on 2nd})$. To finish the problem, we need only compute the probability of getting a 5 when we throw one die.

There are six faces on a die, and on a fair die each is equally likely to come up when you throw the die. Only one face has five dots, so by Formula (2) for equally likely outcomes,

$$P(5 \text{ on die}) = \frac{1}{6}$$

Now we can complete the calculation.

$$P(5 \text{ on 1st die } and\ 5 \text{ on 2nd die}) = P(5 \text{ on 1st}) \cdot P(5 \text{ on 2nd})$$
$$= \frac{1}{6} \cdot \frac{1}{6} = \frac{1}{36}$$

SOLUTION USING THE SAMPLE SPACE: The first task is to write down the sample space. Each die has six equally likely outcomes, and each outcome of the second die can be paired with each of the first. The sample space is shown in Figure 5-2. The total number of outcomes is 36, and only one is favorable to a 5 on the first die *and* a

5 on the second. The 36 outcomes are equally likely, so by Formula (2) for equally likely outcomes,

$$P(5 \text{ on 1st } and \text{ 5 on 2nd}) = \frac{1}{36}$$

The two methods yield the same result. The multiplication rule was easier to use because we did not need to look at all 36 outcomes in the sample space for tossing two dice.   ◇

EXAMPLE 5

Dependent events

Compute the probability of drawing two aces from a well-shuffled deck of 52 cards if the first card is not replaced before the second card is drawn.

MULTIPLICATION RULE METHOD: These events are *dependent*. The probability of an ace on the first draw is 4/52, but on the second draw the probability of an ace is only 3/51 if an ace was drawn for the first card. An ace on the first draw changes the probability of an ace on the second draw. By the multiplication rule for dependent events,

$$P(\text{ace on 1st } and \text{ ace on 2nd}) = P(\text{ace on 1st}) \cdot P(\text{ace on 2nd, } given \text{ ace on 1st})$$

$$= \frac{4}{52} \cdot \frac{3}{51} = \frac{12}{2652} \approx 0.0045$$

SAMPLE SPACE METHOD: We won't actually look at the sample space because each of the 51 possible outcomes for the second card must be paired with each of the 52 possible outcomes for the first card. This gives us a total of 2652 outcomes in the sample space! We'll just think about the sample space and try to list all the outcomes favorable to the event of aces on both cards. The 12 favorable outcomes are shown in Figure 5-3 on the next page. By the formula for equally likely outcomes,

$$P(\text{ace on 1st card } and \text{ ace on 2nd card}) = \frac{12}{2652} \approx 0.0045$$

Again, the two methods agree.   ◇

FIGURE 5-3

Outcomes Favorable to
Drawing Two Aces

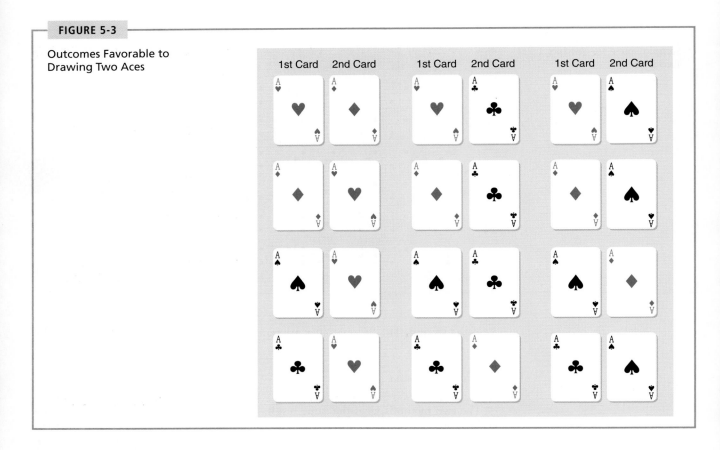

The multiplication rules apply whenever we wish to determine the probability of two events happening *together*. To indicate together, we use *and* between the events. But before you use a multiplication rule to compute the probability of A *and* B, you must determine if A and B are independent or dependent events.

PROCEDURE

How to use the multiplication rules

1. First determine whether A and B are independent events.
   If $P(A) = P(A, \text{given } B)$, then the events are independent.

2. If A and B are independent events,

$$P(A \text{ and } B) = P(A) \cdot P(B) \tag{4}$$

3. If A and B are any events,

$$P(A \text{ and } B) = P(A) \cdot P(B, \text{given } A) \tag{5}$$

$$\text{or} \quad P(A \text{ and } B) = P(B) \cdot P(A, \text{given } B) \tag{6}$$

Let's practice using the multiplication rule.

GUIDED EXERCISE 4

Multiplication rule

Andrew is 55, and the probability that he will be alive in 10 years is 0.72. Ellen is 35, and the probability that she will be alive in 10 years is 0.92. Assuming that the life span of one will have no effect on the life span of the other, what is the probability they will both be alive in 10 years?

(a) Are these events dependent or independent?

⟹ Since the life span of one does not affect the life span of the other, the events are independent.

(b) Use the appropriate multiplication rule to find P(Andrew alive in 10 years *and* Ellen alive in 10 years).

⟹ We use the rule for independent events:

$P(A$ *and* $B) = P(A) \cdot P(B)$

P(Andrew alive *and* Ellen alive)

$= P$(Andrew alive) $\cdot P$(Ellen alive) $= (0.72)(0.92)$

≈ 0.66

GUIDED EXERCISE 5

Dependent events

A quality-control procedure for testing Ready-Flash disposable cameras consists of drawing two cameras at random from each lot of 100 without replacing the first camera before drawing the second. If both are defective, the entire lot is rejected. Find the probability that both cameras are defective if the lot contains 10 defective cameras. Since we are drawing the cameras at random, assume that each camera in the lot has an equal chance of being drawn.

(a) What is the probability of getting a defective camera on the first draw?

⟹ The sample space consists of all 100 cameras. Since each is equally likely to be drawn and there are 10 defective ones,

$$P(\text{defective camera}) = \frac{10}{100} = \frac{1}{10}$$

(b) The first camera drawn is not replaced, so there are only 99 cameras for the second draw. What is the probability of getting a defective camera on the second draw if the first camera was defective?

⟹ If the first camera is defective, then there are only 9 defective cameras left among the 99 remaining cameras in the lot.

P(defective camera on 2nd draw, *given*

defective camera on 1st) $= \dfrac{9}{99} = \dfrac{1}{11}$

Continued

GUIDED EXERCISE 5 continued

(c) Are the probabilities computed in parts (a) and (b) different? Does drawing a defective camera on the first draw change the probability of getting a defective camera on the second draw? Are the events dependent?

⟹ The answer to all these questions is yes.

(d) Use the formula for dependent events,

$P(A \text{ and } B) = P(A) \cdot P(B, \text{ given } A \text{ has occurred})$

to compute $P(1\text{st camera defective } and \text{ 2nd camera defective})$.

⟹ $P(1\text{st defective } and \text{ 2nd defective}) = \dfrac{1}{10} \cdot \dfrac{1}{11}$

$= \dfrac{1}{110}$

≈ 0.009

More than two independent events

The multiplication rule for independent events extends to more than two independent events. If you toss a fair coin, then roll a fair die, and finally draw a card from a standard deck of bridge cards, the three events are independent. To compute the probability of the outcome heads on the coin *and* 5 on the die *and* an ace for the card, we use the extended multiplication rule for independent events together with the facts

$$P(\text{head}) = \frac{1}{2}, P(5) = \frac{1}{6}, P(\text{ace}) = \frac{4}{52} = \frac{1}{13}$$

Then

$$P(\text{head } and \text{ 5 } and \text{ ace}) = \frac{1}{2} \cdot \frac{1}{6} \cdot \frac{1}{13} = \frac{1}{156}$$

Addition Rules

One of the multiplication rules can be used any time we are trying to find the probability of two events happening *together*. Pictorially, we are looking for the probability of the shaded region in Figure 5-4(a).

Probability of *A or B*

Another way to combine events is to consider the possibility of one event *or* another occurring. For instance, if a sports car saleswoman gets an extra bonus if she sells a convertible or a car with leather upholstery, she is interested in the probability that you will buy a car that is a convertible *or* has leather upholstery. Of course, if you bought a convertible with leather upholstery, that would be fine, too. Pictorially, the shaded portion of Figure 5-4(b) represents the outcomes satisfying the *or* condition. Notice that the condition *A or B* is satisfied by any one of the following conditions:

1. Any outcome in *A* occurs.

2. Any outcome in *B* occurs.

3. Any outcome in both *A* and *B* occurs.

It is important to distinguish between the *or* combinations and the *and* combinations because we apply different rules to compute their probabilities.

FIGURE 5-4

(a) The Event *A and B*

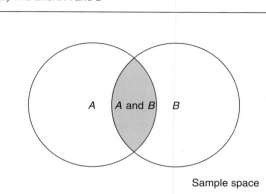

Sample space

(b) The Event *A or B*

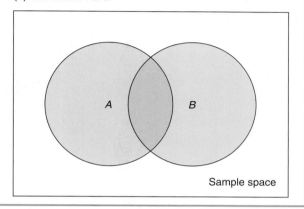

Sample space

GUIDED EXERCISE 6

Combining events

Indicate how each of the following pairs of events are combined. Use either the *and* combination or the *or* combination.

(a) Satisfying the humanities requirement by taking a course in the history of Japan or by taking a course in classical literature   ⟹   Use the *or* combination.

(b) Buying new tires and aligning the tires   ⟹   Use the *and* combination.

(c) Getting an A not only in psychology but also in biology   ⟹   Use the *and* combination.

(d) Having at least one of these pets: cat, dog, bird, rabbit   ⟹   Use the *or* combination.

Once you decide that you are to find the probability of an *or* combination rather than an *and* combination, what formula do you use? Again, it depends on the situation. If you want to compute the probability of drawing either a jack or a king on a single draw from a well-shuffled deck of cards, the formula is simple:

$$P(\text{jack } or \text{ king}) = P(\text{jack}) + P(\text{king}) = \frac{4}{52} + \frac{4}{52} = \frac{8}{52} = \frac{2}{13}$$

since there are 4 jacks and 4 kings in a deck of 52 cards.

If you want to compute the probability of drawing a king or a diamond on a single draw, the formula is a bit more complicated. We have to take the overlap of

FIGURE 5-5

Drawing a King or a Diamond from a Standard Deck

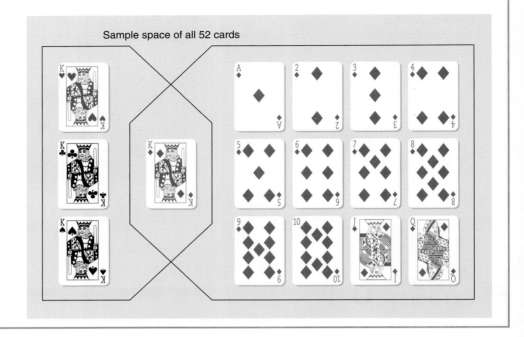

the two events into account so that we do not count the outcomes twice. We can see the overlap of the two events in Figure 5-5.

$$P(\text{king}) = \frac{4}{52} \quad P(\text{diamond}) = \frac{13}{52} \quad P(\text{king } and \text{ diamond}) = \frac{1}{52}$$

If we simply add $P(\text{king})$ and $P(\text{diamond})$, we're including $P(\text{king } and \text{ diamond})$ twice in the sum. To compensate for this double summing, we simply subtract $P(\text{king } and \text{ diamond})$ from the sum. Therefore,

$$P(\text{king } or \text{ diamond}) = P(\text{king}) + P(\text{diamond}) - P(\text{king } and \text{ diamond})$$

$$= \frac{4}{52} + \frac{13}{52} - \frac{1}{52} = \frac{16}{52} = \frac{4}{13}$$

Mutually exclusive events

We say the events A and B are *mutually exclusive* or *disjoint* if they cannot occur together. This means that A and B have no outcomes in common or, put another way, that $P(A \text{ and } B) = 0$.

> Two events are **mutually exclusive** or **disjoint** if they cannot occur together. In particular, events A and B are mutually exclusive if $P(A \text{ and } B) = 0$.

Formula (7) is the *addition rule for mutually exclusive events* A and B.

> **Addition rule for *mutually exclusive* events *A* and *B***
>
> $$P(A \text{ or } B) = P(A) + P(B) \tag{7}$$

If the events are not mutually exclusive, we must use the more general Formula (8), which is the *general addition rule for any events A and B*.

General addition rule for any events *A* and *B*

$$P(A \ or \ B) = P(A) + P(B) - P(A \ and \ B) \tag{8}$$

You may ask: Which formula should I use? The answer is: Use Formula (7) only if you know that *A* and *B* are mutually exclusive (i.e., cannot occur together); if you do not know whether *A* and *B* are mutually exclusive, then use Formula (8). Formula (8) is valid either way. Notice that when *A* and *B* are mutually exclusive, then $P(A \ and \ B) = 0$, so Formula (8) reduces to Formula (7).

PROCEDURE

How to use the addition rules

1. First determine whether *A* and *B* are mutually exclusive events.
   If $P(A \ and \ B) = 0$, then the events are mutually exclusive.

2. If *A* and *B* are mutually exclusive events,

   $$P(A \ or \ B) = P(A) + P(B) \tag{7}$$

3. If *A* and *B* are any events,

   $$P(A \ or \ B) = P(A) + P(B) - P(A \ and \ B) \tag{8}$$

GUIDED EXERCISE 7

Mutually exclusive events

The Cost Less Clothing Store carries seconds in slacks—that is, slacks with manufacturing flaws. If you buy a pair of slacks in your regular waist size without trying them on, the probability that the waist will be too tight is 0.30 and the probability that it will be too loose is 0.10.

(a) Are the events too tight or too loose mutually exclusive?

⟹ The waist cannot be both too tight and too loose at the same time, so the events are mutually exclusive.

(b) If you choose a pair of slacks at random in your regular waist size, what is the probability that the waist will be too tight or too loose?

⟹ Since the events are mutually exclusive,

$P(\text{too tight } or \text{ too loose})$

$= P(\text{too tight}) + P(\text{too loose})$

$= 0.30 + 0.10$

$= 0.40$

GUIDED EXERCISE 8

General addition rule

Professor Jackson is in charge of a program to prepare people for a high school equivalency exam. Records show that 80% of the students need work in math, 70% need work in English, and 55% need work in both areas.

(a) Are the events *needs math* and *needs English* mutually exclusive?

⟹ These events are not mutually exclusive, since some students need both. In fact,

P(needs math *and* needs English) = 0.55

(b) Use the appropriate formula to compute the probability that a student selected at random needs math *or* needs English.

⟹ Since the events are not mutually exclusive, we use Formula (8):

P(needs math *or* needs English)

= P(needs math) + P(needs English)

    − P(needs math *and* English)

= 0.80 + 0.70 − 0.55

= 0.95

More than two mutually exclusive events

The addition rule for mutually exclusive events can be extended so that it applies to the situation in which we have more than two events that are each mutually exclusive to all the other events.

EXAMPLE 6

Mutually exclusive events

Laura is playing Monopoly. On her next move she needs to throw a sum bigger than 8 on the two dice in order to land on her own property and pass Go. What is the probability that Laura will roll a sum bigger than 8?

SOLUTION: When two dice are thrown, the largest sum that can come up is 12. Consequently, the only sums larger than 8 are 9, 10, 11, and 12. These outcomes are mutually exclusive, since only one of these sums can possibly occur on one throw of the dice. The probability of throwing more than 8 is the same as

P(9 *or* 10 *or* 11 *or* 12)

Since the events are mutually exclusive,

$$P(9 \text{ or } 10 \text{ or } 11 \text{ or } 12) = P(9) + P(10) + P(11) + P(12)$$

$$= \frac{4}{36} + \frac{3}{36} + \frac{2}{36} + \frac{1}{36}$$

$$= \frac{10}{36} = \frac{5}{18}$$

To get the specific values of $P(9)$, $P(10)$, $P(11)$, and $P(12)$, we used the sample space for throwing two dice (see Figure 5-2). There are 36 equally likely outcomes—for example, those favorable to 9 are 6, 3; 3, 6; 5, 4; and 4, 5. So $P(9) = 4/36$. The other values can be computed in a similar way. ◇

Further Examples

Most of us have been asked to participate in a survey. Schools, retail stores, news media, and government offices all conduct surveys. There are many types of surveys, and it is not our intention to give a general discussion of this topic. Let us study a very popular method called the *simple tally survey.* Such a survey consists of questions for which the responses can be recorded in the rows and columns of a table called a *contingency table.* These questions are appropriate to the information you want and are designed to cover the *entire* population of interest. In addition, the questions should be designed so that you can partition the sample space of responses into distinct (that is, mutually exclusive) sectors.

If the survey includes responses from a reasonably large random sample, then the results should be representative of your population. In this case, you can estimate simple probabilities, conditional probabilities, and the probabilities of some combinations of events directly from the results of the survey.

EXAMPLE 7

Survey

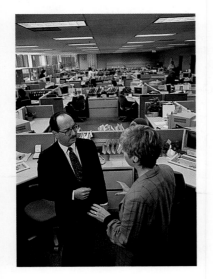

At Hopewell Electronics, all 140 employees were asked about their political affiliations. The employees were grouped by type of work, as executives or production workers. The results with row and column totals are shown in Table 5-2.

Suppose an employee is selected at random from the 140 Hopewell employees. Let us use the following notation to represent different events of our choosing: E = executive; PW = production worker; D = Democrat; R = Republican; I = Independent.

(a) Compute $P(D)$ and $P(E)$.

SOLUTION: To find these probabilities, we look at the *entire* sample space.

$$P(D) = \frac{\text{Number of Democrats}}{\text{Number of employees}} = \frac{68}{140} \approx 0.486$$

$$P(E) = \frac{\text{Number of executives}}{\text{Number of employees}} = \frac{48}{140} \approx 0.343$$

(b) Compute $P(D, \text{ given } E)$.

SOLUTION: For the conditional probability, we *restrict* our attention to the portion of the sample space satisfying the condition of being an executive.

$$P(D, \text{ given } E) = \frac{\text{Number of executives who are Democrats}}{\text{Number of executives}} = \frac{5}{48} \approx 0.104$$

TABLE 5-2 Employee Type and Political Affiliation

	Political Affiliation				
----------------------	-------------	--------------	---------------	---------	
Employee Type	Democrat (D)	Republican (R)	Independent (I)	Row Total	
Executive (*E*)	5	34	9	48	
Production worker (*PW*)	63	21	8	92	
Column Total	68	55	17	140	Grand Total

(c) Are the events D and E independent?

SOLUTION: One way to determine if the events D and E are independent is to see if $P(D) = P(D, given\ E)$ [or equivalently, if $P(E) = P(E, given\ D)$]. Since $P(D) \approx 0.486$ and $P(D, given\ E) \approx 0.104$, we see that $P(D) \neq P(D, given\ E)$. This means that the events D and E are *not* independent. The probability of event D "depends on" whether or not event E has occurred.

(d) Compute $P(D\ and\ E)$.

SOLUTION: This probability is not conditional, so we must look at the entire sample space.

$$P(D\ and\ E) = \frac{\text{Number of executives who are Democrats}}{\text{Total number of employees}} = \frac{5}{140} \approx 0.036$$

Let's recompute this probability using the rules of probability for dependent events.

$$P(D\ and\ E) = P(E) \cdot P(D, given\ E) = \frac{48}{140} \cdot \frac{5}{48} = \frac{5}{140} \approx 0.036$$

The results using the rules are consistent with those using the sample space.

(e) Compute $P(D\ or\ E)$.

SOLUTION: From part (d) we know that the events Democrat or executive are not mutually exclusive, because $P(D\ and\ E) \neq 0$. Therefore,

$$P(D\ or\ E) = P(D) + P(E) - P(D\ and\ E)$$
$$= \frac{68}{140} + \frac{48}{140} - \frac{5}{140} = \frac{111}{140} \approx 0.793 \qquad \diamond$$

GUIDED EXERCISE 9

Survey

Using Table 5-2, let's consider other probabilities regarding the types of employees at Hopewell and their political affiliations. This time let's consider the production worker and the affiliation of Independent. Suppose an employee is selected at random from the group of 140.

(a) Compute $P(I)$ and $P(PW)$.

$$P(I) = \frac{\text{No. of Independents}}{\text{Total no. of employees}} = \frac{17}{140} \approx 0.121$$

$$P(PW) = \frac{\text{No. of production workers}}{\text{Total no. of employees}} = \frac{92}{140} \approx 0.657$$

(b) Compute $P(I, given\ PW)$. This is a conditional probability. Be sure to restrict your attention to production workers, since that is the condition given.

$$P(I, given\ PW) = \frac{\text{No. of Independent production workers}}{\text{No. of production workers}}$$
$$= \frac{8}{92} \approx 0.087$$

Continued

GUIDED EXERCISE 9 continued

(c) Compute $P(I \text{ and } PW)$. In this case, look at the entire sample space and the number of employees who are both Independent and in production.

⟹ $P(I \text{ and } PW) = \dfrac{\text{No. of Independent production workers}}{\text{Total no. of employees}}$

$= \dfrac{8}{140} \approx 0.057$

(d) Use the multiplication rule for dependent events to calculate $P(I \text{ and } PW)$. Is the result the same as that of part (c)?

⟹ By the multiplication rule,

$P(I \text{ and } PW) = P(PW) \cdot P(I, \text{ given } PW)$

$= \dfrac{92}{140} \cdot \dfrac{8}{92} = \dfrac{8}{140} \approx 0.057$

The results are the same.

(e) Compute $P(I \text{ or } PW)$. Are the events mutually exclusive?

⟹ Since the events are not mutully exclusive,

$P(I \text{ or } PW) = P(I) + P(PW) - P(I \text{ and } PW)$

$= \dfrac{17}{140} + \dfrac{92}{140} - \dfrac{8}{140} = \dfrac{101}{140} \approx 0.721$

Basic probability rules

As you apply probability to various settings, keep the following rules in mind.

Summary of basic probability rules

A statistical experiment or statistical observation is any random activity that results in a recordable outcome. The sample space is the set of all simple events that are the outcomes of the statistical experiment and cannot be broken into other "simpler" events. A general event is any subset of the sample space. The notation $P(A)$ designates the probability of the event A.

1. $P(\text{entire sample space}) = 1$

2. For any event A: $0 \le P(A) \le 1$

3. A^c designates the **complement** of A: $P(A^c) = 1 - P(A)$

4. Events A and B are **independent events** if $P(A) = P(A, \text{ given } B)$.

5. Multiplication Rules

   General: $P(A \text{ and } B) = P(A) \cdot P(B, \text{ given } A)$

   Independent events: $P(A \text{ and } B) = P(A) \cdot P(B)$

6. Conditional Probability: $P(A, \text{ given } B) = \dfrac{P(A \text{ and } B)}{P(B)}$

7. Events A and B are **mutually exclusive** if $P(A \text{ and } B) = 0$.

8. Addition Rules

   General: $P(A \text{ or } B) = P(A) + P(B) - P(A \text{ and } B)$

   Mutually exclusive events: $P(A \text{ or } B) = P(A) + P(B)$

In this section, we have studied some important rules that are valid in all probability spaces. The rules and definitions of probability not only are interesting, but they also have extensive *applications* in our everyday lives.

VIEWP◉INT   *The Psychology of Odors*

The Smell and Taste Treatment Research Foundation of Chicago collected data on the time required to complete a maze while subjects were smelling different scents. Data for this survey can be found by visiting the Brase/Brase statistics site at **http://math.college.hmco.com/students** and finding the link to DASL, the Carnegie Mellon University Data and Story Library. Once at the DASL site, select Data Subjects, then Psychology, and then Scents. You can estimate conditional probabilities regarding response times for smokers, nonsmokers, and types of scents.

SECTION 5.2   PROBLEMS

In Problems 1–12, use the appropriate addition or multiplication rules. When possible, verify results by considering the sample space.

1. *General: Candy Colors* M&M plain candies come in various colors. According to the M&M/Mars Department of Consumer Affairs (link to the Mars company web site from the Brase/Brase statistics site at **http://math.college.hmco.com/students**), the distribution of colors for plain M&M candies is

Color	Purple	Yellow	Red	Orange	Green	Blue	Brown
Percentage	20%	20%	20%	10%	10%	10%	10%

Suppose you have a large bag of plain M&M candies and you take one candy at random. Find
(a) *P*(green *or* blue candy). Are these outcomes mutually exclusive? Why?
(b) *P*(yellow *or* red candy). Are these outcomes mutually exclusive? Why?
(c) *P*(*not* purple candy).

2. *General: Candy Colors* According to the Department of Consumer Affairs of M&M/Mars, the color distribution of almond M&M candies is

Color	Purple	Yellow	Red	Green	Blue	Brown
Percentage	20%	20%	20%	20%	10%	10%

Suppose you have a large bag of almond M&M candies and you take one candy at random. Compute the probabilities in parts (a) through (c) of Problem 1 for almond M&M candies. Compare the results with those for plain M&M candies. Do you expect any differences? Why or why not?

3. *General: Candy Colors* Dulce de Leche~Caramel M&M candies have another color distribution, utilizing only six colors. The color distribution for these candies is uniform. There are only six colors: brown, red, yellow, orange, green, and blue. Each color comprises about 16.6% of the mix. Compute the probabilities in parts (a) through (c) of Problem 1 for these candies. Compare the results with those for plain M&M candies. Do you expect any differences? Why or why not?

4. *Environmental: Land Formations* Arches National Park is located in southern Utah. The park is famous for its beautiful desert landscape and its many natural sandstone arches. Park Ranger Edward McCarrick started an inventory (not yet complete) of natural arches within the park that have an opening of at least 3 feet. The following table is based on information taken from the book *Canyon Country Arches and Bridges*, by F. A. Barnes. The height of the arch opening is rounded to the nearest foot.

Height of arch, feet	3–9	10–29	30–49	50–74	75 and higher
Number of arches in park	111	96	30	33	18

For an arch chosen at random in Arches National Park, use the preceding information to estimate the probability that the height of the arch opening is
(a) 3 to 9 feet
(b) 30 feet or taller
(c) 3 to 49 feet
(d) 10 to 74 feet
(e) 75 feet or taller

5. *General: Roll Two Dice* You roll two fair dice, a green one and a red one.
(a) Are the outcomes on the dice independent?
(b) Find $P(5$ on green die *and* 3 on red die).
(c) Find $P(3$ on green die *and* 5 on red die).
(d) Find $P((5$ on green die *and* 3 on red die) *or* (3 on green die *and* 5 on red die)).

6. *General: Roll Two Dice* You roll two fair dice, a green one and a red one.
(a) Are the outcomes on the dice independent?
(b) Find $P(1$ on green die *and* 2 on red die).
(c) Find $P(2$ on green die *and* 1 on red die).
(d) Find $P((1$ on green die *and* 2 on red die) *or* (2 on green die *and* 1 on red die)).

7. *General: Roll Two Dice* You roll two fair dice, a green one and a red one.
(a) What is the probability of getting a sum of 6?
(b) What is the probability of getting a sum of 4?
(c) What is the probability of getting a sum of 6 *or* 4? Are these outcomes mutually exclusive?

8. *General: Roll Two Dice* You roll two fair dice, a green one and a red one.
(a) What is the probability of getting a sum of 7?
(b) What is the probability of getting a sum of 11?
(c) What is the probability of getting a sum of 7 *or* 11? Are these outcomes mutually exclusive?

9. *General: Deck of Cards* You draw two cards from a standard deck of 52 cards without replacing the first one before drawing the second.
   (a) Are the outcomes on the two cards independent? Why?
   (b) Find P(ace on 1st card *and* king on 2nd).
   (c) Find P(king on 1st card *and* ace on 2nd).
   (d) Find the probability of drawing an ace *and* a king in either order.

10. *General: Deck of Cards* You draw two cards from a standard deck of 52 cards without replacing the first one before drawing the second.
    (a) Are the outcomes on the two cards independent? Why?
    (b) Find P(3 on 1st card *and* 10 on 2nd).
    (c) Find P(10 on 1st card *and* 3 on 2nd).
    (d) Find the probability of drawing a 10 *and* a 3 in either order.

11. *General: Deck of Cards* You draw two cards from a standard deck of 52 cards, but before you draw the second card, you put the first one back and reshuffle the deck.
    (a) Are the outcomes on the two cards independent? Why?
    (b) Find P(ace on 1st card *and* king on 2nd).
    (c) Find P(king on 1st card *and* ace on 2nd).
    (d) Find the probability of drawing an ace *and* a king in either order.

12. *General: Deck of Cards* You draw two cards from a standard deck of 52 cards, but before you draw the second card, you put the first one back and reshuffle the deck.
    (a) Are the outcomes on the two cards independent? Why?
    (b) Find P(3 on 1st card *and* 10 on 2nd).
    (c) Find P(10 on 1st card *and* 3 on 2nd).
    (d) Find the probability of drawing a 10 *and* a 3 in either order.

13. *Marketing: Toys* USA Today gave the information shown in the table about ages of children receiving toys. The percentages represent all toys sold.

    What is the probability that a toy is purchased for someone
    (a) 6 years old or older?
    (b) 12 years old or younger?
    (c) between 6 and 12 years old?
    (d) between 3 and 9 years old?

Age (years)	Percentage of Toys
2 and under	15%
3–5	22%
6–9	27%
10–12	14%
13 and over	22%

    A child between 10 and 12 years old looks at this probability distribution and asks, "Why are people more likely to buy toys for kids older than I am (13 and over) than for kids in my age group (10–12)?" How would you respond?

14. *Health Care: Flu* Based on data from the *Statistical Abstract of the United States*, 112th Edition, only about 14% of senior citizens (65 years old or older) get the flu each year. However, about 24% of people under 65 years old get the flu each year. In the general population, there are 12.5% senior citizens (65 years old or older).
    (a) What is the probability that a person selected at random from the general population is a senior citizen who will get the flu this year?
    (b) What is the probability that a person selected at random from the general population is a person under age 65 who will get the flu this year?
    (c) Answer parts (a) and (b) for a community that has 95% senior citizens.
    (d) Answer parts (a) and (b) for a community that has 50% senior citizens.

15. *Focus Problem: Lie Detector Test* In this problem, you are asked to solve the Focus Problem at the beginning of this chapter. In his book *Chances: Risk and Odds in Everyday Life*, James Burke says that there is a 72% chance a polygraph test (lie detector test) will catch a person who is in fact lying. Furthermore, there is approximately a 7% chance that the polygraph will falsely accuse someone of lying.
    (a) Suppose that a person answers 90% of a long battery of questions truthfully. What percentage of the answers will the polygraph *wrongly* indicate are lies?
    (b) Suppose that a person answers 10% of a long battery of questions with lies. What percentage of the answers will the polygraph *correctly* indicate are lies?
    (c) Repeat parts (a) and (b) if 50% of the questions are answered truthfully and 50% are answered with lies.
    (d) Repeat parts (a) and (b) if 15% of the questions are answered truthfully and the rest are answered with lies.

16. *Survey: Medical Tests* Diagnostic tests of medical conditions have several results. The test result can be positive or negative, whether or not a patient has the condition. A positive test $(+)$ indicates the patient has the condition. A negative test $(-)$ indicates the patient does not have the condition. Remember, a positive test does not prove the patient has the condition. Additional medical work may be required. Consider a random sample of 200 patients, some of whom have a medical condition and some of whom do not. Results of a new diagnostic test for the condition are shown.

	Condition Present	Condition Absent	Row Total
Test Result $+$	110	20	130
Test Result $-$	20	50	70
Column Total	130	70	200

Assume the sample is representative of the entire population. For a person selected at random, compute the following probabilities:
    (a) $P(+,$ *given* condition present); this is known as the *sensitivity* of a test.
    (b) $P(-,$ *given* condition present); this is known as the false-negative rate.
    (c) $P(-,$ *given* condition absent); this is known as the *specificity* of a test.
    (d) $P(+,$ *given* condition absent); this is known as the false-positive rate.
    (e) P(condition present *and* $+$); this is the predictive value of the test.
    (f) P(condition present *and* $-$).

17. *Survey: Lung/Heart* In an article entitled "Diagnostic accuracy of fever as a measure of postoperative pulmonary complications" (*Heart Lung* 10, No. 1:61), J. Roberts and colleagues discuss using a fever of 38°C or higher as a diagnostic indicator of postoperative atelectasis (collapse of the lung) as evidenced by x-ray observation. For fever $\geq 38°C$ as the diagnostic test, the results for postoperative patients are

	Condition Present	Condition Absent	Row Total
Test Result $+$	72	37	109
Test Result $-$	82	79	161
Column Total	154	116	270

For the meaning of $+$ and $-$, see Problem 16. Complete parts (a) through (f) from Problem 16.

18. *Survey: Customer Loyalty* Are customers more loyal in the East or in the West? The following table is based on information from *Trends in the United States*, published by the Food Marketing Institute, Washington, D.C. The columns represent length of customer loyalty (in years) at a primary supermarket. The rows represent regions of the United States.

	Less Than 1 Year	1–2 Years	3–4 Years	5–9 Years	10–14 Years	15 or More Years	Row Total
East	32	54	59	112	77	118	452
Midwest	31	68	68	120	63	173	523
South	53	92	93	158	106	158	660
West	41	56	67	78	45	86	373
Column Total	157	270	287	468	291	535	2008

What is the probability that a customer chosen at random
(a) has been loyal 10 to 14 years?
(b) has been loyal 10 to 14 years, given that he or she is from the East?
(c) has been loyal *at least* 10 years?
(d) has been loyal *at least* 10 years, given that he or she is from the West?
(e) is from the West, given that he or she has been loyal less than 1 year?
(f) is from the South, given that he or she has been loyal less than 1 year?
(g) has been loyal *1 or more years,* given that he or she is from the East?
(h) has been loyal *1 or more years,* given that he or she is from the West?
(i) Are the events from the East and loyal 15 or more years independent? Explain.

19. *Survey: Trips to Supermarket* How many times do shoppers go to the supermarket each week? The age group of customers with frequent visits can influence store inventory and marketing methods. The following table is based on information from *Trends in the United States* (see reference in Problem 18). The columns represent number of visits to the primary supermarket in an average week. The rows represent age distribution of customers in years.

Age (years)	One Visit	Two Visits	Three Visits	Four Visits	Five Visits	Six or More Visits	Row Total
18–24	65	58	12	5	4	4	148
25–39	386	230	69	22	17	15	739
40–49	210	161	36	13	9	5	434
50–64	186	102	35	14	7	5	349
65 and over	115	69	18	12	7	3	224
Column Total	962	620	170	66	44	32	1894

What is the probability that a customer chosen at random
(a) has been to the supermarket *at least* 2 times this past week?
(b) has been to the supermarket *at least* 2 times this past week, given that he or she is 25 to 39 years old?
(c) has been to the supermarket *more than* 3 times this past week?
(d) has been to the supermarket *more than* 3 times this past week, given that he or she is *65 or older?*
(e) is *40 or older?*

(f) is *40 or older,* given that he or she has visited the supermarket 4 times this past week?

(g) Are the events age 25–39 years and visits *more than* once a week independent? Explain.

5.3
Trees and Counting Techniques

FOCUS POINTS

✓ Organize outcomes in a sample space using tree diagrams.

✓ Compute number of ordered arrangements of outcomes using permutations.

✓ Compute number of (nonordered) groupings of outcomes using combinations.

✓ Explain how counting techniques relate to probability in everyday life.

Multiplication rule of counting

When outcomes are equally likely, we compute the probability of an event by using the formula

$$P(A) = \frac{\text{Number of outcomes favorable to the event } A}{\text{Number of outcomes in the sample space}}$$

The probability formula requires that we be able to determine the number of outcomes in the sample space. In the problems we have done in previous sections, this task has not been difficult because the number of outcomes was small or the sample space consisted of fairly straightforward events. The tools we present in this section will help you count the number of possible outcomes in larger sample spaces or those formed by more complicated events.

When an outcome of an experiment is composed of a series of events, the multiplication rule gives us the *total number* of outcomes.

Multiplication rule of counting

Consider the series of events E_1 through E_m, where n_1 is the number of possible outcomes for event E_1, n_2 is the number of possible outcomes for event E_2, and n_m designates the number of possible outcomes for event E_m. Then the product

$$n_1 \times n_2 \times \cdots \times n_m$$

gives the total number of possible outcomes for the series of events E_1, followed by E_2, up through event E_m.

EXAMPLE 8

Multiplication rule

Jacqueline is in a nursing program and is required to take a course in psychology and one in physiology (A and P) next semester. She also wants to take Spanish II. If there are two sections of psychology, two of A and P, and three of Spanish II, how many different class schedules can Jacqueline choose from? (Assume that the times of the sections do not conflict.)

SOLUTION: Creating a class schedule can be considered an experiment with a series of three events. There are two possible outcomes for the psychology section, two for the A and P section, and three for the Spanish II section. By the multiplication rule, the total number of class schedules possible is

$$2 \times 2 \times 3 = 12$$

◊

Tree diagram

A *tree diagram* gives a visual display of the total number of outcomes of an experiment consisting of a series of events. From a tree diagram, we can determine not only the total number of outcomes, but also the individual outcomes.

EXAMPLE 9

Tree diagram

Using the information from Example 8, let's make a tree diagram that shows all the possible course schedules for Jacqueline.

SOLUTION: Figure 5-6 shows the tree diagram. Let's study the diagram. There are two branches from Start. These branches indicate the two possible choices for psychology sections. No matter which section of psychology Jacqueline chooses, she can choose from the two available A and P sections. Therefore, we have two branches leading from *each* psychology branch. Finally, after the psychology and A and P sections are selected, there are three choices for Spanish II. That is why there are tree branches from *each* A and P section.

The tree ends with a total of 12 branches. The number of end branches tells us the number of possible schedules. The outcomes themselves can be listed from the tree by following each series of branches from Start to End. For instance, the top branch from Start generates the schedules shown in Table 5-3. The other six schedules can be listed in a similar manner, except they begin with the second section of psychology.   ◊

FIGURE 5-6

Tree Diagram for Selecting Class Schedules

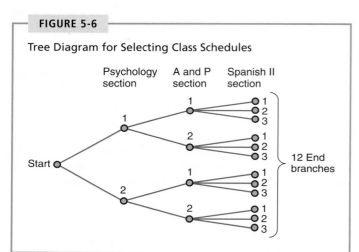

TABLE 5-3   Schedules Utilizing Section 1 of Psychology

Psychology Section	A and P Section	Spanish II Section
1	1	1
1	1	2
1	1	3
1	2	1
1	2	2
1	2	3

GUIDED EXERCISE 10

Tree diagram and multiplication rule

Louis plays three tennis matches. Use a tree diagram to list the possible win and loss sequences Louis can experience for the set of three matches.

(a) On the first match Louis can win or lose. From Start, indicate these two branches.

    FIGURE 5-7 *W* = Win, *L* = Lose

Continued

GUIDED EXERCISE 10 continued

(b) Regardless of whether Louis wins or loses the first match, he plays the second and can again win or lose. Attach branches representing these two outcomes to *each* of the first match results.

FIGURE 5-8

(c) Louis may win or lose the third match. Attach branches representing these two outcomes to *each* of the second match results.

FIGURE 5-9

(d) How many possible win–lose sequences are there for the three matches?

Since there are eight branches at the end, there are eight sequences.

(e) Complete this list of win–lose sequences.

1st	2nd	3rd
W	W	W
W	W	L
W	L	W
W	L	L
___	___	___
___	___	___
___	___	___
___	___	___

The last four sequences all involve a loss on Match 1.

1st	2nd	3rd
L	W	W
L	W	L
L	L	W
L	L	L

(f) Use the multiplication rule to compute the total number of outcomes for the three matches.

The number of outcomes for a series of three events, each with two outcomes, is

$$2 \times 2 \times 2 = 8$$

Tree diagrams help us display the outcomes of an experiment involving several stages. If we label each branch of the tree with an appropriate probability, we can use the tree diagram to help us compute the probability of an outcome displayed on the tree. One of the easiest ways to illustrate this feature of tree diagrams is to use an experiment of drawing balls out of an urn. We do this in the next example.

EXAMPLE 10

Probability

Suppose there are five balls in an urn. They are identical except in color. Three of the balls are red and two are blue. You are instructed to draw out one ball, note its color, and set it aside. Then you are to draw out another ball and note its color. What are the outcomes of the experiment? What is the probability of each outcome?

SOLUTION: The tree diagram in Figure 5-10 will help us answer these questions. Notice that since you did not replace the first ball before drawing the second one, the two stages of the experiment are dependent. The probability associated with the color of the second ball depends on the color of the first ball. For instance, on the top branches, the color of the first ball drawn is red, so we compute the probabilities of the colors on the second ball accordingly. The tree diagram helps us organize the probabilities.

From the diagram, we see that there are four possible outcomes to the experiment. They are

RR = red on 1st *and* red on 2nd
RB = red on 1st *and* blue on 2nd
BR = blue on 1st *and* red on 2nd
BB = blue on 1st *and* blue on 2nd

To compute the probability of each outcome, we will use the multiplication rule for dependent events. As we follow the branches for each outcome, we will find the necessary probabilities.

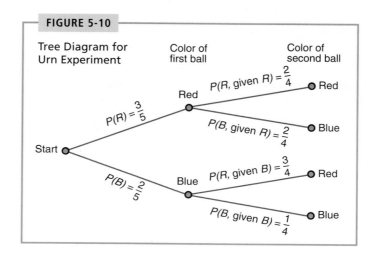

FIGURE 5-10

Tree Diagram for Urn Experiment

$$P(R \text{ on 1st } and \ R \text{ on 2nd}) = P(R) \cdot P(R, \ given \ R) = \frac{3}{5} \cdot \frac{2}{4} = \frac{3}{10}$$

$$P(R \text{ on 1st } and \ B \text{ on 2nd}) = P(R) \cdot P(B, \ given \ R) = \frac{3}{5} \cdot \frac{2}{4} = \frac{3}{10}$$

$$P(B \text{ on 1st } and \ R \text{ on 2nd}) = P(B) \cdot P(R, \ given \ B) = \frac{2}{5} \cdot \frac{3}{4} = \frac{3}{10}$$

$$P(B \text{ on 1st } and \ B \text{ on 2nd}) = P(B) \cdot P(B, \ given \ B) = \frac{2}{5} \cdot \frac{1}{4} = \frac{1}{10}$$

Notice that the probabilities of the outcomes in the sample space add to 1, as they should. ◇

Sometimes when we consider n items, we need to know the number of different *ordered arrangements* of the n items that are possible. The multiplication rules can help us find the number of possible ordered arrangements. Let's consider the classic example of determining the number of different ways in which eight people can be seated at a dinner table. For the first chair at the head of the table, there are eight choices. For the second chair, there are seven choices, since one person is already seated. For the third chair, there are six choices, since two people are already seated. By the time we get to the last chair, there is only one person left for that seat. We can view each arrangement as an outcome of a series of eight events. Event 1 is *fill the first chair,* event 2 is *fill the second chair,* and so forth. The multiplication rule will tell us the number of different outcomes.

Choices for	1st	2nd	3rd	4th	5th	6th	7th	8th	Chair position
	↓	↓	↓	↓	↓	↓	↓	↓	
	(8)	(7)	(6)	(5)	(4)	(3)	(2)	(1)	= 40,320

In all, there are 40,320 different seating arrangements for eight people. It is no wonder that it takes a little time to seat guests at a dinner table!

Factorial notation

The multiplication pattern shown above is not unusual. In fact, it is an example of the multiplication indicated by the factorial notation 8!.

! is read "factorial"

8! is read "8 factorial"

$8! = 8 \cdot 7 \cdot 6 \cdot 5 \cdot 4 \cdot 3 \cdot 2 \cdot 1$

In general, $n!$ indicates the product of n with each of the positive counting numbers less than n. *By special definition, 0! = 1.*

Factorial notation

For a counting number n,

$$0! = 1$$
$$1! = 1$$
$$n! = n(n-1)(n-2) \cdots 1$$

GUIDED EXERCISE 11

Factorial

(a) Evaluate 3!.

$\implies$ $3! = 3 \cdot 2 \cdot 1 = 6$

(b) How many different ways can three objects be arranged in order? How many choices do you have for the first position? for the second position? for the third position?

$\implies$ You have three choices for the first position, two for the second position, and one for the third position. By the multiplication rule, you have

$$(3)(2)(1) = 3! = 6 \text{ arrangements}$$

Permutations

We have considered the number of ordered arrangements of n objects taken as an entire group. But what if order is not important? Specifically, we considered a dinner party for eight and found the number of ordered seating arrangements for all eight people. However, suppose you have an open house and have only five chairs. How many ways can five of the eight people seat themselves in the chairs? The formula we use to compute this number is called the *permutation formula*. As we see in the next example, the *permutations rule* is really another version of the multiplication rule.

Counting rule for permutations

The number of ways to *arrange in order* n distinct objects, taking them r at a time, is

$$P_{n,r} = \frac{n!}{(n-r)!} \tag{9}$$

where n and r are whole numbers and $n \geq r$. Another commonly used notation for permutations is nPr.

EXAMPLE 11

Permutations rule

Let's compute the number of possible ordered seating arrangements for eight people in five chairs.

SOLUTION: In this case, we are considering a total of $n = 8$ different people, and we wish to arrange $r = 5$ of these people. Substituting into Formula (9), we have

$$P_{n,r} = \frac{n!}{(n-r)!}$$

$$P_{8,5} = \frac{8!}{(8-5)!} = \frac{8!}{3!} = \frac{40,320}{6} = 6720$$

Using the multiplication rule, we get the same results

Chair	1		2		3		4		5	
Choices for	8	$\times$	7	$\times$	6	$\times$	5	$\times$	4	= 6720

The permutations rule has the advantage of using factorials. Most scientific calculators have a factorial key ! as well as a permutations key nPr (see the Tech Note). ◇

> **TECH NOTE** Most scientific calculators have a factorial key, often designated x! or n!. Many of these same calculators have the permutation function built in, often labeled nPr. They also have the combination function that is discussed next. The combination function is often labeled nCr.
>
> *TI-84Plus/TI-83Plus* The factorial, permutation, and combination functions are all under **MATH**, then **PRB**.
>
> *Excel* Use the **paste function** (f$_x$), then select **all. Fact** gives factorials, **Permut** gives permutations, and **Combin** gives combinations.

Combinations

In each of our previous counting formulas, we have taken the *order* of the objects or people into account. For instance, suppose that in your political science class, you are given a list of 10 books. You are to select 4 to read during the semester. The order in which you read the books is not important. We are interested in the *different groupings* or *combinations* of 4 books from among the 10 on the list. The next formula tells us how to compute the number of different combinations.

Counting rule for combinations

The number of *combinations* of n objects taken r at a time is

$$C_{n,r} = \frac{n!}{r!(n-r)!} \tag{10}$$

where n and r are whole numbers and $n \geq r$. Other commonly used notations for combinations include nCr and $\binom{n}{r}$.

Notice the difference between the concepts of permutations and combinations. When we consider permutations, we are considering groupings *and order*. When we consider combinations, we are considering only the number of different groupings. For combinations, order within the groupings is not considered. As a result, the number of combinations of n objects taken r at a time is generally smaller than the number of permutations of the same n objects taken r at a time. In fact, the combinations formula is simply the permutations formula with the number of permutations of each distinct group divided out. In the formula for combinations, notice the factor of $r!$ in the denominator.

Now let's look at an example in which we use the *combinations rule* to compute the number of *combinations* of 10 books taken 4 at a time.

EXAMPLE 12

Combinations

In your political science class, you are assigned to read any 4 books from a list of 10 books. How many different groups of 4 are available from the list of 10?

SOLUTION: In this case, we are interested in *combinations* rather than permutations of 10 books taken 4 at a time. Using $n = 10$ and $r = 4$, we have

$$C_{n,r} = \frac{n!}{r!(n-r)!} = \frac{10!}{4!(10-4)!} = 210$$

There are 210 different groups of 4 books that can be selected from the list of 10. An alternate solution method is to use the combinations key (often nCr or $C_{n,r}$) on a calculator. ◇

PROCEDURE

How to determine the number of outcomes of an experiment

1. If the experiment consists of a series of stages with various outcomes, use the multiplication rule or a tree diagram.

2. If the outcomes consist of ordered subgroups of r items taken from a group of n items, use the permutations rule, $P_{n,r}$.

$$P_{n,r} = \frac{n!}{(n-r)!}$$

3. If the outcomes consist of non-ordered subgroups of r items taken from a group of n items, use the combinations rule, $C_{n,r}$.

$$C_{n,r} = \frac{n!}{r!(n-r)!}$$

GUIDED EXERCISE 12

Permutations and combinations

The board of directors at Belford Community Hospital has 12 members.

(i) Three officers—president, vice president, and treasurer—must be elected from the members. How many different slates of officers are possible? We will view a slate of officers as a list of three people, with the president listed first, the vice president listed second, and the treasurer listed third. For instance, if Mr. Acosta, Ms. Hill, and Mr. Smith wish to be on a slate together, there are several different slates possible, depending on the person listed for each office. Not

Continued

GUIDED EXERCISE 12 continued

only are we asking for the number of different groups of three names for a slate, we are also concerned about order.

(a) Do we use the permutations rule or the combinations rule? What is the value of n? What is the value of r?

⟹ We use the permutations rule, since order is important. The size of the group from which the slates of officers are to be selected is n. The size of each slate is r.

$$n = 12 \text{ and } r = 3$$

(b) Use the permutations rule with $n = 12$ and $r = 3$ to compute $P_{12,3}$.

⟹ $P_{n,r} = \dfrac{n!}{(n-r)!} = \dfrac{12!}{(12-3)!} = 1320$

An alternative is to use the permutations key on a calculator.

(ii) Three members from the group of 12 on the board of directors at Belford Community Hospital will be selected to go to a convention (all expenses paid) in Hawaii. How many different groups of 3 are there?

(c) Do we use the permutations rule or the combinations rule? What is the value of n? What is the value of r?

⟹ We use the combinations rule, because order is not important. The size of the board is $n = 12$ and the size of each group going to the convention is $r = 3$.

(d) Use the combinations rule with $n = 12$ and $r = 3$ to compute $C_{12,3}$.

⟹ $C_{n,r} = \dfrac{n!}{r!(n-r)!} = \dfrac{12!}{3!(12-3)!} = 220$

An alternative is to use the combinations key on a calculator.

VIEWP⊙INT

Powerball

Powerball is a multistate lottery game that consists of drawing five distinct whole numbers from the numbers 1 through 55. Then one more number from the numbers 1 through 42 is selected as the Powerball number (this number could be one of the original five). Powerball numbers are drawn every Wednesday and Saturday. If you match all six numbers, you win the jackpot, which is worth at least 10 million dollars. Use methods of this section to show that there are 146,107,962 possible Powerball plays. For more information about the game of Powerball and the probability of winning different prizes, visit the Brase/Brase statistics site at **http://math.college.hmco.com/students** and find the link to the Multi-State Lottery Association. Then select Powerball.

SECTION 5.3   PROBLEMS

1. *Tree Diagram*
   (a) Draw a tree diagram to display all the possible head–tail sequences that can occur when you flip a coin three times.
   (b) How many sequences contain exactly two heads?
   (c) *Probability extension:* Assuming the sequences are all equally likely, what is the probability that you will get exactly two heads when you toss a coin three times?

2. *Tree Diagram*
   (a) Draw a tree diagram to display all the possible outcomes that can occur when you flip a coin and then toss a die.
   (b) How many outcomes contain a head and a number greater than 4?
   (c) *Probability extension:* Assuming the outcomes displayed in the tree diagram are all equally likely, what is the probability that you will get a head *and* a number greater than 4 when you flip a coin and toss a die?

3. *Tree Diagram* There are six balls in an urn. They are identical except for color. Two are red, three are blue, and one is yellow. You are to draw a ball from the urn, note its color, and set it aside. Then you are to draw another ball from the urn and note its color.
   (a) Make a tree diagram to show all possible outcomes of the experiment. Label the probability associated with each stage of the experiment on the appropriate branch.
   (b) *Probability extension:* Compute the probability for each outcome of the experiment.

4. *Tree Diagram*
   (a) Make a tree diagram to show all the possible sequences of answers for three multiple-choice questions, each with four possible responses.
   (b) *Probability extension:* Assuming that you are guessing the answers so that all outcomes listed in the tree are equally likely, what is the probability that you will guess the one sequence that contains all three correct answers?

5. *Multiplication Rule* Four wires (red, green, blue, and yellow) need to be attached to a circuit board. A robotic device will attach the wires. The wires can be attached in any order, and the production manager wishes to determine which order would be fastest for the robot to use. Use the multiplication rule of counting to determine the number of possible sequences of assembly that must be tested. (*Hint:* There are four choices for the first wire, three for the second, two for the third, and only one for the fourth.)

6. *Multiplication Rule* A sales representative must visit four cities: Omaha, Dallas, Wichita, and Oklahoma City. There are direct air connections between each of the cities. Use the multiplication rule of counting to determine the number of different choices the sales representative has for the order in which to visit the cities. How is this problem similar to Problem 5?

7. *Multiplication Rule* Barbara is a research biologist for Green Carpet Lawns. She is studying the effects of fertilizer type, temperature at time of application, and water treatment after application. She has four fertilizer types, three temperature zones, and three water treatments to test. Use the multiplication rule of counting to determine the number of different lawn plots she needs in order to test each fertilizer type, temperature range, and water treatment configuration.

8. *Multiplication Rule* You toss a pair of dice.
   (a) Use the multiplication rule of counting to determine the number of possible pairs of outcomes. (Recall that there are six possible outcomes for each die.)
   (b) There are three even numbers on each die. How many outcomes are possible with even numbers showing on each die?
   (c) *Probability extension:* What is the probability that both dice will show an even number?

9. Compute $P_{5,2}$.

10. Compute $P_{8,3}$.

11. Compute $P_{7,7}$.

12. Compute $P_{9,9}$.

13. Compute $C_{5,2}$.

14. Compute $C_{8,3}$.

15. Compute $C_{7,7}$.

16. Compute $C_{8,8}$.

17. *Permutation: Hiring* There are three nursing positions to be filled at Lilly Hospital. Position 1 is the day nursing supervisor; position 2 is the night nursing supervisor; and position 3 is the nursing coordinator position. There are 15 candidates qualified for all three of the positions. Use the permutations rule to determine the number of different ways the positions can be filled by these applicants.

18. *Permutation: Lottery* In the Cash Now lottery game there are 10 finalists who submitted entry tickets on time. From these 10 tickets, three grand prize winners will be drawn. The first prize is one million dollars, the second prize is one hundred thousand dollars, and the third prize is ten thousand dollars. Use the permutations rule to determine the total number of different ways the winners can be drawn. (Assume that the tickets are not replaced after they are drawn.)

19. *Counting: Hiring* There are 15 qualified applicants for 5 trainee positions in a fast-food management program. How many different groups of trainees can be selected? (*Hint:* Is order important? If not, use the formula for combinations.)

20. *Counting: Shelving* To emphasize the importance of correct shelving of books, a librarian tells a group of students the number of possible orders in which just six books may be placed on a shelf. What is that number?

21. *Counting: Hiring* The qualified applicant pool for six management trainee positions consists of seven women and five men.
    (a) How many different groups of applicants can be selected for the positions?
    (b) How many different groups of trainees would consist entirely of women?
    (c) *Probability extension:* If the applicants are equally qualified and the trainee positions are selected by drawing the names at random so that all groups of six are equally likely, what is the probability that the trainee class will consist entirely of women?

22. *Counting: Grading* One professor grades homework by randomly choosing 5 out of 12 homework problems to grade.
    (a) How many different groups of 5 problems can be chosen from the 12 problems?
    (b) *Probability extension:* Jerry did only 5 problems of one assignment. What is the probability that the problems he did comprised the group that was selected to be graded?
    (c) Silvia did 7 problems. How many different groups of 5 did she complete? What is the probability that one of the groups of 5 she completed comprised the group selected to be graded?

SUMMARY

In this chapter we first examined the question: What is probability? We found that probabilities can be assigned to events by intuition, by the method of relative frequency, or by the method of equally likely outcomes. Next, we studied some probability rules. The most important rules are the multiplication rules for independent and dependent events and the addition rules for mutually exclusive and general events. We also looked at some counting techniques useful in computing probabilities. These techniques included tree diagrams, the multiplication rule for counting, combinations, and permutations.

IMPORTANT WORDS & SYMBOLS

Section 5.1
Probability of an event A, $P(A)$
Relative frequency
Law of large numbers
Equally likely outcomes
Statistical experiment
Simple event
Sample space
Complement of event A

Section 5.2
Independent events
Dependent events
A, given B

Conditional probability
Multiplication rules of probability (for independent and dependent events)
A and B
Mutually exclusive events
Addition rules (for mutually exclusive and general events)
A or B

Section 5.3
Tree diagram
Multiplication rule of counting
Permutations rule
Combinations rule

VIEWPOINT   *Deathday and Birthday*

Can people really postpone death? If so, how much can the timing of death be influenced by psychological, social, or other influential factors? One special event is a birthday. Do famous people try to postpone their deaths until an important birthday? Both Thomas Jefferson and John Adams died on July 4, 1826, when the United States was celebrating its 50th birthday. Is this only a strange coincidence, or is there an unexpected connection between birthdays and deathdays? The probability associated with a death rate decline of famous people just before important birthdays has been studied by Professor D. P. Phillips, of the State University of New York, and is presented in the book *Statistics, A Guide to the Unknown,* edited by J. M. Tanur.

CHAPTER REVIEW PROBLEMS

1. *Salary Raise: Women* Does it pay to ask for a raise? A national survey of heads of households showed the percentage of those who asked for a raise and the percentage who got one (*USA Today*). According to the survey, of the women interviewed, 24% had asked for a raise, and of those women who had asked for a raise, 45% received the raise. If a woman is selected at random from the survey population of women, find the following probabilities: P(woman asked for a raise); P(woman received raise, *given* she asked for one); P(woman asked for raise *and* received raise).

2. *Salary Raise: Men* According to the same survey quoted in Problem 1, of the men interviewed, 20% had asked for a raise, and 59% of the men who had asked for a raise received the raise. If a man is selected at random from the survey population of men, find the following probabilities: P(man asked for a raise); P(man received raise, *given* he asked for one); P(man asked for raise *and* received raise).

3. *General: Deck of Cards* Two cards are drawn at random from a standard deck. (A standard deck has 52 cards: 13 hearts, 13 diamonds, 13 clubs, and 13 spades.)
   (a) Are the outcomes of drawing the two cards independent? Why?
   (b) If the first card is replaced before the second is drawn, what is the probability that both cards will be hearts?
   (c) If the first card is not replaced before the second is drawn, what is the probability that both cards will be hearts?

4. *General: Die and Coin* Suppose you throw a fair die and flip a fair coin. Let's represent the outcomes of 3 on the die and heads on the coin by 3H.
   (a) One outcome is 3H. What are the other outcomes? What is the sample space?
   (b) Are all outcomes in the sample space equally likely? Explain.
   (c) What is the probability of getting heads and a number less than 3?

5. *General: Thumbtack*
   (a) Describe how you could use a relative frequency to estimate the probability that a thumbtack will land with its flat side down.
   (b) What is the sample space of outcomes for the thumbtack?
   (c) How would you make a probability assignment to this sample space if, when you drop 500 tacks, 340 land flat side down?

6. *Survey: Reaction to Poison Ivy* Allergic reactions to poison ivy can be miserable. Plant oils cause the reaction. Researchers at Allergy Institute did a study to see the effects of washing the oil off within 5 minutes of exposure. A random sample of 1000 people with known allergies to poison ivy participated in the study. Oil from the poison ivy plant was rubbed on a patch of skin. For 500 of the subjects, it was washed off *within* 5 minutes. For the other 500 subjects, the oil was washed off *after* 5 minutes. The results are summarized in Table 5-4.

TABLE 5-4 Time in Which Oil Was Washed Off

Reaction	Within 5 Minutes	After 5 Minutes	Row Total
None	420	50	470
Mild	60	330	390
Strong	20	120	140
Column Total	500	500	1000

Let's use the following notation for the various events: W = washing oil off within 5 minutes, A = washing oil off after 5 minutes, N = no reaction, M = mild reaction, and S = strong reaction. Find the following probabilities for a person selected at random from this sample of 1000 subjects.

(a) $P(N)$, $P(M)$, $P(S)$

(b) $P(N, \text{ given } W)$, $P(S, \text{ given } W)$

(c) $P(N, \text{ given } A)$, $P(S, \text{ given } A)$

(d) $P(N \text{ and } W)$, $P(M \text{ and } W)$

(e) $P(N \text{ or } M)$. Are the events N = no reaction and M = mild reaction mutually exclusive? Explain.

(f) Are the events N = no reaction and W = washing oil off within 5 minutes independent? Explain.

7. *General: Two Dice* In a game of craps you roll two fair dice. Whether you win or lose depends on the sum of the numbers showing on the tops of the dice. Let x be the random variable that represents the sum of the numbers on the tops of the dice.

(a) What values can x take on?

(b) What is the probability distribution of these x values (that is, what is the probability that x = 2, 3, etc.)?

8. *Academic: Passing French* Class records at Rockwood College indicate that a student selected at random has probability 0.77 of passing French 101. For the student who passes French 101, the probability is 0.90 that he or she will pass French 102. What is the probability that a student selected at random will pass both French 101 and French 102?

9. *Combination: City Council* There is enough money to send two of eight city council members to a conference in Honolulu. All want to go, so they decide to choose the members to go to the conference by a random process. How many different combinations of two council members can be selected from the eight who want to go to the conference?

10. Compute: (a) $P_{7,2}$ (b) $C_{7,2}$ (c) $P_{3,3}$ (d) $C_{4,4}$

11. *Inspection: Food Processing* Freeze Dry Food, Inc., packages all its foods in clear plastic that is sealed. The quality control for the packaging process checks for three items: (1) that the weight shown is correct, (2) that the label is correct, and (3) that the package is properly sealed. These three processes can be done in any order. A computer-operated device directs the packages to the three inspection stations according to backlog in that area. If there is a larger backlog in one area, products are sent to one of the other two areas first. In how many different ways can a package be cycled through the three inspection stations?

12. *Scheduling: College Courses* A student must satisfy the literature, social science, and philosophy requirements this semester. There are four literature courses to select from, three social science courses, and two philosophy courses. Make a tree diagram showing all the possible sequences of literature, social science, and philosophy courses.

13. *General: Multiplication Rule* There are five multiple-choice questions on an exam, each with four possible answers. Use the multiplication rule of counting to determine the number of possible answer sequences for the five questions. Only one of the sets can contain all five correct answers. If you are guessing, so that you are as likely to choose one sequence of answers as another, what is the probability of getting all five answers correct?

14. *General: Multiplication Rule* A coin is tossed six times. Use the multiplication rule of counting to determine the number of possible head–tail sequences that can occur.

DATA HIGHLIGHTS: GROUP PROJECTS

Break into small groups and discuss the following topics. Organize a brief outline in which you summarize the main points of your group discussion.

Look at Figure 5-11, "Who's Cracking the Books?"

(a) Does the figure show the probability distribution of grade records for male students? for female students? Describe all the grade-record probability distributions shown in Figure 5-11. Find the probability that a male student selected at random has a grade record showing mostly A's.

(b) Is the probability distribution shown for all students making mostly A's? Explain your answer. *Hint:* Do the percentages shown for mostly A's add up to 1? Can Figure 5-11 be used to determine the probability that a student selected at random has mostly A's? Can it be used to determine the probability that a female student selected at random has mostly A's? What is the probability?

(c) Can we use the information shown in the figure to determine the probability that a graduating senior has grades consisting of mostly B's or higher? What is the probability?

(d) Does Figure 5-11 give sufficient information to determine the probability that a student selected at random is in the age range 19 to 23 *and* has grades that are mostly B's? What is the probability that a student selected at random has grades that are mostly B's, *given* he or she is in the age range 19 to 23?

(e) Suppose that 65% of the students at State University are between 19 and 23 years of age. What is the probability that a student selected at random is in this age range *and* has grades that are mostly B's?

FIGURE 5-11

Who's Cracking the Books?

Undergraduate Grade Record by Student Characteristic					
Student characteristic	**C's and D's or lower**	**B's and C's**	**Mostly B's**	**A's and B's**	**Mostly A's**
Gender: Men	38.8 %	16.6 %	22.6 %	9.6 %	12.4 %
Women	29.4	16.2	26.2	12.0	16.2
Class level: Graduating senior	15.8 %	21.9 %	34.5 %	14.7 %	13.0 %
All other class levels	35.4	15.8	23.6	10.5	14.7
Age: 18 or younger	42.6 %	14.7 %	23.4 %	9.4 %	10.0 %
19 to 23	38.1	19.0	25.1	9.4	8.3
24 to 29	33.3	16.9	24.7	10.3	14.9
30 to 39	23.1	13.2	25.9	14.8	23.0
40 and older	20.1	10.1	22.0	14.8	33.0

Source: U.S. Department of Education

LINKING CONCEPTS: WRITING PROJECTS

Discuss each of the following topics in class or review the topics on your own. Then write a brief but complete essay in which you summarize the main points. Please include formulas as appropriate.

1. Discuss the following concepts and give examples from everyday life in which you might encounter each concept. *Hint:* For instance, consider the "experiment" of arriving for class. Some possible outcomes are not arriving (that is, missing class), arriving on time, and arriving late.

   (a) Sample space.

   (b) Probability assignment to a sample space. In your discussion, be sure to include answers to the following questions.

      (i) Is there more than one valid way to assign probabilities to a sample space? Explain and give an example.

      (ii) How can probabilities be estimated by relative frequencies? How can probabilities be computed if events are equally likely?

2. Discuss the concepts of mutually exclusive events and independent events. List several examples of each type of event from everyday life.

   (a) If A and B are mutually exclusive events, does it follow that A and B *cannot* be independent events? Give an example to demonstrate your answer. *Hint:* Discuss an election in which only one person can win the election. Let A be the event that party A's candidate wins, and let B be the event that party B's candidate wins. Does the outcome of one event determine the outcome of the other event? Are A and B mutually exclusive events?

   (b) Discuss conditions under which $P(A \text{ and } B) = P(A) \cdot P(B)$ is true. Under what conditions is this statement not true?

   (c) Discuss conditions under which $P(A \text{ or } B) = P(A) + P(B)$ is true. Under what conditions is this statement not true?

3. Although we learn a good deal about probability in this course, the main emphasis is on statistics. Write a few paragraphs in which you talk about the distinction between probability and statistics. In what types of problems would probability be the main tool? In what types of problems would statistics be the main tool? Give some examples of both types of problems. What kind of outcome or conclusions do we expect from each type of problem?

Using Technology

Demonstration of the Law of Large Numbers

Computers can be used to simulate experiments. With packages such as Excel, Minitab, and SPSS, programs using random-number generators can be designed (see the *Technology Guide*) to simulate activities such as tossing a die.

The following printouts show the results of the simulations for tossing a die 6, 500, 50,000, 500,000, and 1,000,000 times. Notice how the relative frequencies of the outcomes approach the theoretical probabilities of 1/6 or 0.16667 for each outcome. Do you expect the same results every time the simulation is done? Why or why not?

Results of tossing one die 6 times

Outcome	Number of Occurrences	Relative Frequency
⚀	0	.00000
⚁	1	.16667
⚂	2	.33333
⚃	0	.00000
⚄	1	.16667
⚅	2	.33333

Results of tossing one die 500 times

Outcome	Number of Occurrences	Relative Frequency
⚀	87	.17400
⚁	83	.16600
⚂	91	.18200
⚃	69	.13800
⚄	87	.17400
⚅	83	.16600

Results of tossing one die 50,000 times

Outcome	Number of Occurrences	Relative Frequency
⚀	8528	.17056
⚁	8354	.16708
⚂	8246	.16492
⚃	8414	.16828
⚄	8178	.16356
⚅	8280	.16560

Results of tossing one die 500,000 times

Outcome	Number of Occurrences	Relative Frequency
⚀	83644	.16729
⚁	83368	.16674
⚂	83398	.16680
⚃	83095	.16619
⚄	83268	.16654
⚅	83227	.16645

Results of tossing one die 1,000,000 times

Outcome	Number of Occurrences	Relative Frequency
⚀	166643	.16664
⚁	166168	.16617
⚂	167391	.16739
⚃	165790	.16579
⚄	167243	.16724
⚅	166765	.16677

6

The Binomial Probability Distribution and Related Topics

Education is the key to unlock the golden door of freedom.

—George Washington Carver

George Washington Carver won international fame for agricultural research. After graduating from Iowa State College, he was appointed a faculty member in the Iowa State Botany Department. Carver took charge of the greenhouse and started a fungus collection that later included more than 20,000 species. This collection brought him professional acclaim in the field of botany.

At the invitation of his friend Booker T. Washington, Carver joined the faculty of the Tuskegee Institute, where he spent the rest of his long and distinguished career. Carver's creative genius accounted for more than 300 inventions from peanuts, 118 inventions from sweet potatoes, and 75 inventions from pecans.

Gathering and analyzing data were important components of Carver's work. Methods you will learn in this course are widely used in research in every field, including agriculture.

George Washington Carver (1859–1943)

Carver was a winner of the Spingarn Medal for distinguished service in agricultural chemistry and the prestigious Roosevelt Medal for contributions to science. Carver was also a Fellow in the Royal Society of Arts in London, an honor given to very few Americans.

 For on-line student resources, visit **math.college.hmco.com/students** and follow the Statistics links to the Brase/Brase, *Understanding Basic Statistics*, 4th edition web site.

PREVIEW QUESTIONS

◇ What is a random variable? How do you compute μ and σ for a discrete random variable? (SECTION 6.1)

◇ Many of life's experiences consist of some successes together with some failures. Suppose you make n attempts to succeed at a certain project. How can you use the binomial probability distribution to compute the probability of r successes? (SECTION 6.2)

◇ How do you compute μ and σ for the binomial distribution? (SECTION 6.3)

Personality Preference Types: Introvert or Extrovert?

Isabel Briggs Myers was a pioneer in the study of personality types. Her work has been used successfully in counseling, educational, and industrial settings. In the book *A Guide to the Development and Use of the Myers-Briggs Type Indicators,* by Myers and McCaully, it was reported that based on a very large sample (2282 professors), approximately 45% of all university professors are extroverted.

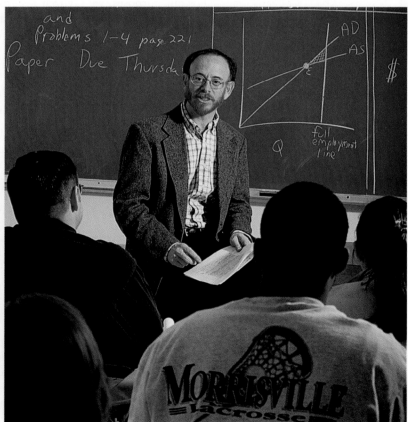

After completing this chapter, you will be able to answer the following questions. Suppose you have classes with six different professors.

(a) What is the probability that all six are extroverts?

(b) What is the probability that none of your professors is an extrovert?

(c) What is the probability that at least two of your professors are extroverts?

(d) In a group of six professors selected at random, what is the *expected number* of extroverts? What is the *standard deviation* of the distribution?

(See Problem 6 of Section 6.3.)

◊ **COMMENT** Both extroverted and introverted professors can be excellent teachers. ◊

6.1   Introduction to Random Variables and Probability Distributions

FOCUS POINTS

✓ Distinguish between discrete and continuous random variables.

✓ Graph discrete probability distributions.

✓ Compute μ and σ for a discrete probability distribution.

Random Variables

For our purposes, we say that a *statistical experiment* or *observation* is any process by which measurements are obtained. Examples are

1. Counting the number of eggs in a robin's nest

2. Measuring daily rainfall in inches

3. Counting the number of defective light bulbs in a case of bulbs

4. Measuring the weight in kilograms of a polar bear cub

Let x represent a quantitative variable that is measured or observed in an experiment. We are interested in the numerical values that x can take on. So x = number of eggs in a robin's nest and x = weight in kilograms of a polar bear cub would be examples of such quantitative variables. Furthermore, we say that the quantitative variable x is a *random variable* because the value that x takes on in a given experiment is a chance or random outcome. We will study two types of random variables: *discrete random variables* and *continuous random variables*.

Discrete random variable

> When the observations of a quantitative random variable can take on only a finite number of values or a countable number of values, we say that the variable is a **discrete random variable.**

We know what a *finite* number of values is, but what is a *countable* number of values? As an example, let the random variable x be the number of wells an oil prospector drills until the first productive well is found. Then x could be any of the values 1, 2, 3. . . . In theory, we have an infinite number of possibilities for the values of x. The set of values of x corresponds to the set of counting numbers. Therefore, this type of infinity is called *countable*, and we say x has a countable number of values. This is an intuitive approach to the concept of a countable set. The reader interested in a more rigorous discussion is referred to the advanced text *Introduction to Mathematical Statistics* by Hogg and Craig (Macmillan Publishing).

In most of the cases we will consider, a *discrete random variable* will be the result of a count (the terms *countable* and *discrete*, however, have different mathematical meanings). For instance, the number of students in a certain section of a statistics course this term is a discrete random variable. The value must be a counting number such as 25, or 57, or 135, and so forth. The values 25.34 or $25\frac{1}{2}$ are not possible. The cost of tuition to the nearest dollar or nearest cent is another example of a discrete random variable. In this case, we are counting dollars or cents.

Continuous random variable

> When the observations of a quantitative random variable can take on any of the countless number of values in a line interval, we say that the variable is a **continuous random variable.**

For our purposes, we will see most *continuous random variables* occurring as the result of a measurement. For example, the air pressure in an automobile tire represents a continuous random variable. The air pressure could in theory take on any value from 0 lb/in^2 (psi) to the bursting pressure of the tire. Values such as 20.126 psi, 20.12678 psi, and so forth are possible. Another example is the height of students in your statistics class. The height could in theory take on any value from a low of, say, 3 feet to a high of, say, 7.25 feet.

The distinction between discrete and continuous random variables is important because of the different mathematical techniques associated with the two kinds of random variables. Although we will not discuss these techniques at great length in this book, the distinction is very important in the study of advanced mathematical statistics.

In general, measurements of quantities such as length, weight, volume, temperature, or time yield continuous random variables. If the temperature changes from 12°C to 13°C, for example, it must take on all the temperature values between 12 and 13. Temperatures cannot just jump from one reading to the next. Discrete random variables often come from counts, such as the number of passing scores on an exam or the number of weeds in a garden.

GUIDED EXERCISE 1

Discrete or continuous random variables

Which of the following random variables are discrete and which are continuous?

(a) *Measure* the time it takes a student selected at random to register for the fall term.

⇒ Time can take on any value, so this is a continuous random variable.

(b) *Count* the number of bad checks drawn on Upright Bank on a day selected at random.

⇒ The number of bad checks can be only a whole number such as 0, 1, 2, 3, etc. This is a discrete variable.

(c) *Measure* the amount of gasoline needed to drive your car 200 miles.

⇒ We are measuring volume, which can assume any value, so this is a continuous random variable.

(d) Pick a random sample of 50 registered voters in a district and find the number who voted in the last county election.

⇒ This is a count, so the variable is discrete.

Probability Distribution of a Discrete Random Variable

A random variable has a probability distribution whether it is discrete or continuous.

Probability distribution

> A **probability distribution** is an assignment of probabilities to the specific values of a random variable or to a range of values of the random variable.

> **Features of the probability distribution of a discrete random variable**
>
> 1. The probability distribution has a probability assigned to *each* value of the random variable.
>
> 2. The sum of all the assigned probabilities must be 1.

EXAMPLE 1

Discrete probability distribution

Dr. Mendoza developed a test to measure boredom tolerance. He administered it to a group of 20,000 adults between the ages of 25 and 35. The possible scores were 0, 1, 2, 3, 4, 5, and 6, with 6 indicating the highest tolerance for boredom. The test results for this group are shown in Table 6-1.

(a) If a subject is chosen at random from this group, the probability that he or she will have a score of 3 is 6000/20,000, or 0.30. In a similar way, we can use the relative frequency to compute the probabilities for the other scores (Table 6-2). These probability assignments make up the probability distribution. Notice that the scores are mutually exclusive: No one subject has two scores. The sum of the probabilities of all the scores is 1.

TABLE 6-1 Boredom Tolerance Test Scores for 20,000 Subjects

Score	Number of Subjects
0	1400
1	2600
2	3600
3	6000
4	4400
5	1600
6	400

TABLE 6-2 Probability Distribution of Scores on Boredom Tolerance Test

Score x	Probability $P(x)$
0	0.07
1	0.13
2	0.18
3	0.30
4	0.22
5	0.08
6	0.02
	$\Sigma P(x) = 1$

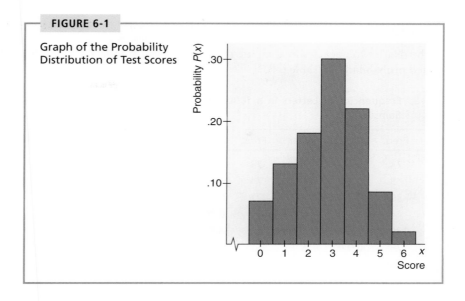

FIGURE 6-1

Graph of the Probability
Distribution of Test Scores

(b) The graph of this distribution is simply a relative-frequency histogram (see Figure 6-1) in which the height of the bar over a score represents the probability of that score. Since each bar is one unit wide, the area of the bar over a score equals the height and thus represents the probability of that score. Since the sum of the probabilities is 1, the area under the graph is also 1.

(c) The Topnotch Clothing Company needs to hire someone with a score on the boredom tolerance test of 5 or 6 to operate the fabric press machine. Since the scores 5 and 6 are mutually exclusive, the probability that someone in the group who took the boredom tolerance test made either a 5 or a 6 is the sum

$$P(5 \text{ or } 6) = P(5) + P(6)$$
$$= 0.08 + 0.02 = 0.10$$

Notice that to find $P(5 \text{ or } 6)$, we could have simply added the *areas* of the bars over 5 and over 6. One out of 10 of the group who took the boredom tolerance test would qualify for the position at Topnotch Clothing.   ◇

GUIDED
EXERCISE **2**

Discrete probability distribution

One of the elementary tools of cryptanalysis (the science of code breaking) is to use relative frequencies of occurrence of different letters in the alphabet to break standard English alphabet codes. Large samples of plain text such as newspaper stories generally yield about the same relative frequencies for letters. A sample 1000 letters long yielded the information in Table 6-3.

Continued

GUIDED EXERCISE 2 continued

(a) Use the relative frequencies to compute the omitted probabilities in Table 6-3.

   Table 6-4 shows the completion of Table 6-3.

TABLE 6-3 Frequencies of Letters in a 1000-Letter Sample

Letter	Freq.	Prob.	Letter	Freq.	Prob.
A	73	———	N	78	0.078
B	9	0.009	O	74	———
C	30	0.030	P	27	0.027
D	44	0.044	Q	3	0.003
E	130	———	R	77	0.077
F	28	0.028	S	63	0.063
G	16	0.016	T	93	0.093
H	35	0.035	U	27	———
I	74	———	V	13	0.013
J	2	0.002	W	16	0.016
K	3	0.003	X	5	0.005
L	35	0.035	Y	19	0.019
M	25	0.025	Z	1	0.001

Source: Elementary Cryptanalysis: A Mathematical Approach, by Abraham Sinkov. Copyright © 1968 by Yale University. Reprinted by permission of Random House, Inc.

TABLE 6-4 Entries for Table 6-3

Letter	Relative Frequency	Probability
A	$\dfrac{73}{1,000}$	0.073
E	$\dfrac{130}{1,000}$	0.130
I	$\dfrac{74}{1,000}$	0.074
O	$\dfrac{74}{1,000}$	0.074
U	$\dfrac{27}{1,000}$	0.027

(b) Do the probabilities of all the individual letters add up to 1?

   Yes.

(c) If a letter is selected at random from a newspaper story, what is the probability that the letter will be a vowel?

If a letter is selected at random,

$$P(a, e, i, o, \text{ or } u) = P(a) + P(e) + P(i) + P(o) + P(u)$$

$$= 0.073 + 0.130 + 0.074 + 0.074 + 0.027 = 0.378$$

Mean and standard deviation of a discrete probability distribution

A probability distribution can be thought of as a relative-frequency distribution based on a very large *n*. As such, it has a mean and standard deviation. If we are referring to the probability distribution of a *population,* then we use the Greek letters μ for the mean and σ for the standard deviation. When we see the Greek letters used, we know the information given is from the *entire population* rather than just a sample. If we have a sample probability distribution, we use $\bar{x}$ (*x* bar) and *s*, respectively, for the mean and standard deviation.

The **mean** and the **standard deviation of a discrete population probability distribution** are found by using these formulas:

$$\mu = \Sigma x P(x); \; \mu \text{ is called the expected value of } x$$
$$\sigma = \sqrt{\Sigma (x - \mu)^2 P(x)} \text{ is called the standard deviation of } x$$

where x is the value of a random variable,
$P(x)$ is the probability of that variable, and
the sum Σ is taken for all the values of the random variable.

Note: μ is the *population mean* and σ is the underlying *population standard deviation* because the sum Σ is taken over *all* values of the random variable (i.e., the entire sample space).

Expected value

The mean of a probability distribution is often called the *expected value* of the distribution. This terminology reflects the idea that the mean represents a "central point" or "cluster point" for the entire distribution. Of course, the mean or expected value is an average value, and, as such, it *need not be a point of the sample space.*

The standard deviation is often represented as a measure of *risk*. A larger standard deviation implies a greater likelihood that the random variable x is different from the expected value μ.

EXAMPLE 2

Expected value, standard deviation

Are we influenced to buy a product by an ad we saw on TV? National Infomercial Marketing Association determined the number of times *buyers* of a product watched a TV infomercial *before* purchasing the product. The results are shown here:

Number of Times Buyers Saw Infomercial	1	2	3	4	5*
Percentage of Buyers	27%	31%	18%	9%	15%

*This category was 5 or more, but will be treated as 5 in this example.

We can treat the information shown as an estimate of the probability distribution because the events are mutually exclusive and the sum of the percentages is 100%. Compute the mean and standard deviation of the distribution.

SOLUTION: We put the data in the first two columns of a computation table and then fill in the other entries (see Table 6-5).

TABLE 6-5   Number of Times Buyers View Infomercial Before Making Purchase

x (number of viewings)	P(x)	xP(x)	x − μ	(x − μ)²	(x − μ)²P(x)
1	0.27	0.27	−1.54	2.372	0.640
2	0.31	0.62	−0.54	0.292	0.091
3	0.18	0.54	0.46	0.212	0.038
4	0.09	0.36	1.46	2.132	0.192
5	0.15	0.75	2.46	6.052	0.908
		$\mu = \Sigma x P(x) = 2.54$			$\Sigma (x - \mu)^2 P(x) = 1.869$

The average number of times a buyer views the infomercial before purchase is

$$\mu = \Sigma x P(x) = 2.54 \text{ (sum of column 3)}$$

To find the standard deviation, we take the square root of the sum of column 6:

$$\sigma = \sqrt{\Sigma(x - \mu)^2 P(x)} \approx \sqrt{1.869} \approx 1.37 \qquad \diamond$$

● **CALCULATOR NOTE**   Some calculators, including the TI-84Plus/TI-83Plus models, accept fractional frequencies. If yours does, you can get μ and σ directly. For instance, on the TI-84Plus/TI-83Plus calculators, enter x values (events) in column L_1 and the corresponding probabilities $P(x)$ in column L_2. Press **Stat ➤ Calc ➤ 1-Var Stats**. Then enter the lists L_1 and L_2 separated by a comma. Press **Enter**. The value of the mean $\bar{x}$ is the expected value, while σ_x gives the standard deviation of the probability distribution.

GUIDED EXERCISE 3

Expected value

At a carnival, you pay $2.00 to play a coin-flipping game with three fair coins. On each coin, one side has the number 0 and the other side has the number 1. You flip the three coins at one time and you win $1.00 for every 1 that appears on top. Are your expected earnings equal to the cost to play? We'll answer this question in several steps.

(a) In this game, the random variable of interest counts the number of 1s that show. What is the sample space for the values of this random variable?

➤ The sample space is {0, 1, 2, 3}, since any of these numbers of 1s can appear.

(b) There are eight equally likely outcomes for throwing three coins. They are 000, 001, 010, 011, 100, 101, _____, and _____.

➤ 110 and 111.

(c) Complete Table 6-6.

TABLE 6-6

Number of 1s, x	Frequency	$P(x)$	$xP(x)$
0	1	0.125	0
1	3	0.375	_____
2	3	_____	_____
3	_____	_____	_____

➤

TABLE 6-7   Completion of Table 6-6

Number of 1s, x	Frequency	$P(x)$	$xP(x)$
0	1	0.125	0
1	3	0.375	0.375
2	3	0.375	0.750
3	1	0.125	0.375

(d) The expected value is the sum

$$\mu = \Sigma x P(x)$$

Sum the appropriate column of Table 6-6 to find this value. Are your expected earnings less than, equal to, or more than the cost of the game?

➤ The expected value can be found by summing the last column of Table 6-7. The expected value is $1.50. It cost $2.00 to play the game; the expected value is less than the cost. The carnival is making money. In the long run, the carnival can expect to make an average of about 50 cents per player.

We have seen probability distributions of discrete variables and the formulas to compute the mean and standard deviation of a discrete population probability distribution. Probability distributions of continuous random variables are similar except that the probability assignments are made to intervals of values rather than to specific values of the random variable. We will see an important example of a discrete probability distribution, the binomial distribution, in the next section, and an example of a continuous probability distribution in Chapter 7 when we study the normal distribution.

VIEWP⊙INT   *The Rosetta Project*

Around 196 B.C., Egyptian priests inscribed a decree on a granite slab affirming the rule of 13-year-old Ptolemy V. The proclamation was in Egyptian hieroglyphics with another translation in a form of ancient Greek. By 1799, the meaning of Egyptian hieroglyphics had been lost for many centuries. However, Napoleon's troops discovered the granite slab (Rosetta Stone). Linguists used the Rosetta Stone and their knowledge of ancient Greek to unlock the meaning of the Egyptian hieroglyphics.

Linguistic experts say that because of industrialization and globalization, by the year 2100 as many as 90% of the world's languages may be extinct. To help preserve some of these languages for future generations, 1000 translations of the first three chapters of Genesis have been inscribed in tiny text onto 3-inch nickel disks and encased in hardened glass balls that are expected to last at least 1000 years. Why Genesis? Because it is the most translated text in the world. The Rosetta Project is sending the disks to libraries and universities all over the world. It is very difficult to send information into the future. However, if in the year 2500 linguists are using the "Rosetta Disks" to unlock the meaning of a lost language, you may be sure they will use statistical methods of cryptanalysis (see Guided Exercise 2). To find out more about the Rosetta Project, visit the Brase/Brase statistics site at **http://math.college.hmco.com/students** and find the link to the Rosetta Project site.

SECTION 6.1   PROBLEMS

1. *Random Variables: Classification* Which of the following are continuous variables and which are discrete?
   (a) Number of traffic fatalities per year in the state of Florida
   (b) Distance a golf ball travels after being hit with a driver
   (c) Time required to drive from home to college on any given day
   (d) Number of ships in Pearl Harbor on any given day
   (e) Your weight before breakfast each morning

2. *Random Variables: Classification* Which of the following are continuous variables and which are discrete?
   (a) Speed of an airplane
   (b) Age of a college professor chosen at random

(c) Number of books in the college bookstore
(d) Weight of a football player chosen at random
(e) Number of lightning strikes in Rocky Mountain National Park on a given day

3. *Probability Distribution* Consider each distribution. Determine whether or not it is a valid probability distribution, and explain your answer.

(a)

x	0	1	2
P(x)	0.25	0.60	0.15

(b)

x	0	1	2
P(x)	0.25	0.60	0.20

4. *Marketing: Age* What is the age distribution of promotion-sensitive shoppers? A *supermarket super shopper* is defined as a shopper for whom at least 70% of the items purchased were on sale or purchased with a coupon. The following table is based on information taken from *Trends in the United States* (Food Marketing Institute, Washington, D.C.).

Age range, years	18–28	29–39	40–50	51–61	62 and over
Midpoint x	23	34	45	56	67
Percent of super shoppers	7%	44%	24%	14%	11%

For the 62 and over age group, use the midpoint 67 years.
(a) Using the age midpoints x and the percentages of super shoppers, do we have a valid probability distribution? Explain.
(b) Use a histogram to graph the probability distribution of part (a).
(c) Compute the expected age μ of a super shopper.
(d) Compute the standard deviation σ for ages of super shoppers.

5. *Marketing: Income* What is the income distribution of super shoppers (see Problem 4)? In the following table, income units are in thousands of dollars, and each interval goes up to but does not include the given high value. The midpoints are given to the nearest thousand dollars.

Income range	5–15	15–25	25–35	35–45	45–55	55 or more
Midpoint x	10	20	30	40	50	60
Percent of super shoppers	21%	14%	22%	15%	20%	8%

(a) Using the income midpoints x and the percentages of super shoppers, do we have a valid probability distribution? Explain.
(b) Use a histogram to graph the probability distribution of part (a).
(c) Compute the expected income μ of a super shopper.
(d) Compute the standard deviation σ for the income of super shoppers.

6. *History: Florence Nightingale* What was the age distribution of nurses in Great Britain at the time of Florence Nightingale? Thanks to Florence Nightingale and the British census of 1851, we have the following information (based on data from the classic text *Notes on Nursing*, by Florence Nightingale). *Note:* In 1851 there were

25,466 nurses in Great Britain. Furthermore, Nightingale made a strict distinction between nurses and domestic servants.

Age range (yr)	20–29	30–39	40–49	50–59	60–69	70–79	80+
Midpoint x	24.5	34.5	44.5	54.5	64.5	74.5	84.5
Percent of nurses	5.7%	9.7%	19.5%	29.2%	25.0%	9.1%	1.8%

(a) Using the age midpoints x and the percentages of nurses, do we have a valid probability distribution? Explain.
(b) Use a histogram to graph the probability distribution of part (a).
(c) Find the probability that a British nurse selected at random in 1851 would be 60 years of age or older.
(d) Compute the expected age μ of a British nurse contemporary to Florence Nightingale.
(e) Compute the standard deviation σ for ages of nurses shown in the distribution.

7. *Criminal Justice: Parole* USA *Today* reported that approximately 25% of all state prison inmates released on parole become repeat offenders while on parole. Suppose the parole board is examining five prisoners up for parole. Let x = number of prisoners out of five on parole who become repeat offenders. The methods of Section 6.2 can be used to compute the probability assignments for the x distribution.

x	0	1	2	3	4	5
$P(x)$	0.237	0.396	0.264	0.088	0.015	0.001

(a) Find the probability that one or more of the five parolees will be repeat offenders. How does this number relate to the probability that none of the parolees will be repeat offenders?
(b) Find the probability that two or more of the five parolees will be repeat offenders.
(c) Find the probability that four or more of the five parolees will be repeat offenders.
(d) Compute μ, the expected number of repeat offenders out of five.
(e) Compute σ, the standard deviation of the number of repeat offenders out of five.

8. *Spring Break: Caribbean Cruise* The college student senate is sponsoring a spring break Caribbean cruise raffle. The proceeds are to be donated to the Samaritan Center for the Homeless. A local travel agency donated the cruise, valued at $2000. The students sold 2852 raffle tickets at $5 per ticket.
(a) Kevin bought six tickets. What is the probability that Kevin will win the spring break cruise to the Caribbean? What is the probability that Kevin will not win the cruise?
(b) Expected earnings can be found by multiplying the value of the cruise by the probability that Kevin will win. What are Kevin's expected earnings? Is this more or less than the amount Kevin paid for the six tickets? How much did Kevin effectively contribute to the Samaritan Center for the Homeless?

9. *Expected Value: Life Insurance* Jim is a 60-year-old Anglo male in reasonably good health. He wants to take out a $50,000 term (that is, straight death benefit) life insurance policy until he is 65. The policy will expire on his 65th birthday. The probability of death in a given year is provided by the Vital Statistics section of the *Statistical Abstract of the United States* (116th Edition).

x = age (yrs)	60	61	62	63	64
P(death at this age)	0.01191	0.01292	0.01396	0.01503	0.01613

Jim is applying to Big Rock Insurance Company for his term insurance policy.
(a) What is the probability that Jim will die in his 60th year? Using this probability and the $50,000 death benefit, what is the expected loss to Big Rock Insurance?
(b) Repeat part (a) for years 61, 62, 63, and 64. What would be the total expected loss to Big Rock Insurance over the years 60 through 64?
(c) If Big Rock Insurance wants to make a profit of $700 above the expected total loss paid out for Jim's death, how much should it charge for the policy?
(d) If Big Rock Insurance Company charges $5000 for the policy, how much profit does the company expect to make?

10. *Expected Value: Life Insurance* Sara is a 60-year-old Anglo female in reasonably good health. She wants to take out a $50,000 term (that is, straight death benefit) life insurance policy until she is 65. The policy will expire on her 65th birthday. The probability of death in a given year is provided by the Vital Statistics section of the *Statistical Abstract of the United States* (116th Edition).

x = age (yrs)	60	61	62	63	64
P(death at this age)	0.00756	0.00825	0.00896	0.00965	0.01035

Sara is applying to Big Rock Insurance Company for her term insurance policy.
(a) What is the probability that Sara will die in her 60th year? Using this probability and the $50,000 death benefit, what is the expected loss to Big Rock Insurance?
(b) Repeat part (a) for years 61, 62, 63, and 64. What would be the total expected loss to Big Rock Insurance over the years 60 through 64?
(c) If Big Rock Insurance wants to make a profit of $700 above the expected total loss paid out for Sara's death, how much should it charge for the policy?
(d) If Big Rock Insurance Company charges $5000 for the policy, how much profit does the company expect to make?

6.2
Binomial Probabilities

Binomial Experiment

FOCUS POINTS
✓ List the defining features of a binomial experiment.
✓ Compute binomial probabilities using the formula $P(r) = C_{n,r}\, p^r q^{n-r}$.
✓ Use the binomial table to find $P(r)$.
✓ Use the binomial probability distribution to solve real-world applications.

On a TV quiz show each contestant has a try at the wheel of fortune. The wheel of fortune is a roulette wheel with 36 slots, one of which is gold. If the ball lands in the gold slot, the contestant wins $50,000. No other slot pays. What is the probability that the quiz show will have to pay the fortune to three contestants out of 100?

In this problem, the contestant and the quiz show sponsors are concerned about only two outcomes from the wheel of fortune: The ball lands on the gold, or the ball does not land on the gold. This problem is typical of an entire class of problems that are characterized by the feature that there are exactly two possible outcomes (for each trial) of interest. These problems are called *binomial experiments,* or *Bernoulli experiments,* after the Swiss mathematician Jacob Bernoulli, who studied them extensively in the late 1600s.

Features of a binomial
experiment

> **Features of a binomial experiment**
>
> 1. There are a *fixed number of trials*. We denote this number by the letter *n*.
>
> 2. The *n* trials are *independent* and repeated under identical conditions.
>
> 3. Each trial has only *two outcomes*: success, denoted by *S*, and failure, denoted by *F*.
>
> 4. For each individual trial, the *probability of success is the same*. We denote the probability of success by *p* and that of failure by *q*. Since each trial results in either success or failure, $p + q = 1$ and $q = 1 - p$.
>
> 5. The central problem of a binomial experiment is to find the *probability of r successes out of n trials*.

EXAMPLE 3

Binomial experiment

Let's see how the wheel of fortune problem meets the criteria of a binomial experiment. We'll take the criteria one at a time.

SOLUTION:

1. Each of the 100 contestants has a trial at the wheel, so there are $n = 100$ trials in this problem.

2. Assuming that the wheel is fair, the *trials are independent,* since the result of one spin of the wheel has no effect on the results of other spins.

3. We are interested in only two outcomes on each spin of the wheel: The ball either lands on the gold, or it does not. Let's call landing on the gold *success* (*S*) and not landing on the gold *failure* (*F*). In general, the assignment of the terms *success* and *failure* to outcomes does not imply good or bad results. These terms are assigned simply for the user's convenience.

4. On each trial the probability *p* of success (landing on the gold) is 1/36, since there are 36 slots and only one of them is gold. Consequently, the probability of failure is

$$q = 1 - p = 1 - \frac{1}{36} = \frac{35}{36}$$

on each trial.

5. We want to know the probability of 3 successes out of 100 trials, so $r = 3$ in this example. It turns out that the probability the quiz show will have to pay the fortune to exactly 3 contestants out of 100 is about 0.23. Later in this section we'll see how this probability was computed. ◇

Any time we make selections from a population *without replacement, we do not have independent trials*. However, replacement is often not practical. If the number of trials is quite small with respect to the population, we *almost* have independent trials, and we can say the situation is *closely approximated* by a binomial experiment. For instance, suppose we select 20 tuition bills at random from a collection of 10,000 bills issued at one college and observe whether or not each bill is in error. If 600 of the 10,000 bills are in error, then the probability that the first one selected is in error is 600/10,000, or 0.0600. If the first is in error, then the probability that the second is in error is 599/9999, or 0.0599. Even if the first 19 bills selected are in error, the probability that the 20th is also in error is 581/9981, or 0.0582. All these probabilities round to 0.06, and we can say that the independence condition is approximately satisfied.

GUIDED EXERCISE 4

Binomial experiment

Let's analyze the following binomial experiment to determine p, q, n, and r.

According to the *Textbook of Medical Physiology*, 5th Edition, by Arthur Guyton, 9% of the population has type B blood. Suppose we choose 18 people at random from the population and test the blood type of each. What is the probability that three of these people have type B blood? (*Note:* Independence is approximated because 18 people is an extremely small sample with respect to the entire population.)

(a) In this experiment, we are observing whether or not a person has type B blood. We will say we have a success if the person has type B blood. What is failure?

⟹ Failure occurs if a person does not have type B blood.

(b) The probability of success is 0.09, since 9% of the population has type B blood. What is the probability of failure, q?

⟹ The probability of failure is
$$q = 1 - p$$
$$= 1 - 0.09 = 0.91$$

(c) In this experiment, there are $n = $ _____ trials.

⟹ In this experiment, $n = 18$.

(d) We wish to compute the probability of 3 successes out of 18 trials. In this case, $r = $ _____.

⟹ In this case, $r = 3$.

Next, we will see how to compute the probability of r successes out of n trials when we have a binomial experiment.

Computing Probabilities for a Binomial Experiment Using the Binomial Distribution Formula

The central problem of a binomial experiment is to find the probability of r successes out of n trials. Now we'll see how to find these probabilities.

A model with three trials

Suppose you are taking a timed final exam. You have three multiple-choice questions left to do. Each question has four suggested answers, and only one of the answers is correct. You have only 5 seconds left to do these three questions, so you decide to mark answers on the answer sheet without even reading the questions. Assuming that your answers are randomly selected, what is the probability that you get zero, one, two, or all three questions correct?

This is a binomial experiment. Each question can be thought of as a trial, so there are $n = 3$ trials. The possible outcomes on each trial are success S,

TABLE 6-8   Outcomes for a Binomial Experiment with $n = 3$ Trials

Outcome	Probability of Outcome	r (number of successes)
SSS	$P(SSS) = P(S)P(S)P(S) = p^3 = (0.25)^3 \approx 0.016$	3
SSF	$P(SSF) = P(S)P(S)P(F) = p^2q = (0.25)^2(0.75) \approx 0.047$	2
SFS	$P(SFS) = P(S)P(F)P(S) = p^2q = (0.25)^2(0.75) \approx 0.047$	2
FSS	$P(FSS) = P(F)P(S)P(S) = p^2q = (0.25)^2(0.75) \approx 0.047$	2
SFF	$P(SFF) = P(S)P(F)P(F) = pq^2 = (0.25)(0.75)^2 \approx 0.141$	1
FSF	$P(FSF) = P(F)P(S)P(F) = pq^2 = (0.25)(0.75)^2 \approx 0.141$	1
FFS	$P(FFS) = P(F)P(F)P(S) = pq^2 = (0.25)(0.75)^2 \approx 0.141$	1
FFF	$P(FFF) = P(F)P(F)P(F) = q^3 = (0.75)^3 \approx 0.422$	0

indicating a correct response, or failure F, meaning a wrong answer. The trials are independent—the outcome of any one trial does not affect the outcome of the others.

What is the probability of success on any question? Since you are guessing and there are four answers from which to select, the probability of a correct answer is 0.25. The probability q of a wrong answer is then 0.75. In short, we have a binomial experiment with $n = 3$, $p = 0.25$, and $q = 0.75$.

Now what are the possible outcomes in terms of success or failure for these three trials? Let's use the notation SSF to mean success on the first question, success on the second, and failure on the third. There are eight possible combinations of S's and F's. They are

$SSS \quad SSF \quad SFS \quad FSS \quad SFF \quad FSF \quad FFS \quad FFF$

To compute the probability of each outcome, we can use the multiplication law, because the trials are independent. For instance, the probability of success on the first two questions and failure on the last is

$$P(SSF) = P(S) \cdot P(S) \cdot P(F) = p \cdot p \cdot q = p^2q = (0.25)^2(0.75) \approx 0.047$$

In a similar fashion, we can compute the probability of each of the eight outcomes. These are shown in Table 6-8, along with the number of successes r associated with each outcome.

Now we can compute the probability of r successes out of three trials for $r = 0, 1, 2,$ or 3. Let's compute $P(1)$. The notation $P(1)$ stands for the probability of one success. For three trials, there are three different outcomes that show exactly one success. They are the outcomes SFF, FSF, and FFS. Since the outcomes are mutually exclusive, we can add the probabilities. So

$$P(1) = P(SFF \text{ or } FSF \text{ or } FFS) = P(SFF) + P(FSF) + P(FFS)$$
$$= pq^2 + pq^2 + pq^2$$
$$= 3pq^2$$
$$= 3(0.25)(0.75)^2$$
$$= 0.422$$

In the same way, we can find $P(0)$, $P(2)$, and $P(3)$. These values are shown in Table 6-9 on the next page.

TABLE 6-9 $P(r)$ for $n = 3$ Trials, $p = 0.25$

r (number of successes)	$P(r)$ (probability of r successes in 3 trials)		$P(r)$ for $p = 0.25$
0	$P(0) = P(FFF)$	$= q^3$	0.422
1	$P(1) = P(SFF) + P(FSF) + P(FFS)$	$= 3pq^2$	0.422
2	$P(2) = P(SSF) + P(SFS) + P(FSS)$	$= 3p^2q$	0.141
3	$P(3) = P(SSS)$	$= p^3$	0.016

We have done quite a bit of work to determine your chances of $r = 0, 1, 2,$ or 3 successes on three multiple-choice questions if you are just guessing. Now we see that there is only a small chance (about 0.016) that you will get them all correct.

Table 6-9 can be used as a model for computing the probability of r successes out of only *three* trials. How can we compute the probability of 7 successes out of 10 trials? We can develop a table for $n = 10$, but this would be a tremendous task because there are 1024 possible combinations of successes and failures on 10 trials. Fortunately, mathematicians have given us a direct formula to compute the probability of r successes for any number of trials.

General formula for binomial probability distribution

Formula for the binomial probability distribution

$$P(r) = \frac{n!}{r!(n-r)!} p^r q^{n-r} = C_{n,r} p^r q^{n-r}$$

where n = number of trials
p = probability of success on each trial
$q = 1 - p$ = probability of failure on each trial
r = random variable representing the number of successes out of n trials ($0 \leq r \leq n$)
$!$ = Factorial notation. Recall from Section 5.3 that the factorial symbol $n!$ designates the product of all the integers between 1 and n. For instance, $4! = 4 \cdot 3 \cdot 2 \cdot 1 = 24$. Special cases are $1! = 1$ and $0! = 1$.

$C_{n,r} = \dfrac{n!}{r!(n-r)!}$ is the binomial coefficient. Many calculators have a combinations key that gives the value of $C_{n,r}$ directly.

Note: The binomial coefficient $C_{n,r}$ represents the number of combinations of n distinct objects (n = number of trials in this case) taken r at a time (r = number of successes). For more information about $C_{n,r}$, see Section 5.3.

Let's look more carefully at the formula for $P(r)$. There are two main parts. The expression $p^r q^{n-r}$ is the probability of getting one outcome with r successes and $n - r$ failures. The binomial coefficient $C_{n,r}$ counts the number of outcomes that have r successes and $n - r$ failures. For instance, in the case of $n = 3$ trials, we saw in Table 6-8 that the probability of getting an outcome with one success and two failures was pq^2. This is the value of $p^r q^{n-r}$ when $r = 1$ and $n = 3$. We also observed that there were three outcomes with one success and two failures, so $C_{3,1}$ is 3.

Now let's take a look at an application of the binomial distribution formula in Example 4.

EXAMPLE 4

Compute P(r) using the binomial distribution formula

Privacy is a concern for many users of the Internet. One survey showed that 59% of Internet users are somewhat concerned about the confidentiality of their e-mail. Based on this information, what is the probability that of a random sample of 10 Internet users, 6 are concerned about the privacy of their e-mail?

SOLUTION:

(a) This is a binomial experiment with 10 trials. If we assign success to an Internet user being concerned about the privacy of e-mail, the probability of success is 59%. We are interested in the probability of 6 successes. We have

$$n = 10 \qquad p = 0.59 \qquad q = 0.41 \qquad r = 6$$

By the formula,

$$\begin{aligned}
P(6) &= C_{10,6}(0.59)^6(0.41)^{10-6} \\
&= 210(0.59)^6(0.41)^4 \qquad \text{Use a calculator.} \\
&\approx 210(0.0422)(0.0283) \qquad \text{Use a calculator.} \\
&\approx 0.25
\end{aligned}$$

There is a 25% chance that *exactly* 6 of the 10 Internet users are concerned about the privacy of e-mail.

FIGURE 6-2

TI-84Plus/TI-83Plus Display

```
10 nCr 6*.59^6*.
41^(10-6)
          .250303  4245
```

(b) Many calculators have a built-in combinations function. On the TI-84Plus and TI-83Plus calculators, you can find the combinations function under the math menu. It is designated nCr. Figure 6-2 displays the process for computing $P(6)$ directly on these calculators. ◇

Using a Binomial Distribution Table

In many cases we will be interested in the probability of a range of successes. In such cases, we need to use the addition rule for mutually exclusive events. For instance, for $n = 6$ and $p = 0.50$,

$$\begin{aligned}
P(4 \text{ or fewer successes}) &= P(r \le 4) \\
&= P(r = 4 \text{ or } 3 \text{ or } 2 \text{ or } 1 \text{ or } 0) \\
&= P(4) + P(3) + P(2) + P(1) + P(0)
\end{aligned}$$

It would be a bit of a chore to use the binomial distribution formula to compute all the required probabilities. Table 2 of the Appendix gives values of $P(r)$ for selected p values and values of n through 20. To use the table, find the appropriate section for n, and then use the entries in the columns headed by the p values and the rows headed by the r values.

Table 6-10 on the next page is an excerpt from Table 2 of the Appendix showing the section for $n = 6$. Notice that all possible r values between 0 and 6 are given as row headers. The value $p = 0.50$ is one of the column headers. For $n = 6$ and $p = 0.50$, you can find the value of $P(4)$ by looking at the entry in the row headed by 4 and the column headed by 0.50. Notice that $P(4) = 0.234$.

Likewise, you can find other values of $P(r)$ from the table. In fact, for $n = 6$ and $p = 0.50$,

$$\begin{aligned}
P(r \le 4) &= P(4) + P(3) + P(2) + P(1) + P(0) \\
&= 0.234 + 0.312 + 0.234 + 0.094 + 0.016 = 0.890
\end{aligned}$$

TABLE 6-10   Excerpt from Table 2 of the Appendix for *n* = 6

n	r	.01	.05	.10	...	.30	...	.50	...	.70	...	.85	.90	.95
⋮														
6	0	.941	.735	.531	...	.118	...	.016	...	.001	...	.000	.000	.000
	1	.057	.232	.354	...	.303	...	.094	...	.010	...	.000	.000	.000
	2	.001	.031	.098	...	.324	...	.234	...	.060	...	.006	.001	.000
	3	.000	.002	.015	...	.185	...	.312	...	.185	...	.042	.015	.002
	4	.000	.000	.001	...	.060	...	.234	...	.324		.176	.098	.031
	5	.000	.000	.000	...	.010	...	.094	...	.303	...	.399	.354	.232
	6	.000	.000	.000	...	.001	...	.016	...	.118	...	.377	.531	.735

Alternatively, to compute $P(r \le 4)$ for $n = 6$, you can use the fact that the total of all $P(r)$ values for r between 0 and 6 is 1. Then

$$P(r \le 4) = 1 - P(5) - P(6)$$
$$= 1 - 0.094 - 0.016 = 0.890$$

Note: In Table 2 of the Appendix, probability entries of 0.000 do not mean that the probability is exactly zero. Rather, to three digits after the decimal, the probability rounds to 0.000.

EXAMPLE 5

Using the binomial distribution table to find P(r)

A biologist is studying a new hybrid tomato. It is known that the seeds of this hybrid tomato have probability 0.70 of germinating. The biologist plants six seeds.

(a) What is the probability that *exactly* four seeds will germinate?

SOLUTION: This is a binomial experiment with $n = 6$ trials. Each seed planted represents an independent trial. We'll say germination is success, so the probability of success on each trial is 0.70.

$$n = 6 \qquad p = 0.70 \qquad q = 0.30 \qquad r = 4$$

We wish to find $P(4)$, the probability of exactly four successes.

In Table 2 of the Appendix, find the section with $n = 6$ (excerpt given in Table 6-10). Then find the entry in the column headed by $p = 0.70$ and the row headed by $r = 4$. This entry is 0.324.

$$P(4) = 0.324$$

(b) What is the probability that *at least* four seeds will germinate?

SOLUTION: In this case, we are interested in the probability of four or more seeds germinating. This means we are to compute $P(r \ge 4)$. Since the events are mutually exclusive, we can use the addition rule

$$P(r \ge 4) = P(r = 4 \quad or \quad r = 5 \quad or \quad r = 6) = P(4) + P(5) + P(6)$$

We already know the value of $P(4)$. We need to find $P(5)$ and $P(6)$.

Use the same part of the table, but find the entries in the row headed by the r value 5 and then the r value 6. Be sure to use the column headed by the value of p, 0.70.

$$P(5) = 0.303 \quad and \quad P(6) = 0.118$$

Now we have all the parts necessary to compute $P(r \geq 4)$.

$$P(r \geq 4) = P(4) + P(5) + P(6)$$
$$= 0.324 + 0.303 + 0.118$$
$$= 0.745$$

◇

In Guided Exercise 5, you'll practice using the formula for $P(r)$ in one part, and then you'll use Table 2 (Appendix) for $P(r)$ values in the second part.

GUIDED EXERCISE 5

Find P(r)

A rarely performed and somewhat risky eye operation is known to be successful in restoring the eyesight of 30% of the patients who undergo the operation. A team of surgeons has developed a new technique for this operation that has been successful for four of six operations. Does it seem likely that the new technique is much better than the old? We'll use the binomial probability distribution to answer this question. We'll compute the probability of at least four successes in six trials for the old technique.

(a) Each operation is a binomial trial. In this case,
$n = \_\_\_\_\_, p = \_\_\_\_\_, q = \_\_\_\_\_, r = \_\_\_\_\_.$

⟹ $n = 6, p = 0.30, q = 1 - 0.30 = 0.70, r = 4$

(b) Use your values of n, p, and q to compute $P(4)$ from the formula:

$P(r) = C_{n,r}p^{r}q^{n-r}$

⟹ $P(4) = C_{6,4}(0.30)^{4}(0.70)^{2}$
$= 15(0.0081)(0.490)$
≈ 0.060

(c) Compute the probability of *at least* four successes out of the six trials.

$P(r \geq 4) = P(r = 4 \text{ or } r = 5 \text{ or } r = 6)$
$= P(4) + P(5) + P(6)$

Use Table 2 of the Appendix to find the values of $P(4)$, $P(5)$, and $P(6)$. Then use these values to compute $P(r \geq 4)$.

⟹ To find $P(4)$, $P(5)$, and $P(6)$ in Table 2 of the Appendix, we look in the section labeled $n = 6$. Then we find the column headed by $p = 0.30$. To find $P(4)$, we use the row labeled $r = 4$. For the values of $P(5)$ and $P(6)$, use the same column but change the row headers to $r = 5$ and $r = 6$, respectively.

$P(r \geq 4) = P(4) + P(5) + P(6)$
$= 0.060 + 0.010 + 0.001 = 0.071$

(d) Under the older operation technique, the probability that at least four patients out of six will regain their eyesight is _____. Does it seem that the new technique is better than the old? Would you encourage the surgeon team to do more work on the new technique?

⟹ It seems the new technique is better than the old since, by pure chance, the probability of four or more successes out of six trials is only 0.071 for the old technique. This means one of the following two things may be happening:

(i) The new method is no better than the old method, and our surgeons have encountered a rare event (probability 0.071), or

(ii) The new method is in fact better. We think it is worth encouraging the surgeons to do more work on the new technique.

Common expressions and
corresponding inequalities

**TABLE 6-11   Common English Expressions and Corresponding Inequalities
(consider a binomial experiment with n trials and r successes)**

Expression	Inequality
Four or more successes At least four successes No fewer than four successes No less than four successes	$r \geq 4$ That is, $r = 4, 5, 6, \ldots, n$
Four or fewer successes At most four successes No more than four successes The number of successes does not exceed four	$r \leq 4$ That is, $r = 0, 1, 2, 3,$ or 4
More than four successes The number of successes exceeds four	$r > 4$ That is, $r = 5, 6, 7, \ldots, n$
Fewer than four successes The number of successes is not as large as four	$r < 4$ That is, $r = 0, 1, 2, 3$

Many times we are asked to compute the probability of a range of successes. For instance, in a binomial experiment with n trials, we may be asked to compute the probability of four or more successes. Table 6-11 shows how common English expressions such as "four or more successes" translate to inequalities involving r.

Using Technology to Compute Binomial Probabilities

Some calculators and computer software packages support the binomial distribution. In general, these technologies will provide both the probability $P(r)$ for an exact number of successes r and the cumulative probability $P(r \leq k)$, where k is a specified value less than or equal to the number of trials n. Note that most of the technologies use the letter x instead of r for the random variable denoting the number of successes out of n trials.

 TECH NOTE   The software packages Minitab and Excel, as well as the TI-84Plus and TI-83Plus calculators, include built-in binomial probability distribution options. These options give the probability $P(r)$ of a specific number of successes r, as well as the cumulative total probability for r or fewer successes.

TI-84Plus/TI-83Plus Press the **DISTR** key and scroll to **binompdf(n, p, r)**. Enter the number of trials n, the probability of success on a single trial p, and the number of successes r. This gives $P(r)$. For the cumulative probability that there are r or fewer successes, use **binomcdf(n, p, r)**.

$$
\begin{array}{l}
\texttt{binompdf(6,.3,4)} \\
\qquad\qquad \texttt{.059535} \\
\texttt{binomcdf(6,.3,4)} \\
\qquad\qquad \texttt{.989065}
\end{array}
$$

$P(r) = 4$

$P(r \le 4)$

Excel Menu Choice: **Paste Function** $\boxed{f_x}$ ➤ **Statistical** ➤ **Binomdist.** In the dialogue box, fill in the values *r, n,* and *p*. For $P(r)$, use false; for P(at most *r* successes), use true.

Minitab First enter the *r* values 0, 1, 2, . . . , *n* in a column. Then use the menu choice **Calc** ➤ **Probability Distribution** ➤ **Binomial.** In the dialogue box, select Probability for $P(r)$ or Cumulative for P(at least *r* successes). Enter the number of trials *n*, the probability of success *p*, and the column containing the *r* values. A sample printout is shown in Problem 15 at the end of this section.

VIEWPOINT   *Lies! Lies!! Lies!!! The Psychology of Deceit*

This is the title of an intriguing book by C. V. Ford, professor of psychiatry. The book recounts the true story of Floyd "Buzz" Fay, who was falsely convicted of murder on the basis of a failed polygraph examination. During his $2\frac{1}{2}$ years of wrongful imprisonment, Buzz became a polygraph expert. He taught inmates, who freely confessed guilt, how to pass a polygraph examination. (For more information on this topic, see Problem 7.)

SECTION 6.2   PROBLEMS

In each of the following problems, the binomial distribution will be used. Answers may vary slightly depending on whether the binomial distribution formula, the binomial distribution table, or distribution results from a calculator or computer are used. Please answer the following questions and then complete the problem.

What makes up a trial? What is a success? What is a failure?

What are the values of *n*, *p*, and *q*?

1. *Binomial Probabilities: Coin Flip* A fair quarter is flipped three times. For each of the following probabilities, use the formula for the binomial distribution and a calculator to compute the requested probability. Next, look up the probability in Table 2 of the Appendix and compare the table result with the computed result.
   (a) Find the probability of getting exactly three heads.
   (b) Find the probability of getting exactly two heads.
   (c) Find the probability of getting two or more heads.
   (d) Find the probability of getting exactly three tails.

2. *Binomial Probabilities: Multiple-Choice Quiz* Richard has just been given a 10-question multiple-choice quiz in his history class. Each question has five answers, of which only one is correct. Since Richard has not attended class recently, he doesn't know any of the answers. Assuming that Richard guesses on all 10 questions, find the indicated probabilities.
   (a) What is the probability that he will answer all questions correctly?
   (b) What is the probability that he will answer all questions incorrectly?
   (c) What is the probability that he will answer at least one of the questions correctly? Compute this probability two ways. First, use the rule for mutually exclusive events and the probabilities shown in Table 2 of the Appendix. Then use the fact that $P(r \geq 1) = 1 - P(r = 0)$. Compare the two results. Should they be equal? Are they equal? If not, how do you account for the difference?
   (d) What is the probability that Richard will answer at least half the questions correctly?

3. *Sociology: Marriage* The percentage of American men who say they would marry the same woman if they had it to do all over again is 80%. The percentage of American women who say they would marry the same man again is 50% (Source: *Harper's Index*).
   (a) What is the probability that in a group of 10 married men, at least 7 will claim that they would marry the same woman again? What is the probability that less than half will say this?
   (b) What is the probability that in a group of 10 married women, at least 7 will claim they would marry the same man again? What is the probability that less than half will say this?

4. *Sociology: Ethics* The one-time fling! Have you ever purchased an article of clothing (dress, sports jacket, etc.), worn the item *once* to a party, and then returned the purchase? This is called a *one-time fling*. About 10% of all adults deliberately do a one-time fling and feel no guilt about it! (Source: *Are You Normal?* by Bernice Kanner, St. Martin's Press.) In a group of seven adult friends, what is the probability that
   (a) no one has done a one-time fling?
   (b) at least one person has done a one-time fling?
   (c) no more than two people have done a one-time fling?

5. *Sociology: Mother-in-Law* The ★#@&#★ mother-in-law! Sociologists say that 90% of married women claim that their husband's mother is the biggest bone of contention in their marriages (sex and money are lower-rated areas of contention). (See the source in Problem 4.) Suppose that six married women are having coffee together one morning. What is the probability that
   (a) all of them dislike their mother-in-law?
   (b) none of them dislike their mother-in-law?
   (c) at least four of them dislike their mother-in-law?
   (d) no more than three of them dislike their mother-in-law?

6. *Sociology: Dress Habits* A research team at Cornell University conducted a study showing that approximately 10% of all businessmen who wear ties wear them so tight that they actually reduce blood flow to the brain, diminishing cerebral functions (Source: *Chances: Risk and Odds in Everyday Life,* by James Burke). At a board meeting of 20 businessmen, all of whom wear ties, what is the probability that
   (a) at least one tie is too tight?
   (b) more than two ties are too tight?
   (c) no tie is too tight?
   (d) at least 18 ties are *not* too tight?

7. *Psychology: Deceit* Aldrich Ames is a convicted traitor who leaked American secrets to a foreign power. Yet Ames took routine lie detector tests and each time passed them. How can this be done? Recognizing control questions, employing unusual breathing patterns, biting one's tongue at the right time, pressing one's toes hard to the floor, and counting backwards by 7 are countermeasures that are difficult to detect but can change the results of a polygraph examination (Source: *Lies! Lies!! Lies!!! The Psychology of Deceit*, by C. V. Ford, professor of psychiatry, University of Alabama). In fact, it is reported in Professor Ford's book that after only 20 minutes of instruction by "Buzz" Fay (a prison inmate), 85% of those trained were able to pass the polygraph examination even when guilty of a crime. Suppose that a random sample of nine students (in a psychology laboratory) are told a "secret" and then given instructions on how to pass the polygraph examination without revealing their knowledge of the secret. What is the probability that
   (a) all the students are able to pass the polygraph examination?
   (b) more than half the students are able to pass the polygraph examination?
   (c) no more than four of the students are able to pass the polygraph examination?
   (d) all the students fail the polygraph examination?

8. *Hardware Store: Income* Trevor is interested in purchasing the local hardware/sporting goods store in the small town of Dove Creek, Montana. After examining accounting records for the past several years, he found that the store has been grossing over $850 per day about 60% of the business days it is open. Estimate the probability that the store will gross over $850
   (a) at least 3 out of 5 business days.
   (b) at least 6 out of 10 business days.
   (c) fewer than 5 out of 10 business days.
   (d) fewer than 6 out of the next 20 business days. If this actually happened, might it shake your confidence in the statement $p = 0.60$? Might it make you suspect that p is less than 0.60? Explain.
   (e) more than 17 out of the next 20 business days. If this actually happened, might you suspect that p is greater than 0.60? Explain.

9. *Fishing: Northern Pike* Manitoba northern pike are hardy, tough fish! Using artificial lures with barbed treble hooks, it was found that the hooking mortality rate was only about 5%. This means that only 5% of pike that were caught and released died (Source: *Proceedings of National Symposium on Catch and Release Fishing*, sponsored by Humboldt State University). Suppose that a group of anglers caught and released 16 northern pike in Manitoba. What is the probability that
   (a) none of the fish died?
   (b) less than 3 of the fish died?
   (c) all the fish lived?
   (d) more than 14 fish lived?

10. *Marketing: Ice Cream* Supreme Chocolate claims its ice cream tastes so good you can distinguish it from all other brands of chocolate ice cream! Five different brands of chocolate ice cream (one of them Supreme Chocolate) are set before six students who are to pick the one that tastes the best. Assume there is really no difference in the way any of these ice creams taste. However, each student picks one ice cream anyway, not knowing which brand it is because all ice creams are presented in identical dishes without brand labels. What is the probability of (a), (b), and (c) below?
   (a) None of the students choose Supreme Chocolate.
   (b) At least three students choose Supreme Chocolate.

(c) All six students choose Supreme Chocolate.

(d) If all six students choose Supreme Chocolate, might this indicate that the given assumption of no difference in taste may be false? Explain.

11. *Psychology: Myers-Briggs* Approximately 75% of all marketing personnel are extroverts, whereas about 60% of all computer programmers are introverts (Source: *A Guide to the Development and Use of the Myers-Briggs Type Indicator,* by Myers and McCaulley).

(a) At a meeting of 15 marketing personnel, what is the probability that 10 or more are extroverts? What is the probability that 5 or more are extroverts? What is the probability that all are extroverts?

(b) In a group of 5 computer programmers, what is the probability that none are introverts? What is the probability that 3 or more are introverts? What is the probability that all are introverts?

12. *Sociology: Dating* In *Chances: Risks and Odds in Everyday Life,* James Burke claims that about 70% of all single men would welcome a woman taking the initiative in asking for a date. A random sample of 20 single men were asked if they would welcome a woman taking the initiative in asking for a date. What is the probability that

(a) at least 18 of the men will say yes?

(b) fewer than 3 of the men will say yes?

(c) none of the men will say yes?

(d) at least 5 of the men will say no?

13. *Health Care: Diabetes* People with diabetes may develop other health complications associated with the disease. The following information is based on a feature in *USA Today* entitled "A Look at Statistics That Shape Our Lives." About 40% of all people with diabetes will also develop hypertension (blood pressure problems), and about 30% of people with diabetes will develop an eye disease. Suppose that you are the director of a health care center that has 10 people with diabetes and no other related health problems. Part of your job is to monitor these patients for symptoms of new illnesses related to diabetes so that corrective measures can be started. What is the probability that

(a) none of the diabetes patients will ever develop related hypertension?

(b) fewer than 5 of the diabetes patients will ever develop related hypertension?

(c) no more than 2 of the diabetes patients will ever develop a related eye disease?

(d) at least 6 of the diabetes patients will never develop a related eye disease?

14. *Business Ethics: Privacy* Are your finances, buying habits, medical records, and phone calls really private? A real concern for many adults is that computers and the Internet are reducing privacy. A survey conducted by Peter D. Hart Research Associates for the Shell Poll was reported in *USA Today.* According to the survey, 37% of adults are concerned that employers are monitoring phone calls. Use the binomial distribution formula to calculate the probability that

(a) out of 5 adults, none is concerned that employers are monitoring phone calls.

(b) out of 5 adults, all are concerned that employers are monitoring phone calls.

(c) out of 5 adults, exactly 3 are concerned that employers are monitoring phone calls.

15. *Business Ethics: Privacy* According to the same poll quoted in Problem 14, 53% of adults are concerned that Social Security numbers are used for general identification. For a group of 8 adults selected at random, we used Minitab to generate the binomial probability distribution and the cumulative binomial probability distribution (menu selections ➤ **Calc** ➤ **Probability Distributions** ➤ **Binomial**).

Number	r	P(r)	P(<=r)
	0	0.002381	0.00238
	1	0.021481	0.02386
	2	0.084781	0.10864
	3	0.191208	0.29985
	4	0.269521	0.56937
	5	0.243143	0.81251
	6	0.137091	0.94960
	7	0.044169	0.99377
	8	0.006226	1.00000

Find the probability that out of 8 adults selected at random,
(a) at most 5 are concerned about Social Security numbers being used for identification. Do the problem by adding the probabilities $P(r = 0)$ through $P(r = 5)$. Is this the same as the cumulative probability $P(r \leq 5)$?
(b) more than 5 are concerned about Social Security numbers being used for identification. First, do the problem by adding the probabilities $P(r = 6)$ through $P(r = 8)$. Then do the problem by subtracting the cumulative probability $P(r \leq 5)$ from 1. Do you get the same results?

16. *Ecology: Wolves* The following is based on information taken from *The Wolf in the Southwest: The Making of an Endangered Species,* edited by David Brown (University of Arizona Press). Before 1918, approximately 55% of the wolves in the New Mexico and Arizona region were male, and 45% were female. However, cattle ranchers in this area have made a determined effort to exterminate wolves. From 1918 to the present, approximately 70% of wolves in the region are male, and 30% are female. Biologists suspect that male wolves are more likely than females to return to an area where the population has been greatly reduced.
(a) Before 1918, in a random sample of 12 wolves spotted in the region, what is the probability that 6 or more were male? What is the probability that 6 or more were female? What is the probability that fewer than 4 were female?
(b) Answer part (a) for the period from 1918 to the present.

17. *Binomial Distribution Table: Symmetry* Study the binomial distribution table (Table 2 of the Appendix). Notice that the probability of success on a single trial p ranges from 0.01 to 0.95. Some binomial distribution tables stop at 0.50 because of the symmetry in the table. Let's look for that symmetry. Consider the section of the table with $n = 5$. Look at the numbers in the columns headed by $p = 0.30$ and $p = 0.70$. Do you detect any similarities? Consider the following probabilities for a binomial experiment with five trials.
(a) Compare $P(3$ successes) where $p = 0.30$ with $P(2$ successes) where $p = 0.70$.
(b) Compare $P(3$ or more successes) where $p = 0.30$ with $P(2$ or fewer successes) where $p = 0.70$.
(c) Find the value of $P(4$ successes) where $p = 0.30$. For what value of r is $P(r$ successes) the same using $p = 0.70$?
(d) What column is symmetrical with the one headed by $p = 0.20$?

6.3
Additional Properties of the Binomial Distribution

FOCUS POINTS

✓ Make histograms for binomial distributions.

✓ Compute μ and σ for a binomial distribution.

Graphing a Binomial Distribution

Any probability distribution may be represented in graphic form. How should we graph the binomial distribution? Remember, the binomial distribution tells us the probability of r successes out of n trials. Therefore, we'll place values of r along the horizontal axis and values of $P(r)$ on the vertical axis. The binomial distribution is a *discrete* probability distribution because r can assume only whole-number values such as 0, 1, 2, 3, ... Therefore, a histogram is an appropriate graph of a binomial distribution.

PROCEDURE

How to graph a binomial distribution

1. Place r values on the horizontal axis.
2. Place $P(r)$ values on the vertical axis.
3. Construct a bar over each r value extending from $r - 0.5$ to $r + 0.5$. The height of the corresponding bar is $P(r)$.

Let's look at an example to see exactly how we'll make these histograms.

EXAMPLE 6

Graph of a binomial distribution

A waiter at the Green Spot Restaurant has learned from long experience that the probability that a lone diner will leave a tip is only 0.7. During one lunch hour he serves six people who are dining by themselves. Make a graph of the binomial probability distribution that shows the probabilities that 0, 1, 2, 3, 4, 5, or all 6 lone diners leave tips.

SOLUTION: This is a binomial experiment with $n = 6$ trials. Success is achieved when the lone diner leaves a tip, so the probability of success is 0.7 and that of failure is 0.3:

$$n = 6 \qquad p = 0.7 \qquad q = 0.3$$

We want to make a histogram showing the probability of r successes when $r = $ 0, 1, 2, 3, 4, 5, or 6. It is easier to make the histogram if we first make a table of r values and the corresponding $P(r)$ values (Table 6-12). We'll use Table 2 of the Appendix to find the $P(r)$ values for $n = 6$ and $p = 0.70$.

To construct the histogram, we'll put r values on the horizontal axis and $P(r)$ values on the vertical axis. Our bars will be one unit wide and will be centered over the appropriate r value. The height of the bar over a particular r value tells the probability of that r (see Figure 6-3).

The probability of a particular value of r is given not only by the height of the bar over that r value but also by the *area* of the bar. Each bar is only one unit wide, so the area (area = height times width) equals its height. Since the area of each bar represents the probability of the r value under it, the sum of the areas of the bars must be 1. In this example, the sum turns out to be 1.001. It is not exactly equal to 1 because of errors created by rounding.

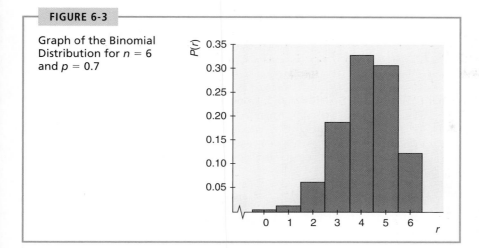

FIGURE 6-3

Graph of the Binomial Distribution for $n = 6$ and $p = 0.7$

TABLE 6-12 Binomial Distribution for $n = 6$ and $p = 0.70$

r	P(r)
0	0.001
1	0.010
2	0.060
3	0.185
4	0.324
5	0.303
6	0.118

Guided Exercise 6 illustrates another binomial distribution with $n = 6$ trials. The graph will be different from that of Figure 6-3 because the probability of success p is different.

GUIDED EXERCISE 6

Graph of a binomial distribution

Jim enjoys playing basketball. He figures that he makes about 50% of the field goals he attempts during a game. Make a histogram showing the probability that Jim will make 0, 1, 2, 3, 4, 5, or 6 shots out of six attempted field goals.

(a) This is a binomial experiment with $n = $ _____ trials. In this situation, we'll say success occurs when Jim makes an attempted field goal. What is the value of p?

⟹ In this example, $n = 6$ and $p = 0.5$.

(b) Use Table 2 of the Appendix to complete Table 6-13 of $P(r)$ values for $n = 6$ and $p = 0.5$.

TABLE 6-13

r	P(r)
0	0.016
1	0.094
2	0.234
3	_____
4	_____
5	_____
6	_____

TABLE 6-14 Completion of Table 6-13

r	P(r)
.	.
.	.
.	.
3	0.312
4	0.234
5	0.094
6	0.016

Continued

GUIDED EXERCISE 6 continued

(c) Use the values of $P(r)$ given in Table 6-14 to complete the histogram in Figure 6-4.

FIGURE 6-4 Beginning of Graph of Binomial Distribution for $n = 6$ and $p = 0.5$

FIGURE 6-5 Completion of Figure 6-4

(d) The area of the bar over $r = 2$ is 0.234. What is the area of the bar over $r = 4$? How does the probability that Jim makes exactly two field goals out of six compare with the probability that he makes exactly four field goals out of six?

The area of the bar over $r = 4$ is also 0.234. Jim is as likely to make two out of six field goals attempted as he is to make four out of six.

In Example 6 and Guided Exercise 6, we see the graphs of two binomial distributions associated with $n = 6$ trials. The two graphs are different because the probability of success p is different in the two cases. In Example 6, $p = 0.7$ and the graph is skewed to the left—that is, the left tail is longer. In Guided Exercise 6, p is equal to 0.5 and the graph is symmetrical—that is, if we fold it in half, the two halves coincide exactly. Whenever p equals 0.5, *the graph of the binomial distribution will be symmetrical no matter how many trials we have.* In Chapter 7, we will see that if the number of trials n is quite large, the binomial distribution is almost symmetrical, even when p is not close to 0.5.

Mean and Standard Deviation of a Binomial Distribution

Mean and standard deviation of binomial probability distributions

Two other features that help describe the graph of any distribution are the balance point of the distribution and the spread of the distribution about that balance point. The *balance point* is the mean μ of the distribution, and the *measure of spread* that is most commonly used is the standard deviation σ. The mean μ is the *expected value* of the number of successes.

For the binomial distribution, we can use two special formulas to compute the mean μ and the standard deviation σ. These are easier to use than the general formulas in Section 6.1 for μ and σ of any discrete probability distribution.

> **PROCEDURE**
>
> **How to compute μ and σ for a binomial distribution**
>
> $\mu = np$ is the **expected number of successes** for the random variable r
>
> $\sigma = \sqrt{npq}$ is the **standard deviation** for the random variable r
>
> where
>
> r is a random variable representing the number of successes in a binomial distribution,
>
> n is the number of trials,
>
> p is the probability of success on a single trial, and
>
> $q = 1 - p$ is the probability of failure on a single trial.

EXAMPLE 7

Compute μ and σ

Let's compute the mean and standard deviation for the distribution of Example 6 that describes that probabilities of lone diners leaving tips at the Green Spot Restaurant.

SOLUTION: In that example,

$$n = 6 \qquad p = 0.7 \qquad q = 0.3$$

For the binomial distribution,

$$\mu = np = 6(0.7) = 4.2$$

The balance point of the distribution is at $\mu = 4.2$. The standard deviation is given by

$$\sigma = \sqrt{npq} = \sqrt{6(0.7)(0.3)} = \sqrt{1.26} \approx 1.12 \qquad \Diamond$$

The mean μ is not only the balance point of the distribution; it is also the *expected value* of r. Specifically, in Example 6, the waiter can expect 4.2 lone diners out of 6 to leave a tip. (The waiter would probably round the expected value to 4 tippers out of 6.)

GUIDED EXERCISE 7

Expected value and standard deviation

When Jim (of Guided Exercise 6) shoots field goals in basketball games, the probability that he makes a shot is only 0.5.

(a) The mean of the binomial distribution is the expected value of r successes out of n trials. Out of six throws, what is the expected number of field goals Jim will make?

⟹ The expected value is the mean μ:

$$\mu = np = 6(0.5) = 3$$

Jim can expect to make three goals out of six tries.

(b) For six trials, what is the standard deviation of the binomial distribution of the number of successful field goals Jim makes?

⟹ $\sigma = \sqrt{npq} = \sqrt{6(0.5)(0.5)} = \sqrt{1.5} \approx 1.22$

VIEWPOINT   *Kodiak Island, Alaska*

Kodiak Island is famous for its giant brown bears. The sea surrounding the island is also famous for its king crab. The state of Alaska, Department of Fish and Game, has collected a huge amount of data regarding ocean latitude, ocean longitude, and size of king crab. Of special interest to commercial fishing skippers is the size of crab. Those too small must be returned to the sea. To find locations and sizes of king crab catches near Kodiak Island, visit the Brase/Brase statistics site at **http://math.college.hmco.com/students** and find the link to the StatLib site hosted by the Department of Statistics at Carnegie Mellon University. Once at StatLib, go to crab data. From this information, it is possible to use methods of this chapter and Chapter 8 to estimate the proportion of legal crab in a sea skipper's catch.

SECTION 6.3   PROBLEMS

1. *Binomial Distribution: Histograms* Consider a binomial distribution with $n = 5$ trials. Use the probabilities given in Table 2 of the Appendix to make histograms showing the probabilities of $r = 0, 1, 2, 3, 4,$ or 5 successes for each of the following. Comment on the skewness of each distribution.
   (a) The probability of success is $p = 0.50$.
   (b) The probability of success is $p = 0.25$.
   (c) The probability of success is $p = 0.75$.
   (d) What is the relationship between the distributions shown in parts (b) and (c)?
   (e) If the probability of success is $p = 0.73$, do you expect the distribution to be skewed to the right or to the left? Why?

2. *Quality Control: Syringes* The quality-control inspector of a production plant will reject a batch of syringes if two or more defective syringes are found in a random sample of eight syringes taken from the batch. Suppose the batch contains 1% defective syringes.
   (a) Make a histogram showing the probabilities of $r = 0, 1, 2, 3, 4, 5, 6, 7,$ or 8 defective syringes in a random sample of eight syringes.
   (b) Find μ. What is the expected number of defective syringes the inspector will find?
   (c) What is the probability that the batch will be accepted?
   (d) Find σ.

3. *Hype: Improved Products* The *Wall Street Journal* reported that approximately 25% of the people who are told a product is *improved* will believe that it is in fact improved. The remaining 75% believe that this is just hype (the same old thing with no real improvement). Suppose a marketing study consists of a random sample of eight people who are given a sales talk about a new, *improved* product.
   (a) Make a histogram showing the probabilities that $r = 0$ to 8 people believe the product is in fact improved.
   (b) Compute the mean and standard deviation of this probability distribution.

4. *Insurance: Auto* The Mountain States Office of State Farm Insurance Company reports that approximately 85% of all automobile damage liability claims were made by people under 25 years of age. A random sample of five automobile insurance liability claims is under study.

(a) Make a histogram showing the probabilities that $r = 0$ to 5 claims are made by people under 25 years of age.

(b) Find the mean and standard deviation of this probability distribution. For samples of size 5, what is the expected number of claims made by people under 25 years of age?

5. *Criminal Justice: Parole* USA Today reports that about 25% of all prison parolees become repeat offenders. Alice is a social worker whose job it is to counsel people on parole. Let us say success means a person does not become a repeat offender. Alice has been given a group of four parolees.

(a) Find the probability $P(r)$ for r successes ranging from 0 to 4.

(b) Make a histogram for the probability distribution of part (a).

(c) What is the expected number of parolees in Alice's group who will not be repeat offenders? What is the standard deviation?

6. *Focus Problem: Personality Types* We now have the tools to solve the Chapter Focus Problem. In the book *A Guide to the Development and Use of the Myers-Briggs Type Indicators* by Myers and McCaully, it was reported that approximately 45% of all university professors are extroverted. Suppose you have classes with six different professors.

(a) What is the probability that all six are extroverts?

(b) What is the probability that none of your professors is an extrovert?

(c) What is the probability that at least two of your professors are extroverts?

(d) In a group of six professors selected at random, what is the *expected number* of extroverts? What is the *standard deviation* of the distribution?

7. *Criminal Justice: Jury Duty* Have you ever tried to get out of jury duty? About 25% of those called will find an excuse (work, poor health, travel out of town, etc.) to avoid jury duty (Source: Bernice Kanner, *Are You Normal?* St. Martin's Press, New York). If 12 people are called for jury duty,

(a) What is the probability that all 12 will be available to serve on the jury?

(b) What is the probability that 6 or more will *not* be available to serve on the jury?

(c) Find the expected number of those available to serve on the jury. What is the standard deviation?

8. *Law Enforcement: Property Crime* Does crime pay? The *FBI Standard Survey of Crimes* showed that for about 80% of all property crimes (burglary, larceny, car theft, etc.), the criminals are never found and the case is never solved (Source: *True Odds,* by James Walsh, Merrit Publishing). Suppose that a neighborhood district in a large city has repeated property crimes, not always by the same criminals. The police are investigating six property crime cases in this district.

(a) What is the probability that none of the crimes will ever be solved?

(b) What is the probability that at least one crime will be solved?

(c) What is the expected number of crimes that will be solved? What is the standard deviation?

9. *Criminal Justice: Convictions* Innocent until proven guilty? In Japanese criminal trials, about 95% of the defendants are found guilty. In the United States, about 60% of the defendants are found guilty in criminal trials (Source: *The Book of Risks,* by Larry Laudan, John Wiley and Sons). Suppose you are a news reporter following seven criminal trials.

(a) If the trials were in Japan, what is the probability that all the defendants would be found guilty? What is this probability if the trials were in the United States?

(b) Of the seven trials, what is the expected number of guilty verdicts in Japan? What is the expected number in the United States? What is the standard deviation in each case?

10. *General: Probability Formula* Let r be a binomial random variable representing the number of successes out of n trials.
    (a) Explain why the sample space for r consists of the set $\{0, 1, 2, \ldots, n\}$ and why the sum of the probabilities of all the entries in the entire sample space must be 1.
    (b) Explain why $P(r \geq 1) = 1 - P(0)$.
    (c) Explain why $P(r \geq 2) = 1 - P(0) - P(1)$.
    (d) Explain why $P(r \geq m) = 1 - P(0) - P(1) - \ldots - P(m - 1)$ for $1 \leq m \leq n$.

SUMMARY

The concepts of discrete and continuous random variables were introduced in this chapter. We looked at the general probability distribution for a discrete random variable and saw how to compute the expected value μ and the standard deviation σ of a discrete probability distribution.

Then we turned our attention to a special discrete probability distribution, the binomial probability distribution. This distribution is used to determine the probabilities of outcomes of a binomial experiment.

A binomial experiment must meet the following criteria:

1. There are a fixed number of trials, denoted by n.

2. The trials are independent and repeated under identical conditions.

3. Each trial has only two outcomes: success S or failure F.

4. For each trial the probability p of success remains the same. The probability of failure is $q = 1 - p$.

5. The central problem is to find the probability of r successes out of n trials.

   The formula for the binomial probability distribution is

   $$P(r) = C_{n,r} p^r q^{n-r}$$

   where $C_{n,r}$ is the binomial coefficient. For certain values of p and n, $P(r)$ can be found directly in Table 2 of the Appendix.

   The mean or expected value and standard deviation of the binomial distribution are given by the formulas

   $$\mu = np$$
   $$\sigma = \sqrt{npq} \qquad \text{where } q = 1 - p$$

IMPORTANT WORDS & SYMBOLS

Section 6.1
Random variable
  Discrete
  Continuous

Mean μ of a probability distribution
Standard deviation σ of a probability distribution
Expected value μ

Section 6.2
Binomial experiment
Independent trials
Successes and failures in a binomial experiment
Probability of success $P(S) = p$
Probability of failure $P(F) = q = 1 - p$

Binomial coefficient $C_{n,r}$
Binomial probability distribution $P(r) = C_{n,r}p^r q^{n-r}$

Section 6.3
Mean for the binomial distribution $\mu = np$
Standard deviation for the binomial distribution $\sigma = \sqrt{npq}$

 What's Your Type?

Are students and professors *really* compatible? One way of answering this question is to look at Myers-Briggs Type Indicators for personality preferences. What is the probability that your professor is introverted and judgmental? What is the probability that you are extroverted and perceptive? Are most of the leaders in student government extroverted and judgmental? Is it true that members of Phi Beta Kappa have personality types more like the professors'? We will consider questions such as these in more detail in Chapter 8 (estimation) and Chapter 9 (hypothesis testing), where we will continue our work with binomial probabilities. In the meantime, you can find many answers regarding careers, probability, and personality types in *Applications of the Myers-Briggs Type Indicator in Higher Education,* edited by J. Provost and S. Anchors.

CHAPTER REVIEW PROBLEMS

1. *Probability Distribution: Auto Leases* Consumer Banker Association released a report showing the lengths of automobile leases for new automobiles. The results are

Lease Length in Months	Percent of Leases
13–24	12.7%
25–36	37.1%
37–48	28.5%
49–60	21.5%
More than 60	0.2%

(a) Use the midpoint of each class, and call the midpoint of the last class 66.5 months, for purposes of computing the expected lease term. Also find the standard deviation of the distribution.

(b) Sketch a graph of the probability distribution for the duration of new auto leases.

2. *Ecology: Predator and Prey* Isle Royale, an island in Lake Superior, has provided an important study site of wolves and their prey. In the National Park Service Scientific Monograph Series 11, *Wolf Ecology and Prey Relationships on Isle Royale,* Peterson gives results of many wolf–moose studies. Of special interest is the study

of the number of moose killed by wolves. In the period from 1958 to 1974, there were 296 moose deaths identified as wolf kills. The age distribution of the kills is

Age of Moose in Years	Number Killed by Wolves
Calf (0.5 yr)	112
1–5	53
6–10	73
11–15	56
16–20	2

(a) For each age group, compute the probability that a moose in that age group is killed by a wolf.
(b) Consider all ages in a class equal to the class midpoint. Find the expected age of a moose killed by a wolf and the standard deviation of the ages.

3. *Insurance: Auto* State Farm Insurance studies show that in Colorado, 55% of the auto insurance claims submitted for property damage were submitted by males under 25 years of age. Suppose 10 property damage claims involving automobiles are selected at random.
(a) Let r be the number of claims that are made by males under age 25. Make a histogram for the r-distribution probabilities.
(b) What is the probability that six or more claims are made by males under age 25?
(c) What is the expected number of claims made by males under age 25? What is the standard deviation of the r-probability distribution?

4. *Quality Control: Pens* A stationery store has decided to accept a large shipment of ball-point pens if an inspection of 20 randomly selected pens yields no more than two defective pens.
(a) Find the probability that this shipment is accepted if 5% of the total shipment is defective.
(b) Find the probability that this shipment is not accepted if 15% of the total shipment is defective.

5. *Criminal Justice: Inmates* According to *Harper's Index*, 50% of all federal inmates are serving time for drug dealing. A random sample of 16 federal inmates is selected.
(a) What is the probability that 12 or more are serving time for drug dealing?
(b) What is the probability that 7 or fewer are serving time for drug dealing?
(c) What is the expected number of inmates serving time for drug dealing?

6. *Airlines: On-Time Arrivals* *Consumer Reports* rated airlines and found that 80% of the flights involved in the study arrived on time (that is, within 15 minutes of scheduled arrival time). Assuming that the on-time arrival rate is representative of the entire commercial airline industry, consider a random sample of 200 flights. What is the expected number that will arrive on time? What is the standard deviation of this distribution?

7. *Agriculture: Grapefruit* It is estimated that 75% of a grapefruit crop is good; the other 25% have rotten centers that cannot be detected unless the grapefruit are cut open. The grapefruit are sold in sacks of 10. Let r be the number of good grapefruit in a sack.
(a) Make a histogram of the probability distribution of r.
(b) What is the probability of getting no more than one bad grapefruit in a sack? What is the probability of getting at least one good grapefruit in a sack?

(c) What is the expected number of good grapefruit in a sack?

(d) What is the standard deviation of the r probability distribution?

8. *Restaurants: Reservations* The Orchard Café has found that about 5% of the diners who make reservations don't show up. If 82 reservations have been made, how many diners can be expected to show up? Find the standard deviation of this distribution.

9. *College Life: Student Government* The student government claims that 85% of all students favor an increase in student fees to buy indoor potted plants for the classrooms. A random sample of 12 students produced 2 in favor of the project. What is the probability that 2 or fewer in the sample will favor the project, assuming that the student government is correct? Do the data support the student government claim, or does it seem that the percentage favoring the increase in fees is less than 85%?

DATA HIGHLIGHTS: GROUP PROJECTS

Break into small groups and discuss the following topics. Organize a brief outline in which you summarize the main points of your group discussion.

1. Powerball! Imagine, you could win a jackpot worth at least $10 million. Some jackpots have been more than $250 million! Powerball is a multistate lottery. To play Powerball, you purchase a $1 ticket. On the ticket you select five distinct white balls (numbered 1 through 53) and then one red Powerball (numbered 1 through 42). The red Powerball number may be any of the numbers 1 through 42, including any of the numbers you selected for the white balls. Every Wednesday and Saturday there is a drawing. If your chosen numbers match those drawn, you win! Figure 6-6 on the next page shows all the prizes and the probability of winning each prize and specifies how many numbers on your ticket must match those drawn to win the prize. The Multi-State Lottery Association maintains a web site that displays the results of each drawing, as well as a history of the results of previous drawings. To find the most current Powerball rules, prizes, and probabilities of winning, visit the Brase/Brase statistics site at **http://math.college.hmco.com/students** and find the link to the Multi-State Lottery Association.

(a) Assume that the jackpot is $10 million and that there will be only one jackpot winner. Figure 6-6 lists the prizes and the probability of winning each prize. What is the probability of *not winning* any prize? Consider all the prizes and their respective probabilities along with the prize of $0 (no win) and its probability. Use all these values to estimate your expected winnings μ if you play one ticket. How much do you effectively contribute to the state in which you purchased the ticket (ignoring the overhead cost of operating Powerball)?

(b) Suppose that the jackpot increased to $25 million (and that there was to be only one winner). Compute your expected winnings if you buy one ticket. Does the probability of winning the jackpot change because the jackpot is higher?

(c) Pretend that you are going to buy 10 Powerball tickets when the jackpot is $10 million. Use the random-number table to select your numbers. Check the Multi-State Lottery Association web site (or any other Powerball site) for the most recent drawing results to see if you would have won a prize.

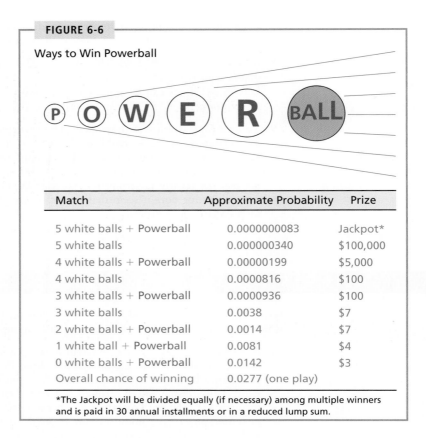

FIGURE 6-6

Ways to Win Powerball

Match	Approximate Probability	Prize
5 white balls + Powerball	0.0000000083	Jackpot*
5 white balls	0.000000340	$100,000
4 white balls + Powerball	0.00000199	$5,000
4 white balls	0.0000816	$100
3 white balls + Powerball	0.0000936	$100
3 white balls	0.0038	$7
2 white balls + Powerball	0.0014	$7
1 white ball + Powerball	0.0081	$4
0 white balls + Powerball	0.0142	$3
Overall chance of winning	0.0277 (one play)	

*The Jackpot will be divided equally (if necessary) among multiple winners and is paid in 30 annual installments or in a reduced lump sum.

(d) The probability of winning any prize is about 0.0277. Suppose that you decide to buy five tickets. Use the binomial distribution to compute the probability of winning (any prize) at least once. *Note:* You will need to use the binomial formula. Carry at least three digits after the decimal.

2. Would you like to travel in space, if given a chance? According to Opinion Research for Space Day Partners, if your answer is yes, you are not alone. Forty-four percent of adults surveyed agreed that they would travel in space if given a chance. Look at Figure 6-7 on the next page, and use the information presented to answer the following questions.

(a) According to Figure 6-7, the probability that an adult selected at random will agree with the statement that humanity should explore planets is 64%. Round this probability to 65%, and use this estimate with the binomial distribution table to determine the probability that of 10 adults selected at random, at least half will agree that humanity should explore planets.

(b) Does space exploration have an impact on daily life? Find the probability that of 10 adults selected at random, at least 9 will agree that space exploration does have an impact on daily life. *Hint:* Use the formula for the binomial distribution.

(c) In a room of 35 adults, what is the expected number who would travel in space, given a chance? What is the standard deviation?

FIGURE 6-7

The Final Frontier: Want to Go?
Percentage of adults who agree with these
statements about the USA's space program

Youth should want to be astronauts.

77%

Humanity should explore planets.

64%

Space exploration impacts daily life.

57%

Given a chance I'd travel in space.

44%

Space will be colonized in my lifetime.

18%

Source: Opinion Research for Space Day Partners

LINKING CONCEPTS: WRITING PROJECTS

Discuss each of the following topics in class or review the topics on your own. Then write a brief but complete essay in which you summarize the main points. Please include formulas and graphs as appropriate.

1. Discuss what we mean by a binomial experiment. As you can see, a binomial process or binomial experiment involves a lot of assumptions! For example, all the trials are supposed to be independent and repeated under identical conditions. Is this always true? Can we always be completely certain that the probability of success does not change from one trial to the next? In the real world there is almost nothing we can be absolutely sure about, so the *theoretical* assumptions of the binomial probability distribution often will not be completely satisfied. Does that mean we cannot use the binomial distribution to solve practical problems? Looking at this chapter, the answer seems to be that we can indeed use the binomial distribution even if not all the assumptions are *exactly* met. We find in practice that the conclusions are sufficiently accurate for our intended application. List three applications of the binomial distribution for which you think, although some of the assumptions are not exactly met, there is adequate reason to apply the binomial distribution anyhow.

2. Why do we need to learn the formula for the binomial probability distribution? Using the formula repeatedly can be very tedious. To cut down on tedious calculations, most people will use a binomial table such as the one found in the Appendix of this book.
   (a) However, there are many applications for which a table in the back of *any* book is not adequate. For instance, compute

   $$P(r = 3) \quad \text{where } n = 5 \text{ and } p = 0.735$$

   Can you find the result in the table? Do the calculation by using the formula. List some other situations in which a table might not be adequate to solve a particular binomial distribution problem.

(b) The formula itself also has limitations. For instance, consider the difficulty of computing

$$P(r \geq 285) \quad \text{where } n = 500 \text{ and } p = 0.6$$

What are some of the difficulties you run into? Consider the calculation of $P(r = 285)$. You will be raising 0.6 and 0.4 to very high powers; this will give you very, very small numbers. Then you need to compute $C_{500,285}$, which is a very, very large number. When combining extremely large and extremely small numbers in the same calculation, most accuracy is lost unless you carry a huge number of significant digits. If this isn't tedious enough, consider the steps you need to compute

$$P(r \geq 285) = P(r = 285) + P(r = 286) + \cdots + P(r = 500)$$

Does it seem clear that we need a better way to estimate $P(r \geq 285)$? In Chapter 7, you will find a much better way to estimate binomial probabilities when the number of trials is large.

3. In Chapter 3, we learned about means and standard deviations. In Section 6.1, we learned that probability distributions also can have a mean and standard deviation. Discuss what is meant by the expected value and standard deviation of a binomial distribution. How does this relate back to the material we learned in Chapter 3 and Section 6.1?

4. In Chapter 2, we looked at the shapes of distributions. Review the concepts of skewness and symmetry; then categorize the following distributions as to skewness or symmetry:
   (a) A binomial distribution with $n = 11$ trials and $p = 0.50$
   (b) A binomial distribution with $n = 11$ trials and $p = 0.10$
   (c) A binomial distribution with $n = 11$ trials and $p = 0.90$

In general, does it seem true that binomial probability distributions in which the probability of success is close to 0 are skewed right, whereas those with probability of success close to 1 are skewed left?

Using Technology

Binomial Distributions

Although tables of binomial probabilities can be found in most libraries, such tables are often inadequate. Either the value of p (the probability of success on a trial) you are looking for is not in the table, or the value of n (the number of trials) you are looking for is too large for the table. In Chapter 7, we will study the normal approximation to the binomial. This approximation is a great help in many practical applications. Even so, we sometimes use the formula for the binomial probability distribution on a computer or graphing calculator to compute the probability we want.

APPLICATIONS

The following percentages were obtained over many years of observation by the U.S. Weather Bureau. All data listed are for the month of December.

Location	Long-Term Mean % of Clear Days in Dec.
Juneau, Alaska	18%
Seattle, Washington	24%
Hilo, Hawaii	36%
Honolulu, Hawaii	60%
Las Vegas, Nevada	75%
Phoenix, Arizona	77%

Adapted from *Local Climatological Data*, U.S. Weather Bureau publication, "Normals, Means, and Extremes" Table.

In the locations listed, the month of December is a relatively stable month with respect to weather. Since weather patterns from one day to the next are more or less the same, it is reasonable to use a binomial probability model.

1. Let r be the number of clear days in December. Since December has 31 days, $0 \le r \le 31$. Using appropriate computer software or calculators available to you, find the probability $P(r)$ for each of the listed locations when $r = 0, 1, 2, \ldots, 31$.

2. For each location, what is the expected value of the probability distribution? What is the standard deviation?

3. Estimate the probability that Juneau will have at most 7 clear days in December.

4. Estimate the probability that Seattle will have from 5 to 10 (including 5 and 10) clear days in December.

5. Estimate the probability that Hilo will have at least 12 clear days in December.

Technology Hints

TI-84Plus/TI-83Plus, Excel, Minitab

The Tech Note in Section 6.2 gives specific instructions for binomial distribution functions on the TI-84Plus and TI-83Plus calculators, Excel, and Minitab.

SPSS

In SPSS, the function **PDF.BINOM(q,n,p)** gives the probability of q successes out of n trials, where p is the probability of success on a single trial. In the data editor, name a variable r and enter values 0 through n. Name another variable Prob_r. Then use the menu choices **Transform ➤ Compute**. In the dialogue box, use Prob_r for the target variable. In the function box, select **PDF.BINOM(q,n,p)**. Use the variable r for q and appropriate values for n and p. Note that the function **CDF.BINOM(q,n,p)** gives the cumulative probability of 0 through q successes.

Cumulative Review Problems

CHAPTERS 4–6

The Hill of Tara is located in south central Meath, not far from Dublin, Ireland. Tara is of great cultural and archaeological importance, since it is by legend the seat of the ancient high kings of Ireland. For more information, see *Tara: An Archaeological Survey,* by Conor Newman, Royal Irish Academy, Dublin.

Magnetic surveying is one technique used by archaeologists to determine anomalies arising from variations in magnetic susceptibility. Unusual changes in magnetic susceptibility might (or might not) indicate an important archaeological discovery. Let x be a random variable that represents a magnetic susceptibility (MS) reading for a randomly chosen site on the Hill of Tara. A random sample of 120 sites gave the readings shown in Table A below.

Table A   Magnetic Susceptibility Readings, centimeter-gram-second $\times 10^{-6}$ (cmg $\times 10^{-6}$)

Comment	Magnetic Susceptibility	Number of Readings	Estimated Probability
"cool"	$0 \le x < 10$	30	$30/120 = 0.25$
"neutral"	$10 \le x < 20$	54	$54/120 = 0.45$
"warm"	$20 \le x < 30$	18	$18/120 = 0.15$
"very interesting"	$30 \le x < 40$	12	$12/120 = 0.10$
"hot spot"	$40 \le x$	6	$6/120 = 0.05$

1. *Sample Space* What is a statistical experiment? How could the magnetic susceptibility intervals $0 \le x < 10$, $10 \le x < 20$, and so on be considered events in the sample space of all possible readings?

2. *Estimated Probability* What is probability? What do we mean by relative frequency as a probability estimate for events? What is the law of large numbers? How would the law of large numbers apply in this context?

3. *Probability Distribution* Do the probabilities shown in Table A add up to 1? Why should they total to 1?

4. *Probability Rules* For a site chosen at random, estimate the following probabilities.
   (a) $P(0 \le x < 30)$ (b) $P(10 \le x < 40)$ (c) $P(x < 20)$
   (d) $P(x \ge 20)$ (e) $P(30 \le x)$ (f) $P(x\ not$ less than 10)
   (g) $P(0 \le x < 10\ or\ 40 \le x)$ (h) $P(40 \le x\ and\ 20 \le x)$

5. *Discrete Probability Distribution* Consider the midpoint of each interval. Assign the value 45 as the midpoint of the interval $40 \le x$. The midpoints constitute the sample

space for a discrete random variable. Using Table A, compute the expected value μ and the standard deviation σ.

Midpoint x	5	15	25	35	45
$P(x)$					

6. *Binomial Distribution* Suppose a reading between 30 and 40 is called "very interesting" from an archaeological point of view. Let us say you take readings at $n = 12$ sites chosen at random. Let r be a binomial random variable that represents the number of "very interesting" readings from these 12 sites.
   (a) Let us call "very interesting" a binomial success. Use Table A to find p, the probability of success on a single trial, where $p = P(\text{success}) = P(30 \leq x < 40)$.
   (b) What is the expected value μ and standard deviation σ for the random variable r?
   (c) What is the probability that you will find *at least* one "very interesting" reading in the 12 sites?
   (d) What is the probability that you will find *fewer than* three "very interesting" readings in the 12 sites?

7. *Linear Regression: Blood Glucose* Let x be a random variable that represents blood glucose level after a 12-hour fast. Let y be a random variable representing blood glucose level 1 hour after drinking sugar water (after the 12-hour fast). Units are in mg/10 ml. A random sample of eight adults gave the following information (Reference: *American Journal of Clinical Nutrition*, vol. 19, pp. 345–351).

x	6.2	8.4	7.0	7.5	8.1	6.9	10.0	9.7
y	9.8	10.7	10.3	11.9	14.2	7.0	14.6	12.2

$\Sigma x = 63.8; \Sigma x^2 = 521.56; \Sigma y = 90.7; \Sigma y^2 = 1070.87; \Sigma xy = 739.65$

(a) Draw a scatter diagram for the data.
(b) Find the equation of the least-squares line and graph it on the scatter diagram.
(c) Find the sample correlation coefficient r and the sample coefficient of determination r^2. Explain the meaning of r^2 in the context of the application.
(d) If $x = 9.0$, use the least-squares line to predict y.

7

Normal Curves and Sampling Distributions

One cannot escape the feeling that these mathematical formulas have an independent existence and an intelligence of their own, that they are wiser than we are, wiser even than their discoverers, that we get more out of them than was originally put into them.

—Heinrich Hertz

How can it be that mathematics, a product of human thought independent of experience, is so admirably adapted to the objects of reality?

—Albert Einstein

**Heinrich Rudolf Hertz
(1857–1894)**

This German physicist was largely responsible for doing pioneering work in electromagnetic theory.

For on-line student resources, visit **math.college.hmco.com/students** and follow the Statistics links to the Brase/Brase, *Understanding Basic Statistics,* 4th edition web site.

Heinrich Hertz was a pioneer in the study of radio waves. His work and the later work of Maxwell and Marconi led the way to modern radio, television, and radar. Albert Einstein is world renowned for his great discoveries in relativity and quantum mechanics. Everyone who has worked in both mathematics and real-world applications cannot help but marvel at how the "pure thought" of the mathematical sciences can predict and explain events in other realms. In this chapter, we will study the most important type of probability distribution in all of mathematical statistics: the normal distribution. Why is the normal distribution so important? Two of the reasons are that it applies to a wide variety of situations and that other distributions tend to become normal under certain conditions.

PREVIEW QUESTIONS

◊ What are some characteristics of a normal distribution? What does the empirical rule tell you about data spread around the mean? (SECTION 7.1)

◊ Can you compare apples and oranges, or maybe elephants and butterflies? In most cases, the answer is no . . . unless you first *standardize* your measurements. What are a *standard normal distribution* and a *standard z score*? (SECTION 7.2)

◊ How do you convert *any* normal distribution to a *standard normal* distribution? How do you find probabilities of "standardized events"? (SECTION 7.3)

◇ As humans, our experiences are finite and limited. Consequently, most of the important decisions in our lives are based on sample (incomplete) information. What is a probability sampling distribution? How will sampling distributions help us make good decisions based on incomplete information? (SECTION 7.4)

◇ There is an old saying: All roads lead to Rome. In statistics, we could recast this saying: All probability distributions average out to be normal distributions (as the sample size increases). How can we take advantage of this in our study of sampling distributions? (SECTION 7.5)

◇ The binomial and normal distributions are two of the most important probability distributions in statistics. Under certain limiting conditions, the binomial can be thought to evolve (or envelope) into the normal distribution. How can you apply this in the real world? (SECTION 7.6)

FOCUS PROBLEM

Impulse Buying

The Food Marketing Institute, Progressive Grocer, New Products News, and Point of Purchaser Advertising Institute are organizations that analyze supermarket sales. One of the interesting discoveries was that the average amount of impulse buying in a grocery store was very time-dependent.

As reported in the *Denver Post*, "when you dilly dally in a store for 10 unplanned minutes, you can kiss nearly $20 goodbye." For this reason, it is in the best interest of the supermarket to keep you in the store longer. In the *Post* article, it was pointed out that long checkout lines (near end-aisle displays), "samplefest" events of tasting free samples, video kiosks, magazine and book sections, and so on help keep customers in the store longer. On average, a single customer who strays from his or her grocery list can plan on impulse spending of $20 for every 10 minutes spent wandering about in the supermarket.

Let x represent the dollar amount spent on supermarket impulse buying in a 10-minute (unplanned) shopping interval. Based on the *Post* article, the mean of the x distribution is about $20 and the (estimated) standard deviation is about $7.

(a) Let us assume that x has a distribution that is approximately normal. What is the probability that x is between $18 and $22?

(b) Consider a random sample of $n = 100$ customers, each of whom has 10 minutes of unplanned shopping time in a supermarket. From the central limit theorem, what can you say about the probability distribution of $\bar{x}$, the *average* amount spent by these customers due to impulse buying? Is the $\bar{x}$ distribution approximately normal? What are the mean and standard deviation of the $\bar{x}$ distribution? Is it necessary to make any assumption about the x distribution? Explain.

(c) What is the probability that $\bar{x}$ is between $18 and $22?

(d) In part (c), we used $\bar{x}$, the *average* amount spent, computed for 100 customers. In part (a), we used x, the amount spent by only *one* individual customer. The answers for parts (c) and (a) are very different. Why would this happen? In this example, $\bar{x}$ is a much more predictable or reliable statistic than x. Consider that almost all marketing strategies and sales pitches are designed for the *average* customer and *not* the *individual* customer. How does the central limit theorem tell us that the average customer is much more predictable than the individual customer? (See Problem 12 of Section 7.5.)

7.1
Graphs of Normal Probability Distributions

FOCUS POINTS

✓ Graph a normal curve and summarize its important properties.

✓ Apply the empirical rule to solve real-world problems.

One of the most important examples of a continuous probability distribution is the *normal distribution*. This distribution was studied by the French mathematician Abraham de Moivre (1667–1754) and later by the German mathematician Carl Friedrich Gauss (1777–1855), whose work is so important that the normal distribution is sometimes called *Gaussian*. The work of these mathematicians provided a foundation on which much of the theory of statistical inference is based.

Applications of a normal probability distribution are so numerous that some mathematicians refer to it as "a veritable Boy Scout knife of statistics." However, before we can apply it, we must examine some of the properties of a normal distribution.

A rather complicated formula, presented later in this section, defines a normal distribution in terms of μ and σ, the mean and standard deviation of the population

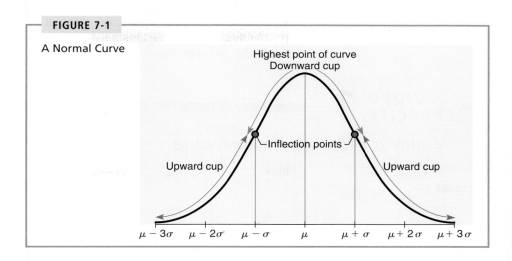

FIGURE 7-1

A Normal Curve

distribution. It is only through this formula that we can verify if a distribution is normal. However, we can look at the graph of a normal distribution and get a good pictorial idea of some of the essential features of any normal distribution.

Normal curve

The graph of a normal distribution is called a *normal curve*. It possesses a shape very much like the cross section of a pile of dry sand. Because of its shape, blacksmiths would sometimes use a pile of dry sand in the construction of a mold for a bell. Thus the normal curve is also called a *bell-shaped curve* (see Figure 7-1).

We see that a general normal curve is smooth and symmetrical about the vertical line extending upward from the mean μ. Notice that the highest point of the curve occurs over μ. If the distribution were graphed on a piece of sheet metal, cut out, and placed on a knife edge, the balance point would be at μ. We also see that the curve tends to level out and approach the horizontal (x axis) like a glider making a landing. However, in mathematical theory, such a glider would never quite finish its landing because a normal curve never touches the horizontal axis.

The parameter σ controls the spread of the curve. The curve is quite close to the horizontal axis at $\mu + 3\sigma$ and $\mu - 3\sigma$. Thus, if the standard deviation σ is large, the curve will be more spread out; if it is small, the curve will be more peaked. Figure 7-1 shows the normal curve cupped downward for an interval on either side of the mean μ. Then it begins to cup upward as we go to the lower part of the bell. The exact places where the *transition* between the upward and downward cupping occurs are above the points $\mu + \sigma$ and $\mu - \sigma$. In the terminology of calculus, transition points such as these are called *inflection points*.

Important properties of a normal curve

1. The curve is bell-shaped with the highest point over the mean μ.

2. The curve is symmetrical about a vertical line through μ.

3. The curve approaches the horizontal axis but never touches or crosses it.

4. The inflection (transition) points between cupping upward and downward occur above $\mu + \sigma$ and $\mu - \sigma$.

The parameters that control the shape of a normal curve are the mean μ and the standard deviation σ. When both μ and σ are specified, a specific normal curve is determined. In brief, μ locates the balance point, and σ determines the extent of the spread.

GUIDED EXERCISE 1

Identify μ and σ on a normal curve

Look at the normal curves in Figure 7-2.

FIGURE 7-2

(a) Do these distributions have the same mean? If so, what is it?

➡ The means are the same, since both graphs have the high point over 6. $\mu = 6$.

(b) One of the curves corresponds to a normal distribution with $\sigma = 3$ and the other to one with $\sigma = 1$. Which curve has which σ?

➡ Curve A has $\sigma = 1$, and curve B has $\sigma = 3$. (Since curve B is more spread out, it has the larger σ value.)

◇ **COMMENT** The normal distribution curve is always above the horizontal axis. The area beneath the curve and above the axis is exactly one. As such, the normal distribution curve is an example of a *density curve*. The formula used to generate the shape of the normal distribution curve is called the *normal density function*. If x is a normal random variable with mean μ and standard deviation σ, the formula for the normal density function is

$$f(x) = \frac{e^{(-1/2)((x-\mu)/\sigma)^2}}{\sigma\sqrt{2\pi}}$$

In this text, we will not use this formula explicitly. However, we will use tables of areas based on the normal density function. ◇

The total area under any normal curve studied in this book will *always* be 1. The graph of the normal distribution is important because the portion of the *area* under the curve above a given interval represents the *probability* that a measurement will lie in that interval.

In Section 3.2, we studied Chebyshev's theorem. This theorem gives us information about the *smallest* proportion of data that lies within 2, 3, or k standard deviations of the mean. This result applies to *any* distribution. However, for normal distributions, we can get a much more precise result, which is given by the *empirical rule*.

Empirical rule

Empirical rule

For a distribution that is symmetrical and bell-shaped (in particular, for a normal distribution):

Approximately 68% of the data values will lie within one standard deviation on each side of the mean.

Approximately 95% of the data values will lie within two standard deviations on each side of the mean.

Approximately 99.7% (or almost all) of the data values will lie within three standard deviations on each side of the mean.

The preceding statement is called the *empirical rule* because, for symmetrical, bell-shaped distributions, the given percentages are observed in practice. Furthermore, for the normal distribution, the empirical rule is a direct consequence of the very nature of the distribution (see Figure 7-3). Notice that the empirical rule is a stronger statement than Chebyshev's theorem in that it gives *definite percentages*, not just lower limits. Of course, the empirical rule applies only to normal or symmetrical, bell-shaped distributions, whereas Chebyshev's theorem applies to all distributions.

EXAMPLE 1

Empirical rule

The playing life of a Sunshine radio is normally distributed with mean $\mu = 600$ hours and standard deviation $\sigma = 100$ hours. What is the probability that a radio selected at random will last from 600 to 700 hours?

SOLUTION: The probability that the playing time will be between 600 and 700 hours is equal to the percentage of the total area under the curve that is shaded in Figure 7-4. Since $\mu = 600$ and $\mu + \sigma = 600 + 100 = 700$, we see that the shaded area is simply the area between μ and $\mu + \sigma$. The area from μ to $\mu + \sigma$ is 34% of the total area. This tells us that the probability a Sunshine radio will last between 600 and 700 playing hours is about 0.34.   ◇

FIGURE 7-3

Area Under a Normal Curve

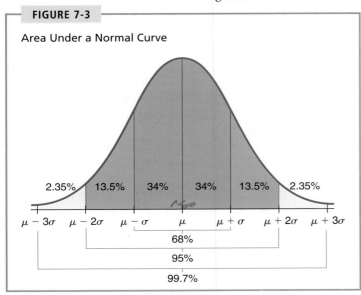

FIGURE 7-4

Distribution of Playing Times

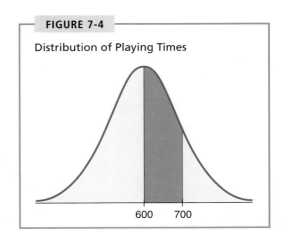

GUIDED EXERCISE 2

Empirical rule

The yearly wheat yield per acre on a particular farm is normally distributed with mean $\mu = 35$ bushels and standard deviation $\sigma = 8$ bushels.

(a) Shade the area under the curve in Figure 7-5 that represents the probability that an acre will yield between 19 and 35 bushels.

⟹ See Figure 7-6.

(b) Is the area the same as the area between $\mu - 2\sigma$ and μ?

⟹ Yes, since $\mu = 35$ and $\mu - 2\sigma = 35 - 2(8) = 19$.

FIGURE 7-5

FIGURE 7-6 Completion of Figure 7-5

(c) Use Figure 7-3 to find the percentage of area over the interval between 19 and 35.

⟹ The area between the values $\mu - 2\sigma$ and μ is 47.5% of the total area.

(d) What is the probability that the yield will be between 19 and 35 bushels per acre?

⟹ The area is 47.5% of the total area, which is 1. Therefore, the probability is 0.475 that the yield will be between 19 and 35 bushels.

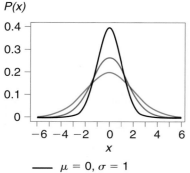

TECH NOTE We can graph normal distributions using the TI-84Plus and TI-83Plus calculators, Excel, and Minitab. In each technology, set the range of x values to between -3.5σ and 3.5σ. Then use the built-in normal density functions to generate the corresponding y values.

TI-84Plus/TI-83Plus Press the **Y=** key. Then, under **DISTR**, select **1:normalpdf** (x,μ,σ) and fill in the desired μ and σ values. Press the **WINDOW** key. Set **Xmin** to $\mu - 3\sigma$ and **Xmax** to $\mu + 3\sigma$. Finally, press the **ZOOM** key and select option **0:ZoomFit.**

Excel In one column, enter x values from -3.5σ to 3.5σ in increments of 0.2σ. In the next column, enter y values by using the menu choices **Paste function** $\boxed{f_x}$ ➤ **Statistical** ➤ **NORMDIST**$(x, \mu, \sigma,$ false). Next, use the chart wizard, and select **XY(scatter).** Choose the first picture with the dots connected and fill in the dialogue boxes.

Minitab In one column, enter x values from -3.5σ to 3.5σ in increments of 0.2σ. In the next column, enter y values by using the menu choices **Calc ➤ Probability Distribution ➤ Normal.** Fill in the dialogue box. Next, use the menu choices **Graph ➤ Plot.** Fill in the dialogue box. Under **Display,** select **Connect.**

VIEWPOINT   *Nenana Ice Classic*

The Nenana Ice Classic is a betting pool offering a large cash prize to the lucky winner who can guess the time, to the nearest minute, of the ice breakup on the Tanana River in the town of Nenana, Alaska. Official breakup time is defined as the time when the surging river dislodges a tripod on the ice. This breaks an attached line and stops a clock set to Yukon Standard Time. The event is so popular that the first state legislature of Alaska (1959) made the Nenana Ice Classic an official statewide lottery. Since 1918, the earliest breakup was April 20, 1940, at 3:27 P.M., and the latest recorded breakup was May 20, 1964, at 11:41 A.M. Want to make a statistical guess predicting when the ice will break up? Breakup times from 1918 to 1996 are recorded in *The Alaska Almanac*, published by Alaska Northwest Books, Anchorage.

SECTION 7.1   PROBLEMS

1. *General: Curves* Which, if any, of the curves in Figure 7-7 below look(s) like a normal curve? If a curve is not a normal curve, tell why.

2. *General: Normal Curves* Look at the normal curve in Figure 7-8 below, and find μ, $\mu + \sigma$, and σ.

FIGURE 7-7

(a)

(b)

(c)

(d)

FIGURE 7-8

16   18   20   22

3. *General: Normal Curves* Look at the two normal curves in Figures 7-9 and 7-10. Which has the larger standard deviation? What is the mean of the curve in Figure 7-9? What is the mean of the curve in Figure 7-10?

FIGURE 7-10

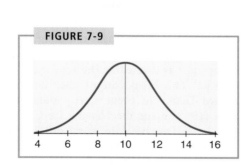

FIGURE 7-9

4. *General: Normal Curves* Sketch a normal curve
   (a) with mean 15 and standard deviation 2.
   (b) with mean 15 and standard deviation 3.
   (c) with mean 12 and standard deviation 2.
   (d) with mean 12 and standard deviation 3.
   (e) Consider two normal curves. If the first one has a larger mean than the second one, must it have a larger standard deviation as well? Explain your answer.

5. *General: Normal Curves* What percentage of the area under the normal curve lies
   (a) to the left of μ?
   (b) between $\mu - \sigma$ and $\mu + \sigma$?
   (c) between $\mu - 3\sigma$ and $\mu + 3\sigma$?

6. *General: Normal Curves* What percentage of the area under the normal curve lies
   (a) to the right of μ?
   (b) between $\mu - 2\sigma$ and $\mu + 2\sigma$?
   (c) to the right of $\mu + 3\sigma$?

7. *Distribution: Heights of Coeds* Assuming that the heights of college women are normally distributed, with mean 65 in. and standard deviation 2.5 in. (based on information from *Statistical Abstract of the United States*, 112th Edition), answer the following questions. (*Hint:* Use Problems 5 and 6 and Figure 7-3.)
   (a) What percentage of women are taller than 65 in.?
   (b) What percentage of women are shorter than 65 in.?
   (c) What percentage of women are between 62.5 in. and 67.5 in.?
   (d) What percentage of women are between 60 in. and 70 in.?

8. *Distribution: Rhode Island Red Chickens* The incubation time for Rhode Island Red chicks is normally distributed with a mean of 21 days and standard deviation of approximately 1 day (based on information from *World Book Encyclopedia*). Look at Figure 7-3 and answer the following questions. If 1000 eggs are being incubated, how many chicks do we expect will hatch
   (a) in 19 to 23 days?
   (b) in 20 to 22 days?
   (c) in 21 days or fewer?
   (d) in 18 to 24 days? (Assume all eggs eventually hatch.)
   (*Note:* In this problem, let us agree to think of a single day or a succession of days as a continuous interval of time.)

9. *Archaeology: Tree Rings* At Burnt Mesa Pueblo, archaeological studies have used the method of tree-ring dating in an effort to determine when prehistoric people lived in the pueblo. Wood from several excavations gave a mean of (year) 1243 with a standard deviation of 36 years (*Bandelier Archaeological Excavation Project: Summer 1989 Excavations at Burnt Mesa Pueblo*, edited by Kohler, Washington State University Department of Anthropology). The distribution of dates was more or less mound-shaped and symmetrical about the mean. Use the empirical rule to
   (a) estimate a range of years centered about the mean in which about 68% of the data (tree-ring dates) will be found.
   (b) estimate a range of years centered about the mean in which about 95% of the data (tree-ring dates) will be found.
   (c) estimate a range of years centered about the mean in which almost all the data (tree-ring dates) will be found.

10. *Vending Machine: Soft Drinks* A vending machine automatically pours soft drinks into cups. The amount of soft drink dispensed into a cup is normally distributed with a mean of 7.6 oz and standard deviation of 0.4 oz. Examine Figure 7-3 and answer the following questions.
   (a) Estimate the probability that the machine will overflow an 8-oz cup.
   (b) Estimate the probability that the machine will not overflow an 8-oz cup.
   (c) The machine has just been loaded with 850 cups. How many of these do you expect will overflow when served?

11. *Pain Management: Laser Therapy* "Effect of Helium-Neon Laser Auriculotherapy on Experimental Pain Threshold" is the title of an article in the journal *Physical Therapy* (Vol. 70, No. 1, pp. 24–30). In this article, laser therapy was discussed as a useful alternative to drugs in pain management of chronically ill patients. To measure pain threshold, a machine was used that delivered low-voltage direct current to different parts of the body (wrist, neck, and back). The machine measured current in milliamperes (mA). The pretreatment experimental group in the study had an average threshold of pain (pain was first detectable) at $\mu = 3.15$ mA with standard deviation $\sigma = 1.45$ mA. Assume that the distribution of threshold pain so measured in milliamperes is symmetrical and more or less mound-shaped. Use the empirical rule to
   (a) estimate a range of milliamperes centered about the mean in which about 68% of the experimental group will have a threshold of pain.
   (b) estimate a range of milliamperes centered about the mean in which about 95% of the experimental group will have a threshold of pain.

7.2   Standard Units and Areas Under the Standard Normal Distribution

FOCUS POINTS

✓ Given μ and σ, convert raw data to z scores.

✓ Given μ and σ, convert z scores to raw data.

✓ Graph the standard normal distribution, and find areas under the standard normal curve.

z Scores and Raw Scores

Normal distributions vary from one another in two ways: The mean μ may be located anywhere on the x axis, and the bell shape may be more or less spread according to the size of the standard deviation σ. The differences among the normal distributions cause difficulties when we try to compute the area under the curve in a specified interval of x values and, hence, the probability that a measurement will fall into that interval.

It would be a futile task to try to set up a table of areas under the normal curve for each different μ and σ combination. We need a way to standardize the distributions so that we can use *one* table of areas for *all* normal distributions. We achieve this standardization by considering how many standard deviations a measurement lies from the mean. In this way, we can compare a value in one normal distribution with a value in another, different normal distribution. The next situation shows how this is done.

Suppose Tina and Jack are in two different sections of the same course. Each section is quite large, and the scores on the midterm exams of each section follow a normal distribution. In Tina's section, the average (mean) was 64 and her score was 74. In Jack's section, the mean was 72 and his score was 82. Both Tina and Jack were pleased that their scores were each 10 points above the average of each respective section. However, the fact that each person's score was 10 points above average does not really tell us how each person did *with respect to the other students in the section*. In Figure 7-11, we see the normal distribution of grades for each section.

Tina's 74 was higher than most of the other scores in her section, while Jack's 82 is only an upper-middle score in his section. Tina's score is far better with respect to her class than Jack's score with respect to his class.

Standard score

The preceding situation demonstrates that it is not sufficient to know the difference between a measurement (x value) and the mean of a distribution. We need also to consider the spread of the curve, or the standard deviation. What we really want to know is the number of standard deviations between a measurement and the mean. This "distance" takes both μ and σ into account.

FIGURE 7-11

Distributions of Midterm Scores

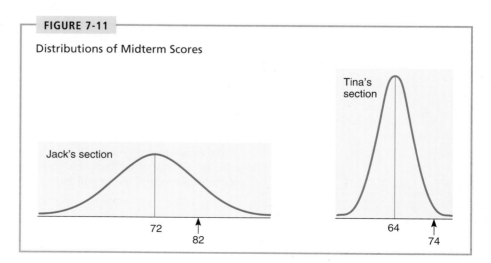

We can use a simple formula to compute the number z of standard deviations between a measurement x and the mean μ of a normal distribution with standard deviation σ:

$$\left(\begin{array}{c} \text{Number of standard deviations} \\ \text{between the measurement and} \\ \text{the mean} \end{array} \right) = \left(\frac{\text{Difference between the}}{\text{measurement and the mean}} \middle/ \text{Standard deviation} \right)$$

z score

The **z value** or **z score** gives the number of standard deviations between the original measurement x and the mean μ of the x distribution.

$$z = \frac{x - \mu}{\sigma}$$

The mean is a special value of a distribution. Let's see what happens when we convert $x = \mu$ to a z value:

$$z = \frac{x - \mu}{\sigma} = \frac{\mu - \mu}{\sigma} = 0$$

The mean of the original distribution is always zero, in standard units. This makes sense because the mean is zero standard deviations from itself.

An x value in the original distribution that is *above* the mean μ has a corresponding z value that is *positive*. Again, this makes sense because a measurement above the mean would be a positive number of standard deviations from the mean. Likewise, an x value *below* the mean has a *negative z value*. (See Table 7-1.)

TABLE 7-1
x Values and Corresponding z Values

x Value in Original Distribution	Corresponding z Value or Standard Unit
$x = \mu$	$z = 0$
$x > \mu$	$z > 0$
$x < \mu$	$z < 0$

Note

Unless otherwise stated, in the remainder of the book we will take the word *average* to be either the sample arithmetic mean $\bar{x}$ or the population mean μ.

EXAMPLE 2

Standard score

A pizza parlor franchise specifies that the average (mean) amount of cheese on a large pizza should be 8 oz and the standard deviation only 0.5 oz. An inspector picks out a large pizza at random in one of the pizza parlors and finds that it is made with 6.9 oz of cheese. Assume that the amount of cheese on a pizza follows a normal distribution. If the amount of cheese is below the mean by more than *three* standard deviations, the parlor will be in danger of losing its franchise. (Remember, in a normal distribution we are unlikely to find measurements more than three standard deviations from the mean, since 99.7% of all measurements fall within three standard deviations of the mean.)

How many standard deviations from the mean is 6.9? Is the pizza parlor in danger of losing its franchise?

SOLUTION: Since we want to know the number of standard deviations from the mean, we want to convert 6.9 to standard z units.

$$z = \frac{x - \mu}{\sigma} = \frac{6.9 - 8}{0.5} = -2.20$$

Therefore, the amount of cheese on the selected pizza is only 2.20 standard deviations below the mean. Note that the fact that z is negative indicates that the amount of cheese was 2.20 standard deviations *below* the mean. The parlor will not lose its franchise based on this sample.   ◇

GUIDED EXERCISE 3

Standard score

A student has computed that it takes an average (mean) of 17 minutes with a standard deviation of 3 minutes to drive from home, park the car, and walk to an early morning class.

(a) One day it took the student 21 minutes to get to class. How many standard deviations from the average is that? Is the z value positive or negative? Explain why it should be either positive or negative.

The number of standard deviations from the mean is given by the z value:

$$z = \frac{x - \mu}{\sigma} = \frac{21 - 17}{3} \approx 1.33$$

The z value is positive. We should expect a positive z value, since 21 minutes is *more* than the mean of 17.

(b) Another day it took only 12 minutes for the student to get to class. What is this measurement in standard units? Is the z value positive or negative? Why should it be positive or negative?

The measurement in standard units is

$$z = \frac{x - \mu}{\sigma} = \frac{12 - 17}{3} \approx -1.67$$

Here the z value is negative, as we should expect, because 12 minutes is less than the mean of 17 minutes.

(c) Another day it took 17 minutes for the student to go from home to class. What is the z value? Why should you expect this answer?

In this case, the z value is

$$z = \frac{x - \mu}{\sigma} = \frac{17 - 17}{3} = 0.00$$

We expect this result because 17 minutes is the mean, and the z value of the mean is always zero.

Raw score

We have seen how to convert from x measurements to standard units z. We can easily reverse the process to find the original *raw score* x if we know the mean and standard deviation of the original x distribution. Simply solve the z score formula for x.

Given an x distribution with mean μ and standard deviation σ, the **raw score** x corresponding to a z score is

$$x = z\sigma + \mu$$

EXAMPLE 3

Raw score

In Example 2, we talked about the amount of cheese required by a franchise for a large pizza. Again, the mean amount of cheese required is 8 oz with a standard deviation of 0.5 oz. The franchise specifies that the minimum amount of cheese for a large pizza is three standard deviations below the mean. A pizza parlor can lose its franchise if the amount of cheese on a large pizza is less than the specified minimum. What is the minimum amount of cheese that can be placed on a large pizza according to the franchise?

SOLUTION: Here we need to convert $z = -3$ to information about x oz of cheese. We use the formula

$$x = z\sigma + \mu = -3(0.5) + 8 = 6.5 \text{ oz}$$

The franchise will not approve a large pizza with less than 6.5 oz of cheese.   ◇

In many testing situations, we hear the terms *raw score* and *z score*. The raw score is just the score in the original measuring units, and the *z* score is the score in standard units. Guided Exercise 4 illustrates these different units.

GUIDED EXERCISE 4

Raw score

Marulla's *z* score on a college entrance exam is 1.3. If the raw scores have a mean of 480 and a standard deviation of 70 points, what is her raw score?

    Here we are given *z*, σ, and μ. We need to find the raw score *x* corresponding to the *z* score 1.3.

$$x = z\sigma + \mu$$
$$= 1.3(70) + 480$$
$$= 571$$

Standard Normal Distribution

If the original distribution of *x values is normal*, then the corresponding *z values have a normal distribution as well*. The *z* distribution has a mean of 0 and a standard deviation of 1. The normal curve with these properties has a special name.

The **standard normal distribution** is a normal distribution with mean $\mu = 0$ and standard deviation $\sigma = 1$ (Figure 7-12 on the next page).

Any normal distribution of *x* values can be converted to the standard normal distribution by converting all *x* values to their corresponding *z* values. Let's look at the graphic interpretation of this transformation in Figure 7-13 on the next page.

The resulting standard distribution will always have mean $\mu = 0$ and standard deviation $\sigma = 1$.

Areas Under the Standard Normal Curve

We have seen how to convert *any* normal distribution to the *standard* normal distribution. We can change any *x* value to a *z* value and back again. But what is the

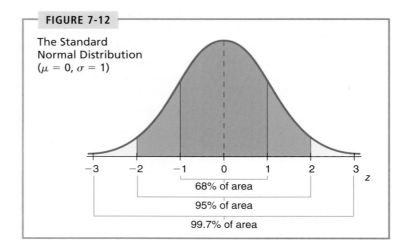

FIGURE 7-12

The Standard
Normal Distribution
($\mu = 0$, $\sigma = 1$)

68% of area

95% of area

99.7% of area

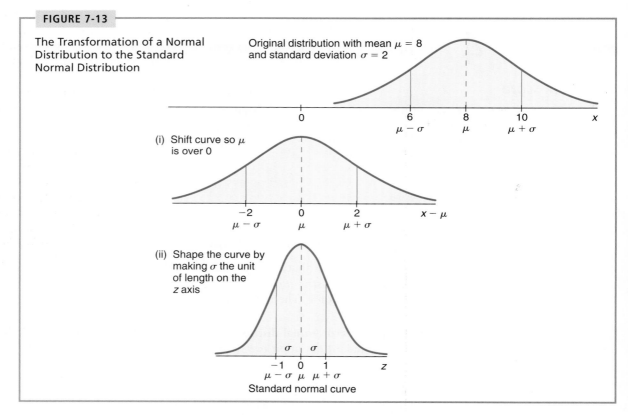

FIGURE 7-13

The Transformation of a Normal
Distribution to the Standard
Normal Distribution

Original distribution with mean $\mu = 8$
and standard deviation $\sigma = 2$

(i) Shift curve so μ
is over 0

(ii) Shape the curve by
making σ the unit
of length on the
z axis

Standard normal curve

advantage of all this work? The advantage is that there are extensive tables that show the *area under the standard normal curve* for almost any interval along the z axis. The areas are important because each area is equal to the *probability* that the measurement of an item selected at random falls in this interval. Thus, the *standard* normal distribution can be a tremendously helpful tool.

For instance, Sunshine Stereo guarantees their cassette decks for a period of 2 years. The company statistician has computed that the cassette deck life is normally distributed with a mean of 2.3 years and a standard deviation 0.4 year. What is the probability that a cassette deck will stop working during the guarantee period?

To answer questions of this type, we convert the given normal distribution to the standard normal distribution. Then we use a table, computer, or calculator to find the area over the interval in question and, hence, the probability that an item selected at random will fall into that interval. Before we can carry out this plan, though, let's practice using Table 3 of the Appendix to find areas under the standard normal curve.

Using a Standard Normal Distribution Table

Using a table to find areas and probabilities associated with the standard normal distribution is a fairly straightforward activity. However, it is important to first observe the range of *z* values for which areas are given. This range is usually depicted in a picture that accompanies the table.

Left-tail style table

In this text, *we will use the left-tail style table*. This style table gives cumulative areas to the left of a specified *z*. Determining other areas under the curve utilizes the fact that the area under the entire curve is 1. Taking advantage of the symmetry of the normal distribution is also useful. The procedures you learn for using the left-tail style normal distribution table apply directly to cumulative normal distribution areas found on calculators and in computer software packages such as Excel and Minitab.

EXAMPLE 4

Standard normal distribution table

Use Table 3 of the Appendix to find the described areas under the standard normal curve.

(a) Find the area under the standard normal curve to the left of $z = -1.00$.

SOLUTION: First, shade the area to be found on the standard normal distribution curve, as shown in Figure 7-14 on the next page. Notice that the *z* value we are using is negative. This means that we will look at the portion of Table 3 of the Appendix in which the *z* values are negative. In the upper-left corner of the table we see the letter *z*. The column under *z* gives us the units value and tenths for *z*. The other column headings indicate the hundredths value of *z*. Table entries give areas under the standard normal curve to the left of the listed *z* values. To find the area to the left of $z = -1.00$, we use the row headed by -1.0 and then move to the column headed by the hundredths position .00. This entry is shaded in Table 7-2. We see that the area is 0.1587.

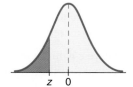

TABLE 7-2   Excerpt from Table 3 of the Appendix Showing Negative z Values

z	.00	.01	...	.07	.08	.09
−3.4	.0003	.0003	...	.0003	.0003	.0002
⋮						
−1.1	.1357	.1335	...	.1210	.1190	.1170
−1.0	.1587	.1562	...	.1423	.1401	.1379
−0.9	.1841	.1814	...	.1660	.1635	.1611
⋮						
−0.0	.5000	.4960	...	.4721	.4681	.4641

(b) Find the area to the left of $z = 1.18$, illustrated in Figure 7-15 on the next page.

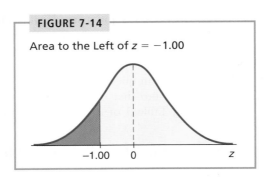

FIGURE 7-14

Area to the Left of $z = -1.00$

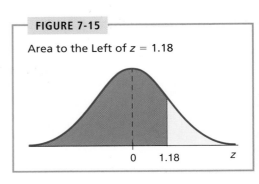

FIGURE 7-15

Area to the Left of $z = 1.18$

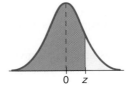

TABLE 7-3   Excerpt from Table 3 of the Appendix Showing Positive z Values

z	.00	.01	.02	...	.08	.09
0.0	.5000	.5040	.5080	...	.5319	.5359
:						
0.9	.8159	.8186	.8212	...	.8365	.8359
1.0	.8413	.8438	.8461	...	.8599	.8621
1.1	.8643	.8665	.8686	...	.8810	.8830
:						
3.4	.9997	.9997	.9997	...	.9997	.9998

SOLUTION: In this case, we are looking for an area to the left of a positive z value, so we look in the portion of Table 3 that shows positive z values. Again we first sketch the area to be found on a standard normal curve, as shown in Figure 7-15. Look in the row headed by 1.1 and move to the column headed by .08. The desired area is shaded (see Table 7-3). We see that the area to the left of 1.18 is 0.8810. ◇

GUIDED EXERCISE 5

Using the standard normal distribution table

Table 3, Areas of a Standard Normal Distribution, is located in the Appendix as well as in the endpapers of the text. Spend a little time studying the table, and then answer these questions.

(a) As z values increase, do the areas to the left of z increase?

⟹ Yes; as z values increase, we move to the right on the normal curve, and the areas increase.

(b) If a z value is negative, is the area to the left of z less than 0.5000?

⟹ Yes. Remember that a negative z value is on the left side of the standard normal distribution. The entire left half of the normal distribution has area 0.5, so any area to the left of $z = 0$ will be less than 0.5.

(c) If a z value is positive, is the area to the left of z greater than 0.5000?

⟹ Yes. Positive z values are on the right side of the standard normal distribution, and any area to the left of a positive z value includes the entire left half of the normal distribution.

Using Table 3 to find other areas

Table 3 gives areas under the standard normal distribution that are to the *left of a z value*. How do we find other areas under the standard normal curve?

PROCEDURE

How to use a left-tail style standard normal distribution table

1. For areas to the left of a specified z value, use the table entry directly.

2. For areas to the right of a specified z value, look up the table entry for z and subtract the area from 1.
   Note: Another way to find the same area is to use the symmetry of the normal curve and look up the table entry for $-z$.

3. For areas between two z values z_1 and z_2 (where $z_2 > z_1$), *subtract* the table area for z_1 from the table area for z_2.

Figure 7-16 illustrates the procedure for using Table 3, Areas of a Standard Normal Distribution, to find any specified area under the standard normal distribution. Again, it is useful to sketch the area in question before you use Table 3.

◇ **COMMENT:** Notice that the z values shown in Table 3 of the Appendix are formatted to the hundredths position. It is convenient to *round or format z values to the hundredths position* before using the table. The areas are all given to four places after the decimal, so give your answers to four places after the decimal. ◇

FIGURE 7-16

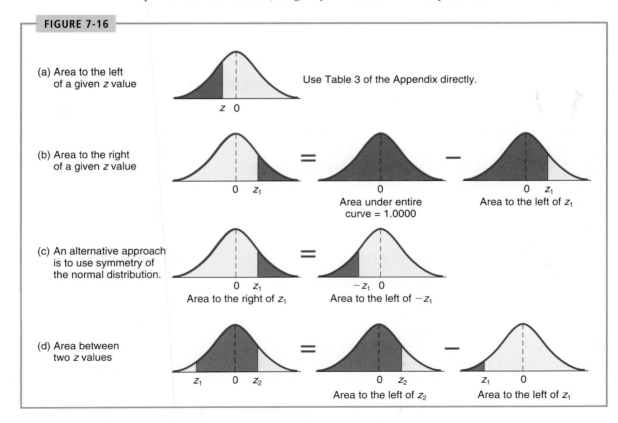

(a) Area to the left of a given z value — Use Table 3 of the Appendix directly.

(b) Area to the right of a given z value — Area under entire curve = 1.0000 ; Area to the left of z_1

(c) An alternative approach is to use symmetry of the normal distribution. — Area to the right of z_1 ; Area to the left of $-z_1$

(d) Area between two z values — Area to the left of z_2 ; Area to the left of z_1

◇ **COMMENT:** The smallest z value shown in Table 3 is -3.49, while the largest value is 3.49. These values are, respectively, far to the left and far to the right on the standard normal distribution, with very little area beyond either value. We will follow the common convention of treating any area to the left of a z value smaller than -3.49 as 0.000. Similarly, we will consider any area to the right of a z value greater than 3.49 as 0.000. We understand that there is some area in these extreme tails. However, these areas are each less than 0.0002. Now let's get real about this! Some very specialized applications, beyond the scope of this book, do need to measure areas and corresponding probabilities in these extreme tails. But in most practical applications, *we follow the convention of treating the areas in the extreme tails as zero.* ◇

Convention for using Table 3 of the Appendix

1. Treat any area to the left of a z value smaller than -3.49 as 0.000.

2. Treat any area to the left of a z value greater than 3.49 as 1.000.

EXAMPLE 5

Using table to find areas

Use Table 3 of the Appendix to find the specified areas.

(a) Find the area between $z = 1.00$ and $z = 2.70$.

SOLUTION: First, sketch a diagram showing the area (see Figure 7-17). Because we are finding the area between two z values, we subtract corresponding table entries.

(Area between 1.00 and 2.70) = (Area left of 2.70) − (Area left of 1.00)
$$= 0.9965 - 0.8413 = 0.1552$$

(b) Find the area to the right of $z = 0.94$.

SOLUTION: First, sketch the area to be found (see Figure 7-18).

(Area to right of 0.94) = (Area under entire curve) − (Area to left of 0.94)
$$= 1.000 - 0.8264 = 0.1736$$

Alternatively,

(Area to right of 0.94) = (Area to left of −0.94)
$$= 0.1736$$

◇

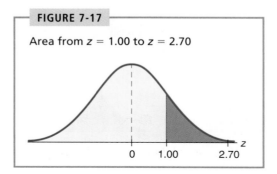

FIGURE 7-17

Area from $z = 1.00$ to $z = 2.70$

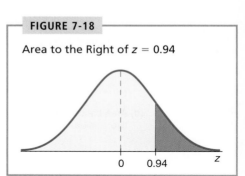

FIGURE 7-18

Area to the Right of $z = 0.94$

Probabilities associated with the standard normal distribution

We have practiced the skill of finding areas under the standard normal curve for various intervals along the z axis. This skill is important because *the probability* that z lies in an interval *is given by the area* under the standard normal curve above that interval.

Because the normal distribution is continuous, there is no area under the curve exactly over a specific z. Therefore, probabilities such as $P(z \geq z_1)$ are the same as $P(z > z_1)$. When dealing with probabilities or areas under a normal curve that are specified with inequalities, *strict inequality* symbols can be used *interchangeably* with *inequality-or-equal* symbols.

GUIDED EXERCISE 6

Probabilities associated with the standard normal distribution

Let z be a random variable with a standard normal distribution.

(a) $P(z \geq 1.15)$ refers to the probability that z values lie to the right of 1.15. Shade the corresponding area under the standard normal curve and find $P(z \geq 1.15)$.

 FIGURE 7-19 Area to Be Found

$P(z \geq 1.15) = 1.000 - P(z \leq 1.15) = 1.000 - 0.8749 = 0.1251$

Alternatively,

$P(z \geq 1.15) = P(z \leq -1.15) = 0.1251$

(b) Find $P(-1.78 \leq z \leq 0.35)$. First, sketch the area under the standard normal curve corresponding to the area.

 FIGURE 7-20 Area to Be Found

$P(-1.78 \leq z \leq 0.35) = P(z \leq 0.35) - P(z \leq -1.78)$
$= 0.6368 - 0.0375 = 0.5993$

 TECH NOTE The TI-84Plus and TI-83Plus calculators, Excel, and Minitab all provide cumulative areas under any normal distribution, including the standard normal. The Tech Note of Section 7.3 shows examples.

VIEWPOINT   *Mighty Oaks from Little Acorns Grow!*

Just how big is that acorn? What if we compare it with other acorns? Is that oak tree taller than an average oak tree? How does it compare with other oak trees? What do you mean, this oak tree has a larger geographic range? Compared with what? Answers to questions such as these can be given only if we resort to *standardized statistical units*. Can you compare a single oak tree with an entire forest of oak trees? The answer is yes, if you use *standardized z scores*. For more information about sizes of acorns, oak trees, and geographic locations, visit the Brase/Brase statistics site at **http://math.college.hmco.com/students** and find the link to DASL, the Carnegie Mellon University Data and Story Library. From the DASL site, find Biology under Data Subjects, and select Acorns. Follow the links to Data Subjects, Biology, and Acorns.

SECTION 7.2   PROBLEMS

In these problems, assume that all the distributions are *normal*. In all problems in Chapter 7, *average* is always taken to be the arithmetic mean $\bar{x}$ or μ.

1. *z Scores: First Aid Course* A college Physical Education Department offered an Advanced First Aid course last semester. The scores on the comprehensive final exam were normally distributed, and the z scores for some of the students are shown below:

Robert, 1.10	Juan, 1.70	Susan, −2.00
Joel, 0.00	Jan, −0.80	Linda, 1.60

   (a) Which of these students scored above the mean?
   (b) Which of these students scored on the mean?
   (c) Which of these students scored below the mean?
   (d) If the mean score was $\mu = 150$ with standard deviation $\sigma = 20$, what was the final exam score for each student?

2. *z Scores: Teaching Duties* What do professors do with their time? They do research, teach classes, serve on academic committees, serve the student body (advise students, sponsor student clubs, attend student events), serve the community (consult, address civic groups), and a lot more! The specific answer depends on the individual professor and his or her special interests. Well, how much time does a professor spend on teaching activities? *The NEA Almanac of Higher Education,* published by the National Education Association, reports that the mean percentage of time professors spend on teaching activities is about $\mu = 51\%$ with standard deviation $\sigma = 25\%$. Find the standardized z values corresponding to the following professors' percentages of time allocated to teaching duties.
   (a) Dr. Taylor, 45%   (b) Mr. Patterson, 72%   (c) Dr. Lee, 75%
   (d) Ms Simms, 65%   (e) Dr. Adams, 33%   (f) Dr. Riley, 55%

3. *z Scores: Honolulu Temperatures* Data collected over a period of years show that the average daily temperature in Honolulu is $\mu = 73°F$ with standard deviation

$\sigma = 5°F$ (U.S. Department of Commerce, Environmental Data Service). Convert each of the following intervals in °F to an interval of z values.
(a) $53°F < x < 93°F$ (b) $x < 65°F$ (c) $78°F < x$

Convert the following intervals of z values to intervals in °F.
(d) $1.75 < z$ (e) $z < -1.90$ (f) $-1.80 < z < 1.65$

4. *z Scores: Fawns* Fawns between 1 and 5 months old in Mesa Verde National Park have a body weight that is approximately normally distributed with mean $\mu = 27.2$ kilograms and standard deviation $\sigma = 4.3$ kilograms (based on information from *The Mule Deer of Mesa Verde National Park*, by G. W. Mierau and J. L. Schmidt, Mesa Verde Museum Association). Let x be the weight of a fawn in kilograms. Convert each of the following x intervals to z intervals.
(a) $x < 30$ (b) $19 < x$ (c) $32 < x < 35$

Convert each of the following z intervals to x intervals.
(d) $-2.17 < z$ (e) $z < 1.28$ (f) $-1.99 < z < 1.44$
(g) If a fawn weighs 14 kilograms, would you say it is an unusually small animal? Explain using z values and Figure 7-12.
(h) If a fawn is unusually large, would you say that the z value for the weight of the fawn will be close to 0, -2, or 3? Explain.

5. *z Scores: Deer Population* The fall deer population in Mesa Verde National Park is approximately normally distributed with mean 4400 deer and standard deviation 620 deer (see reference in Problem 4). Let x be a random variable that represents the size of the deer population in Mesa Verde National Park in the fall of a given year. Convert each of the following x intervals to z intervals.
(a) $3300 < x$ (b) $x < 5400$ (c) $3500 < x < 5300$

Convert each of the following z intervals to x intervals.
(d) $-1.12 < z < 2.43$ (e) $z < 1.96$ (f) $2.58 < z$
(g) If the fall deer population were 2800 deer, would that be considered an unusually low number? If the fall population were 6300, would that be considered an unusually high population? Explain using z values and Figure 7-12.

6. *z Scores: White Blood Cell Count* Let x = white blood cell (WBC) count per cubic millimeter of whole blood. Then x has a distribution that is approximately normal with mean $\mu = 7500$ and standard deviation $\sigma = 1750$ (based on information from *Diagnostic Tests with Nursing Implications*, edited by S. Loeb, Springhouse Press). Convert each of the following x intervals to z intervals.
(a) $9000 < x$ (b) $x < 6000$ (c) $3500 < x < 4500$

Convert each of the following z intervals to x intervals.
(d) $z < 1.15$ (e) $2.19 < z$ (f) $0.25 < z < 1.25$
(g) If someone had a WBC count of 2500, would that be considered unusually high or low? Explain using z values and Figure 7-12.

7. *z Scores: Red Blood Cell Count* Let x = red blood cell (RBC) count in millions per cubic millimeter of whole blood. For healthy females x has an approximately normal distribution with mean $\mu = 4.8$ and standard deviation $\sigma = 0.3$. (See reference in Problem 6.) Convert each of the following x intervals from laboratory tests to z intervals.
(a) $4.5 < x$ (b) $x < 4.2$ (c) $4.0 < x < 5.5$

Convert each of the following z intervals to x intervals.
(d) $z < -1.44$ (e) $1.28 < z$ (f) $-2.25 < z < -1.00$
(g) If a female had an RBC count of 5.9 or higher, would that be considered unusually high? Explain using z values and Figure 7-12.

8. *Normal Curve: Tree Rings* Tree-ring dates were used extensively in archaeological studies at Burnt Mesa Pueblo (*Bandelier Archaeological Excavation Project: Summer 1989 Excavations at Burnt Mesa Pueblo*, edited by Kohler, Washington State University Department of Anthropology). At one site on the mesa, tree-ring dates (for many samples) gave a mean date of $\mu_1 =$ year 1272 with standard deviation $\sigma_1 = 35$ years. At a second, removed site, the tree-ring dates gave a mean of $\mu_2 =$ year 1122 with standard deviation $\sigma_2 = 40$ years. Assume that both sites had dates that were approximately normally distributed. In the first area, an object was found and dated as $x_1 =$ year 1250. In the second area, another object was found and dated as $x_2 =$ year 1234.
   (a) Convert both x_1 and x_2 to z values, and locate both these values under the standard normal curve of Figure 7-12.
   (b) Which of these two items is the more unusual as an archaeological find in its location?

In Problems 9–28, sketch the areas under the standard normal curve over the indicated intervals, and find the specified areas.

9. To the right of $z = 0$.

10. To the left of $z = 0$.

11. To the left of $z = -1.32$.

12. To the left of $z = -0.47$.

13. To the left of $z = 0.45$.

14. To the left of $z = 0.72$.

15. To the right of $z = 1.52$.

16. To the right of $z = 0.15$.

17. To the right of $z = -1.22$.

18. To the right of $z = -2.17$.

19. Between $z = 0$ and $z = 3.18$.

20. Between $z = 0$ and $z = 2.92$.

21. Between $z = -2.01$ and $z = 0$.

22. Between $z = 0$ and $z = -1.93$.

23. Between $z = -2.18$ and $z = 1.34$.

24. Between $z = -1.40$ and $z = 2.03$.

25. Between $z = 0.32$ and $z = 1.92$.

26. Between $z = 1.42$ and $z = 2.17$.

27. Between $z = -2.42$ and $z = -1.77$.

28. Between $z = -1.98$ and $z = -0.03$.

In Problems 29–48, let z be a random variable with a standard normal distribution. Find the indicated probability, and shade the corresponding area under the standard normal curve.

29. $P(z \le 0)$.

30. $P(z \ge 0)$.

31. $P(z \le -0.13)$.

32. $P(z \le -2.15)$.

33. $P(z \le 1.20)$.

34. $P(z \le 3.20)$.

35. $P(z \ge 1.35)$.

36. $P(z \ge 2.17)$.

37. $P(z \ge -1.20)$.

38. $P(z \ge -1.50)$.

39. $P(-1.20 \le z \le 2.64)$.

40. $P(-2.20 \le z \le 1.04)$.

41. $P(-2.18 \le z \le -0.42)$.

42. $P(-1.78 \le z \le -1.23)$.

43. $P(0 \le z \le 1.62)$.

44. $P(0 \le z \le 0.54)$.

45. $P(-0.82 \le z \le 0)$.

46. $P(-2.37 \le z \le 0)$.

47. $P(-0.45 \le z \le 2.73)$.

48. $P(-0.73 \le z \le 3.12)$.

7.3
Areas Under Any Normal Curve

Normal Distribution Areas

In many applied situations, the original normal curve is not the standard normal curve. Generally, there will not be a table of areas available for the original normal curve. This does not mean that we cannot find the probability that a measurement x will fall into an interval from a to b. What we must do is *convert* the original measurements x, a, and b to z values.

PROCEDURE

How to work with normal distributions

To find areas and probabilities for a random variable x that follows a normal distribution with mean μ and standard deviation σ, convert x values to z values using the formula

$$z = \frac{x - \mu}{\sigma}$$

Then use Table 3 of the Appendix to find corresponding areas and probabilities.

EXAMPLE 6

Normal distribution probability

Let x have a normal distribution with $\mu = 10$ and $\sigma = 2$. Find the probability that an x value selected at random from this distribution is between 11 and 14. In symbols, find $P(11 \leq x \leq 14)$.

SOLUTION: Since probabilities correspond to areas under the distribution curve, we want to find the area under the x curve above the interval from $x = 11$ to $x = 14$. To do so, we will convert the x values to standard z values (see Figure 7-21) and then use Table 3 of the Appendix to find the corresponding area under the standard curve.

We use the formula

$$z = \frac{x - \mu}{\sigma}$$

to convert the given x interval to a z interval.

FIGURE 7-21

The Interval $11 \leq x \leq 14$ Corresponds to the Interval $0.50 \leq z \leq 2.00$

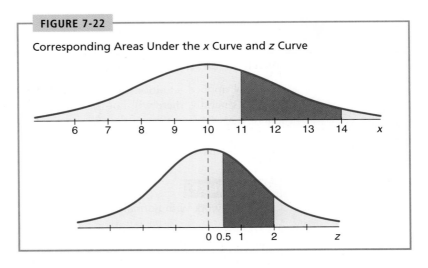

FIGURE 7-22

Corresponding Areas Under the x Curve and z Curve

$$z_1 = \frac{11 - 10}{2} = 0.50 \qquad \text{(Use } x = 11, \ \mu = 10, \ \sigma = 2.\text{)}$$

$$z_2 = \frac{14 - 10}{2} = 2.00 \qquad \text{(Use } x = 14, \ \mu = 10, \ \sigma = 2.\text{)}$$

The corresponding areas under the x and z curves are shown in Figure 7-22. From Figure 7-22 we see that

$$
\begin{aligned}
P(11 \le x \le 14) &= P(0.50 \le z \le 2.00) \\
&= P(z \le 2.00) - P(z \le 0.50) \\
&= 0.9772 - 0.6915 \qquad \text{(From Table 3 of the Appendix)} \\
&= 0.2857
\end{aligned}
$$

The probability is 0.2857 that an x value selected at random from a normal distribution with mean 10 and standard deviation 2 lies between 11 and 14. ◆

GUIDED EXERCISE 7

Normal distribution probability

In Section 7.2, we talked about Sunshine Stereo cassette decks. The cassette deck life was normally distributed with a mean of 2.3 years and a standard deviation of 0.4 year. We wanted to know the probability that a cassette deck will break down during the guarantee period of 2 years.

(a) Let x represent the life of a cassette deck. The statement that the cassette deck breaks during the 2-year guarantee period means the life is less than 2 years, or $x \le 2$. Convert this to a statement about z.

$$z = \frac{x - \mu}{\sigma} = \frac{2 - 2.3}{0.4} = -0.75$$

So $x \le 2$ means $z \le -0.75$.

Continued

GUIDED EXERCISE 7 continued

(b) Indicate the area to be found in Figure 7-23. Does this area correspond to the probability that $z \leq -0.75$?

 See Figure 7-24.
Yes, the shaded area does correspond to the probability that $z \leq -0.75$.

FIGURE 7-23

FIGURE 7-24 $z \leq -0.75$

(c) Use Table 3 of the Appendix to find $P(z \leq -0.75)$.

 0.2266

(d) What is the probability that the cassette deck will break before the end of the guarantee period? [*Hint:* $P(x \leq 2) = P(z \leq -0.75)$.]

 The probability is

$$P(x \leq 2) = P(z \leq -0.75)$$
$$= 0.2266$$

This means that the company will repair or replace about 23% of the cassette decks.

 TECH NOTE   The TI-84Plus and TI-83Plus calculators, Excel, and Minitab all provide areas under any normal distribution. Excel and Minitab give the left-tail area to the left of a specified x value. The TI-84Plus/TI-83Plus has you specify an interval from a lower bound to an upper bound and provides the area under the normal curve for that interval. For example, to solve Guided Exercise 7 regarding the probability that a cassette deck will break during the guarantee period, we find $P(x \leq 2)$ for a normal distribution with $\mu = 2.3$ and $\sigma = 0.4$.

TI-84Plus/TI-83Plus Press the **DISTR** key, select **2:normalcdf (lower bound, upper bound, μ, σ)** and press **Enter**. Type in the specified values. For a left-tail area, use a lower bound setting at about four standard deviations below the mean. Likewise, for a right-tail area, use an upper bound setting about four standard deviations above the mean. For our example, use a lower bound of $\mu - 4\sigma = 2.3 - 4(0.4) = 0.7$.

```
normalcdf(.7,2,2.3,
.4)
            .226955934
```

Excel Select **Paste Function** (fx) ➤ **Statistical** ➤ **NORMDIST.** Fill in the dialogue box, using True for cumulative.

=	=NORMDIST(2,2.3,0.4, TRUE)		
	C	D	E
0.226627			

Minitab Use the menu selection **Calc ➤ Probability Distribution ➤ Normal**. Fill in the dialogue box, marking cumulative.

```
Cumulative Distribution Function
Normal with mean = 2.3 and
standard deviation = 0.4
       x      P(X <= x)
      2.0        0.2266
```

Inverse Normal Distribution

Finding z or x, given a probability

Sometimes we need to find z or x values that correspond to a given area under the normal curve. This situation arises when we want to specify a guarantee period such that a given percentage of the total products produced by a company last at least as long as the duration of the guarantee period. In such cases, we use the standard normal distribution table "in reverse." When we look up an area and find the corresponding z value, we are using the *inverse normal probability distribution*.

EXAMPLE 7
Find x, given probability

Magic Video Games, Inc., sells an expensive video game console. Because the console is so expensive, the company wants to advertise an impressive guarantee for the life expectancy of its game console. The guarantee policy will refund the full purchase price if the console fails during the guarantee period. The research department has done tests which show that the mean life for the console is 30 months, with standard deviation of 4 months. The console life is normally distributed. How long can the guarantee period be if management does not want to refund the purchase price on more than 7% of the Magic Video Game Consoles?

SOLUTION: Let us look at the distribution of lifetimes for the computer game console, and shade the portion of the distribution in which the console lasts fewer months than the guarantee period. (See Figure 7-25.)

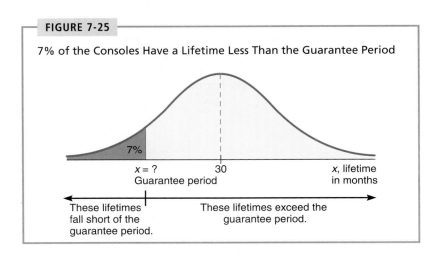

FIGURE 7-25

7% of the Consoles Have a Lifetime Less Than the Guarantee Period

TABLE 7-4   Excerpt from Table 3 of the Appendix

z	.00	...	.07		.08	.09
$\vdots$						
−1.4	.0808		.0708		.0694	.0681
				↑ 0.0700		

If a game console lasts fewer months than the guarantee period, a full-price refund will have to be made. The lifetimes requiring a refund are in the shaded region of Figure 7-25. This region represents 7% of the total area under the curve.

We can use Table 3 of the Appendix to find the z value such that 7% of the total area under the *standard* normal curve lies to the left of the z value. Then we convert the z value to its corresponding x value to find the guarantee period.

We want to find the z value with 7% of the area under the standard normal curve to the left of z. Since we are given the area in a left tail, we can use Table 3 of the Appendix directly to find z. The area value is 0.0700. However, this area is not in our table, so we use the closest area, which is 0.0694, and the corresponding z value of $z = -1.48$ (see Table 7-4).

To translate this value back to an x value (in months), we use the formula

$x = z\sigma + \mu$

$\quad = -1.48(4) + 30 \qquad$ (Use $\sigma = 4$ months and $\mu = 30$ months.)

$\quad = 24.08$ months

The company can guarantee the Magic Video Game Console for $x = 24$ months. For this guarantee period, it expects to refund the purchase price of no more than 7% of the consoles.   ◇

Example 7 had us find a z value corresponding to a given area to the left of z. What if the specified area is to the right of z or between $-z$ and z? Figure 7-26 on the next page shows us how to proceed.

◇ **COMMENT** When we use Table 3 of the Appendix to find a z value corresponding to a given area, we usually use the nearest area value rather than interpolating between values. However, when the area value given is exactly halfway between two area values of the table, we use the z value halfway between the z values of the corresponding table areas. Example 8 demonstrates this procedure. However, this interpolation convention is not always used, especially if the area is changing slowly, as it does in the tail ends of the distribution. *When the z value corresponding to an area is smaller than* -2*, the standard convention is to use the z value corresponding to the smaller area. Likewise, when the z value is larger than 2, the standard convention is to use the z value corresponding to the larger area.* We will see an example of this special case in Example 1 of Section 8.1. ◇

FIGURE 7-26

Inverse Normal: Use Table 3 of the Appendix to Find *z* Corresponding to a Given Area *A* (0 < *A* < 1)

(a) **Left-tail case:**
The given area *A* is to the left of *z*.

or

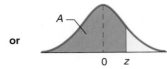

For the left-tail case, look up the number *A* in the body of the table and use the corresponding *z* value.

(b) **Right-tail case:**
The given area *A* is to the right of *z*.

or

For the right-tail case, look up the number 1 − *A* in the body of the table and use the corresponding *z* value.

(c) **Center case:**
The given area *A* is symmetric and centered above *z* = 0. Half of *A* lies to the left and half lies to the right of *z* = 0.

For the center case, look up the number $\dfrac{1 - A}{2}$ in the body of the table and use the corresponding ± *z* value.

EXAMPLE 8

Find z

Find the *z* value such that 90% of the area under the standard normal curve lies between −*z* and *z*.

SOLUTION: Sketch a picture showing the described area (see Figure 7-27).

We find the corresponding area in the left tail.

$$\text{(Area left of } -z) = \frac{1 - 0.9000}{2} = 0.0500$$

Looking at Table 7-5, we see that 0.0500 lies exactly between areas 0.0495 and 0.0505. The halfway value between *z* = −1.65 and *z* = −1.64 is *z* = −1.645. Therefore, we conclude that 90% of the area under the standard normal curve lies between the *z* values −1.645 and 1.645.

FIGURE 7-27

Area Between −*z* and *z* Is 90%

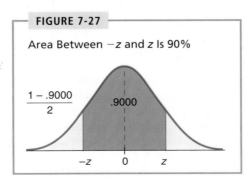

TABLE 7-5   Excerpt from Table 3 of the Appendix

z	...	.04	.05
:			
−1.6		.0505	.0495
		0.0500	

◇

GUIDED EXERCISE 8

Find z

Find the z value such that 3% of the area under the standard normal curve lies to the right of z.

(a) Draw a sketch of the standard normal distribution showing the described area.

FIGURE 7-28 3% of Total Area Lies to the Right of z

97%

3%

0   z

(b) Find the area to the left of z.

The area to the left of $z = 1 − 0.0300 = 0.9700$.

(c) Look up the area in Table 7-6 and find the corresponding z.

The closest area is 0.9699. This area is to the left of $z = 1.88$.

TABLE 7-6   Excerpt from Table 3 of the Appendix

z	.00	.01	.02	.03	.04	.05	.06	.07	.08	.09
1.8	.9641	.9649	.9656	.9664	.9671	.9678	.9686	.9693	.9699	.9706
1.9	.9713	.9719	.9726	.9732	.9738	.9744	.9750	.9756	.9761	.9767

(d) Suppose the time to complete a test is normally distributed with $\mu = 40$ minutes and $\sigma = 5$ minutes. After how many minutes can we expect all but about 3% of the tests to be completed?

We are looking for an x value such that 3% of the normal distribution lies to the right of x. In part (c), we found that 3% of the standard normal curve lies to the right of $z = 1.88$. We convert $z = 1.88$ to an x value.

$$x = z\sigma + \mu$$
$$= 1.88(5) + 40 = 49.4 \text{ minutes}$$

All but about 3% of the tests will be complete after approximately 50 minutes.

Continued

GUIDED EXERCISE 8 continued

(e) Use Table 7-7 to find a *z* value such that 3% of the area under the standard normal curve lies to the left of *z*.

  The closest area is 0.0301. This is the area to the left of $z = -1.88$.

TABLE 7-7   Excerpt from Table 3 of the Appendix

z	.00	.01	.02	.03	.04	.05	.06	.07	.08	.09
−1.9	.0287	.0281	.0274	.0268	.0262	.0256	.0250	.0244	.0239	.0233
−1.8	.0359	.0351	.0344	.0336	.0329	.0322	.0314	.0307	.0301	.0294

(f) Compare the *z* value of part (c) with the *z* value of part (e). Is there any relationship between the *z* values?

One *z* value is the negative of the other. This result is expected because of the symmetry of the normal distribution.

 TECH NOTE   When we are given a *z* value and we find an area to the left of *z*, we are using a normal distribution function. When we are given an area to the left of *z* and we find the corresponding *z*, we are using an inverse normal distribution function. The TI-84Plus and TI-83Plus calculators, Excel, and Minitab all have inverse normal distribution functions for any normal distribution. For instance, to find an *x* value from a normal distribution with mean 40 and standard deviation 5 such that 97% of the area lies to the left of *x*, use the described instructions.

TI-84Plus/TI-83Plus Press the **DISTR** key and select **3:invNorm(area,μ,σ)**.

```
invNorm(.97,40,5)
          49.40396805
```

Excel Select **Paste Function** (f_x) ➤ **Statistical** ➤ **NORMINV**. Fill in the dialogue box.

=	=NORMINV(0.97,40,5)	
	C	D
49.40395		

Minitab Use the menu selection **Calc** ➤ **Probability Distribution** ➤ **Normal**. Fill in the dialogue box, marking Inverse Cumulative.

```
Inverse Cumulative Distribution Function
Normal with mean = 40.000 and
  standard deviation = 5.00000
P(X <= x)          x
    0.9700      49.4040
```

VIEWPOINT   *Want to Be an Archaeologist?*

Each year about 4500 students work with professional archaeologists in scientific research at the Crow Canyon Archaeological Center, Cortez, Colorado. In fact, Crow Canyon was included in *The Princeton Review Guide to America's Top 100 Internships*. The nonprofit, multidisciplinary program at Crow Canyon enables students and laypeople with little or no background to get started in archaeological research. The only requirement is that you be interested in Native American culture and history. By the way, a knowledge of introductory statistics could come in handy in this internship. For more information about the program, visit the Brase/Brase statistics site at **http://math.college.hmco.com/students** and find the link to Crow Canyon.

SECTION 7.3   PROBLEMS

In Problems 1–10, assume that x has a normal distribution, with the specified mean and standard deviation. Find the indicated probabilities.

1. $P(3 \leq x \leq 6)$; $\mu = 4$; $\sigma = 2$

2. $P(10 \leq x \leq 26)$; $\mu = 15$; $\sigma = 4$

3. $P(50 \leq x \leq 70)$; $\mu = 40$; $\sigma = 15$

4. $P(7 \leq x \leq 9)$; $\mu = 5$; $\sigma = 1.2$

5. $P(8 \leq x \leq 12)$; $\mu = 15$; $\sigma = 3.2$

6. $P(40 \leq x \leq 47)$; $\mu = 50$; $\sigma = 15$

7. $P(x \geq 30)$; $\mu = 20$; $\sigma = 3.4$

8. $P(x \geq 120)$; $\mu = 100$; $\sigma = 15$

9. $P(x \geq 90)$; $\mu = 100$; $\sigma = 15$

10. $P(x \geq 2)$; $\mu = 3$; $\sigma = 0.25$

In Problems 11–20, find the z value described and sketch the area described.

11. Find z such that 6% of the standard normal curve lies to the left of z.

12. Find z such that 5.2% of the standard normal curve lies to the left of z.

13. Find z such that 55% of the standard normal curve lies to the left of z.

14. Find z such that 97.5% of the standard normal curve lies to the left of z.

15. Find z such that 8% of the standard normal curve lies to the right of z.

16. Find z such that 5% of the standard normal curve lies to the right of z.

17. Find z such that 82% of the standard normal curve lies to the right of z.

18. Find z such that 95% of the standard normal curve lies to the right of z.

19. Find the z value such that 98% of the standard normal curve lies between $-z$ and z.

20. Find the z value such that 95% of the standard normal curve lies between $-z$ and z.

21. *Medical: Blood Glucose* A person's level of blood glucose and diabetes are closely related. Let x be a random variable measured in milligrams of glucose per deciliter (1/10 of a liter) of blood. After a 12-hour fast, the random variable x will have a distribution that is approximately normal with mean $\mu = 85$ and standard deviation $\sigma = 25$ (*Diagnostic Tests with Nursing Implications*, edited by S. Loeb, Springhouse

Press). *Note:* After 50 years of age, both the mean and standard deviation tend to increase. What is the probability that, for an adult (under 50 years old) after a 12-hour fast,

(a) x is more than 60?
(b) x is less than 110?
(c) x is between 60 and 110?
(d) x is greater than 140 (borderline diabetes starts at 140)?

22. *Medical: Blood Protoplasm* Porphyrin is a pigment in blood protoplasm and other body fluids that is significant in body energy and storage. Let x be a random variable that represents the number of milligrams of porphyrin per deciliter of blood. In healthy adults, x is approximately normally distributed with mean $\mu = 38$ and standard deviation $\sigma = 12$ (see reference in Problem 21). What is the probability that

(a) x is less than 60?
(b) x is greater than 16?
(c) x is between 16 and 60?
(d) x is more than 60? (This may indicate an infection, anemia, or another type of illness.)

23. *Education: SAT and ACT Scores* For a given population of high school seniors, the Scholastic Aptitude Test (SAT) in mathematics has a mean score of 500 with a standard deviation of 100. Another widely used test is the American College Testing (ACT) exam. The mathematics portion of the ACT has a mean of 18 and a standard deviation of 6. (Visit the Brase/Brase statistics site at **http://math.college.hmco.com/ students** and find the link to the College Board.) Both SAT and ACT scores are normally distributed. What is the probability that a randomly selected high school senior's score on the mathematics part of the SAT will be

(a) more than 675?   (b) less than 450?   (c) between 450 and 675?

What is the probability that a randomly selected high school senior's score on the mathematics part of the ACT will be

(d) more than 28?   (e) more than 12?   (f) between 12 and 28?

24. *Inverse Normal Distribution: SAT and ACT Scores* Please refer to the SAT and ACT information from Problem 23.

(a) Suppose that an engineering school honors program will accept only high school seniors with a mathematics SAT or ACT score in the top 10%. What is the minimum SAT score in mathematics for this program? What is the minimum ACT score in mathematics for this program?
(b) Suppose that an engineering school will accept only high school seniors with a mathematics SAT or ACT score in the top 20%. What is the minimum SAT score in mathematics for this program? What is the minimum ACT score in mathematics for this program?
(c) Suppose that an engineering school will accept only high school seniors with a mathematics SAT or ACT score in the top 60%. What is the minimum SAT score in mathematics for this program? What is the minimum ACT score in mathematics for this program?

25. *Guarantee: Batteries* Quick Start Company makes 12-volt car batteries. After many years of product testing, the company knows that the average life of a Quick Start battery is normally distributed, with a mean of 45 months and a standard deviation of 8 months.

(a) If Quick Start guarantees a full refund on any battery that fails within the 36-month period after purchase, what percentage of its batteries will the company expect to replace?

(b) *Inverse Normal Distribution* If Quick Start does not want to make refunds for more than 10% of its batteries under the full-refund guarantee policy, for how long should the company guarantee the batteries (to the nearest month)?

26. *Guarantee: Watches* Accrotime is a manufacturer of quartz crystal watches. Accrotime researchers have shown that the watches have an average life of 28 months before certain electronic components deteriorate, causing the watch to become unreliable. The standard deviation of watch lifetimes is 5 months, and the distribution of lifetimes is normal.

   (a) If Accrotime guarantees a full refund on any defective watch for 2 years after purchase, what percentage of total production will the company expect to replace?

   (b) *Inverse Normal Distribution* If Accrotime does not want to make refunds on more than 12% of the watches it makes, how long should the guarantee period be (to the nearest month)?

27. *Expand Your Knowledge: Estimating the Standard Deviation* Consumer Reports gave information about the ages at which various household products are replaced. For example, color TVs are replaced at an average age of $\mu = 8$ years after purchase, and the (95% of data) range was from 5 to 11 years. Thus, the range was $11 - 5 = 6$ years. Let x be the age (in years) at which a color TV is replaced. Assume that x has a distribution that is approximately normal.

   (a) The empirical rule (Section 7.1) indicates that for a symmetrical and bell-shaped distribution, approximately 95% of the data lie within two standard deviations of the mean. Therefore, a 95% range of data values extending from $\mu - 2\sigma$ to $\mu + 2\sigma$ is often used for "commonly occurring" data values. Note that the interval from $\mu - 2\sigma$ to $\mu + 2\sigma$ is 4σ in length. This leads to a "rule of thumb" for estimating the standard deviation from a 95% range of data values.

From the Empirical Rule

$\mu - 2\sigma$ μ $\mu + 2\sigma$

Estimating the standard deviation

For a symmetric, bell-shaped distribution,

$$\text{standard deviation} \approx \frac{\text{range}}{4} \approx \frac{\text{high value} - \text{low value}}{4}$$

where it is estimated that about 95% of the commonly occurring data values fall into this range.

   Use this "rule of thumb" to approximate the standard deviation of x values, where x is the age (in years) at which a color TV is replaced.

   (b) What is the probability that someone will keep a color TV for more than 5 years before replacement?

   (c) What is the probability that someone will keep a color TV for fewer than 10 years before replacement?

   (d) *Inverse Normal Distribution* Assume that the average life of a color TV is 8 years with a standard deviation of 1.5 years before it breaks. Suppose that a company guarantees color TVs and will replace a TV that breaks while under guarantee with a new one. However, the company does not want to replace more than 10% of the TVs under guarantee. For how long should the guarantee be made (rounded to the nearest tenth of a year)?

28. *Estimating the Standard Deviation: Veterinary Science* The resting heart rate for an adult horse should average about $\mu = 46$ beats per minute with a (95% of data)

range from 22 to 70 beats per minute, based on information from *The Merck Veterinary Manual* (a classic reference used in most veterinary colleges). Let x be a random variable that represents the resting heart rate for an adult horse. Assume that x has a distribution that is approximately normal.

(a) Estimate the standard deviation of the x distribution. *Hint:* See Problem 27.
(b) What is the probability that the heart rate is less than 25 beats per minute?
(c) What is the probability that the heart rate is greater than 60 beats per minute?
(d) What is the probability that the heart rate is between 25 and 60 beats per minute?
(e) *Inverse Normal Distribution* A horse whose resting heart rate is in the upper 10% of the probability distribution of heart rates may have a secondary infection or illness that needs to be treated. What is the heart rate corresponding to the upper 10% cutoff point of the probability distribution?

29. *Insurance: Satellites* A relay microchip in a telecommunications satellite has a life expectancy that follows a normal distribution, with a mean of 90 months and a standard deviation of 3.7 months. When this computer-relay microchip malfunctions, the entire satellite is useless. A large London insurance company is going to insure the satellite for 50 million dollars. Assume that the only part of the satellite in question is the microchip. All other components will work indefinitely.

(a) *Inverse Normal Distribution* For how many months should the satellite be insured for the insurance company to be 99% confident that it will last beyond the insurance date?
(b) If the satellite is insured for 84 months, what is the probability that it will malfunction before the insurance coverage ends?
(c) If the satellite is insured for 84 months, what is the expected loss to the insurance company?
(d) If the insurance company charges $3 million for 84 months of insurance, how much profit does the company expect to make?

7.4
Sampling Distributions

FOCUS POINTS

✓ Review such commonly used terms as random sample, relative frequency, parameter, statistic, and sampling distribution.

✓ From raw data, construct a relative frequency distribution for $\bar{x}$ values and compare the result to a theoretical sampling distribution.

Let us begin with some common statistical terms. Most of these have been discussed before, but this is a good time to review them.

From a statistical point of view, a *population* can be thought of as a set of measurements (or counts), either existing or conceptual. We discussed populations at some length in Chapter 1. A *sample* is a subset of measurements from the population. For our purposes, the most important samples are *random samples*, which were discussed in Section 1.2.

When we compute a descriptive measure such as an average, it makes a difference whether it was computed from a population or from a sample.

Statistic
Parameter

> A **statistic** is a numerical descriptive measure of a *sample*.
> A **parameter** is a numerical descriptive measure of a *population*.

It is important to notice that for a given population, a specified parameter is a fixed quantity. On the other hand, the value of a statistic might vary depending on which sample has been selected.

Some commonly used statistics and corresponding parameters

Measure	Statistic	Parameter
Mean	$\bar{x}$ (x bar)	μ (mu)
Variance	s^2	σ^2 (sigma squared)
Standard deviation	s	σ (sigma)
Proportion	$\hat{p}$ (p hat)	p

Often we do not have access to all the measurements of an entire population because of time, money, effort constraints, etc. So we must use measurements from a sample instead. In such cases, we will use a statistic (such as $\bar{x}$, s, or $\hat{p}$) to make *inferences* about corresponding population parameters (e.g., μ, σ, or p). The principal types of inferences we will make are the following.

Types of inferences

1. **Estimation:** In this type of inference, we estimate the *value* of a population parameter.

2. **Testing:** In this type of inference, we formulate a *decision* about the value of a population parameter.

3. **Regression:** In this type of inference, we make *predictions* or *forecasts* about the value of a statistical variable.

To evaluate the reliability of our inferences, we will need to know the probability distribution for the statistic we are using. Such a probability distribution is called a *sampling distribution*. Perhaps Example 9 below will help clarify this discussion.

Sampling distribution

A **sampling distribution** is a probability distribution of a sample statistic based on all possible simple random samples of the *same* size from the same population.

EXAMPLE 9

Sampling distribution for $\bar{x}$

Pinedale, Wisconsin, is a rural community with a children's fishing pond. Posted rules state that all fish under 6 inches must be returned to the pond, only children under 12 years old may fish, and a limit of five fish may be kept per day. Susan is a college student who was hired by the community last summer to make sure the rules were obeyed and to see that the children were safe from accidents. The pond contains only rainbow trout and has been well stocked for many years. Each child has no difficulty catching his or her limit of five trout.

As a project for her biometrics class, Susan kept a record of the lengths (to the nearest inch) of all trout caught last summer. Hundreds of children visited the pond and caught their limit of five trout, so Susan has a lot of data. To make Table 7-8 (on the next page), Susan selected 100 children at random and listed the lengths of each of the five trout caught by each child in the sample. Then, for each child, she listed the mean length of the five trout that child caught.

TABLE 7-8 Length Measurements of Trout Caught by a Random Sample of 100 Children at the Pinedale Children's Pond

Sample	Length (to nearest inch)					$\bar{x}$ = Sample Mean	Sample	Length (to nearest inch)					$\bar{x}$ = Sample Mean
1	11	10	10	12	11	10.8	51	9	10	12	10	9	10.0
2	11	11	9	9	9	9.8	52	7	11	10	11	10	9.8
3	12	9	10	11	10	10.4	53	9	11	9	11	12	10.4
4	11	10	13	11	8	10.6	54	12	9	8	10	11	10.0
5	10	10	13	11	12	11.2	55	8	11	10	9	10	9.6
6	12	7	10	9	11	9.8	56	10	10	9	9	13	10.2
7	7	10	13	10	10	10.0	57	9	8	10	10	12	9.8
8	10	9	9	9	10	9.4	58	10	11	9	8	9	9.4
9	10	10	11	12	8	10.2	59	10	8	9	10	12	9.8
10	10	11	10	7	9	9.4	60	11	9	9	11	11	10.2
11	12	11	11	11	13	11.6	61	11	10	11	10	11	10.6
12	10	11	10	12	13	11.2	62	12	10	10	9	11	10.4
13	11	10	10	9	11	10.2	63	10	10	9	11	7	9.4
14	10	10	13	8	11	10.4	64	11	11	12	10	11	11.0
15	9	11	9	10	10	9.8	65	10	10	11	10	9	10.0
16	13	9	11	12	10	11.0	66	8	9	10	11	11	9.8
17	8	9	7	10	11	9.0	67	9	11	11	9	8	9.6
18	12	12	8	12	12	11.2	68	10	9	10	9	11	9.8
19	10	8	9	10	10	9.4	69	9	9	11	11	11	10.2
20	10	11	10	10	10	10.2	70	13	11	11	9	11	11.0
21	11	10	11	9	12	10.6	71	12	10	8	8	9	9.4
22	9	12	9	10	9	9.8	72	13	7	12	9	10	10.2
23	8	11	10	11	10	10.0	73	9	10	9	8	9	9.0
24	9	12	10	9	11	10.2	74	11	11	10	9	10	10.2
25	9	9	8	9	10	9.0	75	9	11	14	9	11	10.8
26	11	11	12	11	11	11.2	76	14	10	11	12	12	11.8
27	10	10	10	11	13	10.8	77	8	12	10	10	9	9.8
28	8	7	9	10	8	8.4	78	8	10	13	9	8	9.6
29	11	11	8	10	11	10.2	79	11	11	11	13	10	11.2
30	8	11	11	9	12	10.2	80	12	10	11	12	9	10.8
31	11	9	12	10	10	10.4	81	10	9	10	10	13	10.4
32	10	11	10	11	12	10.8	82	11	10	9	9	12	10.2
33	12	11	8	8	11	10.0	83	11	11	10	10	10	10.4
34	8	10	10	9	10	9.4	84	11	10	11	9	9	10.0
35	10	10	10	10	11	10.2	85	10	11	10	9	7	9.4
36	10	8	10	11	13	10.4	86	7	11	10	9	11	9.6
37	11	10	11	11	10	10.6	87	10	11	10	10	10	10.2
38	7	13	9	12	11	10.4	88	9	8	11	10	12	10.0
39	11	11	8	11	11	10.4	89	14	9	12	10	9	10.8
40	11	10	11	12	9	10.6	90	9	12	9	10	10	10.0
41	11	10	9	11	12	10.6	91	10	10	8	6	11	9.0
42	11	13	10	12	9	11.0	92	8	9	11	9	10	9.4
43	10	9	11	10	11	10.2	93	8	10	9	9	11	9.4
44	10	9	11	10	9	9.8	94	12	11	12	13	10	11.6
45	12	11	9	11	12	11.0	95	11	11	9	9	9	9.8
46	13	9	11	8	8	9.8	96	8	12	8	11	10	9.8
47	10	11	11	11	10	10.6	97	13	11	11	12	8	11.0
48	9	9	10	11	11	10.0	98	10	11	8	10	11	10.0
49	10	9	9	10	10	9.6	99	13	10	7	11	9	10.0
50	10	10	6	9	10	9.0	100	9	9	10	12	12	10.4

TABLE 7-9   Frequency Table for 100 Values of $\bar{x}$

Class	Class Limits		f = Frequency	$f/100$ = Relative Frequency
	Lower	Upper		
1	8.39	8.76	1	0.01
2	8.77	9.14	5	0.05
3	9.15	9.52	10	0.10
4	9.53	9.90	19	0.19
5	9.91	10.28	27	0.27
6	10.29	10.66	18	0.18
7	10.67	11.04	12	0.12
8	11.05	11.42	5	0.05
9	11.43	11.80	3	0.03

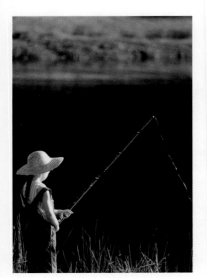

Now let us turn our attention to the following question: What is the average (mean) length of a trout taken from the Pinedale children's pond last summer?

SOLUTION: We can get an idea of the average length by looking at the two $\bar{x}$ columns of Table 7-8. But just looking at 100 of the $\bar{x}$ values doesn't tell us much. Let's organize our $\bar{x}$ values into a frequency table. We used a class width of 0.38 to make Table 7-9.

Note: Techniques of Section 2.1 dictate a class width of 0.4. However, this choice results in the tenth class being beyond the data. Consequently, we shortened the class width slightly and also started the first class with a value slightly smaller than the smallest data value.

The far-right column of Table 7-9 contains relative frequencies $f/100$. Recall that the relative frequencies may be thought of as probabilities, so we effectively have a probability distribution. Because $\bar{x}$ represents the mean length of a trout (based on samples of five trout caught by each child), we estimate the probability of $\bar{x}$ falling into each class by using the relative frequencies. Figure 7-29 is a relative-frequency or probability distribution of the $\bar{x}$ values.

FIGURE 7-29

Estimates of Probabilities of $\bar{x}$ Values

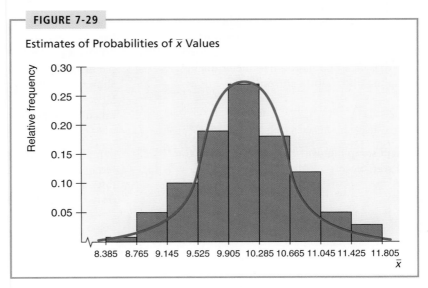

The bars of Figure 7-29 represent our estimated probabilities of $\bar{x}$ values based on the data of Table 7-8. The bell-shaped curve represents the theoretical probability distribution that would be obtained if the number of children (i.e., number of $\bar{x}$ values) were much larger.

Figure 7-29 represents a *probability sampling distribution* for the sample mean $\bar{x}$ of trout lengths based on random samples of size 5. We see that the distribution is mound-shaped and even somewhat bell-shaped. Irregularities are due to the small number of samples used (only 100 sample means) and the rather small sample size (five trout per child). These irregularities would become less obvious and even disappear if the sample of children became much larger, if we used a larger number of classes in Figure 7-29, and if the number of trout used in each sample became larger. In fact, the curve would eventually become a perfect bell-shaped curve. We will discuss this property at some length in the next section, which introduces the *central limit theorem*.   ◇

Let us summarize the information about sampling distributions in the following exercise.

GUIDED EXERCISE 9

Terminology

(a) What is a population parameter? Give an example.

⟹ A population parameter is a numerical descriptive measure of a population. Examples are μ, σ, and p. (There are many others.)

(b) What is a sample statistic? Give an example.

⟹ A sample statistic or a statistic is a numerical descriptive measure of a sample. Examples are $\bar{x}$, s, and $\hat{p}$.

(c) What is a sampling distribution?

⟹ A sampling distribution is a probability distribution for the sample statistic we are using.

(d) In Table 7-8, what makes up the members of the sample? What is the sample statistic corresponding to each sample? What is the sampling distribution? To which population parameter does this sampling distribution correspond?

⟹ There are 100 samples, each of which has five trout lengths. The first sample of five trout has lengths 11, 10, 10, 12, and 11. The sample statistic is the sample mean $\bar{x} = 10.8$. The sampling distribution is shown in Figure 7-29. This sampling distribution relates to the population mean μ of all lengths of trout taken from the Pinedale children's pond (i.e., trout over 6 inches long).

(e) Where will sampling distributions be used in our study of statistics?

⟹ Sampling distributions will be used for statistical inference. (Chapter 8 will concentrate on a method of inference called *estimation*. Chapter 9 will concentrate on a method of inference called *testing*.)

VIEWPOINT   *"Chance Favors the Prepared Mind"*
                                              —Louis Pasteur

It also has been said that a discovery is nothing more than an accident that meets a prepared mind. Sampling can be one of the best forms of preparation. In fact, sampling may be the primary way we humans venture into the unknown. Probability sampling distributions can provide new information for the sociologist, scientist, or economist. In addition, ordinary human sampling of life can help writers and artists develop preferences, style, and insight. Ansel Adams became famous for photographing lyrical, unforgettable landscapes such as "Moonrise, Hernandez, New Mexico." Adams claimed that he was a strong believer in the quote by Pasteur. In fact, he claims that the Hernandez photograph was just such a favored chance happening that his prepared mind readily grasped. During his lifetime, Adams made over $25 million from sales and royalties on the Hernandez photograph.

SECTION 7.4   PROBLEMS

This is a good time to review several important concepts, some of which we have studied earlier. Please write out a careful but brief answer to each of the following questions.

1. What is a population? Give three examples.

2. What is a random sample from a population? (*Hint:* See Section 1.2.)

3. What is a population parameter? Give three examples.

4. What is a sample statistic? Give three examples.

5. What is the meaning of the term *statistical inference*? What types of inferences will we make about population parameters?

6. What is a sampling distribution?

7. How do frequency tables, relative frequencies, and histograms using relative frequencies help us understand sampling distributions?

8. How can relative frequencies be used to help us estimate probabilities occurring in sampling distributions?

9. Give an example of a specific sampling distribution we studied in this section. Outline other possible examples of sampling distributions from areas such as business administration, economics, finance, psychology, political science, sociology, biology, medical science, sports, engineering, chemistry, linguistics, and so on.

7.5
The Central Limit Theorem

The $\bar{x}$ Distribution, Given x Is Normal

FOCUS POINTS

✓ For a normal distribution, use μ and σ to construct the theoretical sampling distribution for the statistic $\bar{x}$.

✓ For large samples, use sample estimates to construct a good approximate sampling distribution for the statistic $\bar{x}$.

✓ Learn the statement and underlying meaning of the central limit theorem well enough to explain it to a friend who is intelligent, but (unfortunately) doesn't know much about statistics.

In Section 7.4, we began a study of the distribution of $\bar{x}$ values, where $\bar{x}$ was the (sample) mean length of five trout caught by children at the Pinedale children's fishing pond. Let's consider this example again in the light of a very important theorem of mathematical statistics.

◇ **THEOREM 7.1 for a Normal Probability Distribution** Let x be a random variable with a *normal distribution* whose mean is μ and whose standard deviation is σ. Let $\bar{x}$ be the sample mean corresponding to random samples of size n taken from the x distribution. Then the following are true:

(a) The $\bar{x}$ distribution is a *normal distribution*.

(b) The mean of the $\bar{x}$ distribution is μ.

(c) The standard deviation of the $\bar{x}$ distribution is $\sigma/\sqrt{n}$.   ◇

We conclude from Theorem 7.1 that when x has a normal distribution, the $\bar{x}$ distribution will be normal *for any sample size n*. Furthermore, we can convert the $\bar{x}$ distribution to the standard normal z distribution using the following formulas.

$$\mu_{\bar{x}} = \mu$$

$$\sigma_{\bar{x}} = \frac{\sigma}{\sqrt{n}}$$

$$z = \frac{\bar{x} - \mu_{\bar{x}}}{\sigma_{\bar{x}}} = \frac{\bar{x} - \mu}{\sigma/\sqrt{n}}$$

where n is the sample size,
μ is the mean of the x distribution, and
σ is the standard deviation of the x distribution.

Theorem 7.1 is a wonderful theorem! It states that the $\bar{x}$ distribution will be normal provided the x distribution is normal. The sample size n could be 2, 3, 4, or any (fixed) sample size we wish. Furthermore, the mean of the $\bar{x}$ distribution is μ (same as for the x distribution), but the standard deviation is $\sigma/\sqrt{n}$ (which is, of course, smaller than σ). The next example illustrates Theorem 7.1.

EXAMPLE 10

Probability regarding x; regarding $\bar{x}$

Suppose that a team of biologists has been studying the Pinedale children's fishing pond. Let x represent the length of a single trout taken at random from the pond. This group of biologists has determined that x has a normal distribution with mean $\mu = 10.2$ inches and standard deviation $\sigma = 1.4$ inches.

(a) What is the probability that a *single trout* taken at random from the pond is between 8 and 12 inches long?

SOLUTION: We use the methods of Section 7.3 with $\mu = 10.2$ and $\sigma = 1.4$ to get

$$z = \frac{x - \mu}{\sigma} = \frac{x - 10.2}{1.4}$$

Therefore,

$$P(8 < x < 12) = P\left(\frac{8 - 10.2}{1.4} < z < \frac{12 - 10.2}{1.4}\right)$$
$$= P(-1.57 < z < 1.29)$$
$$= 0.9015 - 0.0582 = 0.8433$$

Therefore, the probability is about 0.8433 that a *single* trout taken at random is between 8 and 12 inches long.

(b) What is the probability that the *mean length* $\bar{x}$ of five trout taken at random is between 8 and 12 inches?

SOLUTION: If we let $\mu_{\bar{x}}$ represent the mean of the distribution, then Theorem 7.1, part (b), tells us that

$$\mu_{\bar{x}} = \mu = 10.2$$

If $\sigma_{\bar{x}}$ represents the standard deviation of the $\bar{x}$ distribution, then Theorem 7.1, part (c), tells us that

$$\sigma_{\bar{x}} = \sigma/\sqrt{n} = 1.4/\sqrt{5} \approx 0.63$$

To create a standard z variable from $\bar{x}$, we subtract $\mu_{\bar{x}}$ and divide by $\sigma_{\bar{x}}$:

$$z = \frac{\bar{x} - \mu_{\bar{x}}}{\sigma_{\bar{x}}} = \frac{\bar{x} - \mu}{\sigma/\sqrt{n}} \approx \frac{\bar{x} - 10.2}{0.63}$$

To standardize the interval $8 < \bar{x} < 12$, we use 8 and then 12 in place of $\bar{x}$ in the preceding formula for z.

$$8 < \bar{x} < 12$$
$$\frac{8 - 10.2}{0.63} < z < \frac{12 - 10.2}{0.63}$$
$$-3.49 < z < 2.86$$

Theorem 7.1, part (a), tells us that $\bar{x}$ has a normal distribution. Therefore,

$$P(8 < \bar{x} < 12) = P(-3.49 < z < 2.86) = 0.9979 - 0.0002 = 0.9977$$

The probability is about 0.9977 that the mean length based on a sample size of 5 is between 8 and 12 inches.

(c) Looking at the results of parts (a) and (b), we see that the probabilities (0.8433 and 0.9977) are quite different. Why is this the case?

SOLUTION: According to Theorem 7.1, both x and $\bar{x}$ have a normal distribution, and both have the same mean of 10.2 inches. The difference is in the standard deviation for x and $\bar{x}$. The standard deviation of the x distribution is $\sigma = 1.4$. The standard deviation of the $\bar{x}$ distribution is

$$\sigma_{\bar{x}} = \sigma/\sqrt{n} = 1.4/\sqrt{5} \approx 0.63$$

FIGURE 7-30

General Shapes of the x and $\bar{x}$ Distributions

(a) The x distribution with $\mu = 10.2$ and $\sigma = 1.4$

(b) The $\bar{x}$ distribution with $\mu_{\bar{x}} = 10.2$ and $\sigma_{\bar{x}} = 0.63$ for samples of size $n = 5$

The standard deviation of $\bar{x}$ is less than half the standard deviation of x. Figure 7-30 shows the distributions of x and $\bar{x}$.

Looking at Figure 7-30(a) and (b), we see that both curves use the same scale on the horizontal axis. The means are the same, and the shaded area is above the interval from 8 to 12 on each graph. It becomes clear that the smaller standard deviation of the $\bar{x}$ distribution has the effect of gathering together much more of the total probability into the region over its mean. Therefore, the region from 8 to 12 has a much higher probability for the $\bar{x}$ distribution.   ◇

Theorem 7.1 describes the distribution of a particular statistic: namely, the distribution of sample means $\bar{x}$. The standard deviation of a statistic is referred to as the *standard error* of that statistic.

Standard error of the mean

> The **standard error** is the standard deviation of a sampling distribution. For the $\bar{x}$ sampling distribution,
>
> $$\text{standard error} = \sigma_{\bar{x}} = \sigma/\sqrt{n}$$

Statistical software terminology

The expression *standard error* appears commonly on printouts and refers to the standard deviation of the sampling distribution being used. (In Minitab, the expression SE MEAN refers to the standard error of the mean.)

The $\bar{x}$ Distribution, Given x Follows Any Distribution

Central limit theorem

Theorem 7.1 gives complete information about the $\bar{x}$ distribution, provided the original x distribution is known to be normal. What happens if we don't have information about the shape of the original x distribution? The *central limit theorem* tells us what to expect.

◇ **THEOREM 7.2 The Central Limit Theorem for Any Probability Distribution** If x possesses *any* distribution with mean μ and standard deviation σ, then the sample mean $\bar{x}$ based on a random sample of size n will have a distribution that approaches the distribution of a normal random variable with mean μ and standard deviation $\sigma/\sqrt{n}$ as n increases without limit.   ◇

The central limit theorem is indeed surprising! It says that x can have *any* distribution whatsoever, but as the sample size gets larger and larger, the distribution of $\overline{x}$ will approach a *normal* distribution. From this relation, we begin to appreciate the scope and significance of the normal distribution.

In the central limit theorem, the degree to which the distribution of $\overline{x}$ values fits a normal distribution depends on both the selected value of n and the original distribution of x values. A natural question is: How large should the sample size be if we want to apply the central limit theorem? After a great deal of theoretical as well as empirical study, statisticians agree that if n is 30 or larger, the $\overline{x}$ distribution will appear to be normal and the central limit theorem will apply. However, this rule should not be applied blindly. If the x distribution is definitely not symmetrical about its mean, then the $\overline{x}$ distribution also will display a lack of symmetry. In such a case, a sample size larger than 30 may be required to get a reasonable approximation to the normal.

Large sample

In practice, it is a good idea, when possible, to make a histogram of sample x values. If the histogram is approximately mound-shaped, and if it is more or less symmetrical, then we may be assured that, for all practical purposes, the $\overline{x}$ distribution will be well approximated by a normal distribution and the central limit theorem will apply when the sample size is 30 or larger. The main thing to remember is that in almost all practical applications, a sample size of 30 or more is adequate for the central limit theorem to hold. However, in a few rare applications, you may need a sample size larger than 30 to get reliable results.

Let's summarize this information for convenient reference: For almost all x distributions, if we use a random sample of size 30 or larger, the $\overline{x}$ distribution will be approximately normal, and the larger the sample size becomes, the closer the $\overline{x}$ distribution gets to the normal. Furthermore, we may convert the $\overline{x}$ distribution to a standard normal distribution using the following formulas.

Using the central limit theorem to convert the $\overline{x}$ distribution to the standard normal distribution

$$\mu_{\overline{x}} = \mu$$

$$\sigma_{\overline{x}} = \frac{\sigma}{\sqrt{n}}$$

$$z = \frac{\overline{x} - \mu_{\overline{x}}}{\sigma_{\overline{x}}} = \frac{\overline{x} - \mu}{\sigma/\sqrt{n}}$$

where n is the sample size ($n \geq 30$),
      μ is the mean of the x distribution, and
      σ is the standard deviation of the x distribution.

Guided Exercise 10 shows how to standardize $\overline{x}$ when appropriate. Then Example 11 demonstrates the use of the central limit theorem in a decision-making process.

GUIDED EXERCISE 10

Central limit theorem

(a) Suppose x has a *normal* distribution with mean $\mu = 18$ and standard deviation $\sigma = 3$. If you draw random samples of size 5 from the x distribution and $\bar{x}$ represents the sample mean, what can you say about the $\bar{x}$ distribution? How could you standardize the $\bar{x}$ distribution?

Since the x distribution is given to be *normal*, the $\bar{x}$ distribution also will be normal even though the sample size is much less than 30. The mean is $\mu_{\bar{x}} = \mu = 18$. The standard deviation is

$$\sigma_{\bar{x}} = \sigma/\sqrt{n} = 3/\sqrt{5} \approx 1.3$$

We could standardize $\bar{x}$ as follows:

$$z = \frac{\bar{x} - \mu}{\sigma/\sqrt{n}} \approx \frac{\bar{x} - 18}{1.3}$$

(b) Suppose you know that the x distribution has mean $\mu = 75$ and standard deviation $\sigma = 12$, but you have no information as to whether or not the x distribution is normal. If you draw samples of size 30 from the x distribution and $\bar{x}$ represents the sample mean, what can you say about the $\bar{x}$ distribution? How could you standardize the $\bar{x}$ distribution?

Since the sample size is large enough, the $\bar{x}$ distribution will be approximately a normal distribution. The mean of the $\bar{x}$ distribution is

$$\mu_{\bar{x}} = \mu = 75$$

The standard deviation of the distribution is

$$\sigma_{\bar{x}} = \sigma/\sqrt{n} = 12/\sqrt{30} \approx 2.2$$

We could standardize $\bar{x}$ as follows:

$$z = \frac{\bar{x} - \mu}{\sigma/\sqrt{n}} \approx \frac{\bar{x} - 75}{2.2}$$

(c) Suppose you did not know that x had a normal distribution. Would you be justified in saying that the $\bar{x}$ distribution is approximately normal if the sample size were $n = 8$?

No, the sample size should be 30 or larger if we don't know that x has a normal distribution.

EXAMPLE 11

Central limit theorem

A certain strain of bacteria occurs in all raw milk. Let x be the bacteria count per milliliter of milk. The health department has found that if the milk is not contaminated, then x has a distribution that is more or less mound-shaped and symmetrical. The mean of the x distribution is $\mu = 2500$, and the standard deviation is $\sigma = 300$. In a large commercial dairy, the health inspector takes 42 random samples of the milk produced each day. At the end of the day, the bacteria count in each of the 42 samples is averaged to obtain the sample mean bacteria count $\bar{x}$.

(a) Assuming that the milk is not contaminated, what is the distribution of $\bar{x}$?

SOLUTION: The sample size is $n = 42$. Since this value exceeds 30, the central limit theorem applies, and we know that $\bar{x}$ will be approximately normal with mean and standard deviation

$$\mu_{\bar{x}} = \mu = 2500$$
$$\sigma_{\bar{x}} = \sigma/\sqrt{n} = 300/\sqrt{42} \approx 46.3$$

(b) Assuming the milk is not contaminated, what is the probability that the average bacteria count $\bar{x}$ for one day is between 2350 and 2650 bacteria per milliliter?

SOLUTION: We convert the interval

$$2350 \leq \bar{x} \leq 2650$$

to a corresponding interval on the standard z axis.

$$z = \frac{\bar{x} - \mu}{\sigma/\sqrt{n}} \approx \frac{\bar{x} - 2500}{46.3}$$

$\bar{x} = 2350$ converts to $z = \dfrac{2350 - 2500}{46.3} \approx -3.24$

$\bar{x} = 2650$ converts to $z = \dfrac{2650 - 2500}{46.3} \approx 3.24$

Therefore,

$$
\begin{aligned}
P(2350 \leq \bar{x} \leq 2650) &= P(-3.24 \leq z \leq 3.24) \\
&= 0.9994 - 0.0006 \\
&= 0.9988
\end{aligned}
$$

The probability is 0.9988 that $\bar{x}$ is between 2350 and 2650.

(c) At the end of each day, the inspector must decide to accept or reject the accumulated milk that has been held in cold storage awaiting shipment. Suppose that the 42 samples taken by the inspector have a mean bacteria count $\bar{x}$ that is *not* between 2350 and 2650. If you were the inspector, what would be your comment on this situation?

SOLUTION: The probability that $\bar{x}$ is between 2350 and 2650 is very high. If the inspector finds that the average bacteria count for the 42 samples is not between 2350 and 2650, then it is reasonable to conclude that there is something wrong with the milk. If $\bar{x}$ is less than 2350, you might suspect someone added chemicals to the milk to artificially reduce the bacteria count. If $\bar{x}$ is above 2650, you might suspect some other kind of biologic contamination. ◇

PROCEDURE

How to find probabilities regarding $\bar{x}$

Given a probability distribution of x values where

     n = sample size
     μ = mean of the x distribution
     σ = standard deviation of the x distribution

1. If the x distribution is *normal*, then the $\bar{x}$ distribution is *normal*.
2. Even if the x distribution is *not* normal, if the *sample size* $n \geq 30$, then, by the central limit theorem, the $\bar{x}$ distribution is *approximately normal*.
3. Convert $\bar{x}$ to z using the formula

$$z = \frac{\bar{x} - \mu_{\bar{x}}}{\sigma_{\bar{x}}} = \frac{\bar{x} - \mu}{\sigma/\sqrt{n}}$$

4. Use the standard normal distribution to find the corresponding probability of events regarding $\bar{x}$.

GUIDED EXERCISE 11

Probability regarding $\bar{x}$

In mountain country, major highways sometimes use tunnels instead of long, winding roads over high passes. However, too many vehicles in a tunnel at the same time can cause a hazardous situation. Traffic engineers are studying a long tunnel in Colorado. If x represents the time for a vehicle to go through the tunnel, it is known that the x distribution has mean $\mu = 12.1$ minutes and standard deviation $\sigma = 3.8$ minutes under ordinary traffic conditions. From a histogram of x values, it was found that the x distribution is mound-shaped with some symmetry about the mean.

Engineers have calculated that, *on average*, vehicles should spend from 11 to 13 minutes in the tunnel. If the time is less than 11 minutes, traffic is moving too fast for safe travel in the tunnel. If the time is more than 13 minutes, there is a problem of bad air (too much carbon monoxide and other pollutants).

Under ordinary conditions, there are about 50 vehicles in the tunnel at one time. What is the probability that the mean time for 50 vehicles to go through the tunnel will be from 11 to 13 minutes?

We will answer this question in steps.

(a) Let $\bar{x}$ represent the sample mean based on samples of size 50. Describe the $\bar{x}$ distribution.

From the central limit theorem, we expect the $\bar{x}$ distribution to be approximately normal with mean and standard deviation

$$\mu_{\bar{x}} = \mu = 12.1 \qquad \sigma_{\bar{x}} = \frac{\sigma}{\sqrt{n}} = \frac{3.8}{\sqrt{50}} \approx 0.54$$

(b) Find $P(11 < \bar{x} < 13)$.

We convert the interval

$$11 < \bar{x} < 13$$

to a standard z interval and use the standard normal probability table to find our answer. Since

$$z = \frac{\bar{x} - \mu}{\sigma/\sqrt{n}} \approx \frac{\bar{x} - 12.1}{0.54}$$

$$\bar{x} = 11 \text{ converts to } z \approx \frac{11 - 12.1}{0.54} = -2.04 \text{ and}$$

$$\bar{x} = 13 \text{ converts to } z \approx \frac{13 - 12.1}{0.54} = 1.67$$

Therefore,

$$P(11 < \bar{x} < 13) = P(-2.04 < z < 1.67)$$
$$= 0.9525 - 0.0207$$
$$= 0.9318$$

(c) Comment on your answer for part (b).

It seems that about 93% of the time there should be no safety hazard for average traffic flow.

VIEWPOINT   *Chaos!*

Is there a different side to random sampling? Can sampling be used as a weapon? According to *The Wall Street Journal*, the answer could be yes! The acronym for *C*reate *H*avoc *A*round *O*ur *S*ystem is *CHAOS*. The Association of Flight Attendants (AFA) is a union that successfully used **CHAOS** against Alaska Airlines in 1994 as a negotiation tool. **CHAOS** involves a small sample of random strikes—a few flights at a time—instead of a mass walkout. The president of the AFA claims that by striking randomly, "we take control of the schedule." The entire schedule becomes unreliable, and that is something management cannot tolerate. In 1986, TWA flight attendants struck in a mass walkout, and all were permanently replaced! Using **CHAOS**, only a few jobs are put at risk, and these are usually not lost. It appears that random sampling *can* be used as a weapon.

SECTION 7.5   PROBLEMS

In these problems, the word *average* refers to the arithmetic mean $\bar{x}$ or μ, as appropriate.

1. *General* Suppose that x has a distribution with $\mu = 15$ and $\sigma = 14$.
   (a) If a random sample of size $n = 49$ is drawn, find $\mu_{\bar{x}}$, $\sigma_{\bar{x}}$, and $P(15 \le \bar{x} \le 17)$.
   (b) If a random sample of size $n = 64$ is drawn, find $\mu_{\bar{x}}$, $\sigma_{\bar{x}}$, and $P(15 \le \bar{x} \le 17)$.
   (c) Why should you expect the probability of part (b) to be higher than that of part (a)? (*Hint:* Consider the standard deviations in parts (a) and (b).)

2. *General* Suppose that x has a distribution with $\mu = 100$ and $\sigma = 48$.
   (a) If a random sample of size $n = 81$ is drawn, find $\mu_{\bar{x}}$, $\sigma_{\bar{x}}$, and $P(92 \le \bar{x} \le 100)$.
   (b) If a random sample of size $n = 121$ is drawn, find $\mu_{\bar{x}}$, $\sigma_{\bar{x}}$, and $P(92 \le \bar{x} \le 100)$.
   (c) Again, comment on the differences between the probabilities in parts (a) and (b). Why do you expect the differences?

3. *General* Suppose that x has a distribution with $\mu = 25$ and $\sigma = 3.5$.
   (a) If random samples of size $n = 9$ are selected, can we say anything about the $\bar{x}$ distribution of sample means?
   (b) If the original x distribution is normal, can we say anything about the $\bar{x}$ distribution from samples of size $n = 9$? Find $P(23 \le \bar{x} \le 26)$.

4. *General* Suppose that x has a distribution with $\mu = 72$ and $\sigma = 8$.
   (a) If random samples of size $n = 16$ are selected, can we say anything about the $\bar{x}$ distribution of sample means?
   (b) If the original x distribution is *normal*, can we say anything about the $\bar{x}$ distribution of random samples of size 16? Find $P(68 \le \bar{x} \le 73)$.

5. *Coal: Automatic Loader* Coal is carried from a mine in West Virginia to a power plant in New York in hopper cars on a long train. The automatic hopper car loader is set to put 75 tons of coal into each car. The actual weights of coal loaded into each car are *normally distributed* with mean $\mu = 75$ tons and standard deviation $\sigma = 0.8$ ton.
   (a) What is the probability that one car chosen at random will have less than 74.5 tons of coal?
   (b) What is the probability that 20 cars chosen at random will have a mean load weight $\bar{x}$ of less than 74.5 tons of coal?

(c) Suppose that the weight of coal in one car is less than 74.5 tons. Would that fact make you suspect that the loader had slipped out of adjustment? Suppose the weight of coal in 20 cars selected at random has an average $\bar{x}$ less than 74.5 tons. Would that fact make you suspect that the loader had slipped out of adjustment? Why?

6. *Vital Statistics: Heights of Men* The heights of 18-year-old men are approximately *normally distributed*, with mean 68 inches and standard deviation 3 inches (based on information from *Statistical Abstract of the United States*, 112th Edition).
   (a) What is the probability that an 18-year-old man selected at random is between 67 and 69 inches tall?
   (b) If a random sample of nine 18-year-old men is selected, what is the probability that the mean height $\bar{x}$ is between 67 and 69 inches?
   (c) Compare your answers for parts (a) and (b). Is the probability in part (b) much higher? Why would you expect this?

7. *Medical: Blood Glucose* Let x be a random variable that represents the level of glucose in the blood (milligrams per deciliter of blood) after a 12-hour fast. Assume that for people under 50 years old, x has a distribution that is approximately normal with mean $\mu = 85$ and estimated standard deviation $\sigma = 25$ (based on information from *Diagnostic Tests with Nursing Applications*, edited by S. Loeb, Springhouse). A test result $x < 40$ is an indication of severe excess insulin, and medication is usually prescribed.
   (a) What is the probability that, on a single test, $x < 40$?
   (b) Suppose a doctor uses the average $\bar{x}$ for two tests taken about a week apart. What can we say about the probability distribution of $\bar{x}$? *Hint:* See Theorem 7.1. What is the probability that $\bar{x} < 40$?
   (c) Repeat part (b) for $n = 3$ tests taken a week apart.
   (d) Repeat part (b) for $n = 5$ tests taken a week apart.
   (e) Compare your answers for parts (a), (b), (c), and (d). Did the probabilities decrease as n increased? Explain what this might suggest if you were a doctor or a nurse. If a patient had a test result of $\bar{x} < 40$ based on five tests, explain why either you are looking at an extremely rare event or (more likely) the person has a case of excess insulin.

8. *Medical: White Blood Cells* Let x be a random variable that represents white blood cell count per cubic milliliter of whole blood. Assume that x has a distribution that is approximately normal with mean $\mu = 7500$ and estimated standard deviation $\sigma = 1750$ (see reference in Problem 7). A test result of $x < 3500$ is an indication of leukopenia. This indicates bone marrow depression that may be the result of a viral infection.
   (a) What is the probability that, on a single test, x is less than 3500?
   (b) Suppose a doctor uses the average $\bar{x}$ for two tests taken about a week apart. What can we say about the probability distribution of $\bar{x}$? What is the probability of $\bar{x} < 3500$?
   (c) Repeat part (b) for $n = 3$ tests taken a week apart.
   (d) Compare your answers for parts (a), (b), and (c). How did the probabilities change as n increased? If a person had a test result of $\bar{x} < 3500$ based on three tests, what conclusion would you draw as a doctor or a nurse?

9. *Wildlife: Deer* Let x be a random variable that represents the weights in kilograms (kg) of healthy adult female deer (does) in December in Mesa Verde National Park. Then x has a distribution that is approximately normal with mean $\mu = 63.0$ kg and standard deviation $\sigma = 7.1$ kg (Source: *The Mule Deer of Mesa Verde National Park*, by G. W. Mierau and J. L. Schmidt, Mesa Verde Museum Association). Suppose a doe that weighs less than 54 kg is considered undernourished.
   (a) What is the probability that a single doe captured (weighed and released) at random in December is undernourished?

(b) If the park has about 2200 does, what number do you expect to be under-nourished in December?

(c) To estimate the health of the December doe population, park rangers use the rule that the average weight of $n = 50$ does should be more than 60 kg. If the average weight is less than 60 kg, it is thought that the entire population of does might be undernourished. What is the probability that the average weight $\bar{x}$ for a random sample of 50 does is less than 60 kg (assume a healthy population)?

(d) Compute the probability that $\bar{x} < 64.2$ kg for 50 does (assume a healthy population). Suppose park rangers captured, weighed, and released 50 does in December, and the average weight was $\bar{x} = 64.2$ kg. Do you think the doe population is undernourished or not? Explain.

10. *Wildlife: Hummingbirds* Selasphorus sasin* is the scientific name for what is commonly called "Allen's hummingbird." This beautiful hummingbird lives on the West Coast of the United States and is named for C. A. Allen (1841–1930), who studied these birds extensively. Let x be a random variable that represents the incubation time for Allen hummingbird eggs. Based on information from *The Hummingbird Book*, by Donald and Lillian Stokes (Little, Brown and Company), the x distribution has a mean of $\mu = 16$ days. Let us assume that the standard deviation is approximately $\sigma = 2$ days. The distribution of x values is more or less mound-shaped and symmetrical but not necessarily normal. Suppose that we have $n = 30$ eggs in an incubator. Let $\bar{x}$ be the average incubation time for these eggs.

(a) What can we say about the probability distribution of $\bar{x}$? Is it approximately normal? What are the mean and standard deviation?

(b) What is the probability that $\bar{x}$ is between 16 and 17 days?

(c) What is the probability that $\bar{x}$ is less than 15 days?

11. *Finance: Templeton Funds* Templeton World is a mutual fund that invests in both U.S. and foreign markets. Let x be a random variable that represents the monthly percentage return for the Templeton World fund. Based on information from the *Morningstar Guide to Mutual Funds* (available in most libraries), x has mean $\mu = 1.6\%$ and standard deviation $\sigma = 0.9\%$.

(a) Templeton World fund has over 250 stocks that combine together to give the overall monthly percentage return x. We can consider the monthly return of the stocks in the fund to be a sample from the population of monthly returns of all world stocks. Then we see that the overall monthly return x for Templeton World fund is itself an average return computed using all 250 stocks in the fund. Why would this indicate that x has an approximately normal distribution? Explain. *Hint:* See the discussion after Theorem 7.2.

(b) After 6 months, what is the probability that the *average* monthly percentage return $\bar{x}$ will be between 1% and 2%? *Hint:* See Theorem 7.1, and assume that x has a normal distribution as based on part (a).

(c) After 2 years, what is the probability that $\bar{x}$ will be between 1% and 2%?

(d) Compare your answers for parts (b) and (c). Did the probability increase as n (number of months) increased? Why would this happen?

(e) If after 2 years the average monthly percentage return $\bar{x}$ was less than 1%, would that tend to shake your confidence in the statement that $\mu = 1.6\%$? Might you suspect that μ has slipped below 1.6%? Explain.

12. *Focus Problem: Impulse Buying* Let x represent the dollar amount spent on super-market impulse buying in a 10-minute (unplanned) shopping interval. Based on a *Denver Post* article, the mean of the x distribution is about $20 and the estimated standard deviation is about $7.

(a) Let us assume that x has a distribution that is approximately normal. What is the probability that x is between $18 and $22?

(b) Consider a random sample of $n = 100$ customers, each of whom has 10 minutes of unplanned shopping time in a supermarket. From the central limit theorem, what can you say about the probability distribution of $\bar{x}$, the average amount spent by these customers due to impulse buying? What are the mean and standard deviation of the $\bar{x}$ distribution? Is it necessary to make any assumption about the x distribution? Explain.

(c) What is the probability that $\bar{x}$ is between $18 and $22?

(d) In part (c) we used $\bar{x}$, the *average* amount spent, computed for 100 customers. In part (a) we used x, the amount spent by only *one* customer. The answers for parts (c) and (a) are very different. Why would this happen? In this example $\bar{x}$ is a much more predictable or reliable statistic than x. Consider that almost all marketing strategies and sales pitches are designed for the *average* customer and *not the individual* customer. How does the central limit theorem tell us that the average customer is much more predictable than the individual customer?

13. *General: Distribution of Sample Means*

(a) If we have a distribution of x values that is more or less mound-shaped and somewhat symmetrical, what is the sample size needed to claim that the distribution of sample means $\bar{x}$ from random samples of that size is approximately normal?

(b) If the original distribution of x values is known to be normal, do we need to make any restriction about sample size in order to claim that the distribution of sample means $\bar{x}$ taken from random samples of a given size is normal?

7.6
Normal Approximation to the Binomial Distribution

FOCUS POINTS

✓ State the necessary conditions for the normal approximation to the binomial distribution.

✓ Compute μ and σ for the normal approximation.

✓ Use the continuity correction to convert a range of r values to a corresponding range of normal x values.

✓ Convert the x values to a range of standardized z scores and find desired probabilities.

Large sample criteria $np > 5$ and $nq > 5$

The probability that a new vaccine will protect adults from cholera is known to be 0.85. It is administered to 300 adults who must enter an area where the disease is prevalent. What is the probability that more than 280 of these adults will be protected from cholera by the vaccine?

This question falls into the category of a binomial experiment with the number of trials n equal to 300, the probability of success p equal to 0.85, and the number of successes r greater than 280. It is possible to use the formula for the binomial distribution to compute the probability that r is greater than 280. However, this approach would involve a number of tedious and long calculations. There is an easier way to do this problem, for under the conditions stated below, the normal distribution can be used to approximate the binomial distribution.

Normal approximation to the binomial distribution

Consider a binomial distribution where

n = number of trials

r = number of successes

p = probability of success on a single trial

$q = 1 - p$ = probability of failure on a single trial

If $np > 5$ and $nq > 5$, then r has a binomial distribution that is approximated by a normal distribution with

$$\mu = np \quad \text{and} \quad \sigma = \sqrt{npq}$$

Note: As n increases, the approximation becomes better.

Example 12 demonstrates that as n increases, the normal approximation to the binomial distribution improves.

EXAMPLE 12

Binomial distribution graphs

Graph the binomial distributions for which $p = 0.25$, $q = 0.75$, and the number of trials is first $n = 3$, then $n = 10$, then $n = 25$, and finally $n = 50$.

SOLUTION: The authors used a computer program to obtain the binomial distributions for the given values of p, q, and n. The results have been organized and graphed in Figures 7-31, 7-32, 7-33, and 7-34.

When $n = 3$, the outline of the histogram does not even begin to take the shape of a normal curve. But when $n = 10$, 25, or 50, it does begin to take a normal shape, indicated by the red curve. From a theoretical point of view, the histograms in Figures 7-32, 7-33, and 7-34 would have bars for all values of r from $r = 0$ to $r = n$. However, in the construction of these histograms, the bars of height less

FIGURE 7-31

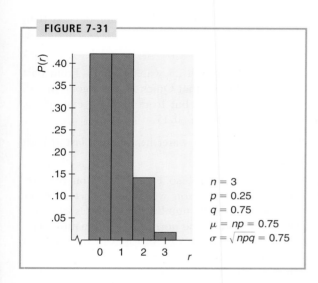

$n = 3$
$p = 0.25$
$q = 0.75$
$\mu = np = 0.75$
$\sigma = \sqrt{npq} = 0.75$

FIGURE 7-32

$n = 10$
$p = 0.25$
$q = 0.75$
$\mu = np = 2.5$
$\sigma = \sqrt{npq} = 1.37$

FIGURE 7-33

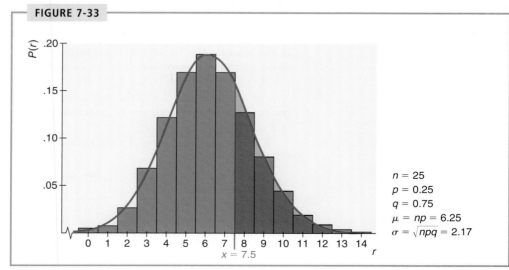

$x = 7.5$

$n = 25$
$p = 0.25$
$q = 0.75$
$\mu = np = 6.25$
$\sigma = \sqrt{npq} = 2.17$

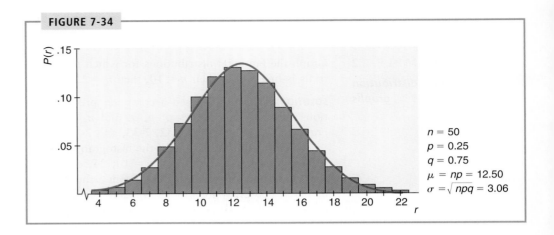

FIGURE 7-34

$n = 50$
$p = 0.25$
$q = 0.75$
$\mu = np = 12.50$
$\sigma = \sqrt{npq} = 3.06$

than 0.001 unit have been omitted—that is, in this example, probabilities less than 0.001 have been rounded to 0. ◆

EXAMPLE 13

Normal approximation

The owner of a new apartment building must install 25 water heaters. From past experience in other apartment buildings, she knows that Quick Hot is a good brand. A Quick Hot heater is guaranteed for 5 years only, but from her past experience, she knows that the probability it will last 10 years is 0.25.

(a) What is the probability that 8 or more of the 25 water heaters will last at least 10 years?

SOLUTION: In this example, $n = 25$ and $p = 0.25$, so Figure 7-33 (on the preceding page) represents the probability distribution we will use. Let r be the binomial random variable corresponding to the number of successes out of $n = 25$ trials. We want to find $P(r \geq 8)$ by using the normal approximation. This probability is represented graphically (Figure 7-33) by the area of the bar over 8 and all bars to the right of the bar over 8.

Let x be a normal random variable corresponding to a normal distribution with $\mu = np = 25(0.25) = 6.25$ and $\sigma = \sqrt{npq} = \sqrt{25(0.25)(0.75)} \approx 2.17$. This normal curve is represented by the red line in Figure 7-33. The area under the normal curve from $x = 7.5$ to the right is approximately the same as the area of the bars from the bar over $r = 8$ to the right. It is important to notice that we start with $x = 7.5$ because the bar over $r = 8$ really starts at $x = 7.5$.

The area of the bars and the area under the corresponding red (normal) curve are approximately equal, so we conclude that $P(r \geq 8)$ is approximately equal to $P(x \geq 7.5)$.

When we convert $x = 7.5$ to standard units, we get

$$z = \frac{x - \mu}{\sigma} = \frac{7.5 - 6.25}{2.17} \qquad \text{(use } \mu = 6.25 \text{ and } \sigma = 2.17\text{)}$$

$$\approx 0.58$$

The probability we want is

$$P(x \geq 7.5) = P(z \geq 0.58)$$
$$= 1 - P(z \leq 0.58)$$
$$= 1 - 0.7190$$
$$= 0.2810$$

(b) How does this result compare with the result we can obtain by using the formula for the binomial probability distribution with $n = 25$ and $p = 0.25$?

SOLUTION: Using the binomial distribution function on the TI-84Plus/TI-83Plus model calculators, the authors computed that $P(r \geq 8) \approx 0.2735$. This means that the probability is approximately 0.27 that 8 or more water heaters will last at least 10 years.

(c) How do the results of parts (a) and (b) compare?

SOLUTION: The error of approximation is the difference between the approximate normal value (0.2810) and the binomial value (0.2735). The error is only $0.2810 - 0.2735 = 0.0075$, which is negligible for most practical purposes.

We knew in advance that the normal approximation to the binomial probability would be good, since $np = 25(0.25) = 6.25$ and $nq \doteq 25(0.75) = 18.75$ are both greater than 5. These are the conditions that assure us that the normal approximation will be sufficiently close to the binomial probability for most practical purposes. ◇

Remember that when using the normal distribution to approximate the binomial, we are computing the areas under bars. The bar over the discrete variable r extends from $r - 0.5$ to $r + 0.5$. This means that the corresponding continuous normal variable x extends from $r - 0.5$ to $r + 0.5$. Adjusting the values of discrete random variables to obtain a corresponding range for a continuous random variable is called making a *continuity correction*.

Continuity correction: converting r values to x values

PROCEDURE

How to make the continuity correction

Convert the discrete random variable r (number of successes) to the continuous normal random variable x by doing the following:

1. If r is a **left-point** of an interval, subtract 0.5 to obtain the corresponding normal variable x; that is, $x = r - 0.5$.

2. If r is a **right-point** of an interval, add 0.5 to obtain the corresponding normal variable x: that is, $x = r + 0.5$.

For instance, $P(6 \leq r \leq 10)$, where r is a binomial random variable, is approximated by $P(5.5 \leq x \leq 10.5)$, where x is the corresponding normal random variable (see Figure 7-35 on the next page).

FIGURE 7-35

$P(6 \le r \le 10)$ Is Approximately Equal to $P(5.5 \le x \le 10.5)$

GUIDED EXERCISE 12

Continuity correction

From many years of observation, a biologist knows that the probability is only 0.65 that any given Arctic tern will survive the migration from its summer nesting area to its winter feeding grounds. A random sample of 500 Arctic terns were banded at their summer nesting area. Use the normal approximation to the binomial and the following steps to find the probability that between 310 and 340 of the banded Arctic terns will survive the migration. Let r be the number of surviving terns.

Arctic tern

(a) To approximate $P(310 \le r \le 340)$, we use the normal curve with $\mu = $ _____ and $\sigma = $ _____ .

   We use the normal curve with

$$\mu = np = 500(0.65) = 325 \quad \text{and}$$
$$\sigma = \sqrt{npq} = \sqrt{500(0.65)(0.35)} \approx 10.67$$

(b) $P(310 \le r \le 340)$ is approximately equal to $P(\underline{\hspace{1cm}} \le x \le \underline{\hspace{1cm}})$, where x is a variable from the normal distribution described in part (a).

   Since 310 is the left endpoint, we subtract 0.5, and since 340 is the right endpoint, we add 0.5. Consequently,

$$P(310 \le r \le 340) \approx P(309.5 \le x \le 340.5)$$

Continued

GUIDED EXERCISE 12 continued

(c) Convert the condition $309.5 \leq x \leq 340.5$ to a condition in standard units.

⟹ Since $\mu = 325$ and $\sigma \approx 10.67$, the condition $309.5 \leq x \leq 340.5$ becomes

$$\frac{309.5 - 325}{10.67} \leq z \leq \frac{340.5 - 325}{10.67} \quad \text{or}$$

$$-1.45 \leq z \leq 1.45$$

(d) $P(310 \leq r \leq 340) = P(309.5 \leq x \leq 340.5)$
$\qquad = P(-1.45 \leq z \leq 1.45)$
$\qquad = \underline{\qquad}$

⟹ $P(-1.45 \leq z \leq 1.45) = P(z \leq 1.45) - P(z \leq -1.45)$
$\qquad\qquad = 0.9265 - 0.0735$
$\qquad\qquad = 0.8530$

(e) Will the normal distribution make a good approximation to the binomial for this problem? Explain your answer.

⟹ Since

$$np = 500(0.65) = 325 \quad \text{and}$$

$$nq = 500(0.35) = 175$$

are both greater than 5, the normal distribution will be a good approximation to the binomial.

VIEWPOINT   *Sunspots, Tree Rings, and Statistics*

Ancient Chinese astronomers recorded extreme sunspot activity with a peak around 1200 A.D. Mesa Verde tree rings in the period between 1276 and 1299 were unusually narrow, indicating a drought and/or a severe cold spell in the region at that time. A cooling trend could have narrowed the window of frost-free days below the approximately 80 days needed for cultivation of aboriginal corn and beans. Is this the reason the ancient Anasazi dwellings in Mesa Verde were abandoned? Is there a connection to the extreme sunspot activity? Much research and statistical work continues to be done on this topic.

Reference: *Prehistoric Astronomy in the Southwest,* by J. McKim Malville and C. Putnam, Department of Astronomy, University of Colorado.

SECTION 7.6   PROBLEMS

Note: When we say *between a and b,* we mean every value from *a* to *b, including a* and *b.* Due to rounding, your answers might vary slightly from answers given in the text.

1. *Health: Lead Contamination* More than a decade ago, high levels of lead in the blood put 88% of children at risk. A concerted effort was made to remove lead from the environment. Now, according to the *Third National Health and Nutrition Examination Survey (NHANES III)* conducted by the Centers for Disease Control, only 9% of children in the United States are at risk of high blood-lead levels.
   (a) In a random sample of 200 children taken more than a decade ago, what is the probability that 50 or more had high blood-lead levels?

(b) In a random sample of 200 children taken now, what is the probability that 50 or more have high blood-lead levels?

2. *Insurance: Claims* Do you try to *pad* an insurance claim to cover your deductible? About 40% of all U.S. adults will try to pad their insurance claims! (Source: *Are You Normal?* by Bernice Kanner, St. Martin's Press.) Suppose that you are the director of an insurance adjustment office. Your office has just received 128 insurance claims to be processed in the next few days. What is the probability that
(a) half or more of the claims have been padded?
(b) fewer than 45 of the claims have been padded?
(c) from 40 to 64 of the claims have been padded?
(d) more than 80 of the claims are *not* padded?

3. *Law Enforcement: Arrests* In Colorado Springs, a local newspaper ran a full page of nearly 100 mug shots of people the police wanted to arrest for serious crimes. Within 1 week, the police received enough information to locate and arrest about 17% of these "wanted" people (reported in *Rocky Mountain News*). If next month the newspaper runs a full page of 125 mug shots of fugitives, what is the probability that the police will receive enough information to locate and arrest (within 1 week)
(a) at least 15 fugitives?
(b) 28 or more fugitives?
(c) between 15 and 28 fugitives?
(d) In the solution to this problem, what is n? p? q? Does it appear that both np and nq are larger than 5? Why is this an important consideration?

4. *Novels: Romance USA Today* reported that 11% of all books sold are of the romance genre. If a local bookstore sells 316 books on a given day, what is the probability that
(a) fewer than 40 are romances?
(b) at least 25 are romances?
(c) between 25 and 40 are romances?
(d) In the solution to this problem, what is n? p? q? Does it appear that both np and nq are larger than 5? Why is this an important consideration?

5. *Longevity: 90th Birthday* It is estimated that 3.5% of the general population will live past their 90th birthday (*Statistical Abstract of the United States*, 112th Edition). In a graduating class of 753 high school seniors, what is the probability that
(a) 15 or more will live beyond their 90th birthday?
(b) 30 or more will live beyond their 90th birthday?
(c) between 25 and 35 will live beyond their 90th birthday?
(d) more than 40 will live beyond their 90th birthday?

6. *Fishing: Billfish* Ocean fishing for billfish is very popular in the Cozumel region of Mexico. In *World Record Game Fishes* (published by the International Game Fish Association), it was stated that in the Cozumel region about 44% of strikes (while trolling) resulted in a catch. Suppose that on a given day a fleet of fishing boats got a total of 24 strikes. What is the probability that the number of fish caught was
(a) 12 or fewer?
(b) 5 or more?
(c) between 5 and 12?
(d) In the solution to this problem, what is n? p? q? Does it appear that both np and nq are larger than 5? Why is this an important consideration?

7. *Grocery Stores: New Products* The *Denver Post* stated that 80% of all new products introduced in grocery stores fail (are taken off the market) within 2 years. If a

grocery store chain introduces 66 new products, what is the probability that within 2 years
(a) 47 or more fail?
(b) 58 or fewer fail?
(c) 15 or more succeed?
(d) fewer than 10 succeed?

8. *Crime: Murder* What are the chances that a person who is murdered actually knew the murderer? The answer to this question explains why a lot of police detective work begins with relatives and friends of the victim! About 64% of the people who are murdered actually knew the person who committed the murder (*Chances: Risk and Odds in Everyday Life,* by James Burke). Suppose that a detective file in New Orleans has 63 current unsolved murders. What is the probability that
(a) at least 35 of the victims knew their murderer?
(b) at most 48 of the victims knew their murderer?
(c) fewer than 30 victims did *not* know their murderer?
(d) more than 20 victims did *not* know their murderer?

9. *Private Investigation: Finding People* Old Friends Information Service is a California company that finds addresses for people who have lost track of each other. Old Friends claims to be 70% successful in reuniting people (*The Wall Street Journal*). In December, Old Friends had 430 requests for addresses of lost acquaintances. What is the probability that the number of addresses found was
(a) more than 280?
(b) at least 320?
(c) between 280 and 320?
(d) In the solution to this problem, what is n? p? q? Does it appear that both np and nq are larger than 5? Why is this an important consideration?

10. *Archaeology: Pottery* Santa Fe black-on-white is a style of pottery that occurs in about 61% of the pot shards found in the Bandelier National Monument area (*Bandelier Archaeological Excavation Project: Summer 1990 Excavations at Burnt Mesa Pueblo,* edited by Kohler, Washington State University). At one excavation site 8641 pot shards have been found that have not yet been cleaned and identified. What is the probability that
(a) fewer than 5200 are Santa Fe black-on-white?
(b) more than 5400 are Santa Fe black-on-white?
(c) between 5200 and 5400 are Santa Fe black-on-white?
(d) In the solution to this problem, what is n? p? q? Does it appear that both np and nq are larger than 5? Why is this an important consideration?

11. *Lawyers: Bar Exam* Over the years, it has been observed that of all the lawyers who take the state bar exam, only 57% pass (information from the National Conference on Bar Examiners, referenced in *The Book of Odds,* by Shook and Shook, Signet). Suppose that this year 850 lawyers are going to take the Ohio bar exam. What is the probability that
(a) 540 or more pass?
(b) 500 or fewer pass?
(c) between 485 and 525 pass?

12. *Ice Cream: Flavors* What's your favorite ice cream? For people who buy ice cream, the all-time favorite is still vanilla. About 25% of ice cream sales are vanilla. Chocolate accounts for only 9% of ice cream sales. (See reference in Problem 2.) Suppose that 175 customers go to a grocery store in Cheyenne, Wyoming, today to buy ice cream.
(a) What is the probability that 50 or more will buy vanilla?

(b) What is the probability that 12 or more will buy chocolate?

(c) A customer who buys ice cream is not limited to one container or one flavor. What is the probability that someone who is buying ice cream will buy chocolate or vanilla? *Hint:* Chocolate flavor and vanilla flavor are not mutually exclusive events. Assume that the choice to buy one flavor is independent of the choice to buy another flavor. Then use the multiplication rule for independent events together with the addition rule for events that are not mutually exclusive to compute the requested probability. (See Section 5.2.)

(d) What is the probability that between 50 and 60 customers buy chocolate or vanilla ice cream? *Hint:* Use the probability of success computed in part (c).

13. *Airline Flights: No-Shows* Based on long experience, an airline found that about 6% of the people making reservations on a flight from Miami to Denver do not show up for the flight. Suppose the airline overbooks this flight by selling 267 ticket reservations for an airplane with only 255 seats.

(a) What is the probability that a person holding a reservation will show up for the flight?

(b) Let $n = 267$ represent the number of ticket reservations. Let r represent the number of people with reservations who show up for the flight. Which expression represents the probability that a seat will be available for everyone who shows up holding a reservation?

$$P(255 \leq r); \qquad P(r \leq 255); \qquad P(r \leq 267); \qquad P(r = 255)$$

(c) Use the normal approximation to the binomial distribution and part (b) to answer the following question: What is the probability that a seat will be available for every person who shows up holding a reservation?

SUMMARY

In this chapter, we examined normal distributions, z scores, raw scores, area under normal curves, $\overline{x}$ sampling distributions, and normal approximations to binomial distributions.

The standard normal distribution has mean $\mu = 0$ and standard deviation $\sigma = 1$. To convert a normal distribution with mean μ and standard deviation σ to the standard normal distribution, we use the formula

$$z = \frac{x - \mu}{\sigma}$$

Probabilities associated with the standard normal distribution are found in Table 3 of the Appendix.

Sampling distributions give us the basis for inferential statistics. By studying the distribution of sample statistics, we can learn about a population parameter.

The central limit theorem describes the sampling distribution of sample means $\overline{x}$ taken from samples of size n. It tells us that for increasing sample size n, the distribution of sample means approaches a normal distribution with mean $\mu_{\overline{x}} = \mu$

and standard deviation $\sigma_{\bar{x}} = \sigma/\sqrt{n}$, where μ and σ are the respective mean and standard deviation of the original x distribution. Using the central limit theorem, we convert $\bar{x}$ values to standard z scores by the formula

$$z = \frac{\bar{x} - \mu}{\sigma/\sqrt{n}}$$

We can use the normal distribution to approximate the binomial distribution if $np > 5$ and $nq > 5$, where n is the number of trials, p is the probability of success on a single trial, and $q = 1 - p$.

IMPORTANT WORDS & SYMBOLS

Section 7.1
Normal distributions
Normal curves
Upward cup and downward cup on normal curves
Symmetry of normal curves
Empirical rule

Section 7.2
z value or z score
Standard units
Standard normal distribution ($\mu = 0$ and $\sigma = 1$)
Raw score, x
Area under the standard normal curve

Section 7.3
Areas under any normal curve

Section 7.4
Population parameter
Statistic
Sampling distribution

Section 7.5
$\mu_{\bar{x}}$
$\sigma_{\bar{x}}$
Standard error of the mean
Central limit theorem

Section 7.6
Normal approximation to the binomial distribution
Continuity correction

VIEWPOINT

Why Wait? Apply Now for a College Loan!

The cost of education is high. The cost of not having an education is higher! What kinds of costs can you expect? What about tuition and student fees? What about room and board? What is the total cost for 1 year at college? Perhaps some averages based on random samples of colleges would be useful. For more information, visit the Brase/Brase statistics site at **http://math.college .hmco.com/students** and find the link to the U.S. News site. Then select Education. Search for the geographic regions of the colleges of interest.

CHAPTER REVIEW PROBLEMS

1. Given that x is a normal variable with mean $\mu = 47$ and standard deviation $\sigma = 6.2$, find
   (a) $P(x \leq 60)$ (b) $P(x \geq 50)$ (c) $P(50 \leq x \leq 60)$

2. Given that x is a normal variable with mean $\mu = 110$ and standard deviation $\sigma = 12$, find
   (a) $P(x \leq 120)$ (b) $P(x \geq 80)$ (c) $P(108 \leq x \leq 117)$

3. Find z such that 5% of the area under the standard normal curve lies to the right of z.

4. Find z such that 99% of the area under the standard normal curve lies between $-z$ and z.

5. *Nursing: Exams* On a practical nursing licensing exam, the mean score is 79 and the standard deviation is 9 points.
   (a) What is the standardized score of a student with a raw score of 87?
   (b) What is the standardized score of a student with a raw score of 79?
   (c) Assuming the scores follow a normal distribution, what is the probability that a score selected at random is above 85?

6. *Aptitude Tests: Mechanical* On an auto mechanic aptitude test, the mean score is 270 points and the standard deviation is 35 points.
   (a) If a student has a standardized score of 1.9, how many points is that?
   (b) If a student has a standardized score of -0.25, how many points is that?
   (c) Assuming the scores follow a normal distribution, what is the probability that a student will get between 200 and 340 points?

7. *Recycling: Aluminum Cans* One environmental group did a study of recycling habits in a California community. It found that 70% of the aluminum cans sold in the area were recycled.
   (a) If 400 cans are sold today, what is the probability that 300 or more will be recycled?
   (b) Of the 400 cans sold, what is the probability that between 260 and 300 will be recycled?

8. *Guarantee: Disc Players* Future Electronics makes compact disc players. Its research department found that the life of the laser beam device is normally distributed, with mean 5000 hours and standard deviation 450 hours.
   (a) Find the probability that the laser beam device will wear out in 5000 hours or less.
   (b) *Inverse Normal Distribution* Future Electronics wants to place a guarantee on the players so that no more than 5% fail during the guarantee period. Because the laser pickup is the part most likely to wear out first, the guarantee period will be based on the life of the laser beam device. How many playing hours should the guarantee cover? (Round to the next playing hour.)

9. *Guarantee: Package Delivery* Express Courier Service has found that the delivery time for packages is normally distributed, with mean 14 hours and standard deviation 2 hours.
   (a) For a package selected at random, what is the probability that it will be delivered in 18 hours or less?

(b) *Inverse Normal Distribution* What should be the guaranteed delivery time on all packages for Express Courier to be 95% sure that the package will be delivered before this time? (*Hint:* Note that 5% of the packages will be delivered at a time beyond the guaranteed time period.)

10. *Medical: Blood Type* Blood type AB is found in only 3% of the population (*Textbook of Medical Physiology,* by A. Guyton, M.D.). If 250 people are chosen at random, what is the probability that
    (a) 5 or more will have this blood type?
    (b) between 5 and 10 will have this blood type?

11. *General Discussion* Let x be a random variable representing the amount of sleep each adult in New York City got last night. Consider a sampling distribution of sample means $\bar{x}$.
    (a) As the sample size becomes increasingly large, what distribution does the $\bar{x}$ distribution approach?
    (b) As the sample size becomes increasingly large, what value will the mean $\mu_{\bar{x}}$ of the $\bar{x}$ distribution approach?
    (c) What value will the standard deviation $\sigma_{\bar{x}}$ of the sampling distribution approach?
    (d) How do the two $\bar{x}$ distributions for sample sizes $n = 50$ and $n = 100$ compare?

12. *Drugs: Effects* A new muscle relaxant is available. Researchers from the firm developing the relaxant have done studies that indicate that the time lapse between administration of the drug and beginning effects of the drug is normally distributed, with mean $\mu = 38$ minutes and standard deviation $\sigma = 5$ minutes.
    (a) The drug is administered to one patient selected at random. What is the probability that the time it takes for the drug to go into effect is 35 minutes or less?
    (b) The drug is administered to a random sample of 10 patients. What is the probability that the average time before the drug is effective for all 10 patients is 35 minutes or less?
    (c) Comment on the differences between the results in parts (a) and (b).

13. *Psychology: IQ Scores* Assume that IQ scores are normally distributed with a standard deviation of 15 points and a mean of 100 points. If 100 people are chosen at random, what is the probability that the sample mean of IQ scores will not differ from the population mean by more than 2 points?

14. *Meteorology: Miami and Fairbanks* Let x be a random variable that represents daily high temperatures (in degrees Fahrenheit) in January. The following information is based on a report from the U.S. Department of Commerce Environmental Data Services. For Miami, Florida, the mean of the x distribution is $\mu = 76$, and the standard deviation is approximately $\sigma = 1.9$. For Fairbanks, Alaska, the mean of the x distribution is $\mu = 0$ with approximate standard deviation $\sigma = 5.3$. Assume that x has a normal distribution.
    (a) For one day chosen at random in January, what is the probability that the high temperature in Miami will be less than 77°F? What is the probability that the high temperature in Fairbanks will be less than 3°F?
    (b) If we choose $n = 7$ days in January, what can we say about the probability distribution of $\bar{x}$, the average high temperature? What is the probability that $\bar{x}$ is less than 77°F for Miami? less than 3°F for Fairbanks?

(c) Suppose we cannot assume that x has a normal distribution, but we can say that the distribution is approximately symmetrical and mound-shaped. In this case, what can we say about the $\bar{x}$ probability distribution? If we use all 31 days in January, what is the probability that $\bar{x} < 77°F$ in Miami? less than 3°F in Fairbanks?

DATA HIGHLIGHTS: GROUP PROJECTS

Break into small groups and discuss the following topics. Organize a brief outline in which you summarize the main points of your group discussion.

Iris setosa is a beautiful wildflower that is found in such diverse places as Alaska, the Gulf of St. Lawrence, much of North America, and even in English meadows and parks. R. A. Fisher, with his colleague Dr. Edgar Anderson, studied these flowers extensively. Dr. Anderson described how he collected information on irises:

> I have studied such irises as I could get to see, in as great detail as possible, measuring iris standard after iris standard and iris fall after iris fall, sitting squat-legged with record book and ruler in mountain meadows, in cypress swamps, on lake beaches, and in English parks. [Anderson, E., "The Irises of the Gaspé Peninsula," *Bulletin, American Iris Society*, 59:2–5, 1935.]

The data in Table 7-10 were collected by Dr. Anderson and were published by his friend and colleague R. A. Fisher in a paper entitled "The Use of Multiple Measurements in Taxonomic Problems" (*Annals of Eugenics*, part II, 179–188, 1936). To find these data, visit the Brase/Brase statistics site at **http://math.college.hmco.com/students** and find the link to DASL, the Carnegie Mellon University Data and Story Library. From the DASL site, look under famous data sets.

Let x be a random variable representing petal length. Using a TI-84Plus/TI-83Plus calculator, it was found that the sample mean for the petal length data is $\bar{x} = 1.46$ cm and the sample standard deviation is $s = 0.17$ cm. Figure 7-36 shows a histogram for the given data generated on a TI-84Plus/TI-83Plus calculator.

(a) Examine the histogram for petal lengths. Would you say that the distribution is approximately mound-shaped and symmetrical? Our sample has only 50 irises; if many thousands of irises had been used, do you think that the distribution would

Wild iris

TABLE 7-10   Petal Length in Centimeters for *Iris setosa*

1.4	1.4	1.3	1.5	1.4
1.7	1.4	1.5	1.4	1.5
1.5	1.6	1.4	1.1	1.2
1.5	1.3	1.4	1.7	1.5
1.7	1.5	1	1.7	1.9
1.6	1.6	1.5	1.4	1.6
1.6	1.5	1.5	1.4	1.5
1.2	1.3	1.4	1.3	1.5
1.3	1.3	1.3	1.6	1.9
1.4	1.6	1.4	1.5	1.4

FIGURE 7-36

Petal Length (cm) for *Iris setosa* (TI-84Plus/TI-83Plus)

look even more like a normal curve? Let x be the petal length of *Iris setosa*. Research has shown that x has an approximately normal distribution, with mean $\mu = 1.5$ cm and standard deviation $\sigma = 0.2$ cm.

(b) Use the empirical rule with $\mu = 1.5$ and $\sigma = 0.2$ to get an interval in which approximately 68% of the petal lengths will fall. Repeat this for 95% and 99.7%. Examine the raw data and compute the percentage of the raw data that actually falls into each of these intervals (the 68% interval, the 95% interval, and the 99.7% interval). Compare your computed percentages with those given by the empirical rule.

(c) Compute the probability that a petal length is between 1.3 and 1.6 cm. Compute the probability that a petal length is greater than 1.6 cm.

(d) Suppose that a random sample of 30 irises is obtained. Compute the probability that the average petal length for this sample is between 1.3 and 1.6 cm. Compute the probability that the average petal length is greater than 1.6 cm.

(e) Compare your answers for parts (c) and (d). Do you notice any differences? Why would these differences occur?

LINKING CONCEPTS: WRITING PROJECTS

Discuss each of the following topics in class or review the topics on your own. Then write a brief but complete essay in which you summarize the main points. Please include formulas and graphs as appropriate.

1. Why are standard z values so important? Is it true that z values have no units of measurement? Why would this be desirable for comparing data sets with *different* units of measurement? How can we assess differences in quality or performance by simply comparing z values under a standard normal curve? Examine the formula to compute standard z values. Notice that it involves *both* the mean and standard deviation. Recall that in Chapter 2 we commented that the mean of a data collection is not entirely adequate to describe the data; you need the standard deviation as well. Discuss this topic again in the light of what you now know about normal distributions and standard z values.

2. Most people would agree that increased information should give better predictions. Discuss how sampling distributions actually enable better predictions by providing more information. Examine Theorem 7.1 again. Suppose that x is a random variable with a *normal* distribution. Then $\bar{x}$, the sample mean based on random samples of size n, also will have a normal distribution for *any* value of $n = 1, 2, 3, \ldots$.

   What happens to the standard deviation of the $\bar{x}$ distribution as n (the sample size) increases? Consider the following table for different values of n.

n	1	2	3	4	10	50	100
$\sigma/\sqrt{n}$	1σ	0.71σ	0.58σ	0.50σ	0.32σ	0.14σ	0.10σ

In this case, "increased information" means a larger sample size n. Give a brief explanation as to why a *large* standard deviation will usually result in poor statistical predictions, whereas a *small* standard deviation usually results in much better predictions. Since the standard deviation of the sampling distribution $\bar{x}$ is $\sigma/\sqrt{n}$, we can decrease the standard deviation by increasing n. In fact, if we look at the preceding table, we see that if we use a sample size of only $n = 4$, we cut the standard deviation of $\bar{x}$ to 50% of the standard deviation σ of x. If we were to use a sample of size $n = 100$, we would cut the standard deviation of $\bar{x}$ to 10% of the standard deviation σ of x.

Give the preceding discussion some thought and explain why you should get much better predictions for μ by using $\bar{x}$ from a sample of size n rather than by just using x. Write a brief essay in which you explain why sampling distributions are an important tool in statistics.

As we have seen in this chapter, the value of a sample statistic such as $\bar{x}$ varies from one sample to another. The central limit theorem describes the distribution of the sample statistic $\bar{x}$ when samples are sufficiently large.

We can use technology tools to generate samples of the same size from the same population. Then we can look at the statistic $\bar{x}$ for each sample, and the resulting $\bar{x}$ distribution.

Project Illustrating the Central Limit Theorem

Step 1: Generate random samples of specified size n from a population.

   The random-number table enables us to sample from the uniform distribution of digits 0 through 9. Use either the random-number table or a random-number generator to generate 30 samples of size 10.

Step 2: Compute the sample mean $\bar{x}$ of the digits in each sample.

Step 3: Compute the sample mean of the means (i.e., $\bar{x}_{\bar{x}}$) as well as the standard deviation $s_{\bar{x}}$ of the sample means.

The population mean of the uniform distribution of digits from 0 through 9 is 4.5. How does $\bar{x}_{\bar{x}}$ compare to this value?

Step 4: Compare the sample distribution of $\bar{x}$ values to a normal distribution having the mean and standard deviation computed in Step 3.

   (a) Use the values of $\bar{x}_{\bar{x}}$ and $s_{\bar{x}}$ computed in Step 3 to create the intervals shown in column 1 of Table 7-11.

   (b) Tally the sample means computed in Step 2 to determine how many fall into each interval of column 2. Then compute the percent of data in each interval and record the results in column 3.

   (c) The percentages listed in column 4 are those from a normal distribution (see Figure 7-3 showing the empirical rule). Compare the percentages in column 3 to those in column 4. How do the sample percentages compare with the hypothetical normal distribution?

Step 5: Create a histogram showing the sample means computed in Step 2.

TABLE 7-11   Frequency Table of Sample Means

1. Interval	2. Frequency	3. Percent	4. Hypothetical Normal Distribution
$\bar{x} - 3s$ to $\bar{x} - 2s$	Tally the sample means computed in step 2 and place here.	Compute percents from column 2 and place here.	2 or 3%
$\bar{x} - 2s$ to $\bar{x} - s$			13 or 14%
$\bar{x} - s$ to $\bar{x}$			About 34%
$\bar{x}$ to $\bar{x} + s$			About 34%
$\bar{x} + s$ to $\bar{x} + 2s$			13 or 14%
$\bar{x} + 2s$ to $\bar{x} + 3s$			2 or 3%

Look at the histogram, and compare it to a normal distribution with the mean and standard deviation of the $\bar{x}$'s (as computed in Step 3).

Step 6: Compare the results of this project to the central limit theorem.

Increase the sample size of Step 1 to 20, 30, and 40 and repeat Steps 1 to 5.

Technology Hints

The TI-84Plus and TI-83Plus calculators, Excel, Minitab, and SPSS all support the process of drawing random samples from a variety of distributions. Macros can be written in Excel, Minitab, and the professional version of SPSS to repeat the six steps of the project. Figure 7-37 shows histograms generated by SPSS for random samples of size 30 and size 100. The samples are taken from a uniform probability distribution.

TI-84Plus/TI-83Plus

You can generate random samples from uniform, normal, and binomial distributions. Press **MATH** and select **PRB**. Selection **5:randInt(lower, upper, sample size m)** generates m random integers from the specified interval. Selection **6:randNorm(μ, σ, sample size m)** generates m random numbers from a normal distribution with mean μ and standard deviation σ. Selection **7:randBin(number of trials n, p, sample size m)** generates m random values (number of successes out of n trials) for a binomial distribution with probability of success p on each trial. You can put these values in lists by using **Edit**

FIGURE 7-37 SPSS-Generated Histograms for Samples of Size 30 and Size 100

(a) $n = 30$

(b) $n = 100$

under **Stat.** Highlight the list header, press Enter, and then select one of the options discussed.

Excel

Use the menu selection **Tools ➤ Data Analysis ➤ Random Number Generator.** The dialogue box provides choices for the population distribution, including uniform, binomial, and normal distributions. Fill in the required parameters and designate the location for the output.

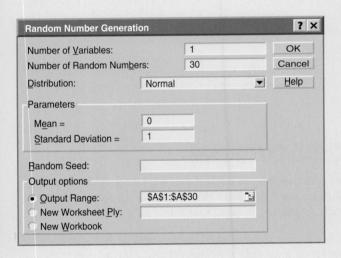

Minitab

Use the menu selection **Calc ➤ Random Data.** Then select the population distribution. The choices include uniform, binomial, and normal distributions. Fill in the

dialogue box, where the number of rows indicates the number of data in the sample.

SPSS

SPSS supports random samples from a variety of distributions, including binomial, normal, and uniform. In data view, generate a column of consecutive integers from 1 to n, where n is the sample size. In variable view, name the variables sample1, sample2, and so on through sample30. These variables head the columns containing each of the 30 samples of size n. Then use the menu choices **Transform ➤ Compute.** In the dialogue box, use sample 1 as the target variable for the first sample, and so forth. In the function box, select **RV.UNIFORM(min,max)** for samples from a uniform distribution. Functions **RV.NORMAL(mean,stddev)** and **RV.BINOM(n,p)** provide random samples from normal and binomial distributions, respectively.

8

Estimation

We dance round in a ring and suppose,
But the Secret sits in the middle and knows.

—Robert Frost,
"The Secret Sits"[*]

In Chapter 1 we said that statistics is the study of how to collect, organize, analyze, and interpret numerical data. That part of statistics concerned with analysis, interpretation, and forming conclusions about the source of the data is called *statistical inference*. Problems of statistical inference require us to draw a *sample* of observations from a larger *population*. A sample usually contains incomplete information, so in a sense we must "dance round in a ring and suppose." Nevertheless, conclusions about the population can be obtained from sample data by the use of statistical estimates. This chapter introduces you to several widely used methods of estimation.

[*]*Source:* From *The Poetry of Robert Frost*, edited by Edward Connery Lathem. Copyright 1942 by Robert Frost, © 1970 by Lesley Frost Ballantine, © 1969 by Henry Holt and Company. Reprinted by permission of Henry Holt and Company, LLC.

**Robert Lee Frost
(1874–1963)**

This celebrated American poet drew poetic symbols largely from common experiences observed in his rural New England.

For on-line student resources, visit **math.college.hmco.com/students** and follow the Statistics links to the Brase/Brase, *Understanding Basic Statistics,* 4th edition web site.

PREVIEW QUESTIONS

◇ How do you estimate the expected value of a random variable? What assumptions are needed? How much confidence should be placed in such estimates? (SECTION 8.1)

◇ If you start out in the beginning design stage of a statistical project, how large a sample size should you plan to get? (SECTION 8.1)

◇ What famous statistician worked for Guinness brewing company in Ireland? What has this to do with constructing estimates from sample data? (SECTION 8.2)

◇ How do you estimate the proportion p for success in a binomial experiment? How does the normal approximation fit into this process? (SECTION 8.3)

FOCUS PROBLEM

Trick or Treat!!!

About 28% of U.S. households turn out the lights and pretend not to be at home on Halloween (*Source: Are You Normal About Money?* by Bernice Kanner, Bloomberg Press).

Alice is a sociology student who is studying the affluent Cherry Creek neighborhood in Denver. As part of a larger survey, Alice interviewed a random sample of 35 households. One of the questions she asked was whether the resident turned out the lights and pretended not to be at home on Halloween. It was found that 11 of the 35 residents actually did this practice.

(a) Compute a 90% confidence interval or p, the proportion of all households in Cherry Creek that pretend not to be at home on Halloween.

(b) What assumptions are necessary to calculate the confidence interval of part (a)? Do you think these assumptions are met in this case? Explain.

(c) The national proportion is about 0.28. Is 0.28 in the confidence interval you computed? Based on your answer, does it seem that the Cherry Creek neighborhood is much different (either higher or lower proportion) from the population of all U.S. households? Explain.

(See Problem 8 of Section 8.3.)

8.1
Estimating μ When σ Is Known

FOCUS POINTS

✓ Explain the meaning of confidence level, error of estimate, and critical value.

✓ Find the critical value corresponding to a given confidence level.

✓ Compute confidence intervals for μ when σ is known. Interpret the results.

✓ Compute the sample size to be used for estimating a mean μ.

Because of time and money constraints, difficulty in finding population members, and so forth, we usually do not have access to *all* measurements of an *entire* population. Instead we rely on information from a sample.

In this section, we develop techniques for estimating the population mean μ using sample data. We assume the population standard deviation σ is known.

Let's begin by listing some basic assumptions used in the development of our formulas for estimating μ when σ is known.

Assumptions about the random variable x

1. We have a *simple random sample* of size n drawn from a population of x values.

2. The value of σ, the population standard deviation of x, *is known*.

3. If the x *distribution is normal*, then our methods work for *any sample size n*.

4. If x has an unknown distribution, then we require a *sample size $n \geq 30$*. However, if the x distribution is distinctly skewed and definitely not mound-shaped, a sample of size 50 or even 100 or higher may be necessary.

Point estimate

An estimate of a population parameter given by a single number is called a *point estimate* for that parameter. It will come as no great surprise that we use $\bar{x}$ (the sample mean) as the point estimate for μ (the population mean).

A **point estimate** of a population parameter is an estimate of the parameter using a single number.

$\bar{x}$ is the **point estimate** for μ.

Margin of error

Even with a large random sample, the value of $\bar{x}$ usually is not *exactly* equal to the population mean μ. The *margin of error* is the magnitude of the difference between the sample point estimate and the true population parameter value.

When using $\bar{x}$ as a point estimate for μ, the **margin of error** is the magnitude of $\bar{x} - \mu$ or $|\bar{x} - \mu|$.

We cannot say exactly how close $\bar{x}$ is to μ when μ is unknown. Therefore, the exact margin of error is unknown when the population parameter is unknown. Of course, μ is usually not known or there would be no need to estimate it. In this section, we will use the language of probability to give us an idea of the size of the margin of error when we use $\bar{x}$ as a point estimate for μ.

First, we need to learn about *confidence levels*. The reliability of an estimate will be measured by the confidence level.

Suppose we want a confidence level of c (see Figure 8-1). Theoretically, you can choose c to be any value between 0 and 1, but usually c is equal to a number such

FIGURE 8-1

Confidence Level c and Corresponding Critical Value z_c Shown on the Standard Normal Curve

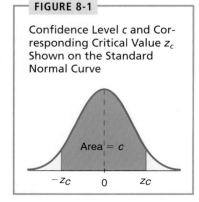

Finding the critical value

as 0.90, 0.95, or 0.99. In each case, the value z_c is the number such that the area under the standard normal curve falling between $-z_c$ and z_c is equal to c. The value z_c is called the *critical value* for a confidence level of c.

> For a confidence level c, the **critical value** z_c is the number such that the area under the standard normal curve between $-z_c$ and z_c equals c.

The area under the normal curve from $-z_c$ to z_c is the probability that the standardized normal variable z lies in that interval. This means that

$$P(-z_c < z < z_c) = c$$

EXAMPLE 1

Find a critical value

Let us use Table 3 of the Appendix to find a number $z_{0.99}$ such that 99% of the area under the standard normal curve lies between $-z_{0.99}$ and $z_{0.99}$. That is, we will find $z_{0.99}$ such that

$$P(-z_{0.99} < z < z_{0.99}) = 0.99$$

SOLUTION: In Section 7.3, we saw how to find the z value when we were given an area between $-z$ and z. The first thing we did was to find the corresponding area to the left of $-z$. If A is the area between $-z$ and z, then $(1 - A)/2$ is the area to the left of z. In our case, the area between $-z$ and z is 0.99. The corresponding area in the left tail is $(1 - 0.99)/2 = 0.005$ (see Figure 8-2).

Next, we use Table 3 of the Appendix to find the z value corresponding to a left-tail area of 0.0050. Table 8-1 shows an excerpt from Table 3 of the Appendix.

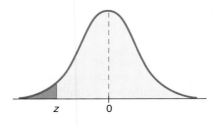

TABLE 8-1   Excerpt from Table 3 of the Appendix

z	.00	...	.07	.08	.09
-3.4	.0003		.0003	.0003	.0002
⋮					
-2.5	.0062		.0051	.0049	.0048
				↑ .0050	

From Table 8-1, we see that the desired area, 0.0050, is exactly halfway between the areas corresponding to $z = -2.58$ and $z = -2.57$. Because the two area values are so close together, we use the more conservative z value -2.58 rather than interpolate. In fact, $z_{0.99} \approx 2.576$. However, to two decimal places, we use $z_{0.99} = 2.58$ as the critical value for a confidence level of $c = 0.99$. We have

$$P(-2.58 < z < 2.58) = 0.99 \qquad \diamond$$

The results of Example 1 will be used a great deal in our later work. For convenience, Table 8-2 gives some levels of confidence and corresponding critical values z_c. The same information is provided in Table 3(b) of the Appendix.

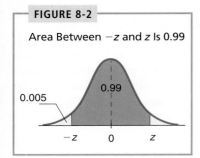

FIGURE 8-2

Area Between $-z$ and z Is 0.99

0.99

0.005

TABLE 8-2 Some Levels of Confidence and Their Corresponding Critical Values

Level of Confidence c	Critical Value z_c
0.70, or 70%	1.04
0.75, or 75%	1.15
0.80, or 80%	1.28
0.85, or 85%	1.44
0.90, or 90%	1.645
0.95, or 95%	1.96
0.98, or 98%	2.33
0.99, or 99%	2.58

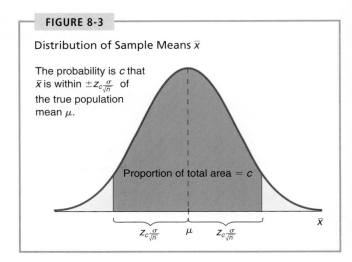

FIGURE 8-3

Distribution of Sample Means $\bar{x}$

The probability is c that $\bar{x}$ is within $\pm z_c \frac{\sigma}{\sqrt{n}}$ of the true population mean μ.

Proportion of total area = c

An estimate is not very valuable unless we have some kind of measure of how "good" it is. The language of probability can give us an idea of the size of the margin of error caused by using the sample mean $\bar{x}$ as an estimate for the population mean.

Remember that $\bar{x}$ is a random variable. Each time we draw a sample of size n from a population, we can get a different value for $\bar{x}$. According to the central limit theorem, if the sample size is large, then $\bar{x}$ has a distribution that is approximately normal with mean $\mu_{\bar{x}} = \mu$, the population mean we are trying to estimate. The standard deviation is $\sigma_{\bar{x}} = \sigma/\sqrt{n}$. If x has a normal distribution, these results are true *for any sample size*. (See Theorem 7.1.)

This information, together with our work on confidence levels, leads us to the probability statement

$$P\left(-z_c\frac{\sigma}{\sqrt{n}} < \bar{x} - \mu < z_c\frac{\sigma}{\sqrt{n}}\right) = c \tag{1}$$

◇ **COMMENT** To derive Equation (1), we start with the probability statement $P(-z_c < z < z_c) = c$. Since $n \geq 30$, we can use the central limit theorem and replace z by $(\bar{x} - \mu)/(\sigma/\sqrt{n})$. Finally, we multiply all parts of the inequality by $(\sigma/\sqrt{n})$ to obtain Equation (1). ◇

Equation (1) uses the language of probability to give us an idea of the size of the margin of error for the corresponding confidence level c. In words, Equation (1) states that the probability is c that our point estimate $\bar{x}$ is within a distance $\pm z_c(\sigma/\sqrt{n})$ of the population mean μ. This relationship is shown in Figure 8-3.

The *margin of error* (or absolute error) using $\bar{x}$ as a point estimate for μ is $|\bar{x} - \mu|$. In most practical problems, μ is unknown, so the margin of error is also unknown. However, Equation (1) allows us to compute an *error tolerance E*, which serves as a bound on the margin of error. Using a $c\%$ level of confidence, we can say that the point estimate $\bar{x}$ differs from the population mean μ by a *maximal margin of error*

Maximal margin of error, E

$$E = z_c\frac{\sigma}{\sqrt{n}} \tag{2}$$

Note: Formula (2) for E is based on the fact that the sampling distribution for $\bar{x}$ is exactly normal, with mean μ and standard deviation $\sigma/\sqrt{n}$. This occurs whenever the x distribution is normal with mean μ and standard deviation σ. If the x distribution is not normal, then according to the central limit theorem, large samples ($n \geq 30$) produce an $\bar{x}$ distribution that is approximately normal with mean μ and standard deviation $\sigma/\sqrt{n}$.

Using Equations (1) and (2), we conclude that

$$P(-E < \bar{x} - \mu < E) = c \tag{3}$$

Confidence interval for μ with σ known

Applying a little algebra to formula (3) produces

$$P(\bar{x} - E < \mu < \bar{x} + E) = c \tag{4}$$

Equation (4) states that there is a chance of c that the interval from $\bar{x} - E$ to $\bar{x} + E$ contains the population mean μ. We call this interval a *c confidence interval for μ.*

> A *c* **confidence interval for μ** is an interval computed from sample data in such a way that c is the probability of generating an interval containing the actual value of μ.

We may get a different confidence interval for each different sample that is taken. Some intervals will contain the population mean μ and others will not. However, in the long run, the proportion of confidence intervals that contain μ is c.

PROCEDURE

How to find a confidence interval for μ when σ is known

Let x be a random variable appropriate to your application. Obtain a simple random sample (of size n) of x values from which you compute the sample mean $\bar{x}$. The value of σ is already known (perhaps from a previous study).

If you can assume that x has a normal distribution, then any sample size n will work. If you cannot assume this, then use a sample size of $n \geq 30$.

Confidence interval for μ when σ is known

$$\bar{x} - E < \mu < \bar{x} + E \tag{5}$$

where $\bar{x}$ = sample mean of a simple random sample

$$E = z_c \frac{\sigma}{\sqrt{n}}$$

c = confidence level ($0 < c < 1$)

z_c = critical value for confidence level c based on the standard normal distribution (See Table 3(b) of the Appendix for frequently used values.)

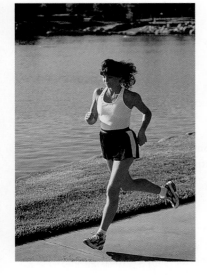

EXAMPLE 2

Confidence interval for μ with σ known

Julia enjoys jogging. She has been jogging over a period of several years, during which time her physical condition has remained constantly good. Usually, she jogs 2 miles per day. The standard deviation of her times is $\sigma = 1.80$ min. During the past year Julia has recorded her times required to run 2 miles. She has a random sample of 90 of these times. For these 90 times the mean was $\bar{x} = 15.60$ minutes. Let μ be the mean jogging time for the entire distribution of Julia's 2-mile running times (taken over the past year). Find a 0.95 confidence interval for μ.

SOLUTION: The interval from $\bar{x} - E$ to $\bar{x} + E$ will be a 95% confidence interval for μ. In this case, $c = 0.95$, so $z_c = 1.96$ (see Table 8-2). The sample size $n = 90$ is large enough for the $\bar{x}$ distribution to be approximately normal, with mean μ and standard deviation $\sigma/\sqrt{n}$. Therefore,

$$E = z_c \frac{\sigma}{\sqrt{n}}$$

$$E = 1.96\left(\frac{1.80}{\sqrt{90}}\right)$$

$$E \approx 0.37$$

Using Equation (5), the given value of $\bar{x}$, and our computed value for E, we get the 95% confidence interval for μ.

$$\bar{x} - E < \mu < \bar{x} + E$$
$$15.60 - 0.37 < \mu < 15.60 + 0.37$$
$$15.23 < \mu < 15.97$$

We conclude with 95% confidence that the interval from 15.23 min. to 15.97 min. is one that contains the population mean μ of jogging times for Julia.   ◇

A few comments are in order about the general meaning of the term *confidence interval*. It is important to realize that the endpoints $\bar{x} \pm E$ are really statistical *variables*. Equation (4) states that we have a chance c of obtaining a sample such that the interval, once it is computed, will contain the parameter μ. Of course, after the confidence interval is numerically fixed, it either does or does not contain μ. So the probability is 1 or 0 that the interval, when it is fixed, will contain μ. A nontrivial probability statement can be made only about variables, not constants. Therefore, Equation (4) really states that if we repeat the experiment many times and get lots of confidence intervals (for the same sample size), then the proportion of all intervals that will turn out to contain the mean μ is c.

In Figure 8-4, the horizontal lines represent 0.90 confidence intervals for various samples of the same size from a distribution. Some of these intervals contain μ, and others do not. Since the intervals are 0.90 confidence intervals, about 90% of all such intervals should contain μ. For each sample, the interval goes from $\bar{x} - E$ to $\bar{x} + E$.

◇ **COMMENT** Please see Using Technology at the end of this chapter for a computer demonstration of this discussion about confidence intervals.   ◇

FIGURE 8-4

0.90 Confidence Intervals for Samples of the Same Size

For each sample the interval goes from $\bar{x} - E$ to $\bar{x} + E$

μ

GUIDED EXERCISE **1**

Confidence interval for μ with σ known

Walter usually meets Julia at the track. He prefers to jog 3 miles. From long experience, he knows that $\sigma = 2.40$ minutes for his jogging times. For a random sample of 90 jogging sessions, his mean time was $\bar{x} = 22.50$ minutes. Let μ be the mean jogging time for the entire distribution of Walter's 3-mile jogging times over the past several years. Find a 0.99 confidence interval for μ.

(a) What is the value of $z_{0.99}$? (See Table 8-2.)

⟹ $z_{0.99} = 2.58$

(b) Is the $\bar{x}$ distribution approximately normal?

⟹ Yes; we know this from the central limit theorem.

(c) What is the value of E?

⟹ $E = z_c \dfrac{\sigma}{\sqrt{n}} = 2.58 \left(\dfrac{2.40}{\sqrt{90}} \right) \approx 0.65$

(d) What are the endpoints for a 0.99 confidence interval for μ?

⟹ The endpoints are given by

$\bar{x} - E \approx 22.50 - 0.65 = 21.85$

$\bar{x} + E \approx 22.50 + 0.65 = 23.15$

(e) How can we interpret the confidence interval?

⟹ We are 99% certain that the interval from 21.85 to 23.15 is an interval that contains the population mean time μ.

When we use samples to estimate the mean of a population, we generate a small error. However, samples are useful even when it is possible to survey the entire population because the use of a sample may yield savings of time or effort in collecting data.

TECH NOTE The TI-84Plus and TI-83Plus calculators, Excel, and Minitab all support confidence intervals for μ when σ is known. The level of support varies according to the technology. When a confidence interval is given, the standard mathematical notation (lower value, upper value) is used. For instance, the notation (15.23, 15.97) means the interval from 15.23 to 15.97.

TI-84Plus/TI-83Plus This calculator gives the most extensive support. The user can opt to enter raw data or just summary statistics. In each case, the value of σ must be specified. Press the **STAT** key and select **TESTS,** then use **7:ZInterval.** The TI-84Plus/ TI-83Plus output shows the results for Example 2.

```
ZInterval
 Inpt:Data Stats
 σ:1.8
 x̄:15.6
 n:90
 C-Level:95
 Calculate
```

```
ZInterval
 (15.228, 15.972)
 x̄=15.6
 n=90
```

Excel Excel gives only the value of the maximal error of estimate E. Use the menu choice **Paste Function** (f_x) ➤ **Statistics** ➤ **Confidence(alpha, σ, n).** In the dialogue box, the value of alpha is $1 -$ confidence level. The Excel output shows the value of E for Example 2.

=	=CONFIDENCE(0.05,1.8,90)		
C	D	E	
0.371876			

An alternate approach incorporating raw data (using the Student's t distribution presented in the next section) uses the menu choices **Tools ➤ Data Analysis ➤ Describe Statistics.** Again, the value of E for the interval is given.

Minitab Raw data are required. Use the menu choices **Stat ➤ Basic Statistics ➤ 1-SampleZ.**

Sample Size for Estimating the Mean μ

In the design stages of statistical research projects, it is a good idea to decide in advance on the confidence level you wish to use and to select the *maximum* margin of error E you want for your project. How you choose to make these decisions depends on the requirements of the project and the practical nature of the problem.

Whatever specifications you make, the next step is to determine the sample size. Solving the formula that gives the maximal margin of error E for n enables us to determine the minimum sample size.

> **PROCEDURE**
>
> **How to find the sample size n for estimating μ when σ is known**
>
> Assuming the distribution of sample means $\overline{x}$ is approximately normal, then
>
> $$n = \left(\frac{z_c \sigma}{E}\right)^2 \tag{6}$$
>
> where E = specified maximal error of estimate
>
> σ = population standard deviation
>
> z_c = critical value from the normal distribution for the desired confidence level c. Commonly used values of z_c can be found in Table 3(b) of the Appendix.
>
> If n is not a whole number, increase n to the next higher whole number. Note that n is the minimal sample size for a specified confidence level and maximal error of estimate E.

◇ **COMMENT:** If you have a *preliminary study* involving a sample size of 30 or larger, then for most practical purposes it is safe to approximate σ with the sample standard deviation s in the formula for sample size.   ◇

EXAMPLE 3

Sample size for estimating μ

A wildlife study is designed to find the mean weight of salmon caught by an Alaskan fishing company. A recent study of a random sample of 50 salmon showed $s \approx 2.15$ lb. How large a sample should be taken to be 99% confident that the sample mean $\overline{x}$ is within 0.20 lb of the true mean weight μ?

SOLUTION: In this problem, $z_{0.99} = 2.58$ (see Table 8-2) and $E = 0.20$. The preliminary study of 50 fish is large enough to permit a good approximation of σ by $s = 2.15$. Therefore, Equation (6) becomes

$$n = \left(\frac{z_c \sigma}{E}\right)^2 \approx \left(\frac{(2.58)(2.15)}{0.20}\right)^2 = 769.2$$

Note: In determining sample size, any fractional value of n is always rounded to the *next higher whole number*. We conclude that a sample size of 770 will be large enough to satisfy the specifications. Of course, a sample size larger than 770 also works.   ◇

Salmon moving upstream

VIEWPOINT   *Music and Techno Theft*

Performing rights organizations ASCAP (American Society of Composers, Authors, and Publishers) and BMI (Broadcast Music, Inc.) collect royalties for songwriters and music publishers. Radio, television, cable, nightclubs, restaurants, elevators, and even beauty parlors play music that is copyrighted by a composer or publisher. The royalty payment for this music turns out to be more than a billion dollars a year (Source: *The Wall Street Journal*). How do ASCAP and BMI know who is playing what music? The answer is, they don't know! Instead of tracking *exactly* what gets played, they use random sampling and *confidence intervals*. For example, each radio station (there are more than 10,000 in the U.S.) has randomly chosen days of programming analyzed every year. The results are used to assess royalty fees. In fact, Deloitte & Touche (a financial services company) administers the sampling process.

Although the system is not perfect, it helps bring order into an otherwise chaotic accounting system. Such methods of "copyright policing" help prevent techno theft, ensuring that many songwriters and recording artists get a reasonable return for their creative work.

SECTION 8.1   PROBLEMS

Answers may vary slightly due to rounding.

1. *Zoology: Hummingbirds* Allen's hummingbird (*Selasphorus sasin*) has been studied by zoologist Bill Alther (Reference: *Hummingbirds*, K. Long and W. Alther). A small group of 15 Allen's hummingbirds has been under study in Arizona. The average weight for these birds is $\bar{x} = 3.15$ gm. Based on previous studies, we can assume that the weights of Allen's hummingbirds have a normal distribution with $\sigma = 0.33$ gm.
   (a) Find an 80% confidence interval for the average weights of Allen's hummingbirds in the study region. What is the margin of error?
   (b) What conditions are necessary for your calculations?
   (c) Give a brief interpretation of your results in the context of this problem.
   (d) *Sample Size* Find the sample size necessary for an 80% confidence level with a maximal error of estimate $E = 0.08$ for the mean weights of the hummingbirds.

2. *Diagnostic Tests: Uric Acid* Overproduction of uric acid in the body can be an indication of cell breakdown. This may be an advance indication of illness such as gout, leukemia, or lymphoma (Reference: *Manual of Laboratory and Diagnostic Tests*, F. Fischbach). Over a period of months, an adult male patient has taken eight blood tests for uric acid. The mean concentration was $\bar{x} = 5.35$ mg/dl. The distribution of uric acid in healthy adult males can be assumed to be normal with $\sigma = 1.85$ mg/dl.
   (a) Find a 95% confidence interval for the population mean concentration of uric acid in this patient's blood. What is the margin of error?
   (b) What conditions are necessary for your calculations?
   (c) Give a brief interpretation of your results in the context of this problem.
   (d) *Sample Size* Find the sample size necessary for a 95% confidence level with maximal error of estimate $E = 1.10$ for the mean concentration of uric acid in this patient's blood.

3. *Diagnostic Tests: Plasma Volume* Total plasma volume is important in determining the required plasma component in blood replacement therapy for a person undergoing surgery. Plasma volume is influenced by the overall health and physical activity of an individual. (Reference: See Problem 2.) Suppose that a random sample of 45 male firefighters are tested and that they have a plasma volume sample mean of $\bar{x} = 37.5$ ml/kg (milliliters plasma per kilogram body weight). Assume that $\sigma = 7.50$ ml/kg for the distribution of blood plasma.
   (a) Find a 99% confidence interval for the population mean blood plasma volume in male firefighters. What is the margin of error?
   (b) What conditions are necessary for your calculations?
   (c) Give a brief interpretation of your results in the context of this problem.
   (d) *Sample Size* Find the sample size necessary for a 99% confidence level with maximal error of estimate $E = 2.50$ for the mean plasma volume in male firefighters.

4. *Agriculture: Watermelon* What price do farmers get for their watermelon crops? In the third week of July, a random sample of 40 farming regions gave a sample mean of $\bar{x} = \$6.88$ per 100 pounds of watermelon. Assume that σ is known to be $\$1.92$ per 100 pounds (Reference: *Agricultural Statistics,* U.S. Department of Agriculture).
   (a) Find a 90% confidence interval for the population mean price (per 100 pounds) that farmers in this region get for their watermelon crop. What is the margin of error?
   (b) *Sample Size* Find the sample size necessary for a 90% confidence level with maximal error of estimate $E = 0.3$ for the mean price per 100 pounds of watermelon.
   (c) A farm brings 15 tons of watermelon to market. Find a 90% confidence interval for the population mean cash value of this crop. What is the margin of error? *Hint:* 1 ton is 2000 pounds.

5. *FBI Report: Larceny* Thirty small communities in Connecticut (population near 10,000 each) gave an average of $\bar{x} = 138.5$ reported cases of larceny per year. Assume that σ is known to be 42.6 cases per year (Reference: *Crime in the United States,* Federal Bureau of Investigation).
   (a) Find a 90% confidence interval for the population mean annual number of reported larceny cases in such communities. What is the margin of error?
   (b) Find a 95% confidence interval for the population mean annual number of reported larceny cases in such communities. What is the margin of error?
   (c) Find a 99% confidence interval for the population mean annual number of reported larceny cases in such communities. What is the margin of error?
   (d) Compare the margins of error for parts (a) through (c). As the confidence level increases, does the margin of error increase?
   (e) Compare the lengths of the confidence intervals for parts (a) through (c). As the confidence level increases, does the confidence interval increase in length?

6. *Salaries: Student Services* Consider college officials in admissions, registration, counseling, financial aid, campus ministry, food services, and so on. How much money do these people make each year? Suppose you read in your local newspaper that 45 officials in student services earned an average of $\bar{x} = \$50,340$ each year (Reference: *Chronicle of Higher Education*).
   (a) Assume that $\sigma = \$16,920$ for salaries of college officials in student services. Find a 90% confidence interval for the population mean salary of such personnel. What is the margin of error?
   (b) Assume that $\sigma = \$10,780$ for salaries of college officials in student services. Find a 90% confidence interval for the population mean salary of such personnel. What is the margin of error?

(c) Assume that $\sigma = \$4830$ for salaries of college officials in student services. Find a 90% confidence interval for the population mean salary of such personnel. What is the margin of error?

(d) Compare the margins of error for parts (a) through (c). As the standard deviation decreases, does the margin of error decrease?

(e) Compare the lengths of the confidence intervals for parts (a) through (c). As the standard deviation decreases, does the length of a 90% confidence interval decrease?

7. *Salaries: College Administrators* How much do college administrators (not teachers or service personnel) make each year? Suppose you read the local newspaper and find that the average annual salary of administrators in the local college is $\bar{x} = \$58,940$. Assume that σ is known to be $\$18,490$ for college administrator salaries (Reference: *The Chronicle of Higher Education*).

(a) Suppose that $\bar{x} = \$58,940$ is based on a random sample of $n = 36$ administrators. Find a 90% confidence interval for the population mean annual salary of local college administrators. What is the margin of error?

(b) Suppose that $\bar{x} = \$58,940$ is based on a random sample of $n = 64$ administrators. Find a 90% confidence interval for the population mean annual salary of local college administrators. What is the margin of error?

(c) Suppose that $\bar{x} = \$58,940$ is based on a random sample of $n = 121$ administrators. Find a 90% confidence interval for the population mean annual salary of local college administrators. What is the margin of error?

(d) Compare the margins of error for parts (a) through (c). As the sample size increases, does the margin of error decrease?

(e) Compare the lengths of the confidence intervals for parts (a) through (c). As the sample size increases, does the length of a 90% confidence interval decrease?

8. *Ecology: Sand Dunes* At wind speeds above 1000 cm/sec, significant sand-moving events begin to occur. Wind speeds below 1000 cm/sec deposit sand and wind speeds above 1000 cm/sec move sand to new locations. The cyclic nature of wind and moving sand determines the shape and location of large dunes (Reference: *Hydraulic, Geologic, and Biologic Research at Great Sand Dunes National Monument and Vicinity, Colorado*, Proceedings of the National Park Service Research Symposium). At a test site, the prevailing direction of the wind did not change noticeably. However, the velocity did change. Sixty wind speed readings gave an average velocity of $\bar{x} = 1075$ cm/sec. Based on long-term experience, σ can be assumed to be 265 cm/sec.

(a) Find a 95% confidence interval for the population mean wind speed at this site.

(b) Does the confidence interval indicate that the population mean wind speed is such that the sand is always moving at this site? Explain.

9. *Profits: Banks* Jobs and productivity! How do banks rate? One way to answer this question is to examine annual profits per employee. *Forbes Top Companies*, edited by J. T. Davis (John Wiley & Sons), gave the following data about annual profits per employee (in units of one thousand dollars per employee) for representative companies in financial services. Companies such as Wells Fargo, First Bank System, and Key Banks were included. Assume $\sigma \approx 10.2$ thousand dollars.

42.9	43.8	48.2	60.6	54.9	55.1	52.9	54.9	42.5	33.0	33.6
36.9	27.0	47.1	33.8	28.1	28.5	29.1	36.5	36.1	26.9	27.8
28.8	29.3	31.5	31.7	31.1	38.0	32.0	31.7	32.9	23.1	54.9
43.8	36.9	31.9	25.5	23.2	29.8	22.3	26.5	26.7		

(a) Use a calculator or appropriate computer software to verify that, for the preceding data, $\bar{x} \approx 36.0$.

(b) Let us say that the preceding data are representative of the entire sector of (successful) financial services corporations. Find a 75% confidence interval for μ, the average annual profit per employee for all successful banks.

(c) Let us say that you are the manager of a local bank with a large number of employees. Suppose the annual profits per employee are less than 30 thousand dollars per employee. Do you think that this might be somewhat low compared with other successful financial institutions? Explain by referring to the confidence interval you computed in part (b).

(d) Suppose the annual profits are more than 40 thousand dollars per employee. As manager of the bank, would you feel somewhat better? Explain by referring to the confidence interval you computed in part (b).

(e) Repeat parts (b), (c), and (d) for a 90% confidence level.

10. *Profits: Retail* Jobs and productivity! How do retail stores rate? One way to answer this question is to examine annual profits per employee. The following data give annual profits per employee (in units of one thousand dollars per employee) for companies in retail sales. (See reference in Problem 9.) Companies such as Gap, Nordstrom, Circuit City, Dillards, JCPenney, Sears, Wal-Mart, Office Depot, and Toys 'Я' Us are included. Assume $\sigma \approx 3.8$ thousand dollars.

4.4	6.5	4.2	8.9	8.7	8.1	6.1	6.0	2.6	2.9	8.1	−1.9
11.9	8.2	6.4	4.7	5.5	4.8	3.0	4.3	−6.0	1.5	2.9	4.8
−1.7	9.4	5.5	5.8	4.7	6.2	15.0	4.1	3.7	5.1	4.2	

(a) Use a calculator or appropriate computer software to verify that, for the preceding data, $\bar{x} \approx 5.1$.

(b) Let us say that the preceding data are representative of the entire sector of retail sales companies. Find an 80% confidence interval for μ, the average annual profit per employee for retail sales.

(c) Let us say that you are the manager of a retail store with a large number of employees. Suppose the annual profits per employee are less than 3 thousand dollars per employee. Do you think that this might be low compared with other retail stores? Explain by referring to the confidence interval you computed in part (b).

(d) Suppose the annual profits are more than 6.5 thousand dollars per employee. As store manager, would you feel somewhat better? Explain by referring to the confidence interval you computed in part (b).

(e) Repeat parts (b), (c), and (d) for a 95% confidence interval.

8.2
Estimating μ When σ Is Unknown

FOCUS POINTS

✓ Learn about degrees of freedom and Student's t distributions.

✓ Find critical values using degrees of freedom and confidence level.

✓ Compute confidence intervals for μ when σ is unknown. What does this information tell you?

In order to use the normal distribution to find confidence intervals for a population mean μ, we need to know the value of σ, the population standard deviation. However, much of the time, when μ is unknown, σ is unknown as well. In such cases, we use the sample standard deviation s to approximate σ. When we use s to approximate σ, the sampling distribution for $\bar{x}$ follows a new distribution called a *Student's t distribution*.

Student's t Distributions

Student's t distributions were discovered in 1908 by W. S. Gosset. He was employed as a statistician by Guinness brewing company, a company that discouraged publication of research by its employees. As a result, Gosset published his research under the pseudonym *Student*. Gosset was the first to recognize the importance of developing statistical methods for obtaining reliable information from samples of populations with unknown σ. Gosset used the variable t when he introduced the distribution in 1908. To this day and in his honor it is still called a Student's t distribution. It might be more fitting to call this distribution *Gosset's t distribution;* however, in the literature of mathematical statistics, it is known as a *Student's t distribution.*

The variable t is defined as follows. A Student's t distribution depends on sample size n.

Assume that x has a normal distribution with mean μ. For samples of size n with sample mean $\bar{x}$ and sample standard deviation s, the **t variable**

$$t = \frac{\bar{x} - \mu}{\dfrac{s}{\sqrt{n}}} \tag{7}$$

has a **Student's t distribution** with **degrees of freedom** $d.f. = n - 1$.

If many random samples of size n are drawn, then we get many t values from Equation (7). These t values can be organized into a frequency table, and a histogram can be drawn, thereby giving us an idea of the shape of the t distribution (for a given n).

Fortunately, all this work is not necessary because mathematical theorems can be used to obtain a formula for the t distribution. However, it is important to observe that these theorems state that the shape of the t distribution depends only on n, provided the basic variable x has a normal distribution. So *when we use a t distribution, we will assume that the x distribution is normal.*

Table 4 of the Appendix gives values of the variable t corresponding to what we call the number of *degrees of freedom,* abbreviated $d.f.$ For the methods used in this section, the number of degrees of freedom is given by the formula

$$d.f. = n - 1 \tag{8}$$

where $d.f.$ stands for the degrees of freedom and n is the sample size being used. Each choice for $d.f.$ gives a different t distribution.

The graph of a t distribution is always symmetrical about its mean, which (as for the z distribution) is 0. The main observable difference between a t distribution and the standard normal z distribution is that a t distribution has somewhat thicker tails.

Figure 8-5 shows a standard normal z distribution and a Student's t distribution with $d.f. = 3$ and $d.f. = 5$.

Degrees of freedom

FIGURE 8-5

A Standard Normal Distribution and a Student's t Distribution with $d.f. = 3$ and $d.f. = 5$

> **Properties of a Student's *t* distribution**
>
> 1. The distribution is *symmetric* about the mean 0.
>
> 2. The distribution depends on the *degrees of freedom, d.f.* ($d.f. = n - 1$ for μ confidence intervals).
>
> 3. The distribution is *bell-shaped*, but has thicker tails than the standard normal distribution.
>
> 4. As the degrees of freedom increase, the *t* distribution *approaches* the standard normal distribution.

FIGURE 8-6

Area Under the *t* Curve Between $-t_c$ and t_c

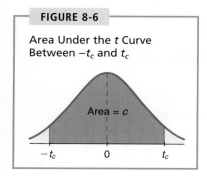

Using Table 4 to Find Critical Values for Confidence Intervals

Table 4 of the Appendix gives various *t* values for different degrees of freedom *d.f.* We will use this table to find *critical values* t_c for a *c* confidence level. In other words, we want to find t_c such that an area equal to *c* under the *t* distribution for a given number of degrees of freedom falls between $-t_c$ and t_c. In the language of probability, we want to find t_c such that

$$P(-t_c < t < t_c) = c$$

This probability corresponds to the shaded area in Figure 8-6.

   Table 4 of the Appendix has been arranged so that *c* is one of the column headings, and the degrees of freedom *d.f.* are the row headings. To find t_c for any specific *c*, we find the column headed by that *c* value and read down until we reach the row headed by the appropriate number of degrees of freedom *d.f.* (You will notice two other column headings: one-tail area and two-tail area. We will use these later, but for the time being, ignore them.)

> **Convention for using a Student's *t* distribution table**
>
> If the degrees of freedom *d.f.* you need are not in the table, use the closest *d.f.* in the table that is *smaller*. This procedure results in a critical value t_c that is more conservative in the sense that it is larger. The resulting confidence interval will be longer and have a probability that is slightly higher than *c*.

EXAMPLE 4

Student's t distribution

Use Table 8-3 (an excerpt from Table 4 of the Appendix) to find the critical value t_c for a 0.99 confidence level for a *t* distribution with sample size $n = 5$.

SOLUTION:

(a) First, we find the column with *c* heading 0.990.

(b) Next, we compute the number of degrees of freedom:
$$d.f. = n - 1 = 5 - 1 = 4.$$

(c) We read down the column under the heading $c = 0.99$ until we reach the row headed by 4 (under *d.f.*). The entry is 4.604. Therefore, $t_{0.99} = 4.604.$ ◇

**TABLE 8-3　Student's *t* Distribution Critical Values
(Excerpt from Table 4, Appendix)**

one-tail area		—	—	—	—
two-tail area		—	—	—	—
d.f.	*c*	... 0.900	0.950	0.980	0.990 ...
⋮					
3		... 2.353	3.182	4.541	5.841 ...
4		... 2.132	2.776	3.747	4.604 ...
⋮					
7		... 1.895	2.365	2.998	3.449 ...
8		... 1.860	2.306	2.896	3.355 ...

GUIDED EXERCISE 2

Student's *t* distribution table

Use Table 4 of the Appendix (or Table 8-3 showing an excerpt from the table) to find t_c for a
0.90 confidence level for a *t* distribution with sample size $n = 9$.

(a) We find the column headed by $c =$ _____.

⇒　$c = 0.900$

(b) The degrees of freedom are given by
$d.f. = n - 1 =$ _____.

⇒　$d.f. = n - 1 = 9 - 1 = 8$

(c) Read down the column found in part (a) until
you reach the entry in the row headed by
$d.f. = 8$. The value of $t_{0.90}$ is _____ for
a sample of size 9.

⇒　$t_{0.90} = 1.860$ for a sample of size $n = 9$.

(d) Find t_c for a 0.95 confidence level for a *t* distribution with sample size $n = 9$.

⇒　$t_{0.95} = 2.306$ for a sample of size $n = 9$.

Maximal margin of error, *E*

　　　In Section 8.1, we found bounds $\pm E$ on the margin of error for a *c* confidence
level. Using the same basic approach, we arrive at the conclusion that

$$E = t_c \frac{s}{\sqrt{n}} \tag{9}$$

is the maximal margin of error for a *c* confidence level when σ is unknown (i.e.,
$|\bar{x} - \mu| < E$ with probability *c*). The analogue of Equation (1) in Section 8.1 is

$$P\left(-t_c \frac{s}{\sqrt{n}} < \bar{x} - \mu < t_c \frac{s}{\sqrt{n}}\right) = c \tag{10}$$

◇ **COMMENT** Comparing Equation (10) with Equation (1) in Section 8.1, it
becomes evident that we are using the same basic method on the *t* distribution
that we did on the *z* distribution.　◇

Likewise, for samples from normal populations with unknown σ, Equation (4) of Section 8.1 becomes

$$P(\bar{x} - E < \mu < \bar{x} + E) = c \tag{11}$$

where $E = t_c(s/\sqrt{n})$. Let us organize what we have been doing in a convenient summary.

Confidence interval for μ with σ unknown

PROCEDURE

How to find a confidence interval for μ when σ is unknown

Let x be a random variable appropriate to your application. Obtain a simple random sample (of size n, $n > 1$) of x values from which you compute the sample mean $\bar{x}$ and the sample standard deviation s.

If you can assume that x has a normal distribution or simply a mound-shaped symmetric distribution, then any sample size n will work. If you cannot assume this, then use a sample size of $n \geq 30$.

Confidence interval for μ when σ is unknown

$$\bar{x} - E < \mu < \bar{x} + E$$

where $\bar{x}$ = sample mean of a simple random sample

$$E = t_c \frac{s}{\sqrt{n}}$$

c = confidence level $(0 < c < 1)$

t_c = critical value for confidence level c and degrees of freedom
$d.f. = n - 1$
(See Table 4 of the Appendix.)

◊ **COMMENT** In our applications of Student's t distributions, we have made the basic assumption that x has a normal distribution. However, the same methods apply even if x is only approximately normal. In fact, the main requirement for using a Student's t distribution is that the distribution of x values be reasonably symmetrical and mound-shaped. If this is the case, then the methods we employ with the t distribution can be considered valid for most practical applications. ◊

EXAMPLE 5

Confidence interval for μ, σ unknown

Suppose an archaeologist discovers only seven fossil skeletons from a previously unknown species of miniature horse. Reconstructions of the skeletons of these seven miniature horses show the shoulder heights (in centimeters) to be

| 45.3 | 47.1 | 44.2 | 46.8 | 46.5 | 45.5 | 47.6 |

For these sample data, the mean is $\bar{x} \approx 46.14$ and the sample standard deviation is $s \approx 1.19$. Let μ be the mean shoulder height (in centimeters) for this entire species of miniature horse, and assume that the population of shoulder heights is approximately normal.

Find a 99% confidence interval for μ, the mean shoulder height of the entire population of such horses.

SOLUTION: In this case, $n = 7$, so $d.f. = n - 1 = 7 - 1 = 6$. For $c = 0.990$, Table 4 of the Appendix gives $t_{0.99} = 3.707$ (for $d.f. = 6$). The sample standard deviation is $s = 1.19$.

$$E = t_c \frac{s}{\sqrt{n}} = (3.707)\frac{1.19}{\sqrt{7}} \approx 1.67$$

The 99% confidence interval is

$$\bar{x} - E < \mu < \bar{x} + E$$
$$46.14 - 1.67 < \mu < 46.14 + 1.67$$
$$44.5 < \mu < 47.8$$

The archaeologist can be 99% confident that the interval from 44.5 cm to 47.8 cm is an interval that contains the population mean μ for shoulder height of this species of miniature horse.   ◆

GUIDED EXERCISE 3

Confidence interval for μ, σ unknown

A company has a new process for manufacturing large artificial sapphires. In a trial run, 37 sapphires are produced. The mean weight for these 37 gems is $\bar{x} = 6.75$ carats, and the sample standard deviation is $s = 0.33$ carat. Let μ be the mean weight for the distribution of all sapphires produced by the new process.

(a) What is $d.f.$ for this setting?

⟹ $d.f. = n - 1$, where n is the sample size. Since $n = 37$, $d.f. = 37 - 1 = 36$.

(b) Use Table 4 of the Appendix to find $t_{0.95}$. Note that $d.f. = 36$ is not in the table. Use the $d.f.$ closest to 36 that is smaller than 36.

⟹ $d.f. = 35$ is the closest $d.f.$ in the table that is smaller than 36. Using $d.f. = 35$ and $c = 0.95$, we find $t_{0.95} = 2.030$.

(c) Find E.

⟹ $E = t_{0.95}\dfrac{s}{\sqrt{n}}$

$\approx 2.030\dfrac{0.33}{\sqrt{37}} \approx 0.11$ carat

(d) Find a 95% confidence interval for μ.

⟹ $\bar{x} - E < \mu < \bar{x} + E$
$6.75 - 0.11 < \mu < 6.75 + 0.11$
6.64 carats $< \mu < 6.86$ carats

(e) Interpret the confidence interval in the context of the problem.

⟹ The company can be 95% confident that the interval from 6.64 to 6.86 is an interval that contains the population mean weight of sapphires produced by the new process.

We have several formulas for confidence intervals for the population mean μ. How do we choose an appropriate one? We need to look at the sample size, the distribution of the original population, and whether or not the population standard deviation σ is known.

Summary: Confidence intervals for the mean

Assume that you have a random sample of size $n > 1$ from an x distribution and that you have computed $\bar{x}$ and s. A confidence interval for μ is

$$\bar{x} - E < \mu < \bar{x} + E$$

where E is the margin of error. How do you find E? It depends on how much you know about the x distribution.

Situation I (most common)

You don't know the population standard deviation σ. In this situation, you use the t distribution with margin of error

$$E = t_c \frac{s}{\sqrt{n}}$$

and degrees of freedom

$$d.f. = n - 1$$

Although a t distribution can be used in many situations, you need to observe some guidelines. If n is less than 30, x should have a distribution that is mound-shaped and approximately symmetric. It's even better if the x distribution is normal. If n is 30 or more, the central limit theorem (Section 7.5) implies that these restrictions can be relaxed.

Situation II (almost never happens!)

You actually know the population value of σ. In addition, you know that x has a normal distribution. If you don't know that the x distribution is normal, then your sample size n must be 30 or larger. In this situation, you use the standard normal z distribution with margin of error

$$E = z_c \frac{\sigma}{\sqrt{n}}$$

Which distribution should you use for $\bar{x}$?

Bootstrap

◇ **COMMENT** To find confidence intervals for μ based on small samples, you need to know that the population distribution is approximately normal. What if this is not the case? A procedure called *bootstrap* utilizes computer power to generate an approximation for the $\bar{x}$ sampling distribution. Essentially, the bootstrap method treats the sample as if it were the population. Then, using repetition, it takes many samples (often thousands) from the original sample. This process is called *resampling*. The sample mean $\bar{x}$ is computed for each resample and a distribution of sample means is created. For example, a 95% confidence interval reflects the range for the middle 95% of the bootstrap $\bar{x}$ distribution. (Reference: *An Introduction to the Bootstrap*, B. Efron and R. Tibshirani). ◇

 TECH NOTE The TI-84Plus and TI-83Plus calculators, Excel, and Minitab support confidence intervals using the Student's t distribution.

TI-84Plus/TI-83Plus Press the **STAT** key, select **TESTS**, and choose the option **8:TInterval.** You may use either raw data in a list or summary statistics.

Excel Excel gives only the value of the maximal margin of error E. You can easily construct the confidence interval by computing $\bar{x} - E$ and $\bar{x} + E$. Use the menu choices **Tools ➤ Data Analysis ➤ Describe Statistics.** In the dialogue box, check summary statistics and check confidence level for mean. Then set the desired confidence level. Under these menu choices, Excel uses the Student's t distribution.

Minitab Use the menu choices **Stat ➤ Basic Statistics ➤ 1-Sample t.** In the dialogue box, indicate the column that contains the raw data. The Minitab output shows the confidence interval for Example 5.

T Confidence Intervals					
Variable	N	Mean	StDev	SE Mean	99.0 % CI
C1	7	46.143	1.190	0.450	(44.475, 47.810)

VIEWP◉INT

Earthquakes!

California, Washington, Nevada, and even Yellowstone National Park all have earthquakes. Some earthquakes are severe! All earthquakes bring fear and anxiety to people living near the quake. Is San Francisco due for a really big quake like the 1906 major earthquake? How big are the sizes of recent earthquakes compared with really big earthquakes? What is the duration of an earthquake? How long is the time span between major earthquakes? One way to answer questions such as these is to use existing data to estimate confidence intervals for the average size, duration, and time interval between quakes. Recent data sets for computing such confidence intervals can be found at the National Earthquake Information Service of the U.S. Geological Survey web site. To access the site, visit the Brase/Brase statistics site at **http://math.college.hmco.com/students** and find the link to National Earthquake Information Service.

SECTION 8.2   PROBLEMS

1. Use Table 4 of the Appendix to find t_c for a 0.95 confidence level when the sample size is 18.

2. Use Table 4 of the Appendix to find t_c for a 0.99 confidence level when the sample size is 4.

3. Use Table 4 of the Appendix to find t_c for a 0.90 confidence level when the sample size is 22.

4. Use Table 4 of the Appendix to find t_c for a 0.95 confidence level when the sample size is 12.

In Problems 5–11, assume that the population of x values has an approximately normal distribution. Answers may vary slightly due to rounding.

5. *Archaeology: Tree Rings* At Burnt Mesa Pueblo, the method of tree ring dating gave the following dates A.D. for an archaeological excavation site (*Bandelier Archaeological Excavation Project: Summer 1990 Excavations at Burnt Mesa Pueblo*, edited by Kohler, Washington State University):

| 1189 | 1271 | 1267 | 1272 | 1268 | 1316 | 1275 | 1317 | 1275 |

(a) Use a calculator with mean and standard deviation keys to verify that the sample mean date is $\bar{x} \approx 1272$ with sample standard deviation $s \approx 37$ years.
(b) Find a 90% confidence interval for the mean of all tree ring dates from this archaeological site.

6. *Wildlife: Wolf Pups* The number of pups in wolf dens of the southwestern United States is recorded below for 16 wolf dens (*The Wolf in the Southwest: The Making of an Endangered Species*, edited by D. E. Brown, University of Arizona Press).

| 5 | 8 | 7 | 5 | 3 | 4 | 3 | 9 |
| 5 | 8 | 5 | 6 | 5 | 6 | 4 | 7 |

(a) Use a calculator with mean and standard deviation keys to verify that the sample mean is $\bar{x} \approx 5.63$ pups with sample standard deviation $s \approx 1.78$ pups.
(b) Compute an 85% confidence interval for the population mean number of wolf pups per den in the southwestern United States.

7. *Wildlife: Mountain Lions* How much do wild mountain lions weigh? *The 77th Annual Report of the New Mexico Department of Game and Fish*, edited by Bill Montoya, gave the following information. Adult wild mountain lions (18 months or older) captured and released for the first time in the San Andres Mountains gave the following weights (lb):

| 68 | 104 | 128 | 122 | 60 | 64 |

(a) Use a calculator with mean and sample standard deviation keys to verify that $\bar{x} = 91.0$ lb and $s \approx 30.7$ lb.
(b) Find a 75% confidence interval for the population average weight μ of all adult mountain lions in the specified region.

8. *Franchise: Candy Store* Do you want to own your own candy store? Wow! With some interest in running your own business and a decent credit rating, you can probably get a bank loan on startup costs for franchises such as Candy Express, The Fudge Company, Karmel Corn, and Rocky Mountain Chocolate Factory. Startup

costs (units in $1000) for a random sample of candy stores are given below (Source: *Entrepreneur Magazine*, Vol. 23, No. 10).

| 95 | 173 | 129 | 95 | 75 | 94 | 116 | 100 | 85 |

Use a calculator with mean and sample standard deviation keys to verify that $\bar{x} \approx 106.9$ thousand dollars and $s \approx 29.4$ thousand dollars. Find a 90% confidence interval for the population average startup costs μ for candy store franchises.

9. *Diagnostic Tests: Total Calcium* Over the past several months, an adult patient has been treated for tetany (severe muscle spasms). This condition is associated with an average total calcium level below 6 mg/dl (Reference: *Manual of Laboratory and Diagnostic Tests*, F. Fischbach). Recently, the patient's total calcium tests gave the following readings (in mg/dl).

| 9.3 | 8.8 | 10.1 | 8.9 | 9.4 | 9.8 | 10.0 |
| 9.9 | 11.2 | 12.1 | | | | |

(a) Use a calculator to verify that $\bar{x} = 9.95$ and $s \approx 1.02$.
(b) Find a 99.9% confidence interval for the population mean of total calcium in this patient's blood.
(c) Based on your results in part (b), do you think this patient still has a calcium deficiency? Explain.

10. *Hospitals: Charity Care* What percentage of hospitals provide at least some charity care? The following problem is based on information taken from *State Health Care Data: Utilization, Spending, and Characteristics* (American Medical Association). Based on a random sample of hospital reports from eastern states, the following information was obtained (units in percentage of hospitals providing at least some charity care):

| 57.1 | 56.2 | 53.0 | 66.1 | 59.0 | 64.7 | 70.1 | 64.7 | 53.5 | 78.2 |

Use a calculator with mean and sample standard deviation keys to verify that $\bar{x} \approx 62.3\%$ and $s \approx 8.0\%$. Find a 90% confidence interval for the population average μ of the percentage of hospitals providing at least some charity care.

11. *Box Plots and Confidence Intervals: Heights* The distribution of heights of 18-year-old men in the United States is approximately normal with mean 68 inches and standard deviation 3 inches (U.S. Census Bureau). In Minitab we can simulate the drawing of random samples of size 20 from this population (➤ **Calc** ➤ **Random Data** ➤ **Normal** with 20 rows from a distribution with mean 68 and standard deviation 3). Then we can have Minitab compute a 95% confidence interval and draw a boxplot of the data (➤ **Stat** ➤ **Basic Statistics** ➤ **1—Sample t**, with boxplot selected in the graphs). The boxplots and confidence intervals for four different samples are shown in the accompanying figures. The four confidence intervals are

VARIABLE	N	MEAN	STDEV	SEMEAN	95.0 % CI
Sample 1	20	68.050	2.901	0.649	(66.692 , 69.407)
Sample 2	20	67.958	3.137	0.702	(66.490 , 69.426)
Sample 3	20	67.976	2.639	0.590	(66.741 , 69.211)
Sample 4	20	66.908	2.440	0.546	(65.766 , 68.050)

(a) Examine the figure [parts (a) to (d)]. How do the boxplots for the four samples differ? Why should you expect the boxplots to differ?

95% Confidence Intervals for Mean Height of 18-Year-Old Men (Sample size 20)

(a) Boxplot of Sample 1
(with 95% *t*-confidence interval for the mean)

(b) Boxplot of Sample 2
(with 95% *t*-confidence interval for the mean)

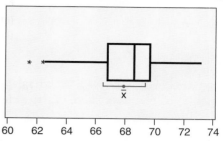

(c) Boxplot of Sample 3
(with 95% *t*-confidence interval for the mean)

(d) Boxplot of Sample 4
(with 95% *t*-confidence interval for the mean)

(b) Examine the 95% confidence intervals for the four samples shown in the printout. Do the intervals differ in length? Do the intervals all contain the expected population mean of 68 inches? If we draw more samples, do you expect all of the resulting 95% confidence intervals to contain $\mu = 68$? Why or why not?

12. *Crime Rate: Denver* The following data represent crime rate per 1000 population for a random sample of 46 Denver neighborhoods (Reference: *The Piton Foundation*, Denver, Colorado).

63.2	36.3	26.2	53.2	65.3	32.0	65.0
66.3	68.9	35.2	25.1	32.5	54.0	42.4
77.5	123.2	66.3	92.7	56.9	77.1	27.5
69.2	73.8	71.5	58.5	67.2	78.6	33.2
74.9	45.1	132.1	104.7	63.2	59.6	75.7
39.2	69.9	87.5	56.0	154.2	85.5	77.5
84.7	24.2	37.5	41.1			

(a) Use a calculator with mean and sample standard deviation keys to verify that $\bar{x} \approx 64.2$ and $s \approx 27.9$ crimes per 1000 population.
(b) Let us say that the preceding data are representative of the population crime rate in Denver neighborhoods. Compute an 80% confidence interval for μ, the population mean crime rate for all Denver neighborhoods.
(c) Suppose you are advising the police department about police patrol assignments. One neighborhood has a crime rate of 57 crimes per 1000 population. Do you think that this rate is below the average population crime rate and that fewer

patrols could safely be assigned to this neighborhood? Use the confidence interval to justify your answer.

(d) Another neighborhood has a crime rate of 75 crimes per 1000 population. Does this crime rate seem to be higher than the population average? Would you recommend assigning more patrols to this neighborhood? Use the confidence interval to justify your answer.

(e) Repeat parts (b), (c), and (d) for a 95% confidence interval.

(f) In previous problems, we assumed that the x distribution was normal or approximately normal. Do we need to make such an assumption in this problem? Why or why not? *Hint:* See the central limit theorem in Section 7.5.

13. *Finance: P/E Ratio* The price of a share of stock divided by the company's estimated future earnings per share is called the P/E ratio. High P/E ratios usually indicate "growth" stocks or maybe stocks that are simply overpriced. Low P/E ratios indicate "value" stocks or bargain stocks. A random sample of 51 of the largest companies in the United States gave the following P/E ratios (Reference: *Forbes*).

11	35	19	13	15	21	40	18	60	72	9	20
29	53	16	26	21	14	21	27	10	12	47	14
33	14	18	17	20	19	13	25	23	27	5	16
8	49	44	20	27	8	19	12	31	67	51	26
19	18	32									

(a) Use a calculator with mean and sample standard deviation keys to verify that $\bar{x} \approx 25.2$ and $s \approx 15.5$.

(b) Find a 90% confidence interval for the P/E population mean μ of all large U.S. companies.

(c) Find a 99% confidence interval for the P/E population mean μ of all large U.S. companies.

(d) Bank One (now merged with J. P. Morgan) had a P/E of 12, AT&T Wireless had a P/E of 72, and Disney had a P/E of 24. Examine the confidence intervals in parts (b) and (c). How would you describe these stocks at this time?

(e) In previous problems, we assumed that the x distribution was normal or approximately normal. Do we need to make such an assumption in this problem? Why or why not? *Hint:* See the central limit theorem in Section 7.5.

14. *Baseball: Home Run Percentage* The home run percentage is the number of home runs per 100 times at bat. A random sample of 43 professional baseball players gave the following data for home run percentages (Reference: *The Baseball Encyclopedia*, Macmillan).

1.6	2.4	1.2	6.6	2.3	0.0	1.8	2.5	6.5	1.8
2.7	2.0	1.9	1.3	2.7	1.7	1.3	2.1	2.8	1.4
3.8	2.1	3.4	1.3	1.5	2.9	2.6	0.0	4.1	2.9
1.9	2.4	0.0	1.8	3.1	3.8	3.2	1.6	4.2	0.0
1.2	1.8	2.4							

(a) Use a calculator with mean and standard deviation keys to verify that $\bar{x} \approx 2.29$ and $s \approx 1.40$.

(b) Compute a 90% confidence interval for the population mean μ of home run percentages for all professional baseball players. *Hint:* If you use Table 4 of the Appendix, be sure to use the closest *d.f.* that is *smaller*.

(c) Compute a 99% confidence interval for the population mean μ of home run percentages for all professional baseball players.

(d) The home run percentages for three professional players are

      Tim Huelett, 2.5   Herb Hunter, 2.0   Jackie Jensen, 3.8

    Examine your confidence intervals and describe how home run percentages for these players compare to the population average.

(e) In previous problems, we assumed that the *x* distribution was normal or approximately normal. Do we need to make such an assumption in this problem? Why or why not? *Hint:* See the central limit theorem in Section 7.5.

15. *Expand Your Knowledge: Alternate Method for Confidence Intervals* When σ is unknown and the sample size is $n \geq 30$, there are two methods for computing confidence intervals for μ.

> **Method 1: Use the Student's *t* distribution with d.f. $= n - 1$.**
>
> This is the method used in the text. It is widely employed in statistical studies. Also, most statistical software packages use this method.

> **Method 2: When $n \geq 30$, use the sample standard deviation *s* as an estimate for σ, and then use the standard normal distribution.**
>
> This method is based on the fact that for large samples, *s* is a fairly good approximation for σ. Also, for large *n*, the critical values for the Student's *t* distribution approach those of the standard normal distribution.

Consider a random sample of size $n = 31$, with sample mean $\bar{x} = 45.2$ and sample standard deviation $s = 5.3$.

(a) Compute 90%, 95%, and 99% confidence intervals for μ using Method 1 with a Student's *t* distribution. Round endpoints to two digits after the decimal.

(b) Compute 90%, 95%, and 99% confidence intervals for μ using Method 2 with the standard normal distribution. Use *s* as an estimate for σ. Round endpoints to two digits after the decimal.

(c) Compare intervals for the two methods. Would you say that confidence intervals using a Student's *t* distribution are more conservative in the sense that they tend to be longer than intervals based on the standard normal distribution?

(d) Repeat parts (a) through (c) for a sample of size $n = 81$. With increased sample size, do the two methods give respective confidence intervals that are more similar?

8.3
Estimating *p* in the Binomial Distribution

FOCUS POINTS

✓ Compute the maximal margin of error for proportions using a given level of confidence.

✓ Compute confidence intervals for *p* and interpret the results.

✓ Interpret poll results.

✓ Compute the sample size to be used for estimating a proportion *p* when we have an estimate for *p*.

✓ Compute the sample size to be used for estimating a proportion *p* when we have no estimate for *p*.

The binomial distribution is completely determined by the number of trials *n* and the probability *p* of success in a single trial. For most experiments, the number of trials is chosen in advance. Then the distribution is completely determined by *p*. In this section, we will consider the problem of estimating *p* under the assumption that *n* has already been selected.

    We are employing what are called *large-sample methods*. We will assume that the normal curve is a good approximation to the binomial distribution, and when necessary, we will use sample estimates for the standard deviation. Empirical studies have shown that these methods are quite good provided that *both*

$$np > 5 \quad \text{and} \quad nq > 5 \quad \text{where } q = 1 - p \text{ is the probability of failure}$$

    Let *r* be the number of successes out of *n* trials in a binomial experiment. We will take the sample proportion of successes $\hat{p}$ (read "*p* hat") $= r/n$ as our *point estimate for p*, the population proportion of successes.

Point estimates of p and q

> The **point estimates for p and q** are
>
> $$\hat{p} = \frac{r}{n}$$
>
> $$\hat{q} = 1 - \hat{p}$$
>
> where n = number of trials and r = number of successes.

For example, suppose that 800 students are selected at random from a student body of 20,000 and that they are each given shots to prevent a certain type of flu. These 800 students are then exposed to the flu, and 600 of them do not get the flu. What is the probability p that the shot will be successful for any single student selected at random from the entire population of 20,000 students? We estimate p for the entire student body by computing r/n from the sample of 800 students. The value $\hat{p} = r/n$ is 600/800, or 0.75. The value $\hat{p} = 0.75$ is then the *point estimate* for p.

The difference between the actual value of p and the estimate $\hat{p}$ is the size of our error caused by using $\hat{p}$ as a point estimate for p. The magnitude of $\hat{p} - p$ is

Margin of error

called the *margin of error* for using $\hat{p} = r/n$ as a point estimate for p. In absolute value notation, the margin of error is $|\hat{p} - p|$.

To compute the bounds for the margin of error, we need some information about the distribution of $\hat{p} = r/n$ values for different samples of the same size n. It turns out that, for large samples, the distribution of $\hat{p}$ values is well approximated by a *normal curve* with

$$\text{mean } \mu = p \quad \text{and} \quad \text{standard error } \sigma = \sqrt{pq/n}$$

Since the distribution of $\hat{p} = r/n$ is approximately normal, we use features of the standard normal distribution to find the bounds for the difference $\hat{p} - p$. Recall that z_c is the number such that an area equal to c under the standard normal curve falls between $-z_c$ and z_c. Then, in terms of the language of probability,

$$P\left(-z_c\sqrt{\frac{pq}{n}} < \hat{p} - p < z_c\sqrt{\frac{pq}{n}}\right) = c \qquad (12)^*$$

Equation (12) states that the chance is c that the numerical difference between $\hat{p}$ and p is between $-z_c\sqrt{pq/n}$ and $z_c\sqrt{pq/n}$. With the c confidence level, our estimate $\hat{p}$ differs from p by no more than

Maximal margin of error, E

$$E = z_c\sqrt{pq/n}$$

As in Section 8.1, we call E the *maximal margin of error*.

---

*Recall from Section 7.6 that when n is large, the binomial distribution of the number of successes r is approximately normal, with mean $\mu = np$ and standard deviation $\sigma = \sqrt{npq}$. Therefore, $z = (r - np)/\sqrt{npq}$. Dividing the numerator and denominator by n shows that $\hat{p} = r/n$ has a normal distribution with mean $\mu = p$ and standard deviation $\sigma = \sqrt{pq/n}$. Beginning with the equation $P(-z_c < z < z_c) = c$, replacing z by $(\hat{p} - p)/\sqrt{pq/n}$, and multiplying all parts of the inequality by $\sqrt{pq/n}$, we obtain Equation (12).

Confidence interval for p

To find a c confidence interval for p, we will use E in place of the expression $z_c\sqrt{pq/n}$ in Equation (12). Then we get

$$P(-E < \hat{p} - p < E) = c \tag{13}$$

Some algebraic manipulation produces the mathematically equivalent statement

$$P(\hat{p} - E < p < \hat{p} + E) = c \tag{14}$$

Equation (14) states that the probability is c that p lies in the interval from $\hat{p} - E$ to $\hat{p} + E$. Therefore, the interval from $\hat{p} - E$ to $\hat{p} + E$ is the c confidence interval for p that we wanted to find.

There is one technical difficulty in computing the c confidence interval for p. The expression $E = z_c\sqrt{pq/n}$ requires that we know the values of p and q. In most situations, we will not know the actual values of p or q, so we will use our point estimates

$$p \approx \hat{p} \qquad \text{and} \qquad q = 1 - p \approx 1 - \hat{p}$$

to estimate E. These estimates are safe for most practical purposes, since we are dealing with large-sample theory ($np > 5$ and $nq > 5$).

For convenient reference, we'll summarize the information about c confidence intervals for p, the probability of success in a binomial distribution.

PROCEDURE

How to find a confidence interval for a proportion p

Consider a binomial experiment with n trials for which p represents the population probability of success and $q = 1 - p$ represents the population probability of failure. Let r be a random variable that represents the number of successes out of the n binomial trials.

The point estimates for p and q are

$$\hat{p} = \frac{r}{n} \qquad \text{and} \qquad \hat{q} = 1 - \hat{p}$$

The number of trials should be sufficiently large so that $np > 5$ and $nq > 5$. Since we do not know p or q, we use the approximations $n\hat{p} > 5$ and $n\hat{q} > 5$.

Confidence interval for p

$$\hat{p} - E < p < \hat{p} + E$$

where $E \approx z_c\sqrt{\dfrac{\hat{p}\hat{q}}{n}} = z_c\sqrt{\dfrac{\hat{p}(1 - \hat{p})}{n}}$

c = confidence level ($0 < c < 1$)

z_c = critical value for confidence level c based on the standard normal distribution (See Table 3(b) of the Appendix for frequently used values.)

EXAMPLE 6

Confidence interval for p

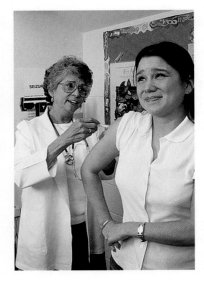

Let's return to our flu shot experiment described at the beginning of this section. Suppose that 800 students were selected at random from a student body of 20,000 and given shots to prevent a certain type of flu. All 800 students were exposed to the flu, and 600 of them did not get the flu. Let p represent the probability that the shot will be successful in preventing the flu for any single student selected at random from the entire population of 20,000. Let q be the probability that the shot is not successful.

(a) What is the number of trials n? What is the value of r?

  SOLUTION: Since each of the 800 students receiving the shot may be thought of as a trial, then $n = 800$, and $r = 600$ is the number of successful trials.

(b) What are the point estimates for p and q?

  SOLUTION: We estimate p by the sample point estimate

$$\hat{p} = \frac{r}{n} = \frac{600}{800} = 0.75$$

  We estimate q by

$$\hat{q} = 1 - \hat{p} = 1 - 0.75 = 0.25$$

(c) Would it seem that the number of trials is large enough to justify a normal approximation to the binomial?

  SOLUTION: Since $n = 800$, $p \approx 0.75$, and $q \approx 0.25$, we have

$$np \approx (800)(0.75) = 600 > 5 \quad \text{and} \quad nq \approx (800)(0.25) = 200 > 5$$

  A normal approximation is certainly justified.

(d) Find a 99% confidence interval for p.

  SOLUTION:

$$z_{0.99} = 2.58 \text{ (see Table 8-2 or Table 3(b) of the Appendix)}$$

$$E \approx z_{0.99}\sqrt{\frac{\hat{p}(1 - \hat{p})}{n}} \approx 2.58\sqrt{\frac{(0.75)(0.25)}{800}} \approx 0.0395$$

  The 99% confidence interval is then

$$\hat{p} - E < p < \hat{p} + E$$
$$0.75 - 0.0395 < p < 0.75 + 0.0395$$
$$0.71 < p < 0.79$$

GUIDED EXERCISE 4

Confidence interval for p

A random sample of 188 books purchased at a local bookstore showed that 66 of the books were murder mysteries. Let p represent the proportion of books sold by this store that are murder mysteries.

(a) What is a point estimate for p?

$$\hat{p} = \frac{r}{n} = \frac{66}{188} = 0.35$$

(b) Find a 90% confidence interval for p.

$$E = z_c \sqrt{\frac{\hat{p}(1 - \hat{p})}{n}}$$

$$= 1.645 \sqrt{\frac{(0.35)(1 - 0.35)}{188}} \approx 0.0572$$

The confidence interval is

$$\hat{p} - E < p < \hat{p} + E$$
$$0.35 - 0.0572 < p < 0.35 + 0.0572$$
$$0.29 < p < 0.41$$

(c) What is the meaning of the confidence interval you just computed?

If we had computed the interval for many different sets of 188 books, we would have found that about 90% of the intervals actually contained p, the population proportion of mysteries. Consequently, we can be 90% confident that our interval is one of the intervals that contains the unknown value p.

(d) To compute the confidence interval, we used a normal approximation. Does this seem justified?

$n = 188$; $p \approx 0.35$; $q \approx 0.65$

Since $np \approx 65.8 > 5$ and $nq \approx 122.2 > 5$, the approximation is justified.

It is interesting to note that our sample point estimate $\hat{p} = r/n$ and the confidence interval for the population proportion p do not depend on the size of the population. In our bookstore example, it made no difference how many books the store sold. On the other hand, the size of the sample does affect the accuracy of a statistical estimate.

 TECH NOTE   The TI-84Plus and TI-83Plus calculators and Minitab provide confidence intervals for proportions.

TI-84Plus/TI-83Plus Press the **STAT** key, select **TESTS**, and choose option **A:1-PropZInt.** The letter x represents the number of successes r. The TI-84Plus/TI-83Plus output shows the results for Guided Exercise 4.

```
1-PropZInt
  (.29381,.40832)
  p̂=.3510638298
  n=188
```

Minitab Use the menu selections **Stat ➤ Basic Statistics ➤ 1 Proportion.** In the dialogue box, select summarized data and fill in the number of trials and the number of successes. Under Options, select a confidence interval. Minitab uses the binomial distribution directly unless normal is checked. The Minitab output shows the results for Guided Exercise 4. Information relating to Chapter 9 material is also shown.

```
Test and Confidence Interval for One Proportion (Using Binomial)
Test of p = 0.5 vs p not = 0.5
                                                           Exact
Sample     X      N    Sample p         90.0 % CI        P-Value
   1      66    188    0.351064   (0.293222, 0.412466)    0.000
```

```
Test and Confidence Interval for One Proportion (Using Normal)
Test of p = 0.5 vs p not = 0.5
Sample   X    N   Sample p        90.0 % CI        Z-Value  P-Value
   1    66  188   0.351064  (0.293805, 0.408323)   -4.08    0.000
```

Interpreting Results from a Poll

Newspapers frequently report the results of an opinion poll. In articles that give more information, a statement about the margin of error accompanies the poll results. In most polls, the margin of error is given for a *95% confidence interval.*

General interpretation of poll results

1. When a poll states the results of a survey, the proportion reported to respond in the designated manner is $\hat{p}$, the sample estimate of the population proportion.

2. The *margin of error* is the maximal error E of a 95% confidence interval for p.

3. A 95% confidence interval for the population proportion p is

   poll report $\hat{p}$ − margin of error $E < p <$ poll report $\hat{p}$ + margin of error E

◇ **COMMENT:** Leslie Kish, a statistician at the University of Michigan, was the first to apply the term *margin of error.* He was a pioneer in the study of population sampling techniques. His book *Survey Sampling* is still widely used all around the world. ◇

Some articles clarify the meaning of the margin of error further by saying that it is an error due to sampling. For instance, the following comments accompany results of a political poll reported in an issue of *The Wall Street Journal.*

How Poll Was Conducted

The Wall Street Journal/NBC News poll was based on nationwide telephone interviews of 1508 adults conducted last Friday through Tuesday by the polling organizations of Peter Hart and Robert Teeter.

The sample was drawn from 315 randomly selected geographic points in the continental U.S. Each region was represented in proportion to its population. Households were selected by a method that gave all telephone numbers . . . an equal chance of being included.

One adult, 18 years or older, was selected from each household by a procedure to provide the correct number of male and female respondents.

Chances are 19 of 20 that if all adults with telephones in the U.S. had been surveyed, the findings would differ from these poll results by no more than 2.6 percentage points in either direction.

GUIDED EXERCISE 5

Reading a poll

Read the last paragraph of the article, "How Poll Was Conducted."

(a) What confidence level corresponds to the phrase "chances are 19 of 20 that if . . ."

→ $\dfrac{19}{20} = 0.95$

A 95% confidence interval is being discussed.

(b) The article indicates that everyone in the sample was asked the question, "Which party, the Democratic Party or the Republican Party, do you think would do a better job handling . . . education?" Possible responses were Democrats, neither, both, or Republicans. The poll reported that 32% of the respondents said "Democrats." Does 32% represent the sample statistic $\hat{p}$ or the population parameter p for the proportion of adults responding "Democrat"?

→ 32% represents a sample statistic $\hat{p}$ because 32% represents the percentage of the adults in the *sample* who responded "Democrats."

(c) Continue reading the last paragraph of the article. It goes on to state, ". . . if all adults with telephones in the U.S. had been surveyed, the findings would differ from these poll results by no more than 2.6 percentage points in either direction." Use this information together with parts (a) and (b) to find a 95% confidence interval for the proportion p of the specified population who would respond "Democrat" to the question.

→ The value 2.6 percentage points represents the margin of error. Since the margin of error is for a 95% confidence interval, the confidence interval is

$$32\% - 2.6\% < p < 32\% + 2.6\%$$
$$29.4\% < p < 34.6\%$$

The poll indicates that at the time of the poll, between 29.4% and 34.6% of the specified population thought Democrats would do a better job handling education.

Sample Size for Estimating p

Suppose you want to specify the maximal margin of error in advance for a confidence interval for p at a given confidence level c. What sample size do you need? The answer depends on whether or not you have a preliminary estimate for the population probability of success p in a binomial distribution.

PROCEDURE

How to find the sample size n for estimating a proportion p

$$n = p(1 - p)\left(\frac{z_c}{E}\right)^2 \text{ if you have a preliminary estimate for } p \qquad (15)$$

$$n = \frac{1}{4}\left(\frac{z_c}{E}\right)^2 \text{ if you do } not \text{ have a preliminary estimate for } p \qquad (16)$$

where E = specified maximal error of estimate

z_c = critical value from the normal distribution for the desired confidence level c. Commonly used values of z_c can be found in Table 3(b) of the Appendix.

If n is not a whole number, increase n to the next higher whole number. Also, if necessary, increase the sample size n to ensure that both $np > 5$ and $nq > 5$. Note that n is the minimal sample size for a specified confidence level and maximal error of estimate.

◇ **COMMENT:** To obtain Equation (15), simply solve the formula that gives the maximal error of estimate E of p for the sample size n. When you don't have an estimate for p, a little algebra can be used to show that the maximum value of $p(1 - p)$ is $1/4$.   ◇

EXAMPLE 7

Sample size for estimating p

A company is in the business of selling wholesale popcorn to grocery stores. The company buys directly from farmers. A buyer for the company is examining a large amount of corn from a certain farmer. Before the purchase is made, the buyer wants to estimate p, the probability that a kernel will pop.

Suppose that a random sample of n kernels is taken and r of these kernels pop. The buyer wants to be 95% sure that the point estimate $\hat{p} = r/n$ for p will be in error either way by less than 0.01.

(a) If no preliminary study is made to estimate p, how large a sample should the buyer use?

SOLUTION: In this case, we use Equation (16) with $z_{0.95} = 1.96$ (see Table 8-2) and $E = 0.01$.

$$n = \frac{1}{4}\left(\frac{z_c}{E}\right)^2 = \frac{1}{4}\left(\frac{1.96}{0.01}\right)^2 = 0.25(38{,}416) = 9604$$

The buyer would need a sample of $n = 9604$ kernels.

(b) A preliminary study showed that p was approximately 0.86. If the buyer uses the results of the preliminary study, how large a sample should be used?

SOLUTION: In this case, we use Equation (15) with $p \approx 0.86$. Again, from Table 8-2, $z_{0.95} = 1.96$, and from the problem, $E = 0.01$.

$$n = p(1 - p)\left(\frac{z_c}{E}\right)^2 = (0.86)(0.14)\left(\frac{1.96}{0.01}\right)^2 = 4625.29$$

The sample size should be at least $n = 4626$ kernels. This sample is less than half the sample size necessary without the preliminary study.   ◇

"Band-Aid" Surgery

Faster recovery time and less pain! Sounds great. An alternate surgical technique called *laparoscopic* ("Band-Aid") *surgery* involves small incisions in which tiny video cameras and long surgical instruments are maneuvered. Instead of a 10-inch incision, surgeons might use four little stabs of about $\frac{1}{2}$-inch in length. However, not every such surgery is successful. An article in the Health Section of *The Wall Street Journal* recommends using a surgeon who has done at least 50 such surgeries. Then the prospective patient should ask about the *rate of conversion,* that is, the proportion p of times the surgeon has been forced by complications to switch in midoperation to conventional surgery. A confidence interval for the proportion p would be useful patient information!

SECTION 8.3   PROBLEMS

For all these problems, carry at least four digits after the decimal in your calculations. Answers may vary slightly due to rounding.

1. *Myers-Briggs: Actors* Isabel Myers was a pioneer in the study of personality types. The following information is taken from *A Guide to the Development and Use of the Myers-Briggs Type Indicator,* by Myers and McCaulley (Consulting Psychologists Press). In a random sample of 62 professional actors, it was found that 39 were extroverts.
   (a) Let p represent the proportion of all actors who are extroverts. Find a point estimate for p.
   (b) Find a 95% confidence interval for p. Give a brief interpretation of the meaning of the confidence interval you have found.
   (c) Do you think that the conditions $np > 5$ and $nq > 5$ are satisfied in this problem? Explain why this would be an important consideration.

2. *Myers-Briggs: Judges* In a random sample of 519 judges, it was found that 285 were introverts (see reference of Problem 1).
   (a) Let p represent the proportion of all judges who are introverts. Find a point estimate for p.
   (b) Find a 99% confidence interval for p. Give a brief interpretation of the meaning of the confidence interval you have found.
   (c) Do you think that the conditions $np > 5$ and $nq > 5$ are satisfied in this problem? Explain why this would be an important consideration.

3. *Navajo Lifestyle: Traditional Hogans* A random sample of 5222 permanent dwellings on the entire Navajo Indian Reservation showed that 1619 were traditional Navajo hogans (*Navajo Architecture: Forms, History, Distributions,* by Jett and Spencer, University of Arizona Press).
   (a) Let p be the proportion of all permanent dwellings on the entire Navajo Reservation that are traditional hogans. Find a point estimate for p.
   (b) Find a 99% confidence interval for p. Give a brief interpretation of the confidence interval.
   (c) Do you think that $np > 5$ and $nq > 5$ are satisfied for this problem? Explain why this would be an important consideration.

4. *Archaeology: Pottery* Santa Fe black-on-white is a type of pottery commonly found at archaeological excavations in Bandelier National Monument. At one excavation site, a sample of 592 potsherds was found, of which 360 were identified as Santa Fe black-on-white (*Bandelier Archaeological Excavation Project: Summer 1990 Excavations at Burnt Mesa Pueblo and Casa del Rito,* edited by Kohler and Root, Washington State University).
   (a) Let p represent the population proportion of Santa Fe black-on-white potsherds at the excavation site. Find a point estimate for p.
   (b) Find a 95% confidence interval for p. Give a brief statement of the meaning of the confidence interval.
   (c) Do you think that the conditions $np > 5$ and $nq > 5$ are satisfied in this problem? Why would this be important?

5. *Health Care: Colorado Physicians* A random sample of 5792 physicians in Colorado showed that 3139 provided at least some charity care (i.e., treated poor people at no cost). These data are based on information from *State Health Care Data: Utilization, Spending, and Characteristics* (American Medical Association).
   (a) Let p represent the proportion of all Colorado physicians who provide some charity care. Find a point estimate for p.
   (b) Find a 99% confidence interval for p. Give a brief explanation of the meaning of your answer in the context of this problem.
   (c) Is the normal approximation to the binomial justified in this problem? Explain.

6. *Law Enforcement: Escaped Convicts* Case studies showed that out of 10,351 convicts who escaped from U.S. prisons, only 7867 were recaptured (*The Book of Odds,* by Shook and Shook, Signet).
   (a) Let p represent the proportion of all escaped convicts who will eventually be recaptured. Find a point estimate for p.
   (b) Find a 99% confidence interval for p. Give a brief statement of the meaning of the confidence interval.
   (c) Is use of the normal approximation to the binomial justified in this problem? Explain.

7. *Fishing: Barbless Hooks* In a combined study of northern pike, cutthroat trout, rainbow trout, and lake trout, it was found that 26 out of 855 fish died when caught and released using barbless hooks on flies or lures. All hooks were removed from the fish (Source: *A National Symposium on Catch and Release Fishing,* Humboldt State University Press).
   (a) Let p represent the proportion of all pike and trout that die (i.e., p is the mortality rate) when caught and released using barbless hooks. Find a point estimate for p.
   (b) Find a 99% confidence interval for p, and give a brief explanation of the meaning of the interval.
   (c) Is the normal approximation to the binomial justified in this problem? Explain.

8. *Focus Problem: Trick or Treat* In a survey of a random sample of 35 households in the Cherry Creek neighborhood of Denver, it was found that 11 households turned out the lights and pretended not to be home on Halloween.
   (a) Compute a 90% confidence interval for *p*, the proportion of all households in Cherry Creek that pretend not to be home on Halloween.
   (b) What assumptions are necessary to calculate the confidence interval of part (a)?
   (c) The national proportion of all households in the United States that turn out the lights and pretend not to be home on Halloween is 0.28. Is 0.28 in the confidence interval you computed? Based on your answer, does it seem that the Cherry Creek neighborhood is much different (either higher or lower proportion) from the population of all U.S. households? Explain.

9. *Marketing: Customer Loyalty* In a marketing survey, a random sample of 730 women shoppers revealed that 628 remained loyal to their favorite supermarket during the past year—i.e., did not switch stores (Source: *Trends in the United States: Consumer Attitudes and the Supermarket*, The Research Department, Food Marketing Institute).
   (a) Let *p* represent the proportion of all women shoppers who remain loyal to their favorite supermarket. Find a point estimate for *p*.
   (b) Find a 95% confidence interval for *p*. Give a brief explanation of the meaning of the interval.
   (c) As a news writer, how would you report the survey results regarding the percentage of supermarket shoppers who remained loyal to their favorite supermarket during the past year? What is the margin of error based on a 95% confidence interval?

10. *Marketing: Bargain Hunters* In a marketing survey, a random sample of 1001 supermarket shoppers revealed that 273 always stock up on an item when they find that item at a real bargain price. See reference in Problem 9.
    (a) Let *p* represent the proportion of all supermarket shoppers who always stock up on an item when they find a real bargain. Find a point estimate for *p*.
    (b) Find a 95% confidence interval for *p*. Give a brief explanation of the meaning of the interval.
    (c) As a news writer, how would you report the survey results on the percentage of supermarket shoppers who stock up on items when they find the item is a real bargain? What is the margin of error based on a 95% confidence interval?

11. *Lifestyle: Smoking* In a survey of 1000 large corporations, 250 said that, given a choice between a job candidate who smokes and an equally qualified nonsmoker, the nonsmoker would get the job (*USA Today*).
    (a) Let *p* represent the proportion of all corporations preferring a nonsmoking candidate. Find a point estimate for *p*.
    (b) Find a 0.95 confidence interval for *p*.
    (c) As a news writer, how would you report the survey results regarding the proportion of corporations that would hire the equally qualified nonsmoker? What is the margin of error based on a 95% confidence interval?

12. *Opinion Poll: Crime and Violence* A *New York Times*/CBS poll asked the question, "What do you think is the most important problem facing this country today?" Nineteen percent of the respondents answered "crime and violence." The margin of sampling error was plus or minus 3 percentage points. Following the convention that the margin of error is based on a 95% confidence interval, find a 95% confidence interval for the percentage of the population that would respond "crime and violence" to the question asked by the pollsters.

13. *Medical: Blood Type* A random sample of medical files is used to estimate the proportion p of all people who have blood type B.
    (a) If you have no preliminary estimate for p, how many medical files should you include in a random sample in order to be 85% sure that the point estimate $\hat{p}$ will be within a distance of 0.05 from p?
    (b) Answer part (a) if you use the preliminary estimate that about 8 out of 90 people have blood type B (Reference: *Manual of Laboratory and Diagnostic Tests*, F. Fischbach).

14. *Business: Phone Contact* How hard is it to reach a businessperson by phone? Let p be the proportion of calls to businesspeople for which the caller reaches the person being called on the *first* try.
    (a) If you have no preliminary estimate for p, how many business phone calls should you include in a random sample to be 80% sure that the point estimate $\hat{p}$ will be within a distance of 0.03 from p?
    (b) The *Book of Odds*, by Shook and Shook (Signet), reports that businesspeople can be reached by a single phone call approximately 17% of the time. Using this (national) estimate for p, answer part (a).

15. *Campus Life: Coeds* What percentage of the campus student body is female? Let p be the proportion of women students on your campus.
    (a) If no preliminary study is made to estimate p, how large a sample is needed to be 99% sure that a point estimate $\hat{p}$ will be within a distance of 0.05 from p?
    (b) The *Statistical Abstract of the United States*, 112th Edition, indicates that approximately 54% of college students are females. Answer part (a) using this estimate for p.

16. *Small Business: Bankruptcy* The National Council of Small Businesses is interested in the proportion of small businesses that declared Chapter 11 bankruptcy last year. Since there are so many small businesses, the National Council intends to estimate the proportion from a random sample. Let p be the proportion of small businesses that declared Chapter 11 bankruptcy last year.
    (a) If no preliminary sample is taken to estimate p, how large a sample is necessary to be 95% sure that a point estimate $\hat{p}$ will be within a distance of 0.10 from p?
    (b) In a preliminary random sample of 38 small businesses, it was found that six had declared Chapter 11 bankruptcy. How many *more* small businesses should be included in the sample to be 95% sure that a point estimate $\hat{p}$ will be within a distance of 0.10 from p?

SUMMARY

How do you get information about a population by looking at a sample? One way is to use point estimates and confidence intervals. In this chapter, you studied point estimates and confidence intervals for population parameters μ and p. The respective point estimates are $\bar{x}$ and $\hat{p}$. Confidence intervals are created by subtracting and adding the margin of error E for a specified confidence level.

The general structure for a c confidence interval is

point estimate $- E <$ parameter $<$ point estimate $+ E$

Specific formulas for E depend on the parameter being estimated, the level of confidence, whether population standard deviations are known, sample sizes, and the shapes of the original population distributions. When estimating μ, follow the convention of using the standard normal distribution for critical values only if the population standard deviation is known. Otherwise, use a Student's t distribution.

Confidence intervals for p require large-sample techniques so that the standard normal distribution can be used for critical values.

Confidence intervals have an associated probability c called the confidence level. The probability is c that the c confidence interval you compute is one of the many possible intervals containing the population parameter.

IMPORTANT WORDS & SYMBOLS

Section 8.1
Large samples, $n \geq 30$
Maximal margin of error E
Confidence level c
Critical values z_c
Point estimate for μ
Confidence interval for μ
c confidence interval

Section 8.2
Student's t variable
Degrees of freedom $(d.f.)$
Critical values t_c

Section 8.3
Point estimate for p, $\hat{p}$
Confidence interval for p
Margin of error for polls

VIEWPOINT   *All Systems Go?*

On January 28, 1986, the Space Shuttle *Challenger* caught fire and blew up only seconds after launch. A great deal of good engineering went into the design of the *Challenger*. However, when a system has several confidence levels operating at once, it can happen, in rare cases, that risks will increase rather than cancel out. Diane Vaughn is a professor of sociology at Boston College and author of the book *The Challenger Launch Decision* (University of Chicago Press). Her book contains an excellent discussion of risks, the normalization of deviants, and cost/safety tradeoffs. Vaughn's book is described as "a remarkable and important analysis of how social structures can induce consequential errors in a decision process" (Robert K. Merton, Columbia University).

CHAPTER REVIEW PROBLEMS

1. In your own words, carefully explain the meaning of the following terms: point estimate, critical value, maximal margin of error, confidence level, and confidence interval.

For Problems 2–10, categorize each problem according to the parameter being estimated, mean μ or proportion p. Then solve the problem.

2. *Auto Insurance: Claims* Anystate Auto Insurance Company took a random sample of 370 insurance claims paid out during a 1-year period. The average claim paid was $1570. Assume $\sigma = \$250$. Find 0.90 and 0.99 confidence intervals for the mean claim payment.

3. *Psychology: Closure* Three experiments investigating the relation between need for cognitive closure and persuasion were reported in "Motivated Resistance and Openness to Persuasion in the Presence or Absence of Prior Information," by A. W. Kruglanski (*Journal of Personality and Social Psychology,* Vol. 65, No. 5, pp. 861–874). Part of the study involved administering a "need for closure scale" to a group of students enrolled in an introductory psychology course. The "need for closure scale" has scores ranging from 101 to 201. For the 73 students in the highest quartile of the distribution, the mean score was $\bar{x} = 178.70$. Assume the population standard deviation $\sigma = 7.81$. These students were all classified as high on their need for closure. Assume that the 73 students represent a random sample of all students who are classified as high on their need for closure. Find a 95% confidence interval for the population mean score μ on the "need for closure scale" for all students with a high need for closure.

4. *Psychology: Closure* How large a sample is needed in Problem 3 if we wish to be 99% confident that the sample mean score is within 2 points of the population mean score for students who are high on the need for closure?

5. *Archaeology: Excavations* The Wind Mountain archaeological site is located in southwestern New Mexico. Wind Mountain was home to an ancient culture of prehistoric Native Americans called Anasazi. A random sample of excavations at Wind Mountain gave the following depths (in centimeters) from present-day surface grade to the location of significant archaeological artifacts (Source: *Mimbres Mogollon Archaeology,* by A. Woosley and A. McIntyre, University of New Mexico Press).

85	45	120	80	75	55	65	60
65	95	90	70	75	65	68	

(a) Use a calculator with mean and sample standard deviation keys to verify that $\bar{x} \approx 74.2$ cm and $s \approx 18.3$ cm.
(b) Compute a 95% confidence interval for the mean depth μ at which archaeological artifacts from the Wind Mountain excavation site can be found.

6. *Archaeology: Pottery* Sherds of clay vessels were put together to reconstruct rim diameters of the original ceramic vessels at the Wind Mountain archaeological site (see source in Problem 5). A random sample of ceramic vessels gave the following rim diameters (in centimeters):

15.9	13.4	22.1	12.7	13.1	19.6	11.7	13.5	17.7	18.1

(a) Use a calculator with mean and sample standard deviation keys to verify that $\bar{x} \approx 15.8$ cm and $s \approx 3.5$ cm.
(b) Compute an 80% confidence interval for the population mean μ of rim diameters for such ceramic vessels found at the Wind Mountain archaeological site.

7. *Telephone Interviews: Survey* The National Study of the Changing Work Force conducted an extensive survey of 2958 wage and salaried workers on issues ranging from relationship with their bosses to household chores. The data were gathered through hour-long telephone interviews with a nationally representative sample (*The Wall Street Journal*). In response to the question, "What does success mean to you?" 1538 responded, "Personal satisfaction from doing a good job." Let p be the population proportion of all wage and salaried workers who would respond the same way to the stated question. Find a 90% confidence interval for p.

8. *Telephone Interviews: Survey* How large a sample is needed in Problem 7 if we wish to be 95% confident that the sample percentage of those equating success with personal satisfaction is within 1% of the population percentage? (*Hint:* Use $p \approx 0.52$ as a preliminary estimate.)

9. *Archaeology: Pottery* Three-circle, red-on-white is one distinctive pattern painted on ceramic vessels of the Anasazi period found at the Wind Mountain archaeological site (see source for Problem 5). At one excavation, a sample of 167 potsherds indicated that 68 were of the three-circle, red-on-white pattern.
   (a) Find a point estimate $\hat{p}$ for the proportion of all ceramic potsherds at this site that are of the three-circle, red-on-white pattern.
   (b) Compute a 95% confidence interval for the population proportion p of all ceramic potsherds with this distinctive pattern found at the site.

10. *Archaeology: Pottery* Consider the three-circle, red-on-white pattern discussed in Problem 9. How many ceramic potsherds must be found and identified if we are to be 95% confident that the sample proportion $\hat{p}$ of such potsherds is within 6% of the population proportion of three-circle, red-on-white patterns found at this excavation site? (*Hint:* Use the results of Problem 9 as a preliminary estimate.)

DATA HIGHLIGHTS: GROUP PROJECTS

Break into small groups and discuss the following topics. Organize a brief outline in which you summarize the main points of your group discussion.

Digging clams

1. Garrison Bay is a small bay in Washington state. A popular recreational activity in the bay is clam digging. For several years, the clam harvest has been monitored and the size distribution of clams recorded. Data for lengths and widths of little neck clams (*Protothaca staminea*) were recorded by a method of systematic sampling in a study done by S. Scherba and V. F. Gallucci ("The Application of Systematic Sampling to a Study of Infaunal Variation in a Soft Substrate Intertidal Environment," *Fishery Bulletin* 74:937–948). The data in Tables 8-4 and 8-5 give lengths and widths for 35 little neck clams.
   (a) Use a calculator to compute the sample mean and sample standard deviation for the lengths and widths. Compute the coefficient of variation for each.
   (b) Compute a 95% confidence interval for the population mean length of all Garrison Bay little neck clams.
   (c) How many more little neck clams would be needed in a sample if you wanted to be 95% sure that the sample mean length is within a maximal margin of error of 10 mm of the population mean length?
   (d) Compute a 95% confidence interval for the population mean width of all Garrison Bay little neck clams.

TABLE 8-4 Lengths of Little Neck Clams (mm)

530	517	505	512	487	481	485	479	452	468
459	449	472	471	455	394	475	335	508	486
474	465	420	402	410	393	389	330	305	169
91	537	519	509	511					

TABLE 8-5 Widths of Little Neck Clams (mm)

494	477	471	413	407	427	408	430	395	417
394	397	402	401	385	338	422	288	464	436
414	402	383	340	349	333	356	268	264	141
77	498	456	433	447					

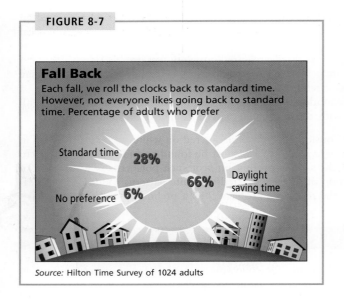

FIGURE 8-7

Fall Back

Each fall, we roll the clocks back to standard time. However, not everyone likes going back to standard time. Percentage of adults who prefer

Standard time **28%**

66% Daylight saving time

No preference **6%**

Source: Hilton Time Survey of 1024 adults

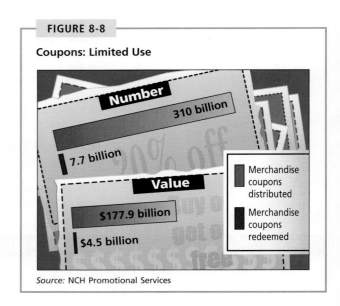

FIGURE 8-8

Coupons: Limited Use

Number
310 billion
7.7 billion

Value
$177.9 billion
$4.5 billion

Merchandise coupons distributed

Merchandise coupons redeemed

Source: NCH Promotional Services

(e) How many more little neck clams would be needed in a sample if you wanted to be 95% sure that the sample mean width is within a maximal margin of error of 10 mm of the population mean width?

2. Examine Figure 8-7, "Fall Back."
   (a) Of the 1024 adults surveyed, 66% were reported to favor daylight saving time. How many people in the sample preferred daylight saving time? Using the statistic $\hat{p} = 0.66$ and sample size $n = 1024$, find a 95% confidence interval for the proportion of people p who favor daylight saving time. How could you report this information in terms of a margin of error?
   (b) Look at Figure 8-7 to find the sample statistic $\hat{p}$ for the proportion of people preferring standard time. Find a 95% confidence interval for the population proportion p of people who favor standard time. Report the same information in terms of a margin of error.

3. Examine Figure 8-8, "Coupons: Limited Use."
   (a) Use Figure 8-8 to estimate the percentage of merchandise coupons that were redeemed. Also estimate the percentage dollar value of the coupons that were redeemed. Are these numbers approximately equal?
   (b) Suppose that you are a marketing executive working for a national chain of toy stores. You wish to estimate the percentage of coupons that will be redeemed for the toy stores. How many coupons should you check to be 95% sure that the percentage of coupons redeemed is within 1% of the population proportion of all coupons redeemed for the toy store?
   (c) Use the results of part (a) as a preliminary estimate for p, the percentage of coupons that are redeemed, and redo part (b).
   (d) Suppose that you sent out 937 coupons and found that 27 were redeemed. Explain why you could be 95% confident that the proportion of such coupons redeemed in the future would be between 1.9% and 3.9%.
   (e) Suppose that the dollar value of a collection of coupons was $10,000. Use the data in Figure 8-8 to find the expected value and standard deviation of the dollar value of the redeemed coupons. What is the probability that between $225 and $275 (out of the $10,000) is redeemed?

LINKING CONCEPTS: WRITING PROJECTS

Discuss each of the following topics in class or review the topics on your own. Then write a brief but complete essay in which you summarize the main points. Please include formulas and graphs as appropriate.

1. In this chapter, we have studied confidence intervals. Carefully read the following statements about confidence intervals:
   (a) Once the endpoints of a confidence interval are numerically fixed, then the parameter in question (either μ or p) does or does not fall inside the "fixed" interval.
   (b) A given fixed interval either does or does not contain the parameter μ or p; therefore, the probability is 1 or 0 that the parameter is in the interval.

   Next, read the following statements. Then discuss all four statements in the context of what we actually mean by a confidence interval.
   (c) Nontrivial probability statements can be made only about variables, not constants.
   (d) The confidence level c represents the proportion of all (fixed) intervals that would contain the parameter if we repeated the process many, many times.

2. Throughout Chapter 8, we have used the normal distribution, the central limit theorem, or the Student's t distribution.
   (a) Give a brief outline describing how confidence intervals for means use the central limit theorem or Student's t distribution in their basic construction.
   (b) Give a brief outline describing how the normal approximation to the binomial distribution is used in the construction of confidence intervals for a proportion p.
   (c) Give a brief outline describing how the sample size for a predetermined error tolerance and level of confidence is determined from the normal distribution or the central limit theorem.

3. When the results of a survey or a poll are published, the sample size is usually given, as well as the margin of error. For example, suppose the *Honolulu Star Bulletin* reported that it surveyed 385 Honolulu residents and 78% said they favor mandatory jail sentences for people convicted of driving under the influence of drugs or alcohol (with margin of error of 3 percentage points in either direction). Usually the confidence level of the interval is not given, but it is standard practice to use the margin of error for a 95% confidence interval when no other confidence level is given.
   (a) The paper reported a point estimate of 78% with margin of error of $\pm 3\%$. Write this information in the form of a confidence interval for p, the population proportion of residents favoring mandatory jail sentences for people convicted of driving under the influence. What is the assumed confidence level?
   (b) The margin of error is simply the error due to using a sample instead of the entire population. It does not take into account the bias that might be introduced by the wording of the question, by the truthfulness of the respondents, or by other factors. Suppose the question was asked in this fashion: "Considering the devastating injuries suffered by innocent victims in auto accidents caused by drunken or drugged drivers, do you favor a mandatory jail sentence for those convicted of driving under the influence of drugs or alcohol?" Do you think the wording of the question would influence the respondents? Do you think the population proportion of those favoring mandatory jail sentences is accurately represented by a confidence interval based on responses to such a question? Explain your answer.

   Suppose the question had been: "Considering the existing overcrowding of our prisons, do you favor a mandatory jail sentence for people convicted of driving under the influence of drugs or alcohol?" Do you think the population proportion of those favoring mandatory jail sentences is accurately represented by a confidence interval based on responses to such a question? Explain your answer.

Using Technology

APPLICATION

Confidence Interval Demonstration

When we generate different random samples of the same size from a population, we discover that $\bar{x}$ varies from sample to sample. Likewise, different samples produce different confidence intervals for μ. The endpoints $\bar{x} \pm E$ of a confidence interval are statistical variables. A 90% confidence interval tells us that if we obtain lots of confidence intervals (for the same sample size), then the proportion of all intervals that will turn out to contain μ is 90%.

(a) Use the technology of your choice to generate 10 large random samples from a population with a known mean μ.

(b) Construct a 90% confidence interval for the mean for each sample.

(c) Examine the confidence intervals and note the percentage of the intervals that contain the population mean μ. We have 10 confidence intervals. Will exactly 90% of 10 intervals always contain μ? Explain. What if we have 1000 intervals?

Technology Hints for Confidence Interval Demonstration

TI-84Plus/TI-83Plus

The TI-84Plus/TI-83Plus generates random samples from uniform, normal, and binomial distributions. Press the **MATH** key and select **PRB**. Choice **5:randInt(lower, upper, sample size n)** generates random samples of size n from the integers between the specified lower and upper values. Choice **6:randNorm(μ, σ, sample size n)** generates random samples of size n from a normal distribution with specified mean and standard deviation.

Choice **7:randBin(number of trials, p, sample size)** generates samples of the specified size from the designated binomial distribution. Under **STAT**, select **EDIT** and highlight the list name such as L1. At the $=$ sign, use the **MATH** key to access the desired population distribution. Finally, use the **Zinterval** under the **TESTS** option of the **STAT** key to generate 90% confidence intervals.

Excel

Use the menu choices **Tools ➤ Data Analysis ➤ Random Number Generator**. In the dialogue box, the number of variables refers to the number of samples. The number of random numbers refers to the number of data in each sample. Select the population distribution (uniform, normal, binomial). The command **Paste function ⨍x ➤ Statistical ➤ Confidence(1 − confidence level, σ, sample size)** gives the maximal margin of error E. To find a 90% confidence interval for each sample, use **Confidence(0.10, σ, sample size)** to find the maximal margin of error E. Note that if you use the population standard deviation σ in the function, the value of E will be the same for all samples of the same size. Next, find the sample mean $\bar{x}$ for each sample (use **Paste function ⨍x ➤ Statistical ➤ Average**). Finally, construct the endpoints $\bar{x} \pm E$ of the confidence interval for each sample.

Minitab

Minitab provides options for sampling from a variety of distributions. To generate random samples from a specific distribution, use the menu selection **Calc ➤ Random Data ➤** and then select the population distribution. In the dialogue box, the *number of rows of data* represents the *sample size*. The *number of samples* corresponds to the number of columns selected for data storage. For example, c1−c10 in data storage produces 10 different random samples of the specified size. Use the menu selection **Stat ➤ Basic Statistics ➤ 1 sample z** to generate confidence intervals for the mean μ from each sample. In the variables box, list all the columns containing your samples. For instance, using c1−c10 in the variables list will produce confidence intervals for each of the 10 samples stored in columns c1 through c10.

The Minitab display shows 90% confidence intervals for 10 different random samples of size 50 taken from a normal distribution with $\mu = 30$ and $\sigma = 4$. Notice that, as expected, 9 out of 10 of the intervals contain $\mu = 30$.

Minitab Display

```
z Confidence Intervals (Samples from a Normal
Population with μ = 30 and σ = 4)
The assumed sigma = 4.00
Variable    N     Mean    StDev   SE Mean        90.0 % CI
C1         50    30.265   4.300    0.566    ( 29.334,  31.195)
C2         50    31.040   3.957    0.566    ( 30.109,  31.971)
C3         50    29.940   4.195    0.566    ( 29.010,  30.871)
C4         50    30.753   3.842    0.566    ( 29.823,  31.684)
C5         50    30.047   4.174    0.566    ( 29.116,  30.977)
C6         50    29.254   4.423    0.566    ( 28.324,  30.185)
C7         50    29.062   4.532    0.566    ( 28.131,  29.992)
C8         50    29.344   4.487    0.566    ( 28.414,  30.275)
C9         50    30.062   4.199    0.566    ( 29.131,  30.992)
C10        50    29.989   3.451    0.566    ( 29.058,  30.919)
```

SPSS

SPSS uses a Student's t distribution to generate confidence intervals for the mean. Use the menu choices **Analyze ➤ Compare Means** and then **One-Sample T Test** for confidence intervals for a single mean. In the dialogue box, use 0 for the test value. Click **Options...** to provide the confidence level.

To generate 10 random samples of size $n = 30$ from a normal distribution with $\mu = 30$ and $\sigma = 4$, first enter consecutive integers from 1 to 30 in a column of the data editor. Then, under variable view, enter the variable names Sample1 through Sample10. Use the menu choices **Transform ➤ Compute**. In the dialogue box, use Sample1 for the target variable, then select the function **RV.Normal(mean, stddev)**. Use 30 for the mean and 4 for the standard deviation. Continue until you have 10 samples. To sample from other distributions, use appropriate functions in the Compute dialogue box.

The SPSS display shows 90% confidence intervals for 10 different random samples of size 30 taken from a normal distribution with $\mu = 30$ and $\sigma = 4$. Notice that, as expected, 9 of the 10 intervals contain the population mean $\mu = 30$.

SPSS Display

```
90% t-confidence intervals for random samples of size
n = 30 from a normal distribution with μ = 30
and σ = 4.
               t    df  Sig(2-tail)    Mean     Lower    Upper
SAMPLE1    42.304   29     .000      29.7149   28.5214  30.9084
SAMPLE2    43.374   29     .000      30.1552   28.9739  31.3365
SAMPLE3    53.606   29     .000      31.2743   30.2830  32.2656
SAMPLE4    35.648   29     .000      30.1490   28.7120  31.5860
SAMPLE5    47.964   29     .000      31.0161   29.9173  32.1148
SAMPLE6    34.718   29     .000      30.3519   28.8665  31.8374
SAMPLE7    34.698   29     .000      30.7665   29.2599  32.2731
SAMPLE8    39.731   29     .000      30.2388   28.9456  31.5320
SAMPLE9    44.206   29     .000      29.7256   28.5831  30.8681
SAMPLE10   49.981   29     .000      29.7273   28.7167  30.7379
```

9

Hypothesis Testing

Charles Lutwidge Dodgson (1832–1898)

Using the pseudonym Lewis Carroll, this English mathematician and author wrote *Alice's Adventures in Wonderland.*

 For on-line student resources, visit **math.college.hmco.com/students** and follow the Statistics links to the Brase/Brase, *Understanding Basic Statistics,* 4th edition web site.

"Would you tell me, please, which way I ought to go from here?"
"That depends a good deal on where you want to get to," said the Cat.
"I don't much care where—" said Alice.
"Then it doesn't matter which way you go," said the Cat.

—Lewis Carroll
Alice's Adventures in Wonderland

Charles Dodgson was an English mathematician who loved to write children's stories in his free time. The dialogue above between Alice and the Cheshire Cat occurs in the masterpiece *Alice's Adventures in Wonderland,* written by Dodgson under the pen name Lewis Carroll. These lines relate to our study of hypothesis testing. Statistical tests cannot answer all of life's questions. They cannot always tell us "where to go," but after this decision has been made on other grounds, they can help us find the best way to get there.

PREVIEW QUESTIONS

◇ Many of life's questions require a yes or no answer. When you must act on incomplete (sample) information, how do you decide whether to accept or reject a proposal? (SECTION 9.1)

◇ What is the *P*-value of a statistical test? What does this measurement have to do with performance reliability? (SECTION 9.1)

◇ How do you construct statistical tests for μ? Does it make a difference whether σ is known or unknown? (SECTION 9.2)

◇ How do you construct statistical tests for the proportion *p* of successes in a binomial experiment? (SECTION 9.3)

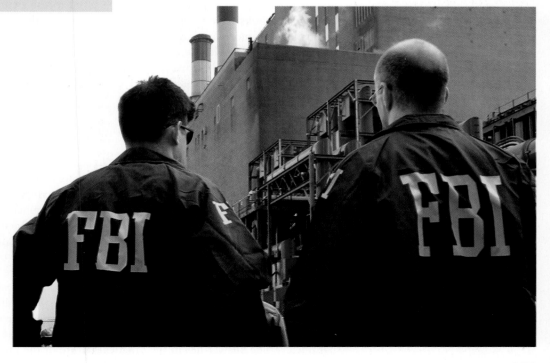

FOCUS PROBLEM

Benford's Law: The Importance of Being Number 1

Benford's Law states that in a wide variety of circumstances, numbers have "1" as their first nonzero digit disproportionately often. Benford's Law applies to such diverse topics as the drainage areas of rivers; properties of chemicals; populations of towns; figures in newspapers, magazines, and government reports; and the half-lives of radioactive atoms!

Specifically, such diverse measurements begin with "1" about 30% of the time, with "2" about 18% of time, and with "3" about 12.5% of the time. Larger digits occur less often. For example, less than 5% of the numbers in circumstances such as these begin with the digit 9. This is in dramatic contrast to a random sampling situation, in which each of the digits 1 through 9 has an equal chance of occurring.

The first nonzero digits of numbers taken from large bodies of numerical records such as tax returns, population studies, government records, and so forth show the following probabilities of occurrence.

359

First nonzero digit	1	2	3	4	5	6	7	8	9
Probability	0.301	0.176	0.125	0.097	0.079	0.067	0.058	0.051	0.046

More than 100 years ago, the astronomer Simon Newcomb noticed that books of logarithm tables were much dirtier near the fronts of the tables. It seemed that people were more frequently looking up numbers with a low first digit. This was regarded as an odd phenomenon and a strange curiosity. The phenomenon was rediscovered in 1938 by physicist Frank Benford (hence the name *Benford's Law*).

More recently, Ted Hill, a mathematician at the Georgia Institute of Technology, studied situations that might demonstrate Benford's Law. Professor Hill showed that such probability distributions are likely to occur when we have a "distribution of distributions." Put another way, large random collections of random samples tend to follow Benford's Law. This seems to be especially true for samples taken from large government data banks, accounting reports for large corporations, large collections of astronomical observations, and so forth. For more information, see *American Scientist,* Vol. 86, pp. 358–363, and *Chance,* American Statistical Association, Vol. 12, No. 3, pp. 27–31.

Can Benford's Law be applied to help solve a real-world problem? Well, one application might be accounting fraud! Suppose the first nonzero digits of the entries in the accounting records of a large corporation (such as Enron or WorldCom) did not follow Benford's Law. Should this set off an accounting alarm for the FBI or the stockholders? How "significant" would this be? Such questions are the subject of statistics.

In Section 9.3 you will see how to use sample data to test whether the proportion of first nonzero digits of the entries in a large accounting report follows Benford's Law. Problems 1 and 2 of Section 9.3 relate to Benford's Law and accounting discrepancies. In one problem you are asked to use sample data to determine if accounting books have been "cooked" by "pumping the numbers up" to make the company look more attractive, or perhaps to provide a cover for money laundering. In the other problem you are asked to determine if accounting books have been "cooked" by artificially lowering the numbers, perhaps to hide profits from the Internal Revenue Service or to divert company profits to unscrupulous employees. (See Problems 1 and 2 of Section 9.3.)

9.1
Introduction to Statistical Tests

FOCUS POINTS

✓ Understand the rationale for statistical tests.

✓ Identify the null and alternate hypotheses in a statistical test.

✓ Identify right-tailed, left-tailed, and two-tailed tests.

✓ Use a test statistic to compute a *P*-value.

✓ Recognize types of errors, level of significance, and power of a test.

✓ Understand the meaning and risks of rejecting or not rejecting the null hypothesis.

In Chapter 1, we emphasized the fact that one of a statistician's most important jobs is to draw inferences about populations based on samples taken from the populations. Most statistical inference centers around the parameters of a population (often the mean or probability of success in a binomial trial). Methods for drawing inferences about parameters are of two types: Either we make decisions concerning the value of the parameter, or we actually estimate the value of the parameter. When we estimate the value (or location) of a parameter, we are using methods of estimation such as those studied in Chapter 8. Decisions concerning the value of a parameter are obtained by *hypothesis testing,* the topic we shall study in this chapter.

Students often ask which method should be used on a particular problem—that is, should the parameter be estimated, or should we test a *hypothesis* involving the parameter? The answer lies in the practical nature of the problem and the questions posed about it. Some people prefer to test theories concerning the parameters.

Others prefer to express their inferences as estimates. Both estimation and hypothesis testing are found extensively in the literature of statistical applications.

Stating Hypotheses

Null hypothesis

Our first step is to establish a working hypothesis about the population parameter in question. This hypothesis is called the *null hypothesis*, denoted by the symbol H_0. The value specified in the null hypothesis is often a historical value, a claim, or a production specification. For instance, if the average height of a professional male basketball player was 6.5 feet 10 years ago, we might use a null hypothesis H_0: $\mu = 6.5$ feet for a study involving the average height of this year's professional male basketball players. If television networks claim that the average length of time devoted to commercials in a 60-minute program is 12 minutes, we would use H_0: $\mu = 12$ minutes as our null hypothesis in a study regarding the length of time devoted to commercials. Finally, if a repair shop claims that it should take an average of 25 minutes to install a new muffler on a passenger automobile, we would use H_0: $\mu = 25$ minutes as the null hypothesis for a study of how well the repair shop is conforming to specified times for a muffler installation.

Alternate hypothesis

Any hypothesis that differs from the null hypothesis is called an *alternate hypothesis*. An alternate hypothesis is constructed in such a way that it is the one to be accepted when the null hypothesis must be rejected. The alternate hypothesis is denoted by the symbol H_1. For instance, if we believe the average height of professional male basketball players is greater than it was 10 years ago, we would use an alternate hypothesis H_1: $\mu > 6.5$ feet with the null hypothesis H_0: $\mu = 6.5$ feet.

> **Null hypothesis H_0:** This is the statement that is under investigation or being tested. Usually the null hypothesis represents a statement of "no effect," "no difference," or, put another way, "things haven't changed."
>
> **Alternate hypothesis H_1:** This is the statement you will adopt in the situation where the evidence (data) is so strong that you reject H_0. A statistical test is designed to assess the strength of the evidence (data) against the null hypothesis.

EXAMPLE 1

Null and alternate hypotheses

A car manufacturer advertises that its new subcompact models get 47 miles per gallon (mpg). Let μ be the mean of the mileage distribution for these cars. You assume that the manufacturer will not underrate the car, but you suspect that the mileage might be overrated.

(a) What shall we use for H_0?

SOLUTION: We want to see if the manufacturer's claim that $\mu = 47$ can be rejected. Therefore, our null hypothesis is simply that $\mu = 47$. We denote the null hypothesis as

$$H_0: \mu = 47$$

(b) What shall we use for H_1?

SOLUTION: From experience with this manufacturer, we have every reason to believe that the advertised mileage is too high. If μ is not 47, we are sure it is less than 47. Therefore, the alternate hypothesis is

$$H_1: \mu < 47$$

◇

GUIDED EXERCISE 1

Null and alternate hypotheses

A company manufactures ball bearings for precision machines. The average diameter of a certain type of ball bearing should be 6.0 mm. To check that the average diameter is correct, the company formulates a statistical test.

(a) What statement should be used for H_0? (*Hint:* What is the company trying to test?)

⇒ If μ is the mean diameter of the ball bearings, the company wants to test whether $\mu = 6.0$ mm. Therefore, H_0: $\mu = 6.0$.

(b) What statement should be used for H_1? (*Hint:* An error either way, too small or too large, would be serious.)

⇒ An error either way could occur, and it would be serious. Therefore, H_1: $\mu \neq 6.0$ (μ is either smaller than or larger than 6.0).

◇ **COMMENT: NOTATION REGARDING THE NULL HYPOTHESIS** In statistical testing, the null hypothesis H_0 always contains the equals symbol. However, in the null hypothesis, some statistical software packages and texts also include the inequality symbol that is the opposite of the symbol used in the alternate hypothesis. For instance, if the alternate hypothesis is "μ is less than 3" ($\mu < 3$), then the corresponding null hypothesis is sometimes written as "μ is greater than or equal to 3" ($\mu \geq 3$). The mathematical construction of a statistical test uses the null hypothesis to assign a specific number (rather than a range of numbers) to the parameter μ in question. The null hypothesis establishes a single fixed value for μ, so we are working with a single distribution having a specific mean. In this case, H_0 assigns $\mu = 3$. So when H_1: $\mu < 3$ is the alternate hypothesis, we follow the commonly used convention of writing the null hypothesis simply as H_0: $\mu = 3$. ◇

Types of Tests

The null hypothesis H_0 always states that the parameter of interest *equals* a specified value. The alternate hypothesis H_1 states that the parameter is *less than, greater than,* or simply *not equal to* the same value. We categorize a statistical test as *left-tailed, right-tailed,* or *two-tailed* according to the alternate hypothesis.

Types of statistical tests

A statistical test is:

    left-tailed if H_1 states that the parameter is less than the value claimed in H_0

    right-tailed if H_1 states that the parameter is greater than the value claimed in H_0

    two-tailed if H_1 states that the parameter is different from (or not equal to) the value claimed in H_0

TABLE 9-1   The Null and Alternate Hypotheses for Tests of the Mean μ

Null Hypothesis	Alternate Hypotheses and Type of Test		
Claim about μ or historical value of μ $H_0: \mu = k$	You believe that μ is less than value stated in H_0. $H_1: \mu < k$ Left-tailed test	You believe that μ is more than value stated in H_0. $H_1: \mu > k$ Right-tailed test	You believe that μ is different from value stated in H_0. $H_1: \mu \neq k$ Two-tailed test

In this introduction to statistical tests, we discuss tests involving a population mean μ. However, you should keep an open mind and be aware that the methods outlined apply to testing other parameters as well (e.g., p, σ, $\mu_1 - \mu_2$, $p_1 - p_2$, and so on). Table 9-1 shows how tests of the mean μ are categorized.

Hypothesis Tests of μ, Given x Is Normal and σ Is Known

Once you have selected the null and alternate hypotheses, how do you decide which hypothesis is likely to be valid? Data from a simple random sample and the sample test statistic, together with the corresponding sampling distribution of the test statistic, will help you decide. Example 2 leads you through the decision process.

First, a quick review of Section 7.4 is in order. Recall that a population *parameter* is a numerical descriptive measurement of the entire population. Examples of population parameters are μ, p, and σ. It is important to remember that for a given population, the parameters are *fixed* values. They do not vary! The null hypothesis H_0 makes a statement about a population parameter.

A *statistic* is a numerical descriptive measurement of a sample. Examples of statistics are $\bar{x}$, $\hat{p}$, and s. Statistics usually *vary* from one sample to the next. The probability distribution of the statistic we are using is called a *sampling distribution*.

For hypothesis testing, we take a simple random sample and compute a *test statistic* corresponding to the parameter in H_0. Based on the sampling distribution of the statistic, we can assess how compatible the test statistic is with H_0.

In this section, we use hypothesis tests about the mean to introduce the concepts and vocabulary of hypothesis testing. In particular, let's suppose that x has *a normal distribution* with mean μ and standard deviation σ. Then, Theorem 7.1 tells us that $\bar{x}$ has a *normal distribution* with mean μ and standard deviation $\sigma/\sqrt{n}$.

Test statistic for μ, given x normal and σ known

Given that x has a *normal distribution* with known standard deviation σ, then

$$\text{test statistic} = z = \frac{\bar{x} - \mu}{\sigma/\sqrt{n}}$$

where $\bar{x}$ = mean of a simple random sample
   μ = value stated in H_0
   n = sample size

EXAMPLE 2

Statistical testing preview

Rosie is an aging sheep dog in Montana who gets regular check-ups from her owner, the local veterinarian. Let x be a random variable that represents Rosie's resting heart rate (in beats per minute). From past experience, the vet knows that x has a normal distribution with $\sigma = 12$. The vet checked the *Merck Veterinary Manual* and found that for dogs of this breed, $\mu = 115$ beats per minute.

Over the past six weeks, Rosie's heart rate (beats/min) measured

| 93 | 109 | 110 | 89 | 112 | 117 |

The sample mean is $\bar{x} = 105.0$. The vet is concerned that Rosie's heart rate may be slowing. Do the data indicate that this is the case?

SOLUTION:

(a) Establish the null and alternate hypotheses.
If "nothing has changed" from Rosie's earlier life, then her heart rate should be nearly average. This point of view is represented by the null hypothesis

$$H_0: \mu = 115$$

However, the vet is concerned about Rosie's heart rate slowing. This point of view is represented by the alternate hypothesis

$$H_1: \mu < 115$$

(b) Are the observed sample data compatible with the null hypothesis?
Are the six observations of Rosie's heart rate compatible with the null hypothesis $H_0: \mu = 115$? To answer this question, you need to know the *probability* of obtaining a sample mean of 105.0 or less from a population with true mean $\mu = 115$. If this probability is small, we conclude that $H_0: \mu = 115$ is not the case. Rather, we accept $H_1: \mu < 115$ and conclude that Rosie's heart rate is slowing.

(c) How do you compute the probability in part (b)?
Well, you probably guessed it! We use the sampling distribution for $\bar{x}$ and compute $P(\bar{x} < 105.0)$. Figure 9-1 shows the $\bar{x}$ distribution and the corresponding standard normal distribution with the desired probability shaded.

FIGURE 9-1

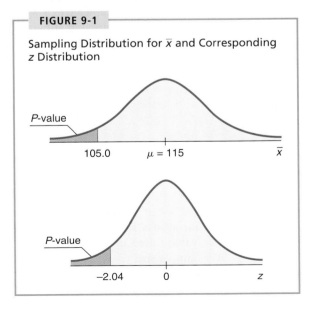

Sampling Distribution for $\bar{x}$ and Corresponding z Distribution

Since x has a normal distribution, $\bar{x}$ will also have a normal distribution for any sample size n and given σ (see Theorem 7.1). Note that using $\mu = 115$ from H_0, $\sigma = 12$, and $n = 6$, the sample $\bar{x} = 105.0$ converts to

$$\text{test statistic} = z = \frac{\bar{x} - \mu}{\sigma/\sqrt{n}} = \frac{105.0 - 115}{12/\sqrt{6}} \approx -2.04$$

Using the standard normal distribution table, we find that

$$P(\bar{x} < 105.0) = P(z < -2.04) = 0.0207$$

P-value

The area in the left tail that is more extreme than $\bar{x} = 105.0$ is called the *P-value* of the test. In this example, P-value $= 0.0207$. We will learn more about P-values later.

(d) What conclusion can be drawn about Rosie's average heart rate?

If H_0: $\mu = 115$ is in fact true, then the probability of getting a sample mean of $\bar{x} \leq 105.0$ is only about 2%. Because this probability is small, we reject H_0: $\mu = 115$ and conclude that H_1: $\mu < 115$. Rosie's average heart rate seems to be slowing.

(e) Have we proved H_0: $\mu = 115$ to be false and H_1: $\mu < 115$ to be true?

No! The sample data do not prove H_0 to be false and H_1 to be true! We do say that H_0 has been "discredited" by a small P-value of 0.0207. Therefore, we abandon the claim H_0: $\mu = 115$ and adopt the claim H_1: $\mu < 115$.   ◇

The *P*-value of a Statistical Test

Rosie the sheep dog has helped us to "sniff out" an important statistical concept.

P-value

Assuming H_0 is true, the *probability* that the test statistic will take on values as extreme as or more extreme than the observed test statistic (computed from sample data) is called the **P-value** of the test. The smaller the P-value computed from sample data, the stronger the evidence against H_0.

The *P*-value is sometimes called the *probability of chance*. The P-value can be thought of as the probability that the results of a statistical experiment are due only to chance. The lower the P-value, the greater the likelihood of obtaining the same results (or very similar results) in a repetition of the statistical experiment. Thus a low P-value is a good indication that your results are not due to random chance alone.

The *P*-value associated with the observed test statistic takes on different values depending on the alternate hypothesis and the type of test. Let's look at *P*-values and types of tests when the test involves the mean and standard normal distribution. Notice that in Example 2, part (c), we computed a *P*-value for a left-tailed test. Guided Exercise 3 asks you to compute a *P*-value for a two-tailed test.

P-values and types of tests

Let $z_{\bar{x}}$ represent the standardized sample test statistic for testing a mean μ using the standard normal distribution. That is, $z_{\bar{x}} = (\bar{x} - \mu)/(\sigma/\sqrt{n})$.

I. Left-tailed Test
$H_0: \mu = k$ $H_1: \mu < k$

P-value $= P(z < z_{\bar{x}})$
This is the probability of getting a test statistic as low as or lower than $z_{\bar{x}}$.

II. Right-tailed Test
$H_0: \mu = k$ $H_1: \mu > k$

P-value $= P(z > z_{\bar{x}})$
This is the probability of getting a test statistic as high as or higher than $z_{\bar{x}}$.

III. Two-tailed Test
$H_0: \mu = k$ $H_1: \mu \neq k$

$$\frac{\text{P-value}}{2} = P(z > |z_{\bar{x}}|); \text{ therefore,}$$

$$\text{P-value} = 2P(z > |z_{\bar{x}}|)$$

This is the probability of getting a test statistic either lower than $-|z_{\bar{x}}|$ or higher than $|z_{\bar{x}}|$.

Types of Errors

If we *reject the null hypothesis when it is*, in fact, *true*, we have made an error that is called a *type I error*. On the other hand, if we *accept the null hypothesis when it is*, in fact, *false*, we have made an error that is called a *type II error*. Table 9-2 indicates how these errors occur.

For tests of hypotheses to be well constructed, they must be designed to minimize possible errors of decision. (Usually, we do not know if an error has been made, and therefore, we can talk only about the probability of making an error.) Usually, for a given sample size, an attempt to reduce the probability of one type

TABLE 9-2   Type I and Type II Errors

	Our Decision	
Truth of H_0	And if we do not reject H_0	And if we reject H_0
If H_0 is true	Correct decision; no error	Type I error
If H_0 is false	Type II error	Correct decision; no error

of error results in an increase in the probability of the other type of error. In practical applications, one type of error may be more serious than another. In such a case, careful attention is given to the more serious error. If we increase the sample size, it is possible to reduce both types of errors, but increasing the sample size may not be possible.

Good statistical practice requires that we announce in advance how much evidence against H_0 will be required to reject H_0. The probability with which we are willing to risk a type I error is called the *level of significance* of a test. The level of significance is denoted by the Greek letter α (pronounced "alpha").

Level of significance

> The **level of significance** $\boldsymbol{\alpha}$ is the probability of rejecting H_0 when it is true. This is the probability of a type I error.

The *probability of making a type II error* is denoted by the Greek letter β (pronounced "beta"). Methods of hypothesis testing require us to choose α and β values to be as small as possible. In elementary statistical applications, we usually choose α first.

Power of a test

The quantity $1 - \beta$ is called the *power of the test* and represents the probability of rejecting H_0 when it is in fact false. For a given level of significance, how much power can we expect from a test? The actual value of the power is usually difficult (and sometimes impossible) to obtain, since it requires us to know the H_1 distribution. However, we can make the following general comments:

1. The power of a statistical test increases as the level of significance α increases. A test performed at the $\alpha = 0.05$ level has more power than one performed at $\alpha = 0.01$. This means that the less stringent we make our significance level α, the more likely we will reject the null hypothesis when it is false.

2. Using a larger value of α will increase the power of a test, but it also will increase the probability of a type I error. Despite this fact, most business executives, administrators, social scientists, and scientists use *small* α values. This choice reflects the conservative nature of administrators and scientists, who are usually more willing to make an error by failing to reject a claim (i.e., H_0) than to make an error by accepting another claim (i.e., H_1) that is false. Table 9-3 on the next page summarizes the probabilities of errors associated with a statistical test.

◇ **COMMENT** Since the calculation of the probability of a type II error is treated in advanced statistics courses, we will restrict our attention to the probability of a type I error. ◇

TABLE 9-3   Probabilities Associated with a Statistical Test

	Our Decision	
Truth of H_0	And if we accept H_0 as true	And if we reject H_0 as false
H_0 is true	Correct decision, with corresponding probability $1 - \alpha$	Type I error, with corresponding probability α, called the *level of significance of the test*
H_0 is false	Type II error, with corresponding probability β	Correct decision, with corresponding probability $1 - \beta$, called the *power of the test*

GUIDED EXERCISE 2

Types of errors

Let's reconsider Guided Exercise 1, in which we were considering the manufacturing specifications for the diameter of ball bearings. The hypotheses were

H_0: $\mu = 6.0$ mm (manufacturer's specification) H_1: $\mu \neq 6.0$ mm (cause for adjusting process)

(a) Suppose the manufacturer requires a 1% level of significance. Describe a type I error, its consequences, and its probability.

 A type I error is caused when sample evidence indicates that we should reject H_0 when, in fact, the average diameter of the ball bearings being produced is 6.0 mm. A type I error will cause a needless adjustment and delay of the manufacturing process. The probability of such an error is 1% because $\alpha = 0.01$.

(b) Discuss a type II error and its consequences.

A type II error occurs if the sample evidence tells us not to reject the null hypothesis H_0: $\mu = 6.0$ mm when, in fact, the average diameter of the ball bearings is either too large or too small to meet specifications. Such an error would mean that the production process would not be adjusted when it really needed to be adjusted. This could possibly result in a large production of ball bearings that do not meet specifications.

Concluding a Statistical Test

Usually, α is specified in advance, before any samples are drawn, so that the results will not influence the choice for the level of significance. To conclude a statistical test, we compare our α value with the P-value computed using sample data and the sampling distribution.

> **PROCEDURE**
>
> ### How to conclude a test using the *P*-value and level of significance α
>
> If *P*-value $\leq \alpha$, we **reject** the null hypothesis and say that the data are **statistically significant** at the level α.
>
> If *P*-value $> \alpha$, we **do not reject** the null hypothesis.

Statistical significance

In what sense are we using the word "significant"? *Webster's Dictionary* gives two interpretations of *significance*: (1) having or signifying *meaning*; or (2) important or momentous.

In statistical work, significance does not necessarily imply momentous importance. For us, "significant" at the α level has a special *meaning*. It says that at the α level of risk, the evidence (sample data) against the null hypothesis H_0 is sufficient to discredit H_0, so we adopt the alternate hypothesis H_1.

In any case, we do not claim that we have "proved" or "disproved" the null hypothesis H_0. We can say that the probability of a type I error (rejecting H_0 when it is in fact true) is α.

> **Basic components of a statistical test**
>
> A statistical test can be thought of as a package of five basic ingredients.
>
> 1. **Null hypothesis H_0, alternate hypothesis H_1, and preset level of significance α**
>   If the evidence (sample data) against H_0 is strong enough, we reject H_0 and adopt H_1. The level of significance α is the probability of rejecting H_0 when it is in fact true.
>
> 2. **Test statistic and sampling distribution**
>   These are mathematical tools used to measure compatibility of sample data and the null hypothesis.
>
> 3. ***P*-value**
>   This is the probability of obtaining a test statistic from the sampling distribution that is as extreme as or more extreme (as specified by H_1) than the sample test statistic computed from the data under the assumption that H_0 is true.
>
> 4. **Test conclusion**
>   If *P*-value $\leq \alpha$, we reject H_0 and say that the data are significant at level α. If *P*-value $> \alpha$, we do not reject H_0.
>
> 5. **Interpretation of the test results**
>   Give a simple explanation of your conclusions in the context of the application.

Constructing a statistical test for μ (normal distribution)

The Environmental Protection Agency has been studying Miller Creek regarding ammonia nitrogen concentration. For many years, the concentration has been 2.3 mg/l. However, a new golf course and housing developments are raising concern that the concentration may have changed because of increased use of lawn fertilizer. Any change (either an increase or a decrease) in the ammonia nitrogen concentration can affect plant and animal life in and around the creek (Reference: *EPA Report 832-R-93-005*). Let x be a random variable representing ammonia nitrogen concentration (in mg/l). Based on recent studies of Miller Creek, we may assume that x has a normal distribution with $\sigma = 0.30$. Recently, a random sample of 8 water tests from the creek gave the following x values.

| 2.1 | 2.5 | 2.2 | 2.8 | 3.0 | 2.2 | 2.4 | 2.9 |

The sample mean is $\bar{x} \approx 2.51$.

Let us construct a statistical test to examine the claim that the concentration of ammonia nitrogen has changed from 2.3 mg/l. Use level of significance $\alpha = 0.01$.

(a) What is the null hypothesis? What is the alternate hypothesis? What is the level of significance α?

⟹ $H_0: \mu = 2.3$
$H_1: \mu \neq 2.3$
$\alpha = 0.01$

(b) Is this a right-tailed, left-tailed, or two-tailed test?

⟹ Since $H_1: \mu \neq 2.3$, this is a two-tailed test.

(c) What sampling distribution shall we use? Note that the value of μ is given in the null hypothesis, H_0.

⟹ Since the x distribution is normal and σ is known, use the standard normal distribution with

$$z = \frac{\bar{x} - \mu}{\frac{\sigma}{\sqrt{n}}} = \frac{\bar{x} - 2.3}{\frac{0.3}{\sqrt{8}}}$$

(d) What is the sample test statistic? Convert the sample mean $\bar{x}$ to a standard z value.

⟹ The sample of 8 measurements has mean $\bar{x} = 2.51$. Converting this measurement to z, we have

$$\text{test statistic} = z = \frac{2.51 - 2.3}{\frac{0.3}{\sqrt{8}}} \approx 1.98$$

(e) Draw a sketch showing the P-value area on the standard normal distribution. Find the P-value. *Hint:* Use Table 3 of the Appendix. Because this is a two-tailed test, we double the area in the right tail beyond $z = 1.98$.

⟹ P-value $= 2P(z > 1.98) = 2(0.0239) = 0.0478$

FIGURE 9-2 *P-value*

Continued

GUIDED EXERCISE 3 continued

(f) Compare the level of significance α and the P-value. What is your conclusion?

⇨ Since P-value $0.0478 > 0.01$, we see that

$$P\text{-value} > \alpha$$

We fail to reject H_0.

(g) Summarize your results in the context of this problem.

⇨ The sample data are not significant at the $\alpha = 1\%$ level. At this point in time there is not enough evidence to conclude that the ammonia nitrogen concentration has changed in Miller Creek.

Meaning of accepting H_0

In most statistical applications, the level of significance is specified to be $\alpha = 0.05$ or $\alpha = 0.01$, although other values can be used. If $\alpha = 0.05$, then we say we are using a 5% level of significance. This means that in 100 similar situations, H_0 will be rejected 5 times, on average, when it should not have been rejected. Using Technology at the end of this chapter shows a simulation of this phenomenon.

When we accept (or fail to reject) the null hypothesis, we should understand that we are *not proving the null hypothesis*. We are saying only that the sample evidence (data) is not strong enough to justify rejection of the null hypothesis. The word *accept* sometimes has a stronger meaning in common English usage than we are willing to give it in our application of statistics. Therefore, we often use the expression *fail to reject* H_0 instead of *accept* H_0. When we *fail to reject* the null hypothesis, it simply means that the evidence in favor of rejection is not strong enough (see Table 9-4). Often, in the case that H_0 cannot be rejected, a confidence interval is used to estimate the parameter in question. The confidence interval gives the statistician a range of possible values for the parameter.

Some comments about P-values and level of significance α should be made. The level of significance α should be a fixed, pre-specified value. Usually α is chosen before any samples are drawn. The level of significance α is the probability of a type I error. So, α is the probability of rejecting H_0 when H_0 is in fact true.

The P-value should *not* be interpreted as the probability of a type I error. The level of significance (in theory) is set in advance before any samples are drawn. The P-value cannot be set in advance, since it is determined from the random sample. The P-value, together with α, should be regarded as tools used to conclude the test. If P-value $\leq \alpha$, then reject H_0, and if P-value $> \alpha$, then do not reject H_0.

TABLE 9-4   Meaning of the Terms *Fail to Reject H_0* and *Reject H_0*

Term	Meaning
Fail to reject H_0	There is not enough evidence in the data (and the test being used) to justify a rejection of H_0. This means that we retain H_0 with the understanding that we have not proved it to be true beyond all doubt.
Reject H_0	There is enough evidence in the data (and the test employed) to justify rejection of H_0. This means that we choose the alternate hypothesis H_1 with the understanding that we have not proved H_1 to be true beyond all doubt.

In most computer applications and journal articles, only the P-value is given. It is understood that the person using this information will supply an appropriate level of significance α. From an historical point of view, the English statistician F. Y. Edgeworth (1845–1926) was one of the first to use the term *significant* to imply that the sample data indicated a "meaningful" difference from a previously held view.

In this book, we are using the most popular method of testing, which is called the *P-value method*. At the end of the next section, you will learn about another (equivalent) method of testing called the *critical region method*. An extensive discussion regarding the P-value method of testing versus the critical region method can be found in *The American Statistician*, Vol. 57, No. 3, pp. 171–178, American Statistical Association.

VIEWPOINT

Lovers Take Heed!!!

If you are going to whisper sweet nothings to your sweetheart, be sure to whisper in the *left* ear. Professor Sim of Sam Houston State University (Huntsville, Texas) found that emotionally loaded words had a higher recall rate when spoken into a person's left ear, not the right. Professor Sim presented his findings at the British Psychology Society European Congress. He told the Congress that his findings are consistent with the hypothesis that the brain's right hemisphere has more influence in the processing of emotional stimuli. The left ear is controlled by the right side of the brain. Sim's research involved statistical tests like the ones you will study in this chapter.

SECTION 9.1   PROBLEMS

1. Discuss each of the following topics in class or review the topics on your own. Then write a brief but complete essay in which you answer the following questions.
   (a) What is a null hypothesis H_0?
   (b) What is an alternate hypothesis H_1?
   (c) What is a type I error? a type II error?
   (d) What is the level of significance of a test? What is the probability of a type II error?

2. In a statistical test, we have a choice of a left-tailed test, right-tailed test, or two-tailed test. Is it the null hypothesis or the alternate hypothesis that determines which type of test is used? Explain your answer.

3. If we fail to reject (i.e., "accept") the null hypothesis, does this mean that we have *proved* it to be true beyond *all* doubt? Explain your answer.

4. If we reject the null hypothesis, does this mean that we have *proved* it to be false beyond *all* doubt? Explain your answer.

5. *Veterinary Science: Colts* The body weight of a healthy 3-month-old colt should be about $\mu = 60$ kg (Source: *The Merck Veterinary Manual*, a standard reference manual used in most veterinary colleges).
   (a) If you want to set up a statistical test to challenge the claim that $\mu = 60$ kg, what would you use for the null hypothesis H_0?

(b) In Nevada, there are many herds of wild horses. Suppose that you want to test the claim that the average weight of a wild Nevada colt (3 months old) is less than 60 kg. What would you use for the alternate hypothesis H_1?

(c) Suppose that you want to test the claim that the average weight of such a wild colt is greater than 60 kg. What would you use for the alternate hypothesis?

(d) Suppose that you want to test the claim that the average weight of such a wild colt is *different* from 60 kg. What would you use for the alternate hypothesis?

(e) For each of the tests in parts (b), (c), and (d), would the area corresponding to the *P*-value be on the left, on the right, or on both sides of the mean? Explain your answer in each case.

6. *Marketing: Shopping Time* How much customers buy is a direct result of how much time they spend in a store. A study of average shopping time in a large national houseware store gave the following information (Source: *Why We Buy: The Science of Shopping* by P. Underhill):

> Women with female companion: 8.3 min.
> Women with male companion: 4.5 min.

Suppose you want to set up a statistical test to challenge the claim that a woman with a female friend spends an average of 8.3 minutes shopping in such a store.

(a) What would you use for the null and alternate hypotheses if you believe that the average shopping time is less than 8.3 minutes? Is this a right-tailed, left-tailed, or two-tailed test?

(b) What would you use for the null and alternate hypotheses if you believe that the average shopping time is different from 8.3 minutes? Is this a right-tailed, left-tailed, or two-tailed test?

Stores that sell mainly to women should figure out a way to engage the interest of men! Perhaps comfortable seats and a big TV with sports programs would do the trick. Suppose such an entertainment center was installed and you now wish to challenge the claim that a woman with a male friend spends only 4.5 minutes shopping in a houseware store.

(c) What would you use for the null and alternate hypotheses if you believe that the average shopping time is more than 4.5 minutes? Is this a right-tailed, left-tailed, or two-tailed test?

(d) What would you use for the null and alternate hypotheses if you believe that the average shopping time is different from 4.5 minutes? Is this a right-tailed, left-tailed, or two-tailed test?

7. *Meteorology: Storms* *Weatherwise* magazine is published in association with the American Meteorological Society. Volume 46, Number 6 has a rating system to classify Nor'easter storms that frequently hit New England states and can cause much damage near the ocean coast. A *severe* storm has an average peak wave height of 16.4 feet for waves hitting the shore. Suppose that a Nor'easter is in progress at the severe storm class rating.

(a) Let us say that we want to set up a statistical test to see if the wave action (i.e., height) is dying down or getting worse. What would be the null hypothesis regarding average wave height?

(b) If you wanted to test the hypothesis that the storm is getting worse, what would you use for the alternate hypothesis?

(c) If you wanted to test the hypothesis that the waves are dying down, what would you use for the alternate hypothesis?

(d) Suppose that you do not know if the storm is getting worse or dying out. You just want to test the hypothesis that the average wave height is *different* from (either higher or lower than) the severe storm class rating. What would you use for the alternate hypothesis?

(e) For each of the tests in parts (b), (c), and (d), would the area corresponding to the *P*-value be on the left, on the right, or on both sides of the mean? Explain your answer in each case.

8. *Chrysler Concorde: Acceleration Consumer Reports* stated that the mean time for a Chrysler Concorde to go from 0 to 60 miles per hour was 8.7 seconds.
   (a) If you want to set up a statistical test to challenge the claim of 8.7 seconds, what would you use for the null hypothesis?
   (b) The town of Leadville, Colorado, has an elevation over 10,000 feet. Suppose you wanted to test the claim that the average time to accelerate from 0 to 60 miles per hour is longer in Leadville (because of less oxygen). What would you use for the alternate hypothesis?
   (c) Suppose you made an engine modification and you think that the average time to accelerate from 0 to 60 miles per hour has been reduced. What would you use for the alternate hypothesis?
   (d) For each of the tests in parts (b) and (c), would the *P*-value area be on the left, on the right, or on both sides of the mean? Explain your answer in each case.

For Problems 9–14, please provide the following information.
(a) What is the level of significance? State the null and alternate hypotheses. Will you use a left-tailed, right-tailed, or two-tailed test?
(b) What sampling distribution will you use? Explain the rationale for your choice of sampling distribution. What is the value of the sample test statistic?
(c) Find (or estimate) the *P*-value. Sketch the sampling distribution and show the area corresponding to the *P*-value.
(d) Based on your answers in parts (a) to (c), will you reject or fail to reject the null hypothesis? Are the data statistically significant at level α?
(e) State your conclusion in the context of the application.

9. *Dividend Yield: Australian Bank Stocks* Let x be a random variable representing dividend yield of Australian bank stocks. We may assume that x has a normal distribution with $\sigma = 2.4\%$. A random sample of 10 Australian bank stocks gave the following yields.

| 5.7 | 4.8 | 6.0 | 4.9 | 4.0 | 3.4 | 6.5 | 7.1 | 5.3 | 6.1 |

The sample mean is $\bar{x} = 5.38\%$. For the entire Australian stock market, the mean dividend yield is $\mu = 4.7\%$ (Reference: *Forbes*). Do these data indicate that the dividend yield of all Australian bank stocks is higher than 4.7%? Use $\alpha = 0.01$.

10. *Glucose Level: Horses* Gentle Ben is a Morgan horse at a Colorado dude ranch. Over the past 8 weeks, a veterinarian took the following glucose readings from this horse (in mg/100 ml).

| 93 | 88 | 82 | 105 | 99 | 110 | 84 | 89 |

The sample mean is $\bar{x} \approx 93.8$. Let x be a random variable representing glucose readings taken from Gentle Ben. We may assume that x has a normal distribution, and we know from past experience that $\sigma = 12.5$. The mean glucose level for horses should be $\mu = 85$ mg/100 ml (Reference: *Merck Veterinary Manual*). Do these data indicate that Gentle Ben has an overall average glucose level higher than 85? Use $\alpha = 0.05$.

11. *Ecology: Hummingbirds* Bill Alther is a zoologist who studies Anna's hummingbird (*Calypte anna*). (Reference: *Hummingbirds*, K. Long, W. Alther.) Suppose that in a

remote part of the Grand Canyon a random sample of six of these birds was caught, weighed, and released. The weights (in gm) were

| 3.7 | 2.9 | 3.8 | 4.2 | 4.8 | 3.1 |

The sample mean is $\bar{x} = 3.75$ gm. Let x be a random variable representing weights of Anna's hummingbirds in this part of the Grand Canyon. We assume that x has a normal distribution and $\sigma = 0.70$ gm. It is known that for the population of all Anna's hummingbirds, the mean weight is $\mu = 4.55$ gm. Do the data indicate that the mean weight of these birds in this part of the Grand Canyon is less than 4.55 gm? Use $\alpha = 0.01$.

12. *Finance: P/E of Stocks* The price to earnings ratio (P/E) is an important tool in financial work. A random sample of 14 large U.S. banks (J. P. Morgan, Bank of America, and others) gave the following P/E ratios (Reference: *Forbes*).

| 24 | 16 | 22 | 14 | 12 | 13 | 17 |
| 22 | 15 | 19 | 23 | 13 | 11 | 18 |

The sample mean is $\bar{x} \approx 17.1$. Generally speaking, a low P/E ratio indicates a "value" or bargain stock. A recent copy of *The Wall Street Journal* indicated that the mean of the P/E ratio of the entire S&P 500 stock index is $\mu = 19$. Let x be a random variable representing the P/E ratio of all large U.S. bank stocks. We assume that x has a normal distribution and $\sigma = 4.5$. Do these data indicate that the P/E ratio of all U.S. bank stocks is less than 19? Use $\alpha = 0.05$.

13. *Insurance: Hail Damage* Nationally, about 11% of the total U.S. wheat crop is destroyed each year by hail (Reference: *Agricultural Statistics*, U.S. Department of Agriculture). An insurance company is studying wheat hail damage claims in Weld County, Colorado. A random sample of 16 claims in Weld County gave the following data (% wheat crop lost to hail).

| 15 | 8 | 9 | 11 | 12 | 20 | 14 | 11 |
| 7 | 10 | 24 | 20 | 13 | 9 | 12 | 5 |

The sample mean is $\bar{x} = 12.5\%$. Let x be a random variable that represents the percentage of wheat crop in Weld County lost to hail. Assume that x has a normal distribution and $\sigma = 5.0\%$. Do these data indicate that the percentage of wheat crops lost to hail in Weld County is different (either way) from the national mean of 11%? Use $\alpha = 0.01$.

14. *Medical: Red Blood Cell Volume* Total blood volume (in ml) per body weight (in kg) is important in medical research. For healthy adults, the red blood cell volume mean is about $\mu = 28$ ml/kg (Reference: *Laboratory and Diagnostic Tests*, F. Fischbach). Red blood cell volume that is too low or too high can indicate a medical problem (see reference). Suppose that Roger has had seven blood tests, and the red blood cell volumes were

| 32 | 25 | 41 | 35 | 30 | 37 | 29 |

The sample mean is $\bar{x} \approx 32.7$ ml/kg. Let x be a random variable that represents Roger's red blood cell volume. Assume that x has a normal distribution and $\sigma = 4.75$. Do the data indicate that Roger's red blood cell volume is different (either way) from $\mu = 28$ ml/kg? Use a 0.01 level of significance.

9.2
Testing the Mean μ

In this section, we continue our study of testing the mean μ. The method we are using is called the *P*-value method. It was used extensively by the famous statistician R. A. Fisher and is the most popular method of testing in use today. At the end of this section, we present another method of testing called the *critical region method* (or *traditional method*). The critical region method was used extensively by the statisticians J. Neyman and E. Pearson. In recent years, the use of this method has been declining. It is important to realize that for a fixed, preset level of significance α, both methods are logically equivalent.

In Section 9.1 we discussed the vocabulary and method of hypothesis testing using *P*-values. Let's quickly review the basic process.

1. We first state a proposed value for a population parameter in the null hypothesis H_0. The alternate hypothesis H_1 states alternative values of the parameter, either $<$, $>$, or $\neq$ the value proposed in H_0. We also set the level of significance α. This is the risk we are willing to take of committing a type I error. That is, α is the probability of rejecting H_0 when it is in fact true.

2. We use a corresponding sample statistic from a simple random sample to challenge the statement made in H_0. We convert the sample statistic to a test statistic, which is the corresponding value of the appropriate sampling distribution.

3. We use the sampling distribution of the test statistic and the type of test to compute the *P*-value of this statistic. Under the assumption that the null hypothesis is true, the *P*-value is the probability of getting a sample statistic as extreme as or more extreme than the observed statistic from our random sample.

4. Next, we conclude the test. If the *P*-value is very small, we have evidence to reject H_0 and adopt H_1. What do we mean by "very small"? We compare the *P*-value to the preset level of significance α. If the *P*-value $\leq \alpha$, then we say that we have evidence to reject H_0 and adopt H_1. Otherwise, we say that the sample evidence is insufficient to reject H_0.

5. Finally, we interpret the results in the context of the application.

Knowing the sampling distribution of the sample test statistic is an essential part of the hypothesis testing process. For tests of μ, we use one of two sampling distributions for $\bar{x}$: the standard normal distribution or a Student's *t* distribution. As discussed in Chapters 7 and 8, the appropriate distribution depends upon our knowledge of the population standard deviation σ, the nature of the *x* distribution, and the sample size.

Part I: Testing μ When σ Is Known

In most real world situations, σ is simply not known. However, in some cases, a preliminary study or other information can be used to get a realistic and accurate value for σ.

> ### PROCEDURE
>
> #### How to test μ when σ is known
>
> Let x be a random variable appropriate to your application. Obtain a simple random sample (of size n) of x values from which you compute the sample mean $\bar{x}$. The value of σ is already known (perhaps from a previous study).
>
> 1. In the context of the application, state the *null and alternate hypotheses* and set the *level of significance α*.
> 2. If you can assume that x has a normal distribution, then any sample size n will work. If you cannot assume this, then use a sample size $n \geq 30$. Use the known σ, the sample size n, the value of $\bar{x}$ from the sample, and μ from the null hypothesis to compute the standardized sample *test statistic*.
>
> $$z = \frac{\bar{x} - \mu}{\dfrac{\sigma}{\sqrt{n}}}$$
>
> 3. Use the standard normal distribution and the type of test, one-tailed or two-tailed, to find the *P-value* corresponding to the test statistic.
> 4. *Conclude* the test. If P-value $\leq \alpha$, then reject H_0. If P-value $> \alpha$, then do not reject H_0.
> 5. *State your conclusion* in the context of the application.

In Section 9.1, we examined P-value tests for normal distributions with relatively small sample size ($n < 30$). The next example does not assume a normal distribution, but has a large sample size ($n \geq 30$).

EXAMPLE 3

Testing μ, σ known

Sunspots have been observed for many centuries. Records of sunspots from ancient Persian and Chinese astronomers go back thousands of years. Some archaeologists think sunspot activity may somehow be related to prolonged periods of drought in the southwestern United States. Let x be a random variable representing the number of sunspots observed in a 4-week period. A random sample of 40 such periods from Spanish colonial times gave the following data (Reference: M. Waldmeir, *Sun Spot Activity*, International Astronomical Union Bulletin).

12.5	14.1	37.6	48.3	67.3	70.0	43.8	56.5	59.7	24.0
12.0	27.4	53.5	73.9	104.0	54.6	4.4	177.3	70.1	54.0
28.0	13.0	6.5	134.7	114.0	72.7	81.2	24.1	20.4	13.3
9.4	25.7	47.8	50.0	45.3	61.0	39.0	12.0	7.2	11.3

The sample mean is $\bar{x} \approx 47.0$. Previous studies of sunspot activity during this period indicate that $\sigma = 35$. It is thought that for thousands of years, the mean number of sunspots per 4-week period was about $\mu = 41$. Sunspot activity above this level may (or may not) be linked to gradual climate change. Do the data indicate that the mean sunspot activity during the Spanish colonial period was higher than 41? Use $\alpha = 0.05$.

SOLUTION:

(a) Establish the null and alternate hypotheses.

Since we want to know whether the average sunspot activity during the Spanish colonial period was higher than the long-term average of $\mu = 41$,

$$H_0: \mu = 41 \quad \text{and} \quad H_1: \mu > 41$$

(b) Compute the test statistic from the sample data.

Since $n \geq 30$ and we know σ, we use the standard normal distribution. Using $\bar{x} = 47$ from the sample, $\sigma = 35$, $\mu = 41$ from H_0, and $n = 40$,

$$z = \frac{\bar{x} - \mu}{\sigma/\sqrt{n}} \approx \frac{47 - 41}{35/\sqrt{40}} \approx 1.08$$

(c) Find the P-value of the test statistic.

Figure 9-3 shows the P-value. Since we have a right-tailed test, the P-value is the area to the right of $z = 1.08$ shown in Figure 9-3. Using Table 3 of the Appendix, we find that

$$P\text{-value} = P(z > 1.08) \approx 0.1401$$

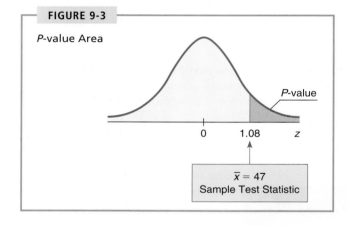

FIGURE 9-3

P-value Area

(d) Conclude the test.

Since the P-value of $0.1401 > 0.05$ for α, we do not reject H_0.

(e) Interpret the results.

At the 5% level of significance, the evidence is not sufficient to reject H_0. Based on the sample data, we do not think that the average sunspot activity during the Spanish colonial period was higher than the long-term mean.   ◇

Part II: Testing μ When σ Is Unknown

In many real-world situations, you have only a random sample of data values. In addition, you may have some limited information about the probability distribution of your data values. Can you still test μ under these circumstances? In most cases, the answer is yes!

> ### PROCEDURE
>
> #### How to test μ when σ is unknown
>
> Let x be a random variable appropriate to your application. Obtain a simple random sample (of size n) of x values from which you compute the sample mean $\bar{x}$ and the sample standard deviation s.
>
> 1. In the context of the application, state the *null and alternate hypotheses* and set the *level of significance α*.
>
> 2. If you can assume that x has a normal distribution or simply has a mound-shaped, symmetric distribution, then any sample size n will work. If you cannot assume this, then use a sample size $n \geq 30$. Use $\bar{x}$, s, and n from the sample with μ from H_0 to compute the sample *test statistic*.
>
> $$t = \frac{\bar{x} - \mu}{\dfrac{s}{\sqrt{n}}} \qquad \text{with degrees of freedom } d.f. = n - 1$$
>
> 3. Use the Student's t distribution and the type of test, one-tailed or two-tailed, to find (or estimate) the *P-value* corresponding to the test statistic.
>
> 4. *Conclude* the test. If P-value $\leq \alpha$, then reject H_0. If P-value $> \alpha$, then do not reject H_0.
>
> 5. *State your conclusion* in the context of the application.

Using the Student's t table to estimate P-values

In Section 8.2, we used Table 4 of the Appendix, Student's t Distribution, to find critical values t_c for confidence intervals. The critical values are in the body of the table. We find P-values in the *rows* headed by "one-tail area" and "two-tail area," depending on whether we have a one-tailed or two-tailed test. If the test statistic t for the sample statistic $\bar{x}$ is negative, look up the P-value for the corresponding *positive* value of t (i.e., look up the P-value for $|t|$).

Note: In Table 4, areas are given in *one tail* beyond positive t on the right or negative t on the left, and in *two tails* beyond $\pm t$. Notice that in each column, two-tail area = 2(one-tail area). Consequently, we use *one-tail areas* as endpoints of the interval containing the P-value for *one-tailed tests*. We use *two-tail areas* as endpoints of the interval containing the P-value for *two-tailed tests*. (See Figure 9-4.)

Example 4 and Guided Exercise 4 show how to use Table 4 of the Appendix to find an interval containing the P-value corresponding to a test statistic t.

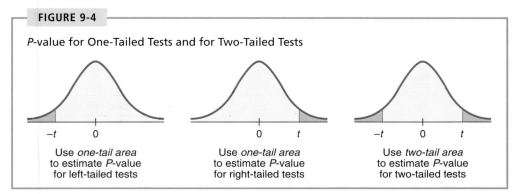

FIGURE 9-4

*P-*value for One-Tailed Tests and for Two-Tailed Tests

Use *one-tail area* to estimate P-value for left-tailed tests

Use *one-tail area* to estimate P-value for right-tailed tests

Use *two-tail area* to estimate P-value for two-tailed tests

EXAMPLE 4

Testing μ, σ unknown

The drug 6-mP (6-mercaptopurine) is used to treat leukemia. The following data represent the remission times (in weeks) for a random sample of 21 patients using 6-mP (Reference: E. A. Gehan, University of Texas Cancer Center).

10	7	32	23	22	6	16	34	32	25	11
20	19	6	17	35	6	13	9	6	10	

The sample mean is $\bar{x} \approx 17.1$ weeks with sample standard deviation $s \approx 10.0$. Let x be a random variable representing the remission time (in weeks) for all patients using 6-mP. Assume the x distribution is mound-shaped and symmetric. A previously used drug treatment had a mean remission time of $\mu = 12.5$ weeks. Do the data indicate that the mean remission time using the drug 6-mP is different (either way) from 12.5 weeks? Use $\alpha = 0.01$.

SOLUTION:

(a) Establish the null and alternate hypotheses.

Since we want to determine if the drug 6-mP provides a mean remission time that is different from that provided by a previously used drug having $\mu = 12.5$ weeks,

$$H_0: \mu = 12.5 \text{ weeks} \quad \text{and} \quad H_1: \mu \neq 12.5 \text{ weeks}$$

(b) Compute the test statistic from the sample data.

Since the x distribution is assumed to be mound-shaped and symmetric, we use the Student's t distribution. Using $\bar{x} \approx 17.1$ and $s \approx 10.0$ from the sample data, $\mu = 12.5$ from H_0, and $n = 21$,

$$t \approx \frac{\bar{x} - \mu}{s/\sqrt{n}} \approx \frac{17.1 - 12.5}{10.0/\sqrt{21}} \approx 2.108$$

(c) Find the P-value or the interval containing the P-value.

Figure 9-5 shows the P-value. Using Table 4 of the Appendix, we find an interval containing the P-value. Since this is a two-tailed test, we use entries from the row headed by *two-tail area*. Look up the t value in the row headed by $d.f. = n - 1 = 21 - 1 = 20$. The sample statistic $t = 2.108$ falls between 2.086 and 2.528. The P-value for the sample t falls between the corresponding two-tail areas 0.050 and 0.020. (See Table 9-5, Excerpt from Table 4.)

$$0.020 < P\text{-value} < 0.050$$

FIGURE 9-5

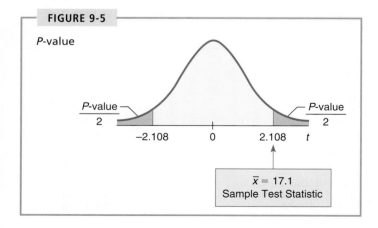

P-value

TABLE 9-5   Excerpt from Student's t Distribution (Table 4, Appendix)

one-tail area	...	...
✓two-tail area	0.050	0.020
$d.f. = 20$	2.086	2.528

↑ Sample $t = 2.108$

(d) Conclude the test.

The following diagram shows the interval that contains the single P-value corresponding to the test statistic. Note that there is just one P-value corresponding to the test statistic. Table 4 of the Appendix does not give that specific value, but it does give a range that contains the specific P-value. As the diagram shows, the entire range is greater than α. This means that the specific P-value is greater than α, so we cannot reject H_0.

Note: Using the raw data, computer software gives P-value ≈ 0.048. This value is in the interval we estimated. It is larger than the α value of 0.01, so we do not reject H_0.

(e) Interpret the results.

At the 1% level of significance, the evidence is not sufficient to reject H_0. Based on the sample data, we cannot say that the drug 6-mP provides a different average remission time than the previous drug.   ◇

GUIDED EXERCISE 4

Testing μ, σ unknown

Archaeologists become excited when they find an anomaly in discovered artifacts. The anomaly may (or may not) indicate a new trading region or a new method of craftsmanship. Suppose the lengths of projectile points (arrowheads) at a certain archaeological site have mean length $\mu = 2.6$ cm. A random sample of 61 recently discovered projectile points in an adjacent cliff dwelling gave the following lengths (in cm) (Reference: A. Woosley and A. McIntyre, *Mimbres Mogollon Archaeology*, University of New Mexico Press).

3.1	4.1	1.8	2.1	2.2	1.3	1.7	3.0	3.7	2.3	2.6	2.2	2.8	3.0
3.2	3.3	2.4	2.8	2.8	2.9	2.9	2.2	2.4	2.1	3.4	3.1	1.6	3.1
3.5	2.3	3.1	2.7	2.1	2.0	4.8	1.9	3.9	2.0	5.2	2.2	2.6	1.9
4.0	3.0	3.4	4.2	2.4	3.5	3.1	3.7	3.7	2.9	2.6	3.6	3.9	3.5
1.9	4.0	4.0	4.6	1.9									

The sample mean is $\bar{x} \approx 2.92$ cm and the sample standard deviation is $s \approx 0.85$, where x is a random variable that represents the lengths (in cm) of all projectile points found at the adjacent cliff dwelling site. Do these data indicate that the mean length of projectile points in the adjacent cliff dwelling is longer than 2.6 cm? Use a 1% level of significance.

(a) State H_0, H_1, and α.

⟹ H_0: $\mu = 2.6$ cm; H_1: $\mu > 2.6$ cm; $\alpha = 0.01$

(b) What sampling distribution should you use? What is the t value of the sample test statistic?

⟹ Because $n \geq 30$ and σ is unknown, use the Student's t distribution with $d.f. = n - 1 = 61 - 1 = 60$. Using $\bar{x} \approx 2.92$, $s \approx 0.85$, $\mu = 2.6$ from H_0, and $n = 61$,

$$t = \frac{\bar{x} - \mu}{s/\sqrt{n}} \approx \frac{2.92 - 2.6}{0.85/\sqrt{61}} \approx 2.940$$

Continued

GUIDED EXERCISE 4 continued

(c) When you use Table 4 of the Appendix to find an interval containing the P-value, do you use one-tail or two-tail areas? Why? Sketch a figure showing the P-value. Find an interval for the P-value.

 This is a right-tailed test, so use a one-tail area (see Figure 9-6).

FIGURE 9-6 *P*-value

TABLE 9-6   Excerpt from Student's *t* Table

✓ one-tail area	...0.005	0.0005
two-tail area	...0.010	0.0010
d.f. = 60	...2.660	3.460

Sample *t* = 2.940

Using $d.f. = 60$, we find that the sample $t = 2.940$ is between the critical values 2.660 and 3.460 (see Table 9-6). The sample P-value is then between the one-tail areas 0.005 and 0.0005.

$$0.0005 < P\text{-value} < 0.005$$

(d) Do we reject or fail to reject H_0?

Since the interval containing the P-value lies to the left of $\alpha = 0.01$, we reject H_0.

$$
\begin{array}{ccc}
\text{0.0005} & \text{0.005} & \overset{\alpha}{0.01}
\end{array}
$$

Note: Using the raw data, computer software gives P-value ≈ 0.0022. This value is in our estimated range and is less than $\alpha = 0.01$, so we reject H_0.

(e) Interpret your results in the context of the application.

At the 1% level of significance, sample evidence is sufficiently strong to reject H_0 and to conclude that the average projectile point length at the adjacent cliff dwelling site is longer than 2.6 cm.

 TECH NOTE   The TI-84Plus and TI-83Plus calculators, Excel, and Minitab all support testing of μ using the standard normal distribution. The TI-84Plus/TI-83Plus and Minitab support testing of μ using a Student's *t* distribution. All the technologies return a P-value for the test.

TI-84Plus/TI-83Plus You can select to enter raw data (**Data**) or summary statistics (**Stats**). Enter the value of μ_0 used in the null hypothesis $H_0: \mu = \mu_0$. Select the symbol used in the alternate hypothesis ($\neq\mu_0$, $<\mu_0$, $>\mu_0$). To test μ using the standard normal distribution, press **Stat**, select **Tests**, and use option **1:Z-Test**. The value for σ is required. To test μ using a Student's *t* distribution, use option **2:T-Test**. Using data from Example 4 regarding remission times, we have the following displays.

```
T-Test                    T-Test
 Inpt:Data Stats           µ≠12.5
 µ₀:12.5                   t=2.105902924
 List:L1                   p=.0480466063
 Freq:1                    x̄=17.0952381
 µ:≠µ₀ <µ₀ >µ₀             Sx=9.999523798
 Calculate Draw           n=21
```

Excel In Excel, the **ZTEST** function finds the *P*-values for a right-tailed test. (*Note:* Ignore the Excel documentation that mistakenly says ZTEST gives the *P*-value for a two-tailed test.) Use the menu choice **Paste Function** $\boxed{f_x}$ ➤ **ZTEST.** In the dialogue box, give the cell range containing your data for the array. Use the value of μ stated in H_0 for *x*. Provide σ. Otherwise, Excel uses the sample standard deviation computed from the data.

Minitab Enter the raw data from a sample. Use the menu selections **Stat ➤ Basic Stat ➤ 1-Sample z** for tests using the standard normal distribution. For tests of μ using a Student's *t* distribution, select **1-Sample t.**

Part III: Testing μ Using Critical Regions (Traditional Method)

The most popular method of statistical testing is the *P*-value method. For that reason, the *P*-value method is emphasized in this book. Another method of testing is called the *critical region method* or *traditional method.*

Critical region method

For a fixed preset value of the level of significance α, both methods are logically equivalent. Because of this, we treat the traditional method as an "optional" topic and consider only the case of testing μ when σ is known.

Consider the null hypothesis $H_0: \mu = k$. We use information from a random sample, together with the sampling distribution for $\overline{x}$ and the level of significance α, to determine whether or not we should reject the null hypothesis. The essential question is, "How much can $\overline{x}$ vary from $\mu = k$ before we suspect that $H_0: \mu = k$ is false and reject it?"

The answer to the question regarding the relative sizes of $\overline{x}$ and μ, as stated in the null hypothesis, depends on the sampling distribution of $\overline{x}$, the alternate hypothesis H_1, and the level of significance α. If the sample test statistic $\overline{x}$ is sufficiently different from the claim about μ made in the null hypothesis, we reject the null hypothesis.

The values of $\overline{x}$ for which we reject H_0 are called the *critical region* of the $\overline{x}$ distribution. Depending on the alternate hypothesis, the critical region is located on the left side, the right side, or both sides of the $\overline{x}$ distribution. Figure 9-7 on the next page shows the relationship of the critical region to the alternate hypothesis and to the level of significance α.

Notice that the total area in the critical region is preset to be the level of significance α. This is *not* the *P*-value discussed earlier! In fact, you cannot set the *P*-value in advance because it is determined from a random sample. Recall that the level of significance α should (in theory) be a fixed, preset number assigned before drawing any samples.

The most commonly used levels of significance are $\alpha = 0.05$ and $\alpha = 0.01$. Critical regions of a standard normal distribution are shown for these levels of significance in Figure 9-8. *Critical values* are the boundaries of the critical region.

FIGURE 9-7

Critical Regions for $H_0: \mu = k$

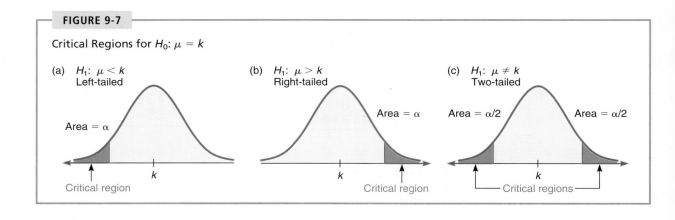

(a) $H_1: \mu < k$
Left-tailed

(b) $H_1: \mu > k$
Right-tailed

(c) $H_1: \mu \neq k$
Two-tailed

FIGURE 9-8

Critical Values z_0 for Tests Involving a Mean (Large Samples)

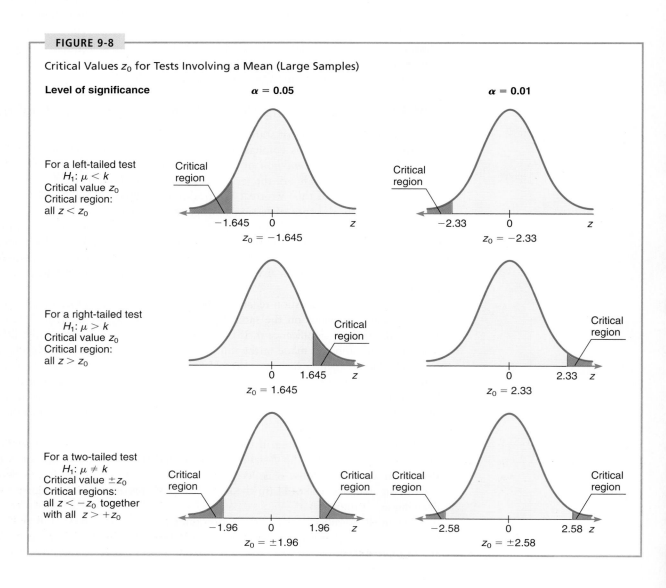

Level of significance $\boldsymbol{\alpha = 0.05}$ $\boldsymbol{\alpha = 0.01}$

For a left-tailed test
$H_1: \mu < k$
Critical value z_0
Critical region:
all $z < z_0$

$z_0 = -1.645$ $z_0 = -2.33$

For a right-tailed test
$H_1: \mu > k$
Critical value z_0
Critical region:
all $z > z_0$

$z_0 = 1.645$ $z_0 = 2.33$

For a two-tailed test
$H_1: \mu \neq k$
Critical value $\pm z_0$
Critical regions:
all $z < -z_0$ together
with all $z > +z_0$

$z_0 = \pm 1.96$ $z_0 = \pm 2.58$

Critical values designated as z_0 for the standard normal distribution are shown in Figure 9-8. For easy reference, they are also included in Table 3(c) of the Appendix, Areas of a Standard Normal Distribution.

The procedure for hypothesis testing using critical regions follows the same first two steps as the procedure using P-values. However, instead of finding a P-value for the sample test statistic, we check whether the sample test statistic falls in the critical region. If it does, we reject H_0. Otherwise, we do not reject H_0.

PROCEDURE

How to test μ when σ is known (critical region method)

Let x be a random variable appropriate to your application. Obtain a simple random sample (of size n) of x values from which you compute the sample mean $\overline{x}$. The value of σ is already known (perhaps from a previous study).

1. In the context of the application, state the *null and alternate hypotheses* and set the *level of significance* α. We use the most popular choices, $\alpha = 0.05$ or $\alpha = 0.01$.

2. If you can assume that x has a normal distribution, then any sample size n will work. If you cannot assume this, then use a sample size $n \geq 30$. Use the known σ, the sample size n, the value of $\overline{x}$ from the sample, and μ from the null hypothesis to compute the standardized sample *test statistic.*

$$z = \frac{\overline{x} - \mu}{\dfrac{\sigma}{\sqrt{n}}}$$

3. Show the *critical region and critical value(s)* on a graph of the sampling distribution. The level of significance α and the alternate hypothesis determine the locations of critical regions and critical values.

4. *Conclude* the test. If the test statistic z computed in Step 2 is in the critical region, then reject H_0. If the test statistic z is not in the critical region, then do not reject H_0.

5. *State your conclusion* in the context of the application.

EXAMPLE 5

Critical region method of testing μ

Consider Example 3 regarding sunspots. Let x be a random variable representing the number of sunspots observed in a 4-week period. A random sample of 40 such periods from Spanish colonial times gave the number of sunspots per period. The raw data are given in Example 3. The sample mean is $\overline{x} \approx 47.0$. Previous studies indicate that for this period, $\sigma = 35$. It is thought that for thousands of years, the mean number of sunspots per 4-week period was about $\mu = 41$. Do the data indicate that the mean sunspot activity during the Spanish colonial period was higher than 41? Use $\alpha = 0.05$.

SOLUTION:

(a) Set the null and alternate hypotheses.
   As in Example 3, we use H_0: $\mu = 41$ and H_1: $\mu > 41$.

(b) Compute the sample test statistic.
   As in Example 3, we use the standard normal distribution with $\bar{x} = 47$, $\sigma = 35$, $\mu = 41$ from H_0, and $n = 40$.

$$z = \frac{\bar{x} - \mu}{\sigma/\sqrt{n}} \approx \frac{47 - 41}{35/\sqrt{40}} \approx 1.08$$

(c) Determine the critical region and critical value based on H_1 and $\alpha = 0.05$.
   Since we have a right-tailed test, the critical region is the rightmost 5% of the standard normal distribution. According to Figure 9-8, the critical value is $z_0 = 1.645$.

(d) Conclude the test.
   We conclude the test by showing the critical region, critical value, and sample test statistic $z = 1.08$ on the standard normal curve. For a right-tailed test with $\alpha = 0.05$, the critical value is $z_0 = 1.645$. Figure 9-9 shows the critical region. As we can see, the sample test statistic does not fall in the critical region. Therefore, we fail to reject H_0.

(e) Interpret the results.
   At the 5% level of significance, the sample evidence is insufficient to justify rejecting H_0. It seems that the average sunspot activity during the Spanish colonial period was the same as the historical average.

(f) How do results of the critical region method compare with the results of the P-value method?
   The results, as expected, are the same. In both cases we fail to reject H_0.

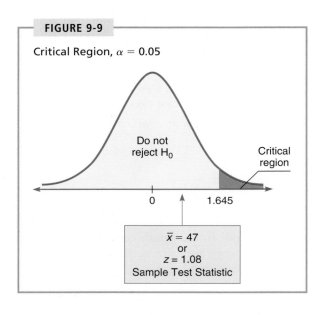

FIGURE 9-9

Critical Region, $\alpha = 0.05$

The critical region method of testing as outlined applies to tests of other parameters. As with the *P*-value method, you need to know the sampling distribution of the sample test statistic. Critical values for distributions are usually found in tables rather than in computer software output. For example, Table 4 of the Appendix provides critical values for Student *t* distributions.

The critical region method of hypothesis testing is very general. The following procedure box outlines the process of concluding a hypothesis test using the critical region method.

PROCEDURE

How to conclude tests using the critical region method

1. Compute the sample test statistic using an appropriate sampling distribution.

2. Using the same sampling distribution, find the critical value(s) as determined by the level of significance α and the nature of the test: right-tailed, left-tailed, or two-tailed.

3. Compare the sample test statistic to the critical value(s).

   (a) For a right-tailed test,
      i. if sample test statistic $\geq$ critical value, reject H_0.
      ii. if sample test statistic $<$ critical value, fail to reject H_0.

   (b) For a left-tailed test,
      i. if sample test statistic $\leq$ critical value, reject H_0.
      ii. if sample test statistic $>$ critical value, fail to reject H_0.

   (c) For a two-tailed test,
      i. if sample test statistic lies beyond critical values, reject H_0.
      ii. if sample test statistic lies between critical values, fail to reject H_0.

VIEWPOINT   *Predator or Prey?*

Consider animals such as the arctic fox, gray wolf, desert lion, and South American jaguar. Each animal is a predator. What are the total sleep time (hours per day), maximum life span (years), and overall danger index from other animals? Now consider prey such as rabbits, deer, wild horses, and the Brazilian tapir (a wild pig). Is there a statistically significant difference in average sleep time, life span, and danger index? What about other variables such as the ratio of brain weight to body weight or the sleep exposure index (sleeping in a well-protected den or out in the open)? How did prehistoric humans fit into this picture? Scientists have collected a lot of data, and a great deal of statistical work has been done regarding such questions. For more information, visit the web site **http://lib.stat.cmu.edu/** and follow the links to Datasets and then Sleep.

SECTION 9.2 PROBLEMS

Please provide the following information for Problems 1–16.
(a) What is the level of significance? State the null and alternate hypotheses.
(b) What sampling distribution will you use? Explain the rationale for your choice of sampling distribution. What is the value of the sample test statistic?
(c) Find (or estimate) the *P*-value. Sketch the sampling distribution and show the area corresponding to the *P*-value.
(d) Based on your answers in parts (a) to (c), will you reject or fail to reject the null hypothesis? Are the data statistically significant at level *α*?
(e) State your conclusion in the context of the application.

Note: For degrees of freedom *d.f.* not given in the Student's *t* table, use the closest *d.f.* that is *smaller*. In some situations, this choice of *d.f.* may increase the *P*-value by a small amount and therefore produce a slightly more "conservative" answer.

1. *Meteorology: Storms* *Weatherwise* is a magazine published by the American Meteorological Society. One issue gives a rating system used to classify Nor'easter storms that frequently hit New England and can cause much damage near the ocean. A severe storm has an average peak wave height of $\mu = 16.4$ feet for waves hitting the shore. Suppose that a Nor'easter is in progress at the severe storm class rating. Peak wave heights are usually measured from land (using binoculars) off fixed cement piers. Suppose that a reading of 36 waves showed an average wave height of $\bar{x} = 17.3$ feet. Previous studies of severe storms indicate that $\sigma = 3.5$ feet. Does this information suggest that the storm is (perhaps temporarily) increasing above the severe rating? Use $\alpha = 0.01$.

2. *Ford Taurus: Assembly Time* Let *x* be a random variable that represents assembly time for the Ford Taurus. *The Wall Street Journal* reported that the average assembly time is $\mu = 38$ hours. A modification to the assembly procedure has been made. Experience with this new method indicates that $\sigma = 1.2$ hours. It is thought that the average assembly time may be reduced by this modification. A random sample of 47 new Ford Taurus automobiles coming off the assembly line showed the average assembly time using the new method to be $\bar{x} = 37.5$ hours. Does this indicate that the average assembly time has been reduced? Use $\alpha = 0.01$.

3. *E-mails: Priority Lists* Message mania! A professional employee in a large corporation receives an average of $\mu = 41.7$ e-mails per day. Most of these e-mails are from other employees in the company. Because of the large number of e-mails, employees find themselves distracted and are unable to concentrate when they return to their tasks (Reference: *The Wall Street Journal*). In an effort to reduce distraction caused by such interruptions, one company established a priority list that all employees were to use before sending an e-mail. One month after the new priority list was put into place, a random sample of 45 employees showed that they were receiving an average of $\bar{x} = 36.2$ e-mails per day. The computer server through which the e-mails are routed showed that $\sigma = 18.5$. Has the new policy had any effect? Use a 5% level of significance to test the claim that there has been a change (either way) in the average number of e-mails received per day per employee.

4. *Medical: Blood Plasma* Let *x* be a random variable that represents the pH of arterial plasma (i.e., acidity of the blood). For healthy adults, the mean of the *x* distribution is $\mu = 7.4$ (Reference: *Merck Manual*, a commonly used reference in medical schools and nursing programs). A new drug for arthritis has been developed. However, it is thought that this drug may change blood pH. A random sample of 31 patients with arthritis took the drug for 3 months. Blood tests showed the average pH to be $\bar{x} = 8.1$

with sample standard deviation $s = 1.9$. Use a 5% level of significance to test the claim that the drug has changed (either way) the mean pH level of the blood.

5. *Wildlife: Coyotes* A random sample of 46 adult coyotes in a region of northern Minnesota showed the average age to be $\bar{x} = 2.05$ years with sample standard deviation $s = 0.82$ year (based on information from the book *Coyotes: Biology, Behavior and Management* by M. Bekoff, Academic Press). However, it is thought that the overall population mean age of coyotes is $\mu = 1.75$. Do the sample data indicate that coyotes in this region of northern Minnesota tend to live longer than the average age of 1.75 years? Use $\alpha = 0.01$.

6. *Fishing: Trout* Pyramid Lake is on the Paiute Indian Reservation in Nevada. The lake is famous for cutthroat trout. Suppose a friend tells you that the average length of trout caught in Pyramid Lake is $\mu = 19$ inches. However, the Creel Survey (published by the Pyramid Lake Paiute Tribe Fisheries Association) reported that for a random sample of 51 fish caught, the mean length was $\bar{x} = 18.5$ inches with estimated standard deviation $s = 3.2$ inches. Do these data indicate that the average length of a trout caught in Pyramid Lake is less than $\mu = 19$ inches? Use $\alpha = 0.05$.

7. *Investing: Stocks* Socially conscious investors screen out stocks of alcohol and tobacco makers, firms with poor environmental records, and companies with poor labor practices. Some examples of "good," socially conscious companies are Johnson and Johnson, Dell Computers, Bank of America, and Home Depot. The question is, are such stocks overpriced? One measure of value is the P/E, or price to earnings ratio. High P/E ratios may indicate that a stock is overpriced. For the S&P Stock Index of all major stocks, the mean P/E ratio is $\mu = 19.4$. A random sample of 36 "socially conscious" stocks gave a P/E ratio sample mean of $\bar{x} = 17.9$ with sample standard deviation $s = 5.2$ (Reference: *Morningstar*, a financial analysis company in Chicago). Does this indicate that the mean P/E ratio of all socially conscious stocks is different (either way) from the mean P/E ratio of the S&P Stock Index? Use $\alpha = 0.05$.

8. *Agriculture: Ground Water* Unfortunately, arsenic occurs naturally in some ground water (Reference: *Union Carbide Technical Report K/UR-1*). A mean arsenic level of $\mu = 8.0$ parts per billion (ppb) is considered safe for agricultural use. A well in Texas is used to water cotton crops. This well is tested on a regular basis for arsenic. A random sample of 37 tests gave a sample mean of $\bar{x} = 7.2$ ppb arsenic with $s = 1.9$ ppb. Does this information indicate that the mean level of arsenic in this well is less than 8 ppb? Use $\alpha = 0.01$.

9. *Medical: Red Blood Cell Count* Let x be a random variable that represents red blood cell count (RBC) in millions of cells per cubic millimeter of whole blood. Then x has a distribution that is approximately normal. For the population of healthy female adults, the mean of the x distribution is about 4.8 (based on information from *Diagnostic Tests with Nursing Implications*, Springhouse Corporation). Suppose that a female patient has taken six laboratory blood tests over the past several months and that the RBC count data sent to the patient's doctor are

4.9   4.2   4.5   4.1   4.4   4.3

i. Use a calculator with sample mean and sample standard deviation keys to verify that $\bar{x} = 4.40$ and $s \approx 0.28$.
ii. Do the given data indicate that the population mean RBC count for this patient is lower than 4.8? Use $\alpha = 0.05$.

10. *Medical: Hemoglobin Count* Let x be a random variable that represents hemoglobin count (HC) in grams per 100 milliliters of whole blood. Then x has a distribution

that is approximately normal, with population mean of about 14 for healthy adult women (see reference in Problem 9). Suppose that a female patient has taken 10 laboratory blood tests during the past year. The HC data sent to the patient's doctor are

| 15 | 18 | 16 | 19 | 14 | 12 | 14 | 17 | 15 | 11 |

i. Use a calculator with sample mean and sample standard deviation keys to verify that $\bar{x} = 15.1$ and $s \approx 2.51$.
ii. Does this information indicate that the population average HC for this patient is higher than 14? Use $\alpha = 0.01$.

11. *Ski Patrol: Avalanches* Snow avalanches can be a real problem for travelers in the western United States and Canada. A very common type of avalanche is called the slab avalanche. These have been studied extensively by David McClung, a professor of civil engineering at the University of British Columbia. Slab avalanches studied in Canada had an average thickness of $\mu = 67$ cm (Source: *Avalanche Handbook,* by D. McClung and P. Schaerer). The ski patrol at Vail, Colorado, is studying slab avalanches in their region. A random sample of avalanches in spring gave the following thicknesses (in cm):

| 59 | 51 | 76 | 38 | 65 | 54 | 49 | 62 |
| 68 | 55 | 64 | 67 | 63 | 74 | 65 | 79 |

i. Use a calculator with mean and standard deviation keys to verify that $\bar{x} \approx$ 61.8 cm and $s \approx 10.6$ cm.
ii. Assume the slab thickness has an approximately normal distribution. Use a 1% level of significance to test the claim that the mean slab thickness in the Vail region is different from that in Canada.

12. *Longevity: Honolulu* USA Today reported that the state with the longest mean life span is Hawaii, where the population mean life span is 77 years. A random sample of 20 obituary notices in the *Honolulu Advertizer* gave the following information about life span (in years) of Honolulu residents:

| 72 | 68 | 81 | 93 | 56 | 19 | 78 | 94 | 83 | 84 |
| 77 | 69 | 85 | 97 | 75 | 71 | 86 | 47 | 66 | 27 |

i. Use a calculator with mean and standard deviation keys to verify that $\bar{x} =$ 71.4 years and $s \approx 20.65$ years.
ii. Assuming that life span in Honolulu is approximately normally distributed, does this information indicate that the population mean life span for Honolulu residents is less than 77 years? Use a 5% level of significance.

13. *Veterinary Science: Lions* The heart rate of a healthy lion is approximately normally distributed, with mean $\mu = 40$ beats per minute (Source: *The Merck Veterinary Manual,* a reference used in most veterinary colleges). A heart rate that is too slow or too fast can indicate a health problem. A veterinarian has removed an abscessed tooth from a young, healthy zoo lion. As the animal slowly starts to come out of the anesthetic, its heart rate (in beats per minute) is taken and recorded for half an hour:

| 30 | 37 | 43 | 38 | 35 | 36 |

i. Use a calculator with mean and standard deviation keys to verify that $\bar{x} = 36.5$ and $s \approx 4.2$.
ii. Use a 5% level of significance to test the claim that the population average heart rate of the lion is different (either way) from 40 beats per minute.

14. *Shopping Time: Housewares* How much customers buy is a direct result of how much time they spend in a store. The mean shopping time for a woman accompanied by children in national houseware stores is 7.3 minutes (Source: *Why We Buy: The Science of Shopping* by P. Underhill). A retail research team is studying shopping habits in the Cherry Creek Mall (Denver). A random sample of women shoppers with children in a large houseware store gave the following shopping times (in minutes):

| 7.7 | 8.1 | 8.2 | 9.0 | 5.8 | 9.3 | 8.4 | 6.9 | 12.1 | 9.4 |
| 8.1 | 6.2 | 7.3 | 7.9 | 8.2 | 8.5 | 7.2 | 6.3 | 9.1 | 8.8 |

i. Use a calculator with mean and standard deviation keys to verify that $\bar{x} \approx 8.1$ min and $s \approx 1.4$ min.

ii. Assume shopping time follows an approximately normal distribution. Use a 5% level of significance to test the claim that the average shopping time for women with children in the Cherry Creek Mall is higher than the national average for this type of store.

15. *Fishing: Atlantic Salmon* Homser Lake, Oregon, has an Atlantic salmon catch-and-release program that has been very successful. The average fisherman's catch has been $\mu = 8.8$ Atlantic salmon per day (Source: *National Symposium on Catch and Release Fishing*, Humboldt State University). Suppose that a new quota system restricting the number of fishermen has been put into effect this season. A random sample of fishermen gave the following catches per day:

| 12 | 6 | 11 | 12 | 5 | 0 | 2 |
| 7 | 8 | 7 | 6 | 3 | 12 | 12 |

i. Use a calculator with mean and sample standard deviation keys to verify that $\bar{x} \approx 7.36$ and sample standard deviation $s \approx 4.03$.

ii. Assuming that the catch per day has an approximately normal distribution, use a 5% level of significance to test the claim that the population average catch per day is now different from 8.8.

16. *Archaeology: Tree Rings* Tree-ring dating at archaeological excavation sites is used in conjunction with other chronologic evidence to estimate occupation dates of prehistoric Indian dwellings in the southwestern United States. It is thought that Burnt Mesa Pueblo was occupied around 1300 A.D. (based on evidence from potsherds and stone tools). The following data give tree-ring dates (A.D.) from adjacent archaeological sites (*Bandelier Archaeological Excavation Project: Summer 1990 Excavations at Burnt Mesa Pueblo*, edited by T. Kohler, Washington State University Department of Anthropology, 1992):

| 1189 | 1267 | 1268 | 1275 | 1275 |
| 1271 | 1272 | 1316 | 1317 | 1230 |

i. Use a calculator with mean and standard deviation keys to verify that $\bar{x} = 1268$ and $s \approx 37.29$ years.

ii. Assuming that the tree-ring dates in this excavation area follow a distribution that is approximately normal, does this information indicate that the population mean of tree-ring dates in the area is different from (either higher or lower than) that for 1300 A.D.? Use a 1% level of significance.

17. *General: One-Tailed versus Two-Tailed Tests*

(a) For the same data and null hypothesis, is the *P*-value of a one-tailed test (right or left) larger or smaller than that of a two-tailed test? Explain.

(b) For the same data, null hypothesis, and level of significance, is it possible that a one-tailed test results in the conclusion to reject H_0 while a two-tailed test results in the conclusion to fail to reject H_0? Explain.

(c) For the same data, null hypothesis, and level of significance, if the conclusion is to reject H_0 based on a two-tailed test, do you also reject H_0 based on a one-tailed test? Explain.

(d) If a report states that certain data were used to reject a given hypothesis, would it be a good idea to know what type of test (one-tailed or two-tailed) was used? Explain.

18. *General: Comparing Hypothesis Tests to U.S. Courtroom System* Compare similarities of statistical testing with legal methods used in a U.S. court setting. Then discuss the following topics in class or consider the topics on your own. Please write a brief but complete essay in which you answer the following questions.

(a) In a court setting, the person charged with a crime is initially considered to be innocent. The claim of innocence is maintained until the jury returns with a decision. Explain how the claim of innocence could be taken to be the null hypothesis. Do we assume that the null hypothesis is true throughout the testing procedure? What would the alternate hypothesis be in a court setting?

(b) The court claims that a person is innocent if the evidence against the person is not adequate to find him or her guilty. This does not mean, however, that the court has necessarily *proved* the person to be innocent. It simply means that the evidence against the person was not adequate for the jury to find him or her guilty. How does this situation compare with a statistical test for which the conclusion is "do not reject" (i.e., accept) the null hypothesis? What would be a type II error in this context?

(c) If the evidence against a person is adequate for the jury to find him or her guilty, then the court claims that the person is guilty. Remember, this does not mean that the court has necessarily *proved* the person to be guilty. It simply means that the evidence against the person was strong enough to find him or her guilty. How does this situation compare with a statistical test for which the conclusion is to "reject" the null hypothesis? What would be a type I error in this context?

(d) In a court setting, the final decision as to whether the person charged is innocent or guilty is made at the end of the trial, usually by a jury of impartial people. In hypothesis testing, the final decision to reject or not reject the null hypothesis is made at the end of the test by using information or data from an (impartial) random sample. Discuss these similarities between statistical hypothesis testing and a court setting.

(e) We hope that you are able to use this discussion to increase your understanding of statistical testing by comparing it with something that is a well-known part of our American way of life. However, all analogies have weak points. It is important not to take the analogy between statistical hypothesis testing and legal court methods too far. For instance, the judge does not set a level of significance and tell the jury to determine a verdict that is wrong only 5% or 1% of the time. Discuss some of these weak points in the analogy between the court setting and hypothesis testing.

19. *Expand Your Knowledge: Confidence Intervals and Two-Tailed Hypothesis Tests* Is there a relationship between confidence intervals and two-tailed hypothesis tests? Let c be the level of confidence used to construct a confidence interval from sample data. Let α be the level of significance for a two-tailed hypothesis test. The following statement applies to hypothesis tests of the mean.

For a two-tailed hypothesis test with level of significance α and null hypothesis H_0: $\mu = k$, we *reject* H_0 whenever k falls *outside* the $c = 1 - \alpha$ confidence interval for μ based on the sample data. When k falls within the $c = 1 - \alpha$ confidence interval, we do not reject H_0.

(A corresponding relationship between confidence intervals and two-tailed hypothesis tests also is valid for other parameters such as p, $\mu_1 - \mu_2$, or $p_1 - p_2$, which we will study in Sections 9.3, 10.2, and 10.3.) Whenever the value of k given in the null hypothesis falls *outside* the $c = 1 - \alpha$ confidence interval for the parameter, we *reject* H_0. For example, consider a two-tailed hypothesis test with $\alpha = 0.01$ and

$$H_0: \mu = 20 \qquad H_1: \mu \neq 20$$

A random sample of size 36 has a sample mean $\bar{x} = 22$ from a population with standard deviation $\sigma = 4$.

(a) What is the value of $c = 1 - \alpha$? Using the methods of Chapter 8, construct a $1 - \alpha$ confidence interval for μ from the sample data. What is the value of μ given in the null hypothesis (i.e., what is k)? Is this value in the confidence interval? Do we reject or fail to reject H_0 based on this information?

(b) Using methods of Chapter 9, find the P-value for the hypothesis test. Do we reject or fail to reject H_0? Compare your result to that of part (a).

20. *Confidence Intervals and Two-Tailed Hypothesis Tests* Change the null hypothesis of Problem 19 to H_0: $\mu = 21$. Repeat parts (a) and (b).

21. *Critical Region Method: Standard Normal* Solve Problem 1 using the critical region method of testing (i.e., traditional method). Compare your conclusion with the conclusion obtained by using the P-value method. Are they the same?

22. *Critical Region Method: Standard Normal* Solve Problem 2 using the critical region method of testing. Compare your conclusion with the conclusion obtained by using the P-value method. Are they the same?

23. *Critical Region Method: Standard Normal* Solve Problem 3 using the critical region method of testing. Compare your conclusion with the conclusion obtained by using the P-value method. Are they the same?

24. *Critical Region Method: Student's t* Table 4 of the Appendix gives critical values for the Student's t distribution. Use an appropriate $d.f.$ as the row header. For a *right-tailed* test, the column header is the value of α found in the *one-tail area* row. For a *left-tailed* test, the column header is the value of α found in the *one-tail area* row, but you must change the sign of the critical value t to $-t$. For a *two-tailed* test, the column header is the value of α from the *two-tail area* row. The critical values are the $\pm t$ values shown. Solve Problem 4 using the critical region method of testing. Compare your conclusion with the conclusion obtained by using the P-value method. Are they the same?

25. *Critical Region Method: Student's t* Solve Problem 5 using the critical region method of testing. *Hint:* See Problem 24. Compare your conclusion with the conclusion obtained by using the P-value method. Are they the same?

26. *Critical Region Method: Student's t* Solve Problem 6 using the critical region method of testing. *Hint:* See Problem 24. Compare your conclusion with the conclusion obtained by using the P-value method. Are they the same?

9.3
Testing a Proportion p

Tests for a single proportion

Many situations arise that call for tests of proportions or percentages rather than means. For instance, a college registrar may want to determine if the proportion of students wanting 3-week intensive courses has increased.

How can we make such a test? In this section, we will study tests involving proportions (i.e., percentages or proportions). Such tests are similar to those in Sections 9.1 and 9.2. The main difference is that we are working with a distribution of proportions.

Throughout this section, we will assume that the situations we are dealing with satisfy the conditions underlying the binomial distribution. In particular, we will let r be a binomial random variable. This means that r is the number of successes out of n independent binomial trials (for the definition of binomial trial, see Section 6.2). We will use $\hat{p} = r/n$ as our estimate for p, the population probability of success on each trial. The letter q represents the population probability of failure on each trial, and so $q = 1 - p$. We also assume that the samples are large (i.e., $np > 5$ and $nq > 5$).

For large samples, the distribution of $\hat{p} = r/n$ values is well approximated by a *normal curve* with mean μ and standard deviation σ as follows:

$$\mu = p$$

$$\sigma = \sqrt{\frac{pq}{n}}$$

The null and alternate hypotheses for tests of proportions are

Left-Tailed Test	Right-Tailed Test	Two-Tailed Test
$H_0: p = k$	$H_0: p = k$	$H_0: p = k$
$H_1: p < k$	$H_1: p > k$	$H_1: p \neq k$

depending on what is asked for in the problem. Notice that since p is a probability, the value k must be between 0 and 1.

Sample test statistic

For tests of proportions, we need to convert the sample test statistic $\hat{p}$ to a z value. Then we can find a *P*-value appropriate for the test. The $\hat{p}$ distribution is approximately normal, with mean p and standard deviation $\sqrt{pq/n}$. Therefore, the conversion of $\hat{p}$ to z follows the formula

$$z = \frac{\hat{p} - p}{\sqrt{\dfrac{pq}{n}}}$$

where $\hat{p} = r/n$ is the sample test statistic

n = number of trials

p = proportion specified in H_0

$q = 1 - p$

Using this mathematical information about the sampling distribution for $\hat{p}$, the basic procedure for testing a proportion is similar to tests you have conducted before.

PROCEDURE

How to test a proportion p

Consider a binomial experiment with n trials, where p represents the population probability of success and $q = 1 - p$ represents the population probability of failure. Let r be a random variable that represents the number of successes out of the n binomial trials.

1. In the context of the application, state the *null and alternate hypotheses* and set the *level of significance* α.

2. The number of trials n should be sufficiently large so that both $np > 5$ and $nq > 5$ (use p from the null hypothesis). In this case, the $\hat{p} = r/n$ distribution can be approximated by the normal distribution using the standardized sample *test statistic*

$$z = \frac{\hat{p} - p}{\sqrt{\dfrac{pq}{n}}}$$

   where p is the value specified in H_0 and $q = 1 - p$.

3. Use the standard normal distribution and the type of test, one-tailed or two-tailed, to find the *P-value* corresponding to the test statistic.

4. *Conclude* the test. If P-value $\leq \alpha$, then reject H_0. If P-value $> \alpha$, then do not reject H_0.

5. *State your conclusion* in the context of the application.

EXAMPLE 6

Testing p

A team of eye surgeons has developed a new technique for a risky eye operation to restore the sight of people blinded from a certain disease. Under the old method, it is known that only 30% of the patients who undergo this operation recover their eyesight.

Suppose that surgeons in various hospitals have performed a total of 225 operations using the new method and that 88 have been successful (the patients fully recovered their sight). Can we justify the claim that the new method is better than the old one? (Use a 1% level of significance.)

SOLUTION:

(a) Establish H_0 and H_1 and note the level of significance.

The level of significance is $\alpha = 0.01$. Let p be the probability that a patient fully recovers his or her eyesight. The null hypothesis is that p is still 0.30, even for the new method. The alternate hypothesis is that the new method has improved the chances of a patient recovering his or her eyesight. Therefore,

$$H_0: p = 0.30 \quad \text{and} \quad H_1: p > 0.30$$

(b) Find the sample test statistic $\hat{p}$ and convert it to a z value, if appropriate.

Using p from H_0, we note that $np = 225(0.3) = 67.5$ is greater than 5 and $nq = 225(0.7) = 157.5$ is also greater than 5, so we can use the normal distribution for the sample statistic $\hat{p}$.

$$\hat{p} = \frac{r}{n} = \frac{88}{225} \approx 0.39$$

The z value corresponding to $\hat{p}$ is

$$z = \frac{\hat{p} - p}{\sqrt{\dfrac{pq}{n}}} \approx \frac{0.39 - 0.30}{\sqrt{\dfrac{0.30(0.70)}{225}}} \approx 2.95$$

In the formula, the value for p is from the null hypothesis. H_0 specifies that $p = 0.30$, so $q = 1 - 0.30 = 0.70$.

(c) Find the P-value of the test statistic.

Figure 9-10 shows the P-value. Since we have a right-tailed test, the P-value is the area to the right of $z = 2.95$ shown in Figure 9-10. Using the normal distribution (Table 3 of the Appendix), we find that P-value $= P(z > 2.95) \approx 0.0016$.

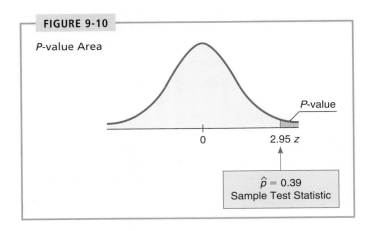

FIGURE 9-10

P-value Area

(d) Conclude the test.

Since the P-value of $0.0016 \leq 0.01$ for α, we reject H_0.

(e) Interpret the results.

At the 1% level of significance, the sample evidence shows that the population probability of success for the new surgery technique is higher than that of the old technique. ◇

GUIDED EXERCISE 5

Testing p

A botanist has produced a new variety of hybrid wheat that is better able to withstand drought than other varieties. The botanist knows that for the parent plants, the proportion of seeds germinating is 80%. The proportion of seeds germinating for the hybrid variety is unknown, but the botanist claims that it is 80%. To test this claim, 400 seeds from the hybrid plant are tested, and it is found that 312 germinated. Use a 5% level of significance to test the claim that the proportion germinating for the hybrid is 80%.

(a) Let p be the proportion of hybrid seeds that will germinate. Notice that we have no prior knowledge about the germination proportion for the hybrid plant. State H_0 and H_1. What is the required level of significance?

$H_0: p = 0.80$; $H_1: p \neq 0.80$; $\alpha = 0.05$

(b) Calculate the sample test statistic $\hat{p}$. Using the value of p in H_0, are both $np > 5$ and $nq > 5$? Can we use the normal distribution for $\hat{p}$?

The number of trials is $n = 400$, and the number of successes is $r = 312$. Thus,

$$\hat{p} = \frac{r}{n} = \frac{312}{400} = 0.78$$

From H_0, $p = 0.80$ and $q = 1 - p = 0.20$.

$np = 400(0.8) = 320 > 5$

$nq = 400(0.2) = 80 > 5$

So, we can use the normal distribution for $\hat{p}$.

(c) Next, we convert the sample test statistic $\hat{p} = 0.78$ to a z value. Based on our choice for H_0, what value should we use for p in our formula? Since $q = 1 - p$, what value should we use for q? Using these values for p and q, convert $\hat{p}$ to a z value.

According to H_0, $p = 0.80$. Then $q = 1 - p = 0.20$. Using these values in the following formula gives

$$z = \frac{\hat{p} - p}{\sqrt{\dfrac{pq}{n}}} = \frac{0.78 - 0.80}{\sqrt{\dfrac{0.80(0.20)}{400}}} = -1.00$$

● **CALCULATOR NOTE**   If you evaluate the denominator separately, be sure to carry at least four digits after the decimal.

(d) Is the test right-tailed, left-tailed, or two-tailed? Find the P-value of the sample test statistic and sketch a standard normal curve showing the P-value.

For a two-tailed test, using the normal distribution (Table 3(a) of the Appendix), we find that

$P\text{-value} = 2P(z < -1.00) = 2(0.1587) = 0.3174$

Continued

GUIDED EXERCISE 5 continued

FIGURE 9-11 P-value

$$\hat{p} = 0.78$$
Sample Test Statistic

(e) Do we reject or fail to reject H_0? State your conclusion in the context of the application.   ⟹   Since

P-value of $0.3174 > 0.05$ for α

we fail to reject H_0. At the 5% level of significance,
there is insufficient evidence to say that the botanist
is wrong.

Critical region method

Since the $\hat{p}$ sampling distribution is approximately normal, we use Table 3 of
the Appendix, Areas of a Standard Normal Distribution, to find critical values.

EXAMPLE 7

Critical region method
for testing p

Let's solve Guided Exercise 5 using the critical region approach. In that problem,
312 of 400 seeds from a hybrid wheat variety germinated. For the parent plants,
the proportion of germinating seeds was 80%. Use a 5% level of significance to test
the claim that the population proportion of germinating seeds for the hybrid wheat
is different from that of the parent plants.

SOLUTION:

(a) As in Guided Exercise 5, we have $\alpha = 0.05$, H_0: $p = 0.80$, and H_1: $p \neq 0.80$.
The next step is to find the sample statistic $\hat{p}$ and the corresponding test statistic z. This was done in Guided Exercise 5, where we found that $\hat{p} = 0.78$ with
corresponding $z = -1.00$.

(b) Now we find the critical value z_0 for a two-tailed test using $\alpha = 0.05$. This
means that we want the total area 0.05 divided between two tails, one to the
right of z_0 and one to the left of $-z_0$. As shown in Figure 9-8 of Section 9.2,
the critical value(s) are ± 1.96. (See also Table 3, part (c), of the Appendix for
critical values of the z distribution.)

(c) Figure 9-12 shows the critical regions and the location of the sample test
statistic.

(d) Finally, we conclude the test and compare the results to Guided Exercise 5. Since
the sample test statistic does not fall in the critical region, we fail to reject H_0
and conclude that at the 5% level of significance, the evidence is not strong

FIGURE 9-12

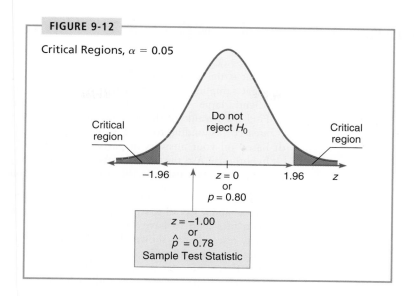

Critical Regions, $\alpha = 0.05$

enough to reject the botanist's claim. This result, as expected, is consistent with the conclusion obtained by using the P-value method.   ◆

TECH NOTE   The TI-84Plus/TI-83Plus calculators and Minitab support tests of proportions. The output for both technologies includes the sample proportion $\hat{p}$ and the P-value of $\hat{p}$. Minitab also includes the z value corresponding to $\hat{p}$.

TI-84Plus/TI-83Plus Press **STAT**, select **TESTS**, and use option **5:1-PropZTest.** The value of p_0 is from the null hypothesis H_0: $p = p_0$. The number of successes is the value for x.

Minitab Menu selections: **Stat ➤ Basic Statistics ➤ 1 Proportion.** Under options, set the test proportion as the value in H_0. Choose to use the normal distribution.

VIEWPOINT

Who Did What?

Art, music, literature, and science share a common need to classify things: Who painted that picture? Who composed that music? Who wrote that document? Who should get that patent? In statistics, such questions are called *classification problems.* For example, the *Federalist Papers* were published anonymously in 1787–1788 by Alexander Hamilton, John Jay, and James Madison. But who wrote what? That question is addressed by F. Mosteller (Harvard University) and D. Wallace (University of Chicago) in the book *Statistics: A Guide to the Unknown,* edited by J. M. Tanur. Other scholars have studied authorship regarding Plato's *Republic* and Plato's *Dialogues,* including the *Symposium.* For more information on this topic, see the source in Problems 9 and 10 of this exercise set.

Please provide the following information for Problems 1–17.

(a) What is the level of significance? State the null and alternate hypotheses.

(b) What sampling distribution will you use? Do you think that the sample size is sufficiently large? Explain. What is the value of the sample test statistic?

(c) Find the *P*-value of the test statistic. Sketch the sampling distribution and show the area corresponding to the *P*-value.

(d) Based on your answers in parts (a) to (c), will you reject or fail to reject the null hypothesis? Are the data statistically significant at level α?

(e) State your conclusion in the context of the application.

1. *Focus Problem: Benford's Law* Please read the focus problem at the beginning of this chapter. Recall that Benford's Law claims that numbers chosen from very large data files tend to have "1" as the first nonzero digit disproportionately often. In fact, research has shown that if you randomly draw a number from a very large data file, the probability of getting a number with "1" as the leading digit is about 0.301 (see the reference in this chapter's Focus Problem).

   Now suppose you are an auditor for a very large corporation. The revenue report involves millions of numbers in a large computer file. Let us say you took a random sample of $n = 215$ numerical entries from the file and $r = 46$ of the entries had a first nonzero digit of 1. Let p represent the population proportion of all numbers in the corporate revenue file that have a first nonzero digit of 1.

   i. Test the claim that p is less than 0.301. Use $\alpha = 0.01$.

   ii. If p is in fact less than 0.301, would it make you suspect that there are not enough numbers in the data file with leading 1's? Could this indicate that the books have been "cooked" by "pumping up" or inflating the numbers? Comment from the viewpoint of a stockholder. Comment from the perspective of the Federal Bureau of Investigation as it looks for money laundering in the form of false profits.

   iii. Comment on the following statement: If we reject the null hypothesis at level of significance α, we have not *proved* H_0 to be false. We can say that the probability is α that we made a mistake in rejecting H_0. Based on the outcome of the test, would you recommend further investigation before accusing the company of fraud?

2. *Focus Problem: Benford's Law* Again suppose that you are the auditor for a very large corporation. The revenue file contains millions of numbers in a large computer data bank (see Problem 1). You draw a random sample of $n = 228$ numbers from this file and $r = 92$ have a first nonzero digit of 1. Let p represent the population proportion of all numbers in the computer revenue file that have a leading digit of 1.

   i. Test the claim that p is more than 0.301. Use $\alpha = 0.01$.

   ii. If p is in fact larger than 0.301, it would seem that there are too many numbers in the file with leading 1's. Could this indicate that the books have been "cooked" by artificially lowering numbers in the file? Comment from the point of view of the Internal Revenue Service. Comment from the perspective of the Federal Bureau of Investigation as it looks for "profit skimming" by unscrupulous employees.

   iii. Comment on the following statement: If we reject the null hypothesis at level of significance α, we have not *proved* H_0 to be false. We can say that the probability is α that we made a mistake in rejecting H_0. Based on the outcome of the test, would you recommend further investigation before accusing the company of fraud?

3. *Sociology: Crime Rate* Is the national crime rate really going down? Some sociologists say yes! They say that the reason for the decline in crime rates in the 1980s and 1990s is demographics. It seems that the population is aging, and older people commit fewer crimes. According to the FBI and the Justice Department, 70% of all arrests are of males aged 15 to 34 years (Source: *True Odds*, by J. Walsh, Merritt Publishing). Suppose that you are a sociologist in Rock Springs, Wyoming, and a random sample of police files showed that of 32 arrests last month, 24 were of males aged 15 to 34 years. Use a 1% level of significance to test the claim that the population proportion of such arrests in Rock Springs is different from 70%.

4. *College Athletics: Graduation Rate* Women athletes at the University of Colorado, Boulder, have a long-term graduation rate of 67% (Source: *The Chronicle of Higher Education*). Over the past several years, a random sample of 38 women athletes at the school showed that 21 eventually graduated. Does this indicate that the population proportion of women athletes who graduate from the University of Colorado, Boulder, is now less than 67%? Use a 5% level of significance.

5. *Highway Accidents: DUI* The U.S. Department of Transportation, National Highway Traffic Safety Administration, reported that 77% of all fatally injured automobile drivers were intoxicated. A random sample of 27 records of automobile driver fatalities in Kit Carson County, Colorado, showed that 15 involved an intoxicated driver. Do these data indicate that the population proportion of driver fatalities related to alcohol is less than 77% in Kit Carson County? Use $\alpha = 0.01$.

6. *Preference: Color* What is your favorite color? A large survey of countries including the United States, China, Russia, France, Turkey, Kenya, and others indicated that most people prefer the color blue. In fact, about 24% of the population claim blue as their favorite color (Reference: Study by J. Bunge and A. Freeman-Gallant, Statistics Center, Cornell University). Suppose a random sample of $n = 56$ college students was surveyed and $r = 12$ of them said that blue is their favorite color. Does this information imply that the color preference of all college students is different (either way) from that of the general population? Use $\alpha = 0.05$.

7. *Wildlife: Wolves* The following is based on information from *The Wolf in the Southwest: The Making of an Endangered Species*, by David E. Brown (University of Arizona Press). Before 1918, the proportion of female wolves in the general population of all southwestern wolves was about 50%. However, after 1918, southwestern cattle ranchers began a widespread effort to destroy wolves. In a recent sample of 34 wolves, there were only 10 females. One theory is that male wolves tend to return sooner than females to their old territory, where their predecessors were exterminated. Do these data indicate that the population proportion of female wolves is now less than 50% in the region? Use $\alpha = 0.01$.

8. *Fishing: Northern Pike* Athabasca Fishing Lodge is located on Lake Athabasca in northern Canada. In one of its recent brochures, the lodge advertises that 75% of its guests catch northern pike over 20 pounds. Suppose that last summer 64 out of a random sample of 83 guests did, in fact, catch northern pike weighing over 20 pounds. Does this indicate that the population proportion of guests who catch pike over 20 pounds is different from 75% (either higher or lower)? Use $\alpha = 0.05$.

9. *Plato's Republic: Syllable Patterns* Prose rhythm is characterized as the occurrence of five-syllable sequences in long passages of text. This characterization may be used to assess the similarity among passages of text and sometimes the identity of authors. The following information is based on an article by D. Wishart and S. V. Leach appearing in *Computer Studies of the Humanities and Verbal Behavior* (Vol. 3, pp. 90–99). Syllables were categorized as long or short. On analyzing

Plato's *Republic*, Wishart and Leach found that about 26.1% of the five-syllable sequences are of the type in which two are short and three are long. Suppose that Greek archaeologists have found an ancient manuscript dating back to Plato's time (about 427–347 B.C.). A random sample of 317 five-syllable sequences from the newly discovered manuscript showed that 61 are of the type two short and three long. Do the data indicate that the population proportion of this type of five-syllable sequence is different (either way) from that of the text of Plato's *Republic*? Use $\alpha = 0.01$.

10. *Plato's* Dialogues: *Prose Rhythm* Symposium is part of a larger work referred to as Plato's *Dialogues*. Wishart and Leach (see source in Problem 9) found that about 21.4% of five-syllable sequences in *Symposium* are of the type in which four are short and one is long. Suppose that an antiquities store in Athens has a very old manuscript that the owner claims is part of Plato's *Dialogues*. A random sample of 493 five-syllable sequences from this manuscript showed that 136 were of the type four short and one long. Do the data indicate that the population proportion of this type of five-syllable sequence is higher than that found in Plato's *Symposium*? Use $\alpha = 0.01$.

11. *Consumers: Product Loyalty* USA Today reported that about 47% of the general consumer population in the United States is loyal to the automobile manufacturer of their choice. Suppose that Chevrolet did a study of a random sample of 1006 Chevrolet owners and found that 490 said they would buy another Chevrolet. Does this indicate that the population proportion of consumers loyal to Chevrolet is more than 47%? Use $\alpha = 0.01$.

12. *Supermarket: Prices* Harper's Index reported that 80% of all supermarket prices end in the digit 9 or 5. Suppose that you check a random sample of 115 items in a supermarket and find that 88 have prices that end in 9 or 5. Does this indicate that less than 80% of the prices in the store end in the digits 9 or 5? Use $\alpha = 0.05$.

13. *Medical: Hypertension* This problem is based on information taken from *The Merck Manual* (a reference manual used in most medical and nursing schools). Hypertension is defined as a blood pressure over 140 mm Hg systolic and/or over 90 mm Hg diastolic. Hypertension, if not corrected, can cause long-term health problems. In the college-age population (18–24 years), about 9.2% have hypertension. Suppose that a blood donor program is occurring in a college dormitory this week (final exams week). Before each student gives blood, the nurse takes a blood pressure reading. Of 196 donors, it was found that 29 have hypertension. Do these data indicate that the population proportion of students with hypertension during final exams week is higher than 9.2%? Use a 5% level of significance.

14. *Medical: Hypertension* Diltiazem is a commonly prescribed drug for hypertension (see source in Problem 13). However, diltiazem causes headaches in about 12% of patients using the drug. It is hypothesized that regular exercise might help reduce the headaches. If a random sample of 209 patients using diltiazem exercised regularly and only 16 had headaches, would this indicate a reduction in the population proportion of patients having headaches? Use a 1% level of significance.

15. *Myers-Briggs: Extroverts* Are most student government leaders extroverts? According to Myers-Briggs estimates, about 82% of college student government leaders are extroverts (Source: *Myers-Briggs Type Indicator Atlas of Type Tables*). Suppose that a Myers-Briggs personality preference test was given to a random sample of 73 student government leaders attending a large national leadership conference and that

56 were found to be extroverts. Does this indicate that the population proportion of extroverts among college student government leaders is different (either way) from 82%? Use $\alpha = 0.01$.

16. *American Attitudes: NAFTA* Generally speaking, would you say that America benefits from being a member of NAFTA (North American Free Trade Agreement)? Nationally, about 28% of the U.S. population believes NAFTA benefits America (Source: *American Attitudes* by S. Mitchell, Sociology Department, Ithaca College). A random sample of 48 interstate truck drivers showed that 19 believe NAFTA benefits America. Does this indicate that the population proportion of interstate truckers who believe NAFTA benefits America is higher than 28%? Use a 5% level of significance.

17. *Careers: College Professors* If you could start your career all over again, would you still choose to be a college professor? About 76% of all U.S. college professors responded yes to this question (Source: *The Chronicle of Higher Education*). A random sample of 59 college professors in Colorado showed that 47 claimed they would choose college teaching again. Does this indicate that the proportion of professors in Colorado who would choose the career again is different from the national rate of 76%? Use a 1% level of significance.

18. *Critical Region Method: Testing Proportions* Solve Problem 3 using the critical region method of testing. Since the sampling distribution of $\hat{p}$ is the normal distribution, you can use critical values from the standard normal distribution as shown in Figure 9-8 or part (c) of Table 3 of the Appendix. Compare your conclusions with the conclusions obtained by using the *P*-value method. Are they the same?

19. *Critical Region Method: Testing Proportions* Solve Problem 5 using the critical region method of testing. *Hint:* See Problem 18. Compare your conclusions with the conclusions obtained by using the *P*-value method. Are they the same?

20. *Critical Region Method: Testing Proportions* Solve Problem 11 using the critical region method of testing. *Hint:* See Problem 18. Compare your conclusions with the conclusions obtained by using the *P*-value method. Are they the same?

SUMMARY

In this chapter, we studied statistical inference methods called *hypothesis testing*. We establish an initial claim about the value of a parameter. This claim is the null hypothesis H_0, which states that the parameter in question equals a certain value. Then we propose an alternate hypothesis H_1, which indicates that the parameter is less than, greater than, or different from the value in the null hypothesis. To determine whether or not to reject the null hypothesis, we use the evidence of the sample data and the predetermined level of significance α.

The basic steps we follow in the procedure of hypothesis testing are

1. Choose the level of significance α. State the null and alternate hypotheses H_0 and H_1.

2. Determine the sampling distribution of the sample test statistic. Convert the sample test statistic to a z value or a t value as appropriate.

3. Find (or estimate) the *P*-value of the sample test statistic.

4. If *P*-value $\leq \alpha$, reject H_0. If *P*-value $> \alpha$, do not reject H_0.

5. Interpret the results in the context of the application.

An alternate way to conclude a test of hypotheses is to use critical regions based on the alternate hypothesis and α. Critical values z_0 are found in Table 3(c) of the Appendix. Critical values t_0 are found in Table 4 of the Appendix. If the sample test statistic falls in the critical region, reject H_0.

In this chapter, we used hypothesis testing to conduct tests involving a single mean μ (σ known or unknown) or a single proportion p. The methods of hypothesis testing are very general, and we will see them used again in later chapters with other parameters and other probability distributions.

IMPORTANT WORDS & SYMBOLS

Section 9.1
Hypothesis testing
Hypotheses
Null hypothesis H_0
Alternate hypothesis H_1
Right-tailed test
Left-tailed test
Two-tailed test
Sample test statistic
P-value
Statistical significance
Type I error
Type II error

α, the level of significance of a test and the probability of a type I error
β, the probability of a type II error
Power of a test $(1 - \beta)$

Section 9.2
d.f. for testing μ when σ is unknown
Critical region
Critical value

Section 9.3
Criteria for using normal approximation to binomial, $np > 5$ and $nq > 5$

VIEWPOINT   *Will It Rain?*

Do cloud seed experiments ever work? If you seed the clouds, will it rain? If it does rain, who will benefit? Who will be displeased by the rain? If you seed the clouds and nothing happens, will taxpayers (who support the effort) complain or rejoice? Maybe this should be studied over a remote island—such as Tasmania (near Australia). Using what you already know about statistical testing, you can conduct your own tests, given the appropriate data. Remember, there are sociological questions (pleased/displeased with result) as well as technical questions (number of inches of rain produced). For data regarding cloud-seeding experiments over Tasmania, visit the Brase/Brase statistics site at **http://math.college.hmco.com/students** and find the link to DASL, the Carnegie Mellon University Data and Story Library. From the DASL site, look under Datasets for Cloud.

CHAPTER REVIEW PROBLEMS

Before you solve each problem, first categorize it by answering the following question: Are we testing a single mean or a single proportion? Then provide the following information for Problems 1–10.

(a) What is the level of significance? State the null and alternate hypotheses.

(b) What sampling distribution will you use? What assumptions are you making? What is the value of the sample test statistic?

(c) Find (or estimate) the P-value. Sketch the sampling distribution and show the area corresponding to the P-value.

(d) Based on your answers in parts (a) to (c), will you reject or fail to reject the null hypothesis? Are the data statistically significant at level α?

(e) State your conclusion in the context of the application.

Note: For degrees of freedom *d.f.* not in the Student's *t* table, use the closest *d.f.* that is *smaller.* In some situations, this choice of *d.f.* may increase the P-value by a small amount, and therefore produce a slightly more "conservative" answer. Answers may vary due to rounding.

1. *Vehicles: Mileage* Based on information from *Statistical Abstract of the United States* (116th Edition), the average annual miles driven per vehicle in the United States is 11.1 thousand miles with $\sigma \approx 600$ miles. Suppose that a random sample of 36 vehicles owned by residents of Chicago showed that the average mileage driven last year was 10.8 thousand miles. Does this indicate that the average miles driven per vehicle in Chicago is different from (higher or lower than) the national average? Use a 0.05 level of significance.

2. *Student Life: Employment* Professor Jennings claims that only 35% of the students at Flora College work while attending school. Dean Renata thinks that the professor has underestimated the number of students with part-time or full-time jobs. A random sample of 81 students showed that 39 have jobs. Do the data indicate that more than 35% of the students have jobs? (Use a 5% level of significance.)

3. *Toys: Electric Trains* The Toylot Company makes an electric train with a motor that it claims will draw an average of only 0.8 ampere (A) under a normal load. A sample of nine motors was tested, and it was found that the mean current was $\bar{x} = 1.4$ A with a sample standard deviation of $s = 0.41$ A. Do the data indicate that the Toylot claim of 0.8 A is too low? (Use a 1% level of significance.)

4. *Unions: Salaries* The Fleetfoot Shoe Company claims that the average yearly salary of its workers is $29,800. The union believes that the average salary is much less. A random sample of 61 employees showed their average salary to be $29,500 with a sample standard deviation of $800. Use a 5% level of significance to test the company's claim.

5. *Medical: Plasma Compress* A hospital reported that the normal death rate for patients with extensive burns (more than 40% of skin area) has been significantly reduced by the use of new fluid plasma compresses. Before the new treatment, the mortality rate for extensive burn patients was about 60%. Using the new compresses, the hospital found that only 40 of 90 patients with extensive burns died. Use a 1% level of significance to test the claim that the mortality rate has dropped.

6. *Matches: Number per Box* The Nero Match Company sells matchboxes that are supposed to have an average of 40 matches per box with $\sigma = 9$. A random sample

of 94 Nero matchboxes showed the average number of matches per box to be 43.1. Using a 1% level of significance, can you say that the average number of matches per box is more than 40?

7. *Student Government: Opinions* The student council is thinking about discontinuing the student poetry magazine because only 20% of the students read it. A vote was taken, and it was decided to continue the magazine if more than 20% of the students are known to read it. A random sample of 200 students showed that 58 of them had read the last issue. Use a 1% level of significance to determine whether the magazine should be continued.

8. *Civil Service: College Degrees* The Congressional Budget Office reports that 36% of federal civilian employees have a bachelor's degree or higher (*The Wall Street Journal*). A random sample of 120 employees in the private sector showed that 33 have a bachelor's degree or higher. Does this indicate that the percentage of employees holding bachelor's degrees or higher in the private sector is less than in the federal civilian sector? Use $\alpha = 0.05$.

9. *Vending Machines: Coffee* A machine in the student lounge dispenses coffee. The average cup of coffee is supposed to contain 7.0 oz. Eight cups of coffee from this machine show the average content to be 7.3 oz with a standard deviation of 0.5 oz. Do you think that the machine has slipped out of adjustment and that the average amount of coffee per cup is different from 7 oz? Use a 5% level of significance.

10. *Sports Car: Fuel Injection* The manufacturer of a sports car claims that the fuel injection system lasts 48 months before it needs to be replaced. A consumer group tests this claim by surveying a random sample of 10 owners who had the fuel injection system replaced. The ages of the cars at the time of replacement were (in months):

29	42	49	48	53	46	30	51	42	52

i. Use your calculator to verify that the mean age of a car when the fuel injection system fails is $\bar{x} = 44.2$ months with standard deviation $s \approx 8.61$ months.

ii. Test the claim that the fuel injection system lasts less than an average of 48 months before needing replacement. Use a 5% level of significance.

DATA HIGHLIGHTS: GROUP PROJECTS

Break into small groups and discuss the following topics. Organize a brief outline in which you summarize the main points of your group discussion.

"With Sampling, There Is Too a Free Lunch"—This is a headline that appeared in *The Wall Street Journal*. The article is about food product samples available at grocery stores. Giving out food samples is expensive and labor-intensive. It clogs supermarket aisles. It is risky. What if a customer tries an item and spits it out on the floor or says the product is awful? It creates litter. Some customers drop toothpicks or small paper cups on the floor or spill the product. However, the budget that companies are willing to spend to have their products sampled is growing. The director of communications for Bigg's "hypermarket" (a combination grocery and general-merchandise store) says that more than 60% of customers sample products and about 37% of those who sample buy the product.

(a) Let's test the hypothesis that 60% of customers sample a particular product. What is the null hypothesis? Do you believe that the percentage of customers who sample products is less than, more than, or just different from 60%? What will you use for the alternate hypothesis?

(b) Choose a level of significance α.

(c) Go to a grocery store when special products are being sampled (not just the usual in-house store samples often available at the deli or bakery). Count the number of customers going by the display when a sample is available and the number of customers who try the sample. Be sure the number of customers n is large enough to use the normal distribution to approximate the binomial.

(d) Using your sample data, conclude the hypothesis test. What is your conclusion?

(e) Do you think different food products might have a higher or lower percentage of customers trying them? For instance, does a higher percentage of customers try samples of pizza than samples of yogurt? How could you use statistics to justify your answer?

(f) Do you want to include young children in your sample? Do they pick up items to include in the customer's basket, or do they just munch the samples?

LINKING CONCEPTS: WRITING PROJECTS

Discuss each of the following topics in class or review the topics on your own. Then write a brief but complete essay in which you summarize the main points. Please include formulas and graphs as appropriate.

The most important questions in life usually cannot be answered with absolute certainty. Many important questions are answered by giving an estimate and a measure of confidence in the estimate. This was the focus of Chapter 8. However, sometimes important questions must be answered in a more straightforward manner by a simple *yes* or *no*. Hypothesis testing is the statistical process of answering questions with a straightforward yes or no *and* providing an estimate of the risk in accepting the answer.

(a) Review and discuss type I and type II errors associated with hypothesis testing.

(b) Review and discuss the level of significance and power of a statistical test.

(c) The following statements are very important. Give them some careful thought and discuss them.

  i. When we fail to reject the null hypothesis, we do not claim that it is absolutely true. We simply claim that at the given level of significance, the data were not sufficient to reject the null hypothesis.

  ii. When we accept the alternate hypothesis, we do not claim that the null hypothesis is absolutely false. We do claim that at the given level of significance, the data presented enough evidence to reject the null hypothesis.

(d) In the text, it is said that a statistical test is a package of five basic ingredients. List these ingredients, discuss them in class, and write a short description of how these ingredients relate to the above discussion questions.

(e) As access to computers becomes more and more prevalent, we see the *P*-value reported in hypothesis testing more frequently. Review the use of the *P*-value in hypothesis testing. What is the difference between the level of significance of a test and the *P*-value? Considering both the *P*-value and level of significance, under what conditions do we reject or fail to reject the null hypothesis?

Using Technology

TI-84PLUS/TI-83PLUS • EXCEL • MINITAB • SPSS

SIMULATION

Recall that the level of significance α is the probability of mistakenly rejecting a true null hypothesis. If $\alpha = 0.05$, then we expect to mistakenly reject a true null hypothesis about 5% of the time. The following simulation conducted with Minitab demonstrates this phenomenon.

We draw 40 random samples of size 50 from a population that is normally distributed with mean $\mu = 30$ and standard deviation $\sigma = 2.5$. The display shows the results of a hypothesis test with

$$H_0: \mu = 30 \qquad H_1: \mu > 30$$

for each of the 40 samples labeled C1 through C40. Because each of the 40 samples is drawn from a population with mean $\mu = 30$, the null hypothesis $H_0: \mu = 30$ is true for the test based on each sample. However, as the display shows, for some samples we reject the true null hypothesis.

(a) How many of the 40 samples have a sample mean $\bar{x}$ above $\mu = 30$? below $\mu = 30$?

(b) Look at the P-value of the sample statistic $\bar{x}$ in each of the 40 samples. How many P-values are less than or equal to $\alpha = 0.05$? What percent of the P-values are less than or equal to α? What percent of the samples have us reject H_0 when, in fact, each of the samples was drawn from a normal distribution with $\mu = 30$, as hypothesized in the null hypothesis?

(c) If you have access to computer or calculator technology that creates random samples from a normal distribution with a specified mean and standard deviation, repeat this simulation. Do you expect to get the same results? Why or why not?

Minitab Display: Random samples of size 50 from a normal population with $\mu = 30$ and $\sigma = 2.5$

```
Z-Test
Test of mu = 30.000 vs. mu > 30.000
The assumed sigma = 2.50
Variable   N    Mean    StDev   SE Mean     Z      P
C1        50   30.002   2.776    0.354    0.01   0.50
C2        50   30.120   2.511    0.354    0.34   0.37
C3        50   30.032   2.721    0.354    0.09   0.46
C4        50   30.504   2.138    0.354    1.43   0.077
C5        50   29.901   2.496    0.354   -0.28   0.61
C6        50   30.059   2.836    0.354    0.17   0.43
C7        50   30.443   2.519    0.354    1.25   0.11
C8        50   29.775   2.530    0.354   -0.64   0.74
C9        50   30.188   2.204    0.354    0.53   0.30
C10       50   29.907   2.302    0.354   -0.26   0.60
C11       50   30.036   2.762    0.354    0.10   0.46
C12       50   30.656   2.399    0.354    1.86   0.032
C13       50   30.158   2.884    0.354    0.45   0.33
C14       50   29.830   3.129    0.354   -0.48   0.68
C15       50   30.308   2.241    0.354    0.87   0.19
C16       50   29.751   2.165    0.354   -0.70   0.76
C17       50   29.833   2.358    0.354   -0.47   0.68
C18       50   29.741   2.836    0.354   -0.73   0.77
C19       50   30.441   2.194    0.354    1.25   0.11
C20       50   29.820   2.156    0.354   -0.51   0.69
C21       50   29.611   2.360    0.354   -1.10   0.86
C22       50   30.569   2.659    0.354    1.61   0.054
C23       50   30.294   2.302    0.354    0.83   0.20
C24       50   29.978   2.298    0.354   -0.06   0.53
C25       50   29.836   2.438    0.354   -0.46   0.68
C26       50   30.102   2.322    0.354    0.29   0.39
C27       50   30.066   2.266    0.354    0.19   0.43
C28       50   29.071   2.219    0.354   -2.63   1.00
C29       50   30.597   2.426    0.354    1.69   0.046
C30       50   30.092   2.296    0.354    0.26   0.40
C31       50   29.803   2.495    0.354   -0.56   0.71
C32       50   29.546   2.335    0.354   -1.28   0.90
C33       50   29.702   1.902    0.354   -0.84   0.80
C34       50   29.233   2.657    0.354   -2.17   0.98
C35       50   30.097   2.472    0.354    0.28   0.39
C36       50   29.733   2.588    0.354   -0.76   0.78
C37       50   30.379   2.976    0.354    1.07   0.14
C38       50   29.424   2.827    0.354   -1.63   0.95
C39       50   30.288   2.396    0.354    0.81   0.21
C40       50   30.195   3.051    0.354    0.55   0.29
```

Technology Hints

TI-84Plus/TI-83Plus

Press **STAT** and select **EDIT.** Highlight the list name, such as L1. Then press **MATH,** select **PRB,** and highlight **6:randNorm(μ, σ, sample size).** Press Enter. Fill in the values of $\mu = 30$, $\sigma = 2.5$, and sample size $= 50$. Press Enter. Now list L1 contains a random sample from the normal distribution specified.

To test the hypothesis H_0: $\mu = 30$ against H_1: $\mu > 30$, press **STAT,** select **TESTS,** and use option **1:Z-Test.** Fill in the value 30 for μ_0, 2.5 for σ, and $> \mu_0$. The output provides the value of the sample statistic $\bar{x}$, its corresponding z value, and the P-value of the sample statistic.

Excel

To draw random samples from a normal distribution with $\mu = 30$ and $\sigma = 2.5$, use the menu choices **Tools ➤ Data Analysis ➤ Random Number Generator.** In the dialogue box, the number of variables is the number of samples. Fill in the rest of the dialogue box using 50 as the number of random numbers, with 30 for the mean and 2.5 for the standard deviation.

To conduct a hypothesis test of H_0: $\mu = 30$ against H_1: $\mu > 30$, use the command **ZTEST(data range, 30, 2.5).** This command is described as returning the two-tailed P-value of the z test. However, it appears to give the P-value of a right-tailed test. Use the **ZTEST** command with caution and check your results against the table results.

Minitab

To generate random samples from a normal distribution, use the menu choices **Calc ➤ Random Data**

➤ Normal. In the dialogue box, the number of rows refers to the sample size. Use 50 rows. Then designate the columns for the samples. Using C1–C40 will generate 40 random samples and put the samples in columns C1 through C40.

To test the hypothesis H_0: $\mu = 30$ against H_1: $\mu > 30$, use the menu choices **Stat ➤ Basic Statistics ➤ 1-SampleZ.** Use columns C1–C40 as the variables. Fill in 30 for the test mean, use greater than for the alternate hypothesis, and use 2.5 for sigma.

SPSS

SPSS uses a Student's t distribution to test the mean and difference of means. SPSS uses the sample standard deviation s even if the population σ is known. Use the menu choices **Analyze ➤ Compare Means** and then **One-Sample T Test** for tests of a single mean. In the dialogue box, fill in the test value of the null hypothesis.

To generate 40 random samples of size $n = 50$ from a normal distribution with $\mu = 30$ and $\sigma = 2.5$, first enter consecutive integers from 1 to 50 in a column of the data editor. Then, under variable view, enter the variable names Sample1 through Sample40. Use the menu choices **Transform ➤ Compute.** In the dialogue box, use Sample1 for the target variable, and then select the function **RV.Normal(mean, stddev).** Use 30 for the mean and 2.5 for the standard deviation. Continue until you have 40 samples. To sample from other distributions, use appropriate functions in the Compute dialogue box.

Cumulative Review Problems

CHAPTERS 7–9

Answers may vary due to rounding.

1. *Normal Distribution* *Oxygen demand* is a term biologists use to describe the oxygen needed by fish and other aquatic organisms for survival. The Environmental Protection Agency conducted a study of a wetland area in Marin County, California. In this wetland environment, the mean oxygen demand was $\mu = 9.9$ mg/L with 95% of the data ranging from 6.5 mg/L to 13.3 mg/L (Reference: EPA Report 832-R-93-005). Let x be a random variable that represents oxygen demand in this wetland environment. Assume x has a probability distribution that is approximately normal.
   (a) Use the 95% data range to estimate the standard deviation for oxygen demand. *Hint:* See Problem 27 of Section 7.3.
   (b) An oxygen demand below 8 indicates that some organisms in the wetland environment may be dying. What is the probability that the oxygen demand will fall below 8 mg/L?
   (c) A high oxygen demand can also indicate trouble. An oxygen demand above 12 may indicate an overabundance of organisms that endanger some types of plant life. What is the probability that the oxygen demand will exceed 12 mg/L?

2. *Normal Approximation to the Binomial* The majority of house burglars simply walk into a house that is unlocked! In fact, about 57% of all house burglars gain entrance through an unlocked window or door (Reference: *The Book of Risks* by Larry Laudan). Suppose that $n = 129$ house burglaries will occur tomorrow in Los Angeles. Let r be a binomial random variable that represents the number of burglaries that required no forced entrance.
   (a) We want to approximate the binomial random variable r by a normal random variable x. Is this appropriate? What requirements must be satisfied before we can do this? Do you think these requirements are satisfied in this case? Explain.
   (b) Compute μ and σ for the normal approximation.
   (c) What is the probability that at least 65 of the burglaries required no forced entry?

Patrol car at scene of house robbery

3. *Terminology* Please give a careful but brief answer to each of the following questions.
   (a) What is a population? How do you get a simple random sample? Give examples.
   (b) What is a sample statistic? What is a sampling distribution? Give examples.
   (c) Give a careful and complete statement of the central limit theorem.
   (d) List at least three areas of everyday life to which the above concepts can be applied. Be specific.

4. *Sampling Distribution* $\bar{x}$ Workers at a large toxic cleanup project are concerned that their white blood cell counts may have been reduced. Let x be a random variable that represents white blood cell count per cubic millimeter of whole blood in a healthy adult. Then $\mu = 7500$ and $\sigma \approx 1750$ (Reference: *Diagnostic Tests with Nursing Applications*, S. Loeb). A random sample of $n = 50$ workers from the toxic cleanup site were given a blood test that showed $\bar{x} = 6820$. What is the probability that for healthy adults $\bar{x}$ will be this low or lower?
   (a) How does the central limit theorem apply? Explain.
   (b) Compute $P(\bar{x} \leq 6820)$.
   (c) Based on your answer to part (b), would you recommend that additional facts be obtained, or would you recommend that the workers' claims be dismissed? Explain.

In Problems 5–7, please use the following steps (i) through (v) for all hypothesis tests.
   i. What is the level of significance? State the null and alternate hypotheses.
   ii. What sampling distribution will you use? What assumptions are you making? What is the value of the sample test statistic?
   iii. Find (or estimate) the P-value. Sketch the sampling distribution and show the area corresponding to the P-value.
   iv. Based on your answers in parts (i) to (iii), will you reject or fail to reject the null hypothesis? Are the data statistically significant at level α?
   v. State your conclusion in the context of the application.

   Note: For degrees of freedom *d.f.* not in the Student's t table, use the closest *d.f.* that is *smaller*. In some situations, this choice of *d.f.* may increase the P-value a small amount, and thereby produce a slightly more "conservative" answer.

5. *Testing and Estimating* μ, σ *Known* Let x be a random variable that represents micrograms of lead per liter of water (ug/l). An industrial plant discharges water into a creek. The Environmental Protection Agency has studied the discharged water and found x to have a normal distribution with $\sigma = 0.7$ ug/l (Reference: *EPA Wetlands Case Studies*).
   (a) The industrial plant says that the population mean value of x is $\mu = 2.0$ ug/l. However, a random sample of $n = 10$ water samples showed that $\bar{x} = 2.56$ ug/l. Does this indicate that the lead concentration population mean is higher than the industrial plant claims? Use $\alpha = 1\%$.
   (b) Find a 95% confidence interval for μ using the sample data and the EPA value for σ.
   (c) *Sample Size* How large a sample should be taken to be 95% confident that the sample mean $\bar{x}$ is within a margin of error $E = 0.2$ ug/l of the population mean?

6. *Testing and Estimating* μ, σ *Unknown* Carboxyhemoglobin is formed when hemoglobin is exposed to carbon monoxide. Heavy smokers tend to have a high percentage of carboxyhemoglobin in their blood (Reference: *Laboratory and Diagnostic Tests*, F. Fishbach). Let x be a random variable representing percentage of carboxyhemoglobin in the blood. For a person who is a regular heavy smoker, x has

a distribution that is approximately normal. A random sample of $n = 12$ blood tests given to a heavy smoker gave the following results (percent carboxyhemoglobin in the blood).

9.1 9.5 10.2 9.8 11.3 12.2 11.6 10.3 8.9 9.7 13.4 9.9

(a) Use a calculator to verify that $\bar{x} \approx 10.49$ and $s \approx 1.36$.
(b) A long-term population mean $\mu = 10\%$ is considered a health risk. However, a long-term population mean above 10% is considered a clinical alert that the person may be asymptomatic. Do the data indicate that the population mean percentage is higher than 10% for this patient? Use $\alpha = 0.05$.
(c) Use the given data to find a 99% confidence interval for μ for this patient.

7. *Testing and Estimating a Proportion p* Although older Americans are most afraid of crime, it is young people who are more likely to be the actual victims of crime. It seems that older people are more cautious about the people with whom they associate. A national survey showed that 10% of all people ages 16–19 have been victims of crime (Reference: *Bureau of Justice Statistics*). At Jefferson High School, a random sample of $n = 68$ students (ages 16–19) showed that $r = 10$ had been victims of a crime.
(a) Do these data indicate that the population proportion of students in this school (ages 16–19) who have been victims of a crime is different (either way) from the national rate for this age group? Use $\alpha = 0.05$. Do you think the conditions $np > 5$ and $nq > 5$ are satisfied in this setting? Why is this important?
(b) Find a 90% confidence interval for the proportion of students in this school (ages 16–19) who have been victims of a crime.
(c) *Sample Size* How large a sample size should be used to be 95% sure that the sample proportion $\hat{p}$ is within a margin of error $E = 0.05$ of the population proportion of all students in this school (ages 16–19) who have been victims of a crime? *Hint:* Use sample data $\hat{p}$ as a preliminary estimate for p.

8. *Essay and Project* In Chapters 7, 8, and 9 you have studied sampling distributions, estimation, and hypothesis testing.
(a) Write a brief essay in which you discuss using information from samples to infer information about populations. Be sure to include methods of estimation and hypothesis testing in your discussion. What two sampling distributions are used in estimation and hypothesis testing of population means and proportions? What are the criteria for determining the appropriate sampling distribution? What is the level of significance of a test? What is the P-value? How is the P-value related to the alternate hypothesis? How is the null hypothesis related to the sample test statistic? Explain.
(b) Suppose you want to study the length of time devoted to commercial breaks for television programs. Identify the type of programs you want to study (e.g., sitcoms,

sports events, movies, news, children's programs, etc.). Write a brief outline for your study. Discuss how to obtain random samples. How large should the sample be for a specified margin of error? Describe the protocol you will follow to measure the times of the commercial breaks. Determine whether you are going to study the average time devoted to commercials or the proportion of time devoted to commercials. What assumptions will you make regarding the population distribution? What graphics might be appropriate? What methods of estimation will you use? What methods of testing will you use?

10

Inferences About Differences

"So what!"

—Anonymous

We have all heard the exclamation, "So what!" Philologists (people who study cultural linguistics) tell us that this expression is a shortened version of "So what is the difference!" They also tell us that there are similar popular or slang expressions about differences in all languages and cultures. It is human nature to challenge the claim that something is better, worse, or just simply different. In this chapter, we will focus on this very human theme by studying a variety of topics regarding questions of whether or not differences exist between two populations.

"Girl with Black Eye" by Norman Rockwell (1894–1978)

Norman Rockwell painted everyday people and situations. In this cover for the *Saturday Evening Post* (May 23, 1953), a young lady is about to have a conference with her school principal. So what!

PREVIEW QUESTIONS

◇ What are the statistical advantages of paired data values? How do we construct statistical tests? (SECTION 10.1)

◇ How do we compare means from two independent populations when we know σ for each population? (SECTION 10.2)

◇ What if we want to compare means from two independent populations, but we do not know σ for each population? (SECTION 10.2)

◇ How do we use sample data to compare proportions from two independent populations? (SECTION 10.3)

For on-line student resources, visit **math.college.hmco.com/students** and follow the Statistics links to the Brase/Brase, *Understanding Basic Statistics,* 4th edition web site.

FOCUS PROBLEM

The Trouble with Wood Ducks

The National Wildlife Federation published an article entitled "The Trouble with Wood Ducks" (*National Wildlife,* Vol. 31, No. 5). In this article, wood ducks are described as beautiful birds living in forested areas such as the Pacific Northwest and Southeast United States. Because of overhunting and habitat destruction, these birds were in danger of extinction. A federal ban on hunting wood ducks in 1918 helped save the species from extinction. Wood ducks like to nest in tree cavities. However, many such trees were disappearing due to heavy timber cutting. For a period of time it seemed that nesting boxes were the solution to disappearing trees. At first, the wood duck population grew, but after a few seasons, the population declined sharply. Good biology research combined with good statistics provided an answer to this disturbing phenomenon.

Cornell University professors of ecology Paul Sherman and Brad Semel found that the nesting boxes were placed too close to each other. Female wood ducks prefer a secluded nest that is a considerable distance from the next wood duck nest. In fact, female wood duck behavior changed when the nests were too close to each other. Some females would lay their eggs in another female's nest. The result was too many eggs in one nest. The biologists found that if there were too many eggs in a nest, the proportion of eggs that hatched was considerably reduced. In the long run, this meant a decline in the population of wood ducks.

In their study, Sherman and Semel used two placements of nesting boxes. Group I boxes were well separated from each other and well hidden by available brush. Group II boxes were highly visible and grouped closely together.

In group I boxes, there were a total of 474 eggs, of which a field count showed that about 270 hatched. In group II boxes, there were a total of 805 eggs, of which a field count showed that, again, about 270 hatched.

(a) Find a 95% confidence interval for $p_1 - p_2$. Does the interval indicate that the proportion of eggs hatched from group I nest box placements is higher than, lower than, or not different from the proportion of eggs hatched from group II nest boxes?

(b) Use a 5% level of significance to test the hypothesis that the proportion of hatches from group I placements is greater than that from group II placements. Do we reject or fail to reject H_0? Is this result consistent with the information from the 95% confidence interval?

(c) What conclusions about placement of nest boxes can be drawn? In the article, additional concerns are raised about the higher cost of placing and maintaining group I nest boxes. Also at issue is the cost efficiency per successful wood duck hatch. Data in the article do not include information that would help us answer questions of *cost* efficiency. However, the data presented do help us answer questions about the proportions of successful hatches in the two nest box configurations.

(See Problem 16 of Section 10.3.)

10.1
Tests Involving Paired Differences (Dependent Samples)

FOCUS POINTS

✓ Identify paired data and dependent samples.

✓ Explain the advantages of paired data tests.

✓ Compute differences and the sample test statistic.

✓ Estimate the *P*-value and conclude the test.

Creating data pairs

Many statistical applications use *paired data* samples to draw conclusions about the difference between two population means. Data *pairs* occur very naturally in "before and after" situations, where the *same* object or item is measured both before and after a treatment. Applied problems in social science, natural science, and business administration frequently involve a study of matching pairs. Psychological studies of identical twins; biological studies of plant growth on plots of land matched for soil type, moisture, and sun; and business studies on sales of matched inventories are examples of paired data studies.

When working with paired data, it is very important to have a definite and uniform method of creating data pairs that clearly utilizes a natural matching of characteristics. The next example and exercise demonstrate this feature.

EXAMPLE 1

Paired data

A shoe manufacturer claims that among the general population of adults in the United States, the average length of the left foot is longer than that of the right. To compare the average length of the left foot with that of the right, we can take a random sample of 15 U.S. adults and measure the length of the left foot and then the length of the right foot for each person in the sample. Is there a natural way of pairing the measurements? How many pairs will we have?

SOLUTION: In this case, we can pair each left foot measurement with the same person's right foot measurement. The person serves as the "matching link" between the two distributions. We will have 15 pairs of measurements.   ◇

GUIDED EXERCISE 1

Paired data

A psychologist has developed a series of exercises called the Instrumental Enrichment (IE) Program, which he claims is useful in overcoming cognitive deficiencies in mentally retarded children. To test the program, extensive statistical tests are being conducted. In one experiment, a random sample of 10-year-old students with IQ scores below 80 was selected. An IQ test was given to these students before they spent 2 years in an IE Program, and an IQ test was given to the same students after the program.

(a) On what basis can you pair the IQ scores?

⟹ Take the "before and after" IQ scores of each individual student.

(b) If there were 20 students in the sample, how many data pairs would you have?

⟹ Twenty data pairs. Note that there would be 40 IQ scores, but only 20 pairs.

◇ **COMMENT** To compare two populations, we cannot always employ paired data tests, but when we can, what are the advantages? Using matched or paired data often can reduce the danger of introducing extraneous or uncontrollable factors into our sample measurements, because the matched or paired data have essentially the *same* characteristics except for the *one* characteristic that is being measured. Furthermore, it can be shown that pairing data has the theoretical effect of reducing measurement variability (i.e., variance), which increases the precision of statistical conclusions. ◇

> Two samples are **dependent** if each data value in one sample can be paired with a corresponding data value in the other sample.

When we wish to compare the means of two samples, the first item to be determined is whether or not there is a natural pairing between the data in the two samples. Again, data pairs are created from "before and after" situations, or from matching data by using studies of the same object, or by a process of taking measurements of closely matched items.

Testing the differences d

When testing *paired* data, we take the differences d of the data pairs *first* and look at the mean difference $\bar{d}$. Then we use a test on $\bar{d}$. Theorem 10.1 provides the basis for our work with paired data.

◇ **THEOREM 10.1** Consider a random sample of n data pairs. Suppose the differences d between the first and second members of each data pair are (approximately) normally distributed with population mean μ_d. Then the t values

$$t = \frac{\bar{d} - \mu_d}{s_d / \sqrt{n}}$$

where $\bar{d}$ is the sample mean of the d values, n is the number of data pairs, and

$$s_d = \sqrt{\frac{\Sigma(d - \bar{d})^2}{n - 1}}$$

is the sample standard deviation of the d values, follow a Student's t distribution with degrees of freedom $d.f. = n - 1$. ◊

Hypotheses for testing the mean of paired differences

When testing the mean of the differences of paired data values, the null hypothesis is that there is no difference among the pairs. That is, the mean of the differences μ_d is zero.

$$H_0: \mu_d = 0$$

The alternate hypothesis depends on the problem and can be

$H_1: \mu_d < 0$	$H_1: \mu_d > 0$	$H_1: \mu_d \neq 0$
(left-tailed)	(right-tailed)	(two-tailed)

Sample test statistic

For paired difference tests, we make our decision regarding H_0 according to the evidence of the sample mean $\overline{d}$ of the differences of measurements. By Theorem 10.1, we convert the sample test statistic $\overline{d}$ to a t value using the formula

$$t = \frac{\overline{d} - \mu_d}{(s_d / \sqrt{n})} \text{ with } d.f. = n - 1$$

where s_d = sample standard deviation of the differences d

n = number of data pairs

μ_d = 0 as specified in H_0

P-values from Table 4 of the Appendix

To find the P-value (or an interval containing the P-value) corresponding to the test statistic t computed from $\overline{d}$, we use the Student's t distribution table (Table 4 of the Appendix). Recall from Section 9.2 that we find the test statistic t (or, if t is negative, $|t|$) in the row headed by $d.f. = n - 1$, where n is the number of data pairs. The P-value for the test statistic is the column entry in the *one-tail area* row for one-tailed tests (right or left). For two-tailed tests, the P-value is the column entry in the *two-tail area* row. Usually the exact test statistic t is not in the table, so we obtain an interval that contains the P-value by using adjacent entries in the table. Table 10-1 gives the basic structure for using the Student's t distribution table to find the P-value or an interval containing the P-value.

TABLE 10-1   Using Student's t Distribution Table for P-values

For one-tailed tests:	one-tail area	P-value	P-value
For two-tailed tests:	two-tail area	P-value	P-value
Use row header	$d.f. = n - 1$		Find t value

With the preceding information, you are now ready to test paired differences. First let's summarize the procedure.

> **PROCEDURE**
>
> **How to test paired differences using the Student's *t* distribution**
>
> Obtain a simple random sample of *n* matched data pairs A, B. Let *d* be a random variable representing the difference between the values in a matched data pair. Compute the sample mean $\bar{d}$ and sample standard deviation s_d.
>
> If you can assume that *d* has a normal distribution or simply has a mound-shaped symmetric distribution, then any sample size *n* will work. If you cannot assume this, then use a sample size $n \geq 30$.
>
> 1. Use the *null hypothesis* of *no difference*, $H_0: \mu_d = 0$. In the context of the application, choose the *alternate hypothesis* to be $H_1: \mu_d > 0$, or $\mu_d < 0$, or $\mu_d \neq 0$. Set the *level of significance* α.
>
> 2. Use $\bar{d}$, s_d, the sample size *n*, and $\mu_d = 0$ from the null hypothesis to compute the sample *test statistic*
>
> $$t = \frac{\bar{d} - 0}{\dfrac{s_d}{\sqrt{n}}} = \frac{\bar{d}\sqrt{n}}{s_d}$$
>
> with degrees of freedom $d.f. = n - 1$.
>
> 3. Use the Student's *t* distribution and the type of test, one-tailed or two-tailed, to find (or estimate) the *P-value* corresponding to the test statistic.
>
> 4. *Conclude* the test. If P-value $\leq \alpha$, then reject H_0. If P-value $> \alpha$, then do not reject H_0.
>
> 5. *State your conclusion* in the context of the application.

EXAMPLE 2

Paired difference test

A team of heart surgeons at Saint Ann's Hospital knows that many patients who undergo corrective heart surgery have a dangerous buildup of anxiety before their scheduled operations. The staff psychiatrist at the hospital has started a new counseling program intended to reduce this anxiety. A test of anxiety is given to patients who know they must undergo heart surgery. Then each patient participates in a series of counseling sessions with the staff psychiatrist. At the end of the counseling sessions, each patient is retested to determine anxiety level. Table 10-2 indicates the results for a random sample of nine patients. Higher scores mean higher levels of anxiety.

TABLE 10-2

Patient	B Score before Counseling	A Score after Counseling	$d = B - A$ Difference
Jan	121	76	45
Tom	93	93	0
Diane	105	64	41
Kamal	115	117	−2
Mike	130	82	48
Bill	98	80	18
Enrique	142	79	63
Carol	118	67	51
Alice	125	89	36

From the given data, can we conclude that the counseling sessions reduce anxiety? Use a 0.01 level of significance.

SOLUTION: Before we answer this question, let us notice two important points: (1) we have a *random sample* of nine patients, and (2) we have a *pair* of measurements taken on the same patient before and after counseling sessions. In our problem, the sample size is $n = 9$ pairs (i.e., patients), and the d values are found in the fourth column of Table 10-2 on the previous page.

(a) Note the level of significance and set the hypotheses.

In the problem statement, $\alpha = 0.01$. We want to test the claim that the counseling sessions reduce anxiety. This means that the anxiety level before counseling is expected to be higher than the anxiety level after counseling. In symbols, $d = B - A$ should tend to be positive, and the population mean of differences μ_d also should be positive. Therefore, we have

$$H_0: \mu_d = 0 \quad \text{and} \quad H_1: \mu_d > 0$$

(b) Find the sample test statistic $\bar{d}$ and convert it to a corresponding test statistic t. First we need to compute $\bar{d}$ and s_d. Using formulas or a calculator and the d values shown in Table 10-2, we find that

$$\bar{d} \approx 33.33 \quad \text{and} \quad s_d \approx 22.92$$

Using these values together with $n = 9$ and $\mu_d = 0$, we have

$$t = \frac{\bar{d} - 0}{(s_d/\sqrt{n})} \approx \frac{33.33}{22.92/\sqrt{9}} \approx 4.363$$

(c) Find the *P*-value for the test statistic and sketch the *P*-value on the *t* distribution. Since we have a right-tailed test, the *P*-value is the area to the right of $t = 4.363$, as shown in Figure 10-1. In Table 4 of the Appendix, we find an interval containing the *P*-value. Use entries from the row headed by $d.f. = n - 1 = 9 - 1 = 8$. The test statistic $t = 4.636$ falls between 3.355 and 5.041. The *P*-value for the sample t falls between the corresponding one-tail areas 0.005 and 0.0005. (See Table 10-3, Excerpt from Table 4 of the Appendix.)

$$0.0005 < \text{P-value} < 0.005$$

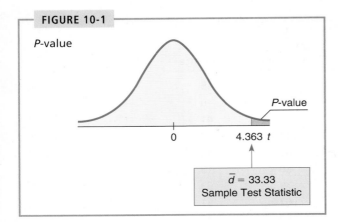

FIGURE 10-1

P-value

TABLE 10-3   Excerpt from Student's *t* Distribution Table (Table 4, Appendix)

✓ one-tail area	0.005	0.0005
two-tail area	0.010	0.0010
d.f. = 8	3.355	5.041

Sample $t = 4.363$

(d) Conclude the test.

$$\text{—(}\underset{0.0005}{\rule{1cm}{0.1cm}}\text{)—}\underset{0.005}{\text{)}}\text{——}\overset{\alpha}{\underset{0.01}{+}}\text{——}$$

Since the interval containing the P-value lies to the left of $\alpha = 0.01$, we reject H_0. *Note:* Using the raw data and software, the P-value ≈ 0.0012.

(e) Interpret the results.

At the 1% level of significance, we conclude that the counseling sessions reduce the average anxiety level of patients about to undergo corrective heart surgery. ◇

The problem we have just solved is a paired difference problem of the "before and after" type. The next guided exercise demonstrates a paired difference problem of the "matched pair" type.

GUIDED EXERCISE 2

Paired difference test

Do educational toys make a difference in the age at which a child learns to read? To study this question, researchers designed an experiment in which one group of preschool children spent 2 hours each day (for 6 months) in a room well supplied with "educational" toys such as alphabet blocks, puzzles, ABC readers, coloring books featuring letters, and so forth. A control group of children spent 2 hours a day for 6 months in a "noneducational" toy room. It was anticipated that IQ differences and home environment might be uncontrollable factors unless identical twins could be used. Therefore, six pairs of identical twins of preschool age were randomly selected. From each pair, one member was randomly selected to participate in the experimental (i.e., educational toy room) group and the other in the control (i.e., noneducational toy room) group. For each twin the data item recorded is the age in months at which the child began reading at the primary level (Table 10-4).

TABLE 10-4　Reading Ages for Identical Twins in Months

Twin Pair	Experimental Group B = Reading Age	Control Group A = Reading Age	Difference $d = B - A$
1	58	60	
2	61	64	
3	53	52	
4	60	65	
5	71	75	
6	62	63	

(a) Compute the entries in the $d = B - A$ column of Table 10-4. Using formulas for the mean and sample standard deviation or a calculator with mean and sample standard deviation keys, compute $\overline{d}$ and s_d.

Pair	$d = B - A$
1	−2
2	−3
3	1
4	−5
5	−4
6	−1

$\overline{d} \approx -2.33$

$s_d \approx 2.16$

Continued

GUIDED EXERCISE 2 continued

(b) What is the null hypothesis?

⇨ $H_0: \mu_d = 0$

(c) To test the claim that the experimental group learned to read at a *different age* (either younger or older), what should the alternate hypothesis be?

⇨ $H_1: \mu_d \neq 0$

(d) Convert the sample test statistic $\bar{d}$ to a t value. Find the degrees of freedom.

⇨ Using $\mu_d = 0$ from H_0, $\bar{d} = -2.33$, $n = 6$, and $s_d = 2.16$, we get

$$t = \frac{\bar{d} - \mu_d}{(s_d/\sqrt{n})} \approx \frac{-2.33 - 0}{(2.16/\sqrt{6})} \approx -2.642$$

$$d.f. = n - 1 = 6 - 1 = 5$$

(e) When we use Table 4 of the Appendix to find an interval containing the P-value, do we use one-tail or two-tail areas? Why? Sketch a figure showing the P-value. Find an interval containing the P-value.

⇨ This is a two-tailed test, so we use two-tail areas.

FIGURE 10-2 *P*-value

TABLE 10-5 Excerpt from Student's *t* Table

one-tail area	0.025	0.010
✓ two-tail area	0.050	0.020
d.f. = 5	2.571	3.365

Sample t = 2.642

The sample t is between 2.571 and 3.365.

$0.020 < P\text{-value} < 0.050$

(f) Using $\alpha = 0.05$, do we reject or fail to reject H_0? Interpret your results in the context of this application.

⇨ Since the interval containing the P-value has values that are all smaller than 0.05, we reject H_0.

At the 5% level of significance, the experiment indicates that educational toys make a difference in the age at which a child learns to read.

Note: Using the raw data and software, $P\text{-value} \approx 0.0457$.

TECH NOTE Both Excel and Minitab support paired difference tests directly. On the TI-84Plus and TI-83Plus calculators, construct a column of differences and then do a t test on the data in that column. For each technology, be sure to relate the alternate hypothesis to the "before and after" assignments. All the displays show the results for the data of Guided Exercise 2.

TI-84Plus/TI-83Plus Enter the "before" data in column L1 and the "after" data in column L2. Highlight L3, type L1 − L2, and press Enter. The column L3 now contains the $B - A$ differences. To conduct the test, press **STAT**, select **TESTS**, and use option **2:T-Test**. Note that the letter x is used in place of d.

L1	L2	L3 3
58	60	-2
61	64	-3
53	52	1
60	65	-5
71	75	-4
62	63	-1
L3(7) =		

```
T-Test
 μ≠0
 t=-2.645751311
 p=.0456591238
 x̄=-2.333333333
 Sx=2.160246899
 n=6
```

Excel Enter the data in two columns. Use the menu choices **Tools ➤ Data Analysis ➤ t-Test: Paired Two-Sample for Means.** Fill in the dialogue box with the hypothesized mean difference of 0. Set alpha.

	B	C	D
	t-Test: Paired Two Sample for Means		
		Variable 1	Variable 2
	Mean	60.83333	63.16666667
	Variance	34.96667	55.76666667
	Observations	6	6
	Pearson Correlation	0.974519	
	Hypothesized Mean Difference	0	
	df	5	
	t Stat	−2.64575	
	P(T<=t) one-tail	0.02283	
	t Critical one-tail	2.015049	
P-value ➤	P(T<=t) two-tail	0.045659	
	t Critical two-tail	2.570578	

Minitab Enter the data in two columns. Use the menu selection **Stat ➤ Basic Statistics ➤ Paired *t*.** Under Options, set the null and alternate hypotheses.

```
Paired T-Test and Confidence Interval
Paired T for B - A
                N       Mean      St Dev SE    Mean
B               6       60.83     5.91         2.41
A               6       63.17     7.47         3.05
Difference      6      -2.333     2.160        0.882
95% CI for mean difference: (-4.601, -0.066)
T-Test of mean difference = 0 (vs not = 0):
        T-Value = -2.65 P-Value = 0.046
```

Traditional Method Using Critical Regions (Optional)

For a fixed preset level of significance α, the P-value method of testing is logically equivalent to the critical region method of testing. This book emphasizes the P-value method because of its great popularity and because it is readily compatible with most computer software. However, for completeness, we provide an optional example utilizing the critical region method.

Recall that the critical region method and the P-value method of testing share a number of steps. Both methods use the same *null and alternate hypotheses*, the same *sample test statistic*, and the same *sampling distribution* for the test statistic. Instead of computing the P-value and comparing it to the level of significance α, the critical region method compares the sample test statistic to a *critical value* from the sampling distribution that is based on α and the alternate hypothesis (left-tailed, right-tailed, or two-tailed).

Test conclusions based on critical values

For a *right-tailed test*, if the sample *test statistic* $\geq$ *critical value*, reject H_0.

For a *left-tailed test*, if the sample *test statistic* $\leq$ *critical value*, reject H_0.

For a *two-tailed test*, if the sample *test statistic lies beyond the critical values* (that is, $\leq$ negative critical value or $\geq$ positive critical value), reject H_0.

Otherwise, in each case, do not reject H_0.

EXAMPLE 3

Critical region method

Let's revisit Guided Exercise 2 regarding educational toys and reading age and conclude the test using the critical region method. Recall that there were six pairs of twins. One twin of each set was given educational toys and the other was not. The difference d in reading ages for each pair of twins was measured, and $\alpha = 0.05$.

SOLUTION: From Guided Exercise 2, we have

$$H_0: \mu_d = 0 \quad \text{and} \quad H_1: \mu_d \neq 0$$

We computed the sample test statistic $\overline{d} \approx -2.33$ with corresponding $t \approx -2.642$.

(a) Find the critical values for $\alpha = 0.05$.

Since the number of pairs is $n = 6$, $d.f. = n - 1 = 5$. In the Student's t distribution table (Table 4 of the Appendix), look in the row headed by 5. To find the column, locate $\alpha = 0.05$ in the *two-tail area* row, since we have a two-tailed test. The critical values are $\pm t_0 = \pm 2.571$.

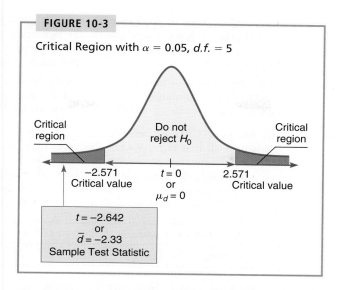

FIGURE 10-3

Critical Region with $\alpha = 0.05$, $d.f. = 5$

Critical region

Do not reject H_0

Critical region

−2.571
Critical value

$t = 0$
or
$\mu_d = 0$

2.571
Critical value

$t = -2.642$
or
$\bar{d} = -2.33$
Sample Test Statistic

(b) Sketch the critical regions and place the t value of the sample test statistic $\bar{d}$ on the sketch. Conclude the test. Compare the result to the result given by the P-value method of Guided Exercise 2.

Since the sample test statistic falls in the critical region (see Figure 10-3), we reject H_0 at the 5% level of significance. At this level, educational toys seem to make a difference in reading age. Notice that this conclusion is consistent with the conclusion obtained using the P-value. ◆

VIEWPOINT   *DUI*

DUI usually means "driving under the influence" of *alcohol*, but driving under the influence of *sleep loss* can be just as dangerous. Researchers in Australia have found that after staying awake for 24 hours straight, a person will be about as impaired as if he or she had had enough alcohol to be legally drunk in most U.S. states (Source: *Rocky Mountain News*). Using driver simulation exams and statistical tests (paired difference tests) found in this section, it is possible to show that the null hypothesis H_0: $\mu_d = 0$ cannot be rejected. Or put another way, the average level of impairment for a given individual from alcohol (at the DUI level) is about the same as the average level of impairment from sleep loss (24 hours without sleep).

SECTION 10.1   PROBLEMS

Please provide the following information for Problems 1–10.
(a) What is the level of significance? State the null and alternate hypotheses. Will you use a left-tailed, right-tailed, or two-tailed test?
(b) What sampling distribution will you use? What assumptions are you making? What is the value of the sample test statistic?
(c) Find (or estimate) the P-value. Sketch the sampling distribution and show the area corresponding to the P-value.

(d) Based on your answers in parts (a) to (c), will you reject or fail to reject the null hypothesis? Are the data statistically significant at level α?

(e) State your conclusion in the context of the application.

In these problems, assume that the distribution of differences is approximately normal.

Note: For degrees of freedom *d.f.* not in the Student's *t* table, use the closest *d.f.* that is *smaller.* In some situations, this choice of *d.f.* may increase the *P*-value a small amount, and therefore produce a slightly more "conservative" answer.

1. *Business: CEO Raises* Are America's top chief executive officers (CEOs) really worth all that money? One way to answer this question is to look at row *B*, the annual company percentage increase in revenue, versus row *A*, the CEO's annual percentage salary increase at that same company (Source: *Forbes*, Vol. 159, No. 10). A random sample of companies such as John Deere & Co., General Electric, Union Carbide, and Dow Chemical yielded the following data:

B: Percent for company	24	23	25	18	6	4	21	37
A: Percent for CEO	21	25	20	14	−4	19	15	30

Do these data indicate that the population mean percentage increase in corporate revenue (row *B*) is different from the population mean percentage increase in CEO salary? Use a 5% level of significance.

2. *Fishing: Shore or Boat?* Is fishing better from a boat or from the shore? Pyramid Lake is on the Paiute Indian Reservation in Nevada. Presidents, movie stars, and people who just want to catch fish go to Pyramid Lake for really large cutthroat trout. Let row *B* represent hours to catch a fish fishing from the shore, and let row *A* represent hours to catch a fish using a boat. The following data are paired by month from October through April (Source: *Pyramid Lake Fisheries*, Paiute Reservation, Nevada).

	Oct.	Nov.	Dec.	Jan.	Feb.	March	April
B: Shore	1.6	1.8	2.0	3.2	3.9	3.6	3.3
A: Boat	1.5	1.4	1.6	2.2	3.3	3.0	3.8

Use a 1% level of significance to test if there is a difference in the population mean hours to catch a fish using a boat compared with fishing from the shore.

3. *Ecology: Rocky Mountain National Park* The following is based on information taken from *Winter Wind Studies in Rocky Mountain National Park,* by D. E. Glidden (Rocky Mountain Nature Association). At five weather stations on Trail Ridge Road in Rocky Mountain National Park, the peak wind gusts (in miles per hour) for January and April are recorded below.

Weather Station	1	2	3	4	5
January	139	122	126	64	78
April	104	113	100	88	61

Does this information indicate that the peak wind gusts are higher in January than in April? Use $\alpha = 0.01$.

4. *Wildlife: Highways* The western United States has a number of four-lane interstate highways that cut through long tracts of wilderness. To prevent car accidents with wild animals, the highways are bordered on both sides with 12-foot-high woven wire fences.

Although the fences prevent accidents, they also disturb the winter migration pattern of many animals. To compensate for this disturbance, the highways have frequent wilderness underpasses designed for exclusive use by deer, elk, and other animals.

In Colorado, there is a large group of deer that spend their summer months in a region on one side of a highway and survive the winter months in a lower region on the other side. To determine if the highway has disturbed deer migration to the winter feeding area, the following data were gathered from a random sample of 10 wilderness districts in the winter feeding area. Row *B* represents the average January deer count for a 5-year period before the highway was built, and row *A* represents the average January deer count for a 5-year period after the highway was built. The highway department claims that the January population has not changed. Test this against the claim that the January population has dropped. Use a 5% level of significance. Units used in the table are hundreds of deer.

Wilderness District	1	2	3	4	5	6	7	8	9	10
B: Before highway	10.3	7.2	12.9	5.8	17.4	9.9	20.5	16.2	18.9	11.6
A: After highway	9.1	8.4	10.0	4.1	4.0	7.1	15.2	8.3	12.2	7.3

5. *Wildlife: Wolves* In environmental studies, sex ratios are of great importance. Wolf society, packs, and ecology have been studied extensively at different locations in the U.S. and foreign countries. Sex ratios for eight study sites in northern Europe are shown below (based on *The Wolf* by L. D. Mech, University of Minnesota Press).

Gender Study of Large Wolf Packs

Location of Wolf Pack	% Males (Winter)	% Males (Summer)
Finland	72	53
Finland	47	51
Finland	89	72
Lapland	55	48
Lapland	64	55
Russia	50	50
Russia	41	50
Russia	55	45

It is hypothesized that in winter, "loner" males (males not present in summer packs) join the pack to increase survival rate. Use a 5% level of significance to test the claim that the average percentage of males in a wolf pack is higher in winter.

6. *Demographics: Birth Rate and Death Rate* In the following data pairs, *A* represents birth rate and *B* represents death rate per 1000 resident population. The data are paired by counties in the Midwest. A random sample of 16 counties gave the following information (Reference: *County and City Data Book*, U.S. Department of Commerce).

A:	12.7	13.4	12.8	12.1	11.6	11.1	14.2	15.1
B:	9.8	14.5	10.7	14.2	13.0	12.9	10.9	10.0

A:	12.5	12.3	13.1	15.8	10.3	12.7	11.1	15.7
B:	14.1	13.6	9.1	10.2	17.9	11.8	7.0	9.2

Do the data indicate a difference (either way) between population average birth rate and death rate in this region? Use $\alpha = 0.01$.

7. *Golf: Tournaments* Do professional golfers play better in their first round? Let row *B* represent the score in the fourth (and final) round, and let row *A* represent the score in the first round of a professional golf tournament. A random sample of finalists in the British Open gave the following data for first and last rounds in the tournament (Source: *Golf Almanac*).

B: Last	73	68	73	71	71	72	68	68	74
A: First	66	70	64	71	65	71	71	71	71

Do the data indicate that the population mean score on the last round is higher than that on the first? Use a 5% level of significance.

8. *Archaeology: Stone Tools* The following is based on information taken from *Bandelier Archaeological Excavation Project: Summer 1990 Excavations at Burnt Mesa Pueblo and Casa del Rito*, edited by T. A. Kohler (Washington State University, Department of Anthropology). The artifact frequency for an excavation of a kiva in Bandelier National Monument gave the following information.

Stratum	Flaked Stone Tools	Nonflaked Stone Tools
1	7	3
2	3	2
3	10	1
4	1	3
5	4	7
6	38	32
7	51	30
8	25	12

Does this information indicate that there tend to be more flaked stone tools than nonflaked stone tools at this excavation site? Use a 5% level of significance.

9. *Archaeology: Pot Sherds* From the same stratum of an excavated block of rooms at Bandelier National Monument, the following information was obtained for number of sherds of service ware found in two different subareas (see reference in Problem 8):

Service Ware	Subarea 1	Subarea 2
Socorro black-on-white	10	4
Santa Fe black-on-white	42	39
Galisteo black-on-white	15	21
Puerco black-on-red	6	9
Wingate black-on-red	11	6

Does this information indicate that there is a difference (either higher or lower) in the population mean number of service ware sherds in subarea 1 compared with subarea 2? Use a 5% level of significance.

10. *Economics: Cost of Living Index* In the following data pairs, *A* represents the cost of living index for housing and *B* represents the cost of living index for groceries. The data are paired by metropolitan areas of the United States. A random sample of 36 metropolitan areas gave the following information (Reference: *Statistical Abstract of the United States*, 121st edition).

A:	132	109	128	122	100	96	100	131	97
B:	125	118	139	104	103	107	109	117	105

A:	120	115	98	111	93	97	111	110	92
B:	110	109	105	109	104	102	100	106	103

A:	85	109	123	115	107	96	108	104	128
B:	98	102	100	95	93	98	93	90	108

A:	121	85	91	115	114	86	115	90	113
B:	102	96	92	108	117	109	107	100	95

i. Let *d* be the random variable $d = A - B$. Use a calculator to verify that $\bar{d} \approx 2.472$ and $s_d \approx 12.124$.

ii. Do the data indicate that the U.S. population mean cost of living index for housing is higher than that for groceries in these areas? Use $\alpha = 0.05$.

11. *Critical Region Method: Student's t* Solve Problem 1 using the critical region method of testing. Compare your conclusions with the conclusions obtained by using the *P*-value method. Are they the same?

12. *Critical Region Method: Student's t* Solve Problem 3 using the critical region method of testing. Compare your conclusions with the conclusions obtained by using the *P*-value method. Are they the same?

10.2
Inferences About the Difference of Two Means $\mu_1 - \mu_2$
Independent Samples

FOCUS POINTS

✓ Identify independent samples and sampling distributions.

✓ Compute the sample test statistic and *P*-value for testing $\mu_1 - \mu_2$.

✓ Find confidence intervals for $\mu_1 - \mu_2$.

Many practical applications of statistics involve a comparison of two population means or two population proportions. In Section 10.1, we considered tests of difference of means for *dependent samples*. With dependent samples, we could pair the data and then consider the differences of the data measurements *d*. In this section, we will turn our attention to inferences regarding differences of means from *independent samples*.

> Two samples are **independent** if the selection of sample data from one population is completely unrelated to the selection of sample data from the other population.

Independent samples occur very naturally when we draw *two random samples*, one from the first population and one from the second population. Because *both* samples are random samples, there is no pairing of measurements between the two populations.

GUIDED EXERCISE 3

Distinguish between independent and dependent samples

For each experiment, categorize the sampling as independent or dependent, and explain your choice.

(a) In many medical experiments, a sample of subjects is randomly divided into two groups. One group is given a specific treatment, and the other group is given a placebo. After a certain period of time, both groups are measured for the same condition. Do the measurements from these two groups constitute independent or dependent samples?

⟹ Since the subjects are *randomly assigned* to the two treatment groups (one receives a treatment, the other a placebo), the resulting measurements would form independent samples.

(b) In an accountability study, a group of students in an English composition course is given a pretest. After the course, the same students are given a posttest covering similar material. Are the two groups of scores independent or dependent?

⟹ Since the pretest scores and the posttest scores are from the same students, the samples are dependent. Each student has both a pretest score and a posttest score, so there is a natural pairing of data values.

Hypothesis Tests and Confidence Intervals for $\mu_1 - \mu_2$ (σ_1 and σ_2 known)

The $\bar{x}_1 - \bar{x}_2$ sampling distribution

In this section, we will use probability distributions that arise from a difference of means. How do we obtain such distributions? Suppose that we have two statistical variables x_1 and x_2, each with its own distribution. We take *independent* random samples of size n_1 from the x_1 distribution and of size n_2 from the x_2 distribution. Then we compute the respective means $\bar{x}_1$ and $\bar{x}_2$. Now consider the difference $\bar{x}_1 - \bar{x}_2$. This expression represents a difference of means. If we repeat this sampling process over and over, we will create lots of $\bar{x}_1 - \bar{x}_2$ values. Figure 10-4 illustrates the sampling distribution of $\bar{x}_1 - \bar{x}_2$.

The values of $\bar{x}_1 - \bar{x}_2$ that come from repeated (independent) sampling of populations 1 and 2 can be arranged in a relative-frequency table and a relative-frequency histogram (see Section 2.1). This would give us an experimental idea of the theoretical probability distribution of $\bar{x}_1 - \bar{x}_2$.

Fortunately, it is not necessary to carry out this lengthy process for each example. The results have been worked out mathematically. The next theorem presents the main results.

◇ **THEOREM 10.2** Let x_1 and x_2 have normal distributions with means μ_1 and μ_2 and standard deviations σ_1 and σ_2, respectively. If we take independent random samples of size n_1 from the x_1 distribution and of size n_2 from the x_2 distribution, then the variable $\bar{x}_1 - \bar{x}_2$ has

1. a normal distribution

2. mean $\mu_1 - \mu_2$

3. standard deviation $\sqrt{\dfrac{\sigma_1^2}{n_1} + \dfrac{\sigma_2^2}{n_2}}$ ◇

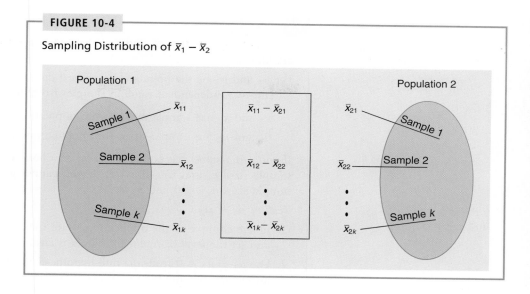

FIGURE 10-4

Sampling Distribution of $\bar{x}_1 - \bar{x}_2$

◇ **COMMENT** The theorem requires that x_1 and x_2 have *normal* distributions. However, if *both* n_1 and n_2 are 30 or larger, then the central limit theorem (Section 7.5) assures us that $\bar{x}_1$ and $\bar{x}_2$ are approximately normally distributed. In this case, the conclusions of the theorem are again valid even if the original x_1 and x_2 distributions are not exactly normal.   ◇

Theorem 10.2 gives us the basis for hypothesis tests and confidence intervals for $\mu_1 - \mu_2$ when σ_1 and σ_2 are both known.

Hypotheses for testing difference of means

When testing the difference of means, it is customary to use the null hypothesis

$$H_0:\ \mu_1 - \mu_2 = 0 \ \text{or, equivalently,}\ H_0:\ \mu_1 = \mu_2$$

As mentioned in Section 9.1, the null hypothesis is set up to see if it can be rejected. When testing the difference of means, we first set up the hypothesis H_0 that there is no difference. The alternate hypothesis could then be any of the ones listed in Table 10-6. The alternate hypothesis and consequent type of test used depend on the particular problem. Note that μ_1 is always listed first.

Using Theorem 10.2 and the central limit theorem (Section 7.5), we can summarize the procedure for testing $\mu_1 - \mu_2$ and finding a confidence interval when both σ_1 and σ_2 are known.

TABLE 10-6   Alternate Hypotheses and Type of Test: Difference of Two Means

H_1			Type of Test
$H_1:\ \mu_1 - \mu_2 < 0$	or equivalently	$H_1:\ \mu_1 < \mu_2$	Left-tailed test
$H_1:\ \mu_1 - \mu_2 > 0$	or equivalently	$H_1:\ \mu_1 > \mu_2$	Right-tailed test
$H_1:\ \mu_1 - \mu_2 \neq 0$	or equivalently	$H_1:\ \mu_1 \neq \mu_2$	Two-tailed test

> **PROCEDURE**
>
> **How to test $\mu_1 - \mu_2$ and find a confidence interval when both σ_1 and σ_2 are known**
>
> Let σ_1 and σ_2 be the population standard deviations of populations 1 and 2. Obtain two independent random samples from populations 1 and 2, where
>
> > $\bar{x}_1$ and $\bar{x}_2$ are sample means from populations 1 and 2
> >
> > n_1 and n_2 are sample sizes from populations 1 and 2
>
> If you can assume that both population distributions 1 and 2 are normal, any sample sizes n_1 and n_2 will work. If you cannot assume this, then use sample sizes $n_1 \geq 30$ and $n_2 \geq 30$.
>
> *Testing $\mu_1 - \mu_2$*
>
> 1. In the context of the application, state the *null and alternate hypotheses* and set the *level of significance* α. It is customary to use $H_0: \mu_1 - \mu_2 = 0$.
>
> 2. Use $\mu_1 - \mu_2 = 0$ from the null hypothesis together with $\bar{x}_1, \bar{x}_2, \sigma_1, \sigma_2, n_1$, and n_2 to compute the sample *test statistic*.
>
> $$z = \frac{(\bar{x}_1 - \bar{x}_2) - (\mu_1 - \mu_2)}{\sqrt{\dfrac{\sigma_1^2}{n_1} + \dfrac{\sigma_2^2}{n_2}}} = \frac{\bar{x}_1 - \bar{x}_2}{\sqrt{\dfrac{\sigma_1^2}{n_1} + \dfrac{\sigma_2^2}{n_2}}}$$
>
> 3. Use the standard normal distribution and the type of test, one-tailed or two-tailed, to find the *P-value* corresponding to the sample test statistic.
>
> 4. *Conclude the test.* If P-value $\leq \alpha$, then reject H_0. If P-value $> \alpha$, then do not reject H_0.
>
> 5. *State your conclusion* in the context of the application.
>
> *Confidence interval for $\mu_1 - \mu_2$*
>
> $$(\bar{x}_1 - \bar{x}_2) - E < \mu_1 - \mu_2 < (\bar{x}_1 - \bar{x}_2) + E$$
>
> where $E = z_c\sqrt{\dfrac{\sigma_1^2}{n_1} + \dfrac{\sigma_2^2}{n_2}}$
>
> > c = confidence level $(0 < c < 1)$
> >
> > z_c = critical value for confidence level c based on the standard normal distribution (See Table 3(b) of the Appendix for commonly used values.)

Hypothesis test for $\mu_1 - \mu_2$ (σ_1 and σ_2 known)

Confidence interval for $\mu_1 - \mu_2$ (σ_1 and σ_2 known)

EXAMPLE 4

Testing the difference of means and finding a confidence interval (σ_1 and σ_2 known)

A consumer group is testing camp stoves. To test the heating capacity of a stove, it measures the time required to bring 2 quarts of water from 50°F to boiling (at sea level). Two competing models are under consideration. Ten stoves of the first model and 12 stoves of the second model are tested. The following results are obtained.

Model 1: Mean time $\bar{x}_1 = 11.4$ min; $\sigma_1 = 2.5$ min; $n_1 = 10$

Model 2: Mean time $\bar{x}_2 = 9.9$ min; $\sigma_2 = 3.0$ min; $n_2 = 12$

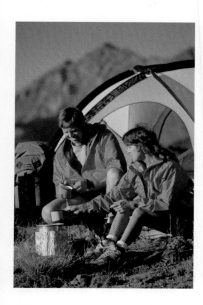

Assume that the time required to bring water to a boil is normally distributed for each stove.

Hypothesis test: Is there any difference (either way) between the performances of these two models? Use a 5% level of significance.

SOLUTION:

(a) State the null and alternate hypotheses and note the value of α.

Let μ_1 and μ_2 be the means of the distributions of times for models 1 and 2, respectively. We set up the null hypothesis to state that there is no difference:

$$H_0: \mu_1 = \mu_2 \quad \text{or} \quad H_0: \mu_1 - \mu_2 = 0$$

The alternate hypothesis states that there is a difference:

$$H_1: \mu_1 \neq \mu_2 \quad \text{or} \quad H_1: \mu_1 - \mu_2 \neq 0$$

The level of significance is $\alpha = 0.05$.

(b) Compute the sample test statistic $\bar{x}_1 - \bar{x}_2$ and then convert it to a z value. Note that we use the standard normal distribution because the original distributions are normal and the standard deviations are known.

We are given the values $\bar{x}_1 = 11.4$ and $\bar{x}_2 = 9.9$. Therefore, the sample test statistic is $\bar{x}_1 - \bar{x}_2 = 11.4 - 9.9 = 1.5$. To convert this to a z value, we use the values $\sigma_1 = 2.5$, $\sigma_2 = 3.0$, $n_1 = 10$, and $n_2 = 12$. From the null hypothesis, $\mu_1 - \mu_2 = 0$.

$$z = \frac{(\bar{x}_1 - \bar{x}_2) - (\mu_1 - \mu_2)}{\sqrt{\dfrac{\sigma_1^2}{n_1} + \dfrac{\sigma_2^2}{n_2}}} = \frac{1.5}{\sqrt{\dfrac{2.5^2}{10} + \dfrac{3.0^2}{12}}} \approx 1.28$$

(c) Find the P-value and sketch the area on the standard normal curve.

Figure 10-5 shows the P-value. Use the standard normal distribution (Table 3 of the Appendix) and the fact that we have a two-tailed test. P-value $\approx 2(0.1003) = 0.2006$.

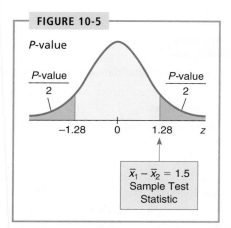

FIGURE 10-5

P-value

$\dfrac{P\text{-value}}{2}$

$\dfrac{P\text{-value}}{2}$

−1.28   0   1.28 z

$\bar{x}_1 - \bar{x}_2 = 1.5$
Sample Test
Statistic

(d) Conclude the test.

The P-value is 0.2006 and $\alpha = 0.05$. Since P-value $> \alpha$, do not reject H_0.

(e) Interpret the results.

At the 5% level of significance, the sample data do not indicate any difference in the population mean times for boiling water for the two stove models.

Confidence interval: Find a 95% confidence interval for the population difference $\mu_1 - \mu_2$ of mean times to boil water for the two stoves. Interpret the results.

SOLUTION:

Note that both σ_1 and σ_2 are known and that the times for each stove to bring 2 quarts of water to a boil are normally distributed. Therefore, by Theorem

10.2, $\bar{x}_1 - \bar{x}_2$ is normal. We use the normal distribution to find the critical value $z_{0.95}$. From Table 3(b) of the Appendix, we see that $z_{0.95} = 1.96$. The confidence interval is

$$(\bar{x}_1 - \bar{x}_2) - E < \mu_1 - \mu_2 < (\bar{x}_1 - \bar{x}_2) + E$$

where $\bar{x}_1 - \bar{x}_2 = 11.4 - 9.9 = 1.5$ min and

$$E = z_c \sqrt{\frac{\sigma_1^2}{n_1} + \frac{\sigma_2^2}{n_2}} = 1.96 \sqrt{\frac{2.5^2}{10} + \frac{3.0^2}{12}} \approx 2.30 \text{ min}$$

The confidence interval is

$$-0.8 \text{ min} < \mu_1 - \mu_2 < 3.8 \text{ min}$$

Notice that the confidence interval contains both negative and positive values. At the 95% confidence level, we cannot conclude that μ_1 is either less than or greater than μ_2. This result is consistent with the conclusion of the hypothesis test—that is, at the 5% level, the evidence is not sufficient to conclude that there is a difference in the average times for boiling 2 quarts of water between the two stoves. ◇

Meaning of confidence interval for $\mu_1 - \mu_2$

In Example 4 we saw that the confidence interval for $\mu_1 - \mu_2$ contained both positive and negative numbers. At the 95% level of confidence, we could not conclude that there was a difference in value between μ_1 and μ_2. There are two other cases: either all the values in the confidence interval are positive, or they are all negative. The next procedure summarizes the interpretation of all three cases.

PROCEDURE

How to interpret confidence intervals for differences

Suppose that we construct a $c\%$ confidence interval for $\mu_1 - \mu_2$. Then three cases arise:

1. The $c\%$ confidence interval contains only *negative values*. In this case, we conclude that $\mu_1 - \mu_2 < 0$, and we are therefore $c\%$ confident that $\mu_1 < \mu_2$.

2. The $c\%$ confidence interval contains only *positive values*. In this case, we conclude that $\mu_1 - \mu_2 > 0$, and we can be $c\%$ confident that $\mu_1 > \mu_2$.

3. The $c\%$ confidence interval contains *both positive and negative values*. In this case, we cannot at the $c\%$ confidence level conclude that either μ_1 or μ_2 is larger. However, if we *reduce* the confidence level c to a *smaller value*, then the confidence interval will, in general, be shorter (explain why). A shorter confidence interval *might* put us back into case 1 or case 2 above (again, explain why).

GUIDED EXERCISE 4

Interpret a confidence interval

(a) A study reported a 90% confidence interval for the difference of means to be

$$10 < \mu_1 - \mu_2 < 20$$

For this interval, what can you conclude about the respective values of μ_1 and μ_2?

⇒ At a 90% level of confidence, we can say that the difference $\mu_1 - \mu_2$ is positive, so $\mu_1 - \mu_2 > 0$ and $\mu_1 > \mu_2$.

(b) A study reported a 95% confidence interval for the difference of means to be

$$-0.32 < \mu_1 - \mu_2 < 0.16$$

From this interval, what can you conclude about the respective values of μ_1 and μ_2?

⇒ At the 95% confidence level, we see that the difference of means ranges from negative to positive values. We cannot tell from this interval if μ_1 is greater than μ_2 or μ_1 is less than μ_2.

◇ **COMMENT:** In the case of large samples ($n_1 \geq 30$ and $n_2 \geq 30$), it is not unusual to see σ_1 and σ_2 approximated by s_1 and s_2. Then Theorem 10.2 is used as a basis for approximating confidence intervals for $\mu_1 - \mu_2$. In other words, when samples are large, sample estimates for σ_1 and σ_2 can be used together with the standard normal distribution to test $\mu_1 - \mu_2$ and find confidence intervals. However, in this text, we follow the more common convention of using a Student's t distribution whenever σ_1 and σ_2 are unknown. ◇

Hypothesis Tests and Confidence Intervals for $\mu_1 - \mu_2$ When σ_1 and σ_2 Are Unknown

When σ_1 and σ_2 are unknown, we turn to a Student's t distribution. As before, when we use a Student's t distribution, we require that our populations be normal or approximately normal (mound-shaped and symmetric) when the sample sizes n_1 and n_2 are less than 30. We also replace σ_1 by s_1 and σ_2 by s_2. Then we consider the approximate t value, attributed to Welch (*Biometrika*, Vol. 29, pp. 350–362).

$$t \approx \frac{(\bar{x}_1 - \bar{x}_2) - (\mu_1 - \mu_2)}{\sqrt{\dfrac{s_1^2}{n_1} + \dfrac{s_2^2}{n_2}}}$$

Unfortunately, this approximation is *not* exactly a Student's t distribution. However, it will be a good approximation provided we adjust the degrees of freedom by one of the following methods.

1. The adjustment for the degrees of freedom is calculated from sample data. The formula is called *Satterthwaite's approximation*. It is rather complicated. Satterthwaite's approximation is used in statistical software packages such as Minitab and in the TI-84Plus/TI-83Plus calculators. See Problem 13 for the formula.

2. An alternative method, which is much simpler, is to approximate the degrees of freedom using the *smaller* of $n_1 - 1$ and $n_2 - 1$.

For hypothesis tests and confidence intervals, we take the degrees of freedom *d.f.* to be the smaller of $n_1 - 1$ and $n_2 - 1$. This commonly used choice for the degrees of freedom is more conservative that Satterthwaite's approximation in the sense that it produces a slightly larger *P*-value for testing or a slightly larger margin of error for confidence intervals.

Applying methods similar to those used for hypothesis tests and confidence intervals for μ when σ is unknown, and using the Welch approximation for *t*, we obtain the following results.

PROCEDURE

How to test $\mu_1 - \mu_2$ and find a confidence interval when σ_1 and σ_2 are unknown

Obtain two independent random samples from populations 1 and 2, where

$\bar{x}_1$ and $\bar{x}_2$ are sample means from populations 1 and 2

s_1 and s_2 are sample standard deviations from populations 1 and 2

n_1 and n_2 are sample sizes from populations 1 and 2

If you can assume that both population distributions 1 and 2 are normal or at least mound-shaped and symmetric, then any sample sizes n_1 and n_2 will work. If you cannot assume this, then use sample sizes $n_1 \geq 30$ and $n_2 \geq 30$.

Testing $\mu_1 - \mu_2$

Hypothesis test for $\mu_1 - \mu_2$
(σ_1 and σ_2 unknown)

1. In the context of the application, state the *null and alternate hypotheses* and set the *level of significance* α. It is customary to use H_0: $\mu_1 - \mu_2 = 0$.

2. Use $\mu_1 - \mu_2 = 0$ from the null hypothesis together with $\bar{x}_1, \bar{x}_2, s_1, s_2, n_1$, and n_2 to compute the sample *test statistic*.

$$t = \frac{(\bar{x}_1 - \bar{x}_2) - (\mu_1 - \mu_2)}{\sqrt{\dfrac{s_1^2}{n_1} + \dfrac{s_2^2}{n_2}}} = \frac{\bar{x}_1 - \bar{x}_2}{\sqrt{\dfrac{s_1^2}{n_1} + \dfrac{s_2^2}{n_2}}}$$

The sample test statistic distribution is approximately that of a Student's *t* with *degrees of freedom d.f.* = *smaller of* $n_1 - 1$ *and* $n_2 - 1$.
Note that statistical software gives a slightly more accurate and larger *d.f.* based on Satterthwaite's approximation (see Problem 13).

3. Use a Student's *t* distribution and the type of test, one-tailed or two-tailed, to find the *P-value* corresponding to the sample test statistic.

4. *Conclude the test.* If *P*-value $\leq \alpha$, then reject H_0. If *P*-value $> \alpha$, then do not reject H_0.

5. *State your conclusion* in the context of the application.

Confidence interval for $\mu_1 - \mu_2$
(σ_1 and σ_2 unknown)

Confidence interval for $\mu_1 - \mu_2$

$$(\bar{x}_1 - \bar{x}_2) - E < \mu_1 - \mu_2 < (\bar{x}_1 - \bar{x}_2) + E$$

where $E \approx t_c \sqrt{\dfrac{s_1^2}{n_1} + \dfrac{s_2^2}{n_2}}$

c = confidence level ($0 < c < 1$)

t_c = critical value for confidence level c (See Table 4 of the Appendix.)

$d.f.$ = *smaller of* $n_1 - 1$ *and* $n_2 - 1$. Note that statistical software gives a slightly more accurate and larger *d.f.* based on Satterthwaite's approximation.

Two competing headache remedies claim to give fast-acting relief. An experiment was performed to compare the mean lengths of time required for bodily absorption of brand A and brand B headache remedies.

Twelve people were randomly selected and given an oral dosage of brand A. Another 12 were randomly selected and given an equal dosage of brand B. The lengths of time in minutes for the drugs to reach a specified level in the blood were recorded. The means, standard deviations, and sizes of the two samples follow.

$$Brand\ A: \bar{x}_1 = 21.8\ min; \qquad s_1 = 8.7\ min; \qquad n_1 = 12$$
$$Brand\ B: \bar{x}_2 = 18.9\ min; \qquad s_2 = 7.5\ min; \qquad n_2 = 12$$

Past experience with the drug composition of the two remedies permits researchers to assume that both distributions are approximately normal.

Hypothesis test: Use a 5% level of significance to test the claim that there is no difference in the mean time required for bodily absorption. Also, find or estimate the *P*-value of the sample test statistic.

SOLUTION:

(a) $\alpha = 0.05$. The null hypothesis is

$$H_0: \mu_1 = \mu_2 \qquad or \qquad H_0: \mu_1 - \mu_2 = 0$$

Since we have no prior knowledge about which brand is faster, the alternate hypothesis is

$$H_1: \mu_1 \neq \mu_2 \qquad or \qquad H_0: \mu_1 - \mu_2 \neq 0$$

(b) Compute the sample test statistic.

We're given $\bar{x}_1 = 21.8$ and $\bar{x}_2 = 18.9$, so the sample difference is $\bar{x}_1 - \bar{x}_2 = 21.8 - 18.9 = 2.9$. Using $s_1 = 8.7$, $s_2 = 7.5$, $n_1 = 12$, $n_2 = 12$, and $\mu_1 - \mu_2 = 0$ from H_0, we compute the sample test statistic.

$$t = \frac{(\bar{x}_1 - \bar{x}_2) - (\mu_1 - \mu_2)}{\sqrt{\dfrac{s_1^2}{n_1} + \dfrac{s_2^2}{n_2}}} = \frac{2.9}{\sqrt{\dfrac{8.7^2}{12} + \dfrac{7.5^2}{12}}} \approx 0.875$$

(c) Estimate the *P*-value and sketch the area on a *t* graph.

Figure 10-6 shows the *P*-value. The degrees of freedom is *d.f.* = 11 (since both samples are of size 12). Because the test is a two-tailed test, the *P*-value is the area to the right of 0.875 together with the area to the left of −0.875. In the Student's *t* distribution table (Table 4 of the Appendix), we find an interval containing the *P*-value. Find 0.875 in the row headed by *d.f.* = 11. The test statistic 0.875 falls between the entries 0.697 and 1.214. Because this is a two-tailed test, we use the corresponding *P*-values 0.500 and 0.250 from the *two-tail area* row (see Table 10-7, Excerpt from Table 4). The *P*-value for the sample *t* is in the interval

$$0.250 < P\text{-value} < 0.500$$

(d) Conclude the test.

Since the interval containing the *P*-value lies to the right of $\alpha = 0.05$, we fail to reject H_0.

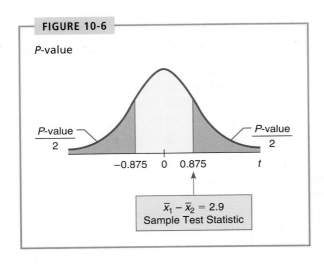

FIGURE 10-6

P-value

$\dfrac{P\text{-value}}{2}$ $\dfrac{P\text{-value}}{2}$

−0.875   0   0.875   *t*

$\bar{x}_1 - \bar{x}_2 = 2.9$
Sample Test Statistic

TABLE 10-7   Excerpt from Table 4 of the Appendix

one-tail area	0.250	0.125
✓two-tail area	0.500	0.250
d.f. = 11	0.697	1.214

↑
Sample *t* = 0.875

Note: Using Satterthwaite's approximation for the degrees of freedom, *d.f.* ≈ 21.53, the *P*-value ≈ 0.3915. This value is in the interval we computed.

(e) Interpret the results.

At the 5% level of significance, there is insufficient evidence to conclude that there is a difference in mean times for the remedies to reach the specified level in the bloodstream.

Confidence interval: Find a 95% confidence interval for the population difference $\mu_1 - \mu_2$ of mean times for the competing drugs to reach a specified level in the blood. Interpret the results.

SOLUTION:

Because neither σ_1 nor σ_2 is known and because the distributions of times for each drug to enter the bloodstream are approximately normal, it is appropriate to use a Student's t distribution. We approximate the degrees of freedom by using the smaller of $n_1 - 1$ and $n_2 - 1$. Since n_1 and n_2 are both 12, *d.f.* = 12 − 1 = 11. From Table 4 of the Appendix, we find that $t_{0.95} = 2.201$. The confidence interval is

$$(\bar{x}_1 - \bar{x}_2) - E < \mu_1 - \mu_2 < (\bar{x}_1 - \bar{x}_2) + E$$

with $\bar{x}_1 - \bar{x}_2 = 21.8 - 18.9 = 2.9$ min and

$$E = t_c \sqrt{\frac{s_1^2}{n_1} + \frac{s_2^2}{n_2}} = 2.201 \sqrt{\frac{8.7^2}{12} + \frac{7.5^2}{12}} \approx 7.3 \text{ min}$$

The confidence interval is

$$-4.4 \text{ min} < \mu_1 - \mu_2 < 10.2 \text{ min}$$

Note: Using Satterthwaite's formula, *d.f.* = 21.53 and the 95% confidence interval is from −3.99 to 9.79 minutes.

Since the confidence interval contains both negative and positive values, we conclude that at the 95% confidence level, there is no difference in the population mean times for the two drugs to reach the bloodstream. This result is consistent with the two-tailed hypothesis test at the 5% level of significance.   ◇

GUIDED
EXERCISE **5**

Testing the difference of means and finding a confidence interval (σ_1 and σ_2 unknown)

Suppose the experiment to measure the time in minutes for the headache remedies to enter the blood-stream (Example 5) yielded sample means, sample standard deviations, and sample sizes as follows:

Brand A: $\bar{x}_1 = 20.1$ min; $s_1 = 8.7$ min; $n_1 = 12$

Brand B: $\bar{x}_2 = 11.2$ min; $s_2 = 7.5$ min; $n_2 = 8$

Brand B claims to be faster.

Hypothesis test: Is this claim justified at the 5% level of significance? (Use the following steps to obtain the answer.)

(a) What is α? State H_0 and H_1.

  $\alpha = 0.05$.

$H_0: \mu_1 = \mu_2$ or $H_0: \mu_1 - \mu_2 = 0$

$H_1: \mu_1 > \mu_2$ (or $H_1: \mu_1 - \mu_2 > 0$). This says that the mean time for brand B is less than the mean time for brand A.

(b) Compute the sample test statistic $\bar{x}_1 - \bar{x}_2$ and convert it to a t value.

$\bar{x}_1 - \bar{x}_2 = 20.1 - 11.2 = 8.9$. Using $s_1 = 8.7$, $s_2 = 7.5$, $n_1 = 12$, $n_2 = 8$, and $\mu_1 - \mu_2 = 0$ from H_0, we have

$$t = \frac{\bar{x}_1 - \bar{x}_2}{\sqrt{\dfrac{s_1^2}{n_1} + \dfrac{s_2^2}{n_2}}} = \frac{8.9}{\sqrt{\dfrac{8.7^2}{12} + \dfrac{7.5^2}{8}}} \approx 2.437$$

(c) What degrees of freedom do you use? To find an interval containing the P-value, do you use one-tail or two-tail areas of Table 4 of the Appendix? Sketch a figure showing the P-value. Find an interval for the P-value.

Since $n_2 < n_1$, $d.f. = n_2 - 1 = 8 - 1 = 7$. Use *one-tail area* of Table 4 of the Appendix.

FIGURE 10-7 P-value

The sample t is between 2.365 and 2.998.

$0.010 < P\text{-value} < 0.025$

TABLE 10-8   Excerpt from Student's t Table

✓one-tail area	0.025	0.010
two-tail area	0.050	0.020
$d.f. = 7$	2.365	2.998
	↑ Sample t = 2.437	

Continued

(d) Do we reject or fail to reject H_0?

 Since the interval containing the *P*-value has values that are all less than 0.05, we reject H_0.

Note: On the calculator with Satterthwaite's approximation for *d.f.*, we have *d.f.* = 16.66 and *P*-value ≈ 0.013.

(e) Interpret the results in the context of the application.

 At the 5% level of significance, there is evidence that the mean time for brand B to enter the bloodstream is less than the mean time for brand A.

Confidence interval: Find a 90% confidence interval for the difference of population means $\mu_1 - \mu_2$ of times for the two competing headache remedies to enter the bloodstream.

(f) Find the degrees of freedom and the critical value $t_{0.90}$.

 Since $n_2 < n_1$, $d.f. = n_2 - 1 = 8 - 1 = 7$.
From Table 4 of the Appendix, $t_{0.90} = 1.895$.

(g) Find the maximal error of estimate E for a 90% confidence interval.

$$E = t_c \sqrt{\frac{s_1^2}{n_1} + \frac{s_2^2}{n_2}} = 1.895 \sqrt{\frac{8.7^2}{12} + \frac{7.5^2}{8}} \approx 6.9 \text{ min}$$

(h) Find the sample difference $\bar{x}_1 - \bar{x}_2$ and a 90% confidence interval for $\mu_1 - \mu_2$.

$\bar{x}_1 - \bar{x}_2 = 20.1 - 11.2 = 8.9$ min

$(\bar{x}_1 - \bar{x}_2) - E < \mu_1 - \mu_2 < (\bar{x}_1 - \bar{x}_2) + E$

$8.9 - 6.9 < \mu_1 - \mu_2 < 8.9 + 6.9$

$2 \text{ min} < \mu_1 - \mu_2 < 15.8 \text{ min}$

With Satterthwaite's formula, *d.f.* = 16.66 and the 90% confidence interval is 2.54 to 15.26 min.

(i) Interpret the results in the context of the application.

The confidence interval contains all positive numbers. This indicates that at the 90% confidence level, $\mu_1 > \mu_2$. It seems to take longer for brand A to enter the bloodstream.

◇ **COMMENT:** In Guided Exercise 5, we used a right-tailed test at the 5% level of significance and a 90% confidence interval. With both techniques, we concluded that the time for brand A to enter the bloodstream was longer than the time for brand B. This agreement of results is not an accident. In general, when dealing with the difference of means (and difference of proportions, as discussed in the next section), we will arrive at the same conclusion using either of the following two combinations.

1. Two-tailed hypothesis test at level of significance α and $(1 - \alpha)$ confidence interval

2. One-tailed hypothesis test at level of significance α and $(1 - 2\alpha)$ confidence interval ◇

Alternate method using pooled standard deviation

There is another method for testing $\mu_1 - \mu_2$ and finding confidence intervals when σ_1 and σ_2 are unknown. Suppose that the sample values s_1 and s_2 are sufficiently close and that there is reason to believe $\sigma_1 = \sigma_2$ (or that the standard deviations are approximately equal). This situation can happen when you make a slight change or alteration to a known process or method of production. The standard deviation may not change much, but the outputs or means could be very different. When there is reason to believe that $\sigma_1 = \sigma_2$, it is best to use a *pooled standard deviation*. The sample test statistic $\bar{x}_1 - \bar{x}_2$ has a corresponding t variable with an *exact* Student's t distribution and degrees of freedom $d.f. = n_1 + n_2 - 2$. Problem 14 at the end of this section provides the details for using the pooled standard deviation in hypothesis tests of and confidence intervals for $\mu_1 - \mu_2$.

Summary

Depending on the information available, there are several methods for testing and constructing confidence intervals for the difference of means $\mu_1 - \mu_2$ from two independent random samples. To use the normal probability distribution, you need to know σ_1 and σ_2. In addition, you need to know that the original population distributions are both normal or that n_1 and n_2 are both of size at least 30. To use a Student's t distribution, you need to know that the original population distributions are both normal or at least mound-shaped, or that n_1 and n_2 are both at least 30. The following decision chart summarizes the appropriate formulas.

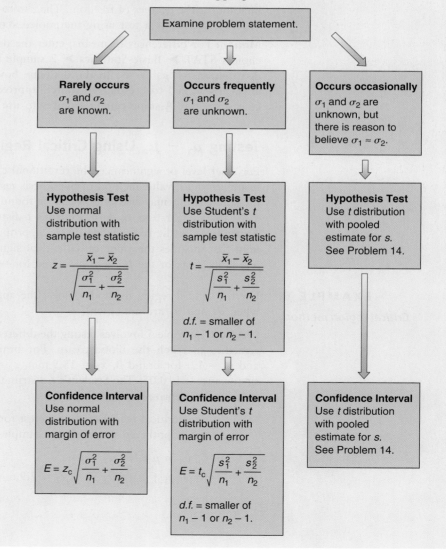

Examine problem statement.

Rarely occurs
σ_1 and σ_2 are known.

Occurs frequently
σ_1 and σ_2 are unknown.

Occurs occasionally
σ_1 and σ_2 are unknown, but there is reason to believe $\sigma_1 \approx \sigma_2$.

Hypothesis Test
Use normal distribution with sample test statistic

$$z = \frac{\bar{x}_1 - \bar{x}_2}{\sqrt{\dfrac{\sigma_1^2}{n_1} + \dfrac{\sigma_2^2}{n_2}}}$$

Hypothesis Test
Use Student's t distribution with sample test statistic

$$t = \frac{\bar{x}_1 - \bar{x}_2}{\sqrt{\dfrac{s_1^2}{n_1} + \dfrac{s_2^2}{n_2}}}$$

$d.f. =$ smaller of $n_1 - 1$ or $n_2 - 1$.

Hypothesis Test
Use t distribution with pooled estimate for s. See Problem 14.

Confidence Interval
Use normal distribution with margin of error

$$E = z_c \sqrt{\frac{\sigma_1^2}{n_1} + \frac{\sigma_2^2}{n_2}}$$

Confidence Interval
Use Student's t distribution with margin of error

$$E = t_c \sqrt{\frac{s_1^2}{n_1} + \frac{s_2^2}{n_2}}$$

$d.f. =$ smaller of $n_1 - 1$ or $n_2 - 1$.

Confidence Interval
Use t distribution with pooled estimate for s. See Problem 14.

TECH NOTE The TI-84Plus and TI-83Plus calculators, Excel, and Minitab all support testing the difference of means for independent samples. The TI-84Plus/TI-83Plus calculators and Minitab also supply confidence intervals for the difference of means.

TI-84Plus/TI-83Plus Enter either summary statistics or raw data. Press **STAT** and select **TESTS**. Options **3:2-SampZTest** and **4:2-SampTTest** test the difference of means using the normal distribution and a Student's t distribution, respectively. Choice **9:2-SampZInt** finds a confidence interval for a difference of means when σ_1 and σ_2 are known. Choice **0:2-SampTInt** finds a confidence interval for a difference of means when σ_1 and σ_2 are unknown. In general, use **No** for Pooled. Then Satterthwaite's approximation for the degrees of freedom is used. However, if $\sigma_1 \approx \sigma_2$, use **Yes** for Pooled.

Excel Enter the data in two columns. Use the menu choices **Tools ➤ Data Analysis**. The choice **z-Test Two Sample Means** tests the difference of means using the normal distribution. The choice **t-Test: Two-Sample Assuming Unequal Variances** tests the difference of means using a Student's t distribution with Satterthwaite's approximation for the degrees of freedom. The choice **t-Test: Two-Sample Assuming Equal Variances** conducts a test using the pooled standard deviation.

Minitab For differences of means, enter the data into two columns. Use the menu choices **STAT ➤ Basic Statistics ➤ 2 sample t**. Minitab always uses a Student's t distribution for $\mu_1 - \mu_2$. In the dialogue box, leave the box **Assume equal variances** unchecked to use Satterthwaite's approximation for the degrees of freedom. Check the box **Assume equal variances** to use the pooled standard deviation.

Testing $\mu_1 - \mu_2$ Using Critical Regions (Optional)

For a set level of significance, the traditional critical region method yields the same results as the P-value method of hypothesis testing. Critical values z_0 for tests using the standard normal distribution can be found in Table 3(c) of the Appendix. Critical values t_0 for tests using a Student's t distribution are found in Table 4 of the Appendix. Use the row headed by the appropriate degrees of freedom and the column that includes the value of α (level of significance) in the *one-tail area row* for one-tailed tests or the *two-tail area row* for two-tailed tests.

EXAMPLE 6

Critical region method

Use the critical region method to solve the application in Example 5 (test $\mu_1 - \mu_2$ when σ_1 and σ_2 are unknown).

SOLUTION: Example 5 involves testing the difference in average times for two headache remedies to reach the bloodstream. For brand A, $\bar{x}_1 = 21.8$ min, $s_1 = 8.7$ min, and $n_1 = 12$; for brand B, $\bar{x}_2 = 18.9$ min, $s_2 = 7.5$ min, and $n_2 = 12$. The level of significance α is 0.05. The Student's t distribution is appropriate because both populations are approximately normal.

(a) To use the critical region method to test for a difference in average times, we use the same hypotheses and the same sample test statistic as in Example 5.

$H_0: \mu_1 = \mu_2; H_1: \mu_1 \neq \mu_2;$

sample test statistic: $\bar{x}_1 - \bar{x}_2 = 2.9$ min; sample $t = 0.875$

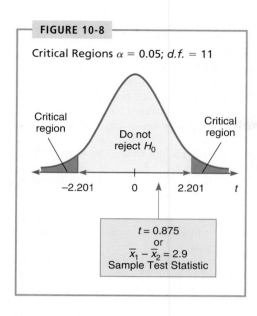

FIGURE 10-8

Critical Regions $\alpha = 0.05$; $d.f. = 11$

Critical region

Critical region

Do not reject H_0

−2.201   0   2.201 t

$t = 0.875$
or
$\bar{x}_1 - \bar{x}_2 = 2.9$
Sample Test Statistic

(b) Instead of finding the *P*-value of the sample test statistic, we use α and H_1 to find the critical values in Table 4 of the Appendix. We have $d.f. = 11$ (since both samples are of size 12). We find $\alpha = 0.05$ in the *two-tail area* row, since we have a two-tailed test. The critical values are $\pm t_0 = \pm 2.201$.

Next compare the sample test statistic $t = 0.875$ to the critical values. Figure 10-8 shows the critical regions and the sample test statistic. We see that the sample test statistic falls in the "do not reject H_0" region. At the 5% level of significance, the sample evidence does not show a difference in times for the drugs to reach the bloodstream. The result is consistent with the result obtained by the *P*-value method of Example 5.   ◇

VIEWPOINT   *Temper! Temper!*

In her book *Red Ink Behaviors,* Jean Hollands discusses inappropriate, problem behaviors of professional employees in the corporate business world. Temper tantrums, flaming e-mails, omitting essential information, sabotaging fellow workers, and the arrogant opinion that others are "dumb and dispensable" create personnel problems that cost companies a lot in the form of wasted time, reduced productivity, and lost revenues. A study of major industries in the Silicon Valley area gave Hollands data for estimating just how much time and money are wasted by such "red ink behaviors." For more information, see Problems 11 and 12 in this section.

SECTION 10.2   PROBLEMS

Please provide the following information for Problems 1–12, part (a).
  (i) What is the level of significance? State the null and alternate hypotheses.
 (ii) What sampling distribution will you use? What assumptions are you making? What is the value of the sample test statistic?
(iii) Find (or estimate) the *P*-value. Sketch the sampling distribution and show the area corresponding to the *P*-value.
(iv) Based on your answers in parts (a) to (c), will you reject or fail to reject the null hypothesis? Are the data statistically significant at level α?
 (v) State your conclusion in the context of the application.
       Note: For degrees of freedom *d.f.* not in the Student's *t* table, use the closest *d.f.* that is *smaller*. In some situations, this choice of *d.f.* may increase the *P*-value a small amount, and therefore produce a slightly more "conservative" answer.
Answers may vary due to rounding.

1. *Medical: REM Sleep* REM (rapid eye movement) sleep is sleep during which most dreams occur. Each night a person has both REM and non-REM sleep. However, it is thought that children have more REM sleep than adults (Reference: *Secrets of Sleep* by Dr. A. Borbely). Assume that REM sleep time is normally distributed for both children and adults. A random sample of $n_1 = 10$ children (9 years old) showed that they had an average REM sleep time of $\bar{x}_1 = 2.8$ hours per night. From previous studies it is known that $\sigma_1 = 0.5$ hour. Another random sample of $n_2 = 10$ adults showed that they had an average REM sleep time of $\bar{x}_2 = 2.1$ hours per night. Previous studies show that $\sigma_2 = 0.7$ hour.
   (a) Do these data indicate that on average, children tend to have more REM sleep than adults? Use a 1% level of significance.
   (b) Find a 98% confidence interval for $\mu_1 - \mu_2$. Explain the meaning of the confidence interval in the context of the problem.

2. *Enviroment: Pollution Index* Based on information from the *Rocky Mountain News*, a random sample of $n_1 = 12$ winter days in Denver gave a sample mean pollution index of $\bar{x}_1 = 43$. Previous studies show that $\sigma_1 = 21$. For Englewood (a suburb of Denver), a random sample of $n_2 = 14$ winter days gave a sample mean pollution index of $\bar{x}_2 = 36$. Previous studies show that $\sigma_2 = 15$. Assume the pollution index is normally distributed in both Englewood and Denver.
   (a) Do these data indicate that the mean population pollution index of Englewood is different (either way) from that of Denver in the winter? Use a 1% level of significance.
   (b) Find a 99% confidence interval for $\mu_1 - \mu_2$. Explain the meaning of the confidence interval in the context of the problem.

3. *Survey: Outdoor Activities* A Michigan study concerning preference for outdoor activities used a questionnaire with a six-point Likert-type response in which 1 designated "not important" and 6 designated "extremely important." A random sample of $n_1 = 46$ adults were asked about fishing as an outdoor activity. The mean response was $\bar{x}_1 = 4.9$. Another random sample of $n_2 = 51$ adults were asked about camping as an outdoor activity. For this group, the mean response was $\bar{x}_2 = 4.3$. From previous studies it is known that $\sigma_1 = 1.5$ and $\sigma_2 = 1.2$. *Note: A Likert scale* usually has to do with approval of or agreement with a statement in a questionnaire. For example, respondents are asked to indicate whether they "strongly agree," "agree," "disagree," or "strongly disagree" with the statement.
   (a) Does this indicate a difference (either way) regarding preference for camping versus preference for fishing as an outdoor activity? Use a 5% level of significance.
   (b) Find a 95% confidence interval for $\mu_1 - \mu_2$. Explain the meaning of the confidence interval in the context of the problem.

4. *Generation Gap: Education* Education influences attitude and lifestyle. Differences in education are a big factor in the "generation gap." Is the younger generation really better educated? Large surveys of people age 65 and older were taken in $n_1 = 32$ U.S. cities. The sample mean for these cities showed that $\bar{x}_1 = 15.2\%$ of the older adults had attended college. Large surveys of young adults (age 25–34) were taken in $n_2 = 35$ U.S. cities. The sample mean for these cities showed that $\bar{x}_2 = 19.7\%$ of the young adults had attended college. From previous studies it is known that $\sigma_1 = 7.2\%$ and $\sigma_2 = 5.2\%$ (Reference: *American Generations*, S. Mitchell).
   (a) Does this information indicate that the population mean percentage of young adults who attended college is higher? Use $\alpha = 0.05$.
   (b) Find a 90% confidence interval for $\mu_1 - \mu_2$. Explain the meaning of the confidence interval in the context of the problem.

5. *Crime Rate: FBI* A random sample of $n_1 = 10$ regions in New England gave the following violent crime rates (per million population).

x_1: **New England crime rate**

| 3.5 | 3.7 | 4.0 | 3.9 | 3.3 | 4.1 | 1.8 | 4.8 | 2.9 | 3.1 |

Another random sample of $n_2 = 12$ regions in the Rocky Mountain states gave the following violent crime rates (per million population).

x_2: **Rocky Mountain states crime rate**

| 3.7 | 4.3 | 4.5 | 5.3 | 3.3 | 4.8 | 3.5 | 2.4 | 3.1 | 3.5 | 5.2 | 2.8 |

(Reference: *Crime in the United States*, Federal Bureau of Investigation.) Assume that the crime rate distribution is approximately normal in both regions. Use a calculator to verify that $\bar{x}_1 \approx 3.51$, $s_1 \approx 0.81$, $\bar{x}_2 \approx 3.87$, and $s_2 \approx 0.94$.

(a) Do the data indicate that the violent crime rate in the Rocky Mountain region is higher than in New England? Use $\alpha = 0.01$.

(b) Find a 98% confidence interval for $\mu_1 - \mu_2$. Explain the meaning of the confidence interval in the context of the problem.

6. *Medical: Hay Fever* A random sample of $n_1 = 16$ communities in western Kansas gave the following information for people under 25 years of age.

x_1: **Rate of hay fever per 1000 population for people under 25**

| 98 | 90 | 120 | 128 | 92 | 123 | 112 | 93 |
| 125 | 95 | 125 | 117 | 97 | 122 | 127 | 88 |

A random sample of $n_2 = 14$ regions in western Kansas gave the following information for people over 50 years old.

x_2: **Rate of hay fever per 1000 population for people over 50**

| 95 | 110 | 101 | 97 | 112 | 88 | 110 |
| 79 | 115 | 100 | 89 | 114 | 85 | 96 |

(Reference: National Center for Health Statistics.)

Use a calculator to verify that $\bar{x}_1 \approx 109.50$, $s_1 \approx 15.41$, $\bar{x}_2 \approx 99.36$, and $s_2 \approx 11.57$.

(a) Assume that the hay fever rate in each age group has an approximately normal distribution. Do the data indicate that the age group over 50 has a lower rate of hay fever? Use $\alpha = 0.05$.

(b) Find a 90% confidence interval for $\mu_1 - \mu_2$. Explain the meaning of the confidence interval in the context of the problem.

7. *Education: Tutoring* In the journal *Mental Retardation*, an article reported the results of a peer tutoring program to help mildly mentally retarded children learn to read. In the experiment, the mildly retarded children were randomly divided into two groups: the experimental group received peer tutoring along with regular instruction, and the control group received regular instruction with no peer tutoring. There were $n_1 = n_2 = 30$ children in each group. The Gates-MacGintie Reading Test was given to both groups before instruction began. For the experimental group, the mean score on the vocabulary portion of the test was $\bar{x}_1 = 344.5$ with sample standard deviation $s_1 = 49.1$. For the control group, the mean score on the same test was $\bar{x}_2 = 354.2$ with sample standard deviation $s_2 = 50.9$.

(a) Use a 5% level of significance to test the hypothesis that there was no difference in the vocabulary scores of the two groups before the instruction began.

(b) Find a 95% confidence interval for $\mu_1 - \mu_2$. Explain the meaning of the confidence interval in the context of the problem.

8. *Education: Tutoring* In the article cited in Problem 7, the results of the following experiment were reported. Form 2 of the Gates-MacGintie Reading Test was

administered to both an experimental group and a control group after 6 weeks of instruction during which the experimental group received peer tutoring and the control group did not. For the experimental group with $n_1 = 30$ children, the mean score on the vocabulary portion of the test was $\bar{x}_1 = 368.4$ with sample standard deviation $s_1 = 39.5$. The average score on the vocabulary portion of the test for the $n_2 = 30$ subjects in the control group was $\bar{x}_2 = 349.2$, with sample standard deviation $s_2 = 56.6$.

(a) Use a 1% level of significance to test the claim that the experimental group performed better than the control group.

(b) Find a 98% confidence interval for $\mu_1 - \mu_2$. Explain the meaning of the confidence interval in the context of the problem.

9. *Wildlife: Fox Rabies* A study of fox rabies in southern Germany gave the following information about different regions and the occurrence of rabies in each region (Reference: B. Sayers, et al., "A Pattern Analysis Study of a Wildlife Rabies Epizootic," *Medical Informatics* 2:11–34). Based on information from this article, a random sample of $n_1 = 16$ locations in region I gave the following information about the number of cases of fox rabies near that location.

x_1: Region I data	1	8	8	8	7	8	8	1
	3	3	3	2	5	1	4	6

A second random sample of $n_2 = 15$ locations in region II gave the following information about the number of cases of fox rabies near that location.

x_2: Region II data	1	1	3	1	4	8	5	4
	4	4	2	2	5	6	9	

Use a calculator with sample mean and sample standard deviation keys to verify that $\bar{x}_1 = 4.75$ with $s_1 \approx 2.82$ in region I and $\bar{x}_2 \approx 3.93$ with $s_2 \approx 2.43$ in region II.

(a) Does this information indicate that there is a difference (either way) in the mean number of cases of fox rabies between the two regions? Use a 5% level of significance. (Assume the distribution of rabies cases in both regions is mound-shaped and approximately normal.)

(b) Find a 95% confidence interval for $\mu_1 - \mu_2$. Explain the meaning of the confidence interval in the context of the problem.

10. *Agriculture: Bell Peppers* The pathogen *Phytophthora capsici* causes bell peppers to wilt and die. Because bell peppers are an important commercial crop, this disease has undergone a great deal of agricultural research. It is thought that too much water aids the spread of the pathogen. Two fields are under study. The first step in the research project is to compare the mean soil water content for the two fields (Source: *Journal of Agricultural, Biological, and Environmental Statistics*, Vol. 2, No. 2). Units are percent water by volume of soil.

Field A samples, x_1:

10.2	10.7	15.5	10.4	9.9	10.0	16.6
15.1	15.2	13.8	14.1	11.4	11.5	11.0

Field B samples, x_2:

8.1	8.5	8.4	7.3	8.0	7.1	13.9	12.2
13.4	11.3	12.6	12.6	12.7	12.4	11.3	12.5

Use a calculator with mean and standard deviation keys to verify that $\bar{x}_1 \approx 12.53$, $s_1 \approx 2.39$, $\bar{x}_2 \approx 10.77$, and $s_2 \approx 2.40$.

(a) Assuming the distribution of soil water content in each field is mound-shaped and symmetric, use a 5% level of significance to test the claim that field A has, on average, a higher soil water content than field B.

(b) Find a 90% confidence interval for $\mu_1 - \mu_2$. Explain the meaning of the confidence interval in the context of the problem.

11. *Management: Lost Time* In her book *Red Ink Behaviors,* Jean Hollands reports on the assessment of leading Silicon Valley companies regarding a manager's lost time due to inappropriate behavior of employees. Consider the following independent random variables. The first variable x_1 measures manager's hours per week lost due to hot tempers, flaming e-mails, and general unproductive tensions:

x_1:	1	5	8	4	2	4	10

The variable x_2 measures manager's hours per week lost due to disputes regarding technical workers' superior attitudes that their colleagues are "dumb and dispensable":

x_2:	10	5	4	7	9	4	10	3

Use a calculator with sample mean and standard deviation keys to verify that $\bar{x}_1 \approx 4.86$, $s_1 \approx 3.18$, $\bar{x}_2 = 6.5$, and $s_2 \approx 2.88$.

(a) Does the information indicate that the population mean time lost due to hot tempers is different (either way) from the population mean time lost due to disputes arising from technical workers' superior attitudes? Use $\alpha = 0.05$. Assume that the two lost-time population distributions are mound-shaped and symmetric.

(b) Find a 95% confidence interval for $\mu_1 - \mu_2$. Explain the meaning of the confidence interval in the context of the problem.

12. *Management: Intimidators and Stressors* This problem is based on information regarding productivity in leading Silicon Valley companies (see reference in Problem 11). In large corporations, an "intimidator" is an employee who tries to stop communication, sometimes sabotages others, and, above all, likes to listen to him- or herself talk. Let x_1 be a random variable representing productive hours per week lost by peer employees of an intimidator.

x_1:	8	3	6	2	2	5	2

A "stressor" is an employee with a hot temper that leads to unproductive tantrums in corporate society. Let x_2 be a random variable representing productive hours per week lost by peer employees of a stressor.

x_2:	3	3	10	7	6	2	5	8

Use a calculator with mean and standard deviation keys to verify that $\bar{x}_1 = 4.00$, $s_1 \approx 2.38$, $\bar{x}_2 = 5.5$, and $s_2 \approx 2.78$.

(a) Assuming that the variables x_1 and x_2 are independent, do the data indicate that the population mean time lost due to stressors is greater than the population mean time lost due to intimidators? Use a 5% level of significance. (Assume that the population distributions of time lost due to intimidators and time lost due to stressors are each mound-shaped and symmetric.)

(b) Find a 90% confidence interval for $\mu_1 - \mu_2$. Explain the meaning of the confidence interval in the context of the problem.

13. *Expand Your Knowledge: Software Approximation for Degrees of Freedom* Given x_1 and x_2 distributions that are normal or approximately normal with unknown σ_1 and σ_2, the value of t corresponding to $\bar{x}_1 - \bar{x}_2$ has a distribution that is approximated by a Student's t distribution. We use the convention that the degrees of freedom

is approximately the smaller of $n_1 - 1$ and $n_2 - 1$. However, a more accurate estimate for the appropriate degrees of freedom is given by Satterthwaite's formula:

$$d.f. \approx \frac{\left(\dfrac{s_1^2}{n_1} + \dfrac{s_2^2}{n_2}\right)^2}{\dfrac{1}{n_1 - 1}\left(\dfrac{s_1^2}{n_1}\right)^2 + \dfrac{1}{n_2 - 1}\left(\dfrac{s_2^2}{n_2}\right)^2}$$

where s_1, s_2, n_1, and n_2 are the respective sample standard deviations and sample sizes of independent random samples from the x_1 and x_2 distributions. This is the approximation used by most statistical software. When both n_1 and n_2 are 5 or larger, it is quite accurate. The degrees of freedom computed from this formula are either truncated or not rounded.

(a) In Problem 5 we tested whether the population average crime rate μ_2 in the Rocky Mountain region is higher than that in New England, μ_1. The data were $n_1 = 10$, $\bar{x}_1 \approx 3.51$, $s_1 \approx 0.81$, $n_2 = 12$, $\bar{x}_2 \approx 3.87$, and $s_2 \approx 0.94$. Use Satterthwaite's formula to compute the degrees of freedom for the Student's t distribution.

(b) When you did Problem 5, you followed the convention that degrees of freedom $d.f. = $ *smaller* of $n_1 - 1$ and $n_2 - 1$. Compare this $d.f.$ with that found by Satterthwaite's formula.

14. *Expand Your Knowledge: Pooled Two-Sample Procedure* Consider independent random samples from two populations that are normal or approximately normal, or the case in which both sample sizes are at least 30. Then, if σ_1 and σ_2 are unknown but we have reason to believe that $\sigma_1 = \sigma_2$, we can pool the standard deviations. Using sample sizes n_1 and n_2, the sample test statistic $\bar{x}_1 - \bar{x}_2$ has a Student's t distribution, where

$$t = \frac{\bar{x}_1 - \bar{x}_2}{s\sqrt{\dfrac{1}{n_1} + \dfrac{1}{n_2}}} \quad \text{with degrees of freedom } d.f. = n_1 + n_2 - 2$$

where the **pooled standard deviation** s is

$$s = \sqrt{\frac{(n_1 - 1)s_1^2 + (n_2 - 1)s_2^2}{n_1 + n_2 - 2}}$$

Hypothesis tests: Use H_0: $\mu_1 = \mu_2$ and an appropriate alternate hypothesis. The test statistic is

$$t = \frac{\bar{x}_1 - \bar{x}_2}{s\sqrt{\dfrac{1}{n_1} + \dfrac{1}{n_2}}} \quad \text{with } d.f. = n_1 + n_2 - 2$$

A c confidence interval: $(\bar{x}_1 - \bar{x}_2) - E < \mu_1 - \mu_2 < (\bar{x}_1 - \bar{x}_2) + E$

where $\quad E = t_c\, s\sqrt{\dfrac{1}{n_1} + \dfrac{1}{n_2}}$

$t_c = $ critical value for confidence level c and degrees of freedom $d.f. = n_1 + n_2 - 2$

Note: With statistical software, select the pooled variance or equal variance options.

There are many situations in which we want to compare means from populations having standard deviations that are equal. This method applies even if the standard deviations are known to be only approximately equal. Consider Problem 9 regarding average incidence of fox rabies in two regions. For region I, $n_1 = 16$, $\bar{x}_1 = 4.75$, and $s_1 \approx 2.82$ and for region II, $n_2 = 15$, $\bar{x}_2 \approx 3.93$, and $s_2 \approx 2.43$. The two sample standard deviations are sufficiently close that we can assume $\sigma_1 = \sigma_2$.
(a) Use the method of pooled standard deviation to redo Problem 9(a).
(b) Use the method of pooled standard deviation to redo Problem 9(b).

15. *Critical Region Method: Testing $\mu_1 - \mu_2$; σ_1, σ_2 Unknown* Redo Problem 5(a) using the critical region method and compare your results to those obtained using the *P*-value method.

16. *Critical Region Method: Testing $\mu_1 - \mu_2$; σ_1, σ_2 Known* Redo Problem 1(a) using the critical region method and compare your results to those obtained using the *P*-value method.

10.3   Inferences About the Difference of Two Proportions $p_1 - p_2$

Testing a Difference of Proportions $p_1 - p_2$

Is the population proportion of people favoring more wilderness areas different between men and women, between younger people and older people, between ranchers and energy employees, etc.? To answer questions of this type, we explore the sampling distribution $\hat{p}_1 - \hat{p}_2$ from two independent binomial experiments.

◇ **THEOREM 10.3** Suppose we have two independent binomial experiments. That is, outcomes from one binomial experiment are in no way paired with outcomes from the other. We use the notation

Binomial Experiment 1	*Binomial Experiment 2*
n_1 = number of trials	n_2 = number of trials
r_1 = number of successes	r_2 = number of successes
p_1 = population probability of success on a single trial	p_2 = population probability of success on a single trial

For *large* values of n_1 and n_2, the distribution of sample differences

$$\hat{p}_1 - \hat{p}_2 = \frac{r_1}{n_1} - \frac{r_2}{n_2}$$

is closely approximated by a *normal distribution* with mean μ and standard deviation σ as shown:

$$\mu = p_1 - p_2 \qquad \sigma = \sqrt{\frac{p_1 q_1}{n_1} + \frac{p_2 q_2}{n_2}}$$

where $q_1 = 1 - p_1$ and $q_2 = 1 - p_2$.   ◇

Pooled estimate $\bar{p}$

For most practical problems involving a comparison of two binomial populations, the experimenters will want to test the null hypothesis $p_1 = p_2$. Consequently, this is the type of test we shall consider. Since the values of p_1 and p_2 are unknown, and since specific values are not assumed under the null hypothesis $p_1 = p_2$, the best estimate for the common value is the total number of successes $(r_1 + r_2)$ divided by the total number of trials $(n_1 + n_2)$. If we denote this *pooled estimate of proportion* by $\bar{p}$ (read "p bar"), then

$$\bar{p} = \frac{r_1 + r_2}{n_1 + n_2}$$

This formula gives the best sample estimate $\bar{p}$ for p_1 and p_2 *under the assumption that $p_1 = p_2$*. Also, $\bar{q} = 1 - \bar{p}$.

Criteria for using the normal approximation to the binomial

◇ **COMMENT** For most practical applications, the sample sizes n_1 and n_2 are considered large samples if each of the four quantities

$$n_1\bar{p} \qquad n_1\bar{q} \qquad n_2\bar{p} \qquad n_2\bar{q}$$

is larger than 5 (see Section 7.6). ◇

Theorem 10.3 leads to the following procedure for testing $p_1 - p_2$.

PROCEDURE

How to test a difference of proportions $p_1 - p_2$

Consider two independent binomial experiments.

Binomial Experiment 1	*Binomial Experiment 2*
n_1 = number of trials	n_2 = number of trials
r_1 = number of successes out of n_1 trials	r_2 = number of successes out of n_2 trials
$\hat{p}_1 = \dfrac{r_1}{n_1}$	$\hat{p}_2 = \dfrac{r_2}{n_2}$
p_1 = population probability of success on a single trial	p_2 = population probability of success on a single trial

1. Use the *null hypothesis* of no difference, $H_0: p_1 - p_2 = 0$. In the context of the application, choose the *alternate hypothesis*. Set the *level of significance* α.

2. The null hypothesis claims that $p_1 = p_2$; therefore, *pooled best estimates* for the population probabilities of success and failure are

$$\bar{p} = \frac{r_1 + r_2}{n_1 + n_2} \qquad \text{and} \qquad \bar{q} = 1 - \bar{p}$$

The number of trials should be sufficiently large so that all four quantities $n_1\bar{p}$, $n_1\bar{q}$, $n_2\bar{p}$, and $n_2\bar{q}$ are each larger than 5. In this case you compute the sample *test statistic*

$$z = \frac{\hat{p}_1 - \hat{p}_2}{\sqrt{\dfrac{\bar{p}\,\bar{q}}{n_1} + \dfrac{\bar{p}\,\bar{q}}{n_2}}}$$

3. Use the standard normal distribution and a type of test, one-tailed or two-tailed, to find the *P-value* corresponding to the sample test statistic.

4. *Conclude the test.* If P-value $\le \alpha$, then reject H_0. If P-value $> \alpha$, then do not reject H_0.

5. *State your conclusion* in the context of the application.

EXAMPLE 7

Testing the difference of proportions

The Macek County Clerk wishes to improve voter registration. One method under consideration is to send reminders in the mail to all citizens in the county who are eligible to register. As part of a pilot study to determine if this method will actually improve voter registration, a random sample of 1250 potential voters was taken. This sample was then randomly divided into two groups.

Group 1: There were 625 people in this group. No reminders to register were sent to them. The number of potential voters from this group who registered was 295.

Group 2: This group also contained 625 people. Reminders were sent in the mail to each member in the group, and the number who registered to vote was 350.

The county clerk claims that the proportion of people who registered was significantly greater in group 2. On the basis of this claim, the clerk recommends that the project be funded for the entire population of Macek County. Use a 5% level of significance to test the claim that the proportion of potential voters who registered was greater in group 2, the group that received reminders.

SOLUTION:

(a) Note that $\alpha = 0.05$. Let p_1 be the proportion of voters who registered from group 1, and let p_2 be the proportion who registered from group 2. The null hypothesis is that there is no difference in proportions, so

$$H_0: p_1 = p_2 \quad \text{or} \quad H_0: p_1 - p_2 = 0$$

The alternate hypothesis is that the proportion of voters who registered is greater for the group that received reminders.

$$H_1: p_1 < p_2 \quad \text{or} \quad H_1: p_1 - p_2 < 0$$

(b) Compute the sample statistic $\hat{p}_1 - \hat{p}_2$ and convert it to a z value.

● **CALCULATOR NOTE** Carry the values for $\hat{p}_1$, $\hat{p}_2$, and the pooled estimates $\bar{p}$ and $\bar{q}$ to at least three places after the decimal. Then round the z value of the corresponding test statistic to two places after the decimal.

For the first group, the number of successes is $r_1 = 295$ out of $n_1 = 625$ trials. For the second group, there are $r_2 = 350$ successes out of $n_2 = 625$ trials. Since

$$\hat{p}_1 = \frac{r_1}{n_1} = \frac{295}{625} = 0.472 \quad \text{and} \quad \hat{p}_2 = \frac{r_2}{n_2} = \frac{350}{625} = 0.560$$

then

$$\hat{p}_1 - \hat{p}_2 = 0.472 - 0.560 = -0.088$$

To convert this $\hat{p}_1 - \hat{p}_2$ value to a z value, we need to find the *pooled estimate* $\bar{p}$ for the common values of p_1 and p_2 and the corresponding value for $\bar{q}$.

$$\bar{p} = \frac{r_1 + r_2}{n_1 + n_2} = \frac{295 + 350}{625 + 625} = 0.516 \quad \text{and} \quad \bar{q} = 1 - \bar{p} = 0.484$$

Using these values, we find that

$$z = \frac{\hat{p}_1 - \hat{p}_2}{\sqrt{\dfrac{\bar{p}\bar{q}}{n_1} + \dfrac{\bar{p}\bar{q}}{n_2}}} = \frac{-0.088}{\sqrt{\dfrac{(0.516)(0.484)}{625} + \dfrac{(0.516)(0.484)}{625}}} \approx -3.11$$

(c) Find the P-value and sketch the area on the standard normal curve.
Figure 10-9 shows the P-value. This is a left-tailed test, so the P-value is the area to the left of −3.11. Using the standard normal distribution (Table 3 of the Appendix), we find P-value = $P(z < -3.11) \approx 0.0009$.

FIGURE 10-9

P-value

FIGURE 10-10

Critical Region, $\alpha = 0.05$

(d) Conclude the test.
Since P-value of $0.0009 \le 0.05$ for α, we reject H_0.

(e) Interpret the results.
At the 5% level of significance, the data indicate that the population proportion of potential voters who registered was greater in group 2, the group that received reminders.

(f) **Critical region method (optional):** Use the critical region method to conclude the test at the 5% level of significance. Compare your results with the P-value method.
In part (b), we found that the sample test statistic is $z = -3.11$. In Table 3(c) of the Appendix, we see that the critical value $z_0 = -1.645$ for a left-tailed test with $\alpha = 0.05$. In Figure 10-10, we see that the sample test statistic falls in the critical region, so we reject H_0. This conclusion is consistent with the conclusion obtained using the P-value method. There is sufficient evidence to conclude that at the 5% level of significance, the population of potential voters who registered was greater in the group receiving reminders.   ◊

GUIDED EXERCISE 6

Testing the difference of proportions

In Example 7 about voter registration, suppose that a random sample of 1100 potential voters was randomly divided into two groups.

  Group 1: 500 potential voters; no registration reminders sent; 248 registered to vote

  Group 2: 600 potential voters; registration reminders sent; 332 registered to vote

Do these data support the claim that the proportion of voters who registered was greater in the group that received reminders than in the group that did not? Use a 1% level of significance.

(a) What is α? State H_0 and H_1.

$\Rightarrow$ $\alpha = 0.01$. As before, $H_0: p_1 = p_2$ and $H_1: p_1 < p_2$.

(b) Under the null hypothesis $p_1 = p_2$, calculate the *pooled estimates* $\overline{p}$ and $\overline{q}$.

$\Rightarrow$ $n_1 = 500$, $r_1 = 248$; $n_2 = 600$, $r_2 = 332$

$$\overline{p} = \frac{r_1 + r_2}{n_1 + n_2} = \frac{248 + 332}{500 + 600} \approx 0.527$$

$$\overline{q} = 1 - \overline{p} \approx 1 - 0.527 \approx 0.473$$

(c) What is the value of the sample test statistic $\hat{p}_1 - \hat{p}_2$?

$\Rightarrow$ $\hat{p}_1 = \dfrac{r_1}{n_1} = \dfrac{248}{500} = 0.496$ $\qquad$ $\hat{p}_2 = \dfrac{r_2}{n_2} = \dfrac{332}{600} \approx 0.553$

$\hat{p}_1 - \hat{p}_2 = -0.057$

(d) Convert the sample test statistic $\hat{p}_1 - \hat{p}_2 = -0.057$ to a z value.

$\Rightarrow$ $z = \dfrac{\hat{p}_1 - \hat{p}_2}{\sqrt{\dfrac{\overline{p}\,\overline{q}}{n_1} + \dfrac{\overline{p}\,\overline{q}}{n_2}}} = \dfrac{-0.057}{\sqrt{\dfrac{(0.527)(0.473)}{500} + \dfrac{(0.527)(0.473)}{600}}} \approx -1.89$

(e) Find the *P*-value and sketch the area on the standard normal curve.

$\Rightarrow$ Figure 10-11 shows the *P*-value. It is the area to the left of $z = -1.89$. Using Table 3 of the Appendix, we find *P*-value = $P(z < -1.89) = 0.0294$.

FIGURE 10-11 *P*-value

(f) Conclude the test and interpret the results in the context of the application.

$\Rightarrow$ Since *P*-value of 0.0294 > 0.01 for α, we cannot reject H_0. At the 1% level of significance, the data do not support the claim that the reminders increase the proportion of registered voters.

Estimating a Difference of Proportions $p_1 - p_2$

We conclude this section with a discussion of confidence intervals for $p_1 - p_2$, the difference of two proportions from two independent binomial probability distributions. Theorem 10.3 gives us the basis for constructing such confidence intervals. Using the notation of Theorem 10.3, recall that for sufficiently large sample sizes n_1 and n_2, the sampling distribution $\hat{p}_1 - \hat{p}_2$ of differences of proportions from two independent binomial probability distributions is approximately normal, with mean $\mu = p_1 - p_2$ and standard deviation $\sigma = \sqrt{p_1 q_1/n_1 - p_2 q_2/n_2}$.

There is one technical difficulty in computing the standard deviation σ of the $\hat{p}_1 - \hat{p}_2$ distribution. We don't know the values of p_1 or p_2. However, if all four quantities $n_1 \hat{p}_1$, $n_1 \hat{q}_1$, $n_2 \hat{p}_2$, and $n_2 \hat{q}_2$ are greater than 5, then a good approximation for the standard deviation σ of the $\hat{p}_1 - \hat{p}_2$ distribution is given by

$$\sigma \approx \hat{\sigma} = \sqrt{\frac{\hat{p}_1 \hat{q}_1}{n_1} + \frac{\hat{p}_2 \hat{q}_2}{n_2}}$$

This leads to the following procedure for confidence intervals.

PROCEDURE

How to find a confidence interval for $p_1 - p_2$

Consider two independent binomial experiments.

Binomial Experiment 1	*Binomial Experiment 2*
n_1 = number of trials	n_2 = number of trials
r_1 = number of successes out of n_1 trials	r_2 = number of successes out of n_2 trials
$\hat{p}_1 = \dfrac{r_1}{n_1}; \quad \hat{q}_1 = 1 - \hat{p}_1$	$\hat{p}_2 = \dfrac{r_2}{n_2}; \quad \hat{q}_2 = 1 - \hat{p}_2$
p_1 = population probability of success	p_2 = population probability of success

The number of trials should be sufficiently large so that all four of the following inequalities are true:

$$n_1 \hat{p}_1 > 5; \quad n_1 \hat{q}_1 > 5; \quad n_2 \hat{p}_2 > 5; \quad n_2 \hat{q}_2 > 5$$

Confidence interval for $p_1 - p_2$

$$(\hat{p}_1 - \hat{p}_2) - E \le p_1 - p_2 \le (\hat{p}_1 - \hat{p}_2) + E$$

where

$$E \approx z_c \hat{\sigma} = z_c \sqrt{\frac{\hat{p}_1 \hat{q}_1}{n_1} + \frac{\hat{p}_2 \hat{q}_2}{n_2}}$$

c = confidence level, $0 < c < 1$

z_c = critical value for confidence level c based on the standard normal distribution (See Table 3(b) of the Appendix for commonly used values.)

EXAMPLE 8

Confidence interval for $p_1 - p_2$

In his book *Secrets of Sleep*, Professor Borbely describes research on dreams in the sleep laboratory at the University of Zurich Medical School. During normal sleep, there is a phase known as *REM* (rapid eye movement). For most people, REM sleep occurs about every 90 minutes or so, and it is thought that dreams occur just before or during the REM phase. Using electronic equipment in the sleep laboratory, it is possible to detect the REM phase in a sleeping person. If a person is wakened immediately after the REM phase, he or she usually can describe a dream that has just taken place. Based on a study of over 650 people in the Zurich sleep laboratory, it was found that about one-third of all dream reports contain feelings of fear, anxiety, or aggression. There is a conjecture that if a person is in a good mood when going to sleep, the proportion of "bad" dreams (fear, anxiety, aggression) might be reduced.

Suppose that two groups of subjects were randomly chosen for a sleep study. In group I, before going to sleep, the subjects spent 1 hour watching a comedy movie. In this group, there were a total of $n_1 = 175$ dreams recorded, of which $r_1 = 49$ were dreams with feelings of anxiety, fear, or aggression. In group II, the subjects did not watch a movie but simply went to sleep. In this group, there were a total of $n_2 = 180$ dreams recorded, of which $r_2 = 63$ were dreams with feelings of anxiety, fear, or aggression.

(a) Why could groups I and II be considered independent binomial distributions? Why do we have a "large-sample" situation?

SOLUTION: Since the two groups were chosen randomly, it is reasonable to assume that neither group's response would be related to the other's. In both groups, each recorded dream could be thought of as a trial, with success being a dream with feelings of fear, anxiety, or aggression.

$$\hat{p}_1 = \frac{r_1}{n_1} = \frac{49}{175} = 0.28 \quad \text{and} \quad \hat{q}_1 = 1 - \hat{p}_1 = 0.72$$

$$\hat{p}_2 = \frac{r_2}{n_2} = \frac{63}{180} = 0.35 \quad \text{and} \quad \hat{q}_2 = 1 - \hat{p}_2 = 0.65$$

Since

$$n_1\hat{p}_1 = 49 > 5 \qquad n_1\hat{q}_1 = 126 > 5$$
$$n_2\hat{p}_2 = 63 > 5 \qquad n_2\hat{q}_2 = 117 > 5$$

then large-sample theory is appropriate.

(b) What is $p_1 - p_2$? Compute a 95% confidence interval for $p_1 - p_2$.

SOLUTION: p_1 is the population proportion of successes (bad dreams) for all people who watch comedy movies before bed. Thus, p_1 can be thought of as the percentage of bad dreams for all people who are in a "good mood" when they go to bed. Likewise, p_2 is the percentage of bad dreams for the population of all people who just go to bed (no movie). The difference $p_1 - p_2$ is the population difference.

To find a confidence interval for $p_1 - p_2$, we need the values of z_c, $\hat{\sigma}$, and then E. From Table 3(b) of the Appendix, we see that $z_{0.95} = 1.96$, so

$$\hat{\sigma} = \sqrt{\frac{\hat{p}_1\hat{q}_1}{n_1} + \frac{\hat{p}_2\hat{q}_2}{n_2}} = \sqrt{\frac{(0.28)(0.72)}{175} + \frac{(0.35)(0.65)}{180}}$$

$$\approx \sqrt{0.0024} \approx 0.0492$$

$$E = z_c\hat{\sigma} = 1.96(0.0492) \approx 0.096$$

$$(\hat{p}_1 - \hat{p}_2) - E < p_1 - p_2 < (\hat{p}_1 - \hat{p}_2) + E$$

$$(0.28 - 0.35) - 0.096 < p_1 - p_2 < (0.28 - 0.35) + 0.096$$

$$-0.166 < p_1 - p_2 < 0.026$$

(c) Explain the meaning of the confidence interval that you constructed in part (b).

SOLUTION: We are 95% sure that the interval between -16.6% and 2.6% is one that contains the percentage difference of "bad" dreams for group I and group II. Since the interval -0.166 to 0.026 is not all negative (or all positive), we cannot say that $p_1 - p_2 < 0$ (or $p_1 - p_2 > 0$). Thus, at the 95% confidence level, we *cannot* conclude that $p_1 < p_2$ or $p_1 > p_2$. The comedy movies before bed help some people reduce the percentage of "bad" dreams, but at the 95% confidence level, we cannot say that the *population difference* is reduced.   ◊

TECH NOTE   The TI-84Plus and TI-83Plus calculators and Minitab support both testing and confidence intervals for the difference of proportions. **TI-84Plus/TI-83Plus** Use the **STAT** key and highlight **TESTS**. The menu choices **B:2-PropZInt** and **6:2-PropZTest** provide confidence intervals and testing, respectively. Note that the symbol x is used to designate the number of successes r.

Minitab Use the menu choices **STAT ➤ Basic Statistics ➤ 2 proportions**. In the dialogue box, under Options, select the null and alternate hypotheses and set the confidence level.

VIEWPOINT   *What's the Difference?*

Will two 15-minute piano lessons a week significantly improve a child's analytical reasoning skills? Why piano? Why not computer keyboard instruction or maybe voice lessons? Professor Frances Rauscher, University of Wisconsin, and Professor Gordon Shaw, University of California at Irvine, claim that there is a difference! How could this be measured? A large number of piano students were given complicated tests of mental ability. Independent control groups of other students were given the same tests. Techniques involving the study of differences of means and proportions were used to draw the conclusion that students taking piano lessons did better on tests measuring analytical reasoning skills (Reported in *The Denver Post*).

SECTION 10.3   PROBLEMS

Please provide the following information for Problems 1–8.
(a) What is the level of significance? State the null and alternate hypotheses.
(b) What sampling distribution will you use? What assumptions are you making? What is the value of the sample test statistic?

(c) Find the *P*-value. Sketch the sampling distribution and show the area corresponding to the *P*-value.
(d) Based on your answers in parts (a) to (c), will you reject or fail to reject the null hypothesis? Are the data statistically significant at level α?
(e) State your conclusion in the context of the application.

Note: Answers may vary due to rounding.

1. *Federal Tax Money: Art Funding* Would you favor spending more federal tax money on the arts? This question was asked by a research group on behalf of *The National Institute* (Reference: *Painting by Numbers*, J. Wypijewski, University of California Press). Of a random sample of $n_1 = 220$ women, $r_1 = 59$ responded yes. Another random sample of $n_2 = 175$ men showed that $r_2 = 56$ responded yes. Does this information indicate a difference (either way) between the population proportion of women and the population proportion of men who favor spending more federal tax dollars on the arts? Use $\alpha = 0.05$.

2. *Art Funding: Politics* Would you favor spending more federal tax money on the arts? This question was asked by a research group on behalf of *The National Institute* (Reference: *Painting by Numbers*, J. Wypijewski, University of California Press). Of a random sample of $n_1 = 93$ politically conservative voters, $r_1 = 21$ responded yes. Another random sample of $n_2 = 83$ politically moderate voters showed that $r_2 = 22$ responded yes. Does this information indicate that the population proportion of conservative voters inclined to spend more federal tax money on funding the arts is less than the proportion of moderate voters so inclined? Use $\alpha = 0.05$.

3. *Sociology: Trusting People* Generally speaking, would you say that most people can be trusted? A random sample of $n_1 = 250$ people in Chicago ages 18–25 showed that $r_1 = 45$ said yes. Another random sample of $n_2 = 280$ people in Chicago ages 35–45 showed that $r_2 = 71$ said yes (based on information from the *National Opinion Research Center*, University of Chicago). Does this indicate that the population proportion of trusting people in Chicago is higher for the older group? Use $\alpha = 0.05$.

4. *Political Science: Voters* This problem is based on information taken from *Life in America's Fifty States*, by G. S. Thomas. A random sample of $n_1 = 288$ voters registered in the state of California showed that 141 voted in the last general election. A random sample of $n_2 = 216$ registered voters in the state of Colorado showed that 125 voted in the most recent general election. Do these data indicate that the population proportion of voter turnout in Colorado is higher than that in California? Use a 5% level of significance.

5. *Extraterrestrials: Believe It?* Based on information from *Harper's Index*, $r_1 = 37$ out of a random sample of $n_1 = 100$ adult Americans who did not attend college believe in extraterrestrials. However, out of a random sample of $n_2 = 100$ adult Americans who did attend college, $r_2 = 47$ claim that they believe in extraterrestrials. Does this indicate that the proportion of people who attended college and who believe in extraterrestrials is higher than the proportion who did not attend college? Use $\alpha = 0.01$.

6. *Art: Politics* Do you prefer paintings in which the people are fully clothed? This question was asked by a professional survey group on behalf of the National Arts Society (see reference in Problem 2). A random sample of $n_1 = 59$ people who are conservative voters showed that $r_1 = 45$ said yes. Another random sample of $n_2 = 62$ people who are liberal voters showed that $r_2 = 36$ said yes. Does this indicate that the population proportion of conservative voters who prefer art with fully clothed people is higher? Use $\alpha = 0.05$.

7. *Hotels: Nonsmoking* A random sample of $n_1 = 378$ hotel guests was taken 1 year ago, and it was found that $r_1 = 194$ requested nonsmoking rooms. Recently, a random sample of $n_2 = 516$ hotel guests showed that $r_2 = 320$ requested nonsmoking rooms. Do these data indicate that the proportion of hotel guests requesting nonsmoking rooms has increased? Use a 1% level of significance.

8. *Sociology: College Degrees* A random sample of $n_1 = 78$ women ages 21–29 in Denver showed that $r_1 = 23$ have a college degree. Another random sample of $n_2 = 73$ men in Denver in the same age group showed that $r_2 = 20$ have a college degree (based on information from *Educational Attainment in the United States,* Bureau of the Census). Does this indicate that the population proportion of Denver women ages 21–29 with college degrees is different (either way) from that of men in this age group? Use $\alpha = 0.05$.

9. *Critical Region Method: Testing $p_1 - p_2$* Redo Problem 1 using the critical region method and compare your results to those obtained using the P-value method.

10. *Critical Region Method: Testing $p_1 - p_2$* Redo Problem 2 using the critical region method and compare your results to those obtained using the P-value method.

11. *Myers-Briggs: Marriage Counseling* Isabel Myers was a pioneer in the study of personality types. She identified four basic personality preferences that are described at length in the book *A Guide to the Development and Use of the Myers-Briggs Type Indicator,* by Myers and McCaulley (Consulting Psychologists Press). Marriage counselors know that couples who have none of the four preferences in common may have a stormy marriage. Myers took a random sample of 375 married couples and found that 289 had two or more personality preferences in common. In another random sample of 571 married couples, it was found that only 23 had no preferences in common. Let p_1 be the population proportion of all married couples who have two or more personality preferences in common. Let p_2 be the population proportion of all married couples who have no personality preferences in common.
   (a) Find a 99% confidence interval for $p_1 - p_2$.
   (b) Explain the meaning of the confidence interval in part (a) in the context of this problem. Does the confidence interval contain all positive, all negative, or both positive and negative numbers? What does this tell you (at the 99% confidence level) about the proportion of married couples with two or more personality preferences in common compared with the proportion of married couples sharing no personality preferences in common?

12. *Myers-Briggs: Marriage Counseling* Most married couples have two or three personality preferences in common (see reference in Problem 11). Myers used a random sample of 375 married couples and found that 132 had three preferences in common. Another random sample of 571 couples showed that 217 had two personality preferences in common. Let p_1 be the population proportion of all married couples who have three personality preferences in common. Let p_2 be the population proportion of all married couples who have two personality preferences in common.
   (a) Find a 90% confidence interval for $p_1 - p_2$.
   (b) Examine the confidence interval in part (a) and explain what it means in the context of this problem. Does the confidence interval contain all positive, all negative, or both positive and negative numbers? What does this tell you about the proportion of married couples with three personality preferences in common compared with the proportion of couples with two preferences in common (at the 90% confidence level)?

13. *Navajo Culture: Traditional Hogans* S. C. Jett is a professor of geography at the University of California, Davis. He and a colleague, V. E. Spencer, are experts on modern Navajo culture and geography. The following information is taken from

their book *Navajo Architecture: Forms, History, Distributions* (University of Arizona Press). On the Navajo Reservation, a random sample of 210 permanent dwellings in the Fort Defiance region showed that 65 were traditional Navajo hogans. In the Indian Wells region, a random sample of 152 permanent dwellings showed that 18 were traditional hogans. Let p_1 be the population proportion of all traditional hogans in the Fort Defiance region, and let p_2 be the population proportion of all traditional hogans in the Indian Wells region.

(a) Find a 99% confidence interval for $p_1 - p_2$.

(b) Examine the confidence interval and comment on its meaning. Does it include numbers that are all positive? all negative? mixed? What if it is hypothesized that Navajo who follow the traditional culture of their people tend to occupy hogans? Comment on the confidence interval for $p_1 - p_2$ in this context.

14. *Archaeology: Cultural Affiliation* "Unknown cultural affiliations and loss of identity at high elevations." These are words used to propose the hypothesis that archaeological sites tend to lose their identity as altitude extremes are reached. This idea is based on the notion that prehistoric people tended *not* to take trade wares to temporary settings and/or isolated areas (Source: *Prehistoric New Mexico: Background for Survey*, by D. E. Stuart and R. P. Gauthier, University of New Mexico Press). As elevation zones of prehistoric people (in what is now the state of New Mexico) increased, there seemed to be a loss of artifact identification. Consider the following information.

Elevation Zone	Number of Artifacts	Number Unidentified
7000–7500 ft	112	69
5000–5500 ft	140	26

Let p_1 be the population proportion of unidentified archaeological artifacts at the elevation zone 7000–7500 ft in the given archaeological area. Let p_2 be the population proportion of unidentified archaeological artifacts at the elevation zone 5000–5500 ft in the given archaeological area.

(a) Find a 99% confidence interval for $p_1 - p_2$.

(b) Explain the meaning of the confidence interval in part (a) in the context of this problem. Does the confidence interval contain all positive numbers? all negative numbers? both positive and negative numbers? What does this tell you (at the 99% confidence level) about the population proportion of unidentified artifacts at high elevations (7000–7500 ft) compared with the population proportion of unidentified artifacts at lower elevations (5000–5500 ft)? How does this relate to the stated hypothesis?

15. *General: Different Confidence Levels*

(a) Suppose that a 95% confidence interval for a difference of proportions contains both positive and negative numbers. Will a 99% confidence interval based on the same data necessarily contain both positive and negative numbers? Explain. What about a 90% confidence interval? Explain.

(b) Suppose that a 95% confidence interval for a difference of proportions contains all positive numbers. Will a 99% confidence interval based on the same data necessarily contain all positive numbers as well? Explain. What about a 90% confidence interval? Explain.

16. *Focus Problem: Wood Duck Nests* In the Focus Problem at the beginning of this chapter, a study was described comparing the hatch ratios of wood duck nesting boxes. Group I nesting boxes were well separated from each other and well hidden by available brush. There were a total of 474 eggs in group I boxes, of which a field count

showed about 270 hatched. Group II nesting boxes were placed in highly visible locations and grouped closely together. There were a total of 805 eggs in group II boxes, of which a field count showed about 270 hatched.

(a) Find a point estimate $\hat{p}_1$ for p_1, the proportion of eggs that hatch in group I nest box placements. Find a 95% confidence interval for p_1.

(b) Find a point estimate $\hat{p}_2$ for p_2, the proportion of eggs that hatch in group II nest box placements. Find a 95% confidence interval for p_2.

(c) Find a 95% confidence interval for $p_1 - p_2$. Does the interval indicate that the proportion of eggs hatched from group I nest boxes is higher than, lower than, or equal to the proportion of eggs hatched from group II nest boxes?

(d) What conclusions about placement of nest boxes can be drawn? In the article discussed in the Focus Problem, additional concerns are raised about the higher cost of placing and maintaining group I nest boxes. Also at issue is the cost efficiency per successful wood duck hatch.

SUMMARY

In this chapter, we continued our discussion of hypothesis testing and confidence intervals. We considered paired data from dependent samples and tested the population mean μ_d of differences between the members of the data pairs. For two independent samples, we considered the population difference of means $\mu_1 - \mu_2$, where μ_1 is the population mean of the first sample and μ_2 is that of the second sample. Hypothesis tests and confidence intervals were developed for the difference of means. The sample statistic $\bar{x}_1 - \bar{x}_2$ follows a normal or Student's t distribution, depending on the given conditions and whether the population standard deviations σ_1 and σ_2 are known. Appropriate methods of testing and confidence intervals were developed for each case.

Finally, we looked at the population difference of proportions $p_1 - p_2$ from two large, independent samples. We studied both hypothesis testing and confidence intervals for the difference of proportions.

IMPORTANT WORDS & SYMBOLS

Section 10.1
Dependent samples
Data pairs
μ_d, difference of means from data pairs

Section 10.2
Independent samples

$d.f.$ for testing $\mu_1 - \mu_2$ when σ_1 and σ_2 are unknown
Pooled standard deviation

Section 10.3
Pooled estimate of proportion $\bar{p}$

VIEWPOINT

Who Watches Cable TV?

Consider the following claim: Average cable TV viewers are, generally speaking, as affluent as newspaper readers and better off than radio or magazine audiences. How do we know that this claim is true? One way to answer such a question is to construct several individual tests of difference of means. One test would compare cable TV viewers with newspaper readers, a second test would compare cable TV viewers with radio audiences, and a third test would compare cable TV viewers with magazine audiences. Another way to handle all three tests at once would be to use techniques of ANOVA (analysis of variance)—a subject often introduced in a second course in statistics. For more information and data, see *American Demographics* (Vol. 17, No. 6).

CHAPTER REVIEW PROBLEMS

For each hypothesis test in Problems 1–8, please provide the following information.

(i) What is the level of significance? State the null and alternate hypotheses.
(ii) What sampling distribution will you use? What assumptions are you making? What is the value of the sample test statistic?
(iii) Find (or estimate) the *P*-value. Sketch the sampling distribution and show the area corresponding to the *P*-value.
(iv) Based on your answers in parts (i) to (iii), will you reject or fail to reject the null hypothesis? Are the data statistically significant at level α?
(v) State your conclusion in the context of the application.

Note: For degrees of freedom *d.f.* not in the Student's *t* table, use the closest *d.f.* that is smaller. In some cases this choice will increase the *P*-value by a small amount or increase the length of a confidence interval, thereby making the answer slightly more "conservative." Answers may vary due to rounding.

1. *Agriculture: Bell Peppers* The following data represent soil water content (percent water by volume) for independent random samples of soil taken from two experimental fields growing bell peppers (Reference: *Journal of Agricultural, Biological, and Environmental Statistics*). *Note:* These data are also available with other software on the statSpace CD-ROM.

Soil water content from field I: x_1; $n_1 = 72$

15.1	11.2	10.3	10.8	16.6	8.3	9.1	12.3	9.1	14.3
10.7	16.1	10.2	15.2	8.9	9.5	9.6	11.3	14.0	11.3
15.6	11.2	13.8	9.0	8.4	8.2	12.0	13.9	11.6	16.0
9.6	11.4	8.4	8.0	14.1	10.9	13.2	13.8	14.6	10.2
11.5	13.1	14.7	12.5	10.2	11.8	11.0	12.7	10.3	10.8
11.0	12.6	10.8	9.6	11.5	10.6	11.7	10.1	9.7	9.7
11.2	9.8	10.3	11.9	9.7	11.3	10.4	12.0	11.0	10.7
8.8	11.1								

Soil water content from field II: x_2; $n_2 = 80$

12.1	10.2	13.6	8.1	13.5	7.8	11.8	7.7	8.1	9.2
14.1	8.9	13.9	7.5	12.6	7.3	14.9	12.2	7.6	8.9
13.9	8.4	13.4	7.1	12.4	7.6	9.9	26.0	7.3	7.4
14.3	8.4	13.2	7.3	11.3	7.5	9.7	12.3	6.9	7.6
13.8	7.5	13.3	8.0	11.3	6.8	7.4	11.7	11.8	7.7
12.6	7.7	13.2	13.9	10.4	12.8	7.6	10.7	10.7	10.9
12.5	11.3	10.7	13.2	8.9	12.9	7.7	9.7	9.7	11.4
11.9	13.4	9.2	13.4	8.8	11.9	7.1	8.5	14.0	14.2

(a) Use a calculator with mean and standard deviation keys to verify that $\bar{x}_1 \approx 11.42$, $s_1 \approx 2.08$, $\bar{x}_2 \approx 10.65$, and $s_2 \approx 3.03$.

(b) Let μ_1 be the population mean for x_1 and let μ_2 be the population mean for x_2. Find a 95% confidence interval for $\mu_1 - \mu_2$.

(c) Examine the confidence interval and explain what it means in the context of this problem. Does the interval consist of numbers that are all positive? all negative? of different signs? At the 95% level of confidence, is the population mean soil water content of the first field higher than that of the second field?

(d) Which distribution (standard normal or Student's t) did you use? Why? Do you need information about the soil water content distributions?

(e) Use $\alpha = 0.01$ to test the claim that the population mean soil water content of the first field is higher than that of the second.

2. *Stocks: Retail and Utility* How profitable are different sectors of the stock market? One way to answer such a question is to examine profit as a percentage of stockholder equity. A random sample of 32 retail stocks such as Toys 'Я' Us, Best Buy, and Gap was studied for x_1, profit as a percentage of stockholder equity. The result was $\bar{x}_1 = 13.7$. A random sample of 34 utility (gas and electric) stocks such as Boston Edison, Wisconsin Energy, and Texas Utilities was studied for x_2, profit as a percentage of stockholder equity. The result was $\bar{x}_2 = 10.1$ (Source: *Fortune 500*, Vol. 135, No. 8). Assume $\sigma_1 = 4.1$ and $\sigma_2 = 2.7$.

(a) Let μ_1 represent the population mean profit as a percentage of stockholder equity for retail stocks, and let μ_2 represent the population mean profit as a percentage of stockholder equity for utility stocks. Find a 95% confidence interval for $\mu_1 - \mu_2$.

(b) Examine the confidence interval and explain what it means in the context of this problem. Does the interval consist of numbers that are all positive? all negative? of different signs? At the 95% level of confidence, does it appear that the profit as a percentage of stockholder equity for retail stocks is higher than that for utility stocks?

(c) Test the claim that the profit as a percentage of stockholder equity for retail stocks is higher than that for utility stocks. Use $\alpha = 0.01$.

3. *Wildlife: Wolves* A random sample of 18 adult male wolves from the Canadian Northwest Territories gave an average weight $\bar{x}_1 = 98$ lb with estimated sample standard deviation $s_1 = 6.5$ lb. Another sample of 24 adult male wolves from Alaska gave an average weight $\bar{x}_2 = 90$ lb with estimated sample standard deviation $s_2 = 7.3$ lb (Source: *The Wolf*, by L. D. Mech, University of Minnesota Press).

(a) Let μ_1 represent the population mean weight of adult male wolves from the Northwest Territories, and let μ_2 represent the population mean weight of adult male wolves from Alaska. Find a 75% confidence interval for $\mu_1 - \mu_2$.

(b) Examine the confidence interval and explain what it means in the context of this problem. Does the interval consist of numbers that are all positive? all negative? of different signs? At the 75% level of confidence, does it appear that the average weight of adult male wolves from the Northwest Territories is greater than that of the Alaska wolves?

(c) Test the claim that the average weight of adult male wolves from the Northwest Territories is different from that of Alaska wolves. Use $\alpha = 0.01$.

4. *Wildlife: Wolves* A random sample of 17 wolf litters in Ontario, Canada, gave an average of $\bar{x}_1 = 4.9$ wolf pups per litter with estimated sample standard deviation $s_1 = 1.0$. Another random sample of 6 wolf litters in Finland gave an average of $\bar{x}_2 = 2.8$ wolf pups per litter with sample standard deviation $s_2 = 1.2$ (see source for Problem 3).

(a) Find an 85% confidence interval for $\mu_1 - \mu_2$, the difference in population mean litter size between Ontario and Finland.

(b) Examine the confidence interval and explain what it means in the context of this problem. Does the interval consist of numbers that are all positive? all negative? of different signs? At the 85% level of confidence, does it appear that the average litter size of wolf pups in Ontario is greater than the average litter size in Finland?

(c) Test the claim that the average litter size of wolf pups in Ontario is greater than the average litter size of wolf pups in Finland. Use $\alpha = 0.01$.

5. *Survey Response: Validity* The book *Survey Responses: An Evaluation of Their Validity*, by E. J. Wentland and K. Smith (Academic Press), includes studies reporting accuracy of answers to questions from surveys. A study by Locander et al. considered the question, "Are you a registered voter?" Accuracy of response was confirmed by a check of city voting records. Two methods of survey were used: a face-to-face interview and a telephone interview. A random sample of 93 people was asked the voter registration question face to face. Seventy-nine respondents gave accurate answers (as verified by city records). Another random sample of 83 people was asked the same question during a telephone interview. Seventy-four respondents gave accurate answers. Assume that the samples are representative of the general population.

(a) Let p_1 be the population proportion of all people who answer the voter registration question accurately during a face-to-face interview. Let p_2 be the population proportion of all people who answer the question accurately during a telephone interview. Find a 95% confidence interval for $p_1 - p_2$.

(b) Does the interval contain numbers that are all positive? all negative? mixed? Comment on the meaning of the confidence interval in the context of this problem. At the 95% level, do you detect any difference in the proportion of accurate responses from face-to-face interviews compared with the proportion of accurate responses from telephone interviews?

(c) Test the claim that there is a difference in the proportion of accurate responses from face-to-face interviews compared with telephone interviews. Use $\alpha = 0.05$.

6. *Survey Response: Validity* Locander et al. (see reference in Problem 5) also studied the accuracy of responses on questions involving more sensitive material than voter registration. From public records, individuals were identified as having been charged with drunken driving not less than 6 months or more than 12 months from the starting date of the study. Two random samples from this group were studied. In the first sample of 30 individuals, the respondents were asked in a face-to-face interview if they had been charged with drunken driving in the last 12 months. Of these 30 people interviewed face-to-face, 16 answered the question accurately. The second random sample consisted of 46 people who had been charged with drunken driving. During a telephone interview, 25 of these responded accurately to the question asking if they had been charged with drunken driving during the past 12 months. Assume that the samples are representative of all people recently charged with drunken driving.

(a) Let p_1 represent the population proportion of all people with recent charges of drunken driving who respond accurately to a face-to-face interview asking if they have been charged with drunken driving during the past 12 months. Let p_2 represent the population proportion of people who respond accurately to the same question when it is asked in a telephone interview. Find a 90% confidence interval for $p_1 - p_2$.

(b) Does the interval found in part (a) contain numbers that are all positive? all negative? mixed? Comment on the meaning of the confidence interval in the context of this problem. At the 90% level, do you detect any differences in the proportion of accurate responses to the question from face-to-face interviews as compared with the proportion of accurate responses from telephone interviews?

(c) Test the claim that there is a difference in the proportion of accurate responses from face-to-face interviews compared with the proportion of accurate responses from telephone interviews. Use $\alpha = 0.05$.

7. *Marketing: Sporting Goods* A marketing consultant was hired to visit a random sample of five sporting goods stores across the state of California. Each store was part of a large franchise of sporting goods stores. The consultant taught the managers of each store better ways to advertise and display their goods. The net sales for 1 month before and 1 month after the consultant's visit were recorded as follows for each store (in thousands of dollars):

Store	1	2	3	4	5
Before visit	57.1	94.6	49.2	77.4	43.2
After visit	63.5	101.8	57.8	81.2	41.9

Do the data indicate that the average net sales improved? (Use $\alpha = 0.05$.)

8. *Psychology: Creative Thinking* Six sets of identical twins were randomly selected from a population of identical twins. One child was taken at random from each pair to form an experimental group. These children participated in a program designed to promote creative thinking. The other child from each pair was part of the control group that did not participate in the program to promote creative thinking. At the end of the program, a creative problem-solving test was given with the results shown in the following table:

Twin pair	A	B	C	D	E	F
Experimental group	53	35	12	25	33	47
Control group	39	21	5	18	21	42

Higher scores indicate better performance in creative problem solving. Do the data support the claim that the program of the experimental group did promote creative problem solving? (Use $\alpha = 0.01$.)

DATA HIGHLIGHTS: GROUP PROJECTS

Break into small groups and discuss the following topic. Organize a brief outline in which you summarize the main points of your group discussion.

"Sweets May Not Be Culprit in Hyper Kids" was a *USA Today* (February 3, 1994) headline reporting results of a study that appeared in the *New England Journal of Medicine*.

In this study, the subjects were 25 normal preschoolers aged 3 to 5, and 23 kids aged 6 to 10, who had been described as "sensitive to sugar." The kids and their families were put on three different diets for 3 weeks each. One diet was high in sugar, one was low in sugar and contained aspartame, and one was low in sugar and contained saccharin. The diets were all free of additives, artificial food coloring, preservatives, and chocolate. All food in the households was removed, and then meals were delivered to the families. Researchers gathered information about the kids' behavior from parents, babysitters, and teachers. In addition, researchers tested the kids for memory, concentration, reading, and math skills. The result: "We couldn't find any difference in terms of their behavior or their learning on any of the three diets," said Mark Wolraich, professor of pediatrics at Vanderbilt University Medical Center, who oversaw the project. In another interview, Dr. Wolraich was quoted as saying, "Our study would say there is no evidence sugar has an adverse effect on children's behavior."

(a) This research involved comparisons of several means, not just two. However, let us take a simplified view of the problem and consider the difference in behavior when children consumed the diet with sugar compared with their behavior when they consumed the diet with aspartame and low sugar. List some variables that might be measured to reflect the behavior of the children.

(b) Let's assume that the general null hypothesis was that there is no difference in children's behavior when they have a diet high in sugar. Was the evidence sufficient to allow the researchers to reject the null hypothesis and conclude that there are differences in children's behavior when they have a diet high in sugar? When we cannot reject H_0, have we *proved* that H_0 is true? In your own words, paraphrase the comments made by Dr. Wolraich.

LINKING CONCEPTS: WRITING PROJECTS

Discuss each of the following topics in class or review the topics on your own. Then write a brief but complete essay in which you summarize the main points. Please include formulas and graphs as appropriate.

Is there a relationship between confidence intervals and two-tailed hypothesis tests? The answer is yes. Let c be the level of confidence used to construct a confidence interval from sample data. Let α be the level of significance for a two-tailed hypothesis test. The following statement applies to hypothesis tests of the mean.

> For a two-tailed hypothesis test with level of significance α and null hypothesis H_0: $\mu = k$, we *reject* H_0 whenever k falls *outside* the $c = 1 - \alpha$ confidence interval for μ based on the sample data. When k falls within the $c = 1 - \alpha$ confidence interval, we do not reject H_0.
>
> For a one-tailed hypothesis test with level of significance α and null hypothesis H_0: $\mu = k$, we *reject* H_0 whenever k falls *outside* the $c = 1 - 2\alpha$ confidence interval for μ based on the sample data. When k falls within the $c = 1 - 2\alpha$ confidence interval, we do not reject H_0.

A corresponding relationship between confidence intervals and two-tailed hypothesis tests is also valid for other parameters such as p, $\mu_1 - \mu_2$, and $p_1 - p_2$.

(a) Consider the hypotheses H_0: $\mu_1 - \mu_2 = 0$ and H_1: $\mu_1 - \mu_2 \neq 0$. Suppose a 95% confidence interval for $\mu_1 - \mu_2$ contains only positive numbers. Should you reject the null hypothesis when $\alpha = 0.05$? Why or why not?

(b) Consider the hypotheses H_0: $p_1 - p_2 = 0$ and H_1: $p_1 - p_2 > 0$. Suppose a 98% confidence interval for $p_1 - p_2$ contains only positive numbers. Should you reject or fail to reject H_0 at the $\alpha = 0.01$ level of significance?

Using Technology

TI-84PLUS/TI-83PLUS • EXCEL • MINITAB • SPSS

APPLICATION

Paired Difference Test

Suppose a random sample of eight nurses' schedules were changed from the day shift to a rotating shift of some night work and some day work. For each of these nurses, the information shown in the table below was recorded about level of tension and anxiety at the end of a day shift and also at the end of a night shift.

Data for Nurses Working Both Shifts

Nurse	1	2	3	4	5	6	7	8
Day shift (B)	1.5	3	2	3	2	2	1	2
Night shift (A)	3.5	2	4	4	3.5	2	3.5	3

(a) Explain why the sample data for the day shift cannot be thought of as independent of the sample data for the night shift.

(b) Let us say that A is the random variable representing tension levels of night nurses and B is the random variable representing tension levels of day nurses. If we wanted to test the claim that nurses have a higher level of tension after the night shift, what would we use for the null hypothesis? What would we use for the alternate hypothesis? Choose the appropriate hypotheses and enter your choices on the computer. Use a 2% level of significance. Shall we accept or reject the claim that after a night shift, nurses express more feelings of tension on average than they do after a day shift?

(c) What is the smallest level of significance at which these data will allow us to accept the claim that after a night shift, nurses express more feelings of tension?

Technology Hints: Paired Difference Test

TI-84Plus/TI-83Plus

Enter the first number of each data pair in the list L_1 and the corresponding value in the second list L_2. Create the list L_3 by subtracting L_2 from L_1. List L_3 contains the differences d. Our next step is to conduct a t test on the differences in L_3. Press **STAT**, select **TESTS**, and choose **Option 2:T-Test.** Use **Inpt:Data.** The value for μ_0 is 0 because we are testing the hypothesis $H_0: \mu_0 = 0$. Indicate that the data are in list L_3 with **Freq: 1.** Select the appropriate symbol ($\neq$, $<$, or $>$) for the alternate hypothesis, and then choose **Calculate,** which gives the value of the sample test statistic along with its t value and P-value, or **Draw,** which shows the area corresponding to the P-value of the sample test statistic and gives the t value and P-value of the sample test statistic.

Excel

Enter the data in two columns. Then use the menu choices ➤ **Tools** ➤ **Data Analysis** ➤ **t-Test: Paired Two-Sample for Means.** The output contains the mean and variance for each data column, the degrees of freedom for the test, the sample t statistic, the P-value for a one-tailed test, the P-value for a two-tailed test, and the critical values t_0 for the specified level of significance for both a one-tailed test and a two-tailed test.

Minitab

Enter the data in two columns. Then use the menu selections ➤ **Stats** ➤ **Basic Statistics** ➤ **Paired-t.** The output includes an option for a confidence interval. Other items include the number of data pairs n, the mean, the standard deviation, and the standard error of the mean, for each data set as well as for the differences. The t value of the sample test statistic is given along with the P-value. There is also an option to generate a histogram, dotplot, or boxplot for the differences.

SPSS

Enter the data in two columns in the Data View window. In the Variable View window, name and label the two columns. Be sure the data type is numeric. Use the commands **Analyze ➤ Compare Means ➤ Paired-Samples T Test.** In the dialogue box, select Options to set the confidence level for a confidence interval. Results for a two-tailed test with H_0: $\mu_d = 0$ and H_1: $\mu_d \neq 0$ are given, with test statistic, standard deviation of the paired differences, standard error, t value of the test statistic, degrees of freedom, and P-value of the test statistic. In the output, **Sig(2-tailed)** is the P-value of the test statistic for a two-tailed test. A confidence interval for the mean of the paired differences is also given, as well as the mean, standard deviation, and standard error for each column of data.

Technology Hints: Inferences for $\mu_1 - \mu_2$

TI-84Plus/TI-83Plus

You have the option of using raw data entered into two separate lists or summary statistics. Press the **STAT** key, select the **TESTS** option, and then use option **3:2-SampZTest** or option **4:2-SampTTest.** The output gives the z ot t value of the sample test statistic and the P-value for the test. For confidence intervals, use option **9:2-SampZInt** or option **0:2-SampTTest** under the Tests option.

Excel

Enter the data in two columns. Then use the menu selection ➤ **Tools ➤ Data Analysis ➤ z-Test Two Sample for Means** if you know σ_1 and σ_2. Otherwise, use **t-Test:Two Sample Assuming Unequal Variances.** The output provides the mean and variance for each variable, the z or t value of the sample test statistic, the

P-values for a one-tailed test and a two-tailed test, and the critical z_0 or t_0 values for a one-tailed test and a two-tailed test.

Minitab

When testing the difference of means from independent samples, Minitab always uses the t distribution. The P-value of the sample test statistic will be slightly larger than the P-value generated using the normal distribution. Enter the data in two columns. Then use the menu selections ➤ **Stat ➤ Basic Statistics ➤ 2-Sample t.** Do not check equal variances. The output gives an option for a confidence interval as well as for dotplots or boxplots of the two variables. The output displays the mean, standard deviation, and standard error of the mean for each of the variables. The t value of the sample test statistic and the P-value are based on the Student's t distribution.

SPSS

Enter all the data in one column. In an adjacent column, enter a grouping variable with two values to separate the cases into two independent samples. For instance, use the value 1 to indicate that a data value is from the first sample, and the value 2 to indicate that a data value is from the second sample. Then use the menu choices **Analyze ➤ Compare Means ➤ Independent-Samples T Test.** In the dialogue box, move the column containing the data into the Test Variable box and the column containing the grouping variables into the Grouping Variable box. Then press Define Groups and enter the grouping values, such as 1 and 2. A confidence interval can be set by using the Options button. The output gives the mean, standard deviation, and standard error for each sample. Test results show the t value, degrees of freedom, and P-value for a two-tailed test for both the case of equal variances and the case of unequal variances. Confidence intervals are also included in the output.

11

Additional Topics Using Inference

Make everything as simple as possible, but no simpler.

—Albert Einstein

Today Professor Einstein's theories are well accepted as part of modern physics. However, this was not always the case. When Einstein first discovered relativity and the bending of light in large gravitational fields, his theories were held suspect. Physicists studied starlight as it passed near our sun (a large gravitational field). They discovered that starlight did not travel in a straight line. Instead it bent very slightly, exactly as Einstein had predicted!

Many studies in natural science, medicine, social science, economics, and business require testing one established theory against another new theory. Statistical tests you will learn in this chapter are of great value in such work.

Albert Einstein (1879–1955)
This brilliant German-born American physicist formulated the theory of relativity.

PREVIEW QUESTIONS

◇ How do we decide if random variables are dependent or independent?   (SECTION 11.1)

◇ How do we decide if two distributions are not only dependent, but actually the same distribution?   (SECTION 11.2)

◇ How do we conduct tests for σ?   (SECTION 11.3)

◇ How do we test a correlation coefficient?   (SECTION 11.4)

◇ What is the standard error of estimate? How do we compute it, and where is it used?   (SECTION 11.4)

◇ How do we compute confidence intervals for a least-squares prediction?   (SECTION 11.4)

◇ The slope of the least-squares line represents rate of growth. How can we determine if the rate of growth is statistically significant?   (SECTION 11.4)

 For on-line student resources, visit **math.college.hmco.com/students** and follow the Statistics links to the Brase/Brase, *Understanding Basic Statistics*, 4th edition web site.

FOCUS PROBLEM

Stone Age Tools and Archaeology

Archaeologists at Washington State University did an extensive summer excavation at Burnt Mesa Pueblo in Bandelier National Monument. Their work is published in the book *Bandelier Archaeological Excavation Project: Summer 1990 Excavations at Burnt Mesa Pueblo and Casa del Rito*, edited by T. A. Kohler.

One question the archaeologists asked was: Is raw material used by prehistoric Indians for stone tool manufacture independent of the archaeological excavation site? Two different excavation sites at Burnt Mesa Pueblo gave the information in the following table.

Use a chi-square test with 1% level of significance to test the claim that raw material used for construction of stone tools and excavation site are independent. (See Problem 9, Section 11.1.)

Stone Tool Construction Material, Burnt Mesa Pueblo

Material	Site A	Site B	Row Total
Basalt	3,657	1,238	4,895
Obsidian	497	68	565
Pedernal chert	3,606	232	3,838
Other	357	36	393
Column total	8,117	1,574	9,691

Verde National Park

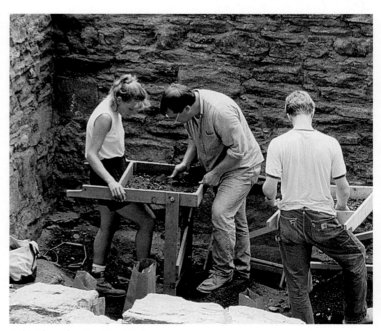

Archaeological excavation site

Overview of the Chi-Square Distribution

So far, we have used several probability distributions for hypothesis testing and confidence intervals, with the most frequently used being the normal distribution and the Student's t distribution. In this chapter, we will use another probability distribution, namely, the chi-square distribution (where *chi* is pronounced like the first two letters in the word *kite*). In Part I, we will see applications of the chi-square distribution.

Chi is a Greek letter denoted by the symbol χ, so chi-square is denoted by the symbol χ^2. Because the distribution is of chi-*square* values, the χ^2 values begin at 0 and then are all positive. The graph of the χ^2 distribution is not symmetrical, and like the Student's t distribution, it depends on the number of degrees of freedom. Figure 11-1 shows the χ^2 distribution for several degrees of freedom (*d.f.*).

As the degrees of freedom increase, the graph of the chi-square distribution becomes more bell-like and begins to look more and more symmetric.

> The **mode (high point)** of a chi-square distribution with n degrees of freedom occurs over $n - 2$ (for $n \geq 3$).

Table 5 of the Appendix shows critical values of chi-square distributions for which a designated area falls to the *right* of the critical value. Table 11-1 gives an excerpt from Table 5. Notice that the row headers are degrees of freedom, and the column headers are areas in the *right* tail of the distribution. For instance, according to the table, for a χ^2 distribution with 3 degrees of freedom, the area occurring to the *right* of $\chi^2 = 0.072$ is 0.995. For a χ^2 distribution with 4 degrees of freedom, the area falling to the *right* of $\chi^2 = 13.28$ is 0.010.

In the next three sections, we will see how to apply the chi-square distribution to different applications.

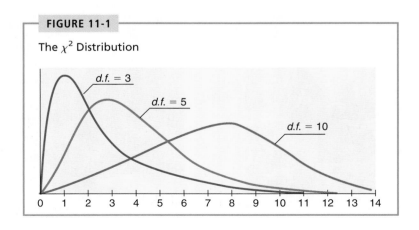

FIGURE 11-1

The χ^2 Distribution

d.f. = 3
d.f. = 5
d.f. = 10

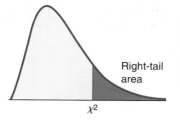

TABLE 11-1   Excerpt from Table 5 (Appendix): The χ^2 Distribution

d.f.	0.995	0.990	0.975	...	0.010	0.005
⋮	⋮	⋮	⋮	⋮	⋮	⋮
3	0.072	0.115	0.216		11.34	12.84
4	0.207	0.297	0.484		13.28	14.86

Area of the Right Tail

Right-tail area

χ^2

11.1
Chi-Square: Tests of Independence

FOCUS POINTS

✓ Set up a test to investigate independence of random variables.
✓ Use contingency tables to compute the sample χ^2 statistic.
✓ Estimate the *P*-value and complete the test.

Innovative Machines Incorporated has developed two new letter arrangements for computer keyboards. The company wishes to see if there is any relationship between the arrangement of letters on the keyboard and the number of hours it takes a new typing student to learn to type at 20 words per minute. Or, from another point of view, is the time it takes a student to learn to type *independent* of the arrangement of the letters on a keyboard?

To answer questions of this type, we test the hypotheses

> H_0: Keyboard arrangement and learning times *are independent.*
>
> H_1: Keyboard arrangement and learning times *are not independent.*

Chi-square distribution

In problems of this sort, we are testing the *independence* of two factors. The probability distribution we use to make the decision is the *chi-square distribution*. Recall from the overview of the chi-square distribution that *chi* is pronounced like the first two letters of the word *kite* and is a Greek letter denoted by the symbol χ; thus chi-square is denoted by χ^2.

The first task for Innovative Machines is to gather data. Suppose that the company took a random sample of 300 beginning typing students and randomly assigned them to learn to type on one of three keyboards. The learning times for this sample are shown in Table 11-2.

TABLE 11-2   Keyboard Arrangement versus Time to Learn to Type at 20 wpm

Keyboard	21–40 h	41–60 h	61–80 h	Row Total
A	#1 25	#2 30	#3 25	80
B	#4 30	#5 71	#6 19	120
Standard	#7 35	#8 49	#9 16	100
Column total	90	150	60	300 Sample size

Contingency table

Table 11-2 is called a *contingency table*. The *shaded boxes*, numbered 1 through 9, that contain observed frequencies are called *cells*. The row and column totals are not considered to be cells. This contingency table is of size 3 × 3 (read, "three-by-three") because there are three rows of cells and three columns. When giving the size of a contingency table, we always list the number of *rows first*.

> To determine the **size** of a contingency table, count the number of rows containing data and the number of columns containing data. The size is
>
> Number of rows × number of columns
>
> where the symbol "×" is read "by." The number of rows is always given first.

Expected frequency

We are testing the null hypothesis that the keyboard arrangement and the time it takes a student to learn to type are *independent*. We use this hypothesis to determine the *expected frequency* of each cell.

For instance, to compute the expected frequency of cell 1 in Table 11-2, we observe that cell 1 consists of all the students in the sample who learned to type on keyboard A and who mastered the skill at the 20-words-per-minute level in 21 to 40 hours. By the assumption (null hypothesis) that the two events are independent, we use the multiplication law to obtain the probability that a student is in cell 1.

$$P(\text{cell 1}) = P(\text{keyboard A } and \text{ skill in 21–40 h})$$
$$= P(\text{keyboard A}) \cdot P(\text{skill in 21–40 h})$$

Because there are 300 students in the sample and 80 used keyboard A,

$$P(\text{keyboard A}) = \frac{80}{300}$$

Also, 90 of the 300 students learned to type in 21–40 hours, so

$$P(\text{skill in 21–40 h}) = \frac{90}{300}$$

Using these two probabilities and the assumption of independence,

$$P(\text{keyboard A } and \text{ skill in 21–40 h}) = \frac{80}{300} \cdot \frac{90}{300}$$

Finally, because there are 300 students in the sample, we have the *expected frequency E* for cell 1.

$$E = P(\text{student in cell 1}) \cdot (\text{no. of students in sample})$$
$$= \frac{80}{300} \cdot \frac{90}{300} \cdot 300 = \frac{80 \cdot 90}{300} = 24$$

We can repeat this process for each cell. However, the last step yields an easier formula for the expected frequency *E*.

> **Formula for expected frequency *E***
>
> $$E = \frac{(\text{Row total})(\text{Column total})}{\text{Sample size}}$$

Note: If the expected value is not a whole number, do *not* round it to the nearest whole number.

Let's use this formula in Example 1 to find the expected frequency for cell 2.

EXAMPLE 1

Expected frequency

Find the expected frequency for cell 2 of contingency Table 11-2.

SOLUTION: Cell 2 is in row 1 and column 2. The *row total* is 80, and the *column total* is 150. The size of the sample is still 300.

$$E = \frac{(\text{Row total})(\text{Column total})}{\text{Sample size}}$$

$$= \frac{(80)(150)}{300} = 40$$

◇

GUIDED EXERCISE 1

Expected frequency

Table 11-3 contains the *observed frequencies* O and *expected frequencies* E for the contingency table giving keyboard arrangement and number of hours it takes a student to learn to type at 20 words per minute. Fill in the missing expected frequencies in cells numbered 3, 5, 6, and 7.

TABLE 11-3   Complete Contingency Table of Keyboard Arrangement versus Time to Learn to Type

Keyboard	21–40 h	41–60 h	61–80 h	Row Total
A	#1 O = 25 E = 24	#2 O = 30 E = 40	#3 O = 25 E = ——	80
B	#4 O = 30 E = 36	#5 O = 71 E = ——	#6 O = 19 E = ——	120
Standard	#7 O = 35 E = ——	#8 O = 49 E = 50	#9 O = 16 E = 20	100
Column Total	90	150	60	300 Sample Size

For cell 3, we have

$$E = \frac{(80)(60)}{300} = 16$$

For cell 5, we have

$$E = \frac{(120)(150)}{300} = 60$$

For cell 6, we have

$$E = \frac{(120)(60)}{300} = 24$$

For cell 7, we have

$$E = \frac{(100)(90)}{300} = 30$$

TABLE 11-4   Difference Between Observed and Expected Frequencies

Cell	Observed O	Expected E	Difference $(O - E)$
1	25	24	1
2	30	40	−10
3	25	16	9
4	30	36	−6
5	71	60	11
6	19	24	−5
7	35	30	5
8	49	50	−1
9	16	20	−4
			$\Sigma(O - E) = 0$

Computing the sample test statistic χ^2

Now we are ready to compute the sample statistic χ^2 for the typing students. The χ^2 value is a measure of the sum of the differences between observed frequency O and expected frequency E in each cell. These differences are listed in Table 11-4.

As you see, if we sum the differences between the observed frequencies and the expected frequencies of the cells, we get the value zero. This total certainly does not reflect the fact that there were differences between the observed and expected frequencies. To obtain a measure whose sum *does* reflect the magnitude of the differences, we square the differences and work with the quantities $(O - E)^2$. But instead of using the terms $(O - E)^2$, we use the values $(O - E)^2/E$. We use this expression because a small difference between the observed and expected frequency is not nearly as important when the expected frequency is large as it is when the expected frequency is small. For instance, for both cells 1 and 8, the squared difference $(O - E)^2$ is 1. However, this difference is more meaningful in cell 1, where the expected frequency is 24, than it is in cell 8, where the expected frequency is 50. When we divide the quantity $(O - E)^2$ by E, we take the size of the difference with respect to the size of the expected value. We use the sum of these values to form the sample statistic χ^2:

$$\chi^2 = \Sigma \frac{(O - E)^2}{E}$$

where the sum is over all cells in the contingency table.

◇ **COMMENT** If you look up the word *irony* in a dictionary, you will find that one of its meanings is described as "the difference between actual (or observed) results and expected results." Because irony is so prevalent in much of our human experience, it is not surprising that statisticians have incorporated a related chi-square distribution into their work. ◇

GUIDED EXERCISE 2

Sample χ^2

(a) Complete Table 11-5.

TABLE 11-5 Data of Table 11-4

Cell	O	E	O − E	$(O − E)^2$	$(O − E)^2/E$
1	25	24	1	1	0.04
2	30	40	−10	100	2.50
3	25	16	9	81	5.06
4	30	36	−6	36	1.00
5	71	60	11	121	2.02
6	19	24	−5	25	1.04
7	35	30	5	25	0.83
8	49	50	___	___	___
9	16	20	___	___	___

$$\Sigma\frac{(O − E)^2}{E} = \underline{\hspace{2em}}$$

⇨ The last two rows of Table 11-5 are

Cell	O	E	O − E	$(O − E)^2$	$(O − E)^2/E$
8	49	50	−1	1	0.02
9	16	20	−4	16	0.80

$$\Sigma\frac{(O − E)^2}{E} = \text{total of last column} = 13.31$$

(b) Compute the statistic χ^2 for this sample.

⇨ Since $\chi^2 = \Sigma\dfrac{(O − E)^2}{E}$, then $\chi^2 = 13.31$.

Notice that when the observed frequency and the corresponding expected frequency of each cell are very close, the quantities $(O − E)^2$ are close to zero, and so the statistic χ^2 is near zero. As the difference increases, the statistic χ^2 also increases. To determine how large the sample statistic can be before we must reject the null hypothesis of independence, we find the P-value of the statistic in the chi-square distribution, Table 5 of the Appendix, and compare it to the specified level of significance α. The P-value depends on the number of degrees of freedom. To test independence, the degrees of freedom d.f. are determined by the following formula.

Degrees of freedom for test of independence

Degrees of freedom = (Number of rows − 1) · (Number of columns − 1)

or $d.f. = (R − 1)(C − 1)$

where R = number of cell rows

C = number of cell columns

GUIDED EXERCISE 3

Degrees of freedom

Determine the number of degrees of freedom in the example of keyboard arrangements (see Table 11-2). Recall that the contingency table had three rows and three columns.

➡ $d.f. = (R - 1)(C - 1)$
$= (3 - 1)(3 - 1) = (2)(2) = 4$

Finding the *P*-value for tests of independence

To test the hypothesis that the letter arrangement on a keyboard and the time it takes to learn to type at 20 words per minute are independent at the $\alpha = 0.05$ level of significance, we estimate the *P*-value shown in Figure 11-2 for the sample test statistic $\chi^2 = 13.31$ (calculated in Guided Exercise 2). We then compare the *P*-value to the specified level of significance α.

For tests of independence, we always use a *right-tailed* test on the chi-square distribution. This is because we are testing to see if the χ^2 measure of the difference between the observed and expected frequencies is too large to be due to chance alone.

In Guided Exercise 3 we found that the degrees of freedom for the example of keyboard arrangements is 4. From Table 5 of the Appendix, in the row headed by $d.f. = 4$, we see that the sample $\chi^2 = 13.31$ falls between the entries 13.28 and 14.86.

The corresponding *P*-value falls between 0.005 and 0.010.

$$\overline{(\underline{})\overset{\textstyle\alpha}{|}}$$

0.005   0.010   0.05

FIGURE 11-2

P-value

P-value

Sample $\chi^2 = 13.31$

Right-tail Area	0.010	0.005
$d.f. = 4$	13.28	14.86
	↑ Sample $\chi^2 = 13.31$	

Since the *P*-value is less than the level of significance $\alpha = 0.05$, we reject the null hypothesis of independence and conclude that the keyboard arrangement and learning time are *not* independent.

Tests of independence for two statistical variables involve a number of steps. A summary of the procedure follows.

PROCEDURE

How to test for independence of two statistical variables

Construct a contingency table in which the rows represent one statistical variable and the columns represent the other. Obtain a random sample of observations, which are assigned to the cells described by the rows and columns. These assignments are called the **observed values O** from the sample.

1. Set the level of significance α and use the hypotheses

    H_0: The variables are independent.

    H_1: The variables are not independent.

2. For each cell, compute the **expected frequency E** (do not round, but give as a decimal number).

$$E = \frac{(\text{Row total})(\text{Column total})}{\text{Sample size}}$$

    You need a sample size large enough so that, for each cell, $E \geq 5$. Now each cell has two numbers, the observed frequency O from the sample and the expected frequency E.

    Next compute the sample *chi-square test statistic*

$$\chi^2 = \Sigma \frac{(O - E)^2}{E} \text{ with degrees of freedom } d.f. = (R - 1)(C - 1)$$

    where the sum is over all cells in the contingency table and

    R = number of rows in contingency table

    C = number of columns in contingency table

3. Use the chi-square distribution (Table 5 of the Appendix) and a *right-tailed test* to find (or estimate) the *P-value* corresponding to the test statistic.

4. *Conclude* the test. If *P*-value $\leq \alpha$, then reject H_0. If *P*-value $> \alpha$, then do not reject H_0.

5. *State your conclusion* in the context of the application.

GUIDED EXERCISE 4

Testing independence

Super Vending Machines Company is to install soda pop machines in elementary schools and high schools. The market analysts wish to know if flavor preference and school level are independent. A random sample of 200 students was taken. Their school level and soda pop preferences are given in Table 11-6. Is independence indicated at the $\alpha = 0.01$ level of significance?

Step 1: State the null and alternate hypotheses.

H_0: School level and soda pop preference are independent.

H_1: School level and soda pop preference are not independent.

Step 2:

(a) Complete the contingency Table 11-6 by filling in the required expected frequencies.

The expected frequency

for cell 5 is $\dfrac{(40)(80)}{200} = 16$

for cell 6 is $\dfrac{(40)(120)}{200} = 24$

for cell 7 is $\dfrac{(20)(80)}{200} = 8$

for cell 8 is $\dfrac{(20)(120)}{200} = 12$

TABLE 11-6   School Level and Soda Pop Preference

Soda Pop	High School	Elementary School	Row Total
Kula Kola	O = 33 #1 E = 36	O = 57 #2 E = 54	90
Mountain Mist	O = 30 #3 E = 20	O = 20 #4 E = 30	50
Jungle Grape	O = 5 #5 E = ___	O = 35 #6 E = ___	40
Diet Pop	O = 12 #7 E = ___	O = 8 #8 E = ___	20
Column Total	80	120	200 Sample Size

Note: In this example, the expected frequencies are all whole numbers. If the expected frequency has a decimal part such as 8.45, do *not* round the value to the nearest whole number; rather, give the expected frequency as the decimal number.

(b) Fill in Table 11-7 and use the table to find the sample statistic χ^2.

The last three rows of Table 11-7 should read as follows:

TABLE 11-7   Computational Table for χ^2

Cell	O	E	O − E	(O − E)²	(O − E)²/E
1	33	36	−3	9	0.25
2	57	54	3	9	0.17
3	30	20	10	100	5.00
4	20	30	−10	100	3.33
5	5	16	−11	121	7.56
6	35	24	11	___	___
7	12	8	___	___	___
8	8	12	___	___	___

Cell	O	E	O − E	(O − E)²	(O − E)²/E
6	35	24	11	121	5.04
7	12	8	4	16	2.00
8	8	12	−4	16	1.33

χ^2 = total of last column

$= \Sigma \dfrac{(O - E)^2}{E} = 24.68$

Continued

GUIDED EXERCISE 4 continued

(c) What is the size of the contingency table? Use the number of rows and the number of columns to determine the degrees of freedom.

➡ The contingency table is of size 4×2. Since there are four rows and two columns,

$$d.f. = (4 - 1)(2 - 1) = 3$$

Step 3: Use Table 5 of the Appendix to estimate the P-value of the sample statistic $\chi^2 = 24.68$ with $d.f. = 3$.

➡

Right-tail Area	0.005
$d.f. = 3$	12.84

As the χ^2 values increase, the area to the right decreases, so

P-value < 0.005

Step 4: Conclude the test by comparing the P-value of the sample statistic χ^2 to the level of significance $\alpha = 0.01$.

➡

Since the P-value is less than α, we reject the null hypothesis of independence.

Step 5: Interpret the test result in the context of the application.

➡ At the 1% level of significance, we conclude that school level and soda pop preference are dependent.

TECH NOTE The TI-84Plus and TI-83Plus calculators, Excel, and Minitab all support chi-square tests of independence. In each case, the observed data are entered in the format of the contingency table.

TI-84Plus/TI-83Plus Enter the observed data into a matrix. Set the dimension of matrix **[B]** to match that of the matrix of observed values. Expected values will be placed in matrix **[B]**. Press **STAT, TESTS,** and select option **C:χ^2-Test.** The output gives the sample χ^2 with the P-value.

Excel Enter the table of observed values. Use the formulas of this section to compute the expected values. Enter the corresponding table of expected values. Finally, select **paste function** (f$_x$) ➤ **Statistical** ➤ **Chitest.** Excel returns the P-value of the sample χ^2.

Minitab Enter the contingency table of observed values. Use the menu selection **Stat** ➤ **Tables** ➤ **Chi-Square Test.** The output shows the contingency table with expected values and the sample χ^2 with P-value.

VIEWPOINT

Loyalty! Going, Going, Gone!

Was there a time in the past when people worked for the same company all their lives, regularly purchased the same brand names, always voted for candidates from the same political party, and loyally cheered for the same sports team? One way to look at this question is to consider tests of *statistical independence*. Is customer loyalty independent of company profits? Can a company maintain its productivity independent of loyal workers? Can politicians do whatever they please independent of the voters back home? Americans may be ready to act on a pent-up desire to restore a sense of loyalty in their lives. For more information, see *American Demographics,* vol. 19, no. 9.

SECTION 11.1 PROBLEMS

For each problem, please provide the following information.
(a) What is the level of significance? State the null and alternate hypotheses.
(b) Find the value of the chi-square statistic for the sample. Are all the expected frequencies greater than 5? What sampling distribution will you use? What are the degrees of freedom?
(c) Find or estimate the *P*-value of the sample test statistic.
(d) Based on your answers in parts (a) to (c), will you reject or fail to reject the null hypothesis of independence?
(e) State your conclusion in the context of the application.

Use the expected values E to the hundredths place.

1. *Psychology: Myers-Briggs* The following table shows the Myers-Briggs personality preferences for a random sample of 406 people in the listed professions (*Atlas of Type Tables,* by Macdaid, McCaulley, and Kainz). E refers to extroverted, and I refers to introverted.

	Personality Preference Type		
Occupation	E	I	Row Total
Clergy (all denominations)	62	45	107
M.D.	68	94	162
Lawyer	56	81	137
Column total	186	220	406

Use the chi-square test to determine if the listed occupations and personality preferences are independent at the 0.05 level of significance.

2. *Psychology: Myers-Briggs* The following table shows the Myers-Briggs personality preferences for a random sample of 519 people in the listed professions (*Atlas of Type Tables,* by Macdaid, McCaulley, and Kainz). T refers to thinking, and F refers to feeling.

	Personality Preference Type		
Occupation	T	F	Row Total
Clergy (all denominations)	57	91	148
M.D.	77	82	159
Lawyer	118	94	212
Column total	252	267	519

Use the chi-square test to determine if the listed occupations and personality preferences are independent at the 0.01 level of significance.

3. *Archaeology: Pottery* The following table shows site type and type of pottery for a random sample of 628 sherds at a location in Sand Canyon Archaeological Project, Colorado (*The Sand Canyon Archaeological Project*, edited by Lipe).

	Pottery Type			
Site Type	Mesa Verde Black-on-White	McElmo Black-on-White	Mancos Black-on-White	Row Total
Mesa Top	75	61	53	189
Cliff-Talus	81	70	62	213
Canyon Bench	92	68	66	226
Column total	248	199	181	628

Use a chi-square test to determine if site type and pottery type are independent at the 0.01 level of significance.

4. *Archaeology: Pottery* The following table shows ceremonial ranking and type of pottery sherd for a random sample of 434 sherds at a location in the Sand Canyon Archaeological Project, Colorado (*The Architecture of Social Integration in Prehistoric Pueblos*, edited by Lipe and Hegmon).

Ceremonial Ranking	Cooking Jar Sherds	Decorated Jar Sherds (Noncooking)	Row Total
A	86	49	135
B	92	53	145
C	79	75	154
Column total	257	177	434

Use a chi-square test to determine if ceremonial ranking and pottery type are independent at the 0.05 level of significance.

5. *Ecology: Buffalo* The following table shows age distribution and location of a random sample of 166 buffalo in Yellowstone National Park (based on information from *The Bison of Yellowstone National Park*, National Park Service Scientific Monograph Series).

Age	Lamar District	Nez Perce District	Firehole District	Row Total
Calf	13	13	15	41
Yearling	10	11	12	33
Adult	34	28	30	92
Column total	57	52	57	166

Use a chi-square test to determine if age distribution and location are independent at the 0.05 level of significance.

6. *Psychology: Myers-Briggs* The following table shows the Myers-Briggs personality preference and area of study for a random sample of 519 college students (*Applications of the Myers-Briggs Type Indicator in Higher Education*, edited by Provost and Anchors). In the table IN refers to introvert, intuitive; EN refers to extrovert, intuitive; IS refers to introvert, sensing; and ES refers to extrovert, sensing.

Myers-Briggs Preference	Arts & Science	Business	Allied Health	Row Total
IN	64	15	17	96
EN	82	42	30	154
IS	68	35	12	115
ES	75	42	37	154
Column total	289	134	96	519

Use a chi-square test to determine if Myers-Briggs preference type is independent of area of study at the 0.05 level of significance.

7. *Sociology: Movie Preference* Mr. Acosta, a sociologist, is doing a study to see if there is a relationship between the age of a young adult (18 to 35 years old) and the type of movie preferred. A random sample of 93 adults revealed the following data. Test if age and type of movie preferred are independent at the 0.05 level.

Movie	Person's Age			Row Total
	18–23 yr	24–29 yr	30–35 yr	
Drama	8	15	11	34
Science fiction	12	10	8	30
Comedy	9	8	12	29
Column total	29	33	31	93

8. *Sociology: Ethnic Groups* After a large fund drive to help the Boston City Library, the following information was obtained from a random sample of contributors to the library fund. Using a 1% level of significance, test the claim that the amount contributed to the library fund is independent of ethnic group.

Ethnic Group	Number of People Making Contribution					Row Total
	$1–50	$51–100	$101–150	$151–200	Over $200	
A	83	62	53	35	18	251
B	94	77	48	25	20	264
C	78	65	51	40	32	266
D	105	89	63	54	29	340
Column total	360	293	215	154	99	1121

9. *Focus Problem: Archaeology* The Focus Problem at the beginning of the chapter refers to excavations at Burnt Mesa Pueblo in Bandelier National Monument. One question the archaeologists asked was: Is raw material used by prehistoric Indians for stone tool manufacture independent of the archaeological excavation site? Two different excavation sites at Burnt Mesa Pueblo gave the information in the following table. Use a chi-square test with 5% level of significance to test the claim that raw material used for construction of stone tools and excavation site are independent.

Material	Stone Tool Construction Material, Burnt Mesa Pueblo		Row Total
	Site A	Site B	
Basalt	731	584	1315
Obsidian	102	93	195
Pedernal chert	510	525	1035
Other	85	94	179
Column total	1428	1296	2724

10. *Political Affiliation: Funding* A random sample of senators and representatives in Washington, D.C., gave the following information about party affiliation and number of dollars spent on federal projects in their home districts. Using a 1% level of significance, test the claim that federal spending level in home districts is independent of party affiliation.

Party	Dollars Spent on Federal Projects in Home District			Row Total
	Less than 5 Billion	5 to 10 Billion	More than 10 Billion	
Democratic	8	15	22	45
Republican	12	19	16	47
Column total	20	34	38	92

11.2
Chi-Square: Goodness of Fit

FOCUS POINTS

✓ Set up a test to investigate how well a sample distribution fits a given distribution.

✓ Use observed and expected frequencies to compute the sample χ^2 statistic.

✓ Estimate the *P*-value and complete the test.

Last year the labor union bargaining agents listed five categories and asked each employee to mark the *one* most important to her or him. The categories and corresponding percentages of favorable responses are shown in Table 11-8. The bargaining agents need to determine if the *current* distribution of responses "fits" last year's distribution, or if it is different.

TABLE 11-8   Bargaining Categories (last year)

Category	Percentage of Favorable Responses
Vacation time	4%
Salary	65%
Safety regulations	13%
Health and retirement benefits	12%
Overtime policy and pay	6%

In questions of this type, we are asking if a population follows a specified distribution. In other words, we are testing the hypotheses

Hypotheses

H_0: The population fits the given distribution.

H_1: The population has a different distribution.

We use the chi-square distribution to test "goodness-of-fit" hypotheses.

Computing sample χ^2 for goodness-of-fit test

Just as with tests of independence, we compute the sample statistic:

$$\chi^2 = \Sigma \frac{(O - E)^2}{E} \text{ with degrees of freedom} = k - 1$$

where E = expected frequency

O = observed frequency

$\frac{(O - E)^2}{E}$ is summed for each category in the distribution

k = number of categories in the distribution

Next we use the chi-square distribution table (Table 5 of the Appendix) to estimate the *P*-value of the sample χ^2 statistic. Finally, we compare the *P*-value to the level of significance α and conclude the test.

In the case of a *goodness-of-fit test*, we use the null hypothesis to compute the expected values for the categories. Let's look at the bargaining category problem to see how this is done.

In the bargaining category problem, the two hypotheses are

H_0: The present distribution of responses is the same as last year's.

H_1: The present distribution of responses is different.

The null hypothesis tells us that the expected frequencies of the present response distribution should follow the percentages indicated in last year's survey. To test this hypothesis, a random sample of 500 employees was taken. If the null hypothesis is true, then there should be 4%, or 20 responses, out of the 500 rating vacation time as the most important bargaining issue. Table 11-9 gives the other expected values and all the information necessary to compute the sample statistic χ^2. We see that the sample statistic is

$$\chi^2 = \Sigma \frac{(O - E)^2}{E} = 14.15$$

Larger values of the sample statistic χ^2 indicate greater differences between the proposed distribution and the distribution followed by the sample. The larger the χ^2 statistic, the stronger the evidence is to reject the null hypothesis that the population distribution fits the given distribution. Consequently, goodness-of-fit tests are always *right-tailed* tests.

> For *goodness-of-fit tests*, we use a *right-tailed test* on the chi-square distribution. This is because we are testing to see if the χ^2 measure of the difference between the observed and expected frequencies is too large to be due to chance alone.

To test the hypothesis that the present distribution of responses to bargaining categories is the same as last year's, we use the chi-square distribution (Table 5 of

Bargaining session with union

Type of test

Degrees of freedom

TABLE 11-9   Observed and Expected Frequencies for Bargaining Categories

Category	O	E	$(O - E)^2$	$(O - E)^2/E$
Vacation time	30	4% of 500 = 20	100	5.00
Salary	290	65% of 500 = 325	1225	3.77
Safety	70	13% of 500 = 65	25	0.38
Health and retirement	70	12% of 500 = 60	100	1.67
Overtime	40	6% of 500 = 30	100	3.33
	$\Sigma O = 500$	$\Sigma E = 500$		$\Sigma \frac{(O - E)^2}{E} = 14.15$

the Appendix) to estimate the P-value of the sample statistic $\chi^2 = 14.15$. To estimate the P-value, we need to know the number of degrees of freedom. In the case of a goodness-of-fit test, the degrees of freedom are found by the following formula.

Degrees of freedom for goodness-of-fit test

$$d.f. = k - 1$$

where k = number of categories

Notice that when we compute the expected values E, we must use the null hypothesis to compute all but the last one. To compute the last one, we can subtract the previous expected values from the sample size. For instance, for the bargaining issues, we could have found the number of responses for overtime policy by adding up the other expected values and subtracting that sum from the sample size 500. We would again get an expected value of 30 responses. The degrees of freedom, then, is the number of E values that *must* be computed by using the null hypothesis.

For the bargaining issues, we have

$$d.f. = 5 - 1 = 4$$

where $k = 5$ is the number of categories.

P-value   We now have the tools necessary to use Table 5 of the Appendix to estimate the P-value of $\chi^2 = 14.15$. Figure 11-3 shows the P-value. In Table 5, we use the row headed by $d.f. = 4$. We see that $\chi^2 = 14.15$ falls between the entries 13.28 and 14.86. Therefore, the P-value falls between the corresponding right-tail areas 0.005 and 0.010.

To test the hypothesis that the distribution of responses to bargaining issues is the same as last year's at the 1% level of significance, we compare the P-value of the statistic to $\alpha = 0.01$.

$$\overset{\qquad\qquad\alpha}{\underline{\quad(\overline{\quad\quad\quad\quad})\quad}}$$
0.005   0.010

FIGURE 11-3

P-value

Sample $\chi^2 = 14.15$

Right-tail Area	0.010	0.005
$d.f. = 4$	13.28	14.86

Sample $\chi^2 = 14.15$

We see that the P-value is less than α, so we reject the null hypothesis that the distribution of responses to bargaining issues is the same as last year's. At the 1% level of significance, we can say that the evidence supports the conclusion that this year's responses to the issues are different from last year's.

Goodness-of-fit tests involve several steps that can be summarized as follows.

PROCEDURE

How to test for goodness of fit

The members of a population need to be classified into exactly one of several different categories. Next you need a specific (theoretical) distribution that assigns a fixed probability (or percentage) that a member of the population will fall into one of the categories. You then need a random sample size n from the population. Let O represent the *observed number* of data from the sample that fall into each category. Let E represent the *expected number* of data from the sample that in theory would fall into each category.

> O = observed frequency count of a category using sample data
>
> E = expected frequency of a category
>
> E = (sample size n)(probability assigned to category)

The sample size n should be large enough so that $E \geq 5$ in each category.

1. Set the *level of significance* α and use the *hypotheses*

    H_0: The population fits the specified distribution of categories.

    H_1: The population has a different distribution.

2. For each category, compute $(O - E)^2/E$ and then compute the sample *test statistic*

$$\chi^2 = \Sigma \frac{(O - E)^2}{E} \quad \text{with } d.f. = k - 1$$

    where the sum is taken over all categories and k = number of categories.

3. Use the chi-square distribution (Table 5 of the Appendix) and a *right-tailed test* to find (or estimate) the *P-value* corresponding to the sample test statistic.

4. *Conclude* the test. If P-value $\leq \alpha$, then reject H_0. If P-value $> \alpha$, then do not reject H_0.

5. *State your conclusion* in the context of the application.

One important application of goodness-of-fit tests is to genetic theories. Such an application is shown in Guided Exercise 5.

GUIDED EXERCISE 5

Goodness-of-fit test

According to genetics theory, red-green colorblindness in humans is a recessive sex-linked characteristic. In this case, the gene is carried on the X chromosome only. We will denote an X chromosome with the gene by X_c and one without the gene by X_n. Women have two X chromosomes, and they will be red-green colorblind only if both chromosomes have the gene, designated X_cX_c. A woman can have normal vision but still carry the colorblind gene if only one of the chromosomes has the gene, designated X_cX_n. A man carries an X and a Y chromosome; if the X chromosome carries the colorblind gene (X_cY), the man is colorblind.

According to genetics theory, if a man with normal vision (X_nY) and a woman carrier (X_cX_n) have a child, the probabilities that the child will have red-green colorblindness, will have normal vision and not carry the gene, or will have normal vision and carry the gene are given by the *equally likely* events in Table 11-10.

TABLE 11-10
Red-Green Colorblindness

Mother	Father X_n	Y
X_c	X_cX_n	X_cY
X_n	X_nX_n	X_nY

$P(\text{child has normal vision and is not a carrier}) = P(X_nY) + P(X_nX_n) = \dfrac{1}{2}$

$P(\text{child has normal vision and is a carrier}) = P(X_cX_n) = \dfrac{1}{4}$

$P(\text{child is red-green colorblind}) = P(X_cY) = \dfrac{1}{4}$

To test this genetics theory, Genetics Labs took a random sample of 200 children whose mothers were carriers of the colorblind gene and whose fathers had normal vision. The results are shown in Table 11-11. We wish to test the hypothesis that the population follows the distribution predicted by genetics theory (see Table 11-10). Use a 1% level of significance.

(a) State the null and alternate hypotheses. What is α?

$\Rightarrow$ H_0: The population fits the distribution predicted by genetics theory.

H_1: The population does not fit the distribution predicted by genetics theory.

$\alpha = 0.01$

(b) Fill in the rest of Table 11-11 and use the table to compute the sample statistic χ^2.

Continued

GUIDED EXERCISE 5 continued

TABLE 11-11   Colorblindness Sample

Event	O	E	$(O - E)^2$	$(O - E)^2/E$
Red-green colorblind	35	50	225	4.50
Normal vision, noncarrier	105	___	___	___
Normal vision, carrier	60	___	___	___

TABLE 11-12   Completion of Table 11-11

Event	O	E	$(O - E)^2$	$(O - E)^2/E$
Red-green colorblind	35	50	225	4.50
Normal vision, noncarrier	105	100	25	0.25
Normal vision, carrier	60	50	100	2.00

The sample statistic is $\chi^2 = \Sigma \dfrac{(O - E)^2}{E} = 6.75$.

(c) There are $k = 3$ categories listed in Table 11-11. Use this information to compute the degrees of freedom.

$d.f. = k - 1$

$\qquad = 3 - 1 = 2$

(d) Find the *P*-value for $\chi^2 = 6.75$.

Using Table 5 of the Appendix and the fact that goodness-of-fit tests are right-tailed tests, we see that

Right-tail Area	0.050	0.025
$d.f. = 2$	5.99	7.38
	↑ Sample $\chi^2 = 6.75$	

$0.025 < P\text{-value} < 0.050$

(e) Conclude the test for $\alpha = 0.01$.

For $\alpha = 0.01$, we have

Since *P*-value $> \alpha$, do not reject H_0.

(f) State the conclusion in the context of the application.

At the 1% level of significance, there is insufficient evidence to conclude that the population follows a distribution different from that predicted by genetics theory.

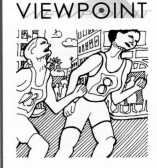

VIEWPOINT   *Run! Run! Run!*

What description would you use for marathon runners? How about age distribution? Body weight? Length of stride? Heart rate? Blood pressure? What countries do these runners come from? What are their best running times? Make your own estimated distribution for these variables, and then consider a goodness-of-fit test for your distribution compared with available data. For more information on marathon runners, visit the Brase/Brase statistics site at **http://math.college.hmco.com/students** and find links to the Honolulu marathon site and to the *Runners World* site.

SECTION 11.2   PROBLEMS

For Problems 1–10, please provide the following information.
(a) What is the level of significance? State the null and alternate hypotheses.
(b) Find the value of the chi-square statistic for the sample. Are all the expected frequencies greater than 5? What sampling distribution will you use? What are the degrees of freedom?
(c) Find or estimate the *P*-value of the sample test statistic.
(d) Based on your answers in parts (a) to (c), will you reject or fail to reject the null hypothesis that the population fits the specified distribution of categories?
(e) State your conclusion in the context of the application.

1. *Census: Age* The age distribution of the Canadian population and the age distribution of a random sample of 455 residents in the Indian community of Red Lake (Northwest Territories) are shown below (based on *U.S. Bureau of the Census, International Data Base*).

Age (years)	Percent of Canadian Population	Observed Number in Red Lake Village
Under 5	7.2%	47
5 to 14	13.6%	75
15 to 64	67.1%	288
65 and older	12.1%	45

Use a 5% level of significance to test the claim that the age distribution of the general Canadian population fits the age distribution of the residents of Red Lake Village.

2. *Census: Type of Household* The type of household for the U.S. population and for a random sample of 411 households in the community of Dove Creek, Montana, are shown (based on *Statistical Abstract of the United States*).

Type of Household	Percent of U.S. Households	Observed Number of Households in Dove Creek
Married, with children	26%	102
Married, no children	29%	112
Single parent	9%	33
One person	25%	96
Other (e.g., roommates, siblings)	11%	68

Use a 5% level of significance to test the claim that the distribution of U.S. households fits the Dove Creek distribution.

3. *Archaeology: Stone Tools* The types of raw material used to construct stone tools found at the archaeological site Casa del Rito are shown below (*Bandelier Archaeological Excavation Project*, edited by Kohler and Root). A random sample of 1486 stone tools were obtained from a current excavation site.

Raw Material	Regional Percent of Stone Tools	Observed Number of Tools at Current Excavation Site
Basalt	61.3%	906
Obsidian	10.6%	162
Welded tuff	11.4%	168
Pedernal chert	13.1%	197
Other	3.6%	53

Use a 1% level of significance to test the claim that the regional distribution of raw materials fits the distribution at the current excavation site.

4. *Ecology: Deer* The type of browse favored by deer is shown in the following table (*The Mule Deer of Mesa Verde National Park*, edited by Mierau and Schmidt). Using binoculars, volunteers observed the feeding habits of a random sample of 320 deer.

Type of Browse	Plant Composition in Study Area	Observed Number of Deer Feeding on This Plant
Sage brush	32%	102
Rabbit brush	38.7%	125
Salt brush	12%	43
Service berry	9.3%	27
Other	8%	23

Use a 5% level of significance to test the claim that the natural distribution of browse fits the deer feeding pattern.

5. *Meteorology: Normal Distribution* The following problem is based on information from the *National Oceanic and Atmospheric Administration (NOAA) Environmental Data Service*. Let x be a random variable that represents the average daily temperature (in degrees Fahrenheit) in July in the town of Kit Carson, Colorado. The x distribution has a mean μ of approximately 75°F and standard deviation σ of approximately

8°F. A 20-year study (620 July days) gave the entries in the rightmost column of the following table.

I Region under Normal Curve	II $x°F$	III Expected % from Normal Curve	IV Observed Number of Days in 20 Years
$\mu - 3\sigma \leq x < \mu - 2\sigma$	$51 \leq x < 59$	2.35%	16
$\mu - 2\sigma \leq x < \mu - \sigma$	$59 \leq x < 67$	13.5%	78
$\mu - \sigma \leq x < \mu$	$67 \leq x < 75$	34%	212
$\mu \leq x < \mu + \sigma$	$75 \leq x < 83$	34%	221
$\mu + \sigma \leq x < \mu + 2\sigma$	$83 \leq x < 91$	13.5%	81
$\mu + 2\sigma \leq x < \mu + 3\sigma$	$91 \leq x < 99$	2.35%	12

(i) Remember that $\mu = 75$ and $\sigma = 8$. Examine Figure 7-3 in Chapter 7. Write a brief explanation for columns I, II, and III in the context of this problem.

(ii) Use a 1% level of significance to test the claim that the average daily July temperature follows a normal distribution with $\mu = 75$ and $\sigma = 8$.

6. *Meteorology: Normal Distribution* Let x be a random variable that represents the average daily temperature (in degrees Fahrenheit) in January in the town of Hana, Maui. The x variable has a mean μ of approximately 68°F and standard deviation σ of approximately 4°F (see reference in Problem 5). A 20-year study (620 January days) gave the entries in the rightmost column of the following table.

I Region under Normal Curve	II $x°F$	III Expected % from Normal Curve	IV Observed Number of Days in 20 Years
$\mu - 3\sigma \leq x < \mu - 2\sigma$	$56 \leq x < 60$	2.35%	14
$\mu - 2\sigma \leq x < \mu - \sigma$	$60 \leq x < 64$	13.5%	86
$\mu - \sigma \leq x < \mu$	$64 \leq x < 68$	34%	207
$\mu \leq x < \mu + \sigma$	$68 \leq x < 72$	34%	215
$\mu + \sigma \leq x < \mu + 2\sigma$	$72 \leq x < 76$	13.5%	83
$\mu + 2\sigma \leq x < \mu + 3\sigma$	$76 \leq x < 80$	2.35%	15

(i) Remember that $\mu = 68$ and $\sigma = 4$. Examine Figure 7-3 in Chapter 7. Write a brief explanation for columns I, II, and III in the context of this problem.

(ii) Use a 1% level of significance to test the claim that the average daily January temperature follows a normal distribution with $\mu = 68$ and $\sigma = 4$.

7. *Ecology: Fish* The Fish and Game Department stocked Lake Lulu with fish in the following proportions: 30% catfish, 15% bass, 40% bluegill, and 15% pike. Five years later it sampled the lake to see if the distribution of fish had changed. It found that the 500 fish in the sample were distributed as follows.

Catfish	Bass	Bluegill	Pike
120	85	220	75

In the 5-year interval, did the distribution of fish change at the 0.05 level?

8. *Library: Book Circulation* The director of library services at Fairmont College did a survey of types of books (by subject) in the circulation library. Then she used library records to take a random sample of 888 books checked out last term and classified the books in the sample by subject. The results are shown below.

Subject Area	Percent of Books on This Subject in Circulation Library	Number of Books on This Subject in Sample
Business	32%	268
Humanities	25%	214
Natural science	20%	215
Social science	15%	115
All other subjects	8%	76

Using a 5% level of significance, test the claim that the subject distribution of books in the library fits the distribution of books checked out by students.

9. *Census: California* The accuracy of a census report from a city in southern California was questioned by some government officials. A random sample of 1215 people living in the city was used to check the report, and the results are shown here:

Ethnic Origin	Census Percent	Sample Result
Black	10%	127
Asian	3%	40
Anglo	38%	480
Latino/Latina	41%	502
Native American	6%	56
All others	2%	10

Using a 1% level of significance, test the claim that the census distribution and the sample distribution agree.

10. *Accounting Records: Benford's Law* Benford's Law states that the first nonzero digits of numbers drawn at random from a large complex data file have the following probability distribution. (Reference: American Statistical Association, *Chance*, vol. 12, no. 3, pp. 27–31; see also the Focus Problem of Chapter 9.)

First nonzero digit	1	2	3	4	5	6	7	8	9
Probability	0.301	0.176	0.125	0.097	0.079	0.067	0.058	0.051	0.046

Suppose that $n = 275$ numerical entries were drawn at random from a large accounting file of a major corporation. The first nonzero digits were recorded for the sample.

First nonzero digit	1	2	3	4	5	6	7	8	9
Sample frequency	83	49	32	22	25	18	13	17	16

Use a 1% level of significance to test the claim that the distribution of first nonzero digits in this accounting file follows Benford's Law.

11.3
Testing a Single Variance or Standard Deviation

FOCUS POINTS

✓ Set up a test for a single variance σ^2.
✓ Compute the sample χ^2 statistic.
✓ Use the χ^2 distribution to estimate a P-value and conclude the test.

Testing σ^2

Many problems arise that require us to make decisions about variability. In this section, we will test hypotheses about the variance (or standard deviation) of a population. It is customary to talk about variance instead of standard deviation because our techniques employ the sample variance rather than the standard deviation. Of course, the standard deviation is just the square root of the variance, so any discussion about variance is easily converted to a similar discussion about standard deviation.

Let us consider a specific example in which we might wish to test a hypothesis about the variance. Almost everyone has had to wait in line. In a grocery store, bank, post office, or registration center, there are usually several checkout or service areas. Frequently, each service area has its own independent line. However, many businesses and government offices are adopting a "single-line" procedure.

In a single-line procedure, there is only one waiting line for everyone. As any service area becomes available, the next person in line gets served. The old independent-lines procedure has a line at each service center. An incoming customer simply picks the shortest line and hopes it will move quickly. In either procedure, the number of clerks and the rate at which they work is the same, so the average waiting time is the *same*. What is the advantage of the single-line procedure? The difference is in the *attitudes* of the people who wait in the lines. A lengthy waiting line will be more acceptable if the variability of waiting times is smaller, even though the average waiting time is the same. When the variability is small, the inconvenience of waiting (although it might not be reduced) does become more predictable. This means impatience is reduced and people are happier.

To test the hypothesis that variability is less in a single-line process, we use the chi-square distribution. The next theorem tells us how to use the sample and population variance to compute values of χ^2.

◇ **THEOREM 11.1** If we have a *normal* population with variance σ^2, and a random sample of n measurements is taken from this population with sample variance s^2, then

$$\chi^2 = \frac{(n-1)s^2}{\sigma^2}$$

has a chi-square distribution with degrees of freedom $d.f. = n - 1$.   ◇

Recall that the chi-square distribution is *not* symmetrical and that there are different chi-square distributions for different degrees of freedom. Table 5 of the Appendix gives chi-square values for which the area α is to the *right* of the given chi-square value.

Table 11-13 summarizes the techniques for using the chi-square distribution (Table 5 of the Appendix) to find P-values for a right-tailed test, a left-tailed test, and a two-tailed test. Example 2 demonstrates the technique of finding P-values for a left-tailed test. Example 3 demonstrates the technique for a two-tailed test, and Guided Exercise 6 uses a right-tailed test.

TABLE 11-13   *P*-values for Chi-Square Distribution Table (Table 5 of the Appendix)

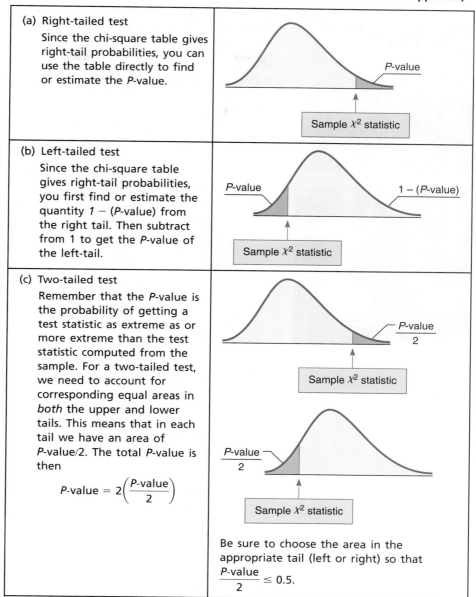

(a) Right-tailed test

Since the chi-square table gives right-tail probabilities, you can use the table directly to find or estimate the *P*-value.

(b) Left-tailed test

Since the chi-square table gives right-tail probabilities, you first find or estimate the quantity $1 - (P\text{-value})$ from the right tail. Then subtract from 1 to get the *P*-value of the left-tail.

(c) Two-tailed test

Remember that the *P*-value is the probability of getting a test statistic as extreme as or more extreme than the test statistic computed from the sample. For a two-tailed test, we need to account for corresponding equal areas in *both* the upper and lower tails. This means that in each tail we have an area of *P*-value/2. The total *P*-value is then

$$P\text{-value} = 2\left(\frac{P\text{-value}}{2}\right)$$

Be sure to choose the area in the appropriate tail (left or right) so that

$$\frac{P\text{-value}}{2} \leq 0.5.$$

Now let's use Theorem 11.1 and our knowledge of the chi-square distribution to determine if a single-line procedure has less variance of waiting times than an independent-lines procedure.

EXAMPLE 2

Testing the variance (left-tailed test)

A large discount hardware store in San Antonio has been using the independent-lines procedure to check out customers. After long observation, the manager knows that the standard deviation of waiting times is 7 minutes. The manager decides to introduce the single-line procedure on a trial basis to see if a reduction in waiting time variability occurs. A random sample of 25 customers are monitored, and their waiting times for checkout are determined. The sample standard deviation is $s = 5$ minutes. We will use a 5% level of significance to test the claim that the variance of waiting times has been reduced.

SOLUTION: As a null hypothesis, we assume that the variance of waiting times is the same as that of the former independent-lines procedure. The alternate hypothesis is that the variance for the single-line procedure is less than that for the independent-lines procedure. If we let σ be the standard deviation of waiting times for the single-line procedure, then σ^2 is the variance, and we have

$$H_0: \sigma^2 = 49 \qquad (\text{use } 7^2 = 49)$$
$$H_1: \sigma^2 < 49$$

We use the chi-square distribution to test the hypotheses. Assuming that the waiting times are normally distributed, we compute our observed value of χ^2 by using Theorem 11.1.

$$n = 25$$
$$s = 5 \quad \text{so} \quad s^2 = 25 \qquad (\text{observed from sample})$$
$$\sigma = 7 \quad \text{so} \quad \sigma^2 = 49 \qquad (\text{from } H_0: \sigma^2 = 49)$$
$$\chi^2 = \frac{(n-1)s^2}{\sigma^2} = \frac{(25-1)25}{49} \approx 12.24$$
$$d.f. = n - 1 = 25 - 1 = 24$$

Next we estimate the P-value for $\chi^2 = 12.24$. Since we have a left-tailed test, the P-value is the area of the chi-square distribution that lies to the *left* of $\chi^2 = 12.24$, as shown in Figure 11-4.

To estimate the P-value on the left, we consider the fact that the area of the right tail is between 0.975 and 0.990. To find an estimate for the area of the left tail, we *subtract* each right-tail endpoint from 1. The P-value (area of the left tail) is in the interval

$$1 - 0.990 < P\text{-value of left tail} < 1 - 0.975$$
$$0.010 < P\text{-value} < 0.025$$

To conclude the test, we compare the P-value to the level of significance $\alpha = 0.05$.

Checkout lines

Establish H_0 and H_1

Sample χ^2 value and degrees of freedom

P-value

Test conclusion

FIGURE 11-4

P-value

P-value   Right-tail area $1 - (P\text{-value})$

Sample $\chi^2 = 12.24$

Right-tail Area	0.990	0.975
$d.f. = 24$	10.86	12.40

Sample $\chi^2 = 12.24$

Since the P-value is less than α, we reject H_0. At the 5% level of significance, we conclude that the variance of waiting times for a single line is less than the variance of waiting times for multiple lines.   ◇

The steps used in Example 2 for testing the variance σ^2 are summarized as follows.

> **PROCEDURE**
>
> **How to test σ^2**
>
> You first need to know that a random variable x has a normal distribution. In testing σ^2, the normal assumption must be strictly observed (whereas in testing means, we can say normal or approximately normal). Next you need a random sample (size $n \geq 2$) of values from the x distribution for which you compute the sample variance s^2.
>
> 1. In the context of the problem, state the *null hypothesis* H_0 and the *alternate hypothesis* H_1, and set the *level of significance* α.
>
> 2. Use the value of σ^2 given in the null hypothesis H_0, the sample variance s^2, and the sample size n to compute the sample *test statistic*
>
> $$\chi^2 = \frac{(n-1)s^2}{\sigma^2} \quad \text{with degrees of freedom } d.f. = n - 1$$
>
> 3. Use a chi-square distribution and the type of test to find or estimate the *P-value*. Use the procedures shown in Table 11-13 and Table 5 of the Appendix.
>
> 4. *Conclude* the test. If P-value $\leq \alpha$, then reject H_0. If P-value $> \alpha$, then do not reject H_0.
>
> 5. *State your conclusion* in the context of the application.

EXAMPLE 3

Testing the variance (two-tailed test)

Let x be a random variable that represents weight loss (in pounds) after following a certain diet for 6 months. After extensive study, it is found that x has a normal distribution with $\sigma = 5.7$ lb. A new modification of the diet has been implemented. A random sample of $n = 21$ people use the modified diet for 6 months. For these people, the sample standard deviation of weight loss is $s = 4.1$ lb. Does this result indicate that the variance of weight loss for the modified diet is different (either way) from the variance of weight loss for the original diet? Use $\alpha = 0.01$.

(a) What is the level of significance? State the null and alternate hypotheses.

   SOLUTION: We are using $\alpha = 0.01$. The standard deviation of weight loss for the original diet is $\sigma = 5.7$ lb, so the variance is $\sigma^2 = 32.49$. The null hypothesis is that the weight loss variance for the modified diet is the same as that for the original diet. The alternate hypothesis is that the variance is different.

   $$H_0: \sigma^2 = 32.49 \qquad H_1: \sigma^2 \neq 32.49$$

FIGURE 11-5

Right-tail Area	0.975	0.950
d.f. = 20	8.59	10.85

(b) Compute the sample χ^2 statistic and the degrees of freedom.

SOLUTION: Using sample size $n = 21$, sample standard deviation $s = 4.1$ lb, and $\sigma^2 = 32.49$ from the null hypothesis, we have

$$\chi^2 = \frac{(n-1)s^2}{\sigma^2} = \frac{(21-1)4.1^2}{32.49} \approx 10.35$$

with degrees of freedom $d.f. = n - 1 = 21 - 1 = 20$.

(c) Use the chi-square distribution (Table 5 of the Appendix) to estimate the P-value.

SOLUTION: For a *two-tailed* test, the area beyond the sample χ^2 represents *half* the total P-value or $(P\text{-value})/2$. Figure 11-5 shows this region, which is to the left of $\chi^2 \approx 10.35$. However, Table 5 of the Appendix gives the areas in the *right tail*. We use Table 5 to find the area in the right tail and then subtract from 1 to find the corresponding area in the left tail.

From the table, we see that the right-tail area falls in the interval between 0.950 and 0.975. Subtracting each endpoint of the interval from 1 gives us an interval containing $(P\text{-value})/2$. Multiplying by 2 gives an interval for the P-value.

$$1 - 0.975 < \frac{P\text{-value}}{2} < 1 - 0.950 \quad \text{Subtract right-tail-area endpoints from 1.}$$

$$0.025 < \frac{P\text{-value}}{2} < 0.050$$

$$0.05 < P\text{-value} < 0.10 \qquad \text{Multiply each part by 2.}$$

(d) Conclude the test.

SOLUTION: The P-value is greater than $\alpha = 0.01$, so we do not reject H_0.

(e) State the conclusion in the context of the application.

SOLUTION: At the 1% level of significance, there is insufficient evidence to conclude that the variance of weight loss using the modified diet is different from the variance of weight loss using the original diet.

GUIDED EXERCISE 6

Testing the variance (right-tailed test)

Certain industrial machines require overhaul when wear on their parts introduces too much variability to pass inspection. A government official is visiting a dentist's office to inspect the operation of an x-ray machine. If the machine emits too little radiation, clear photographs cannot be obtained. However, too much radiation can be harmful to the patient. Government regulations specify an average emission of 60 millirads with standard deviation σ of 12 millirads, and the machine has been set for these readings. After examining the machine, the inspector is satisfied that the average emission is still 60 millirads. However, there is wear on certain mechanical parts. To test variability, the inspector takes a random sample of 30 x-ray emissions and finds the sample standard deviation to be $s = 15$ millirads. Does this support the claim that the variance is too high (i.e., the machine should be overhauled)? Use a 1% level of significance.

Let σ be the (population) standard deviation of emissions (in millirads) of the machine in its present condition.

(a) What is α? State H_0 and H_1.

⟹ $\alpha = 0.01$. Government regulations specify that $\sigma = 12$. This means that the variance $\sigma^2 = 144$. We are to test the claim that the variance is higher than government specifications allow.

H_0: $\sigma^2 = 144$ and H_1: $\sigma^2 > 144$

(b) Compute the sample statistic χ^2 and corresponding degrees of freedom.

⟹ Using $n = 30$, $s = 15$, and $\sigma^2 = 144$ from H_0,

$$\chi^2 = \frac{(n-1)s^2}{\sigma^2} = \frac{(30-1)15^2}{144} \approx 45.3$$

Degrees of freedom $d.f. = n - 1 = 30 - 1 = 29$

(c) Estimate the P-value for the sample $\chi^2 = 45.3$ with $d.f. = 29$.

⟹ Since this is a *right-tailed* test, we look up P-values directly in the chi-square table (Table 5 of the Appendix).

FIGURE 11-6 *P*-value

Sample $\chi^2 = 45.3$

Right-tail Area	0.050	0.025
d.f. = 29	42.56	45.72

↑
Sample $\chi^2 = 45.3$

$0.025 < P\text{-value} < 0.050$

(d) Conclude the test.

⟹ The P-value for $\chi^2 = 45.3$ is greater than $\alpha = 0.01$.

Fail to reject H_0.

Continued

GUIDED EXERCISE 6 continued

(e) Interpret the conclusion in the context of the application.

 At the 1% level of significance, there is insufficient evidence to conclude that the variance of the radiation emitted by the machine is greater than that specified by government regulations. The evidence does not indicate that an adjustment is necessary at this time.

VIEWPOINT   *Adoption—A Good Choice!*

Cuckoos are birds that are known to lay their eggs in the nests of other (host) birds. The host birds then hatch the eggs and adopt the cuckoo chicks as their own. Birds such as the meadow pipit, tree pipit, hedge sparrow, robin, and wren have all played host to cuckoo eggs and adopted their chicks. L. H. C. Tippett (1902–1985) was a pioneer in the field of statistical quality control who collected data on cuckoo eggs found in the nests of other birds. For more information and data from Tippett's study, visit the Brase/Brase statistics site at **http://math.college.hmco.com/students** and find a link to DASL, the Carnegie Mellon University Data and Story Library. Find Biology under Data Subjects, and then select the Cuckoo Egg Length Data file.

SECTION 11.3   PROBLEMS

For each problem, please provide the following information.

(a) What is the level of significance? State the null and alternate hypotheses.

(b) Find the value of the chi-square statistic for the sample. What are the degrees of freedom? What assumptions are you making about the original distribution?

(c) Find or estimate the *P*-value of the sample test statistic.

(d) Based on your answers in parts (a) to (c), will you reject or fail to reject the null hypothesis of independence?

(e) State your conclusion in the context of the application.

In each of the following problems, assume a normal population distribution.

1. *Archaeology: Chaco Canyon* The following problem is based on information from *Archaeological Surveys of Chaco Canyon, New Mexico,* by A. Hayes, D. Brugge, and W. Judge, University of New Mexico Press. A *transect* is an archaeological study area that is 1/5 mile wide and 1 mile long. A *site* in a transect is the location of a significant archaeological find. Let x represent the number of sites per transect. In a section of Chaco Canyon, a large number of transects showed that x has a population variance $\sigma^2 = 42.3$. In a different section of Chaco Canyon, a random sample of 23 transects gave a sample variance $s^2 = 46.1$ for the number of sites per transect. Use a 5% level of significance to test the claim that the variance of the number of sites per transect in the new section is greater than 42.3.

2. *Sociology: Marriage* The following problem is based on information from an article by N. Keyfitz in *The American Journal of Sociology* (vol. 53, pp. 470–480). Let x = age in years of a rural Quebec woman at the time of her first marriage. In the year 1941, the population variance of x was approximately $\sigma^2 = 5.1$. Suppose that a recent study of age at first marriage for a random sample of 41 women in rural Quebec gave a sample variance $s^2 = 3.3$. Use a 5% level of significance to test the claim that the current variance is less than 5.1.

3. *Mountain Climbing: Accidents* The following problem is based on information taken from *Accidents in North American Mountaineering* (jointly published by The American Alpine Club and The Alpine Club of Canada). Let x represent the number of mountain climbers killed each year. The long-term variance of x is approximately $\sigma^2 = 136.2$. Suppose that for the past 8 years the variance has been $s^2 = 115.1$. Use a 1% level of significance to test the claim that the recent variance for number of mountain-climber deaths is less than 136.2.

4. *Professors: Salaries* The following problem is based on information taken from *Academe, Bulletin of the American Association of University Professors*. Let x represent the average annual salary of college and university professors (in thousands of dollars) in the United States. For all colleges and universities in the United States, the population variance of x is approximately $\sigma^2 = 47.1$. However, a random sample of 15 colleges and universities in Kansas showed that x has a sample variance $s^2 = 83.2$. Use a 5% level of significance to test the claim that the variance for colleges and universities in Kansas is greater than 47.1.

5. *Medical: Clinical Test* A new kind of typhoid shot is being developed by a medical research team. The old typhoid shot was known to protect the population for a mean of 36 months with a standard deviation of 3 months. To test the variability of the new shot, a random sample of 23 people were given the new shot. Regular blood tests showed that the sample standard deviation of protection times was 1.9 months. Using a 0.05 level of significance, test the claim that the new typhoid shot has a smaller variance of protection times.

6. *Veterinary Science: Tranquilizer* Jim Mead is a veterinarian who visits a Vermont farm to examine prize bulls. In order to examine a bull, Jim first gives the animal a tranquilizer shot. The effect of the shot is supposed to last an average of 65 minutes, and it usually does. However, Jim sometimes gets chased out of the pasture by a bull that recovers too soon, and other times he becomes worried about prize bulls that take too long to recover. By reading journals, Jim has found that the tranquilizer should have a mean duration of 65 minutes with standard deviation of 15 minutes. A random sample of 10 of Jim's bulls had a mean tranquilized duration time of close to 65 minutes but a standard deviation of 24 minutes. At the 1% level of significance, is Jim justified in claiming that the variance is larger than that stated in his journal?

7. *Engineering: Jet Engines* The fan blades on commercial jet engines must be replaced when wear on these parts indicates too much variability to pass inspection. If a single fan blade broke during operation, it could severely endanger a flight. A large engine contains thousands of fan blades, and safety regulations require that variability measurements on the population of all blades not exceed $\sigma^2 = 0.18$ mm^2. An engine inspector took a random sample of 61 fan blades from an engine. She measured each blade and found a sample variance of 0.27 mm^2. Using a 0.01 level of significance, is the inspector justified in claiming that all the engine fan blades must be replaced?

8. *Law: Bar Exam* A factor in determining the usefulness of an examination as a measure of demonstrated ability is the amount of spread that occurs in the grades. If the

spread or variation of examination scores is very small, it usually means that the examination was either too hard or too easy. However, if the variance of scores is moderately large, then there is a definite difference in scores between "better," "average," and "poorer" students. A group of attorneys in a Midwest state has been given the task of making up this year's bar examination for the state. The examination has 500 total possible points, and from the history of past examinations, it is known that a standard deviation of around 60 points is desirable. Of course, too large or too small a standard deviation is not good. The attorneys want to test their examination to see how good it is. A preliminary version of the examination (with slight modification to protect the integrity of the real examination) is given to a random sample of 24 newly graduated law students. Their scores give a sample standard deviation of 72 points. Using a 0.01 level of significance, test the claim that the population standard deviation for the new examination is 60 against the claim that the population standard deviation is different from 60.

9. *Engineering: Solar Batteries* A set of solar batteries is used in a research satellite. The satellite can run on only one battery, but it runs best if more than one battery is used. The variance σ^2 of lifetimes of these batteries affects the useful lifetime of the satellite before it goes dead. If the variance is too small, all the batteries will tend to die at once. Why? If the variance is too large, the batteries are simply not dependable. Why? Engineers have determined a variance of $\sigma^2 = 23$ months (squared) is most desirable for these batteries. A random sample of 22 batteries gave a sample variance of 14.3 months (squared). Using a 0.05 level of significance, test the claim that $\sigma^2 = 23$ against the claim that σ^2 is different from 23.

PART II: INFERENCES RELATING TO LINEAR REGRESSION

11.4
Inferences for Correlation and Regression

FOCUS POINTS

✓ Test the correlation coefficient ρ.

✓ Use sample data to compute the standard error of estimate S_e.

✓ Find a confidence interval for the value of y predicted for a specified value of x.

✓ Test the slope β of the least-squares line.

Learn more, earn more! We have probably all heard this platitude. The question is whether or not there is some truth in the statement. Do college graduates have an improved chance at a better income? Is there a trend in the general population to support the "learn more, earn more" statement?

Consider the following variables: x = percentage of the population 25 or older with at least 4 years of college and y = percentage *growth* in per capita income over the past 7 years. A random sample of six communities in Ohio gave the information (based on *Life in America's Small Cities,* by G. S. Thomas) shown in Table 11-14.

If we use what we learned in Sections 4.1 and 4.2, we can compute the correlation coefficient r and the least-squares line $\hat{y} = a + bx$ using the data of Table 11-14. However, r is only a *sample* correlation coefficient and $\hat{y} = a + bx$ is only a "sample-based" least-squares line. What if we used *all* possible data pairs (x, y) from *all* U.S. cities, not just the six towns in Ohio? If we accomplished this seemingly impossible task, we would have the *population* of all (x, y) pairs.

TABLE 11-14   Education and Income Growth Percentages

x	9.9	11.4	8.1	14.7	8.5	12.6
y	37.1	43.0	33.4	47.1	26.5	40.2

From this population of (x, y) pairs we could (in theory) compute the *population correlation coefficient*, which we call ρ (Greek letter rho, pronounced like "row"). We could also compute the least-squares line for the entire population, which we denote as $y = \alpha + \beta x$ using more Greek letters, α (alpha) and β (beta).

Sample Statistic		Population Parameter
r	$\rightarrow$	ρ
a	$\rightarrow$	α
b	$\rightarrow$	β
$\hat{y} = a + bx$	$\rightarrow$	$y = \alpha + \beta x$

Assumptions for inferences
concerning linear regression

To make inferences regarding the population correlation coefficient ρ and the slope β of the population least-squares line, we need to be sure that

(a) The set (x, y) of ordered pairs is a *random sample* from the population of all possible such (x, y) pairs.

(b) For each fixed value of x, the y values have a normal distribution. All of the y distributions have the same variance, and, for a given x value, the distribution of y values has a mean that lies on the least-squares line. We also assume that for a fixed y, each x has its own normal distribution. In most cases, the results are still accurate if the distributions are simply mound-shaped and symmetric, and the y variances are approximately equal.

We assume these conditions are met for all inferences presented in this section.

Testing the Correlation Coefficient

The first topic we want to study is the statistical significance of the sample correlation coefficient r. To do this, we construct a statistical test of ρ, the population correlation coefficient. The test will be based on the following theorem.

◇ **THEOREM 11.2** Let r be the sample correlation coefficient computed using data pairs (x, y). We use the null hypothesis

   H_0: x and y have no linear correlation, so $\rho = 0$

The alternate hypothesis may be

   H_1: $\rho > 0$ or H_1: $\rho < 0$ or H_1: $\rho \neq 0$

The conversion of r to a Student's t distribution is

$$t = \frac{r\sqrt{n-2}}{\sqrt{1-r^2}} \quad \text{with } d.f. = n - 2$$

where n is the number of sample data pairs (x, y) $(n \geq 3)$.   ◇

PROCEDURE

How to test the population correlation coefficient ρ

1. Use the *null hypothesis* H_0: $\rho = 0$. In the context of the application, state the *alternate hypothesis* ($\rho > 0$ or $\rho < 0$ or $\rho \neq 0$) and set the *level of significance* α.

2. Obtain a random sample of $n \geq 3$ data pairs (x, y), and compute the sample correlation coefficient r and the corresponding sample *test statistic*

$$t = \frac{r\sqrt{n-2}}{\sqrt{1-r^2}} \quad \text{with degrees of freedom } d.f. = n - 2$$

3. Use a Student's t distribution and the type of test, one-tailed or two-tailed, to find (or estimate) the *P-value* corresponding to the test statistic.

4. *Conclude* the test. If P-value $\leq \alpha$, then reject H_0. If P-value $> \alpha$, then do not reject H_0.

5. *State your conclusion* in the context of the application.

EXAMPLE 4

Testing ρ

Let's return to our data from Ohio regarding the percentage of the population with at least 4 years of college and the percentage of growth in per capita income (Table 11-14). We'll develop a test for the population correlation coefficient ρ.

SOLUTION: First, we compute the sample correlation coefficient r. Using a calculator, statistical software, or "by-hand" calculation from Section 4.1, we find

$$r \approx 0.887$$

Now we test the correlation coefficient ρ. Remember that x represents percentage college graduates and y represents percentage salary increases in the general population. We suspect that the population correlation is positive, $\rho > 0$. Let's use a 1% level of significance:

H_0: $\rho = 0$ (no linear correlation)

H_1: $\rho > 0$ (positive linear correlation)

Convert the sample test statistic $r = 0.887$ to t using $n = 6$.

$$t = \frac{r\sqrt{n-2}}{\sqrt{1-r^2}} = \frac{0.887\sqrt{6-2}}{\sqrt{1-0.887^2}} \approx 3.84 \quad \text{with } d.f. = n - 2 = 6 - 2 = 4$$

The P-value for the sample test statistic $t = 3.84$ is shown in Figure 11-7. Since we have a right-tailed test, we use the one-tail area in the Student's t distribution (Table 4 of the Appendix).

From Table 11-15 we see that

$$0.005 < P\text{-value} < 0.010$$

Since the interval containing the P-value is less than the level of significance $\alpha = 0.01$, we reject H_0 and conclude that the population correlation coefficient between x and y is positive.

FIGURE 11-7

P-value

✓one-tail area	0.010	0.005
two-tail area	0.020	0.010
d.f. = 4	3.747	4.604

TABLE 11-15   Excerpt from Student's t Distribution

Sample t = 3.84

Note: Although we have shown that x and y are positively correlated, we have not shown that an increase in education *causes* an increase in earnings.   ◊

Standard Error of Estimate

Sometimes a scatter diagram clearly indicates the existence of a linear relationship between x and y, but it can happen that the points are widely scattered around the least-squares line. We need a method (besides just looking) for measuring the spread of a set of points about the least-squares line. There are three common methods of measuring the spread. One method uses the *standard error of estimate*. The others are the *coefficient of correlation* and the *coefficient of determination*.

For the standard error of estimate, we use a measure of spread that is in some ways like the standard deviation of measurements of a single variable. Let

$$\hat{y} = a + bx$$

be the predicted value of y from the least-squares line. Then $y - \hat{y}$ is the difference between the y value of the *data point* (x, y) shown on the scatter diagram (Figure 11-8) and the $\hat{y}$ value of the point on the *least-squares line* with the same x value. The quantity $y - \hat{y}$ is known as the *residual*. To avoid the difficulty of

Residual

FIGURE 11-8

The Distance Between Points (x, y) and $(x, \hat{y})$

having some positive and some negative values, we square the quantity $(y - \hat{y})$. Then we sum the squares and, for technical reasons, divide this sum by $n - 2$. Finally, we take the square root to obtain the *standard error of estimate*, denoted by S_e.

$$\text{Standard error of estimate} = S_e = \sqrt{\frac{\Sigma(y - \hat{y})^2}{n - 2}} \qquad (1)$$

where $\hat{y} = a + bx$ and $n \geq 3$.

Note: To compute the standard error of estimate, we require that there be at least three points on the scatter diagram. If we had only two points, the line would be a perfect fit, since two points determine a line. In such a case, there would be no need to compute S_e.

The nearer the scatter points lie to the least-squares line, the smaller S_e will be. In fact, if $S_e = 0$, it follows that each $y - \hat{y}$ is also zero. This means that all the scatter points lie *on* the least-squares line if $S_e = 0$. The larger S_e becomes, the more scattered the points are.

The formula for the standard error of estimate is reminiscent of the formula for the standard deviation. It, too, is a measure of dispersion. However, the standard deviation involves differences of data values from a mean, whereas the standard error of estimate involves the differences between experimental and predicted y values for a given x (i.e., $y - \hat{y}$).

The actual computation of S_e using Equation (1) is quite long because the formula requires us to use the least-squares line equation to compute a predicted value $\hat{y}$ for *each* x value in the data pairs. There is a computational formula that we strongly recommend you use. However, as with all the computation formulas, be careful about rounding. This formula is sensitive to rounding, and you should carry as many digits as seems reasonable for your problem. Answers will vary, depending on rounding used. We give the formula here and follow it with an example of its use.

PROCEDURE

How to find the standard error of estimate S_e

1. Obtain a random sample of $n \geq 3$ data pairs (x, y).

2. Use the procedures of Section 4.2 to find a and b from the sample least-squares line $\hat{y} = a + bx$.

3. The standard error of estimate is

$$S_e = \sqrt{\frac{\Sigma y^2 - a\Sigma y - b\Sigma xy}{n - 2}} \qquad (2)$$

With a considerable amount of algebra, Equations (1) and (2) can be shown to be mathematically equivalent. Equation (1) shows the strong similarity between the standard error of estimate and standard deviation. Equation (2) is a shortcut calculation formula because it involves few subtractions. The sums Σx, Σy, Σx^2, Σy^2, and Σxy are provided directly on most calculators that support two-variable statistics.

In the next example, we show you how to compute the standard error of estimate using the computation formula.

EXAMPLE 5

Least-squares line and S_e

In this example, we find the equation of the least-squares line and the standard error of estimate for the data from Ohio regarding x = percentage of the population with at least 4 years of college and y = percentage growth in per capita income.

x	9.9	11.4	8.1	14.7	8.5	12.6
y	37.1	43.0	33.4	47.1	26.5	40.2

SOLUTION: To find the equation of the least-squares line $\hat{y} = a + bx$ and the value of S_e, we note that $n = 6$ and compute the following sums.

$$\Sigma x = 65.2; \Sigma y = 227.3; \Sigma x^2 = 740.68; \Sigma y^2 = 8877.67;$$
$$\Sigma xy = 2552.17$$

Using formulas (3) and (4) from Chapter 4, we have

$$b = \frac{n\Sigma xy - (\Sigma x)(\Sigma y)}{n\Sigma x^2 - (\Sigma x)^2} = \frac{6(2552.17) - (65.2)(227.3)}{6(740.68) - (65.2)^2} \approx 2.554$$

$$\bar{x} = \frac{\Sigma x}{n} = \frac{65.2}{6} \approx 10.87 \quad \text{and} \quad \bar{y} = \frac{\Sigma y}{n} = \frac{227.3}{6} \approx 37.88$$

$$a = \bar{y} - b\bar{x} \approx 37.88 - 2.554(10.87) \approx 10.12$$

The equation of the least-squares line is

$$\hat{y} \approx 10.12 + 2.554x$$

Note: The values of a and b for the least-squares line are readily available on calculators supporting two-variable statistics.

$$S_e = \sqrt{\frac{\Sigma y^2 - a\Sigma y - b\Sigma xy}{n - 2}}$$

$$\approx \sqrt{\frac{8877.67 - 10.12(227.3) - 2.554(2552.17)}{6 - 2}} \approx \sqrt{\frac{59.152}{4}} \approx 3.8 \qquad \diamond$$

TECH NOTE Although many calculators that support two-variable statistics and linear regression do not provide the value of the standard error of estimate S_e directly, they do provide the sums required for the calculation of S_e. The TI-84Plus/TI-83Plus, Excel, and Minitab all provide the value of S_e.

TI-84Plus/TI-83Plus The value for S_e is given as s under **STAT, TEST,** option **E: LinRegTTest.**

Excel Use the **paste function** (f_x), select **Statistical,** and choose the function **STEYX.**

Minitab Use the menu choices **Stat ➤ Regression ➤ Regression.** The value for S_e is given as s in the display.

Inferences About the Slope β

Recall that $\hat{y} = a + bx$ is the sample-based least-squares line and $y = \alpha + \beta x$ is the population least-squares line computed (in theory) from the population of all (x, y) data pairs. In many real world applications, the slope β is very important because β measures the rate at which y changes per unit change in x. Our next topic is to develop statistical tests for β. Our work is based on the following theorem.

◇ **THEOREM 11.3** Let b be the slope of the sample least-squares line $\hat{y} = a + bx$ computed from a random sample of $n \geq 3$ data pairs (x, y). Let β be the slope of the population least-squares line $y = \alpha + \beta x$, which is in theory computed from the population of all (x, y) data pairs. Let S_e be the standard error of estimate computed from the sample. Then

$$t = \frac{b - \beta}{S_e \Big/ \sqrt{\Sigma x^2 - \frac{1}{n}(\Sigma x)^2}}$$

has a Student's t distribution with degrees of freedom $d.f. = n - 2$.   ◇

◇ **COMMENT:** The expression $S_e \Big/ \sqrt{\Sigma x^2 - \frac{1}{n}(\Sigma x)^2}$ is called the *standard error* for b.   ◇

Using this theorem, we can construct a procedure for statistical tests of β.

PROCEDURE

How to test β

Obtain a random sample of $n \geq 3$ data pairs (x, y). Use the procedure of Section 4.2 to find b, the slope of the sample least-squares line. Use Equation (2) of this section to find S_e, the standard error of estimate.

For a statistical test of β

1. Use the *null hypothesis* H_0: $\beta = 0$. Use an *alternate hypothesis* H_1 appropriate to your application ($\beta > 0$ or $\beta < 0$ or $\beta \neq 0$). Set the level of significance α.

2. Use the null hypothesis H_0: $\beta = 0$ and the values of S_e, n, Σx, Σx^2, and b to compute the *sample test statistic*

$$t = \frac{b}{S_e} \sqrt{\Sigma x^2 - \frac{1}{n}(\Sigma x)^2} \qquad \text{with } d.f. = n - 2$$

3. Use a Student's t distribution and the type of test, one-tailed or two-tailed, to find (or estimate) the *P-value* corresponding to the test statistic.

4. *Conclude* the test. If P-value $\leq \alpha$, then reject H_0. If P-value $> \alpha$, then do not reject H_0.

5. *State your conclusion* in the context of the application.

EXAMPLE 6

Testing β

Returning to the sample data regarding x = percentage of the population 25 or older with at least 4 years of college and y = percentage growth in per capita income over the past 7 years (data in Table 11-14), test the claim that the slope β of the least-squares line is positive. Use $\alpha = 0.01$.

SOLUTION: In Example 5, we found the equation of the least-squares line and the standard error of estimate S_e to be

$$\hat{y} \approx 10.12 + 2.554x \qquad \text{and} \qquad S_e \approx 3.8$$

We also found the sums $\Sigma x^2 = 740.68$ and $\Sigma x = 65.2$. Note that the number of data pairs is $n = 6$.

To test the claim that β is positive, use the hypotheses

$$H_0: \beta = 0 \qquad \text{and} \qquad H_1: \beta > 0$$

Convert the sample test statistic $b = 2.554$ to t:

$$t = \frac{b}{S_e}\sqrt{\Sigma x^2 - \frac{1}{n}(\Sigma x)^2} \approx \frac{2.554}{3.8}\sqrt{740.68 - \frac{1}{6}(65.2)^2} \approx 3.81$$

with $d.f. = n - 2 = 6 - 2 = 4$.

To conclude the test, we estimate the P-value of the sample test statistic. Scanning Table 4 of the Appendix, we see that in the row with $d.f. = 4$, the sample t value 3.81 falls between the entries 3.747 and 4.604. These entries correspond to the one-tail area between 0.010 and 0.005. Therefore,

$$0.005 < P\text{-value} < 0.010$$

Since P-value $\leq \alpha$ of 0.01, we reject H_0 and conclude that the population slope of the least-squares line is positive. This means that at the 1% level of significance, the evidence indicates that the percentage growth in per capita income increases as the percentage of the population 25 or older with at least 4 years of college increases.   ◇

Both Examples 4 and 6 utilize the data of Table 11-14 regarding education levels and income growth. It is interesting to note that for the same data, the t value of the sample correlation coefficient r and the t value of the sample slope b are essentially the same. This is not an accident! Recall from Section 4.2, formula (6), that

$$b = r\left(\frac{s_y}{s_x}\right) \qquad \begin{array}{l}\text{where } s_y \text{ and } s_x \text{ are the standard deviations of the } y \text{ and } x \\ \text{values of the data pairs, respectively}\end{array}$$

Using this relationship and some algebra, it can be shown that:

> For tests of the correlation coefficient r and the slope b of the least-squares line, both b and r convert to the same t value, with $d.f. = n - 2$, where n is the number of data pairs.

In the next Guided Exercise, we take advantage of this fact.

◇ **COMPUTATION HINTS**

(a) Most two-variable calculators provide the value of the correlation coefficient r. Find the t value for r. The t value for b is the same.

(b) Most computer-based statistical packages provide the t value for b. The t value for r is the same.   ◇

GUIDED EXERCISE **7**

Inference for ρ and β

How fast do puppies grow? That depends on the puppy. How about male wolf pups in the Helsinki Zoo (Finland)? Let x = age in weeks and y = weight in kilograms for a random sample of male wolf pups. The following data are based on the article *Studies of the Wolf in Finland Canis lupus L (Ann. Zool. Fenn.* 2: 215–259) by E. Pulliainen, University of Helsinki.

x	8	10	14	20	28	40	45
y	7	13	17	23	30	34	35

$\Sigma x = 165; \Sigma y = 159; \Sigma x^2 = 5169; \Sigma y^2 = 4317; \Sigma xy = 4659$

(a) Verify the following values.

$r \approx 0.959; b \approx 0.712$

⟹ Find the values for r and b on your calculator or use the formulas of Sections 4.1 and 4.2.

(b) Use a 1% level of significance to test the claim that $\rho > 0$.

⟹ Convert the sample correlation coefficient $r \approx 0.959$ to a t value.

$$t = \frac{r\sqrt{n-2}}{\sqrt{1-r^2}} \approx \frac{0.959\sqrt{5}}{\sqrt{1-0.959^2}} \approx 7.56$$

$H_0: \rho = 0; H_1: \rho > 0; d.f. = 5$. Using the Student's t Distribution, Table 4 of the Appendix, we see that the P-value corresponding to the sample t value of 7.56 is less than 0.0005. Since the P-value is less than α of 0.01, we reject H_0 and conclude that there is a positive correlation between age and weight.

(c) Use a 1% level of significance to test the claim that $\beta > 0$.

⟹ Convert $b \approx 0.712$ to a t value. Since the t value for b equals the t value for r, we use the result of part (b) and conclude that $t \approx 7.56$.

$H_0: \beta = 0; H_1: \beta > 0; d.f. = 5$. As in part (b), the P-value corresponding to the sample t value of 7.56 is less than 0.0005. We reject H_0 at the 1% level of significance and conclude that the slope of the least-squares line is positive.

TECH NOTE The t value corresponding to the correlation coefficient r is the same as the t value corresponding to b, the slope of the least-squares line. Consequently, the two tests H_0: $\rho = 0$ and H_0: $\beta = 0$ (with similar corresponding alternate hypotheses) have the same conclusions. The TI-84Plus/ TI-83Plus uses this fact explicitly. Minitab and Excel show the two-tailed P value for the slope b of the least-squares line. Excel also shows confidence intervals for β. The displays show data from Guided Exercise 7 regarding the age and weight of wolf pups.

TI-84Plus/TI-83Plus Under **STAT**, select **TEST** and use option **E:LinRegTTest**.

```
LinRegTTest
 y=a+bx
 B>0 and ρ>0
 t=7.5632
 p=3.2037ᴇ⁻4
 df=5.0000
↓a=5.9317
```

```
LinRegTTest
 y=a+bx
 B≠0 and p≠0
↑b=.7120
 s=3.3676
 r²=.9196
 r=.9590
```

Note that the value of S_e is given as s.

Excel Use the menu selection **Tools ➤ Data Analysis ➤ Regression.**

Regression Statistics	
Multiple R	0.958966516
R Square	0.919616778
Adjusted R Square	0.903540133
Standard Error	3.367628886	⟵ Value of S_e
Observations	7

	Coefficients	Standard Error	t Stat	P-value	Lower 95%	Upper 95%
Intercept	5.931681179	2.558126184	2.318760198	0.068158803	-0.644180779	12.50754314
X Variable 1	0.711989283	0.094138596	7.563202697	0.000640746	0.469998714	0.953979853

                b for two-tailed test

Minitab Use the menu selection **Stat ➤ Regression ➤ Regression.** The value of S_e is S; P is the P-value of a two-tailed test. For a one-tailed test, divide the P-value by 2.

```
Regression Analysis
The regression equation is
y = 5.93 + 0.712 x
Predictor        Coef        StDev         T          P
Constant        5.932        2.558       2.32       0.068
x              0.71199      0.09414      7.56       0.001
S  =  3.368      R-Sq  =  92.0%      R-Sq(adj)  =  90.4%
```

Confidence Intervals for y

The least-squares line gives us a predicted value $\hat{y}$ for a specified x value. However, we used sample data to get the equation of the line. The line derived from the population of all data pairs is likely to have a slightly different slope, which we designate by the symbol β for population slope, and a slightly different y intercept, which we designate by the symbol α for population intercept. In addition, there is some random error ϵ, so the true y value is

$$y = \alpha + \beta x + \epsilon$$

Because of the random variable ϵ, for each x value there is a corresponding distribution of y values. The methods of linear regression were developed so that the distribution of y values for a given x would be centered on the population regression line. Furthermore, the distributions of y values corresponding to each x value all have the same standard deviation, estimated by the standard error of estimate S_e.

Using all this background, the theory tells us that for a specific x, a *c confidence interval for y* is given by the next procedure.

PROCEDURE

How to find a confidence interval for a predicted y from the least-squares line

1. Obtain a random sample of $n \geq 3$ data pairs (x, y).

2. Use the procedure of Section 4.2 to find $\hat{y} = a + bx$. You also need to find $\bar{x}$ from the sample data and the standard error of estimate S_e using Equation (2) of this section.

3. The *c* confidence interval for y for a **specified value of x** is

$$\hat{y} - E < y < \hat{y} + E$$

where

$$E = t_c S_e \sqrt{1 + \frac{1}{n} + \frac{n(x - \bar{x})^2}{n\Sigma x^2 - (\Sigma x)^2}}$$

$\hat{y} = a + bx$ is the predicted value of y from the least-squares line for a *specified x* value

c = confidence level $(0 < c < 1)$

n = number of data pairs $(n \geq 3)$

t_c = critical value from Student's t distribution for c confidence level using $d.f. = n - 2$

S_e = standard error of estimate

The formulas involved in the computation of a c confidence interval look complicated. However, they involve quantities we have already computed or values we can easily look up in tables. The next example illustrates this point.

EXAMPLE 7

Confidence interval for prediction

June and Jim are partners in the chemistry lab. Their assignment is to determine how much copper sulfate ($CuSO_4$) will dissolve in water at 10, 20, 30, 40, 50, 60, and 70°C. Their lab results are shown in the table, where y is the weight in grams of copper sulfate that will dissolve in 100 g of water at x°C.

x	10	20	30	40	50	60	70
y	17	21	25	28	33	40	49

Find the equation of the least-squares line and find a 95% confidence interval for the amount of copper sulfate that will dissolve in 100 g of water at 45°C.

SOLUTION: Using a calculator with appropriate formulas, we find

$$\Sigma x = 280; \ \Sigma y = 213; \ \Sigma x^2 = 14{,}000; \ \Sigma y^2 = 7229; \ \Sigma xy = 9940$$
$$\bar{x} = 40; \ \bar{y} \approx 30.429; \ b \approx 0.50714; \ a \approx 10.143; \ S_e \approx 2.35$$

Next we use the equation of the least-squares line to find $\hat{y}$ for $x = 45$°C.

$$\hat{y} = a + bx$$
$$\hat{y} \approx 10.14 + 0.51x$$
$$\hat{y} \approx 10.14 + 0.51(45) \quad \text{Use 45 in place of } x.$$
$$\hat{y} \approx 33$$

A 95% confidence interval is then

$$\hat{y} - E < y < \hat{y} + E$$
$$33 - E < y < 33 + E$$

where $E = t_c S_e \sqrt{1 + \dfrac{1}{n} + \dfrac{n(x - \bar{x})^2}{n\Sigma x^2 - (\Sigma x)^2}}$.

Using $n - 2 = 7 - 2 = 5$ degrees of freedom, we find from Table 4 of the Appendix that $t_{0.95} = 2.571$.

$$E \approx (2.571)(2.35)\sqrt{1 + \frac{1}{7} + \frac{7(45 - 40)^2}{7(14{,}000) - (280)^2}}$$
$$\approx (2.571)(2.35)\sqrt{1.15179} \approx 6.5$$

A 95% confidence interval for y is

$$33 - 6.5 \leq y \leq 33 + 6.5$$
$$26.5 \leq y \leq 39.5$$

This means that we are 95% sure that the interval between 26.5 g and 39.5 g is one that contains the predicted amount of copper sulfate that will dissolve in 100 g of water at 45°C. The interval is fairly wide but would decrease with more sample data. ◇

GUIDED EXERCISE 8

Confidence interval for prediction

Let's use the data of Example 7 to compute a 95% confidence interval for y = amount of copper sulfate that will dissolve at $x = 15°C$.

(a) From Example 7, we have

$\hat{y} \approx 10.14 + 0.51x$

Evaluate $\hat{y}$ for $x = 15$.

$\implies$ $\hat{y} \approx 10.14 + 0.51x$
$\approx 10.14 + 0.51(15)$
≈ 17.8

(b) The bound E on the error of estimate is

$$E = t_c S_e \sqrt{1 + \frac{1}{n} + \frac{n(x - \bar{x})^2}{n\Sigma x^2 - (\Sigma x)^2}}$$

From Example 7, we know that $S_e \approx 2.35$, $\Sigma x = 280$, $\Sigma x^2 = 14,000$, $\bar{x} = 40$, and $n = 7$. Find $t_{0.95}$ and compute E.

$\implies$ $t_{0.95} = 2.571$ for $d.f. = n - 2 = 5$

$$E \approx (2.571)(2.35)\sqrt{1 + \frac{1}{7} + \frac{7(15 - 40)^2}{7(14,000) - (280)^2}}$$

$\approx (2.571)(2.35)\sqrt{1.366071} \approx 7.1$

(c) Find a 95% confidence interval for y.

$\hat{y} - E \leq y \leq \hat{y} + E$

$\implies$ The confidence interval is

$17.8 - 7.1 \leq y \leq 17.8 + 7.1$
$10.7 \leq y \leq 24.9$

As we compare the results of Guided Exercise 8 and Example 7, we notice that the 95% confidence interval of y values for $x = 15°C$ is 7.1 units above and below the least-squares line, while the 95% confidence interval of y values for $x = 45°C$ is only 6.5 units above and below the least-squares line. This comparison reflects the general property that confidence intervals for y are narrower the nearer we are to the mean $\bar{x}$ of the x values. As we move near the extremes of the x distribution, the confidence intervals for y become wider. This is another reason that we should not try to use the least-squares line to predict y values for x values beyond the data extremes of the sample x distribution.

If we were to compute a 95% confidence interval for all x values in the range of the sample x values, the confidence interval band would curve away from the least-squares line, as shown in Figure 11-9.

TECH NOTE Minitab provides confidence intervals for predictions. Use the menu selection **Stat ➤ Regression ➤ Regression**. Under options, enter the observed x value and set the confidence level. In the output, the confidence interval for predictions is designated by %PI.

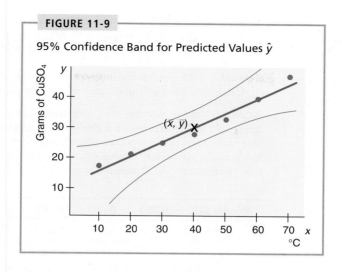

FIGURE 11-9

95% Confidence Band for Predicted Values $\hat{y}$

VIEWPOINT

Hawaiian Island Hopping!

Suppose you want to go camping in Hawaii. Yes! Hawaii has both state and federal parks where you can enjoy camping on the beach or in the mountains. However, you will probably need to rent a car to get to the different campgrounds. How much will the car rental cost? That depends on the islands you visit. For car rental data and regression statistics you can compute regarding costs on different Hawaiian Islands, visit the Brase/Brase statistics site at **http://math.college.hmco.com/students** and find the link to Hawaiian Islands.

SECTION 11.4   PROBLEMS

In Problems 1–6, parts (a) and (b) relate to testing ρ. Part (c) requests the value of S_e. Parts (d) and (e) relate to confidence intervals for prediction. Part (f) relates to testing β. Answers may vary due to rounding.

1. *Basketball: Free Throws and Field Goals* Let x be a random variable that represents the percentage of successful free throws a professional basketball player makes in a season. Let y be a random variable that represents the percentage of successful field goals a professional basketball player makes in a season. A random sample of $n = 6$ professional basketball players gave the following information (Reference: *The Official NBA Basketball Encyclopedia*, Villard Books).

x	67	65	75	86	73	73
y	44	42	48	51	44	51

   (a) Verify that $\Sigma x = 439$, $\Sigma y = 280$, $\Sigma x^2 = 32{,}393$, $\Sigma y^2 = 13{,}142$, $\Sigma xy = 20{,}599$, and $r \approx 0.784$.

(b) Use a 5% level of significance to test the claim that $\rho > 0$.

(c) Verify that $S_e \approx 2.6964$, $a \approx 16.542$, $b \approx 0.4117$, and $\bar{x} \approx 73.167$.

(d) Find the predicted percentage $\hat{y}$ of successful field goals for a player with $x = 70\%$ successful free throws.

(e) Find a 90% confidence interval for y when $x = 70$.

(f) Use a 5% level of significance to test the claim that $\beta > 0$.

2. *Baseball: Batting Average and Strikeouts* Let x be a random variable that represents the batting average of a professional baseball player. Let y be a random variable that represents the percentage of strikeouts of a professional baseball player. A random sample of $n = 6$ professional baseball players gave the following information (Reference: *The Baseball Encyclopedia*, Macmillan).

x	0.328	0.290	0.340	0.248	0.367	0.269
y	3.2	7.6	4.0	8.6	3.1	11.1

(a) Verify that $\Sigma x = 1.842$, $\Sigma y = 37.6$, $\Sigma x^2 = 0.575838$, $\Sigma y^2 = 290.78$, $\Sigma xy = 10.87$, and $r \approx -0.891$.

(b) Use a 5% level of significance to test the claim that $\rho \neq 0$.

(c) Verify that $S_e \approx 1.6838$, $a \approx 26.247$, and $b \approx -65.081$.

(d) Find the predicted percentage of strikeouts for a player with an $x = 0.300$ batting average.

(e) Find an 80% confidence interval for y when $x = 0.300$.

(f) Use a 5% level of significance to test the claim that $\beta \neq 0$.

3. *Scuba Diving: Depth* What is the optimal time for a scuba diver to be on the bottom of the ocean? That depends on the depth of the dive. The U.S. Navy has done a lot of research on this topic. The Navy defines the "optimal time" to be the time at each depth for the best balance between length of work period and decompression time after surfacing. Let x = depth of dive in meters, and let y = optimal time in hours. A random sample of divers gave the following data (based on information taken from *Medical Physiology* by A. C. Guyton, M.D.).

x	14.1	24.3	30.2	38.3	51.3	20.5	22.7
y	2.58	2.08	1.58	1.03	0.75	2.38	2.20

(a) Verify that $\Sigma x = 201.4$, $\Sigma y = 12.6$, $\Sigma x^2 = 6735.46$, $\Sigma y^2 = 25.607$, $\Sigma xy = 311.292$, and $r \approx -0.976$.

(b) Use a 1% level of significance to test the claim that $\rho < 0$.

(c) Verify that $S_e \approx 0.1660$, $a \approx 3.366$, and $b \approx -0.0544$.

(d) Find the predicted optimal time in hours for a dive depth of $x = 18$ meters.

(e) Find an 80% confidence interval for y when $x = 18$ meters.

(f) Use a 1% level of significance to test the claim that $\beta < 0$.

4. *Physiology: Oxygen* Aviation and high-altitude physiology is a specialty in the study of medicine. Let x = partial pressure of oxygen in the alveoli (air cells in the lungs) when breathing naturally available air. Let y = partial pressure when breathing pure oxygen. The (x, y) data pairs correspond to elevations from 10,000 feet up to 30,000 feet in 5000-foot intervals for a random sample of volunteers. Although the medical data were collected using airplanes, they will apply equally well to Mt. Everest climbers (summit 29,028 feet).

x	6.7	5.1	4.2	3.3	2.1 (units: mm Hg/10)
y	43.6	32.9	26.2	16.2	13.9 (units: mm Hg/10)

(Based on information taken from *Medical Physiology* by A. C. Guyton, M.D.)
(a) Verify that $\Sigma x = 21.4$, $\Sigma y = 132.8$, $\Sigma x^2 = 103.84$, $\Sigma y^2 = 4125.46$, $\Sigma xy = 652.6$, and $r \approx 0.984$.
(b) Use a 1% level of significance to test the claim that $\rho > 0$.
(c) Verify that $S_e \approx 2.5319$, $a \approx -2.869$, and $b \approx 6.876$.
(d) Find the predicted pressure from breathing pure oxygen when the pressure from breathing available air is $x = 4.0$.
(e) Find a 90% confidence interval for y when $x = 4.0$.
(f) Use a 1% level of significance to test the claim that $\beta > 0$.

5. *New Car: Negotiating Price* Suppose you are interested in buying a new Toyota Corolla. You are standing on the sales lot looking at a model with different options. The list price is on the vehicle. As a salesperson approaches, you wonder what the dealer invoice price is for this model with its options. The following data are based on information taken from *Consumer Guide* (vol. 677). Let x be the list price (in thousands of dollars) for a random selection of Toyota Corollas of different models and options. Let y be the dealer invoice (in thousands of dollars) for the given vehicle.

x	12.6	13.0	12.8	13.6	13.4	14.2
y	11.6	12.0	11.5	12.2	12.0	12.8

(a) Verify that $\Sigma x = 79.6$, $\Sigma y = 72.1$, $\Sigma x^2 = 1057.76$, $\Sigma y^2 = 867.49$, $\Sigma xy = 957.84$, and $r \approx 0.956$.
(b) Use a 1% level of significance to test the claim that $\rho > 0$.
(c) Verify that $S_e \approx 0.1527$, $a \approx 1.965$, and $b \approx 0.758$.
(d) Find the predicted dealer invoice when the list price is $x = 14$ (thousand dollars).
(e) Find an 85% confidence interval for y when $x = 14$ (thousand dollars).
(f) Use a 1% level of significance to test the claim that $\beta > 0$.

6. *New Car: Negotiating Price* Suppose you are interested in buying a new Lincoln Navigator or Town Car. You are standing on the sales lot looking at a model with different options. The list price is on the vehicle. As a salesperson approaches, you wonder what the dealer invoice price is for this model with its options. The following data are based on information taken from *Consumer Guide* (vol. 677). Let x be the list price (in thousands of dollars) for a random selection of these cars of different models and options. Let y be the dealer invoice (in thousands of dollars) for the given vehicle.

x	32.1	33.5	36.1	44.0	47.8
y	29.8	31.1	32.0	42.1	42.2

(a) Verify that $\Sigma x = 193.5$, $\Sigma y = 177.2$, $\Sigma x^2 = 7676.71$, $\Sigma y^2 = 6432.5$, $\Sigma xy = 7023.19$, and $r \approx 0.977$.
(b) Use a 1% level of significance to test the claim that $\rho > 0$.
(c) Verify that $S_e \approx 1.5223$, $a \approx 1.4084$, and $b \approx 0.8794$.

(d) Find the predicted dealer invoice when the list price is $x = 40$ (thousand dollars).

(e) Find a 95% confidence interval for y when $x = 40$ (thousand dollars).

(f) Use a 1% level of significance to test the claim that $\beta > 0$.

7. *Expand Your Knowledge: Sample Size and Significance of r*

(a) Suppose that $n = 6$ and the sample correlation coefficient is $r = 0.90$. Is r significant at the 1% level of significance (based on a two-tailed test)?

(b) Suppose that $n = 10$ and the sample correlation coefficient is $r = 0.90$. Is r significant at the 1% level of significance (based on a two-tailed test)?

(c) Explain why the test results of parts (a) and (b) are different even though the sample correlation coefficient $r = 0.90$ in both parts. Does it appear that sample size plays an important role in determining the significance of a correlation coefficient? Explain.

SUMMARY

In this chapter, we saw more applications of inferential statistics. In Part I, we looked at three applications of the chi-square distribution. We used the distribution to test for independence and goodness of fit. In each of these cases, we computed expected values and then used the differences between the expected values and the observed values to compute a sample χ^2 statistics. We then used the chi-square distribution table to determine if the sample χ^2 value was significant. Finally, we used the chi-square distribution to test the value of the variance of a normal distribution.

In Part II, we returned to the linear-regression model introduced in Chapter 4. We tested the sample correlation coefficient r and the sample slope b of the least-squares line. Then we computed confidence intervals for predicted values.

IMPORTANT WORDS & SYMBOLS

Section 11.1

Test of independence

Chi-square distribution, χ^2

Degrees of freedom, $d.f. = (R - 1)(C - 1)$, for χ^2 distribution and tests of independence

Contingency table with cells

Expected frequency of a cell, E

Observed frequency of a cell, O

Row total

Column total

Section 11.2

Test of goodness of fit

Degrees of freedom $d.f.$ for χ^2 distribution and goodness-of-fit tests

Section 11.3

Hypothesis test about σ^2

Section 11.4

Population correlation coefficient ρ

Population slope β of the least-squares line

Standard error of estimate S_e

Confidence interval for y

VIEWPOINT

Movies and Money!

Young adults are the movie industry's best customers. However, going to the movies is expensive, which may explain why attendance rates increase with household income. Using what you have learned in this chapter, you can create appropriate chi-square tests to determine how good a fit exists between national percentage rates of attendance by household income and attendance rates in your demographic area. For more information and national data, see *American Demographics* (vol. 18, no. 12).

CHAPTER REVIEW PROBLEMS

Part I: Inferences Using the Chi-Square Distribution

In each problem, when a test is to be performed, please do the following:
  (i) Give the value of the level of significance. State the null and alternate hypotheses.
  (ii) Find the sample test statistic.
  (iii) Find or estimate the *P*-value of the sample test statistic.
  (iv) Conclude the test.
  (v) Interpret the conclusion in the context of the application.

1. *Sociology: Age Distribution* A sociologist is studying the age of the population in Blue Valley. Ten years ago, the population was such that 20% was under 20 years old, 15% was in the 20- to 35-year-old bracket, 30% was between 36 and 50, 25% was between 51 and 65, and 10% was over 65. A study done this year used a random sample of 210 residents. This sample showed

Under 20	20–35	36–50	51–65	Over 65
26	27	69	68	20

At the 0.01 level of significance, has the age distribution of the population of Blue Valley changed?

2. *Education: Exams* Professor Fair believes that extra time does not improve grades on exams. He randomly divided a group of 300 students into two groups and gave them all the same test. One group had exactly 1 hour in which to finish the test, and the other group could stay as long as desired. The results are shown in the following table. Test at the 0.01 level of significance that time to complete a test and test results are independent.

Time	A	B	C	F	Row Total
1 h	23	42	65	12	142
Unlimited	17	48	85	8	158
Column total	40	90	150	20	300

3. *Tires: Blowouts* A consumer agency is investigating the blowout pressures of Soap Stone tires. A Soap Stone tire is said to blow out when it separates from the wheel rim due to impact forces usually caused by hitting a rock or a pothole in the road. A random sample of 30 Soap Stone tires were inflated to the recommended pressure, and then forces measured in foot-pounds were applied to each tire (1 foot-pound is the force of 1 pound dropped from a height of 1 foot). The customer complaint is that some Soap Stone tires blow out under small-impact forces, while other tires seem to be well made and don't have this fault. For the 30 test tires, the sample standard deviation of blowout forces was 1353 foot-pounds. Soap Stone claims its tires will blow out at an average pressure of 20,000 foot-pounds with a standard deviation of 1020 foot-pounds. The average blowout force is not in question, but the variability of blowout forces is in question. Using a 0.01 level of significance, test the claim that the variance of blowout pressures is more than Soap Stone claims it is.

4. *Packaging: Corn Flakes* A machine that puts corn flakes into boxes is adjusted to put an average of 15 oz into each box, with standard deviation of 0.25 oz. If a random sample of 12 boxes gave a sample standard deviation of 0.38 oz, do these data support the claim that the variance has increased and the machine needs to be brought back into adjustment? (Use a 0.01 level of significance.)

5. *Teacher Ratings: Grades* Professor Stone complains that student teacher ratings depend on the grade the student receives. In other words, according to Professor Stone, a teacher who gives good grades gets good ratings, and a teacher who gives bad grades gets bad ratings. To test this claim, the Student Assembly took a random sample of 300 teacher ratings on which the student's grade for the course also was indicated. The results are given in the following table. Test the hypothesis that teacher ratings and student grades are independent at the 0.01 level of significance.

Rating	A	B	C	F (or withdrawal)	Row Total
Excellent	14	18	15	3	50
Average	25	35	75	15	150
Poor	21	27	40	12	100
Column total	60	80	130	30	300

6. *Fair Dice: Uniform Distribution* A gambler complained about the dice. They seemed to be loaded! The dice were taken off the table and tested one at a time. One die was rolled 300 times and the following frequencies were recorded.

Outcome	1	2	3	4	5	6
Observed frequency O	62	45	63	32	47	51

Do these data indicate that the die is unbalanced? Use a 1% level of significance. *Hint:* If the die is balanced, all outcomes should have the same expected frequency.

Part II: Inferences Relating to Linear Regression

7. *Baseball: Batting Averages and Home Runs* In baseball, is there a linear correlation between batting average and home run percentage? Let x represent the batting average of a professional baseball player. Let y represent the home run percentage (number of home runs per 100 times at bat). A random sample of $n = 7$ professional

baseball players gave the following information (Reference: *The Baseball Encyclopedia*, Macmillan Publishing Company).

x	0.243	0.259	0.286	0.263	0.268	0.339	0.299
y	1.4	3.6	5.5	3.8	3.5	7.3	5.0

$\Sigma x = 1.957$; $\Sigma y = 30.1$; $\Sigma x^2 \approx 0.553$; $\Sigma y^2 = 150.15$; $\Sigma xy \approx 8.753$

(a) Verify that $S_e \approx 0.647$.
(b) Verify that $r \approx 0.948$. Test that ρ is positive. Use $\alpha = 0.01$.
(c) Verify that $b \approx 55.166$. Test that β is positive. Use $\alpha = 0.01$.
(d) Verify that $\hat{y} \approx -11.123 + 55.166x$. Find a 90% confidence interval for the predicted home run percentage for a player with a batting average of 0.310.

8. *Physiology: Children* The following problem is based on information taken from the pediatrics section of *The Merck Manual* (a commonly used reference in medical schools and nursing programs). Let x be the body weight of a child (in kilograms), and let y be the metabolic rate of the child (in 100 kcal/24 h).

x	3.0	5.0	9.0	11.0	15.0	17.0	19.0	21.0
y	1.4	2.7	5.0	6.0	7.1	7.8	8.3	8.8

$\Sigma x = 100$; $\Sigma y = 47.1$; $\Sigma x^2 = 1552$; $\Sigma y^2 = 327.83$; $\Sigma xy = 710.3$

(a) Verify that $S_e \approx 0.518$.
(b) Verify that $r \approx 0.984$. Test that ρ is positive. Use $\alpha = 0.01$.
(c) Verify that $b \approx 0.402$. Test that β is positive. Use $\alpha = 0.01$.
(d) Verify that $\hat{y} \approx 0.856 + 0.402x$. Find a 90% confidence interval for the predicted metabolic rate for a child weighing 10 kg.

DATA HIGHLIGHTS: GROUP PROJECTS

Distribution of Drunk Driver Arrests by Age

Age	National Percentage	Number in Freemont County
16–17	3.7	8
18–24	18.9	35
25–29	12.9	23
30–34	10.3	19
35–39	8.5	12
40–44	7.9	14
45–49	8.0	16
50–54	7.9	13
55–59	6.8	10
60–64	5.7	9
65 and over	9.4	15
	100%	174

Break into small groups and discuss the following topics. Organize a brief outline in which you summarize the main points of your group discussion.

The Statistical Abstract of the United States reported information about the percentage of arrests of all drunk drivers according to age group. In the table at the left, the entry 3.7 in the first row means that in the entire United States, about 3.7% of all people arrested for drunk driving were in the age group 16 to 17 years. The Freemont County Sheriff's Office obtained data about the number of drunk drivers arrested in each age group over the past several years. In the table, the entry 8 in the first row means that eight people in the age group 16 to 17 years were arrested for drunk driving in Freemont County.

Use a chi-square test with 5% level of significance to test the claim that the age distribution of drunk drivers arrested in Freemont County is the same as the national age distribution of drunk drivers arrested.

(a) State the null and alternate hypotheses.
(b) Find the value of the chi-square statistic from the sample.
(c) Find the degrees of freedom and the appropriate chi-square critical value.
(d) Sketch the critical region and locate your sample chi-square value and critical chi-square value on the sketch.
(e) Decide whether you should reject or not reject the null hypothesis. State your conclusion in the context of the problem.

LINKING CONCEPTS: WRITING PROJECTS

Discuss each of the following topics in class or review the topics on your own. Then write a brief but complete essay in which you summarize the main points. Please include formulas and graphs as appropriate.

Consider the results of a study conducted by the makers of Advil. A random sample of patients were assigned to one of two groups: One received ibuprofen and the other received a placebo. Then patients were asked if they experienced stomach upset (yes or no). The results of the study follow.

Group	Stomach Upset		Row Total
	Yes	No	
Ibuprofen	8	664	672
Placebo	6	645	651
Column total	14	1309	1323

1. In Chapter 5 on probability (Section 5.2), we considered contingency tables and the probabilities of events described by different combinations of the rows and columns. Use these techniques to compute the probability that a patient had stomach upset, *given* that the patient was in the ibuprofen group. Compute the probability that a patient had stomach upset, *given* that the patient was in the placebo group.

2. Are the proportions of patients having stomach upset in the two different treatment groups the same? We treated questions of this type in Section 10.3, where we applied the normal distribution to test the difference of proportions. Use such a test to determine whether or not the proportions are different at the 5% level of significance.

3. Now consider the 2 × 2 contingency table. We can apply techniques of tests of independence to see if the proportions of patients experiencing stomach upset in the two treatment groups are the same or not. When we apply these techniques to tests of proportions, we assume that the sample size for each treatment group is *assigned* ahead of time and is not itself a random variable. In such a case, we apply a test of independence, but we change the hypotheses to H_0: The proportions are equal and H_1: The proportions are not equal. Perform such a test.

4. Compare the results of Problems 2 and 3. Do the test conclusions agree? When testing two proportions, you can use either the normal distribution test of Section 10.3 or a chi-square test. Can you think of any advantages of one choice over the other?

Using Technology

APPLICATION

Tests of Independence

A study involving people who are food processors gave the following information about work shift and number of sick days.

	Number of Sick Days				
Shift	0	1	2	3	4 or more
Day	134	44	24	10	61
Aft/ev	90	39	23	18	99
Night	107	37	21	20	82
Rotating	56	20	14	17	92

Source: United States Department of Health, Education, and Welfare, NIOSH Technical Report. Tasto, Colligan, *et al. Health Consequences of Shift Work*. Washington: GPO, 1978, 29. (*Note:* This table was adapted from Table 7 on page 25 of the source.)

Use a 1% level of significance to test the null hypothesis that work shift and number of sick days are independent against the alternate hypothesis that they are not independent. What is the sample chi-square value? What is the test conclusion?

Technology Hints

TI-84Plus/TI-83Plus

Press the **Matrix** key and enter the observed values in a matrix. Name the matrix [A]. Then enter dimension matrix [B] to the same dimensions. Matrix [B] will hold the expected values. Press the **STAT** key and under the **TESTS** menu, select option **C:χ^2-Test. Calculate** will give the sample χ^2 value and its *P* value. **Draw** will show the sample test statistic on the χ^2 distribution with the *P*-value shaded.

Excel

There are no built-in commands for executing a chi-square test. The *Technology Guide* shows a multistep process for conducting a chi-square test. The Tech Note of Section 11.1 gives a brief outline of the process.

Minitab

In Minitab, enter data for tests of independence in columns. Be sure to enter data only and not row or column totals. Then use the menu choices ➤ **Stat** ➤ **Tables** ➤ **Chisquare Test.**

SPSS

SPSS utilizes raw data to make a contingency table and then provides an option for a chi-square test of independence. For example, rather than entering the data for number of sick days versus shift as a table, in SPSS you enter all 1009 cases, where the shift variable shows the row category (day, aft/eve, night, rotating) of the entry and the sick-days variable shows the corresponding column category (number of sick days). Specifically, you would enter 134 cases with shift variable "day" and sick-day variable "0," etc. Then use the menu choices **Analyze** ➤ **Descriptive Statistics** ➤ **Crosstabs....** In the dialogue box, move the row variable and the column variable to the designated boxes. Select the Statistics option and check Chi-square. To see the expected values, select the Cells option and check Expected. The output includes a contingency table, the sample χ^2 test statistic, degrees of freedom, and the *P*-value of the test statistic.

Cumulative Review Problems

For all hypothesis tests, please provide the following information.

(i) What is the level of significance? State the null and alternate hypotheses.

(ii) What sampling distribution will you use? What assumptions are you making? What is the value of the sample test statistic?

(iii) Find (or estimate) the P-value. Sketch the sampling distribution and show the area corresponding to the P-value.

(iv) Based on your answers in parts (i) to (iii), will you reject or fail to reject the null hypothesis? Are the data statistically significant at level α?

(v) State your conclusion in the context of the application.

1. *Inferences for Linear Regression* Plate tectonics and the spread of the ocean floor are very important in modern studies of earthquakes and earth science in general. A random sample of islands in the Indian Ocean gave the following information, where

   x = age of volcanic island in the Indian Ocean (units in 10^6 years)

   y = distance of the island from the center of the midoceanic ridge (units in 100 km)

x	120	83	60	50	35	30	20	17
y	30	16	15.5	14.5	22	18	12	0

Source: King, Cuchaine A.M. *Physical Geography.* Oxford: Basil Blackwell, 1980, pp. 77–86 and 196–206. Reprinted by permission of the publisher.

$$\Sigma x = 415; \ \Sigma y = 128; \ \Sigma x^2 = 30{,}203; \ \Sigma y^2 = 2558.5; \ \Sigma xy = 8133$$

(a) Verify that the standard error of estimate $S_e \approx 6.50$.

(b) Verify that the sample correlation coefficient $r \approx 0.709$. Use a 5% level of significance to test that ρ is positive.

(c) Verify that the equation of the least-squares line is $\hat{y} \approx 7.07 + 0.172x$. Use a 5% level of significance to test that β is positive.

(d) Given that the age of a volcanic island is 55 (units in 10^6 years), predict how far the island is from the center of the midoceanic ridge (units in 100 km). Find an 85% confidence interval for the prediction.

2. *Goodness of Fit* A recent national study gave the following information about declared majors of undergraduate college students: humanities, 15%; science, 23%; business, 29%; education, 11%; social science, 10%; all other fields, 12% (Reference: *Statistical Abstract of the United States*). A random sample of 215 college students in Colorado gave the following counts regarding college majors: humanities, 24; science, 54; business, 70; education, 16; social science, 30; all other fields, 21. Does this information indicate that the distribution of college majors for Colorado students is different from the national distribution? Use $\alpha = 0.01$.

3. *Test of Independence: Agriculture* Three types of fertilizer were used on 132 identical plots of maize. Each plot was harvested and the yield (in kg) was recorded (Reference: Caribbean Agricultural Research and Development Institute).

Yield (kg)	Type of Fertilizer			Row Total
	I	II	III	
0–2.9	12	10	15	37
3.0–5.9	18	21	11	50
6.0–8.9	16	19	10	45
Column total	46	50	36	132

Use a 5% level of significance to test the hypothesis that type of fertilizer and yield of maize are independent.

4. *Testing and Estimating Variances: Iris* Random samples of two species of iris gave the following petal lengths (in cm) (Reference: R. A. Fisher, *Annals of Eugenics*, vol. 7).

x_1, *Iris virginica*	5.1	5.9	4.5	4.9	5.7	4.8	5.8	6.4	5.6	5.9
x_2, *Iris versicolor*	4.5	4.8	4.7	5.0	3.8	5.1	4.4	4.2		

(a) Use a 5% level of significance to test the claim that the population standard deviation of x_1 is larger than 0.55.
(b) Find a 90% confidence interval for the population standard deviation of x_1.

5. *Testing Paired Differences* Phosphorous is a chemical that is found in many household cleaning products. Unfortunately, phosphorous also finds its way into surface water where it can harm fish, plants, and other wildlife. Two methods of phosphorous reduction are being studied. At a random sample of seven locations, both methods were used and the total phosphorous reduction (mg/l) was recorded (Reference: *Environmental Protection Agency Case Study 832-R-93-005*).

Site	1	2	3	4	5	6	7
Method I:	0.013	0.030	0.015	0.055	0.007	0.002	0.010
Method II:	0.014	0.058	0.017	0.039	0.017	0.001	0.013

Do these data indicate a difference (either way) in the average reduction of phosphorous between the two methods? Use $\alpha = 0.05$.

6. *Testing and Estimating $\mu_1 - \mu_2$, σ_1 and σ_2 Unknown* In the airline business, "on-time" flight arrival is important for connecting flights and general customer satisfaction. Is there a difference between summer and winter average on-time flight arrivals? Let x_1 be a random variable that represents percentage of on-time arrivals at major airports in the summer. Let x_2 be a random variable that represents percentage of on-time arrivals at major airports in the winter. A random sample of $n_1 = 16$ major airports showed that $\bar{x}_1 = 74.8\%$ with $s_1 = 5.2\%$. A random sample of $n_2 = 18$ major airports showed that $\bar{x}_2 = 70.1\%$ with $s_2 = 8.6\%$ (Reference: *Statistical Abstract of the United States*).

(a) Does this information indicate a difference (either way) in the population mean percentage of on-time arrivals in summer compared to winter? Use $\alpha = 0.05$.

(b) Find a 95% confidence interval for $\mu_1 - \mu_2$.

(c) What assumptions about the original populations have you made for the methods used?

7. *Testing and Estimating a Difference of Proportions $p_1 - p_2$* How often do you go out dancing? This question was asked by a professional survey group on behalf of the National Arts Survey. A random sample of $n_1 = 95$ single men showed that $r_1 = 23$ went out dancing occasionally. Another random sample of $n_2 = 92$ single women showed that $r_2 = 19$ went out dancing occasionally.

(a) Do these data indicate that the proportion of single men who go out dancing occasionally is higher than the proportion of single women? Use a 5% level of significance. List the assumptions you made in solving this problem. Do you think these assumptions are realistic?

(b) Compute a 90% confidence interval for the population difference of proportions $p_1 - p_2$ of single men and single women who occasionally go out dancing.

Appendix   Tables

1. Random Numbers
2. Binomial Probability Distribution
   $C_{n,r}p^r q^{n-r}$
3. Areas of a Standard Normal Distribution
4. Critical Values for Student's t Distribution
5. The χ^2 Distribution

TABLE 1   Random Numbers

92630	78240	19267	95457	53497	23894	37708	79862	76471	66418
79445	78735	71549	44843	26104	67318	00701	34986	66751	99723
59654	71966	27386	50004	05358	94031	29281	18544	52429	06080
31524	49587	76612	39789	13537	48086	59483	60680	84675	53014
06348	76938	90379	51392	55887	71015	09209	79157	24440	30244
28703	51709	94456	48396	73780	06436	86641	69239	57662	80181
68108	89266	94730	95761	75023	48464	65544	96583	18911	16391
99938	90704	93621	66330	33393	95261	95349	51769	91616	33238
91543	73196	34449	63513	83834	99411	58826	40456	69268	48562
42103	02781	73920	56297	72678	12249	25270	36678	21313	75767
17138	27584	25296	28387	51350	61664	37893	05363	44143	42677
28297	14280	54524	21618	95320	38174	60579	08089	94999	78460
09331	56712	51333	06289	75345	08811	82711	57392	25252	30333
31295	04204	93712	51287	05754	79396	87399	51773	33075	97061
36146	15560	27592	42089	99281	59640	15221	96079	09961	05371
29553	18432	13630	05529	02791	81017	49027	79031	50912	09399
23501	22642	63081	08191	89420	67800	55137	54707	32945	64522
57888	85846	67967	07835	11314	01545	48535	17142	08552	67457
55336	71264	88472	04334	63919	36394	11196	92470	70543	29776
10087	10072	55980	64688	68239	20461	89381	93809	00796	95945
34101	81277	66090	88872	37818	72142	67140	50785	21380	16703
53362	44940	60430	22834	14130	96593	23298	56203	92671	15925
82975	66158	84731	19436	55790	69229	28661	13675	99318	76873
54827	84673	22898	08094	14326	87038	42892	21127	30712	48489
25464	59098	27436	89421	80754	89924	19097	67737	80368	08795
67609	60214	41475	84950	40133	02546	09570	45682	50165	15609
44921	70924	61295	51137	47596	86735	35561	76649	18217	63446
33170	30972	98130	95828	49786	13301	36081	80761	33985	68621
84687	85445	06208	17654	51333	02878	35010	67578	61574	20749
71886	56450	36567	09395	96951	35507	17555	35212	69106	01679
00475	02224	74722	14721	40215	21351	08596	45625	83981	63748
25993	38881	68361	59560	41274	69742	40703	37993	03435	18873
92882	53178	99195	93803	56985	53089	15305	50522	55900	43026
25138	26810	07093	15677	60688	04410	24505	37890	67186	62829
84631	71882	12991	83028	82484	90339	91950	74579	03539	90122

Source: Reprinted from *A Million Random Digits with 100,000 Normal Deviates* by the Rand Corporation (New York: The Free Press, 1955). Copyright 1955 and 1983 by the Rand Corporation. Used by permission.

TABLE 2 Binomial Probability Distribution $C_{n,r}\, p^r q^{n-r}$

This table shows the probability of r successes in n independent trials, each with probability of success p.

													p								
n	r	.01	.05	.10	.15	.20	.25	.30	.35	.40	.45	.50	.55	.60	.65	.70	.75	.80	.85	.90	.95
2	0	.980	.902	.810	.723	.640	.563	.490	.423	.360	.303	.250	.203	.160	.123	.090	.063	.040	.023	.010	.002
	1	.020	.095	.180	.255	.320	.375	.420	.455	.480	.495	.500	.495	.480	.455	.420	.375	.320	.255	.180	.095
	2	.000	.002	.010	.023	.040	.063	.090	.123	.160	.203	.250	.303	.360	.423	.490	.563	.640	.723	.810	.902
3	0	.970	.857	.729	.614	.512	.422	.343	.275	.216	.166	.125	.091	.064	.043	.027	.016	.008	.003	.001	.000
	1	.029	.135	.243	.325	.384	.422	.441	.444	.432	.408	.375	.334	.288	.239	.189	.141	.096	.057	.027	.007
	2	.000	.007	.027	.057	.096	.141	.189	.239	.288	.334	.375	.408	.432	.444	.441	.422	.384	.325	.243	.135
	3	.000	.000	.001	.003	.008	.016	.027	.043	.064	.091	.125	.166	.216	.275	.343	.422	.512	.614	.729	.857
4	0	.961	.815	.656	.522	.410	.316	.240	.179	.130	.092	.062	.041	.026	.015	.008	.004	.002	.001	.000	.000
	1	.039	.171	.292	.368	.410	.422	.412	.384	.346	.300	.250	.200	.154	.112	.076	.047	.026	.011	.004	.000
	2	.001	.014	.049	.098	.154	.211	.265	.311	.346	.368	.375	.368	.346	.311	.265	.211	.154	.098	.049	.014
	3	.000	.000	.004	.011	.026	.047	.076	.112	.154	.200	.250	.300	.346	.384	.412	.422	.410	.368	.292	.171
	4	.000	.000	.000	.001	.002	.004	.008	.015	.026	.041	.062	.092	.130	.179	.240	.316	.410	.522	.656	.815
5	0	.951	.774	.590	.444	.328	.237	.168	.116	.078	.050	.031	.019	.010	.005	.002	.001	.000	.000	.000	.000
	1	.048	.204	.328	.392	.410	.396	.360	.312	.259	.206	.156	.113	.077	.049	.028	.015	.006	.002	.000	.000
	2	.001	.021	.073	.138	.205	.264	.309	.336	.346	.337	.312	.276	.230	.181	.132	.088	.051	.024	.008	.001
	3	.000	.001	.008	.024	.051	.088	.132	.181	.230	.276	.312	.337	.346	.336	.309	.264	.205	.138	.073	.021
	4	.000	.000	.000	.002	.006	.015	.028	.049	.077	.113	.156	.206	.259	.312	.360	.396	.410	.392	.328	.204
	5	.000	.000	.000	.000	.000	.001	.002	.005	.010	.019	.031	.050	.078	.116	.168	.237	.328	.444	.590	.774
6	0	.941	.735	.531	.377	.262	.178	.118	.075	.047	.028	.016	.008	.004	.002	.001	.000	.000	.000	.000	.000
	1	.057	.232	.354	.399	.393	.356	.303	.244	.187	.136	.094	.061	.037	.020	.010	.004	.002	.000	.000	.000
	2	.001	.031	.098	.176	.246	.297	.324	.328	.311	.278	.234	.186	.138	.095	.060	.033	.015	.006	.001	.000
	3	.000	.002	.015	.042	.082	.132	.185	.236	.276	.303	.312	.303	.276	.236	.185	.132	.082	.042	.015	.002
	4	.000	.000	.001	.006	.015	.033	.060	.095	.138	.186	.234	.278	.311	.328	.324	.297	.246	.176	.098	.031
	5	.000	.000	.000	.000	.002	.004	.010	.020	.037	.061	.094	.136	.187	.244	.303	.356	.393	.399	.354	.232
	6	.000	.000	.000	.000	.000	.001	.001	.002	.004	.008	.016	.028	.047	.075	.118	.178	.262	.377	.531	.735
7	0	.932	.698	.478	.321	.210	.133	.082	.049	.028	.015	.008	.004	.002	.001	.000	.000	.000	.000	.000	.000
	1	.066	.257	.372	.396	.367	.311	.247	.185	.131	.087	.055	.032	.017	.008	.004	.001	.000	.000	.000	.000
	2	.002	.041	.124	.210	.275	.311	.318	.299	.261	.214	.164	.117	.077	.047	.025	.012	.004	.001	.000	.000
	3	.000	.004	.023	.062	.115	.173	.227	.268	.290	.292	.273	.239	.194	.144	.097	.058	.029	.011	.003	.000
	4	.000	.000	.003	.011	.029	.058	.097	.144	.194	.239	.273	.292	.290	.268	.227	.173	.115	.062	.023	.004
	5	.000	.000	.000	.001	.004	.012	.025	.047	.077	.117	.164	.214	.261	.299	.318	.311	.275	.210	.124	.041
	6	.000	.000	.000	.000	.000	.001	.004	.008	.017	.032	.055	.087	.131	.185	.247	.311	.367	.396	.372	.257
	7	.000	.000	.000	.000	.000	.000	.000	.001	.002	.004	.008	.015	.028	.049	.082	.133	.210	.321	.478	.698
8	0	.923	.663	.430	.272	.168	.100	.058	.032	.017	.008	.004	.002	.001	.000	.000	.000	.000	.000	.000	.000
	1	.075	.279	.383	.385	.336	.267	.198	.137	.090	.055	.031	.016	.008	.003	.001	.000	.000	.000	.000	.000
	2	.003	.051	.149	.238	.294	.311	.296	.259	.209	.157	.109	.070	.041	.022	.010	.004	.001	.000	.000	.000

TABLE 2 *continued*

n	r											p										
		.01	.05	.10	.15	.20	.25	.30	.35	.40	.45	.50	.55	.60	.65	.70	.75	.80	.85	.90	.95
8	3	.000	.005	.033	.084	.147	.208	.254	.279	.279	.257	.219	.172	.124	.081	.047	.023	.009	.003	.000	.000
	4	.000	.000	.005	.018	.046	.087	.136	.188	.232	.263	.273	.263	.232	.188	.136	.087	.046	.018	.005	.000
	5	.000	.000	.000	.003	.009	.023	.047	.081	.124	.172	.219	.257	.279	.279	.254	.208	.147	.084	.033	.005
	6	.000	.000	.000	.000	.001	.004	.010	.022	.041	.070	.109	.157	.209	.259	.296	.311	.294	.238	.149	.051
	7	.000	.000	.000	.000	.000	.000	.001	.003	.008	.016	.031	.055	.090	.137	.198	.267	.336	.385	.383	.279
	8	.000	.000	.000	.000	.000	.000	.000	.000	.001	.002	.004	.008	.017	.032	.058	.100	.168	.272	.430	.663
9	0	.914	.630	.387	.232	.134	.075	.040	.021	.010	.005	.002	.001	.000	.000	.000	.000	.000	.000	.000	.000
	1	.083	.299	.387	.368	.302	.225	.156	.100	.060	.034	.018	.008	.004	.001	.000	.000	.000	.000	.000	.000
	2	.003	.063	.172	.260	.302	.300	.267	.216	.161	.111	.070	.041	.021	.010	.004	.001	.000	.000	.000	.000
	3	.000	.008	.045	.107	.176	.234	.267	.272	.251	.212	.164	.116	.074	.042	.021	.009	.003	.001	.000	.000
	4	.000	.001	.007	.028	.066	.117	.172	.219	.251	.260	.246	.213	.167	.118	.074	.039	.017	.005	.001	.000
	5	.000	.000	.001	.005	.017	.039	.074	.118	.167	.213	.246	.260	.251	.219	.172	.117	.066	.028	.007	.001
	6	.000	.000	.000	.001	.003	.009	.021	.042	.074	.116	.164	.212	.251	.272	.267	.234	.176	.107	.045	.008
	7	.000	.000	.000	.000	.000	.001	.004	.010	.021	.041	.070	.111	.161	.216	.267	.300	.302	.260	.172	.063
	8	.000	.000	.000	.000	.000	.000	.000	.001	.004	.008	.018	.034	.060	.100	.156	.225	.302	.368	.387	.299
	9	.000	.000	.000	.000	.000	.000	.000	.000	.000	.001	.002	.005	.010	.021	.040	.075	.134	.232	.387	.630
10	0	.904	.599	.349	.197	.107	.056	.028	.014	.006	.003	.001	.000	.000	.000	.000	.000	.000	.000	.000	.000
	1	.091	.315	.387	.347	.268	.188	.121	.072	.040	.021	.010	.004	.002	.000	.000	.000	.000	.000	.000	.000
	2	.004	.075	.194	.276	.302	.282	.233	.176	.121	.076	.044	.023	.011	.004	.001	.000	.000	.000	.000	.000
	3	.000	.010	.057	.130	.201	.250	.267	.252	.215	.166	.117	.075	.042	.021	.009	.003	.001	.000	.000	.000
	4	.000	.001	.011	.040	.088	.146	.200	.238	.251	.238	.205	.160	.111	.069	.037	.016	.006	.001	.000	.000
	5	.000	.000	.001	.008	.026	.058	.103	.154	.201	.234	.246	.234	.201	.154	.103	.058	.026	.008	.001	.000
	6	.000	.000	.000	.001	.006	.016	.037	.069	.111	.160	.205	.238	.251	.238	.200	.146	.088	.040	.011	.000
	7	.000	.000	.000	.000	.001	.003	.009	.021	.042	.075	.117	.166	.215	.252	.267	.250	.201	.130	.057	.010
	8	.000	.000	.000	.000	.000	.000	.001	.004	.011	.023	.044	.076	.121	.176	.233	.282	.302	.276	.194	.075
	9	.000	.000	.000	.000	.000	.000	.000	.000	.002	.004	.010	.021	.040	.072	.121	.188	.268	.347	.387	.315
	10	.000	.000	.000	.000	.000	.000	.000	.000	.000	.000	.001	.003	.006	.014	.028	.056	.107	.197	.349	.599
11	0	.895	.569	.314	.167	.086	.042	.020	.009	.004	.001	.000	.000	.000	.000	.000	.000	.000	.000	.000	.000
	1	.099	.329	.384	.325	.236	.155	.093	.052	.027	.013	.005	.002	.001	.000	.000	.000	.000	.000	.000	.000
	2	.005	.087	.213	.287	.295	.258	.200	.140	.089	.051	.027	.013	.005	.002	.001	.000	.000	.000	.000	.000
	3	.000	.014	.071	.152	.221	.258	.257	.225	.177	.126	.081	.046	.023	.010	.004	.001	.000	.000	.000	.000
	4	.000	.001	.016	.054	.111	.172	.220	.243	.236	.206	.161	.113	.070	.038	.017	.006	.002	.001	.000	.000
	5	.000	.000	.002	.013	.039	.080	.132	.183	.221	.236	.226	.193	.147	.099	.057	.027	.010	.002	.000	.000
	6	.000	.000	.000	.002	.010	.027	.057	.099	.147	.193	.226	.236	.221	.183	.132	.080	.039	.013	.002	.000
	7	.000	.000	.000	.000	.002	.006	.017	.038	.070	.113	.161	.206	.236	.243	.220	.172	.111	.054	.016	.001
	8	.000	.000	.000	.000	.000	.001	.004	.010	.023	.046	.081	.126	.177	.225	.257	.258	.221	.152	.071	.014

TABLE 2 *continued*

											p										
n	r	.01	.05	.10	.15	.20	.25	.30	.35	.40	.45	.50	.55	.60	.65	.70	.75	.80	.85	.90	.95
11	9	.000	.000	.000	.000	.000	.000	.001	.002	.005	.013	.027	.051	.089	.140	.200	.258	.295	.287	.213	.087
	10	.000	.000	.000	.000	.000	.000	.000	.000	.001	.002	.005	.013	.027	.052	.093	.155	.236	.325	.384	.329
	11	.000	.000	.000	.000	.000	.000	.000	.000	.000	.000	.000	.001	.004	.009	.020	.042	.086	.167	.314	.569
12	0	.886	.540	.282	.142	.069	.032	.014	.006	.002	.001	.000	.000	.000	.000	.000	.000	.000	.000	.000	.000
	1	.107	.341	.377	.301	.206	.127	.071	.037	.017	.008	.003	.001	.000	.000	.000	.000	.000	.000	.000	.000
	2	.006	.099	.230	.292	.283	.232	.168	.109	.064	.034	.016	.007	.002	.001	.000	.000	.000	.000	.000	.000
	3	.000	.017	.085	.172	.236	.258	.240	.195	.142	.092	.054	.028	.012	.005	.001	.000	.000	.000	.000	.000
	4	.000	.002	.021	.068	.133	.194	.231	.237	.213	.170	.121	.076	.042	.020	.008	.002	.001	.000	.000	.000
	5	.000	.000	.004	.019	.053	.103	.158	.204	.227	.223	.193	.149	.101	.059	.029	.011	.003	.001	.000	.000
	6	.000	.000	.000	.004	.016	.040	.079	.128	.177	.212	.226	.212	.177	.128	.079	.040	.016	.004	.000	.000
	7	.000	.000	.000	.001	.003	.011	.029	.059	.101	.149	.193	.223	.227	.204	.158	.103	.053	.019	.004	.000
	8	.000	.000	.000	.000	.001	.002	.008	.020	.042	.076	.121	.170	.213	.237	.231	.194	.133	.068	.021	.002
	9	.000	.000	.000	.000	.000	.000	.001	.005	.012	.028	.054	.092	.142	.195	.240	.258	.236	.172	.085	.017
	10	.000	.000	.000	.000	.000	.000	.000	.001	.002	.007	.016	.034	.064	.109	.168	.232	.283	.292	.230	.099
	11	.000	.000	.000	.000	.000	.000	.000	.000	.000	.001	.003	.008	.017	.037	.071	.127	.206	.301	.377	.341
	12	.000	.000	.000	.000	.000	.000	.000	.000	.000	.000	.000	.001	.002	.006	.014	.032	.069	.142	.282	.540
15	0	.860	.463	.206	.087	.035	.013	.005	.002	.000	.000	.000	.000	.000	.000	.000	.000	.000	.000	.000	.000
	1	.130	.366	.343	.231	.132	.067	.031	.013	.005	.002	.000	.000	.000	.000	.000	.000	.000	.000	.000	.000
	2	.009	.135	.267	.286	.231	.156	.092	.048	.022	.009	.003	.001	.000	.000	.000	.000	.000	.000	.000	.000
	3	.000	.031	.129	.218	.250	.225	.170	.111	.063	.032	.014	.005	.002	.000	.000	.000	.000	.000	.000	.000
	4	.000	.005	.043	.116	.188	.225	.219	.179	.127	.078	.042	.019	.007	.002	.001	.000	.000	.000	.000	.000
	5	.000	.001	.010	.045	.103	.165	.206	.212	.186	.140	.092	.051	.024	.010	.003	.001	.000	.000	.000	.000
	6	.000	.000	.002	.013	.043	.092	.147	.191	.207	.191	.153	.105	.061	.030	.012	.003	.001	.000	.000	.000
	7	.000	.000	.000	.003	.014	.039	.081	.132	.177	.201	.196	.165	.118	.071	.035	.013	.003	.001	.000	.000
	8	.000	.000	.000	.001	.003	.013	.035	.071	.118	.165	.196	.201	.177	.132	.081	.039	.014	.003	.000	.000
	9	.000	.000	.000	.000	.001	.003	.012	.030	.061	.105	.153	.191	.207	.191	.147	.092	.043	.013	.002	.000
	10	.000	.000	.000	.000	.000	.001	.003	.010	.024	.051	.092	.140	.186	.212	.206	.165	.103	.045	.010	.001
	11	.000	.000	.000	.000	.000	.000	.001	.002	.007	.019	.042	.078	.127	.179	.219	.225	.188	.116	.043	.005
	12	.000	.000	.000	.000	.000	.000	.000	.000	.002	.005	.014	.032	.063	.111	.170	.225	.250	.218	.129	.031
	13	.000	.000	.000	.000	.000	.000	.000	.000	.000	.001	.003	.009	.022	.048	.092	.156	.231	.286	.267	.135
	14	.000	.000	.000	.000	.000	.000	.000	.000	.000	.000	.000	.002	.005	.013	.031	.067	.132	.231	.343	.366
	15	.000	.000	.000	.000	.000	.000	.000	.000	.000	.000	.000	.000	.000	.002	.005	.013	.035	.087	.206	.463
16	0	.851	.440	.185	.074	.028	.010	.003	.001	.000	.000	.000	.000	.000	.000	.000	.000	.000	.000	.000	.000
	1	.138	.371	.329	.210	.113	.053	.023	.009	.003	.001	.000	.000	.000	.000	.000	.000	.000	.000	.000	.000
	2	.010	.146	.275	.277	.211	.134	.073	.035	.015	.006	.002	.001	.000	.000	.000	.000	.000	.000	.000	.000

TABLE 2 *continued*

		p																			
n	r	.01	.05	.10	.15	.20	.25	.30	.35	.40	.45	.50	.55	.60	.65	.70	.75	.80	.85	.90	.95
16	3	.000	.036	.142	.229	.246	.208	.146	.089	.047	.022	.009	.003	.001	.000	.000	.000	.000	.000	.000	.000
	4	.000	.006	.051	.131	.200	.225	.204	.155	.101	.057	.028	.011	.004	.001	.000	.000	.000	.000	.000	.000
	5	.000	.001	.014	.056	.120	.180	.210	.201	.162	.112	.067	.034	.014	.005	.001	.000	.000	.000	.000	.000
	6	.000	.000	.003	.018	.055	.110	.165	.198	.198	.168	.122	.075	.039	.017	.006	.001	.000	.000	.000	.000
	7	.000	.000	.000	.005	.020	.052	.101	.152	.189	.197	.175	.132	.084	.044	.019	.006	.001	.000	.000	.000
	8	.000	.000	.000	.001	.006	.020	.049	.092	.142	.181	.196	.181	.142	.092	.049	.020	.006	.001	.000	.000
	9	.000	.000	.000	.000	.001	.006	.019	.044	.084	.132	.175	.197	.189	.152	.101	.052	.020	.005	.000	.000
	10	.000	.000	.000	.000	.000	.001	.006	.017	.039	.075	.122	.168	.198	.198	.165	.110	.055	.018	.003	.000
	11	.000	.000	.000	.000	.000	.000	.001	.005	.014	.034	.067	.112	.162	.201	.210	.180	.120	.056	.014	.001
	12	.000	.000	.000	.000	.000	.000	.000	.001	.004	.011	.028	.057	.101	.155	.204	.225	.200	.131	.051	.006
	13	.000	.000	.000	.000	.000	.000	.000	.000	.001	.003	.009	.022	.047	.089	.146	.208	.246	.229	.142	.036
	14	.000	.000	.000	.000	.000	.000	.000	.000	.000	.001	.002	.006	.015	.035	.073	.134	.211	.277	.275	.146
	15	.000	.000	.000	.000	.000	.000	.000	.000	.000	.000	.000	.001	.003	.009	.023	.053	.113	.210	.329	.371
	16	.000	.000	.000	.000	.000	.000	.000	.000	.000	.000	.000	.000	.000	.001	.003	.010	.028	.074	.185	.440
20	0	.818	.358	.122	.039	.012	.003	.001	.000	.000	.000	.000	.000	.000	.000	.000	.000	.000	.000	.000	.000
	1	.165	.377	.270	.137	.058	.021	.007	.002	.000	.000	.000	.000	.000	.000	.000	.000	.000	.000	.000	.000
	2	.016	.189	.285	.229	.137	.067	.028	.010	.003	.001	.000	.000	.000	.000	.000	.000	.000	.000	.000	.000
	3	.001	.060	.190	.243	.205	.134	.072	.032	.012	.004	.001	.000	.000	.000	.000	.000	.000	.000	.000	.000
	4	.000	.013	.090	.182	.218	.190	.130	.074	.035	.014	.005	.001	.000	.000	.000	.000	.000	.000	.000	.000
	5	.000	.002	.032	.103	.175	.202	.179	.127	.075	.036	.015	.005	.001	.000	.000	.000	.000	.000	.000	.000
	6	.000	.000	.009	.045	.109	.169	.192	.171	.124	.075	.037	.015	.005	.001	.000	.000	.000	.000	.000	.000
	7	.000	.000	.002	.016	.055	.112	.164	.184	.166	.122	.074	.037	.015	.005	.001	.000	.000	.000	.000	.000
	8	.000	.000	.000	.005	.022	.061	.114	.161	.180	.162	.120	.073	.035	.014	.004	.001	.000	.000	.000	.000
	9	.000	.000	.000	.001	.007	.027	.065	.116	.160	.177	.160	.119	.071	.034	.012	.003	.000	.000	.000	.000
	10	.000	.000	.000	.000	.002	.010	.031	.069	.117	.159	.176	.159	.117	.069	.031	.010	.002	.000	.000	.000
	11	.000	.000	.000	.000	.000	.003	.012	.034	.071	.119	.160	.177	.160	.116	.065	.027	.007	.001	.000	.000
	12	.000	.000	.000	.000	.000	.001	.004	.014	.035	.073	.120	.162	.180	.161	.114	.061	.022	.005	.000	.000
	13	.000	.000	.000	.000	.000	.000	.001	.005	.015	.037	.074	.122	.166	.184	.164	.112	.055	.016	.002	.000
	14	.000	.000	.000	.000	.000	.000	.000	.001	.005	.015	.037	.075	.124	.171	.192	.169	.109	.045	.009	.000
	15	.000	.000	.000	.000	.000	.000	.000	.000	.001	.005	.015	.036	.075	.127	.179	.202	.175	.103	.032	.002
	16	.000	.000	.000	.000	.000	.000	.000	.000	.000	.001	.005	.014	.035	.074	.130	.190	.218	.182	.090	.013
	17	.000	.000	.000	.000	.000	.000	.000	.000	.000	.000	.001	.004	.012	.032	.072	.134	.205	.243	.190	.060
	18	.000	.000	.000	.000	.000	.000	.000	.000	.000	.000	.000	.001	.003	.010	.028	.067	.137	.229	.285	.189
	19	.000	.000	.000	.000	.000	.000	.000	.000	.000	.000	.000	.000	.000	.002	.007	.021	.058	.137	.270	.377
	20	.000	.000	.000	.000	.000	.000	.000	.000	.000	.000	.000	.000	.000	.000	.001	.003	.012	.039	.122	.358

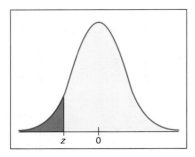

The table entry for z is the area to the left of z.

TABLE 3   Areas of a Standard Normal Distribution

(a) Table of Areas to the Left of z

z	.00	.01	.02	.03	.04	.05	.06	.07	.08	.09
−3.4	.0003	.0003	.0003	.0003	.0003	.0003	.0003	.0003	.0003	.0002
−3.3	.0005	.0005	.0005	.0004	.0004	.0004	.0004	.0004	.0004	.0003
−3.2	.0007	.0007	.0006	.0006	.0006	.0006	.0006	.0005	.0005	.0005
−3.1	.0010	.0009	.0009	.0009	.0008	.0008	.0008	.0008	.0007	.0007
−3.0	.0013	.0013	.0013	.0012	.0012	.0011	.0011	.0011	.0010	.0010
−2.9	.0019	.0018	.0018	.0017	.0016	.0016	.0015	.0015	.0014	.0014
−2.8	.0026	.0025	.0024	.0023	.0023	.0022	.0021	.0021	.0020	.0019
−2.7	.0035	.0034	.0033	.0032	.0031	.0030	.0029	.0028	.0027	.0026
−2.6	.0047	.0045	.0044	.0043	.0041	.0040	.0039	.0038	.0037	.0036
−2.5	.0062	.0060	.0059	.0057	.0055	.0054	.0052	.0051	.0049	.0048
−2.4	.0082	.0080	.0078	.0075	.0073	.0071	.0069	.0068	.0066	.0064
−2.3	.0107	.0104	.0102	.0099	.0096	.0094	.0091	.0089	.0087	.0084
−2.2	.0139	.0136	.0132	.0129	.0125	.0122	.0119	.0116	.0113	.0110
−2.1	.0179	.0174	.0170	.0166	.0162	.0158	.0154	.0150	.0146	.0143
−2.0	.0228	.0222	.0217	.0212	.0207	.0202	.0197	.0192	.0188	.0183
−1.9	.0287	.0281	.0274	.0268	.0262	.0256	.0250	.0244	.0239	.0233
−1.8	.0359	.0351	.0344	.0336	.0329	.0322	.0314	.0307	.0301	.0294
−1.7	.0446	.0436	.0427	.0418	.0409	.0401	.0392	.0384	.0375	.0367
−1.6	.0548	.0537	.0526	.0516	.0505	.0495	.0485	.0475	.0465	.0455
−1.5	.0668	.0655	.0643	.0630	.0618	.0606	.0594	.0582	.0571	.0559
−1.4	.0808	.0793	.0778	.0764	.0749	.0735	.0721	.0708	.0694	.0681
−1.3	.0968	.0951	.0934	.0918	.0901	.0885	.0869	.0853	.0838	.0823
−1.2	.1151	.1131	.1112	.1093	.1075	.1056	.1038	.1020	.1003	.0985
−1.1	.1357	.1335	.1314	.1292	.1271	.1251	.1230	.1210	.1190	.1170
−1.0	.1587	.1562	.1539	.1515	.1492	.1469	.1446	.1423	.1401	.1379
−0.9	.1841	.1814	.1788	.1762	.1736	.1711	.1685	.1660	.1635	.1611
−0.8	.2119	.2090	.2061	.2033	.2005	.1977	.1949	.1922	.1894	.1867
−0.7	.2420	.2389	.2358	.2327	.2296	.2266	.2236	.2206	.2177	.2148
−0.6	.2743	.2709	.2676	.2643	.2611	.2578	.2546	.2514	.2483	.2451
−0.5	.3085	.3050	.3015	.2981	.2946	.2912	.2877	.2843	.2810	.2776
−0.4	.3446	.3409	.3372	.3336	.3300	.3264	.3228	.3192	.3156	.3121
−0.3	.3821	.3783	.3745	.3707	.3669	.3632	.3594	.3557	.3520	.3483
−0.2	.4207	.4168	.4129	.4090	.4052	.4013	.3974	.3936	.3897	.3859
−0.1	.4602	.4562	.4522	.4483	.4443	.4404	.4364	.4325	.4286	.4247
−0.0	.5000	.4960	.4920	.4880	.4840	.4801	.4761	.4721	.4681	.4641

For values of z less than −3.49, use 0.000 to approximate the area.

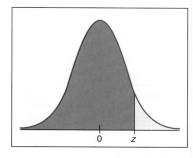

The table entry for z is the area to the left of z.

TABLE 3(a) *continued*

z	.00	.01	.02	.03	.04	.05	.06	.07	.08	.09
0.0	.5000	.5040	.5080	.5120	.5160	.5199	.5239	.5279	.5319	.5359
0.1	.5398	.5438	.5478	.5517	.5557	.5596	.5636	.5675	.5714	.5753
0.2	.5793	.5832	.5871	.5910	.5948	.5987	.6026	.6064	.6103	.6141
0.3	.6179	.6217	.6255	.6293	.6331	.6368	.6406	.6443	.6480	.6517
0.4	.6554	.6591	.6628	.6664	.6700	.6736	.6772	.6808	.6844	.6879
0.5	.6915	.6950	.6985	.7019	.7054	.7088	.7123	.7157	.7190	.7224
0.6	.7257	.7291	.7324	.7357	.7389	.7422	.7454	.7486	.7517	.7549
0.7	.7580	.7611	.7642	.7673	.7704	.7734	.7764	.7794	.7823	.7852
0.8	.7881	.7910	.7939	.7967	.7995	.8023	.8051	.8078	.8106	.8133
0.9	.8159	.8186	.8212	.8238	.8264	.8289	.8315	.8340	.8365	.8389
1.0	.8413	.8438	.8461	.8485	.8508	.8531	.8554	.8577	.8599	.8621
1.1	.8643	.8665	.8686	.8708	.8729	.8749	.8770	.8790	.8810	.8830
1.2	.8849	.8869	.8888	.8907	.8925	.8944	.8962	.8980	.8997	.9015
1.3	.9032	.9049	.9066	.9082	.9099	.9115	.9131	.9147	.9162	.9177
1.4	.9192	.9207	.9222	.9236	.9251	.9265	.9279	.9292	.9306	.9319
1.5	.9332	.9345	.9357	.9370	.9382	.9394	.9406	.9418	.9429	.9441
1.6	.9452	.9463	.9474	.9484	.9495	.9505	.9515	.9525	.9535	.9545
1.7	.9554	.9564	.9573	.9582	.9591	.9599	.9608	.9616	.9625	.9633
1.8	.9641	.9649	.9656	.9664	.9671	.9678	.9686	.9693	.9699	.9706
1.9	.9713	.9719	.9726	.9732	.9738	.9744	.9750	.9756	.9761	.9767
2.0	.9772	.9778	.9783	.9788	.9793	.9798	.9803	.9808	.9812	.9817
2.1	.9821	.9826	.9830	.9834	.9838	.9842	.9846	.9850	.9854	.9857
2.2	.9861	.9864	.9868	.9871	.9875	.9878	.9881	.9884	.9887	.9890
2.3	.9893	.9896	.9898	.9901	.9904	.9906	.9909	.9911	.9913	.9916
2.4	.9918	.9920	.9922	.9925	.9927	.9929	.9931	.9932	.9934	.9936
2.5	.9938	.9940	.9941	.9943	.9945	.9946	.9948	.9949	.9951	.9952
2.6	.9953	.9955	.9956	.9957	.9959	.9960	.9961	.9962	.9963	.9964
2.7	.9965	.9966	.9967	.9968	.9969	.9970	.9971	.9972	.9973	.9974
2.8	.9974	.9975	.9976	.9977	.9977	.9978	.9979	.9979	.9980	.9981
2.9	.9981	.9982	.9982	.9983	.9984	.9984	.9985	.9985	.9986	.9986
3.0	.9987	.9987	.9987	.9988	.9988	.9989	.9989	.9989	.9990	.9990
3.1	.9990	.9991	.9991	.9991	.9992	.9992	.9992	.9992	.9993	.9993
3.2	.9993	.9993	.9994	.9994	.9994	.9994	.9994	.9995	.9995	.9995
3.3	.9995	.9995	.9995	.9996	.9996	.9996	.9996	.9996	.9996	.9997
3.4	.9997	.9997	.9997	.9997	.9997	.9997	.9997	.9997	.9997	.9998

For z values greater than 3.49, use 1.000 to approximate the area.

TABLE 3 *continued*

(c) Hypothesis Testing, Critical Values z_0		
Level of Significance	$\alpha = 0.05$	$\alpha = 0.01$
Critical value z_0 for a left-tailed test	−1.645	−2.33
Critical value z_0 for a right-tailed test	1.645	2.33
Critical values $\pm z_0$ for a two-tailed test	±1.96	±2.58

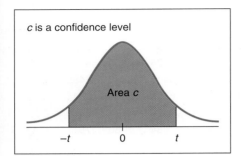

c is a confidence level

Area c

−t   0   t

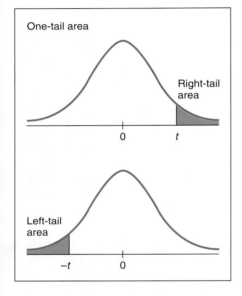

One-tail area

Right-tail
area

0   t

Left-tail
area

−t   0

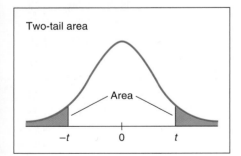

Two-tail area

Area

−t   0   t

TABLE 4   Critical Values for Student's t Distribution

one-tail area	0.250	0.125	0.100	0.075	0.050	0.025	0.010	0.005	0.0005
two-tail area	0.500	0.250	0.200	0.150	0.100	0.050	0.020	0.010	0.0010
d.f. \ c	0.500	0.750	0.800	0.850	0.900	0.950	0.980	0.990	0.999
1	1.000	2.414	3.078	4.165	6.314	12.706	31.821	63.657	636.619
2	0.816	1.604	1.886	2.282	2.920	4.303	6.965	9.925	31.599
3	0.765	1.423	1.638	1.924	2.353	3.182	4.541	5.841	12.924
4	0.741	1.344	1.533	1.778	2.132	2.776	3.747	4.604	8.610
5	0.727	1.301	1.476	1.699	2.015	2.571	3.365	4.032	6.869
6	0.718	1.273	1.440	1.650	1.943	2.447	3.143	3.707	5.959
7	0.711	1.254	1.415	1.617	1.895	2.365	2.998	3.499	5.408
8	0.706	1.240	1.397	1.592	1.860	2.306	2.896	3.355	5.041
9	0.703	1.230	1.383	1.574	1.833	2.262	2.821	3.250	4.781
10	0.700	1.221	1.372	1.559	1.812	2.228	2.764	3.169	4.587
11	0.697	1.214	1.363	1.548	1.796	2.201	2.718	3.106	4.437
12	0.695	1.209	1.356	1.538	1.782	2.179	2.681	3.055	4.318
13	0.694	1.204	1.350	1.530	1.771	2.160	2.650	3.012	4.221
14	0.692	1.200	1.345	1.523	1.761	2.145	2.624	2.977	4.140
15	0.691	1.197	1.341	1.517	1.753	2.131	2.602	2.947	4.073
16	0.690	1.194	1.337	1.512	1.746	2.120	2.583	2.921	4.015
17	0.689	1.191	1.333	1.508	1.740	2.110	2.567	2.898	3.965
18	0.688	1.189	1.330	1.504	1.734	2.101	2.552	2.878	3.922
19	0.688	1.187	1.328	1.500	1.729	2.093	2.539	2.861	3.883
20	0.687	1.185	1.325	1.497	1.725	2.086	2.528	2.845	3.850
21	0.686	1.183	1.323	1.494	1.721	2.080	2.518	2.831	3.819
22	0.686	1.182	1.321	1.492	1.717	2.074	2.508	2.819	3.792
23	0.685	1.180	1.319	1.489	1.714	2.069	2.500	2.807	3.768
24	0.685	1.179	1.318	1.487	1.711	2.064	2.492	2.797	3.745
25	0.684	1.198	1.316	1.485	1.708	2.060	2.485	2.787	3.725
26	0.684	1.177	1.315	1.483	1.706	2.056	2.479	2.779	3.707
27	0.684	1.176	1.314	1.482	1.703	2.052	2.473	2.771	3.690
28	0.683	1.175	1.313	1.480	1.701	2.048	2.467	2.763	3.674
29	0.683	1.174	1.311	1.479	1.699	2.045	2.462	2.756	3.659
30	0.683	1.173	1.310	1.477	1.697	2.042	2.457	2.750	3.646
35	0.682	1.170	1.306	1.472	1.690	2.030	2.438	2.724	3.591
40	0.681	1.167	1.303	1.468	1.684	2.021	2.423	2.704	3.551
45	0.680	1.165	1.301	1.465	1.679	2.014	2.412	2.690	3.520
50	0.679	1.164	1.299	1.462	1.676	2.009	2.403	2.678	3.496
60	0.679	1.162	1.296	1.458	1.671	2.000	2.390	2.660	3.460
70	0.678	1.160	1.294	1.456	1.667	1.994	2.381	2.648	3.435
80	0.678	1.159	1.292	1.453	1.664	1.990	2.374	2.639	3.416
100	0.677	1.157	1.290	1.451	1.660	1.984	2.364	2.626	3.390
500	0.675	1.152	1.283	1.442	1.648	1.965	2.334	2.586	3.310
1000	0.675	1.151	1.282	1.441	1.646	1.962	2.330	2.581	3.300
∞	0.674	1.150	1.282	1.440	1.645	1.960	2.326	2.576	3.291

For degrees of freedom d.f. not in the table, use the closest d.f. that is *smaller*.

TABLE 5   The χ^2 Distribution

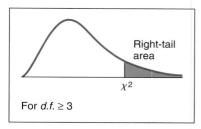

Right-tail area

χ^2

For $d.f. \geq 3$

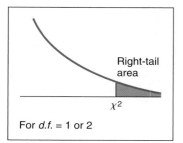

Right-tail area

χ^2

For $d.f. = 1$ or 2

d.f.	Right-tail Area									
	.995	.990	.975	.950	.900	.100	.050	.025	.010	.005
1	0.0^4393	0.0^3157	0.0^3982	0.0^2393	0.0158	2.71	3.84	5.02	6.63	7.88
2	0.0100	0.0201	0.0506	0.103	0.211	4.61	5.99	7.38	9.21	10.60
3	0.072	0.115	0.216	0.352	0.584	6.25	7.81	9.35	11.34	12.84
4	0.207	0.297	0.484	0.711	1.064	7.78	9.49	11.14	13.28	14.86
5	0.412	0.554	0.831	1.145	1.61	9.24	11.07	12.83	15.09	16.75
6	0.676	0.872	1.24	1.64	2.20	10.64	12.59	14.45	16.81	18.55
7	0.989	1.24	1.69	2.17	2.83	12.02	14.07	16.01	18.48	20.28
8	1.34	1.65	2.18	2.73	3.49	13.36	15.51	17.53	20.09	21.96
9	1.73	2.09	2.70	3.33	4.17	14.68	16.92	19.02	21.67	23.59
10	2.16	2.56	3.25	3.94	4.87	15.99	18.31	20.48	23.21	25.19
11	2.60	3.05	3.82	4.57	5.58	17.28	19.68	21.92	24.72	26.76
12	3.07	3.57	4.40	5.23	6.30	18.55	21.03	23.34	26.22	28.30
13	3.57	4.11	5.01	5.89	7.04	19.81	22.36	24.74	27.69	29.82
14	4.07	4.66	5.63	6.57	7.79	21.06	23.68	26.12	29.14	31.32
15	4.60	5.23	6.26	7.26	8.55	22.31	25.00	27.49	30.58	32.80
16	5.14	5.81	6.91	7.96	9.31	23.54	26.30	28.85	32.00	34.27
17	5.70	6.41	7.56	8.67	10.09	24.77	27.59	30.19	33.41	35.72
18	6.26	7.01	8.23	9.39	10.86	25.99	28.87	31.53	34.81	37.16
19	6.84	7.63	8.91	10.12	11.65	27.20	30.14	32.85	36.19	38.58
20	7.43	8.26	8.59	10.85	12.44	28.41	31.41	34.17	37.57	40.00
21	8.03	8.90	10.28	11.59	13.24	29.62	32.67	35.48	38.93	41.40
22	8.64	9.54	10.98	12.34	14.04	30.81	33.92	36.78	40.29	42.80
23	9.26	10.20	11.69	13.09	14.85	32.01	35.17	38.08	41.64	44.18
24	9.89	10.86	12.40	13.85	15.66	33.20	36.42	39.36	42.98	45.56
25	10.52	11.52	13.12	14.61	16.47	34.38	37.65	40.65	44.31	46.93
26	11.16	12.20	13.84	15.38	17.29	35.56	38.89	41.92	45.64	48.29
27	11.81	12.88	14.57	16.15	18.11	36.74	40.11	43.19	46.96	49.64
28	12.46	13.56	15.31	16.93	18.94	37.92	41.34	44.46	48.28	50.99
29	13.21	14.26	16.05	17.71	19.77	39.09	42.56	45.72	49.59	52.34
30	13.79	14.95	16.79	18.49	20.60	40.26	43.77	46.98	50.89	53.67
40	20.71	22.16	24.43	26.51	29.05	51.80	55.76	59.34	63.69	66.77
50	27.99	29.71	32.36	34.76	37.69	63.17	67.50	71.42	76.15	79.49
60	35.53	37.48	40.48	43.19	46.46	74.40	79.08	83.30	88.38	91.95
70	43.28	45.44	48.76	51.74	55.33	85.53	90.53	95.02	100.4	104.2
80	51.17	53.54	57.15	60.39	64.28	96.58	101.9	106.6	112.3	116.3
90	59.20	61.75	65.65	69.13	73.29	107.6	113.1	118.1	124.1	128.3
100	67.33	70.06	74.22	77.93	82.36	118.5	124.3	129.6	135.8	140.2

Source: From H. L. Herter, *Biometrika*, June 1964. Printed by permission of the Biometrika Trustees.

Photo Credits

Answers and Key Steps to Odd-Numbered Problems

Section 1.1

1. (a) Response regarding frequency of eating at fast-food restaurants. (b) Qualitative. (c) Responses for *all* adults in the U.S.
3. (a) Student/faculty ratio at colleges. (b) Quantitative. (c) Student/faculty ratio at *all* colleges in the nation.
5. (a) Nitrogen concentration (mg nitrogen/l water). (b) Quantitative. (c) Nitrogen concentration (mg nitrogen/l water) in the entire lake.
   7. (a) Ratio. (b) Interval. (c) Nominal. (d) Ordinal. (e) Ratio. (f) Ratio.
   9. (a) Nominal. (b) Ratio. (c) Interval. (d) Ordinal. (e) Ratio. (f) Interval.

Section 1.2

1. See text.
3. Select a starting place in the table and group the digits in groups of four. Scan the table by rows and include the first six groups with numbers between 0001 and 8615.
5. (a) Yes, when a die is rolled several times, the same number may appear more than once. Outcome on the 4th roll is 2. (b) No, for a fair die, the outcomes are random.
7. Use a random-number table to select four distinct numbers corresponding to people in your class. (a) Reasons may vary. For instance, the first four students may make a special effort to get to class on time. (b) Reasons may vary. For instance, four students who come in late might all be nursing students enrolled in an anatomy and physiology class that meets the hour before in a far-away building. They may be more motivated than other students to complete a degree requirement. (c) Reasons may vary. For instance, four students sitting in the back row might be less inclined to participate in class discussions. (d) Reasons may vary. For instance, the tallest students might all be male.
9. Since there are five possible outcomes for each question, read single digits from a random-number table. Select a starting place, and proceed until you have 10 digits from 1 to 5. Repetition is required. The correct answer for each question will be the letter choice corresponding to the digit chosen for that question.
11. (a) Simple random sample. (b) Cluster sample. (c) Convenience sample. (d) Systematic sample. (e) Stratified sample.

Section 1.3

1. (a) Observational study. (b) Experiment. (c) Experiment. (d) Observational study.
3. (a) Use random selection to pick 10 calves to inoculate; test all calves; no placebo. (b) Use random selection to pick 9 schools to visit; survey all schools; no placebo. (c) Use random selection to pick 40 volunteers for skin patch with drug; survey all volunteers; placebo used.

Chapter 1 Review

1. Depends on article.
3. In the random-number table use groups of two digits. Select the first six distinct groups of two digits that fall in the range from 01 to 42. Choices vary according to the starting place in the random-number table.
5. (a) Observational study. (b) Experiment.
7. Possible directions on survey questions: Give height in inches, give age as of last birthday, give GPA to one decimal place, and so forth. Think about the types of responses you wish to have on each question.
9. (a) Experiment, since a treatment is imposed on one colony. (b) The control group receives normal daylight/darkness conditions. The treatment group has light 24 hours per day. (c) The number of fireflies living at the end of 72 hours. (d) Ratio.

CHAPTER 2

Section 2.1

1. (a) Class width = 25.
   (b)

Class Limits	Boundaries	Midpoint	Frequency	Relative Frequency
236–260	235.5–260.5	248	4	0.07
261–285	260.5–285.5	273	9	0.16
286–310	285.5–310.5	298	25	0.44
311–335	310.5–335.5	323	16	0.28
336–360	335.5–360.5	348	3	0.05

(c–d) Hours to Complete the Iditarod—Histogram, Relative-Frequency Histogram

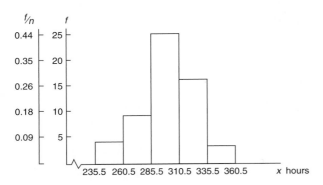

(c–d) Fuel Consumption (mpg)—Histogram, Relative-Frequency Histogram

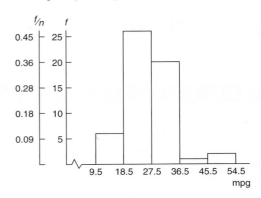

3. (a) Class width = 12.
   (b)

Class Limits	Boundaries	Midpoint	Frequency	Relative Frequency
1–12	0.5–12.5	6.5	6	0.14
13–24	12.5–24.5	18.5	10	0.24
25–36	24.5–36.5	30.5	5	0.12
37–48	36.5–48.5	42.5	13	0.31
49–60	48.5–60.5	54.5	8	0.19

(c–d) Months Before Tumor Recurrence—Histogram, Relative-Frequency Histogram

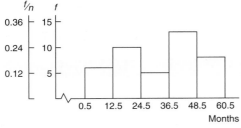

5. (a) Class width = 9.
   (b)

Class Limits	Boundaries	Midpoint	Frequency	Relative Frequency
10–18	9.5–18.5	14	6	0.11
19–27	18.5–27.5	23	26	0.47
28–36	27.5–36.5	32	20	0.36
37–45	36.5–45.5	41	1	0.02
46–54	45.5–54.5	50	2	0.04

7. (a) Version 1 is skewed left; version 2 is uniform; version 3 is symmetrical; version 4 is bimodal; version 5 is skewed right.   (b) Answers will vary.

9. (a) Clear the decimals.
   (b, c) Class width = 0.40.

Class Limits	Boundaries	Midpoint	Frequency
0.46–0.85	0.455–0.855	0.655	4
0.86–1.25	0.855–1.255	1.055	5
1.26–1.65	1.255–1.655	1.455	10
1.66–2.05	1.655–2.055	1.855	5
2.06–2.45	2.055–2.455	2.255	5
2.46–2.85	2.455–2.855	2.655	3

(c) Tonnes of Wheat—Histogram

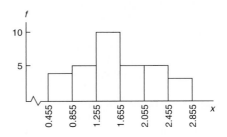

11. (a) One.   (b) 5/51 or 9.8%.   (c) Interval from 650 to 750.

13. Dotplot for Months Before Tumor Recurrence

Section 2.2

1. Highest Level of Education and Average Annual Household Income (in thousands of dollars)

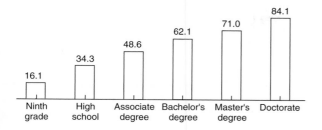

3. Annual Harvest (1000 Metric Tons)—Pareto Chart

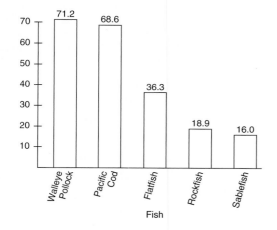

5. Where We Hide the Mess

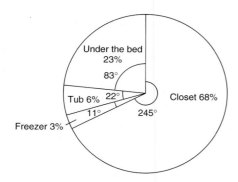

7. (a) Hawaii Crime Rate per 100,000 Population

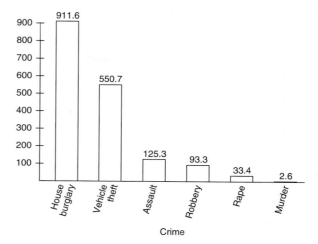

(b) A circle graph is not appropriate because the data do not reflect all types of crime. Also, the same person may have been the victim of more than one crime.

9. Elevation of Pyramid Lake Surface—Time Plot

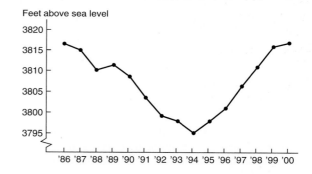

Section 2.3

1. (a) Longevity of Cowboys

4	7 = 47 years
4	7
5	2 7 8 8
6	1 6 6 8 8
7	0 2 2 3 3 5 6 7
8	4 4 4 5 6 6 7 9
9	0 1 1 2 3 7

(b) Yes, certainly these cowboys lived long lives.

3. Average Length of Hospital Stay

5	2 = 5.2 days
5	2 3 5 5 6 7
6	0 2 4 6 6 7 7 8 8 8 8 9 9
7	0 0 0 0 0 1 1 1 2 2 2 3 3 3 3 4 4 5 5 6 6 8
8	4 5 7
9	4 6 9
10	0 3
11	1

The distribution is skewed right.

5. (a) Minutes Beyond 2 Hours (1961–1980)

0	9 = 9 minutes past 2 hours
0	9 9
1	0 0 2 3 3 4
1	5 5 6 6 7 8 8 9
2	0 2 3 3

(b) Minutes Beyond 2 Hours (1981–2000)

0	7 = 7 minutes past 2 hours
0	7 7 7 8 8 8 8 9 9 9 9 9 9 9 9 9
1	0 0 1 1 4

(c) In more recent times, the winning times have been closer to 2 hours, with all the times between 7 and 14 minutes over two hours. In the earlier period, more than half the times were more than 2 hours and 14 minutes.

7. Milligrams of Tar per Cigarette

1	0 = 1.0 mg tar		
1	0	11	4
2		12	0 4 8
3		13	7
4	1 5	14	1 5 9
5		15	0 1 2 8
6		16	0 6
7	3 8	17	0
8	0 6 8		
9	0		
10		29	8

9. Milligrams of Nicotine per Cigarette

0	1 = 0.1 milligram
0	1 4 4
0	5 6 6 6 7 7 7 8 8 9 9 9
1	0 0 0 0 0 0 1 2
1	
2	0

Chapter 2 Review

1. (a) Yes, with lines used instead of bars. However, because of the perspective nature of the drawing, the lengths of the bars do not represent the mileages. The scale for each bar changes. (b) Yes. The scale does not change, and the viewer is not distracted by the graphic of the highway.

3. Problems with Tax Returns

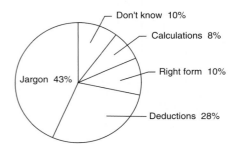

5. (a) Class width = 11.

Class Limits	Boundaries	Midpoint	Frequency	Relative Frequency
69–79	68.5–79.5	74	2	0.03
80–90	79.5–90.5	85	3	0.05
91–101	90.5–101.5	96	8	0.13
102–112	101.5–112.5	107	19	0.32
113–123	112.5–123.5	118	22	0.37
124–134	123.5–134.5	129	3	0.05
135–145	134.5–145.5	140	3	0.05

(b–c) Trunk Circumference (mm)—Histogram, Relative-Frequency Histogram

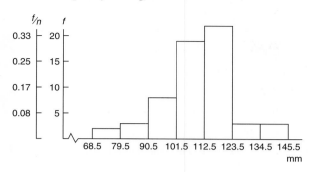

7. (a) 1240s had 40 data. (b) 75. (c) From 1203 to 1212. Little if any repairs or new construction.

CHAPTER 3

Section 3.1

1. $\bar{x} \approx 167.3\ °F$; median $= 171\ °F$; mode $= 178\ °F$.
3. (a) $\bar{x} \approx 3.27$; median $= 3$; mode $= 3$. (b) $\bar{x} \approx 4.21$; median $= 2$; mode $= 1$. (c) Lower Canyon mean is greater; median and mode are less. (d) Trimmed mean $= 3.75$ and is closer to Upper Canyon mean.
5. (a) $\bar{x} = \$136.15$; median $= \$66.50$; mode $= \$60$. (b) 5% trimmed mean $\approx \$121.28$; yes, but still higher than the median. (c) Median. The low and high prices would be useful.
7. (a) If the largest data value is *replaced* by a larger value, the mean will increase because the sum of the data values will increase, but the number of values will remain the same. The median will not change. The same value will still be in the eighth position when the data are ordered. (b) If the largest value is replaced by a value that is smaller (but still higher than the median), the mean will decrease because the sum of the data values will decrease. The median will not change. The same value will be in the eighth position in increasing order. (c) If the largest value is replaced by a value that is smaller than the median, the mean will decrease because the sum of the data values will decrease. The median also will decrease because the value formerly in the eighth position will move to the ninth position in increasing order. The median will be the new value in the eighth position.
9. $\Sigma wx = 85$; $\Sigma w = 10$; weighted average $= 8.5$.

Section 3.2

1. (a) 15. (b) Use a calculator. (c) 37; 608. (d) 37; 6.08. (e) $\sigma^2 \approx 29.59$; $\sigma \approx 5.44$.
3. (a) 7.87. (b) Use a calculator. (c) $\bar{x} \approx 1.24$; $s^2 \approx 1.78$; $s \approx 1.33$. (d) $CV \approx 107\%$. The standard deviation of the time to failure is just slightly larger than the average time.
5. (a) Use a calculator. (b) $\bar{x} = 49$; $s^2 \approx 687.49$; $s \approx 26.22$. (c) $\bar{y} = 44.8$; $s^2 \approx 508.50$; $s \approx 22.55$. (d) Mallard nests, $CV \approx 53.5\%$; Canada goose nests, $CV \approx 50.3\%$. The CV gives the ratio of the standard deviation to the mean; the CV for mallard nests is slightly higher.
7. Since $CV = s/\bar{x}$, then $s = CV(\bar{x})$; $s = 0.033$.
9. Midpoints: 25.5, 35.5, 45.5; $\bar{x} \approx 35.80$; $s^2 \approx 61.1$; $s \approx 7.82$.
11. Midpoints: 10.55, 14.55, 18.55, 22.55, 26.55; $\bar{x} \approx 15.6$; $s^2 \approx 23.4$; $s \approx 4.8$.

Section 3.3

1. 82% or more of the scores were at or below Angela's score; 18% or fewer of the scores were above Angela's score.
3. No, the score 82 might have a percentile rank less than 70.
5. Low $= 2$; Nurses' Length of Employment (months)
$Q_1 = 9.5$;
median $= 23$;
$Q_3 = 28.5$;
high $= 42$;
$IQR = 19$.

7. (a) Low $= 17$;
$Q_1 = 22$;
median $= 24$;
$Q_3 = 27$;
high $= 38$;
$IQR = 5$.
(b) Third quartile, since it is between the median and Q_3.

Bachelor's Degree Percentage by State

9. (a) California has the lowest premium. Pennsylvania has the highest. (b) Pennsylvania has the highest median premium. (c) California has the smallest range. Texas has the smallest interquartile range. (d) Part (a) is the five-number summary for Texas. It has the smallest IQR. Part (b) is the five-number summary for Pennsylvania. It has the largest minimum. Part (c) is the five-number summary for California. It has the lowest minimum.

Chapter 3 Review

1. (a) $\bar{x} = 109.5$; $s \approx 31.7$; $CV \approx 28.9\%$; range $= 69$.
   (b) $\bar{x} = 110.125$; $s \approx 7.2$; $CV \approx 6.5\%$; range $= 20$.
   (c) The first distribution is more spread than the second.
3. (a) Low $= 31$;
   $Q_1 = 40$;
   median $= 45$;
   $Q_3 = 52.5$;
   high $= 68$;
   $IQR = 12.5$.

Percentage of Democratic Vote by County

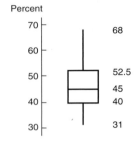

(b) Class width $= 8$.

Class	Midpoint	f
31–38	34.5	11
39–46	42.5	24
47–54	50.5	15
55–62	58.5	7
63–70	66.5	3

$\bar{x} \approx 46.1$; $s \approx 8.64$; 28.82 to 63.38.
   (c) $\bar{x} = 46.15$; $s \approx 8.63$.
5. Mean weight $= 156.25$ lb.
7. (a) No. (b) $23,478 to $57,478. (c) $7,775.
9. $\Sigma w = 16$, $\Sigma wx = 121$, average $= 7.56$.

CUMULATIVE REVIEW PROBLEMS
CHAPTERS 1–3

1. Assign consecutive numbers to all the wells in the study region. Then use a random number table, computer, or calculator to select 102 values that are less than or equal to the highest number assigned to a well in the study region. The sample consists of the wells with numbers corresponding to those selected.
2. Ratio.

---

3.   7 | 0 represents a pH level of 7.0

7	00000001111111111
7	22222222233333333333
7	44444444455555555
7	666666666777777
7	8888899999
8	01111111
8	2222222
8	45
8	67
8	88

4. Clear the decimals. Then the highest value is 88 and the lowest is 70. The class width for the whole numbers is 4. For the actual data, the class width is 0.4.

Class Limits	Boundaries	Midpoint	Frequency	Relative Frequency
7.0–7.3	6.95–7.35	7.15	39	0.38
7.4–7.7	7.35–7.75	7.55	32	0.31
7.8–8.1	7.75–8.15	7.95	18	0.18
8.2–8.5	8.15–8.55	8.35	9	0.09
8.6–8.9	8.55–8.95	8.75	4	0.04

Levels of pH in West Texas Wells—Histogram, Relative-Frequency Histogram

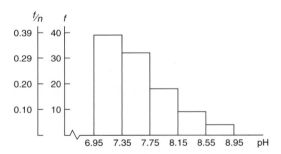

5. Range $= 1.8$; $\bar{x} \approx 7.58$; median $= 7.5$; mode $= 7.3$.
6. (a) Use a calculator or computer.
   (b) $s^2 \approx 0.20$; $s \approx 0.45$; $CV \approx 5.9\%$.
7. 6.68 to 8.48.
8. Levels of pH in West Texas Wells

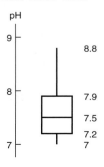

$IQR = 0.7$.

9. Skewed right. Lower values are more common.
10. No, there are no gaps in the plot, but only 6 out of 102, or about 6%, have pH levels at or above 8.4. Eight wells are neutral.
11. Half the wells have pH levels between 7.2 and 7.9. The data are skewed toward the high values, with the upper half of the pH levels spread out more than the lower half. The upper half ranges between 7.5 and 8.8, while the lower half is clustered between 7 and 7.5.
12. The report should emphasize the relatively low mean, median, and mode, and the fact that half the wells have a pH level less than 7.5. The data are clustered at the low end of the range.

CHAPTER 4

Section 4.1

1. (a) Moderate. (b) None. (c) High.
3. (a) No. (b) Increasing population might be a lurking variable causing both variables to increase.
5. (a) No. (b) One lurking variable responsible for average annual income increases is inflation. Better training might be a lurking variable responsible for shorter times to run the mile.
7. (a) Ages and Average Weights of Shetland Ponies

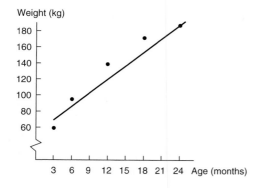

Line slopes upward.
(b) Strong; positive. (c) $r \approx 0.972$; increase.

9. (a) Lowest Barometric Pressure and Maximum Wind Speed for Tropical Cyclones

Line slopes downward.
(b) Strong; negative. (c) $r \approx -0.990$; decrease.
11. (a) Body Diameter and Height of Prehistoric Pottery

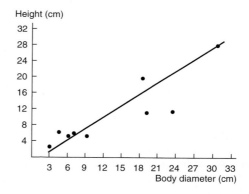

Line slopes upward.
(b) High; positive. (c) $r \approx 0.896$; increase.
13. (a) Unit Length on y Same as That on x

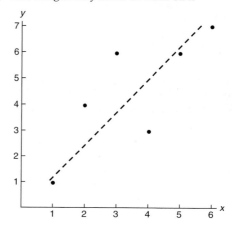

(b) Unit Length on *y* Twice That on *x*

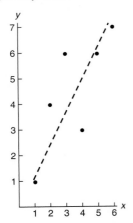

(c) Unit Length on *y* Half That on *x*

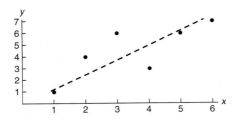

(d) The line in part b appears steeper than the line in part a, while the line in part c appears flatter than the line in part a. The slopes actually are all the same, but the lines look different because of the change in unit lengths on the *y* and *x* axes.

15. (a) $r \approx 0.972$ with $n = 5$ is significant for $\alpha = 0.05$. For this α, we conclude that age and weight of Shetland ponies are correlated. (b) $r \approx -0.990$ with $n = 6$ is significant for $\alpha = 0.01$. For this α, we conclude that lowest barometric pressure reading and maximum wind speed for cyclones are correlated.

Section 4.2

1. (a) Total Number of Jobs and Number of Entry-Level Jobs

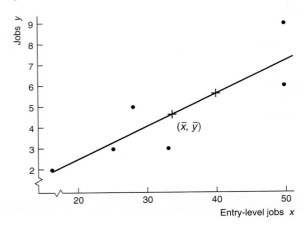

(b) Use a calculator. (c) $\bar{x} \approx 33.67$ jobs; $\bar{y} \approx 4.67$ entry-level jobs; $a \approx -0.748$; $b \approx 0.161$; $\hat{y} \approx -0.748 + 0.161x$. (d) See figure in part a. (e) $r^2 \approx 0.740$; 74.0% of variation explained and 26.0% unexplained. (f) 5.69 jobs.

3. (a) Weight of Cars and Gasoline Mileage

(b) Use a calculator. (c) $\bar{x} = 37.375$; $\bar{y} = 20.875$ mpg; $a \approx 43.326$; $b \approx -0.6007$; $\hat{y} \approx 43.326 - 0.6007x$. (d) See figure in part a. (e) $r^2 \approx 0.895$; 89.5% of variation explained and 10.5% unexplained. (f) 20.5 mpg.

5. (a) Age and Percentage of Fatal Accidents Due to Speeding

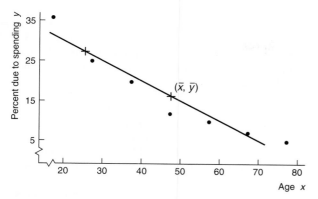

(b) Use a calculator. (c) $\bar{x} = 47$ years; $\bar{y} \approx 16.43\%$; $a \approx 39.761$; $b \approx -0.496$; $\hat{y} \approx 39.761 - 0.496x$.
(d) See figure of part a. (e) $r^2 \approx 0.920$; 92.0% of variation explained and 8.0% unexplained.
(f) 27.36%.

7. (a) Elevation of Archaeological Sites and Percentage of Unidentified Artifacts

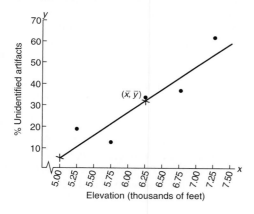

(b) Use a calculator. (c) $\bar{x} = 6.25$; $\bar{y} = 32.8$; $a = -104.7$; $b = 22$; $\hat{y} = -104.7 + 22x$. (d) See figure of part a. (e) $r^2 \approx 0.833$; 83.3% of variation explained, 16.7% unexplained. (f) 38.3.

9. (a) Yes. The pattern of residuals appears randomly scattered around the horizontal line at 0. (b) No. There do not appear to be any outliers.

11. (a) Result checks. (b) Result checks. (c) Yes.
(d) The equation $x = 0.9337y - 0.1335$ does not match

part b. (e) No. The least-squares equation changes depending on which variable is the explanatory variable and which is the response variable.

Chapter 4 Review

1. (a) Age and Mortality Rate for Bighorn Sheep

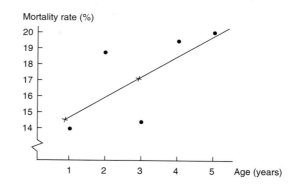

(b) $\bar{x} = 3$; $\bar{y} \approx 17.38$; $b \approx 1.27$; $\hat{y} \approx 13.57 + 1.27x$.
(c) $r \approx 0.685$; $r^2 \approx 0.469$; 46.9% explained.

3. (a) Weight of One-Year-Old versus Weight of Adult

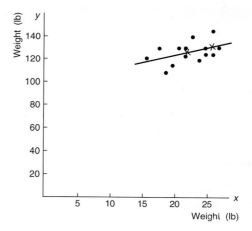

(b) $\bar{x} \approx 21.43$; $\bar{y} \approx 126.79$; $b \approx 1.285$; $\hat{y} \approx 99.25 + 1.285x$. (c) $r \approx 0.468$; $r^2 \approx 0.219$; 21.9% explained.
(d) 124.95 lb. However, since r is low, this prediction may not be useful. Other lurking variables seem to have an effect on adult weight.

5. (a) Weight of Mail versus Number of Employees Required

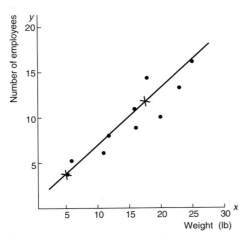

(b) $\bar{x} \approx 16.38$; $\bar{y} \approx 10.13$; $b \approx 0.554$; $\hat{y} \approx 1.051 + 0.554x$.
(c) $r \approx 0.913$; $r^2 \approx 0.833$; 83.3% explained. (d) 9.36.

CHAPTER 5

Section 5.1

1. See text.
3. b, since 4.1 is greater than 1; d, since -0.5 is less than 0; h, since 150% is greater than 100% or 1.
5. Answers vary. Probability as a relative frequency. One concern is whether the students in the class are more or less adept at wiggling their ears than people in the general population.
7. (a) $P(0) = 15/375$; $P(1) = 71/375$; $P(2) = 124/375$; $P(3) = 131/375$; $P(4) = 34/375$. (b) Yes, the listed numbers of similar preferences form the sample space.
9. (a) $P(\text{best idea 6 A.M.–12 noon}) = 290/966 \approx 0.30$; $P(\text{best idea 12 noon–6 P.M.}) = 135/966 \approx 0.14$; $P(\text{best idea 6 P.M.–12 midnight}) = 319/966 \approx 0.33$; $P(\text{best idea 12 midnight–6 A.M.}) = 222/966 \approx 0.23$. (b) The probabilities add up to 1. They should add up to 1 provided the intervals do not overlap and each inventor chose only one interval. The sample space is the set of four time intervals.
11. (a) $P(\text{enter if walks by}) = 58/127 \approx 0.46$. (b) $P(\text{buy if entered}) = 25/58 \approx 0.43$. (c) $P(\text{walk in and buy}) = 25/127 \approx 0.20$. (d) $P(\text{not buy}) = 1 - P(\text{buy}) \approx 1 - 0.43 = 0.57$.

Section 5.2

1. (a) 0.2; yes. (b) 0.4; yes. (c) $1.0 - 0.2 = 0.8$.
3. (a) 0.332; yes. (b) 0.332; yes. (c) 1 (no purple).
5. (a) Yes. (b) $P(5 \text{ on green } and \text{ 3 on red}) = P(5) \cdot P(3) = (1/6)(1/6) = 1/36 \approx 0.028$. (c) $P(3 \text{ on green } and \text{ 5 on red}) = P(3) \cdot P(5) = (1/6)(1/6) = 1/36 \approx 0.028$. (d) $P((5 \text{ on green } and \text{ 3 on red}) \text{ } or \text{ } (3 \text{ on green } and \text{ 5 on red})) = (1/36) + (1/36) = 1/18 \approx 0.056$.
7. (a) $P(\text{sum of 6}) = P(1 \text{ } and \text{ } 5) + P(2 \text{ } and \text{ } 4) + P(3 \text{ } and \text{ } 3) + P(4 \text{ } and \text{ } 2) + P(5 \text{ } and \text{ } 1) = (1/36) + (1/36) + (1/36) + (1/36) + (1/36) = 5/36$. (b) $P(\text{sum of 4}) = P(1 \text{ } and \text{ } 3) + P(2 \text{ } and \text{ } 2) + P(3 \text{ } and \text{ } 1) = (1/36) + (1/36) + (1/36) = 3/36$ or $1/12$. (c) $P(\text{sum of 6 } or \text{ sum of 4}) = P(\text{sum of 6}) + P(\text{sum of 4}) = (5/36) + (3/36) = 8/36$ or $2/9$; yes.
9. (a) No, after the first draw the sample space becomes smaller and probabilities for events on the second draw change. (b) $P(\text{ace on 1st } and \text{ king on 2nd}) = P(\text{ace}) \cdot P(\text{king, } given \text{ ace}) = (4/52)(4/51) = 4/663$. (c) $P(\text{king on 1st } and \text{ ace on 2nd}) = P(\text{king}) \cdot P(\text{ace, } given \text{ king}) = (4/52)(4/51) = 4/663$. (d) $P(\text{ace and king in either order}) = P(\text{ace on 1st } and \text{ king on 2nd}) + P(\text{king on 1st } and \text{ ace on 2nd}) = (4/663) + (4/663) = 8/663$.
11. (a) Yes, replacement of the card restores the sample space and all probabilities for the second draw remain unchanged, regardless of the outcome of the first card. (b) $P(\text{ace on 1st } and \text{ king on 2nd}) = P(\text{ace}) \cdot P(\text{king}) = (4/52)(4/52) = 1/169$. (c) $P(\text{king on 1st } and \text{ ace on 2nd}) = P(\text{king}) \cdot P(\text{ace}) = (4/52)(4/52) = 1/169$. (d) $P(\text{ace and king in either order}) = P(\text{ace on 1st } and \text{ king on 2nd}) + P(\text{king on 1st } and \text{ ace on 2nd}) = (1/169) + (1/169) = 2/169$.
13. (a) $P(\text{6 years old } or \text{ older}) = P(6–9) + P(10–12) + P(13 \text{ and over}) = 0.27 + 0.14 + 0.22 = 0.63$. (b) $P(\text{12 years old } or \text{ younger}) = P(2 \text{ and under}) + P(3–5) + P(6–9) + P(10–12) = 0.15 + 0.22 + 0.27 + 0.14 = 0.78$. (c) $P(\text{between 6 and 12}) = P(6–9) + P(10–12) = 0.27 + 0.14 = 0.41$. (d) $P(\text{between 3 and 9}) = P(3–5) + P(6–9) = 0.22 + 0.27 = 0.49$. The category 13 and over contains far more ages than the group 10–12. It is not surprising that more toys are purchased for this group, since there are more children in this group.
15. The information from James Burke can be viewed as conditional probabilities. $P(\text{report lie, } given \text{ person is lying}) = 0.72$ and $P(\text{report lie, } given \text{ person is not lying}) = 0.07$. (a) $P(\text{person is not lying}) = 0.90$; $P(\text{person is not}$

lying *and* polygraph reports lie) = P(person is not lying) × P(reports lie, *given* person not lying) = (0.90)(0.07) = 0.063 or 6.3%.   (b) P(person is lying) = 0.10; P(person is lying *and* polygraph reports lie) = P(person is lying) × P(reports lie, *given* person is lying) = (0.10)(0.72) = 0.072 or 7.2%.   (c) P(person is not lying) = 0.5; P(person is lying) = 0.5; P(person is not lying *and* polygraph reports lie) = P(person is not lying) × P(reports lie, *given* person not lying) = (0.50)(0.07) = 0.035 or 3.5%. P(person is lying *and* polygraph reports lie) = P(person is lying) × P(reports lie, *given* person is lying) = (0.50)(0.72) = 0.36 or 36%.   (d) P(person is not lying) = 0.15; P(person is lying) = 0.85; P(person is not lying *and* polygraph reports lie) = P(person is not lying) × P(reports lie, *given* person is not lying) = (0.15)(0.07) = 0.0105 or 1.05%. P(person is lying *and* polygraph reports lie) = P(person is lying) × P(reports lie, *given* person is lying) = (0.85)(0.72) = 0.612 or 61.2%.

17. (a) 72/154.   (b) 82/154.   (c) 79/116.   (d) 37/116.
   (e) 72/270.   (f) 82/270.

19. (a) 932/1894.   (b) 353/739.   (c) 142/1894.
   (d) 22/224.   (e) 1007/1894.   (f) 39/66.   (g) No; probabilities computed in parts (a) and (b) are not equal. (*Note:* More than once is two or more times.)

Section 5.3

1. (a) Outcomes for Tossing a Coin Three Times

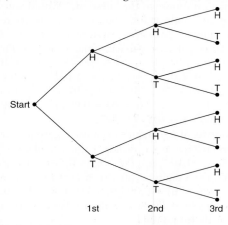

   (b) 3.   (c) 3/8.

3. (a) Outcomes for Drawing Two Balls (without replacement)

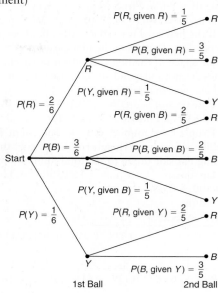

1st Ball   2nd Ball

   (b) P(R *and* R) = 2/6 · 1/5 = 1/15.
      P(R 1st *and* B 2nd) = 2/6 · 3/5 = 1/5.
      P(R 1st *and* Y 2nd) = 2/6 · 1/5 = 1/15.
      P(B 1st *and* R 2nd) = 3/6 · 2/5 = 1/5.
      P(B 1st *and* B 2nd) = 3/6 · 2/5 = 1/5.
      P(B 1st *and* Y 2nd) = 3/6 · 1/5 = 1/10.
      P(Y 1st *and* R 2nd) = 1/6 · 2/5 = 1/15.
      P(Y 1st *and* B 2nd) = 1/6 · 3/5 = 1/10.

5. $4 \cdot 3 \cdot 2 \cdot 1 = 24$ ways.

7. $4 \cdot 3 \cdot 3 = 36$.

9. $P_{5,2} = (5!/3!) = 5 \cdot 4 = 20$.

11. $P_{7,7} = (7!/0!) = 7! = 5040$.

13. $C_{5,2} = (5!/(2!3!)) = 10$.

15. $C_{7,7} = (7!/(7!0!)) = 1$.

17. $P_{15,3} = 2730$.

19. $C_{15,5} = (15!/(5!10!)) = 3003$.

21. (a) $C_{12,6} = (12!/(6!6!)) = 924$.
   (b) $C_{7,6} = (7!/(6!1!)) = 7$.   (c) $7/924 \approx 0.008$.

Chapter 5 Review

1. $P(\text{asked}) = 24\%$; $P(\text{received}, given \text{ asked}) = 45\%$; $P(\text{ask } and \text{ receive}) = (0.24)(0.45) = 10.8\%$.
3. (a) If the first card is replaced, the outcomes are independent. Replacing the first card restores the original sample space. If the first card is not replaced, the outcomes are not independent, because removing the first card changes the sample space.
   (b) $P(\text{heart } and \text{ heart}) = (13/52)(13/52) \approx 0.063$.
   (c) $P(\text{heart } and \text{ heart}) = (13/52)(12/51) \approx 0.059$.
5. (a) Drop a fixed number of tacks and count how many land flat side down. Then form the ratio of the number landing flat side down to the total number dropped.
   (b) Up, down. (c) $P(\text{up}) = 160/500 = 0.32$; $P(\text{down}) = 340/500 = 0.68$.
7. (a) and (b)

Outcomes x	2	3	4	5	6
$P(x)$	0.028	0.056	0.083	0.111	0.139

x	7	8	9	10	11	12
$P(x)$	0.167	0.139	0.111	0.083	0.056	0.028

9. $C_{8,2} = (8!/(2!6!)) = (8 \cdot 7/2) = 28$.
11. $3 \cdot 2 \cdot 1 \approx 6$.
13. $4 \cdot 4 \cdot 4 \cdot 4 \cdot 4 = 1024$ choices; $P(\text{all correct}) = 1/1024 \approx 0.00098$.

CHAPTER 6

Section 6.1

1. (a) Discrete. (b) Continuous. (c) Continuous.
   (d) Discrete. (e) Continuous.
3. (a) Yes. (b) No; probabilities total to more than 1.
5. (a) Yes, events are distinct and probabilities total to 1.
   (b) Income Distribution ($1000)

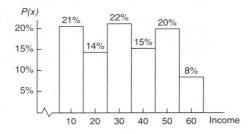

(c) 32.3 thousand dollars. (d) 16.12 thousand dollars.
7. (a) 0.763; complement. (b) 0.368. (c) 0.016.
   (d) 1.25. (e) 0.97.
9. (a) 0.01191; $595.50. (b) $646; $698; $751.50; $806.50; $3497.50 total. (c) $4197.50. (d) $1502.50.

Section 6.2

1. A trial is one flip of a fair quarter. Success = coin shows heads. Failure = coin shows tails. $n = 3$; $p = 0.5$; $q = 0.5$. (a) $P(r = 3 \text{ heads}) = C_{3,3}p^3q^0 = 1(0.5)^3(0.5)^0 = 0.125$. To find this value in Table 2 of the Appendix, use the group in which $n = 3$, the column headed by $p = 0.5$, and the row headed by $r = 3$. (b) $P(r = 2 \text{ heads}) = C_{3,2}p^2q^1 = 3(0.5)^2(0.5)^1 = 0.375$. To find this value in Table 2 of the Appendix, use the group in which $n = 3$, the column headed by $p = 0.5$, and the row headed by $r = 2$. (c) $P(r \text{ is 2 or more}) = P(r = 2 \text{ heads}) + P(r = 3 \text{ heads}) = 0.375 + 0.125 = 0.500$. (d) The probability of getting three tails when you toss a coin three times is the same as getting zero heads. Therefore, $P(3 \text{ tails}) = P(r = 0 \text{ heads}) = C_{3,0}p^0q^3 = 1(0.5)^0(0.5)^3 = 0.125$. To find this value in Table 2 of the Appendix, use the group in which $n = 3$, the column headed by $p = 0.5$, and the row headed by $r = 0$.
3. (a) A trial is a man's response to the question, "Would you marry the same woman again?" Success = a positive response. Failure = a negative response. $n = 10$; $p = 0.80$; $q = 0.20$. Using values in Table 2 of the Appendix, $P(r \text{ is at least } 7) = P(r = 7) + P(r = 8) + P(r = 9) + P(r = 10) = 0.201 + 0.302 + 0.268 + 0.107 = 0.878$. $P(r \text{ is less than half of } 10) = P(r < 5) = P(r = 0) + P(r = 1) + P(r = 2) + P(r = 3) + P(r = 4) = 0.000 + 0.000 + 0.000 + 0.001 + 0.006 = 0.007$. (b) A trial is a woman's response to the question, "Would you marry the same man again?" Success = a positive response. Failure = a negative response. $n = 10$; $p = 0.5$; $q = 0.5$. Using values in Table 2 of the Appendix, $P(r \text{ is at least } 7) = P(r = 7) + P(r = 8) + P(r = 9) + P(r = 10) = 0.117 + 0.044 + 0.010 + 0.001 = 0.172$. $P(r \text{ is less than half of } 10) = P(r < 5) = P(r = 0) + P(r = 1) + P(r = 2) + P(r = 3) + P(r = 4) = 0.001 + 0.010 + 0.044 + 0.117 + 0.205 = 0.377$.
5. A trial consists of a woman's response regarding her mother-in-law. Success = dislike. Failure = like. $n = 6$; $p = 0.90$; $q = 0.10$. (a) $P(r = 6) = 0.531$. (b) $P(r = 0) = 0.000$ (to 3 digits). (c) $P(r \geq 4) = P(r = 4) + P(r = 5) + P(r = 6) = 0.098 + 0.354 + 0.531 = 0.983$. (d) $P(r \leq 3) = 1 - P(r \geq 4) \approx 1 - 0.983 = 0.017$ or 0.016 directly from table.
7. A trial is taking a polygraph exam. Success = pass. Failure = fail. $n = 9$; $p = 0.85$; $q = 0.15$. (a) $P(r = 9) = 0.232$. (b) $P(r \geq 5) = P(r = 5) + P(r = 6) + P(r = 7) + P(r = 8) + P(r = 9) = 0.028 + 0.107 + 0.260 + 0.368 + 0.232 = 0.995$. (c) $P(r \leq 4) = 1 - P(r \geq 5) \approx 1 - 0.995 = 0.005$ or 0.006 directly from table. (d) $P(r = 0) = 0.000$ (to 3 digits).

9. A trial is catching and releasing a pike. Success = pike dies. Failure = pike lives. $n = 16$; $p = 0.05$; $q = 0.95$.
   (a) $P(r = 0) = 0.440$.   (b) $P(r < 3) = 0.957$.
   (c) $P(r = 0) = 0.440$ (all live is equivalent to none die).
   (d) Change success to live; $p = 0.95$; $P(r > 14) = 0.811$.

11. (a) A trial consists of using the Myers-Briggs instrument to determine if a person in marketing is an extrovert. Success = extrovert. Failure = not extrovert. $n = 15$; $p = 0.75$; $q = 0.25$. $P(r \geq 10) = 0.851$; $P(r \geq 5) = 0.999$; $P(r = 15) = 0.013$.   (b) A trial consists of using the Myers-Briggs instrument to determine if a computer programmer is an introvert. Success = introvert. Failure = not introvert. $n = 5$; $p = 0.60$; $q = 0.40$. $P(r = 0) = 0.010$; $P(r \geq 3) = 0.683$; $P(r = 5) = 0.078$.

13. (a) $n = 10$; $p = 0.40$; $P(r = 0) = 0.006$.   (b) $n = 10$; $p = 0.40$; $P(r < 5) = 0.633$.   (c) $n = 10$; $p = 0.30$; $P(r \leq 2) = 0.382$.   (d) $n = 10$; $p = 0.70$; $P(r \geq 6) = 0.849$.

15. $n = 8$; $p = 0.53$; $q = 0.47$.   (a) 0.812515; yes, truncated at 5 digits.   (b) 0.187486; 0.18749; yes, rounded to 5 digits.

17. (a) They are the same.   (b) They are the same.
   (c) $r = 1$.   (d) The one headed by $p = 0.80$.

Section 6.3

1. (a) Binomial Distribution
   The distribution is symmetrical.

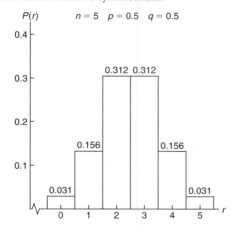

(b) Binomial Distribution
   The distribution is skewed right.

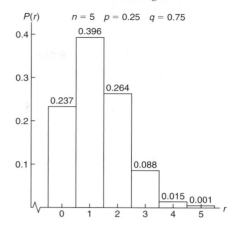

(c) Binomial Distribution
   The distribution is skewed left.

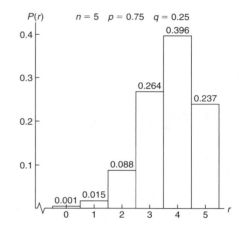

(d) The distributions are mirror images of one another.
(e) The distribution would be skewed left for $p = 0.73$ because the more likely numbers of successes are to the right of the middle.

3. (a) Binomial Distribution for Number of Gullible Consumers

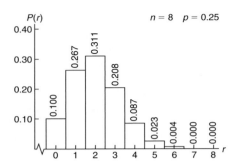

$n = 8 \quad p = 0.25$

(b) $\mu = 2; \sigma \approx 1.225$.

5. (a) $P(r = 0) = 0.004; P(r = 1) = 0.047; P(r = 2) = 0.211; P(r = 3) = 0.422; P(r = 4) = 0.316$.

(b) Binomial Distribution for Number of Parolees Who Do Not Become Repeat Offenders

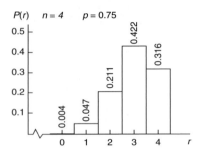

$n = 4 \qquad p = 0.75$

(c) $\mu = 3; \sigma \approx 0.866$.

7. $n = 12; p = 0.25$ do not serve; $p = 0.75$ serve.
   (a) $P(r = 12 \text{ serve}) = 0.032$.   (b) $P(r \geq 6 \text{ do not serve}) = 0.053$.   (c) For serving, $\mu = 9; \sigma = 1.50$.

9. (a) $P(r = 7 \text{ guilty in U.S.}) = 0.028; P(r = 7 \text{ guilty in Japan}) = 0.698$.   (b) For guilty in Japan, $\mu = 6.65, \sigma \approx 0.58$; for guilty in U.S., $\mu = 4.2; \sigma \approx 1.30$.

Chapter 6 Review

1. (a) 38; 11.6.
   (b) Duration of Leases in Months

x months

---

3. (a) Number of Claimants Under 25

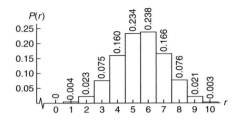

(b) $P(r \geq 6) = 0.504$.   (c) $\mu = 5.5; \sigma \approx 1.57$.

5. (a) 0.039.   (b) 0.403.   (c) 8.

7. (a) Number of Good Grapefruit

(b) 0.244, 0.999.   (c) 7.5.   (d) 1.37.

9. $P(r \leq 2) = 0.000$ (to 3 digits). The data seem to indicate that the percent favoring the increase in fees is less than 85%.

**CUMULATIVE REVIEW PROBLEMS
CHAPTERS 4–6**

1. The specified ranges of readings are disjoint and cover all possible readings.

2. Essay.

3. Yes; the events constitute the entire sample space.

4. (a) 0.85.   (b) 0.70.   (c) 0.70.
   (d) 0.30.   (e) 0.15.   (f) 0.75.
   (g) 0.30.   (h) 0.05.

5.

x	$P(x)$
5	0.25
15	0.45
25	0.15
35	0.10
45	0.05

$\mu \approx 17.5; \sigma \approx 10.9$.

6. (a) $p = 0.10$.   (b) $\mu = 1.2; \sigma \approx 1.04$.   (c) 0.718.
   (d) 0.889.

7. (a) Blood Glucose Level

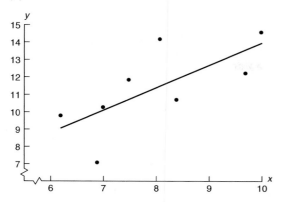

(b) $\hat{y} \approx 1.135 + 1.279x$. (c) $r \approx 0.700$; $r^2 \approx 0.490$; 49% of the variance in y is explained by the model and the variance in x. (d) 12.65.

CHAPTER 7

Section 7.1

1. (a) No, the curve is skewed. (b) No, the curve crosses the horizontal axis. (c) No, the curve has three peaks. (d) No, the curve is not smooth.
3. Figure 7-9 has the larger standard deviation. The mean of Figure 7-9 is $\mu = 10$. The mean of Figure 7-10 is $\mu = 4$.
5. (a) 50%. (b) 68%. (c) 99.7%.
7. (a) 50%. (b) 50%. (c) 68%. (d) 95%.
9. (a) From 1207 to 1279. (b) From 1171 to 1315. (c) From 1135 to 1351.
11. (a) From 1.70 mA to 4.60 mA. (b) From 0.25 mA to 6.05 mA.

Section 7.2

1. (a) Robert, Juan, and Linda each scored above the mean. (b) Joel scored on the mean. (c) Susan and Jan scored below the mean. (d) Robert, 172; Juan, 184; Susan, 110; Joel, 150; Jan, 134; Linda, 182.
3. (a) $-4.00 < z < 4.00$. (b) $z < -1.6$. (c) $1.00 < z$. (d) $81.75°F < \bar{x}$. (e) $x < 63.5°F$. (f) $64°F < x < 81.25°F$.
5. (a) $-1.77 < z$. (b) $z < 1.61$. (c) $-1.45 < z < 1.45$. (d) $3706 < x < 5907$. (e) $x < 5615$. (f) $6000 < x$. (g) A population of 2800 deer corresponds to a z value of -2.58. Data values this far below the mean occur less than 2.5% of the time. This would be an unusually low number. The population 6300 corresponds to a z value of 3.06. Fall deer populations are practically never so large. Such a population would be considered an unusually high population.

7. (a) $-1.00 < z$. (b) $z < -2.00$. (c) $-2.67 < z < 2.33$. (d) $x < 4.4$. (e) $5.2 < x$. (f) $4.1 < x < 4.5$.
(g) A red blood cell count of 5.9 or higher corresponds to a standard z score of 3.67. Practically no data values occur this far above the mean. Such a count would be considered unusually high for a healthy female.
9. 0.5000. 11. 0.0934. 13. 0.6736. 15. 0.0643.
17. 0.8888. 19. 0.4993. 21. 0.4778. 23. 0.8953.
25. 0.3471. 27. 0.0306. 29. 0.5000. 31. 0.4483.
33. 0.8849. 35. 0.0885. 37. 0.8849. 39. 0.8808.
41. 0.3226. 43. 0.4474. 45. 0.2939. 47. 0.6704.

Section 7.3

1. $P(3 \leq x \leq 6) = P(-0.50 \leq z \leq 1.00) = 0.5328$.
3. $P(50 \leq x \leq 70) = P(0.67 \leq z \leq 2.00) = 0.2286$.
5. $P(8 \leq x \leq 12) = P(-2.19 \leq z \leq -0.94) = 0.1593$.
7. $P(x \geq 30) = P(z \geq 2.94) = 0.0016$.
9. $P(x \geq 90) = P(z \geq -0.67) = 0.7486$.
11. -1.555. 13. 0.13. 15. 1.41. 17. -0.92.
19. ± 2.33.
21. (a) $P(x > 60) = P(z > -1) = 0.8413$.
(b) $P(x < 110) = P(z < 1) = 0.8413$.
(c) $P(60 \leq x \leq 110) = P(-1.00 \leq z \leq 1.00) = 0.8413 - 0.1587 = 0.6826$. (d) $P(x > 140) = P(z > 2.20) = 0.0139$.
23. (a) $P(x > 675) = P(z > 1.75) = 0.0401$.
(b) $P(x < 450) = P(z < -0.50) = 0.3085$.
(c) $P(450 \leq x \leq 675) = P(-0.50 \leq z \leq 1.75) = 0.6514$. (d) $P(x > 28) = P(z > 1.67) = 0.0475$.
(e) $P(x > 12) = P(z > -1.00) = 0.8413$.
(f) $P(12 \leq x \leq 28) = P(-1.00 \leq z \leq 1.67) = 0.7938$.
25. (a) $P(x < 36 \text{ mo}) = P(z < -1.13) = 0.1292$. The company will replace 13% of its batteries. (b) $P(z < z_0) = 10\%$ for $z_0 = -1.28$; $x = -1.28(8) + 45 = 34.76$. Guarantee the batteries for 35 months.
27. (a) According to the empirical rule, about 95% of the data lies between $\mu - 2\sigma$ and $\mu + 2\sigma$. Since this interval is 4σ wide, we have $4\sigma \approx 6$ years, so $\sigma \approx 1.5$ years. (b) $P(x > 5) = P(z > -2.00) = 0.9772$. (c) $P(x < 10) = P(z < 1.33) = 0.9082$. (d) $P(z < z_0) = 0.10$ for $z_0 = -1.28$; $x = -1.28(1.5) + 8 = 6.08$ years. Guarantee the TVs for about 6.1 years.
29. (a) $P(z \geq z_0) = 0.99$ for $z_0 = -2.33$; $x = -2.33(3.7) + 90 \approx 81.38$ mo. Guarantee the microchips for 81 months. (b) $P(x \leq 84) = P(z \leq -1.62) = 0.0526$. (c) Expected loss $= (50,000,000)(0.0526) = \$2,630,000$. (d) Profit $= \$370,000$.

Section 7.4

1. A population is a set of measurements or counts either existing or conceptual. For example, the population of

ages of all people in Colorado; the population of weights of all students in your school; the population count of all antelope in Wyoming.

3. A population parameter is a numerical descriptive measure of a population, such as μ, the population mean; σ, the population standard deviation; or σ^2, the population variance.

5. A statistical inference is a conclusion about the value of a population parameter. We will do both estimation and testing.

7. They help us visualize the sampling distribution by using tables and graphs that approximately represent the sampling distribution.

9. We studied the sampling distribution of mean trout lengths based on samples of size 5. Other such sampling distributions abound.

Section 7.5

Note: Answers may differ slightly depending on the number of digits carried in the standard deviation.

1. (a) $\mu_{\bar{x}} = 15$; $\sigma_{\bar{x}} = 2.0$; $P(15 \leq \bar{x} \leq 17) = P(0 \leq z \leq 1.00) = 0.3413$. (b) $\mu_{\bar{x}} = 15$; $\sigma_{\bar{x}} = 1.75$; $P(15 \leq \bar{x} \leq 17) = P(0 \leq z \leq 1.14) = 0.3729$. (c) The standard deviation is smaller in part (b) because of the larger sample size. Therefore, the distribution about $\mu_{\bar{x}}$ is narrower in part (b).

3. (a) No; the sample size is only 9 and so is too small. (b) Yes; the $\bar{x}$ distribution also will be normal with $\mu_{\bar{x}} = 25$; $\sigma_{\bar{x}} = 3.5/3$; $P(23 \leq \bar{x} \leq 26) = P(-1.71 \leq z \leq 0.86) = 0.7615$.

5. (a) $P(x < 74.5) = P(z < -0.63) = 0.2643$. (b) $P(\bar{x} < 74.5) = P(z < -2.79) = 0.0026$. (c) No. If the weight of only one car were less than 74.5 tons, we could not conclude that the loader is out of adjustment. If the mean weight for a sample of 20 cars were less than 74.5 tons, we would suspect that the loader is malfunctioning. As we see in part (b), the probability of this happening is very low if the loader is correctly adjusted.

7. (a) $P(x < 40) = P(z < -1.80) = 0.0359$. (b) Since the x distribution is approximately normal, the $\bar{x}$ distribution is approximately normal with mean 85 and standard deviation 17.678. $P(\bar{x} < 40) = P(z < -2.55) = 0.0054$. (c) $P(\bar{x} < 40) = P(z < -3.12) = 0.0009$. (d) $P(\bar{x} < 40) = P(z < -4.02) < 0.0002$. (e) Yes; if the average value based on five tests were less than 40, the patient is almost certain to have excess insulin.

9. (a) $P(x < 54) = P(z < -1.27) = 0.1020$. (b) The expected number undernourished is $2200(0.1020)$, or about 224. (c) $P(\bar{x} \leq 60) = P(z \leq -2.99) = 0.0014$. (d) $P(\bar{x} < 64.2) = P(z < 1.20) = 0.8849$. Since the sample average is above the mean, it is quite unlikely that the doe population is undernourished.

11. (a) Since x itself represents a sample mean return based on a large (random) sample of stocks, x has a distribution that is approximately normal (central limit theorem). (b) $P(1\% \leq \bar{x} \leq 2\%) = P(-1.63 \leq z \leq 1.09) = 0.8105$. (c) $P(1\% \leq \bar{x} \leq 2\%) = P(-3.27 \leq z \leq 2.18) = 0.9849$. (d) Yes. The standard deviation decreases as the sample size increases. (e) $P(\bar{x} < 1\%) = P(z < -3.27) = 0.0005$. This is very unlikely if $\mu = 1.6\%$. One would suspect that μ has slipped below 1.6%.

13. (a) 30 or more. (b) No.

Section 7.6

Note: Answers may differ slightly depending on how many digits are carried in the computation of the standard deviation and z.

1. (a) $P(r \geq 50) = P(x \geq 49.5) = P(z \geq -27.53) \approx 1$ or almost certain. (b) $P(r \geq 50) = P(x \geq 49.5) = P(z \geq 7.78) \approx 0$ or almost impossible for a random sample.

3. (a) $P(r \geq 15) = P(x \geq 14.5) = P(z \geq -1.61) = 0.9463$. (b) $P(r \geq 28) = P(x \geq 27.5) = P(z \geq 1.49) = 0.0681$. (c) $P(15 \leq r \leq 28) = P(14.5 \leq x \leq 28.5) = P(-1.61 \leq z \leq 1.73) = 0.9045$. (d) $n = 125$; $p = 0.17$. Since both np and nq are larger than 5, the normal approximation is appropriate.

5. (a) $P(r \geq 15) = P(x \geq 14.5) = P(z \geq -2.35) = 0.9906$. (b) $P(r \geq 30) = P(x \geq 29.5) = P(z \geq 0.62) = 0.2676$. (c) $P(25 \leq r \leq 35) = P(24.5 \leq x \leq 35.5) = P(-0.37 \leq z \leq 1.81) = 0.6092$. (d) $P(r > 40) = P(r \geq 41) = P(x \geq 40.5) = P(z \geq 2.80) = 0.0026$.

7. (a) $P(r \geq 47) = P(x \geq 46.5) = P(z \geq -1.94) = 0.9738$. (b) $P(r \leq 58) = P(x \leq 58.5) = P(z \leq 1.75) = 0.9599$. In parts c and d, let r be the number of products that succeed, and use $p = 1 - 0.80 = 0.20$. (c) $P(r \geq 15) = P(x \geq 14.5) = P(z \geq 0.40) = 0.3446$. (d) $P(r < 10) = P(r \leq 9) = P(x \leq 9.5) = P(z \leq -1.14) = 0.1271$.

9. (a) $P(r > 280) = P(r \geq 281) = P(x > 280.5) = P(z \geq -2.16) = 0.9846$. (b) $P(r \geq 320) = P(x \geq 319.5) = P(z \geq 1.95) = 0.0256$. (c) $P(280 \leq r \leq 320) = P(279.5 \leq x \leq 320.5) = P(-2.26 \leq z \leq 2.05) = 0.9679$. (d) $n = 430$; $p = 0.70$; $q = 0.30$; np and nq are both greater than 5. These conditions mean that the normal approximation to the binomial is appropriate.

11. (a) $P(r \geq 540) = P(x \geq 539.5) = P(z \geq 3.81) \approx 0.000$. (b) $P(r \leq 500) = P(x \leq 500.5) = P(z \leq 1.11) = 0.8665$. (c) $P(485 \leq r \leq 525) = P(484.5 \leq x \leq 525.5) = P(0 \leq z \leq 2.84) = 0.4977$.

13. (a) 0.94. (b) $P(r \leq 255)$. (c) $P(r \leq 255) = P(x \leq 255.5) = P(z \leq 1.16) = 0.8770$.

Chapter 7 Review

1. (a) 0.9821. (b) 0.3156. (c) 0.2977.
3. 1.645.
5. (a) 0.89. (b) 0. (c) 0.2514.
7. (a) 0.0166. (b) 0.975.
9. (a) 0.9772. (b) 17.3 hr.
11. (a) A normal distribution. (b) The mean μ of the x distribution. (c) $\sigma/\sqrt{n}$, where σ is the standard deviation of the x distribution. (d) They will both be approximately normal with the same mean, but the standard deviations will be $\sigma/\sqrt{50}$ and $\sigma/\sqrt{100}$, respectively.
13. $P(98 \le \bar{x} \le 102) = P(-1.33 \le z \le 1.33) = 0.8164$.

CHAPTER 8

Section 8.1

1. (a) 3.04 gm to 3.26 gm; 0.11 gm. (b) Distribution of weights is normal with known σ. (c) There is an 80% chance that the confidence interval is one of the intervals that contains the population average weight of Allen's hummingbirds in this region. (d) $n = 28$.
3. (a) 34.62 ml/kg to 40.38 ml/kg; 2.88 ml/kg. (b) The sample size is large (30 or more) and σ is known. (c) There is a 99% chance that the confidence interval is one of the intervals that contains the population average blood plasma level for male firefighters. (d) $n = 60$.
5. (a) 125.7 to 151.3 larceny cases; 12.8 larceny cases. (b) 123.3 to 153.7 larceny cases; 15.2 larceny cases. (c) 118.4 to 158.6 larceny cases; 20.1 larceny cases. (d) Yes. (e) Yes.
7. (a) $53,871 to $64,009; $5069. (b) $55,138 to $62,742; $3802. (c) $56,175 to $61,705; $2765. (d) Yes. (e) Yes.
9. (a) The mean and standard deviation round to the values given. (b) Using the rounded values of part (a), the 75% interval is from 34.19 thousand to 37.81 thousand. (c) Yes. 30 thousand dollars is below the lower bound of the 75% confidence interval. We can say with 75% confidence that the mean lies between 34.19 thousand and 37.81 thousand. (d) Yes. 40 thousand is above the upper bound of the 75% confidence interval. (e) 33.41 thousand to 38.59 thousand. We can say with 90% confidence that the mean lies between 33.4 thousand and 38.6 thousand dollars. 30 thousand is below the lower bound and 40 thousand is above the upper bound.

Section 8.2

1. 2.110.
3. 1.721.

5. (a) The mean and standard deviation round to the values given. (b) Using the rounded values for the mean and standard deviation given in part (a), the interval is from 1249 to 1295.
7. (a) Use a calculator. (b) 74.7 lb to 107.3 lb.
9. (a) The mean and standard deviation round to the given values. (b) 8.41 to 11.49. (c) Since all values in the 99.9% confidence interval are above 6, we can be almost certain that this patient no longer has a calcium deficiency.
11. (a) Boxplots differ in length of interquartile box, location of median, and length of whiskers. The boxplots come from different samples. (b) Yes; yes; for 95% confidence intervals, we expect about 95% of the samples to generate intervals that contain the mean of the population.
13. (a) The mean and standard deviation round to the given values. (b) 21.6 to 28.8. (c) 19.4 to 31.0. (d) Using both confidence intervals, we can say that the P/E for Bank One is well below the population average. The P/E for AT&T Wireless is well above the population average. The P/E for Disney is within both confidence intervals. It appears that the P/E for Disney is close to the population average P/E. (e) By the central limit theorem, when n is large, the $\bar{x}$ distribution is approximately normal. In general, $n \ge 30$ is considered large.
15. (a) $d.f. = 30$; 43.59 to 46.82; 43.26 to 47.14; 42.58 to 47.81. (b) 43.63 to 46.77; 43.33 to 47.07; 42.74 to 47.66. (c) Yes; the respective intervals based on the Student's t distribution are slightly longer. (d) For Student's t, $d.f. = 80$; 44.22 to 46.18; 44.03 to 46.37; 43.65 to 46.75. For standard normal, 44.23 to 46.17; 44.05 to 46.35; 43.68 to 46.72. The intervals using the t distribution are still slightly longer than the corresponding intervals using the standard normal distribution. However, with a larger sample size, the differences between the two methods is less pronounced.

Section 8.3

1. (a) $\hat{p} = 39/62 = 0.6290$. (b) 0.51 to 0.75. If this experiment were repeated many times, about 95% of the intervals would contain p. (c) Both np and nq are greater than 5. If either is less than 5, the normal curve will not necessarily give a good approximation to the binomial.
3. (a) $\hat{p} = 1619/5222 = 0.3100$. (b) 0.29 to 0.33. If we repeat the survey with many different samples of 5222 dwellings, about 99% of the intervals will contain p. (c) Both np and nq are greater than 5. If either is less than 5, the normal curve will not necessarily give a good approximation to the binomial.

5. (a) $\hat{p} = 0.5420$.   (b) 0.53 to 0.56.   (c) Yes. Both np and nq are greater than 5.
7. (a) $\hat{p} = 0.0304$.   (b) 0.02 to 0.05.   (c) Yes. Both np and nq are greater than 5.
9. (a) $\hat{p} = 0.8603$.   (b) 0.84 to 0.89.   (c) A recent study showed that 86% of women shoppers remained loyal to their favorite supermarket last year. The margin of error was 2.5 percentage points.
11. (a) $\hat{p} = 0.25$.   (b) 0.22 to 0.28.   (c) A survey of 1000 large corporations has shown that 25% will choose a nonsmoking job candidate over an equally qualified smoker. The margin of error was 2.7%.
13. (a) 208.   (b) 68.
15. (a) 666.   (b) 662.

Chapter 8 Review

1. See text.
3. Interval for a mean; 176.91 to 180.49.
5. Interval for a mean.
   (a) Use a calculator.   (b) 64.1 to 84.3.
7. Interval for a proportion; 0.50 to 0.54.
9. Interval for a proportion.
   (a) $\hat{p} = 0.4072$.   (b) 0.333 to 0.482.

CHAPTER 9

Section 9.1

1. See text.
3. No, if we fail to reject the null hypothesis, we have not proven it beyond all doubt. We have only failed to find sufficient evidence to reject it.
5. (a) $H_0: \mu = 60$ kg.   (b) $H_1: \mu < 60$ kg.   (c) $H_1: \mu > 60$ kg.   (d) $H_1: \mu \neq 60$ kg.   (e) For part b, the P-value area region is on the left. For part c, the P-value area is on the right. For part d, the P-value area is on both sides of the mean.
7. (a) $H_0: \mu = 16.4$ feet.   (b) $H_1: \mu > 16.4$ feet.   (c) $H_1: \mu < 16.4$ feet.   (d) $H_1: \mu \neq 16.4$ feet.   (e) For part b, the P-value area is on the right. For part c, the P-value area is on the left. For part d, the P-value area is on both sides of the mean.
9. (a) $\alpha = 0.01$; $H_0: \mu = 4.7\%$; $H_1: \mu > 4.7\%$; right-tailed.   (b) Normal; $\overline{x} = 5.38$; $z \approx 0.90$.   (c) P-value ≈ 0.1841; on standard normal curve, shade area to the right of 0.90.   (d) P-value of $0.1841 > 0.01$ for α; fail to reject H_0.   (e) Insufficient evidence at the 0.01 level to reject the claim that average yield for bank stocks equals average yield for all stocks.
11. (a) $\alpha = 0.01$; $H_0: \mu = 4.55$ gm; $H_1: \mu < 4.55$ gm; left-tailed.   (b) Normal; $\overline{x} = 3.75$ gm; $z \approx -2.80$.   (c) P-value ≈ 0.0026; on standard normal curve, shade

area to the left of -2.80.   (d) P-value of $0.0026 \leq 0.01$ for α; reject H_0.   (e) The sample evidence is sufficient at the 0.01 level to justify rejecting H_0. It seems that the hummingbirds in the Grand Canyon region have a lower average weight.
13. (a) $\alpha = 0.01$; $H_0: \mu = 11\%$; $H_1: \mu \neq 11\%$; two-tailed.   (b) Normal; $\overline{x} = 12.5\%$; $z = 1.20$.   (c) P-value = $2(0.1151) = 0.2302$; on standard normal curve, shade areas to the right of 1.20 and to the left of -1.20.   (d) P-value of $0.2302 > 0.01$ for α; fail to reject H_0.   (e) There is insufficient evidence at the 0.01 level to reject H_0. It seems that the average hail damage to wheat crops in Weld County matches the national average.

Section 9.2

1. (a) $\alpha = 0.01$; $H_0: \mu = 16.4$ ft; $H_1: \mu > 16.4$ ft.   (b) Standard normal; $z \approx 1.54$.   (c) P-value ≈ 0.0618; on standard normal curve shade area to the right of $z \approx 1.54$.   (d) P-value of $0.0618 > 0.01$ for α; fail to reject H_0.   (e) At the 1% level, there is insufficient evidence to say that the average storm level is increasing.
3. (a) $\alpha = 0.05$; $H_0: \mu = 41.7$; $H_1: \mu \neq 41.7$.   (b) Standard normal; $z \approx -1.99$.   (c) P-value $\approx 2(0.0233) \approx 0.0466$; on standard normal curve shade areas to the right of 1.99 and to the left of -1.99.   (d) P-value of $0.0466 \leq 0.05$ for α; reject H_0.   (e) At the 5% level, there is sufficient evidence to say that the average number of e-mails is different with the new priority system.
5. (a) $\alpha = 0.01$; $H_0: \mu = 1.75$ yr; $H_1: \mu > 1.75$ yr.   (b) Student's t, $d.f. = 45$; $t \approx 2.481$.   (c) $0.005 < P$-value < 0.010; on t graph shade area to the right of 2.481.   (d) Entire P-interval ≤ 0.01 for α; reject H_0.   (e) At the 1% level of significance, the sample data indicate that the average age of the Minnesota region coyotes is higher than 1.75 years.
7. (a) $\alpha = 0.05$; $H_0: \mu = 19.4$; $H_1: \mu \neq 19.4$.   (b) Student's t, $d.f. = 35$; $t \approx -1.731$.   (c) $0.050 < P$-value < 0.100; on t graph shade areas to the right of 1.731 and to the left of -1.731.   (d) P-value interval > 0.05 for α; fail to reject H_0.   (e) At the 5% level of significance, the sample evidence does not support rejecting the claim that the average P/E of socially responsible funds is different from that of the S&P stock index.
9. i. Use a calculator. Rounded values are used in part ii.
   ii. (a) $\alpha = 0.05$; $H_0: \mu = 4.8$; $H_1: \mu < 4.8$.   (b) Student's t, $d.f. = 5$; $t \approx -3.499$.   (c) $0.005 < P$-value < 0.010; on t graph shade area to the left of -3.499.   (d) P-value interval ≤ 0.05 for α; reject H_0.   (e) At the 5% level of significance, sample evidence supports the claim that the average RBC count for this patient is less than 4.8.

11. i. Use a calculator. Rounded values are used in part ii.
    ii. (a) $\alpha = 0.01$; H_0: $\mu = 67$; H_1: $\mu \neq 67$. (b) Student's t, $d.f. = 15$; $t \approx -1.962$. (c) $0.050 < P\text{-value} < 0.100$; on t graph shade areas to the right of 1.962 and to the left of -1.962. (d) P-value interval > 0.01; fail to reject H_0. (e) At the 1% level of significance, the sample evidence does not support the claim that the average thickness of slab avalanches in Vail is different from that in Canada.
13. i. Use a calculator. Rounded values are used in part ii.
    ii. (a) $\alpha = 0.05$; H_0: $\mu = 40$ beats per min; H_1: $\mu \neq 40$ beats per min. (b) Student's t, $d.f. = 5$; $t \approx -2.041$. (c) $0.050 < P\text{-value} < 0.100$; on t graph shade areas to the right of 2.041 and to the left of -2.041. (d) P-value interval > 0.05; fail to reject H_0. (e) At the 5% level of significance, the population average heart rate for the lion is not significantly different.
15. i. Use a calculator. Rounded values are used in part ii.
    ii. (a) $\alpha = 0.05$; H_0: $\mu = 8.8$; H_1: $\mu \neq 8.8$. (b) Student's t, $d.f. = 13$; $t \approx -1.337$. (c) $0.200 < P\text{-value} < 0.250$; on t graph shade areas to the right of 1.337 and to the left of -1.337. (d) P-value interval > 0.05; fail to reject H_0. (e) At the 5% level of significance, we cannot conclude that the catch is different from 8.8 fish per day.
17. (a) The P-value of a one-tailed test is smaller. For a two-tailed test, the P-value is doubled because it includes the area in both tails. (b) Yes; the P-value of a one-tailed test is smaller, so it might be smaller than α, whereas the P-value of a two-tailed test is larger than α. (c) Yes; if the two-tailed P-value is less than α, the smaller one-tail area is also less than α. (d) Yes, the conclusions can be different. The conclusion based on the two-tailed test is more conservative in the sense that the sample data must be more extreme (differ more from H_0) in order to reject H_0.
19. (a) For $\alpha = 0.01$, confidence level $c = 0.99$; interval from 20.28 to 23.72; hypothesized $\mu = 20$ is not in the interval; reject H_0. (b) H_0: $\mu = 20$; H_1: $\mu \neq 20$; $z = 3.000$; P-value ≈ 0.0026; P-value of $0.0026 \leq 0.01$ for α; reject H_0; conclusions are the same.
21. Critical value $z_0 = 2.33$; critical region is values to the right of 2.33; since the sample statistic $z = 1.54$ is not in the critical region, fail to reject H_0. At the 1% level, there is insufficient evidence to say that the average storm level is increasing. Conclusion is same as with P-value method.
23. Critical values $z_0 = \pm 1.96$; critical regions are values to the left of -1.96 together with values to the right of 1.96. Since the sample test statistic $z = -1.99$ is in the critical region, reject H_0. At the 5% level, there is sufficient evidence to say that the average number of e-mails is different with the new priority system. Conclusion is same as with P-value method.

25. Critical value is $t_0 = 2.412$ for one-tailed test with $d.f. = 45$; critical region is values to the right of 2.412. Since the sample test statistic $t = 2.481$ is in the critical region, reject H_0. At the 1% level, the sample data indicate that the average age of Minnesota region coyotes is higher than 1.75 yr. Conclusion is same as with P-value method.

Section 9.3

1. i. (a) $\alpha = 0.01$; H_0: $p = 0.301$; H_1: $p < 0.301$. (b) Standard normal; yes, $np \approx 64.7 > 5$ and $nq \approx 150.3 > 5$; $\hat{p} \approx 0.214$; $z \approx -2.78$. (c) P-value ≈ 0.0027; on standard normal curve shade area to the left of -2.78. (d) P-value of $0.0027 \leq 0.01$ for α; reject H_0. (e) At the 1% level of significance, the sample data indicate that the population proportion of numbers with a leading "1" in the revenue file is less than the probability 0.301 predicted by Benford's Law.
   ii. Yes; the revenue data file seems to include more numbers with higher first nonzero digits than Benford's Law predicts.
   iii. We have not proved H_0 to be false. However, because our sample data led us to reject H_0 and to conclude that there are too few numbers with a leading digit of 1, more investigation is merited.
3. (a) $\alpha = 0.01$; H_0: $p = 0.70$; H_1: $p \neq 0.70$. (b) Standard normal; $\hat{p} = 0.75$; $z \approx 0.62$. (c) P-value $= 2(0.2676) = 0.5352$; on standard normal curve shade areas to the right of 0.62 and to the left of -0.62. (d) P-value of $0.5352 > 0.01$ for α; fail to reject H_0. (e) At the 1% level of significance, we cannot say that the population proportion of arrests of males aged 15 to 34 in Rock Springs is different from 70%.
5. (a) $\alpha = 0.01$; H_0: $p = 0.77$; H_1: $p < 0.77$. (b) Standard normal; $\hat{p} \approx 0.5556$; $z \approx -2.65$. (c) P-value ≈ 0.004; on standard normal curve shade area to the left of -2.65. (d) P-value of $0.004 \leq 0.01$ for α; reject H_0. (e) At the 1% level of significance, the data show that the population proportion of driver fatalities related to alcohol is less than 77% in Kit Carson County.
7. (a) $\alpha = 0.01$; H_0: $p = 0.50$; H_1: $p < 0.50$. (b) Standard normal; $\hat{p} \approx 0.2941$; $z \approx -2.40$. (c) P-value $= 0.0082$; on standard normal curve shade region to the left of -2.40. (d) P-value of $0.0082 \leq 0.01$ for α; reject H_0. (e) At the 1% level of significance, the data indicate that the population proportion of female wolves is now less than 50% in the region.
9. (a) $\alpha = 0.01$; H_0: $p = 0.261$; H_1: $p \neq 0.261$. (b) Standard normal; $\hat{p} \approx 0.1924$; $z \approx -2.78$. (c) P-value $= 2(0.0027) = 0.0054$; on standard normal curve shade areas to the right of 2.78 and to the left of -2.78. (d) P-value of $0.0054 \leq 0.01$ for α; reject H_0. (e) At the 1% level of significance, the sample data indicate that the

population proportion of the five-syllable sequence is different from that of Plato's *Republic*.

11. (a) $\alpha = 0.01$; H_0: $p = 0.47$; H_1: $p > 0.47$. (b) Standard normal; $\hat{p} \approx 0.4871$; $z \approx 1.09$. (c) P-value $= 0.1379$; on standard normal curve shade area to the right of 1.09. (d) P-value of $0.1379 > 0.01$ for α; fail to reject H_0. (e) At the 1% level of significance, there is insufficient evidence to support the claim that the population proportion of customers loyal to Chevrolet is more than 47%.

13. (a) $\alpha = 0.05$; H_0: $p = 0.092$; H_1: $p > 0.092$. (b) Standard normal; $\hat{p} \approx 0.1480$; $z \approx 2.71$. (c) P-value $= 0.0034$; on standard normal curve shade region to the right of 2.71. (d) P-value of $0.0034 \leq 0.05$ for α; reject H_0. (e) At the 5% level of significance, the data indicate that the population proportion of students with hypertension during final exams week is higher than 9.2%.

15. (a) $\alpha = 0.01$; H_0: $p = 0.82$; H_1: $p \neq 0.82$. (b) Standard normal; $\hat{p} \approx 0.7671$; $z \approx -1.18$. (c) P-value $= 2(0.1190) = 0.2380$; on standard normal curve shade areas to the right of 1.18 and to the left of -1.18. (d) P-value of $0.2380 > 0.01$ for α; fail to reject H_0. (e) At the 1% level of significance, the evidence is insufficient to indicate that the population proportion of extroverts among college student government leaders is different from 82%.

17. (a) $\alpha = 0.01$; H_0: $p = 0.76$; H_1: $p \neq 0.76$. (b) Standard normal; $\hat{p} \approx 0.7966$; $z = 0.66$. (c) P-value $= 2(0.2546) = 0.5092$; on standard normal curve shade areas to the right of 0.66 and to the left of -0.66. (d) P-value of $0.5092 > 0.01$ for α; fail to reject H_0. (e) At the 1% level of significance, the evidence is insufficient to conclude that the population proportion of professors in Colorado who would choose the career again is different from the national rate of 76%.

19. Critical value is $z_0 = -2.33$. The critical region consists of values less than -2.33. The sample test statistic $z = -2.65$ is in the critical region, so we reject H_0. This result is consistent with the P-value conclusion.

Chapter 9 Review

1. (a) $\alpha = 0.05$; H_0: $\mu = 11.1$; H_1: $\mu \neq 11.1$. (b) Standard normal; $z = -3.00$. (c) P-value $= 0.0026$; on standard normal curve shade areas to the right of 3.00 and to the left of -3.00. (d) P-value of $0.0026 \leq 0.05$ for α; reject H_0. (e) At the 5% level of significance, the evidence is sufficient to say that the miles driven per vehicle in Chicago is different from the national average.

3. (a) $\alpha = 0.01$; H_0: $\mu = 0.8$; H_1: $\mu > 0.8$. (b) Student's t, $d.f. = 8$; $t \approx 4.390$. (c) $0.0005 < P$-value < 0.005; on t graph shade area to the right of 4.390. (d) P-value interval ≤ 0.01 for α; reject H_0. (e) At the 1% level of

significance, the evidence is sufficient to say that the Toylot claim of 0.8 A is too low.

5. (a) $\alpha = 0.01$; H_0: $p = 0.60$; H_1: $p < 0.60$. (b) Standard normal; $z = -3.01$. (c) P-value $= 0.0013$; on standard normal curve shade area to the left of -3.01. (d) P-value of $0.0013 \leq 0.01$ for α; reject H_0. (e) At the 1% level of significance, the evidence is sufficient to claim that the mortality rate has dropped.

7. (a) $\alpha = 0.01$; H_0: $p = 0.20$; H_1: $p > 0.20$. (b) Standard normal; $z = 3.18$. (c) P-value $= 0.0007$; on standard normal curve shade area to the right of 3.18. (d) P-value of $0.0007 \leq 0.01$ for α; reject H_0. (e) At the 1% level of significance, the evidence is sufficient to claim that the population proportion of students who read the magazine is larger than 0.20.

9. (a) $\alpha = 0.05$; H_0: $\mu = 7$ oz; H_1: $\mu \neq 7$ oz. (b) Student's t, $d.f. = 7$; $t \approx 1.697$. (c) $0.100 < P$-value < 0.150; on t graph shade areas to the right of 1.697 and to the left of -1.697. (d) P-value interval > 0.05 for α; do not reject H_0. (e) At the 5% level of significance, the evidence is insufficient to claim that the population mean amount of coffee per cup is different from 7 oz.

CUMULATIVE REVIEW PROBLEMS
CHAPTERS 7–9

1. (a) $\sigma \approx 1.7$. (b) 0.1314. (c) 0.1075.
2. (a) The normal approximation to the binomial is appropriate because np and nq are both greater than 5. (b) $\mu \approx 73.5$ and $\sigma \approx 5.6$. (c) $P(r \geq 65) \approx P(x \geq 64.5) \approx P(z \geq -1.61) \approx 0.9463$.
3. Essay based on material from Chapter 7 and Section 1.2.
4. (a) Because of the large sample size, the central limit theorem describes the $\bar{x}$ distribution (approximately). (b) $P(\bar{x} \leq 6820) = P(z \leq -2.75) = 0.0030$. (c) The probability that the average white blood cell count for 50 healthy adults is as low as or lower than 6820 is very small, 0.0030. Based on this result, it would be reasonable to gather additional facts.
5. (a) i. $\alpha = 0.01$; H_0: $\mu = 2.0$ ug/L; H_1: $\mu > 2.0$ ug/L.
   ii. Standard normal; $z = 2.53$.
   iii. P-value ≈ 0.0057; on standard normal curve shade area to the right of 2.53.
   iv. P-value of $0.0057 \leq 0.01$ for α; reject H_0.
   v. At the 1% level of significance, the evidence is sufficient to say that the population mean discharge level of lead is higher.
   (b) 2.13 ug/L to 2.99 ug/L. (c) $n = 48$.
6. (a) Use rounded results to compute t in part (b).
   (b) i. $\alpha = 0.05$; H_0: $\mu = 10\%$; H_1: $\mu > 10\%$.
   ii. Student's t, $d.f. = 11$; $t \approx 1.248$.
   iii. $0.100 < P$-value < 0.125; on t graph shade area to the right of 1.248.
   iv. P-value interval > 0.05 for α; fail to reject H_0.

v. At the 5% level of significance, the evidence does not indicate that the patient is asymptomatic.

(c) 9.27% to 11.71%.

7. (a) i. $\alpha = 0.05$; H_0: $p = 0.10$; H_1: $p \neq 0.10$; yes, $np > 5$ and $nq > 5$; necessary to use normal approximation to the binominal.

ii. Standard normal; $\hat{p} \approx 0.147$; $z = 1.29$.

iii. P-value $= 2P(z > 1.29) \approx 0.1970$; on standard normal curve shade areas to the right of 1.29 and to the left of -1.29.

iv. P-value of $0.1970 > 0.05$ for α; fail to reject H_0.

v. At the 5% level of significance, the data do not indicate any difference from the national average for the population proportion of crime victims.

(b) 0.063 to 0.231.   (c) From sample, $p \approx \hat{p} \approx 0.147$; $n = 193$.

8. (a) Essay.   (b) Outline of study.

CHAPTER 10

Section 10.1

1. (a) $\alpha = 0.05$; H_0: $\mu_d = 0$; H_1: $\mu_d \neq 0$.   (b) Student's t, $d.f. = 7$; $\bar{d} \approx 2.25$; $t \approx 0.818$.   (c) $0.250 < P$-value < 0.500; on t graph shade areas to the left of -0.818 and to the right of 0.818.   (d) P-value interval > 0.05 for α; fail to reject H_0.   (e) At the 5% level of significance, the evidence is insufficient to claim a difference in population mean percentage increases for corporate revenue and CEO salary.

3. (a) $\alpha = 0.01$; H_0: $\mu_d = 0$; H_1: $\mu_d > 0$.   (b) Student's t, $d.f. = 4$; $\bar{d} \approx 12.6$; $t \approx 1.243$.   (c) $0.125 < P$-value < 0.250; on t graph shade area to the right of 1.243. (d) P-value interval > 0.01 for α; fail to reject H_0. (e) At the 1% level of significance, the evidence is insufficient to claim that the average peak wind gusts are higher in January.

5. (a) $\alpha = 0.05$; H_0: $\mu_d = 0$; H_1: $\mu_d > 0$.   (b) Student's t, $d.f. = 7$; $\bar{d} \approx 6.125$; $t \approx 1.762$.   (c) $0.050 < P$-value < 0.075; on t graph shade area to the right of 1.762. (d) P-value interval > 0.05 for α; fail to reject H_0. (e) At the 5% level of significance, the evidence is insufficient to indicate that the population average percentage of male wolves in winter is higher.

7. (a) $\alpha = 0.05$; H_0: $\mu_d = 0$; H_1: $\mu_d > 0$.   (b) Student's t, $d.f. = 8$; $\bar{d} = 2.0$; $t \approx 1.333$.   (c) $0.100 < P$-value < 0.125; on t graph shade area to the right of 1.333. (d) P-value interval > 0.05 for α; fail to reject H_0. (e) At the 5% level of significance, the evidence is insufficient to claim that the population score on the last round is higher than that on the first.

9. (a) $\alpha = 0.05$; H_0: $\mu_d = 0$; H_1: $\mu_d \neq 0$.   (b) Student's t, $d.f. = 4$; $\bar{d} = 1.0$; $t \approx 0.427$.   (c) P-value > 0.500

(note that the t value 0.427 is smaller than any entry in the $d.f. = 4$ row, so the P-value is larger than the largest value 0.500 in the two-tail area row); on t graph shade areas to the left of -0.427 and to the right of 0.427. (d) P-value interval > 0.05 for α; fail to reject H_0.   (e) At the 5% level of significance, the evidence is insufficient to indicate a difference in the population mean number of service ware sherds in subarea 1 as compared with subarea 2.

11. For a two-tailed test with $\alpha = 0.05$ and $d.f. = 7$, the critical values are $\pm t_0 = \pm 2.365$. The sample test statistic $t = 0.818$ is between -2.365 and 2.365, so we do not reject H_0. This conclusion is the same as that reached by the P-value method.

Section 10.2

1. (a) (i) $\alpha = 0.01$; H_0: $\mu_1 = \mu_2$; H_1: $\mu_1 > \mu_2$.   (ii) Standard normal; $\bar{x}_1 - \bar{x}_2 = 0.7$; $z \approx 2.57$.   (iii) P-value $= P(z > 2.57) \approx 0.0051$; on standard normal curve shade area to the right of 2.57.   (iv) P-value of $0.0051 \leq 0.01$ for α; reject H_0.   (v) At the 1% level of significance, the evidence is sufficient to indicate that the population mean REM sleep time for children is more than that for adults.   (b) 0.07 to 1.33; Interval contains values that are all positive. At the 98% confidence level, it appears that the population mean REM sleep time for children is greater than that for adults.

3. (a) (i) $\alpha = 0.05$; H_0: $\mu_1 = \mu_2$; H_1: $\mu_1 \neq \mu_2$.   (ii) Standard normal; $\bar{x}_1 - \bar{x}_2 = 0.6$; $z \approx 2.16$.   (iii) P-value $= 2P(z > 2.16) \approx 2(0.0154) = 0.0308$; on standard normal curve shade areas to the right of 2.16 and to the left of -2.16.   (iv) P-value of $0.0308 \leq 0.05$ for α; reject H_0. (v) At the 5% level of significance, the evidence is sufficient to show that there is a difference between mean responses regarding preference for camping or fishing. (b) 0.06 to 1.14; Interval contains values that are all positive. At the 95% confidence level, it appears that the population mean response for camping is higher than that for fishing.

5. Use rounded results to compute t.

(a) (i) $\alpha = 0.01$; H_0: $\mu_1 = \mu_2$; H_1: $\mu_1 < \mu_2$.   (ii) Student's t, $d.f. = 9$; $\bar{x}_1 - \bar{x}_2 = -0.36$; $t \approx -0.965$.   (iii) $0.125 < P$-value < 0.250; on t graph shade area to the left of -0.965.   (iv) P-value interval > 0.01 for α; do not reject H_0.   (v) At the 1% level of significance, the evidence is insufficient to indicate that violent crime in the Rocky Mountain region is higher than in New England.   (b) $d.f. = 9$; $E \approx 1.05$; -1.41 to 0.69; Interval contains both negative and positive values. At the 98% confidence level, we cannot conclude that the population mean violent crime rate in the Rocky Mountain region is different from that in New England.

7. (a) (i) $\alpha = 0.05$; H_0: $\mu_1 = \mu_2$; H_1: $\mu_1 \neq \mu_2$. (ii) Student's t, d.f. = 29; $\bar{x}_1 - \bar{x}_2 = -9.7$; $t \approx -0.751$. (iii) $0.250 < P\text{-value} < 0.500$; on t graph shade areas to the right of 0.751 and to the left of -0.751. (iv) P-value interval > 0.05 for α; do not reject H_0. (v) At the 5% level of significance, the evidence is insufficient to indicate that there is a difference between the control and experimental groups in the mean score on the vocabulary portion of the test. (b) d.f. = 29; $E \approx 26.4$; -36.1 to 16.7; Interval contains both negative and positive values. At the 95% confidence level, we cannot conclude that the population mean vocabulary score was different between the two groups before instruction began.

9. Use rounded results to compute t.
(a) (i) $\alpha = 0.05$; H_0: $\mu_1 = \mu_2$; H_1: $\mu_1 \neq \mu_2$. (ii) Student's t, d.f. = 14; $\bar{x}_1 - \bar{x}_2 = 0.82$; $t \approx 0.869$. (iii) $0.250 < P\text{-value} < 0.500$; on t graph shade areas to the right of 0.869 and to the left of -0.869. (iv) P-value interval > 0.05 for α; do not reject H_0. (v) At the 5% level of significance, the evidence is insufficient to indicate that there is a difference in the mean number of cases of fox rabies between the two regions. (b) d.f. = 14; $E \approx 2.02$; -1.2 to 2.84; Interval contains both negative and positive values. At the 95% confidence level, we cannot conclude that there is any difference in the population mean number of fox rabies cases in the two regions.

11. Use rounded results to compute t.
(a) (i) $\alpha = 0.05$; H_0: $\mu_1 = \mu_2$; H_1: $\mu_1 \neq \mu_2$. (ii) Student's t, d.f. = 6; $\bar{x}_1 - \bar{x}_2 = -1.64$; $t \approx -1.041$. (iii) $0.250 < P\text{-value} < 0.500$; on t graph shade areas to the right of 1.041 and to the left of -1.041. (iv) P-value interval > 0.05 for α; do not reject H_0. (v) At the 5% level of significance, the evidence is insufficient to indicate that the mean time lost due to hot tempers is different from time lost due to technical workers' attitudes. (b) d.f. = 6; $E \approx 3.85$; -5.49 to 2.21; Interval contains both negative and positive values. At the 95% confidence level, we cannot conclude that there is any difference in the population mean time lost due to the two types of inappropriate behavior.

13. (a) d.f. = 19.96 (Some software will truncate this to 19.) (b) d.f. = 9; the convention of using the smaller of $n_1 - 1$ and $n_2 - 1$ leads to a d.f. that is always less than or equal to that computed by Satterthwaite's formula.

15. H_0: $\mu_1 = \mu_2$; H_1: $\mu_1 < \mu_2$; for d.f. = 9, $\alpha = 0.01$ in the *one-tail area* row, the critical value $t_0 = -2.821$; sample test statistic $t = -0.965$ is not in the critical region; fail to reject H_0. This result is consistent with that obtained by the P-value method.

Section 10.3

1. (a) $\alpha = 0.05$; H_0: $p_1 = p_2$; H_1: $p_1 \neq p_2$. (b) Standard normal; $\bar{p} \approx 0.2911$; $\hat{p}_1 - \hat{p}_2 \approx -0.052$; $z \approx -1.13$. (c) $P\text{-value} \approx 2P(z < -1.13) \approx 2(0.1292) = 0.2584$; on standard normal curve shade areas to the right of 1.13 and to the left of -1.13. (d) P-value of $0.2584 > 0.05$ for α; fail to reject H_0. (e) At the 5% level of significance, there is insufficient evidence to conclude that the population proportion of women favoring more tax dollars for the arts is different from the proportion of men.

3. (a) $\alpha = 0.05$; H_0: $p_1 = p_2$; H_1: $p_1 < p_2$. (b) Standard normal; $\bar{p} \approx 0.2189$; $\hat{p}_1 - \hat{p}_2 \approx -0.074$; $z \approx -2.04$. (c) $P\text{-value} \approx P(z < -2.04) \approx 0.0207$; on standard normal curve shade area to the left of -2.04. (d) P-value of $0.0207 \leq 0.05$ for α; reject H_0. (e) At the 5% level of significance, there is sufficient evidence to conclude that the population proportion of trusting people in Chicago is higher for the older group.

5. (a) $\alpha = 0.01$; H_0: $p_1 = p_2$; H_1: $p_1 < p_2$. (b) Standard normal; $\bar{p} = 0.42$; $\hat{p}_1 - \hat{p}_2 = -0.10$; $z \approx -1.43$. (c) $P\text{-value} \approx P(z < -1.43) \approx 0.0764$; on standard normal curve shade area to the left of -1.43. (d) P-value of $0.0764 > 0.01$ for α; fail to reject H_0. (e) At the 1% level of significance, there is insufficient evidence to conclude that the population proportion of adults who believe in extraterrestrials and who attended college is higher than the proportion who did not attend college.

7. (a) $\alpha = 0.01$; H_0: $p_1 = p_2$; H_1: $p_1 < p_2$. (b) Standard normal; $\bar{p} \approx 0.5749$; $\hat{p}_1 - \hat{p}_2 \approx -0.1070$; $z \approx -3.19$. (c) $P\text{-value} \approx P(z < -3.19) \approx 0.0007$; on standard normal curve shade area to the left of -3.19. (d) P-value of $0.0007 \leq 0.01$ for α; reject H_0. (e) At the 1% level of significance, there is sufficient evidence to conclude that the population proportion of guests requesting nonsmoking rooms has increased.

9. For a two-tailed test with $\alpha = 0.05$, the critical values are $\pm z_0 = \pm 1.96$. The sample test statistic $z = -1.13$ is between -1.96 and 1.96, so we do not reject H_0. This conclusion is the same as that reached by the P-value method.

11. (a) $\hat{\sigma} = 0.0232$; $E = 0.0599$; the interval is from 0.67 to 0.79. (b) The confidence interval contains values that are all positive, so we can be 99% sure that $p_1 > p_2$.

13. (a) $\hat{p}_1 = 0.3095$; $\hat{p}_2 = 0.1184$; $\hat{\sigma} = 0.0413$; interval from 0.085 to 0.297. (b) The interval contains numbers that are all positive. A greater proportion of hogans occurs in Fort Defiance.

15. (a) Based on the same data, a 99% confidence interval is longer than a 95% confidence interval. Therefore, if the 95% confidence interval has both positive and negative values, so will the 99% confidence interval. However, for the same data, a 90% confidence interval is shorter than a 95% confidence interval. The 90% confidence interval might contain only positive or only negative values even if the 95% interval contains both. (b) Based on the same data, a 99% confidence interval is longer than a 95% confidence interval. Even if the 95% confidence interval contains values that are all positive, the longer 99% interval could contain both positive and negative values. Since, for the same data, a 90% confidence interval is shorter than a 95% confidence interval, if the 95% confidence interval contains only positive values, so will the 90% confidence interval.

Chapter 10 Review

1. Difference of means.
   (a) Use a calculator. (b) $d.f. \approx 71$; to use Table 4, round down to $d.f. \approx 70$; $E \approx 0.83$; interval from -0.06 to 1.6. (c) Because the interval contains both positive and negative values, we cannot conclude at the 95% confidence level that there is any difference in soil water content in the two fields. (d) Student's t distribution, because σ_1 and σ_2 are unknown. Both samples are large, so no assumptions about the original distributions are needed. (e) (i) $\alpha = 0.01$; H_0: $\mu_1 = \mu_2$; H_1: $\mu_1 > \mu_2$. (ii) Student's t; $d.f. = 71$ (use $d.f. = 70$ in Table 4 of the Appendix); $t \approx 1.841$. (iii) $0.025 < P\text{-value} < 0.050$; on t graph shade area to the right of 1.841. (iv) P-value interval > 0.01 for α; fail to reject H_0. At the 1% level of significance, the evidence does not show that the population mean soil water content of the first field is higher than that of the second.
3. Difference of means.
   (a) $d.f. \approx 17$; $E \approx 2.5$; interval from 5.5 to 10.5 lb.
   (b) Yes. The interval contains values that are all positive. At the 75% level of confidence, it appears that the average weight of adult male wolves from the Northwest Territories is greater. (c) (i) $\alpha = 0.01$; H_0: $\mu_1 = \mu_2$; H_1: $\mu_1 \neq \mu_2$. (ii) Student's t; $d.f. = 17$; $t \approx 3.743$. (iii) $0.001 < P\text{-value} < 0.010$; on t graph shade areas to the right of 3.743 and to the left of -3.743. (iv) P-value interval ≤ 0.01 for α; reject H_0. (v) At the 1% level of significance, the evidence is sufficient to conclude that the average weight of adult male wolves in the Northwest Territories is different from that of Alaska wolves.
5. Difference of proportions.
   (a) $\hat{p}_1 = 0.8495$; $\hat{p}_2 = 0.8916$; -0.1409 to 0.0567.

(b) No. The interval contains both negative and positive numbers. We do not detect a difference in the proportions at the 95% confidence level. (c) (i) $\alpha = 0.05$; H_0: $p_1 = p_2$; H_1: $p_1 \neq p_2$. (ii) Normal distribution; $z \approx -0.83$. (iii) $P\text{-value} = 2(0.2033) = 0.4066$; on the normal graph, shade areas to the left of -0.83 and to the right of 0.83. (iv) P-value of $0.4066 > \alpha = 0.05$; fail to reject H_0. (v) At the 5% level of significance, there is insufficient evidence to conclude that the proportion of accurate responses from face-to-face interviews differs from the proportion for telephone interviews.
7. (a) $\alpha = 0.05$; H_0: $\mu_d = 0$; H_1: $\mu_d < 0$. (b) Student's t, $d.f. = 4$; $\bar{d} \approx -4.94$; $t = -2.832$. (c) $0.010 < P\text{-value} < 0.025$; on t graph shade area to the left of -2.832. (d) P-value interval ≤ 0.05 for α; reject H_0. (e) At the 5% level of significance, there is sufficient evidence to claim that the population average net sales improved.

CHAPTER 11

Section 11.1

1. (a) $\alpha = 0.05$; H_0: Myers-Briggs preference and profession are independent; H_1: Myers-Briggs preference and profession are not independent. (b) $\chi^2 = 8.649$; $d.f. = 2$. (c) $0.010 < P\text{-value} < 0.025$. (d) Reject H_0. (e) At the 5% level of significance, there is sufficient evidence to conclude that Myers-Briggs preference and profession are not independent.
3. (a) $\alpha = 0.01$; H_0: Site type and pottery type are independent; H_1: Site type and pottery type are not independent. (b) $\chi^2 = 0.5552$; $d.f. = 4$. (c) $0.950 < P\text{-value} < 0.975$. (d) Do not reject H_0. (e) At the 1% level of significance, there is insufficient evidence to conclude that site and pottery type are not independent.
5. (a) $\alpha = 0.05$; H_0: Age distribution and location are independent; H_1: Age distribution and location are not independent. (b) $\chi^2 = 0.6704$; $d.f. = 4$. (c) $0.950 < P\text{-value} < 0.975$. (d) Do not reject H_0. (e) At the 5% level of significance, there is insufficient evidence to conclude that age distribution and location are not independent.
7. (a) $\alpha = 0.05$; H_0: Age of young adult and movie preference are independent; H_1: Age of young adult and movie preference are not independent. (b) $\chi^2 = 3.6230$; $d.f. = 4$. (c) $0.100 < P\text{-value} < 0.900$. (d) Do not reject H_0. (e) At the 5% level of significance, there is insufficient evidence to conclude that age of young adult and movie preference are not independent.

9. (a) $\alpha = 0.05$; H_0: Stone tool construction material and site are independent; H_1: Stone tool construction material and site are not independent. (b) $\chi^2 = 11.15$; $d.f. = 3$. (c) $0.010 < P\text{-value} < 0.025$. (d) Reject H_0. (e) At the 5% level of significance, there is sufficient evidence to conclude that stone tool construction material and site are not independent.

Section 11.2

1. (a) $\alpha = 0.05$; H_0: The distributions are the same; H_1: The distributions are different. (b) Sample $\chi^2 = 11.788$; $d.f. = 3$. (c) $0.005 < P\text{-value} < 0.010$. (d) Reject H_0. (e) At the 5% level of significance, the evidence is sufficient to conclude that the age distribution of the Red Lake Village population does not fit the age distribution of the general Canadian population.

3. (a) $\alpha = 0.01$; H_0: The distributions are the same; H_1: The distributions are different. (b) Sample $\chi^2 = 0.1984$; $d.f. = 4$. (c) $P\text{-value} > 0.995$. (Note that as the χ^2 values decrease, the area in the right tail increases, so $\chi^2 < 0.207$ means that the corresponding $P\text{-value} > 0.995$.) (d) Do not reject H_0. (e) At the 1% level of significance, the evidence is insufficient to conclude that the regional distribution of raw materials does not fit the distribution at the current excavation site.

5. (i) Essay. (ii) (a) $\alpha = 0.01$; H_0: The distributions are the same; H_1: The distributions are different. (b) Sample $\chi^2 = 1.5693$; $d.f. = 5$. (c) $0.900 < P\text{-value} < 0.950$. (d) Do not reject H_0. (e) At the 1% level of significance, the evidence is insufficient to conclude that the average daily July temperature does not follow a normal distribution.

7. (a) $\alpha = 0.05$; H_0: The distributions are the same; H_1: The distributions are different. (b) Sample $\chi^2 = 9.333$; $d.f. = 3$. (c) $0.025 < P\text{-value} < 0.050$. (d) Reject H_0. (e) At the 5% level of significance, the evidence is sufficient to conclude that the current fish distribution is different than it was 5 years ago.

9. (a) $\alpha = 0.01$; H_0: The distributions are the same; H_1: The distributions are different. (b) Sample $\chi^2 = 13.70$; $d.f. = 5$. (c) $0.010 < P\text{-value} < 0.025$. (d) Do not reject H_0. (e) At the 1% level of significance, the evidence is insufficient to conclude that the census ethnic origin distribution and the ethnic origin distribution of city residents are different.

Section 11.3

1. (a) $\alpha = 0.05$; H_0: $\sigma^2 = 42.3$; H_1: $\sigma^2 > 42.3$. (b) $\chi^2 \approx 23.98$; $d.f. = 22$. (c) $0.100 < P\text{-value} < 0.900$. (d) Do not reject H_0. (e) At the 5% level of signifi-

cance, there is insufficient evidence to conclude that the variance is greater in the new section.

3. (a) $\alpha = 0.01$; H_0: $\sigma^2 = 136.2$; H_1: $\sigma^2 < 136.2$. (b) $\chi^2 \approx 5.92$; $d.f. = 7$. (c) Right-tailed area between 0.900 and 0.100; $0.100 < P\text{-value} < 0.900$. (d) Do not reject H_0. (e) At the 1% level of significance, there is insufficient evidence to conclude that the variance for number of mountain-climber deaths is less than 136.2.

5. (a) $\alpha = 0.05$; H_0: $\sigma^2 = 9$; H_1: $\sigma^2 < 9$. (b) $\chi^2 \approx 8.82$; $d.f. = 22$. (c) Right-tail area is between 0.995 and 0.990; $0.005 < P\text{-value} < 0.010$. (d) Reject H_0. (e) At the 5% level of significance, there is sufficient evidence to conclude that the variance of protection times for the new typhoid shot is less than 9.

7. (a) $\alpha = 0.01$; H_0: $\sigma^2 = 0.18$; H_1: $\sigma^2 > 0.18$. (b) $\chi^2 = 90$; $d.f. = 60$. (c) $0.005 < P\text{-value} < 0.010$. (d) Reject H_0. (e) At the 1% level of significance, there is sufficient evidence to conclude that the variance of measurements for the fan blades is higher than the specified amount. The inspector is justified in claiming that the blades must be replaced.

9. (a) $\alpha = 0.05$; H_0: $\sigma^2 = 23$; H_1: $\sigma^2 \neq 23$. (b) $\chi^2 \approx 13.06$; $d.f. = 21$. (c) The area to the left of $\chi^2 = 13.06$ is less than 50%, so we double the left-tail area to find the P-value for the two-tailed test. The right-tail area is between 0.950 and 0.900. Subtracting each value from 1, we find that the left-tail area is between 0.050 and 0.100. Doubling the left-tail area for a two-tailed test gives $0.100 < P\text{-value} < 0.200$. (d) Do not reject H_0. (e) At the 5% level of significance, there is insufficient evidence to conclude that the variance of battery life is different from 23.

Section 11.4

1. (a) Use a calculator. (b) $\alpha = 0.05$; H_0: $\rho = 0$; H_1: $\rho > 0$; sample $t \approx 2.522$; $d.f. = 4$; $0.025 < P\text{-value} < 0.050$; reject H_0. There seems to be a positive correlation between x and y. (c) Use a calculator. (d) 45.36%. (e) Interval from 39.05 to 51.67. (f) $\alpha = 0.05$; H_0: $\beta = 0$; H_1: $\beta > 0$; sample $t \approx 2.522$; $d.f. = 4$; $0.025 < P\text{-value} < 0.050$; reject H_0. There seems to be a positive slope between x and y.

3. (a) Use a calculator. (b) $\alpha = 0.01$; H_0: $\rho = 0$; H_1: $\rho < 0$; sample $t \approx -10.06$; $d.f. = 5$; $P\text{-value} < 0.0005$; reject H_0. The sample evidence supports a negative correlation. (c) Use a calculator. (d) 2.39 hours. (e) Interval from 2.12 to 2.66 hours. (f) $\alpha = 0.01$; H_0: $\beta = 0$; H_1: $\beta < 0$; sample $t \approx -10.06$; $d.f. = 5$; $P\text{-value} < 0.0005$; reject H_0. The sample evidence supports a negative slope.

5. (a) Use a calculator. (b) $\alpha = 0.01$; H_0: $\rho = 0$; H_1: $\rho > 0$; sample $t \approx 6.534$; $d.f. = 4$; $0.0005 < P\text{-value} < 0.005$; reject H_0. The sample evidence supports a positive correlation. (c) Use a calculator. (d) $12.577 thousand. (e) Interval from 12.247 to 12.907 (thousand dollars). (f) $\alpha = 0.01$; H_0: $\beta = 0$; H_1: $\beta > 0$; sample $t \approx 6.534$; $d.f. = 4$; $0.0005 < P\text{-value} < 0.005$; reject H_0. The sample evidence supports a positive slope.

7. (a) H_0: $\rho = 0$; H_1: $\rho \neq 0$; $d.f. = 4$; sample $t = 4.129$; $0.01 < P\text{-value} < 0.02$; do not reject H_0; r is not significant at the 0.01 level of significance. (b) H_0: $\rho = 0$; H_1: $\rho \neq 0$; $d.f. = 8$; sample $t = 5.840$; $P\text{-value} < 0.001$; reject H_0; r is significant at the 0.01 level of significance. (c) As n increases, the t value corresponding to r also increases, resulting in a smaller P-value.

Chapter 11 Review

1. Chi-square test of goodness of fit. (i) $\alpha = 0.01$; H_0: The distributions are the same; H_1: The distributions are different. (ii) $\chi^2 \approx 11.93$; $d.f. = 4$. (iii) $0.010 < P\text{-value} < 0.025$. (iv) Do not reject H_0. (v) At the 1% level of significance, there is insufficient evidence to claim that the age distribution of the population of Blue Valley has changed.

3. Chi-square test of σ^2. (i) $\alpha = 0.01$; H_0: $\sigma^2 = 1,040,400$; H_1: $\sigma^2 > 1,040,400$. (ii) $\chi^2 \approx 51.03$; $d.f. = 29$. (iii) $0.005 < P\text{-value} < 0.010$. (iv) Reject H_0. (v) At the 1% level of significance, there is sufficient evidence to conclude that the variance is greater than claimed.

5. Chi-square test of independence. (i) $\alpha = 0.01$; H_0: Student grade and teacher rating are independent; H_1: Student grade and teacher rating are not independent. (ii) $\chi^2 \approx 9.80$; $d.f. = 6$. (iii) $0.100 < P\text{-value} < 0.900$. (iv) Do not reject H_0. (v) At the 1% level of significance, there is insufficient evidence to claim that student grade and teacher rating are not independent.

7. (a) Use a calculator. (b) (i) $\alpha = 0.01$; H_0: $\rho = 0$; H_1: $\rho > 0$. (ii) $t \approx 6.665$; $d.f. = 5$. (iii) $0.0005 < P\text{-value} < 0.005$. (iv) Reject H_0. (v) At the 1% level of significance, there is evidence that ρ is positive. (c) (i) $\alpha = 0.01$; H_0: $\beta = 0$; H_1: $\beta > 0$. (ii) $t \approx 6.665$; $d.f. = 5$. (iii) $0.0005 < P\text{-value} < 0.005$. (iv) Reject H_0. (v) At the 1% level of significance, there is evidence that β is positive. (d) $\hat{y} \approx 5.98$; $E \approx 3.27$; 2.72 to 9.24.

CUMULATIVE REVIEW PROBLEMS
CHAPTERS 10–11

1. (a) Use a calculator. (b) (i) $\alpha = 0.05$; H_0: $\rho = 0$; H_1: $\rho > 0$. (ii) Student's t, $d.f. = 6$; $t \approx 2.466$. (iii) $0.010 <$

$P\text{-value} < 0.025$. On the t graph, shade area to the right of 2.466. (iv) P-value interval $< \alpha = 0.05$; reject H_0. (v) At the 5% level of significance, there is evidence of a positive correlation between age of a volcanic island in the Indian Ocean and distance of the island from the center of the midoceanic ridge. (c) (i) $\alpha = 0.05$; H_0: $\beta = 0$; H_1: $\beta > 0$. (ii) Student's t, $d.f. = 6$; $t \approx 2.466$. (iii) $0.010 < P\text{-value} < 0.025$. On the t graph, shade area to the right of 2.466. (iv) P-value interval $< \alpha = 0.05$; reject H_0. (v) At the 5% level of significance, there is evidence of a positive slope for the regression line for age of a volcanic island in the Indian Ocean and distance of the island from the center of the midoceanic ridge. (d) $\hat{y} \approx 16.5$ (units in 100 km); $d.f. = 6$; $t_{0.85} = 1.650$; $E \approx 11.4$; 5.1 to 27.9 (units in 100 km).

2. (i) $\alpha = 0.01$; H_0: Colorado major distribution is the same as national distribution; H_1: Colorado major distribution is different from national distribution. (ii) Chi-square; $d.f. = 5$; $\chi^2 \approx 10.196$. (iii) $0.050 < P\text{-value} < 0.100$; shade region to the right of 10.196. (iv) P-value interval $> \alpha = 0.01$; fail to reject H_0. At the 1% level of significance, the evidence is insufficient to claim that the distribution of college majors selected by Colorado students is different from the national distribution of college majors.

3. (i) $\alpha = 0.05$; H_0: Yield and fertilizer type are independent; H_1: Yield and fertilizer type are not independent. (ii) Chi-square distribution $\chi^2 \approx 5.005$; $d.f. = 4$. (iii) $0.100 < P\text{-value} < 0.900$. (iv) Do not reject H_0. (v) At the 5% level of significance, the evidence is insufficient to conclude that fertilizer type and yield are not independent.

4. (a) (i) $\alpha = 0.05$; H_0: $\sigma = 0.55$; H_1: $\sigma > 0.55$. (ii) Chi-square distribution $s \approx 0.602$; $d.f. = 9$; $\chi^2 \approx 10.78$. (iii) $0.100 < P\text{-value} < 0.900$. (iv) Do not reject H_0. (v) At the 5% level of significance, there is insufficient evidence to conclude that the standard deviation of petal lengths is greater than 0.55. (b) Interval from 0.44 to 0.99.

5. (i) $\alpha = 0.05$; H_0: $\mu_d = 0$; H_1: $\mu_d \neq 0$. (ii) Student's t, $d.f. = 6$; $\bar{d} \approx -0.0039$, $t \approx -0.771$. (iii) $0.250 < P\text{-value} < 0.500$; on t graph shade areas to the right of 0.771 and to the left of -0.771. (iv) P-value interval > 0.05 for α; fail to reject H_0. (v) At the 5% level of significance, the evidence does not show a population mean difference in phosphorous reduction between the two methods.

6. (a) (i) $\alpha = 0.05$; H_0: $\mu_1 = \mu_2$; H_1: $\mu_1 \neq \mu_2$. (ii) Student's t, $d.f. = 15$; $t \approx 1.952$. (iii) $0.050 < P\text{-value} < 0.100$; on t graph shade areas to the right of 1.952 and to the left of -0.1952. (iv) P-value interval > 0.05 for α; fail to reject H_0. (v) At the 5% level of significance, the evidence does not show any difference in the

population mean proportion of on-time arrivals in summer versus winter. (b) -0.43% to 9.835%. (c) x_1 and x_2 distributions are approximately normal (mound-shaped and symmetric).

7. (a) (i) $\alpha = 0.05$; H_0: $p_1 = p_2$; H_1: $p_1 > p_2$. (ii) Standard normal; $\hat{p}_1 \approx 0.242$; $\hat{p}_2 \approx 0.207$; $\bar{p} \approx 0.2246$; $z \approx 0.58$. (iii) P-value ≈ 0.2810; on standard normal curve shade area to the right of 0.58. (iv) P-value interval >

0.05 for α; fail to reject H_0. (v) At the 5% level of significance, the evidence does not indicate that the population proportion of single men who go out dancing occasionally differs from the proportion of single women. Since $n_1\bar{p}$, $n_1\bar{q}$, $n_2\bar{p}$, and $n_2\bar{q}$ are all greater than 5, the normal approximation to the binomial is justified. (b) -0.065 to 0.139.

Index

FREQUENTLY USED FORMULAS

n = sample size N = population size f = frequency

Chapter 2

Class Width = $\dfrac{\text{high} - \text{low}}{\text{number classes}}$ (increase to next integer)

Class Midpoint = $\dfrac{\text{upper limit} + \text{lower limit}}{2}$

Lower boundary = lower boundary of previous class + class width

Chapter 3

Sample mean $\bar{x} = \dfrac{\Sigma x}{n}$

Population mean $\mu = \dfrac{\Sigma x}{N}$

Weighted average = $\dfrac{\Sigma xw}{\Sigma w}$

Range = largest data value − smallest data value

Sample standard deviation $s = \sqrt{\dfrac{\Sigma(x - \bar{x})^2}{n - 1}}$

Computation formula $s = \sqrt{\dfrac{\Sigma x^2 - (\Sigma x)^2/n}{n - 1}}$

Population standard deviation $\sigma = \sqrt{\dfrac{\Sigma(x - \mu)^2}{N}}$

Sample variance s^2

Population variance σ^2

Sample Coefficient of Variation $CV = \dfrac{s}{\bar{x}} \cdot 100$

Sample mean for grouped data $\bar{x} = \dfrac{\Sigma xf}{n}$

Sample standard deviation for grouped data

$s = \sqrt{\dfrac{\Sigma(x - \bar{x})^2 f}{n - 1}} = \sqrt{\dfrac{\Sigma x^2 f - (\Sigma xf)^2/n}{n - 1}}$

Chapter 4

Regression and Correlation

Pearson product moment correlation coefficient

$r = \dfrac{n\Sigma xy - (\Sigma x)(\Sigma y)}{\sqrt{n\Sigma x^2 - (\Sigma x)^2}\sqrt{n\Sigma y^2 - (\Sigma y)^2}}$

Least-squares line $\hat{y} = a + bx$

where $b = \dfrac{n\Sigma xy - (\Sigma x)(\Sigma y)}{n\Sigma x^2 - (\Sigma x)^2}$

$a = \bar{y} - b\bar{x}$

Coefficient of determination $= r^2$

Chapter 5

Probability of the complement of event A
$P(\text{not } A) = 1 - P(A)$

Multiplication rule for independent events
$P(A \text{ and } B) = P(A) \cdot P(B)$

General multiplication rules
$P(A \text{ and } B) = P(A) \cdot P(B, \text{ given } A)$
$P(A \text{ and } B) = P(B) \cdot P(A, \text{ given } B)$

Addition rule for mutually exclusive events
$P(A \text{ or } B) = P(A) + P(B)$

General addition rule
$P(A \text{ or } B) = P(A) + P(B) - P(A \text{ and } B)$

Permutation rule $P_{n,r} = \dfrac{n!}{(n - r)!}$

Combination rule $C_{n,r} = \dfrac{n!}{r!(n - r)!}$

Chapter 6

Mean of a discrete probability distribution $\mu = \Sigma x P(x)$

Standard deviation of a discrete probability distribution
$\sigma = \sqrt{\Sigma(x - \mu)^2 P(x)}$

For Binomial Distributions

r = number of successes; p = probability of success;
$q = 1 - p$

Binomial probability distribution $P(r) = C_{n,r} p^r q^{n-r}$

Mean $\mu = np$

Standard deviation $\sigma = \sqrt{npq}$

Chapter 7

Raw score $x = z\sigma + \mu$

Standard score $z = \dfrac{x - \mu}{\sigma}$

Mean of $\bar{x}$ distribution $\mu_{\bar{x}} = \mu$

Standard deviation of $\bar{x}$ distribution $\sigma_{\bar{x}} = \dfrac{\sigma}{\sqrt{n}}$

Standard score for $\bar{x}$ $z = \dfrac{\bar{x} - \mu}{\sigma/\sqrt{n}}$

Chapter 8

Confidence Interval

for μ

$$\bar{x} - E < \mu < \bar{x} + E$$

where $E = z_c \dfrac{\sigma}{\sqrt{n}}$ when σ is known

$$E = t_c \dfrac{s}{\sqrt{n}} \text{ when } \sigma \text{ is unknown}$$
$$\text{with } d.f. = n - 1$$

for p ($np > 5$ and $n(1 - p) > 5$)

$$\hat{p} - E < p < \hat{p} + E$$

where $E = z_c \sqrt{\dfrac{p(1 - p)}{n}}$

$$\hat{p} = \dfrac{r}{n}$$

Sample Size for Estimating

means $n = \left(\dfrac{z_c \sigma}{E}\right)^2$

proportions

$n = p(1 - p)\left(\dfrac{z_c}{E}\right)^2$ with preliminary estimate for p

$n = \dfrac{1}{4}\left(\dfrac{z_c}{E}\right)^2$ without preliminary estimate for p

Chapter 9

Sample Test Statistics for Tests of Hypotheses

for μ (σ known) $\qquad z = \dfrac{\bar{x} - \mu}{\sigma/\sqrt{n}}$

for μ (σ unknown) $\qquad t = \dfrac{\bar{x} - \mu}{s/\sqrt{n}}$; $d.f. = n - 1$

for p ($np > 5$ and $nq > 5$) $\qquad z = \dfrac{\hat{p} - p}{\sqrt{pq/n}}$

where $q = 1 - p$; $\hat{p} = r/n$

Chapter 10

Sample Test Statistics for Tests of Hypotheses

for paired differences $d \qquad t = \dfrac{\bar{d} - \mu_{\bar{d}}}{s_d/\sqrt{n}}$; $d.f. = n - 1$

for difference of means, σ_1 and σ_2 known

$$z = \dfrac{\bar{x}_1 - \bar{x}_2}{\sqrt{\dfrac{\sigma_1^2}{n_1} + \dfrac{\sigma_2^2}{n_2}}}$$

for difference of means, σ_1 or σ_2 unknown

$$t = \dfrac{\bar{x}_1 - \bar{x}_2}{\sqrt{\dfrac{s_1^2}{n_1} + \dfrac{s_2^2}{n_2}}}$$

$d.f. = $ smaller of $n_1 - 1$ and $n_2 - 1$

(*Note:* Software uses Satterthwaite's approximation for degrees of freedom $d.f.$)

for difference of proportions

$$z = \dfrac{\hat{p}_1 - \hat{p}_2}{\sqrt{\dfrac{\bar{p}\,\bar{q}}{n_1} + \dfrac{\bar{p}\,\bar{q}}{n_2}}}$$

where $\bar{p} = \dfrac{r_1 + r_2}{n_1 + n_2}$ and $\bar{q} = 1 - \bar{p}$

$$\hat{p}_1 = r_1/n_1; \ \hat{p}_2 = r_2/n_2$$

Confidence Interval

for $\mu_1 - \mu_2$ (independent samples)

$$(\bar{x}_1 - \bar{x}_2) - E < \mu_1 - \mu_2 < (\bar{x}_1 - \bar{x}_2) + E$$

where $E = z_c \sqrt{\dfrac{\sigma_1^2}{n_1} + \dfrac{\sigma_2^2}{n_2}}$ when σ_1 and σ_2 are known

$E = t_c \sqrt{\dfrac{s_1^2}{n_1} + \dfrac{s_2^2}{n_2}}$ when σ_1 or σ_2 is unknown

with $d.f. = $ smaller of $n_1 - 1$ and $n_2 - 1$

(*Note:* Software uses Satterthwaite's approximation for degrees of freedom $d.f.$)

for difference of proportions $p_1 - p_2$

$$(\hat{p}_1 - \hat{p}_2) - E < p_1 - p_2 < (\hat{p}_1 - \hat{p}_2) + E$$

where $E = z_c \sqrt{\dfrac{\hat{p}_1 \hat{q}_1}{n_1} + \dfrac{\hat{p}_2 \hat{q}_2}{n_2}}$

$$\hat{p}_1 = r_1/n_1; \ \hat{p}_2 = r_2/n_2$$
$$\hat{q}_1 = 1 - \hat{p}_1; \ \hat{q}_2 = 1 - \hat{p}_2$$

Chapter 11

$$\chi^2 = \sum \frac{(O - E)^2}{E} \text{ where } E = \frac{(\text{row total})(\text{column total})}{\text{sample size}}$$

Tests of independence $d.f. = (R - 1)(C - 1)$

Goodness of fit $d.f. = (\text{number of categories}) - 1$

Sample test statistic for σ^2

$$\chi^2 = \frac{(n - 1)s^2}{\sigma^2} \text{ with } d.f. = n - 1$$

Linear Regression

Sample test statistic for r

$$t = \frac{r\sqrt{n - 2}}{\sqrt{1 - r^2}} \text{ with } d.f. = n - 2$$

Standard error of estimate $S_e = \sqrt{\dfrac{\Sigma y^2 - a\Sigma y - b\Sigma xy}{n - 2}}$

Confidence interval for y

$$\hat{y} - E < y < \hat{y} + E$$

$$\text{where } E = t_c S_e \sqrt{1 + \frac{1}{n} + \frac{n(x - \bar{x})^2}{n\Sigma x^2 - (\Sigma x)^2}}$$

$$\text{with } d.f. = n - 2$$

Sample test statistic for slope b

$$t = \frac{b}{S_e}\sqrt{\Sigma x^2 - \frac{1}{n}(\Sigma x)^2} \text{ with } d.f. = n - 2$$

Table entry for z is the area to the left of z.

Areas of a Standard Normal Distribution

(a) Table of Areas to the Left of z

z	.00	.01	.02	.03	.04	.05	.06	.07	.08	.09
−3.4	.0003	.0003	.0003	.0003	.0003	.0003	.0003	.0003	.0003	.0002
−3.3	.0005	.0005	.0005	.0004	.0004	.0004	.0004	.0004	.0004	.0003
−3.2	.0007	.0007	.0006	.0006	.0006	.0006	.0006	.0005	.0005	.0005
−3.1	.0010	.0009	.0009	.0009	.0008	.0008	.0008	.0008	.0007	.0007
−3.0	.0013	.0013	.0013	.0012	.0012	.0011	.0011	.0011	.0010	.0010
−2.9	.0019	.0018	.0018	.0017	.0016	.0016	.0015	.0015	.0014	.0014
−2.8	.0026	.0025	.0024	.0023	.0023	.0022	.0021	.0021	.0020	.0019
−2.7	.0035	.0034	.0033	.0032	.0031	.0030	.0029	.0028	.0027	.0026
−2.6	.0047	.0045	.0044	.0043	.0041	.0040	.0039	.0038	.0037	.0036
−2.5	.0062	.0060	.0059	.0057	.0055	.0054	.0052	.0051	.0049	.0048
−2.4	.0082	.0080	.0078	.0075	.0073	.0071	.0069	.0068	.0066	.0064
−2.3	.0107	.0104	.0102	.0099	.0096	.0094	.0091	.0089	.0087	.0084
−2.2	.0139	.0136	.0132	.0129	.0125	.0122	.0119	.0116	.0113	.0110
−2.1	.0179	.0174	.0170	.0166	.0162	.0158	.0154	.0150	.0146	.0143
−2.0	.0228	.0222	.0217	.0212	.0207	.0202	.0197	.0192	.0188	.0183
−1.9	.0287	.0281	.0274	.0268	.0262	.0256	.0250	.0244	.0239	.0233
−1.8	.0359	.0351	.0344	.0336	.0329	.0322	.0314	.0307	.0301	.0294
−1.7	.0446	.0436	.0427	.0418	.0409	.0401	.0392	.0384	.0375	.0367
−1.6	.0548	.0537	.0526	.0516	.0505	.0495	.0485	.0475	.0465	.0455
−1.5	.0668	.0655	.0643	.0630	.0618	.0606	.0594	.0582	.0571	.0559
−1.4	.0808	.0793	.0778	.0764	.0749	.0735	.0721	.0708	.0694	.0681
−1.3	.0968	.0951	.0934	.0918	.0901	.0885	.0869	.0853	.0838	.0823
−1.2	.1151	.1131	.1112	.1093	.1075	.1056	.1038	.1020	.1003	.0985
−1.1	.1357	.1335	.1314	.1292	.1271	.1251	.1230	.1210	.1190	.1170
−1.0	.1587	.1562	.1539	.1515	.1492	.1469	.1446	.1423	.1401	.1379
−0.9	.1841	.1814	.1788	.1762	.1736	.1711	.1685	.1660	.1635	.1611
−0.8	.2119	.2090	.2061	.2033	.2005	.1977	.1949	.1922	.1894	.1867
−0.7	.2420	.2389	.2358	.2327	.2296	.2266	.2236	.2206	.2177	.2148
−0.6	.2743	.2709	.2676	.2643	.2611	.2578	.2546	.2514	.2483	.2451
−0.5	.3085	.3050	.3015	.2981	.2946	.2912	.2877	.2843	.2810	.2776
−0.4	.3446	.3409	.3372	.3336	.3300	.3264	.3228	.3192	.3156	.3121
−0.3	.3821	.3783	.3745	.3707	.3669	.3632	.3594	.3557	.3520	.3483
−0.2	.4207	.4168	.4129	.4090	.4052	.4013	.3974	.3936	.3897	.3859
−0.1	.4602	.4562	.4522	.4483	.4443	.4404	.4364	.4325	.4286	.4247
−0.0	.5000	.4960	.4920	.4880	.4840	.4801	.4761	.4721	.4681	.4641

For values of z less than −3.49, use 0.000 to approximate the area.

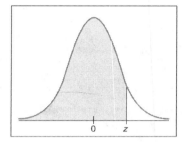

Table entry for z is the area to the left of z.

Areas of a Standard Normal Distribution *continued*

z	.00	.01	.02	.03	.04	.05	.06	.07	.08	.09
0.0	.5000	.5040	.5080	.5120	.5160	.5199	.5239	.5279	.5319	.5359
0.1	.5398	.5438	.5478	.5517	.5557	.5596	.5636	.5675	.5714	.5753
0.2	.5793	.5832	.5871	.5910	.5948	.5987	.6026	.6064	.6103	.6141
0.3	.6179	.6217	.6255	.6293	.6331	.6368	.6406	.6443	.6480	.6517
0.4	.6554	.6591	.6628	.6664	.6700	.6736	.6772	.6808	.6844	.6879
0.5	.6915	.6950	.6985	.7019	.7054	.7088	.7123	.7157	.7190	.7224
0.6	.7257	.7291	.7324	.7357	.7389	.7422	.7454	.7486	.7517	.7549
0.7	.7580	.7611	.7642	.7673	.7704	.7734	.7764	.7794	.7823	.7852
0.8	.7881	.7910	.7939	.7967	.7995	.8023	.8051	.8078	.8106	.8133
0.9	.8159	.8186	.8212	.8238	.8264	.8289	.8315	.8340	.8365	.8389
1.0	.8413	.8438	.8461	.8485	.8508	.8531	.8554	.8577	.8599	.8621
1.1	.8643	.8665	.8686	.8708	.8729	.8749	.8770	.8790	.8810	.8830
1.2	.8849	.8869	.8888	.8907	.8925	.8944	.8962	.8980	.8997	.9015
1.3	.9032	.9049	.9066	.9082	.9099	.9115	.9131	.9147	.9162	.9177
1.4	.9192	.9207	.9222	.9236	.9251	.9265	.9279	.9292	.9306	.9319
1.5	.9332	.9345	.9357	.9370	.9382	.9394	.9406	.9418	.9429	.9441
1.6	.9452	.9463	.9474	.9484	.9495	.9505	.9515	.9525	.9535	.9545
1.7	.9554	.9564	.9573	.9582	.9591	.9599	.9608	.9616	.9625	.9633
1.8	.9641	.9649	.9656	.9664	.9671	.9678	.9686	.9693	.9699	.9706
1.9	.9713	.9719	.9726	.9732	.9738	.9744	.9750	.9756	.9761	.9767
2.0	.9772	.9778	.9783	.9788	.9793	.9798	.9803	.9808	.9812	.9817
2.1	.9821	.9826	.9830	.9834	.9838	.9842	.9846	.9850	.9854	.9857
2.2	.9861	.9864	.9868	.9871	.9875	.9878	.9881	.9884	.9887	.9890
2.3	.9893	.9896	.9898	.9901	.9904	.9906	.9909	.9911	.9913	.9916
2.4	.9918	.9920	.9922	.9925	.9927	.9929	.9931	.9932	.9934	.9936
2.5	.9938	.9940	.9941	.9943	.9945	.9946	.9948	.9949	.9951	.9952
2.6	.9953	.9955	.9956	.9957	.9959	.9960	.9961	.9962	.9963	.9964
2.7	.9965	.9966	.9967	.9968	.9969	.9970	.9971	.9972	.9973	.9974
2.8	.9974	.9975	.9976	.9977	.9977	.9978	.9979	.9979	.9980	.9981
2.9	.9981	.9982	.9982	.9983	.9984	.9984	.9985	.9985	.9986	.9986
3.0	.9987	.9987	.9987	.9988	.9988	.9989	.9989	.9989	.9990	.9990
3.1	.9990	.9991	.9991	.9991	.9992	.9992	.9992	.9992	.9993	.9993
3.2	.9993	.9993	.9994	.9994	.9994	.9994	.9994	.9995	.9995	.9995
3.3	.9995	.9995	.9995	.9996	.9996	.9996	.9996	.9996	.9996	.9997
3.4	.9997	.9997	.9997	.9997	.9997	.9997	.9997	.9997	.9997	.9998

For z values greater than 3.49, use 1.000 to approximate the area.

Areas of a Standard Normal Distribution *continued*

(b) Confidence Interval Critical Values z_c	
Level of Confidence c	Critical Value z_c
0.70, or 70%	1.04
0.75, or 75%	1.15
0.80, or 80%	1.28
0.85, or 85%	1.44
0.90, or 90%	1.645
0.95, or 95%	1.96
0.98, or 98%	2.33
0.99, or 99%	2.58

Areas of a Standard Normal Distribution *continued*

(c) Hypothesis Testing, Critical Values z_0		
Level of Significance	$\alpha = 0.05$	$\alpha = 0.01$
Critical value z_0 for a left-tailed test	−1.645	−2.33
Critical value z_0 for a right-tailed test	1.645	2.33
Critical values $\pm z_0$ for a two-tailed test	±1.96	±2.58

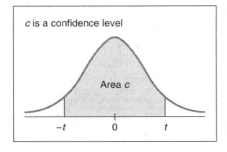

c is a confidence level

Area c

−t   0   t

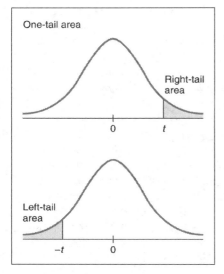

One-tail area

Right-tail area

0   t

Left-tail area

−t   0

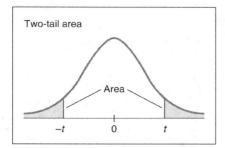

Two-tail area

Area

−t   0   t

Critical Values for Student's *t* Distribution

one-tail area	0.250	0.125	0.100	0.075	0.050	0.025	0.010	0.005	0.0005
two-tail area	0.500	0.250	0.200	0.150	0.100	0.050	0.020	0.010	0.0010
d.f. c	0.500	0.750	0.800	0.850	0.900	0.950	0.980	0.990	0.999
1	1.000	2.414	3.078	4.165	6.314	12.706	31.821	63.657	636.619
2	0.816	1.604	1.886	2.282	2.920	4.303	6.965	9.925	31.599
3	0.765	1.423	1.638	1.924	2.353	3.182	4.541	5.841	12.924
4	0.741	1.344	1.533	1.778	2.132	2.776	3.747	4.604	8.610
5	0.727	1.301	1.476	1.699	2.015	2.571	3.365	4.032	6.869
6	0.718	1.273	1.440	1.650	1.943	2.447	3.143	3.707	5.959
7	0.711	1.254	1.415	1.617	1.895	2.365	2.998	3.499	5.408
8	0.706	1.240	1.397	1.592	1.860	2.306	2.896	3.355	5.041
9	0.703	1.230	1.383	1.574	1.833	2.262	2.821	3.250	4.781
10	0.700	1.221	1.372	1.559	1.812	2.228	2.764	3.169	4.587
11	0.697	1.214	1.363	1.548	1.796	2.201	2.718	3.106	4.437
12	0.695	1.209	1.356	1.538	1.782	2.179	2.681	3.055	4.318
13	0.694	1.204	1.350	1.530	1.771	2.160	2.650	3.012	4.221
14	0.692	1.200	1.345	1.523	1.761	2.145	2.624	2.977	4.140
15	0.691	1.197	1.341	1.517	1.753	2.131	2.602	2.947	4.073
16	0.690	1.194	1.337	1.512	1.746	2.120	2.583	2.921	4.015
17	0.689	1.191	1.333	1.508	1.740	2.110	2.567	2.898	3.965
18	0.688	1.189	1.330	1.504	1.734	2.101	2.552	2.878	3.922
19	0.688	1.187	1.328	1.500	1.729	2.093	2.539	2.861	3.883
20	0.687	1.185	1.325	1.497	1.725	2.086	2.528	2.845	3.850
21	0.686	1.183	1.323	1.494	1.721	2.080	2.518	2.831	3.819
22	0.686	1.182	1.321	1.492	1.717	2.074	2.508	2.819	3.792
23	0.685	1.180	1.319	1.489	1.714	2.069	2.500	2.807	3.768
24	0.685	1.179	1.318	1.487	1.711	2.064	2.492	2.797	3.745
25	0.684	1.198	1.316	1.485	1.708	2.060	2.485	2.787	3.725
26	0.684	1.177	1.315	1.483	1.706	2.056	2.479	2.779	3.707
27	0.684	1.176	1.314	1.482	1.703	2.052	2.473	2.771	3.690
28	0.683	1.175	1.313	1.480	1.701	2.048	2.467	2.763	3.674
29	0.683	1.174	1.311	1.479	1.699	2.045	2.462	2.756	3.659
30	0.683	1.173	1.310	1.477	1.697	2.042	2.457	2.750	3.646
35	0.682	1.170	1.306	1.472	1.690	2.030	2.438	2.724	3.591
40	0.681	1.167	1.303	1.468	1.684	2.021	2.423	2.704	3.551
45	0.680	1.165	1.301	1.465	1.679	2.014	2.412	2.690	3.520
50	0.679	1.164	1.299	1.462	1.676	2.009	2.403	2.678	3.496
60	0.679	1.162	1.296	1.458	1.671	2.000	2.390	2.660	3.460
70	0.678	1.160	1.294	1.456	1.667	1.994	2.381	2.648	3.435
80	0.678	1.159	1.292	1.453	1.664	1.990	2.374	2.639	3.416
100	0.677	1.157	1.290	1.451	1.660	1.984	2.364	2.626	3.390
500	0.675	1.152	1.283	1.442	1.648	1.965	2.334	2.586	3.310
1000	0.675	1.151	1.282	1.441	1.646	1.962	2.330	2.581	3.300
∞	0.674	1.150	1.282	1.440	1.645	1.960	2.326	2.576	3.291

For degrees of freedom *d.f.* not in the table, use the closest *d.f.* that is *smaller*.

STUDENT SOLUTIONS MANUAL

TO ACCOMPANY

UNDERSTANDING BASIC STATISTICS
FOURTH EDITION
BRASE/BRASE

Charles Henry Brase
Regis University

Corrinne Pellillo Brase
Arapahoe Community College

Contents

Chapter 1 Getting Started

Section 1.1

1. **(a)** The variable is the response regarding frequency of eating at fast-food restaurants.
   (b) The variable is qualitative. The categories are the number of times one eats in fast-food restaurants.
   (c) The implied population is responses for all adults in the U.S.

3. **(a)** The variable is student/faculty ratio at colleges.
   (b) The variable is quantitative because arithmetic operations can be applied to the ratios.
   (c) The implied population is student/faculty ratio at all colleges in the nation.

5. **(a)** The variable is the nitrogen concentration (mg nitrogen/l water).
   (b) The variable is quantitative because arithmetic operations can be applied to the time intervals.
   (c) The implied population is the nitrogen concentration (mg nitrogen/l water) in the entire lake.

7. **(a)** *Length of time to complete an exam* is a ratio level of measurement. The data may be arranged in order, differences and ratios are meaningful, and a time of 0 is the starting point for all measurements.
   (b) *Time of first class* is an interval level of measurement. The data may be arranged in order and differences are meaningful.
   (c) *Major field of study* is a nominal level of measurement. The data consists of names only.
   (d) *Course evaluation scale* is an ordinal level of measurement. The data may be arranged in order.
   (e) *Score on last exam* is a ratio level of measurement. The data may be arranged in order, differences and ratios are meaningful, and a score of 0 is the starting point for all measurements.
   (f) *Age of student* is a ratio level of measurement. The data may be arranged in order, differences and ratios are meaningful, and an age of 0 is the starting point for all measurements.

9. **(a)** *Species of fish* is a nominal level of measurement. Data consist of names only.
   (b) *Cost of rod and reel* is a ratio level of measurement. The data may be arranged in order, differences and ratios are meaningful, and a cost of 0 is the starting point for all measurements.
   (c) *Time of return home* is an interval level of measurement. The data may be arranged in order and differences are meaningful.
   (d) *Guidebook rating* is an ordinal level of measurement. Data may be arranged in order.
   (e) *Number of fish* caught is a ratio level of measurement. The data may be arranged in order, differences and ratios are meaningful, and 0 fish caught is the starting point for all measurements.
   (f) *Temperature of the water* is an interval level of measurement. The data may be arranged in order and differences are meaningful.

Section 1.2

1. Essay

3. Answers vary. Use groups of 4 digits.

5. **(a)** Yes, it is appropriate that the same number appears more than once because the outcome of a die roll can repeat. The outcome of the 4th roll is 2.
   (b) No, we do not expect the same sequence because the process is random.

7. **(a)** Reasons may vary. For instance, the first four students may make a special effort to get to class on time.

   (b) Reasons may vary. For instance, four students who come in late might all be nursing students enrolled in an anatomy and physiology class that meets the hour before in a far-away building. They may be more motivated than other students to complete a degree requirement.

   (c) Reasons may vary. For instance, four students sitting in the back row might be less inclined to participate in class discussions.

   (d) Reasons may vary. For instance, the tallest students might all be male.

9. Answers vary. Use single digits with correct answer placed in corresponding position.

11. **(a)** This technique is simple random sampling. Every sample of size n from the population has an equal chance of being selected and every member of the population has an equal chance of being included in the sample.

   (b) This technique is cluster sampling. The state, Hawaii, is divided into regions using, say, the first 3 digits of the Zip code. Within each region a random sample of 10 Zip code areas is selected using, say, all 5 digits of the Zip code. Then, within each selected Zip codes, <u>all</u> businesses are surveyed. The sampling units, defined by 5 digit Zip codes, are clusters of businesses, and within each selected Zip code, the benefits package the businesses offer their employees differs business to business.

   (c) This technique is convenience sampling. This technique uses results or data that are conveniently and readily obtained.

   (d) This technique is systematic sampling. Every k^{th} element is included in the sample.

   (e) This technique is stratified sampling. The population was divided into strata (10 business types), then a simple random sample was drawn from each stratum.

Section 1.3

1. **(a)** This is an observational study because observations and measurements of individuals are conducted in a way that doesn't change the response or the variable being measured.

   (b) This is an experiment because a treatment is deliberately imposed on the individuals in order to observe a possible change in the response or variable being measured.

   (c) This is an experiment because a treatment is deliberately imposed on the individuals in order to observe a possible change in the response or variable being measured.

   (d) This is an observational study because observations and measurements of individuals are conducted in a way that doesn't change the response or the variable being measured.

3. **(a)** Use random selection to pick 10 calves to inoculate. Then test all calves to see if there is a difference in resistance to infection between the two groups. There is no placebo being used.

   (b) Use random selection to pick 9 schools to visit. Then survey all the schools to see if there is a difference in views between the two groups. There is no placebo being used.

   (c) Use random selection to pick 40 volunteers for skin patch with drug. Then survey all volunteers to see if a difference exists between the two groups. A placebo for the remaining 35 volunteers in the second group is used.

Chapter 1 Review

1. Answers vary.

3. In the random number table use groups of 2 digits. Select the first six distinct groups of 2 digits that fall in the range from 01 to 42. Choices vary according to the starting place in the random number table.

5. (a) This is an observational study because observations and measurements of individuals are conducted in a way that doesn't change the response or the variable being measured.

   (b) This is an experiment because a treatment is deliberately imposed on the individuals in order to observe a possible change in the response or variable being measured.

7. This is a good problem for class discussion. Some items such as age and grade point average might be sensitive information. You could ask the class to design a data form that can be filled out anonymously. Other issues to discuss involve the accuracy and honesty of the responses.

9. (a) This is an experiment, since a treatment is imposed on one colony.

   (b) The control group receives normal daylight/darkness condition. The treatment group has light 24 hours per day.

   (c) The number of fireflies living at the end of 72 hours.

   (d) The variable is a ratio level of measurement. The data may be arranged in order, differences and ratios are meaningful, and the number 0 fireflies is the starting point for all measurements.

Chapter 2 Organizing Data

Section 2.1

1. **(a)** largest data value $= 360$

   smallest data value $= 236$

   number of classes specified $= 5$

   class width $= \dfrac{360 - 236}{5} = 24.8$, increased to next whole number, 25

   (b) The lower class limit of the first class is the smallest value, 236.

   The lower class limit of the next class is the previous class's lower class limit plus the class width; for the second class, this is $236 + 25 = 261$.

   The upper class limit is one value less than lower class limit of the next class; for the first class, the upper class limit is $261 - 1 = 260$.

   The class boundaries are the halfway points between (i.e., the average of) the (adjacent) upper class limit of one class and the lower class limit of the next class. The lower class boundary of the first class is the lower class limit minus one-half unit. The upper class boundary for the last class is the upper class limit plus one-half unit. For the first class, the class boundaries are $236 - \dfrac{1}{2} = 235.5$ and

   $\dfrac{260 + 261}{2} = 260.5$. For the last class, the class boundaries are $\dfrac{335 + 336}{2} = 335.5$ and $360 + \dfrac{1}{2} = 360.5$.

   The class mark or midpoint is the average of the class limits for that class. For the first class, the midpoint is $\dfrac{236 + 260}{2} = 248$.

   The class frequency is the number of data values that belong to that class; call this value f.

   The relative frequency of a class is the class frequency, f, divided by the total number of data values, i.e., the overall sample size, n.

   For the first class, $f = 4$, $n = 57$, and the relative frequency is $f/n = \dfrac{4}{57} \approx 0.07$.

   The cumulative frequency of a class is the sum of the frequencies for all previous classes, plus the frequency of that class. For the first and second classes, the class cumulative frequencies are 4 and $4 + 9 = 13$, respectively.

Class Limits	Boundaries	Midpoint	Frequency	Relative Frequency	Cumulative Frequency
236–260	235.5–260.5	248	4	0.07	4
261–285	260.5–285.5	273	9	0.16	13
286–310	285.5–310.5	298	25	0.44	38
311–335	310.5–335.5	323	16	0.28	54
336–360	335.5–360.5	348	3	0.05	57

   (c) The histogram plots the class frequencies on the y-axis and the class boundaries on the x-axis. Since adjacent classes share boundary values, the bars touch each other. [Alternatively, the bars may be centered over the class marks (midpoints).]

(d) In the relative-frequency histogram, each class of the frequency table in part (b) has a corresponding bar with horizontal width extending from the lower boundary to the upper boundary of the respective class; the height of each bar is the corresponding relative frequency, f/n (whereas for the histogram the height is given by the actual frequency, f).

The following figure shows the histogram, frequency polygon, and relative-frequency histogram overlaying one another. (Note that two vertical scales are shown.)

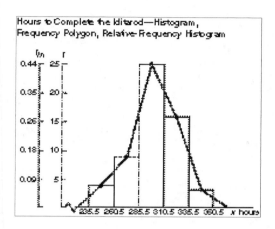

3. (a) largest data value = 59

smallest data value = 1

number of classes specified = 5

class width $= \dfrac{59-1}{5} = 11.6$, increased to next whole number, 12

(b) The lower class limit of the first class is the smallest value, 1.

The lower class limit of the next class is the previous class's lower class limit plus the class width; for the second class, this is 1 + 12 = 13.

The upper class limit is one value less than lower class limit of the next class; for the first class, the upper class limit is 13 − 1 = 12.

The class boundaries are the halfway points between (i.e., the average of) the (adjacent) upper class limit of one class and the lower class limit of the next class. The lower class boundary of the first class is the lower class limit minus one-half unit. The upper class boundary for the last class is the upper class limit plus one-half unit. For the first class, the class boundaries are $1 - \dfrac{1}{2} = 0.5$ and

$\dfrac{12+13}{2} = 12.5$. For the last class, the class boundaries are $\dfrac{48+49}{2} = 48.5$ and $60 + \dfrac{1}{2} = 60.5$.

The class mark or midpoint is the average of the class limits for that class. For the first class, the midpoint is $\dfrac{1+12}{2} = 6.5$.

The class frequency is the number of data values that belong to that class; call this value f.

The relative frequency of a class is the class frequency, f, divided by the total number of data values, i.e., the overall sample size, n.

For the first class, $f = 6$, $n = 42$, and the relative frequency is $f/n = 6/42 \approx 0.14$.

The cumulative frequency of a class is the sum of the frequencies for all previous classes, plus the frequency of that class. For the first and second classes, the class cumulative frequencies are 6 and $6 + 10 = 16$, respectively.

Class Limits	Class Boundaries	Midpoint	Frequency	Relative Frequency	Cumulative Frequency
1–12	0.5–12.5	6.5	6	0.14	6
13–24	12.5–24.5	18.5	10	0.24	16
25–36	24.5–36.5	30.5	5	0.12	21
37–48	36.5–48.5	42.5	13	0.31	34
49–60	48.5–60.5	54.5	8	0.19	42

(c) The histogram plots the class frequencies on the *y*-axis and the class boundaries on the *x*-axis. Since adjacent classes share boundary values, the bars touch each other. [Alternatively, the bars may be centered over the class marks (midpoints).]

(d) In the relative-frequency histogram, each class of the frequency table in part (b) has a corresponding bar with horizontal width extending from the lower boundary to the upper boundary of the respective class; the height of each bar is the corresponding relative frequency, f/n (whereas for the histogram the height is given by the actual frequency, f).

The following figure shows the histogram, frequency polygon, and relative-frequency histogram overlaying one another. (Note that two vertical scales are shown.)

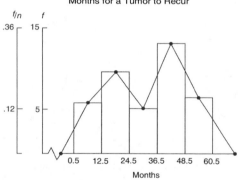

Months for a Tumor to Recur

5. (a) largest data value $= 52$

smallest data value $= 10$

number of classes specified $= 5$

class width $= \dfrac{52-10}{5} = 8.4$, increased to next whole number, 9

(b) The lower class limit of the first class is the smallest value, 10.

The lower class limit of the next class is the previous class's lower class limit plus the class width; for the second class, this is $10 + 9 = 19$.

The upper class limit is one value less than lower class limit of the next class; for the first class, the upper class limit is $19 - 1 = 18$.

The class boundaries are the halfway points between (i.e., the average of) the (adjacent) upper class limit of one class and the lower class limit of the next class. The lower class boundary of the first class is the lower class limit minus one-half unit. The upper class boundary for the last class is the upper class limit plus one-half unit. For the first class, the class boundaries are $10 - \frac{1}{2} = 9.5$ and $\frac{18+19}{2} = 18.5$. For the last class, the class boundaries are $\frac{45+46}{2} = 45.5$ and $54 + \frac{1}{2} = 54.5$.

The class mark or midpoint is the average of the class limits for that class. For the first class, the midpoint is $\frac{10+18}{2} = 14$.

The class frequency is the number of data values that belong to that class; call this value f.

The relative frequency of a class is the class frequency, f, divided by the total number of data values, i.e., the overall sample size, n.

For the first class, $f = 6$, $n = 55$, and the relative frequency is $f/n = 6/55 \approx 0.11$.

The cumulative frequency of a class is the sum of the frequencies for all previous classes, plus the frequency of that class. For the first and second classes, the class cumulative frequencies are 6 and $6 + 26 = 32$, respectively.

Highway Fuel Consumption (mpg)

Class Limits	Class Boundaries	Midpoint	Frequency	Relative Frequency	Cumulative Frequency
10–18	9.5–18.5	14	6	0.11	6
19–27	18.5–27.5	23	26	0.47	32
28–36	27.5–36.5	32	20	0.36	52
37–45	36.5–45.5	41	1	0.02	53
46–54	45.5–54.5	50	2	0.04	55

(c) The histogram plots the class frequencies on the y-axis and the class boundaries on the x-axis. Since adjacent classes share boundary values, the bars touch each other. [Alternatively, the bars may be centered over the class marks (midpoints).]

(d) In the relative-frequency histogram, each class of the frequency table in part (b) has a corresponding bar with horizontal width extending from the lower boundary to the upper boundary of the respective class; the height of each bar is the corresponding relative frequency, f/n (whereas for the histogram the height is given by the actual frequency, f).

The following figure shows the histogram, frequency polygon, and relative-frequency histogram overlaying one another. (Note that two vertical scales are shown.)

7. (a) Uniform is rectangular, symmetric looks like mirror images on each side of the middle, bimodal has two modes (peaks), and skewed distributions have long tails on one side, and are skewed in the direction of the tail ("skew, few"). (Note that uniform distributions are also symmetric, but "uniform" is more descriptive.)

(a) skewed left, (b) uniform, (c) symmetric, (d) bimodal, (e) skewed right.

(b) Answers vary. Students would probably like (a) since there are many high scores and few low scores. Students would probably dislike (e) since there are few high scores but lots of low scores. (b) is designed to give approximately the same number of As, Bs, etc. (d) has more Bs and Ds, for example. (c) is the way many tests are designed: As and Fs for the exceptionally high and low scores with most students receiving Cs.

9. (a) $2.71 \times 100 = 271$, $1.62 \times 100 = 162,\ldots, 0.70 \times 100 = 70$.

(b) largest value = 282, smallest value = 46

class width = $\dfrac{282 - 46}{6} \approx 39.3$; use 40

Class Limits	Class Boundaries	Midpoint	Frequency
46–85	45.5–85.5	65.5	4
86–125	85.5–125.5	105.5	5
126–165	125.5–165.5	145.5	10
166–205	165.5–205.5	185.5	5
206–245	205.5–245.5	225.5	5
246–285	245.5–285.5	265.5	3

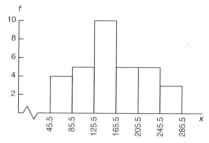

Tons of Wheat—Histogram

(c) class width is $\dfrac{40}{100} = 0.40$

Class Limits	Class Boundaries	Midpoint	Frequency
0.46–0.85	0.455–0.855	0. 655	4
0.86–1.25	0.855–1.255	1.055	5
1.26–1.65	1.255–1.655	1.455	10
1.66–2.05	1.655–2.055	1.855	5
2.06–2.45	2.055–2.455	2.255	5
2.46–2.85	2.455–2.855	2.655	3

11. **(a)** There is one dot below 600, so 1 state has 600 or fewer licensed drivers per 1000 residents.

  (b) 5 values are close to 800; $\dfrac{5}{51} \approx 0.0980 \approx 9.8\%$

  (c) 9 values below 650
    37 values between 650 and 750
    5 values above 750
    From either the counts or the dotplot, the interval from 650 to 750 licensed drivers per 1000 residents has the most "states."

13. The dotplot shows some of the characteristics of the histogram, such as the concentration of most of the data in two peaks, one from 13 to 24 and another from 37 to 48.

  However, they are somewhat difficult to compare since the dotplot can be thought of as a histogram with one value, the class mark, i.e., the data value, per class.

  Because the definitions of the classes and, therefore, the class widths differ, it is difficult to compare the two figures.

Section 2.2

1. Highest Level of Education and Average Annual
   Household Income (in thousands of dollars)

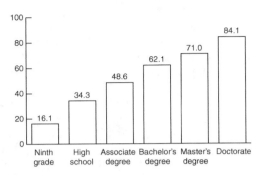

3.   Pareto Chart
   Annual Harvest for Commercial
   Fishing in the Gulf of Alaska
   (in thousand metric tons)

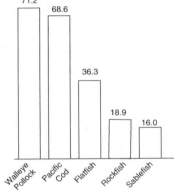

5.

Hiding place	Percentage	Number of Degrees
In the closet	68%	$68\% \times 360° \approx 245°$
Under the bed	23%	$23\% \times 360° \approx 83°$
In the bathtub	6%	$6\% \times 360° \approx 22°$
In the freezer	3%	$3\% \times 360° \approx 11°$
Total	100%	361°*

*Total does not add to 360° due to rounding.

Where We Hide the Mess

7. **(a)**

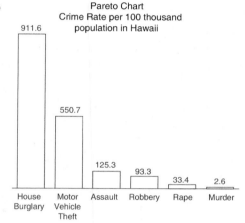

Pareto Chart
Crime Rate per 100 thousand
population in Hawaii

(b) No. In a circle graph, wedges of a circle display proportional parts of the total population that share a common characteristic. The crimes that are listed are not all possible forms. Other forms of crime such as arson are not included in the information. Also, if two or more crimes occur together, the circle graph is not the correct display to choose.

9. Elevation of Pyramid Lake Surface—Time-Series Graph

Section 2.3

1. (a) The smallest value is 47 and the largest is 97, so we need stems 4, 5, 6, 7, 8, and 9. Use the tens digit as the stem and the ones digit as the leaf.

Longevity of Cowboys

4	7 = 47 years
4	7
5	2 7 8 8
6	1 6 6 8 8
7	0 2 2 3 3 5 6 7
8	4 4 4 5 6 6 7 9
9	0 1 1 2 3 7

(b) Yes, certainly these cowboys lived long lives, as evidenced by the high frequency of leaves for stems 7, 8, and 9 (i.e., 70-, 80-, and 90-year olds).

3. The longest average length of stay is 11.1 days in North Dakota and the shortest is 5.2 days in Utah. We need stems from 5 to 11. Use the digit(s) to the left of the decimal point as the stem, and the digit to the right as the leaf.

Average Length of Hospital Stay

5	2 = 5.2 days
5	2 3 5 5 6 7
6	0 2 4 6 6 7 7 8 8 8 8 9 9
7	0 0 0 0 0 0 1 1 1 2 2 2 3 3 3 3 4 4 5 5 6 6 8
8	4 5 7
9	4 6 9
10	0 3
11	1

The distribution is skewed right.

5. (a) The longest time during 1961–1980 was 23 minutes (i.e., 2:23) and the shortest time was 9 minutes (2:09). We need stems 0, 1, and 2. We'll use the tens digit as the stem and the ones digit as the leaf, placing leaves 0, 1, 2, 3, and 4 on the first stem and leaves 5, 6, 7, 8, and 9 on the second stem.

Minutes Beyond 2 Hours (1961-1980)

0	9 = 9 minutes past 2 hours
0	9 9
1	0 0 2 3 3
1	5 5 6 6 7 8 8 9
2	0 2 3 3

(b) The longest time during the period 1981–2000 was 14 (2:14), and the shortest was 7 (2:07), so we'll need stems 0 and 1 only.

Minutes Beyond 2 Hours (1981-2000)

0	7 = 7 minutes past 2 hours
0	7 7 7 8 8 8 8 9 9 9 9 9 9 9 9
1	0 0 1 1 4

(c) In more recent times, the winning times have been closer to 2 hours, with all 20 times between 7 and 14 minutes over two hours. In the earlier period, more than half the times (12 or 20) were more than 2 hours and 14 minutes.

7. The largest value in the data is 29.8 mg of tar per cigarette smoked, and the smallest value is 1.0. We will need stems from 1 to 29, and we will use the numbers to the right of the decimal point as the leaves.

Milligrams of Tar per Cigarette

1	0 = 1.0 mg tar
1	0
2	
3	
4	1 5
5	
6	
7	3 8
8	0 6 8
9	0
10	
11	4
12	0 4 8
13	7
14	1 5 9
15	0 1 2 8
16	0 6
17	0
29	8

9. The largest value in the data set is 2.03 mg nicotine per cigarette smoked. The smallest value is 0.13. We will need stems 0, 1, and 2. We will use the number to the left of the decimal point as the stem and the first number to the right of the decimal point as the leaf. The number 2 places to the right of the decimal point (the hundredths digit) will be truncated (chopped off; _not_ rounded off).

Milligrams of Nicotine per Cigarette

0	1 = 0.1 milligram
0	1 4 4
0	5 6 6 6 7 7 7 8 8 9 9 9
1	0 0 0 0 0 0 1 2
1	
2	0

Chapter 2 Review

1. (a) Figure 2-1 (a) (in the text) is essentially a bar graph with a "horizontal" axis showing years and a "vertical" axis showing miles per gallon. However, in depicting the data as a highway and showing it in perspective, the ability to correctly compare bar heights visually has been lost. For example, determining what would appear to be the bar heights by measuring from the white line on the road to the edge of the road along a line drawn from the year to its mpg value, we get the bar height for 1983 to be approximately 7/8 inch and the bar height for 1985 to be approximately 1 3/8 inches (i.e., 11/8 inches). Taking the ratio of the given bar heights, we see that the bar for 1985 should be $\frac{27.5}{26} \approx 1.06$ times the length of the 1983 bar. However, the measurements show a ratio of

$$\frac{\frac{11}{8}}{\frac{7}{8}} = \frac{11}{7} \approx 1.60,$$ i.e., the 1985 bar is (visually) 1.6 times the length of the 1983 bar. Also, the years are evenly spaced numerically, but the figure shows the more recent years to be more widely spaced due to the use of perspective.

(b) Figure 2-1(b) is a time-series graph, showing the years on the x-axis and miles per gallon on the y-axis. Everything is to scale and not distorted visually by the use of perspective. It is easy to see the mpg standards for each year, and you can also see how fuel economy standards for new cars have changed over the eight years shown (i.e., a steep increase in the early years and a leveling off in the later years).

3.

Most Difficult Task	Percentage	Degrees
IRS jargon	43%	$0.43 \times 360° \approx 155°$
Deductions	28%	$0.28 \times 360° \approx 101°$
Right form	10%	$0.10 \times 360° = 36°$
Calculations	8%	$0.08 \times 360° \approx 29°$
Don't know	10%	$0.10 \times 360° = 36°$

Note: Degrees do not total 360° due to rounding.

Problems with Tax Returns

5. (a) The largest value is 142 mm, and the smallest value is 69. For seven classes we need a class width of
$\frac{142-69}{7} \approx 10.4$; use 11. The lower class limit of the first class is 69, and the lower class limit of the
second class is $69 + 11 = 80$.

The class boundaries are the average of the upper class limit of one class and the lower class limit of
the next higher class. The midpoint is the average of the class limits for that class. There are 60 data
values total so the relative frequency is the class frequency divided by 60.

Class Limits	Class Boundaries	Midpoint	Frequency	Relative Frequency	Cumulative Frequency
69–79	68.5–79.5	74	2	0.03	2
80–90	79.5–90.5	85	3	0.05	5
91–101	90.5–101.5	96	8	0.13	13
102–112	101.5–112.5	107	19	0.32	32
113–123	112.5–123.5	118	22	0.37	54
124–134	123.5–134.5	129	3	0.05	57
135–145	134.5–145.5	140	3	0.05	60

(b) The histogram shows the bars centered over the midpoints of each class.

(c) The frequency histogram and the relative frequency histogram are the same except in the latter, the
vertical scale is relative frequency, not frequency.

Trunk Circumference (mm)

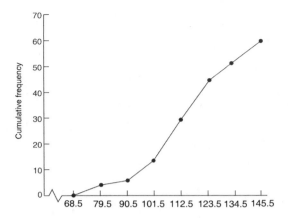

7. **(a)** To determine the decade which contained the most samples, count <u>both</u> rows (if shown) of leaves; recall leaves 0–4 belong on the first line and 5–9 belong on the second line when two lines per stem are used. The greatest number of leaves is found on stem 124, i.e., the 1240s (the 40s decade in the 1200s), with 40 samples.

   (b) The number of samples with tree ring dates 1200 A.D. to 1239 A.D. is 28 + 3 + 19 + 25 = 75.

   (c) The dates of the longest interval with no sample values are 1204 through 1211 A.D. This might mean that for these eight years, the pueblo was unoccupied (thus no new or repaired structures) or that the population remained stable (no new structures needed) or that, say, weather conditions were favorable these years so existing structures didn't need repair. If relatively few new structures were built or repaired during this period, their tree rings might have been missed during sample selection.

Chapter 3 Averages and Variation

Calculations may vary slightly due to rounding.

Section 3.1

1. Mean = $\bar{x} = \dfrac{\Sigma x}{n} = \dfrac{146+152+168+\cdots+144}{14}$

$= \dfrac{2342}{14}$

$= 167.3$

The mean is 167.3°F.

Organize the data from smallest to largest.

| 144 | 146 | 152 | 152 | 165 | 168 | 168 |
| 174 | 178 | 178 | 178 | 179 | 180 | 180 |

To find the median, add the two middle values and divide by 2 since there is an even number of values.

$$\text{Median} = \frac{168+174}{2} = 171$$

The median is 171° F.

The mode is 178° F because it is the value that occurs most frequently.

3. First organize the data from smallest to largest. Then compute the mean, median, and mode.

(a) Upper Canyon

| 1 | 1 | 1 | 2 | 3 | 3 | 3 | 3 | 4 | 6 | 9 |

Mean = $\bar{x} = \dfrac{\Sigma x}{n} = \dfrac{36}{11} \approx 3.27$

Median = 3   (middle value)

Mode = 3   (occurs most frequently)

(b) Lower Canyon

| 0 | 0 | 1 | 1 | 1 | 1 | 2 | 2 | 3 | 6 | 7 | 8 | 13 | 14 |

Mean = $\bar{x} = \dfrac{\Sigma x}{n} = \dfrac{59}{14} \approx 4.21$

Median = $\dfrac{2+2}{2} = 2$

Mode = 1   (occurs most frequently)

(c) The mean for the Lower Canyon is greater than that of the Upper Canyon. However, the median and mode for the Lower Canyon are less than those of the Upper Canyon.

(d) 5% of 14 is 0.7 which rounds to 1. So, eliminate one data value from the bottom of the list and one from the top. Then compute the mean of the remaining 12 values. The mean is 3.75.

$$5\% \text{ trimmed mean} = \frac{\Sigma x}{n} = \frac{45}{12} = 3.75$$

Now this value is closer to the Upper Canyon mean.

5. (a) Mean $= \bar{x} = \dfrac{\Sigma x}{n} = \dfrac{2723}{20} = 136.15$

The mean is $136.15.

The median is $66.50.

The mode is $60.

(b) 5% of 20 is 1. Eliminate one data value from the bottom and one from the top of the ordered data. In this case eliminate $40 and $500.

$$\text{Mean} = \bar{x} = \frac{\Sigma x}{n} = \frac{2183}{18} \approx 121.28$$

The 5% trimmed mean is $121.28.

Yes, the trimmed mean more accurately reflects the general level of the daily rental cost, but is still higher than the median.

(c) Median. The low and high prices would be helpful also.

7. (a) If the largest data value is *replaced* by a larger value, the mean will increase because the sum of the data values will increase, but the number of them will remain the same. The median will not change. The same value will still be in the eighth position when the data are ordered.

(b) If the largest value is replaced by a value that is smaller (but still higher than the median), the mean will decrease because the sum of the data values will decrease. The median will not change. The same value will be in the eighth position in increasing order.

(c) If the largest value is replaced by a value that is smaller than the median, the mean will decrease because the sum of the data values will decrease. The median also will decrease because the former value in the eighth position will move to the ninth position in increasing order. The median will be the new value in the eighth position.

9. Weighted average $= \dfrac{\Sigma xw}{\Sigma w}$

$$= \frac{9(2) + 7(3) + 6(1) + 10(4)}{2 + 3 + 1 + 4}$$

$$= \frac{85}{10}$$

$$= 8.5$$

Section 3.2

1. (a) Range $=$ largest value $-$ smallest value

$$= 30 - 15$$

$$= 15$$

(b) Use a calculator to verify that $\Sigma x = 110$ and $\Sigma x^2 = 2568$.

(c) Computation formula (sample data) for s^2.

$$s = \sqrt{\frac{\Sigma x^2 - \frac{(\Sigma x)^2}{n}}{n-1}}$$

$$= \sqrt{\frac{2568 - \frac{(110)^2}{5}}{5-1}}$$

$$\approx 6.08$$

$$s^2 = 6.08^2$$

$$\approx 37$$

(d) $\bar{x} = \dfrac{\Sigma x}{n} = \dfrac{110}{5} = 22$

Defining formula (sample data) for s^2.

$$s = \sqrt{\frac{\Sigma(x-\bar{x})^2}{n-1}}$$

$$= \sqrt{\frac{(23-22)^2 + (17-22)^2 + \cdots + (25-22)^2}{5-1}}$$

$$\approx 6.08$$

$$s^2 = 6.08^2$$

$$\approx 37$$

(e) $\mu = 22$

$$\sigma = \sqrt{\frac{\Sigma(x-\mu)^2}{N}}$$

$$= \sqrt{\frac{(23-22)^2 + (17-22)^2 + \cdots + (25-22)^2}{5}}$$

$$\approx 5.44$$

$$\sigma^2 = 5.44^2$$

$$\approx 29.59$$

3. (a) Range = largest value − smallest value

$$= 7.89 - 0.02$$

$$= 7.87$$

(b) Use a calculator to verify that $\Sigma x = 62.11$ and $\Sigma x^2 = 164.23$.

(c) $\bar{x} = \dfrac{\Sigma x}{n} = \dfrac{62.11}{50} \approx 1.24$

$$s = \sqrt{\dfrac{\Sigma x^2 - \dfrac{(\Sigma x)^2}{n}}{n-1}}$$

$$= \sqrt{\dfrac{164.23 - \dfrac{(62.11)^2}{50}}{50-1}}$$

≈ 1.333

≈ 1.33

$s^2 = 1.333^2$

≈ 1.78

(d) $CV = \dfrac{s}{x} \cdot 100 = \dfrac{1.33}{1.24} \cdot 100 \approx 107\%$

s is 107% of $\bar{x}$.

The standard deviation of the time to failure is just slightly larger than the average time. Since the coefficient of variation can be thought of as a measure of the spread of the data relative to the average of the data, a small CV indicates more consistent data whereas a larger CV indicates less consistent data.

5. (a) Students verify results with a calculator.

(b) $\bar{x} = \dfrac{\Sigma x}{n} = \dfrac{245}{5} = 49$

$$s = \sqrt{\dfrac{\Sigma x^2 - \dfrac{(\Sigma x)^2}{n}}{n-1}}$$

$$= \sqrt{\dfrac{14,755 - \dfrac{(245)^2}{5}}{5-1}}$$

≈ 26.22

$s^2 = 26.22^2 \approx 687.49$

(c) $\bar{y} = \dfrac{\Sigma y}{n} = \dfrac{224}{5} = 44.8$

$$s = \sqrt{\dfrac{\Sigma y^2 - \dfrac{(\Sigma y)^2}{n}}{n-1}}$$

$$= \sqrt{\dfrac{12,070 - \dfrac{(224)^2}{5}}{5-1}}$$

≈ 22.55

$s^2 = 22.55^2 \approx 508.50$

(d) Mallard nest: $CV = \dfrac{s}{x} \cdot 100 = \dfrac{26.22}{49} \cdot 100 \approx 53.5\%$

Canada Goose nest: $CV = \dfrac{s}{y} \cdot 100 = \dfrac{22.55}{44.8} \cdot 100 \approx 50.3\%$

The CV gives the ratio of the standard deviation to the mean. The CV for mallard nests is slightly higher.

7. $CV = \dfrac{s}{\bar{x}} \cdot 100$

$\dfrac{\bar{x} \cdot CV}{100} = s$

$s = \dfrac{\bar{x} \cdot CV}{100}$

$s = \dfrac{2.2(1.5)}{100}$

$s = 0.033$

9.

Class	$x\bar{x}$	x	xf	$x - \bar{x}$	$(x - \bar{x})^2$	$(x - \bar{x})^2 f$
21–30	260	25.5	6630	−10.3	106.09	27,583.4
31–40	348	35.5	12,354	−0.3	0.09	31.3
41 and over	287	45.5	13,058.5	9.7	94.09	27,003.8
	$n = \Sigma f = 895$		$\Sigma xf = 32,042.5$			$\Sigma (x - \bar{x})^2 f = 54,619$

$\bar{x} = \dfrac{\Sigma xf}{n} = \dfrac{32,042.5}{895} \approx 35.80$

$s^2 = \dfrac{\Sigma (x - \bar{x})^2 \cdot f}{n - 1} = \dfrac{54,619}{894} \approx 61.1$

$s = \sqrt{61.1} \approx 7.82$

11.

Class	f	x	xf	$x - \bar{x}$	$(x - \bar{x})^2$	$(x - \bar{x})^2 f$
8.6–12.5	15	10.55	158.25	−5.05	25.502	382.537
12.6–16.5	20	14.55	291.00	−1.05	1.102	22.050
16.6–20.5	5	18.55	92.75	2.95	8.703	43.513
20.6–24.5	7	22.55	157.85	6.95	48.303	338.118
24.6–28.5	3	26.55	79.65	10.95	119.903	359.708
	$n = \Sigma f = 50$		$x \quad f$			$\Sigma (x - \bar{x})^2 f = 1145.9$

$\bar{x} = \dfrac{\Sigma xf}{n} = \dfrac{779.5}{50} \approx 15.6$

$s^2 = \dfrac{\Sigma (x - \bar{x})^2 f}{n - 1} = \dfrac{1145.9}{49} \approx 23.4$

$s = \sqrt{23.4} \approx 4.8$

Section 3.3

1. 82% or more of the scores were at or below her score. 100% − 82% = 18% or less of the scores were above her score. Note: This answer is correct, but it relies on a more precise definition than that given in the text on page 124. An adequate answer, matching the definition in the text would be: 82% of the scores were at or below her score, and (100 − 82)% = 18% of the scores were at or above her score.

3. No, the score 82 might have a percentile rank less than 70.

5. Order the data from smallest to largest.

$$\text{Lowest value} = 2$$
$$\text{Highest value} = 42$$

There are 20 data values.

$$\text{Median} = \frac{23 + 23}{2} = 23$$

There are 10 values less than the Q_2 position and 10 values greater than the Q_2 position.

$$Q_1 = \frac{8 + 11}{2} = 9.5$$

$$Q_3 = \frac{28 + 29}{2} = 28.5$$

$$IQR = Q_3 - Q_1 = 28.5 - 9.5 = 19$$

Nurses' Length of Employment (months)

7. **(a)**
$$\text{Lowest value} = 17$$
$$\text{Highest value} = 38$$

There are 50 data values.

$$\text{Median} = \frac{24 + 24}{2} = 24$$

There are 25 values above and 25 values below the Q_2 position.

$$Q_1 = 22$$
$$Q_3 = 27$$
$$IQR = 27 - 22 = 5$$

Bachelor's Degree Percentage by State

(b) 26% is in the 3rd quartile, since it is between the median and Q_3.

9. (a) California has the lowest premium since its left whisker is farthest to the left. Pennsylvania has the highest premium since its right whisker is farthest to the right.

(b) Pennsylvania has the highest median premium since its line in the middle of the box is farthest to the right.

(c) California has the smallest range of premiums since the distance between the ends of the whiskers is the smallest. Texas has the smallest interquartile range since the distance between the ends of the boxes is the smallest.

(d) Based on the answers to (a)-(c) above, we can determine that part (a) of Figure 3-9 is for Texas, part (b) of Figure 3-9 is for Pennsylvania, and part (c) of Figure 3-9 is for California.

Chapter 3 Review

1. (a) $\bar{x} = \dfrac{\sum x}{n} = \dfrac{876}{8} = 109.5$

$$s = \sqrt{\dfrac{\sum (x - \bar{x})^2}{n-1}} = \sqrt{\dfrac{7044}{7}} = \sqrt{1006.3} \approx 31.7$$

$$CV = \dfrac{s}{\bar{x}} \cdot 100 = \dfrac{31.7}{109.5} \cdot 100 \approx 28.9\%$$

range = maximum value − minimum value
$$= 142 - 73 = 69$$

(b) $\bar{x} = \dfrac{\sum x}{n} = \dfrac{881}{8} = 110.125$

$$s = \sqrt{\dfrac{\sum (x - \bar{x})^2}{n-1}} = \sqrt{\dfrac{358.87}{7}} \approx 7.2$$

$$CV = \dfrac{s}{\bar{x}} \cdot 100 = \dfrac{7.2}{110.125} \cdot 100 \approx 6.5\%$$

range = maximum value − minimum value
$$= 120 - 100 = 20$$

(c) The means are about the same. The first distribution has greater spread. The standard deviation, *CV*, and range for the first set of measurements are greater than those for the second set of measurements.

3. (a)

$$\text{Lowest value} = 31$$
$$\text{Highest value} = 68$$

There are 60 data values.

$$\text{Median} = \frac{45+45}{2} = 45$$

There are 30 values above and 30 values below the Q_2 position.

$$Q_1 = \frac{40+40}{2} = 40$$

$$Q_3 = \frac{52+53}{2} = 52.5$$

$$IQR = 52.5 - 40 = 12.5$$

Percentage of Democratic Vote
by Counties in Georgia

(b) Class width = 8

Class	x Midpoint	f	xf	$x^2 f$
31–38	34.5	11	379.5	13,092.8
39–46	42.5	24	1020	43,350.0
47–54	50.5	15	757.5	38,253.8
55–62	58.5	7	409.5	23,955.8
63–70	66.5	3	199.5	13,266.8
		$n = \sum f = 60$	$\sum xf = 2766$	$\sum x^2 f = 131,919$

$$\bar{x} = \frac{\sum xf}{n} = \frac{2766}{60} = 46.1$$

$$s = \sqrt{\frac{\sum x^2 f - \frac{(\sum xf)^2}{n}}{n-1}} = \sqrt{\frac{131,919 - \frac{(2766)^2}{60}}{59}} = \sqrt{\frac{4406.4}{59}} \approx 8.64$$

$$\bar{x} - 2s = 46.1 - 2(8.64) = 28.82$$
$$\bar{x} + 2s = 46.1 + 2(8.64) = 63.38$$

We expect at least 75% of the data to fall in the interval 28.82 to 63.38.

(c) $\bar{x} = 46.15,\ s \approx 8.63$

5. Mean weight $= \dfrac{2500}{16} = 156.25$

The mean weight is 156.25 lb.

7. (a) No; 77% is an average, which is not a guarantee that it will be this value for each college graduate.

   (b) $\bar{x} - 2s = 40,478 - 2(8,500) = 23,478$

   $\bar{x} + 2s = 40,478 + 2(8,500) = 57,478$

   We expect at least 75% of the earnings to fall in the interval \$23,478 to \$57,478.

   (c) Weighted average $= \dfrac{\Sigma xw}{\Sigma w}$

   $= \dfrac{\begin{array}{c}3500(0.51) + 6000(0.21) + 10,000(0.06) + 14,000(0.08)\\ + 18,000(0.07) + 25,000(0.07)\end{array}}{1}$

   $= 7775$

   The weighted average is \$7,775.

9. Weighted average $= \dfrac{\Sigma xw}{\Sigma w}$

   $= \dfrac{5(2) + 8(3) + 7(3) + 9(5) + 7(3)}{2 + 3 + 3 + 5 + 3}$

   $= \dfrac{121}{16}$

   ≈ 7.56

Chapter 4 Correlation and Regression

Section 4.1

1. **(a)** The points seem close to a straight line, so there is moderate linear correlation.

   (b) No straight line is realistically a good fit, so there is no linear correlation.

   (c) The points seem very close to a straight line, so there is high linear correlation.

3. **(a)** No. The correlation coefficient is a mathematical tool for measuring the strength of a linear relationship between two variables. As such, it makes no implication about cause or effect. Just because two variables tend to increase or decrease together does not mean a change in one is *causing* a change in the other. A strong correlation between x and y is sometimes due to other (either known or unknown) variables. Such variables are called *lurking variables*.

   (b) Increasing population might be a lurking variable causing both variables to increase.

5. **(a)** No. The correlation coefficient is a mathematical tool for measuring the strength of a linear relationship between two variables. As such, it makes no implication about cause or effect. Just because two variables tend to increase or decrease together does not mean a change in one is *causing* a change in the other. A strong correlation between x and y is sometimes due to other (either known or unknown) variables. Such variables are called *lurking variables*.

   (b) One lurking variable for average annual income increases is inflation. Better training might be a lurking variable responsible for short times to run the mile.

7. **(a)** Ages and Average Weights of Shetland Ponies

Draw the line you think fits best. (Method to find equation is in Section 4.2.)

   (b) Since the points are very close to a straight line, the correlation is strong and positive (since it goes up from left to right).

   (c) $r = \dfrac{n\sum xy - (\sum x)(\sum y)}{\sqrt{n\sum x^2 - (\sum x)^2}\,\sqrt{n\sum y^2 - (\sum y)^2}} = \dfrac{5(9930) - (63)(650)}{\sqrt{5(1089) - (63)^2}\,\sqrt{5(95,350) - (650)^2}} \approx 0.972$

   Since r is positive, y should increase as x increases.

9. (a) Lowest Barometric Pressure and Maximum Wind Speed for Tropical Cyclones

Draw the line you think fits best. (Method to find equation is in Section 4.2.)

(b) Since the points are very close to a straight line, the correlation is strong and negative (since it goes down from left to right).

(c) $r = \dfrac{n\sum xy - (\sum x)(\sum y)}{\sqrt{n\sum x^2 - (\sum x)^2}\sqrt{n\sum y^2 - (\sum y)^2}} = \dfrac{6(556,315) - (5823)(580)}{\sqrt{6(5,655,779) - (5823)^2}\sqrt{6(65,750) - (580)^2}} \approx -0.990$

Since r is negative, y should decrease as x increases.

11. (a) Body Diameter and Height of Prehistoric Pottery

Draw the line you think fits best. (Method to find equation is in Section 4.2.)

(b) Since the points are fairly close to a straight line, the correlation is moderate and positive (since it goes up from left to right).

(c) $r = \dfrac{n\sum xy - (\sum x)(\sum y)}{\sqrt{n\sum x^2 - (\sum x)^2}\sqrt{n\sum y^2 - (\sum y)^2}} = \dfrac{9(1897.19) - (123.1)(94.6)}{\sqrt{9(2452.45) - (123.1)^2}\sqrt{9(1584.3) - (94.6)^2}} \approx 0.896$

Since r is positive, y should increase as x increases.

13. (a)   Unit Length on *y* Same as That on *x*

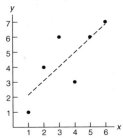

(b)   Unit Length on *y* Twice That on *x*

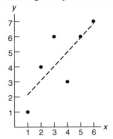

(c)   Unit Length on *y* Half That on *x*

(d) Draw the lines you think best fit the data points.
Stretching the scale on the *y*-axis makes the line appear steeper. Shrinking the scale on the *y*-axis makes the line appear flatter. Or, shrinking the scale on the *y*-axis makes the line appear flatter. The slope of the line does not change. Only the appearance (visual impression) of slope changes as the scale of the *y*-axis changes.

15. (a) $r \approx 0.972$ with $n = 5$
Since $|0.972| = 0.972 \geq 0.88$ for $\alpha = 0.05$, r is significant for this α. For this α, we conclude that age and weight of Shetland ponies are correlated.

(b) $r \approx -0.990$ with $n = 6$
Since $|-0.990| = 0.990 \geq 0.92$ for $\alpha = 0.01$, r is significant for $\alpha = 0.01$.
For this α, we conclude that the lowest barometric pressure reading and maximum wind speed for cyclones are correlated.

Section 4.2

Note: In this section and the next two, answers may vary slightly, depending on how many significant digits are used throughout the calculations.

1. (a)

Number of Jobs (in hundreds)

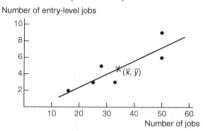

(b) Use a calculator to verify.

(c) $\bar{x} = \dfrac{\sum x}{n} = \dfrac{202}{6} \approx 33.67$ jobs

$\bar{y} = \dfrac{\sum y}{n} = \dfrac{28}{6} \approx 4.67$ entry-level jobs

$b = \dfrac{n\sum xy - (\sum x)(\sum y)}{n\sum x^2 - (\sum x)^2} = \dfrac{6(1096) - (202)(28)}{6(7754) - (202)^2} \approx 0.161$

$a = \bar{y} - b\bar{x} \approx 4.67 - (0.161)(33.67) \approx -0.748$

$\hat{y} = a + bx$ or $\hat{y} \approx -0.748 + 0.161x$

(d) See figure of part (a).

(e) $r^2 = (0.860)^2 \approx 0.740$

This means that 74.0% of the variation in y = number of entry-level jobs can be explained by the corresponding variation in x = total number of jobs using the least squares line.
100% − 74.0% = 26.0% of the variation is unexplained.

(f) Use $x = 40$.

$\hat{y} = -0.748 + 0.161(40)$

$\hat{y} = 5.69$ entry-level jobs

3. (a) Weight of Cars and Gasoline Mileage

(b) Use a calculator to verify.

(c) $\bar{x} = \dfrac{\sum x}{n} = \dfrac{299}{8} = 37.375$

$\bar{y} = \dfrac{\sum y}{n} = \dfrac{167}{8} = 20.875$

$b = \dfrac{n\sum xy - (\sum x)(\sum y)}{n\sum x^2 - (\sum x)^2} = \dfrac{8(5814) - (299)(167)}{8(11,887) - (167)^2} \approx -0.6007$

$a = \bar{y} - b\bar{x} = 20.875 - (-0.6007)(37.375) \approx 43.326$

$\hat{y} = a + bx$ or $\hat{y} = 43.326 - 0.6007x$

(d) See figure of part (a).

(e) $r^2 = (-0.946)^2 \approx 0.895$

This means that 89.5% of the variation in y = miles per gallon can be explained by the corresponding variation in x = weight using the least squares line. $100\% - 89.5\% = 10.5\%$ of the variation is unexplained.

(f) Use $x = 38$.

$\hat{y} = 43.326 - 0.6007(38) = 20.5$ mpg

5. (a) Drivers' Ages and Percent Fatal Accidents Due to Speeding

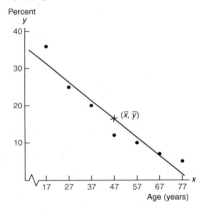

(b) Use a calculator to verify.

(c) $\bar{x} = \dfrac{\sum x}{n} = \dfrac{329}{7} = 47$ years

$\bar{y} = \dfrac{\sum y}{n} = \dfrac{115}{7} \approx 16.43\%$

$b = \dfrac{n\sum xy - (\sum x)(\sum y)}{n\sum x^2 - (\sum x)^2} = \dfrac{7(4015) - (329)(115)}{7(18,263) - (329)^2} \approx -0.496$

$a = \bar{y} - b\bar{x} \approx 16.43 - (-0.496)(47) \approx 39.761$

$\hat{y} = a + bx$ or $\hat{y} = 39.761 - 0.496x$

(d) See figure of part (a).

(e) $r^2 = (-0.959)^2 \approx 0.920$

This means that 92% of the variation in y = percentage of all fatal accidents due to speeding can be explained by the corresponding variation in x = age in years of a licensed automobile driver using the least squares line. $100\% - 92\% = 8\%$ of the variation is unexplained.

(f) Use $x = 25$.
$\hat{y} = 39.761 - 0.496(25) \approx 27.36\%$

7. (a) Cultural Affiliation and Elevation of Archaeological Sites

(b) Use a calculator to verify.

(c) $\bar{x} = \dfrac{\sum x}{n} = \dfrac{31.25}{5} = 6.25$

$\bar{y} = \dfrac{\sum y}{n} = \dfrac{164}{5} = 32.8$

$b = \dfrac{n\sum xy - (\sum x)(\sum y)}{n\sum x^2 - (\sum x)^2} = \dfrac{5(1080) - (31.25)(164)}{5(197.813) - (31.25)^2} = 22.0$

$a = \bar{y} - b\bar{x} = 32.8 - 22.0(6.25) = -104.5$

$\hat{y} = a + bx$ or $\hat{y} = -104.7 + 22.0x$

(d) See figure of part (a).

(e) $r^2 = (0.913)^2 \approx 0.833$

This means that 83.3% of the variation in y = % unidentified artifacts can be explained by the corresponding variation in x = elevation. $100\% - 83.3\% = 16.7\%$ of the variation is unexplained.

(f) Use $x = 6.5$.
$\hat{y} = -104.7 + 22.0(6.5) = 38.3$ percent

9. (a) Yes. The pattern of residuals appears randomly scattered around the horizontal line at 0.

(b) No. There do not appear to be any outliers.

11. (a) Result checks.

(b) Result checks.

(c) Yes.

(d) $y = 0.143 + 1.071x$

$$y - 0.143 = 1.071x$$

$$\frac{y - 0.143}{1.071} = x$$

$$\frac{1}{1.071}y - \frac{0.143}{1.071} = x$$

or

$$x = 0.9337y - 0.1335$$

The equation $x = 0.9337y - 0.1335$ does not match part (b), with the symbols x and y exchanged.

(e) In general, switching x and y values produces a different least-squares equation. It is important that when you perform a linear regression, you know which variable is the explanatory variable and which is the response variable.

Chapter 4 Review

1. (a)   Age and Mortality Rate for Bighorn Sheep

(b) $\bar{x} = \dfrac{\sum x}{n} = \dfrac{15}{5} = 3$

$\bar{y} = \dfrac{\sum y}{n} = \dfrac{86.9}{5} = 17.38$

$b = \dfrac{n\sum xy - \left(\sum x\right)\left(\sum y\right)}{n\sum x^2 - \left(\sum x\right)^2} = \dfrac{5(273.4) - (15)(86.9)}{5(55) - (15)^2} = 1.27$

$a = \bar{y} - b\bar{x} = 17.38 - 1.27(3) = 13.57$

$y = a + bx$ or $y = 13.57 + 1.27x$

(c) $r = \dfrac{n\sum xy - \left(\sum x\right)\left(\sum y\right)}{\sqrt{n\sum x^2 - \left(\sum x\right)^2}\sqrt{n\sum y^2 - \left(\sum y\right)^2}} = \dfrac{5(273.4) - (15)(86.9)}{\sqrt{5(55) - (15)^2}\sqrt{5(1544.73) - (86.9)^2}} \approx 0.685$

$r^2 = (0.685)^2 \approx 0.469$

The correlation coefficient r measures the strength of the linear relationship between a bighorn sheep's age and the mortality rate. The coefficient of determination r^2 means that 46.9% of the variation in y = mortality rate in this age groups can be explained by the corresponding variation in x = age of a bighorn sheep using the least squares line.

3. (a) Weight of One-Year-Old versus
Weight of Adult
Adult Weight (Pounds)

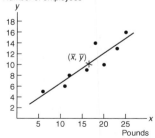

(b) $\bar{x} = \dfrac{\sum x}{n} = \dfrac{300}{14} = 21.43$

$\bar{y} = \dfrac{\sum y}{n} = \dfrac{1775}{14} = 126.79$

$b = \dfrac{n\sum xy - (\sum x)(\sum y)}{n\sum x^2 - (\sum x)^2} = \dfrac{14(38,220) - (300)(1775)}{14(6572) - (300)^2} \approx 1.285$

$a = \bar{y} - b\bar{x} = 126.79 - (1.285)(21.43) = 99.25$

$\hat{y} = a + bx$ or $\hat{y} = 99.25 + 1.285x$

See the figure in part (a).

(c) $r = \dfrac{n\sum xy - (\sum x)(\sum y)}{\sqrt{n\sum x^2 - (\sum x)^2}\sqrt{n\sum y^2 - (\sum y)^2}} = \dfrac{14(38,220) - (300)(1775)}{\sqrt{14(6572) - (300)^2}\sqrt{14(226,125) - (1775)^2}} \approx 0.468$

$r^2 = (0.468)^2 \approx 0.219$

The coefficient of determination r^2 means that 21.9% of the variation in y = weight of a mature adult (30 years old) can be explained by the corresponding variation in x = weight of a 1-year-old baby using the least squares line.

(d) Let $x = 20$.

$\hat{y} = 99.25 + 1.285(20) = 124.95$

The predicted weight is 124.95 pounds.

5. (a) Pounds of Mail versus
Number of Employees
Number of employees

(b) $\bar{x} = \dfrac{\sum x}{n} = \dfrac{131}{8} = 16.375 \approx 16.38$

$\bar{y} = \dfrac{\sum y}{n} = \dfrac{81}{8} = 10.125 \approx 10.13$

$b = \dfrac{n\sum xy - (\sum x)(\sum y)}{n\sum x^2 - (\sum x)^2} = \dfrac{8(1487) - (131)(81)}{8(2435) - (131)^2} \approx 0.554118 \approx 0.554$

$a = \bar{y} - b\bar{x} = 10.125 - 0.554118(16.375) = 1.051$

$\hat{y} = a + bx$ or $\hat{y} = 1.051 + 0.554x$

See the figure in part (a).

(c) $r = \dfrac{n\sum xy - (\sum x)(\sum y)}{\sqrt{n\sum x^2 - (\sum x)^2}\sqrt{n\sum y^2 - (\sum y)^2}} = \dfrac{8(1487) - (131)(81)}{\sqrt{8(2435) - (131)^2}\sqrt{8(927) - (81)^2}} \approx 0.913$

$r^2 = (0.913)^2 \approx 0.833$

The coefficient of determination r^2 means that 83.3% of the variation in y = number of employees can be explained by the corresponding variation in x = weight of incoming mail using the least squares line.

(d) Use $x = 15$.

$\hat{y} = 1.051 + 0.554(15) = 9.36$

About 9 or 10 employees should be assigned mail duty.

Chapter 5 Elementary Probability Theory

Section 5.1

1. Answers vary. Probability is a number between 0 and 1, inclusive, that expresses the likelihood that a specific event will occur. Three ways to find or assign a probability to an event are (1) through intuition (subjective probability), (2) by considering the long-term relative frequency of recurrence of an event in repeated independent trials (empirical probability), and (3) by computing the ratio of the number of favorable outcomes to the total number of possible outcomes, assuming all outcomes are equally likely (classical probability).

3. These are not probabilities: (b) because it is greater than 1, (d) because it is less than zero (negative), (h) 150% = 1.50, because it is greater than 1.

5. Answers vary. The result is a sample, although not necessarily a good one, showing the relative frequency of people able to wiggle their ears.

7. (a) $P(\text{no similar preferences}) = P(0) = \dfrac{15}{375}$, $P(1) = \dfrac{71}{375}$, $P(2) = \dfrac{124}{375}$, $P(3) = \dfrac{131}{375}$, $P(4) = \dfrac{34}{375}$

   (b) $\dfrac{15 + 71 + 124 + 131 + 34}{375} = \dfrac{375}{375} = 1$, yes

   Personality types were classified into 4 main preferences; all possible numbers of shared preferences were considered. The sample space is 0, 1, 2, 3, and 4 shared preferences.

9. (a) Note: "includes the left limit but not the right limit" means 6 A.M. $\le$ time $t <$ noon, noon $\le t < 6$ P.M., 6 P.M. $\le t <$ midnight, midnight $\le t < 6$ A.M. $P(\text{best idea 6 A.M.–12 noon}) = \dfrac{290}{966} \approx 0.30$; $P(\text{best idea 12 noon–6 P.M.}) = \dfrac{135}{966} \approx 0.14$; $P(\text{best idea 6 P.M.–12 midnight}) \dfrac{319}{966} \approx 0.33$; $P(\text{best idea from 12 midnight to 6 A.M.}) = \dfrac{222}{966} \approx 0.23$.

   (b) The probabilities add up to 1. They should add up to 1 provided that the intervals do not overlap and each inventor chose only one interval. The sample space is the set of four time intervals.

11. Make a table showing the information known about the 127 people who walked by the store: [Example 6 in Section 5.2 uses this technique.]

	Buy	Did not buy	Row Total
Came into the store	25	$58 - 25 = 33$	58
Did not come in	0	69	$127 - 58 = 69$
Column Total	25	102	127

If 58 came in, 69 didn't; 25 of the 58 bought something, so 33 came in but didn't buy anything. Those who did not come in, couldn't buy anything. The row entries must sum to the row totals; the column entries must sum to the column totals; and the row totals, as well as the column totals, must sum to the overall total, i.e., the 127 people who walked by the store. Also, the four inner cells must sum to the overall total: $25 + 33 + 0 + 69 = 127$.

This kind of problem relies on formula (2), $P(\text{event } A) = \dfrac{\text{number outcomes favorable to } A}{\text{total number of outcomes}}$. The "trick" is to decide what belongs in the denominator *first*. If the denominator is a row total, stay in that row. If the denominator is a column total, stay in that column. If the denominator is the overall total, the numerator can be a row total, a column total, or the number in any one of the four "cells" inside the table.

(a) total outcomes: people walking by, overall total, 127
favorable outcomes: enter the store, row total, 58 (that's all we know about them)
$$P(A) = \frac{58}{127} \approx 0.46$$

(b) total outcomes: people who walk into the store, row total 58
favorable outcomes: staying in the row, those who buy: 25
$$P(A) = \frac{25}{58} \approx 0.43$$

(c) total outcomes: people walking by, overall total 127
favorable outcomes: people coming in *and* buying, the cell at the *intersection* of the "coming in" row and the "buying" column (the upper left corner), 25 (Recall from set theory that "and" means both things happen, that the two sets *intersect*: >)
$$P(A) = \frac{25}{127} \approx 0.20$$

(d) total outcomes: people coming into the store, row total, 58
favorable outcomes: staying in the row, those who do not buy, 33
$$P(A) = \frac{33}{58} \approx 0.57$$

$$\left(\text{alternate method: this is the complement to (b): } P(A) = 1 - \frac{25}{58} = \frac{33}{58} \approx 0.57 \right)$$

Section 5.2

1. (a) Green and blue are mutually exclusive because each M&M candy is only 1 color.
$P(\text{green } or \text{ blue}) = P(\text{green}) + P(\text{blue}) = 10\% + 10\% = 20\% = 0.20$

(b) Yellow and red are mutually exclusive, again, because each candy is only one color, and if the candy is yellow, it can't be red, too.
$P(\text{yellow } or \text{ red}) = P(\text{yellow}) + P(\text{red}) = 20\% + 20\% = 40\% = 0.40$

(c) It is faster here to use the complementary event rule than to add up the probabilities of all the colors except purple.
$P(not \text{ purple}) = 1 - P(\text{purple}) = 1 - 0.20 = 0.80$, or 80%

3. (a) Mutually exclusive: $P(\text{green } or \text{ blue}) = P(\text{green}) + P(\text{blue}) = 16.6\% + 16.6\% = 33.2\% = 0.332$

(b) Mutually exclusive: $P(\text{yellow } or \text{ red}) = P(\text{yellow}) + P(\text{red}) = 16.6\% + 16.6\% = 33.2\% = 0.332$

(c) $P(not \text{ purple}) = 1 - P(\text{purple}) = 1 - 0 = 1$ (there is no purple)
Since the color distributions differ for plain and caramel M&Ms, if the answers were the same, it would only be by coincidence.

Hint for Problems 5–7: Refer to Figure 5–2 if necessary. (Without loss of generality, let the red die be the first die and the green die be the second die in Figure 5–2.) Think of the outcomes as an (x, y) ordered pair. Then, without loss of generality, $(1, 6)$ means 1 on the red die and 6 on the green die. (We are "ordering" the dice for convenience only – which is first and which is second have no bearing on this problem.) The only important fact is that they are distinguishable outcomes, so that (1 on red, 2 on green) is different from (2 on red, 1 on green).

5. (a) Yes, the outcome of the red die does not influence the outcome of the green die.

(b) $P(5 \text{ on green } and \text{ 3 on red}) = P(5 \text{ on green}) \cdot P(3 \text{ on red}) = \left(\frac{1}{6}\right)\left(\frac{1}{6}\right) = \frac{1}{36} \approx 0.028$ because they are independent.

(c) $P(3 \text{ on green } and \text{ 5 on red}) = P(3 \text{ on green}) \cdot P(5 \text{ on red}) = \left(\frac{1}{6}\right)\left(\frac{1}{6}\right) = \frac{1}{36} \approx 0.028$

(d) $P[(5 \text{ on green } and \text{ 3 on red}) \text{ or } (3 \text{ on green } and \text{ 5 on red})]$
$= P(5 \text{ on green } and \text{ 3 on red}) + P(3 \text{ on green } and \text{ 5 on red})]$
$= \frac{1}{36} + \frac{1}{36} = \frac{2}{36} = \frac{1}{18} \approx 0.056$ [because they are mutually exclusive outcomes]

7. (a) $1 + 5 = 6, 2 + 4 = 6, 3 + 3 = 6, 4 + 2 = 6, 5 + 1 = 6$
$P(\text{sum} = 6) = P[(1, 5) \text{ or } (2, 4) \text{ or } (3 \text{ on red, 3 on green}) \text{ or } (4, 2) \text{ or } (5, 1)]$
$= P(1, 5) + P(2, 4) + P(3, 3) + P(4, 2) + P(5, 1)$
since the (red, green) outcomes are mutually exclusive
$= \left(\frac{1}{6}\right)\left(\frac{1}{6}\right) + \left(\frac{1}{6}\right)\left(\frac{1}{6}\right) + \left(\frac{1}{6}\right)\left(\frac{1}{6}\right) + \left(\frac{1}{6}\right)\left(\frac{1}{6}\right) + \left(\frac{1}{6}\right)\left(\frac{1}{6}\right)$
because the red die outcome is independent of the green die outcome
$= \frac{1}{36} + \frac{1}{36} + \frac{1}{36} + \frac{1}{36} + \frac{1}{36} = \frac{5}{36}$

(b) $1 + 3 = 4, 2 + 2 = 4, 3 + 1 = 4$
$P(\text{sum is } 4) = P[(1, 3) \text{ or } (2, 2) \text{ or } (3, 1)]$
$= P(1, 3) + P(2, 2) + P(3, 1)$
because the (red, green) outcomes are mutually exclusive
$= \left(\frac{1}{6}\right)\left(\frac{1}{6}\right) + \left(\frac{1}{6}\right)\left(\frac{1}{6}\right) + \left(\frac{1}{6}\right)\left(\frac{1}{6}\right)$
because the red die outcome is independent of the green die outcome
$= \frac{1}{36} + \frac{1}{36} + \frac{1}{36} = \frac{3}{36} = \frac{1}{12}$

(c) Since a sum of six can't simultaneously be a sum of four, these are mutually exclusive events;
$P(\text{sum of 6 } or \text{ 4}) = P(\text{sum of 6}) + P(\text{sum of 4}) = \frac{5}{36} + \frac{3}{36} = \frac{8}{36} = \frac{2}{9}$

9. (a) No, the key idea here is "without replacement," which means the draws are dependent, because the outcome of the second card drawn depends on what the first card drawn was. Let the card draws be represented by an (x, y) ordered pair. For example, (K, 6) means the first card drawn was a king and the second card drawn was a 6. Here the order of the cards is important.

(b) $P(\text{ace on 1st } and \text{ king on second}) = P(\text{ace, king}) = \left(\frac{4}{52}\right)\left(\frac{4}{51}\right) = \frac{16}{2652} = \frac{4}{663}$

There are 4 aces and 4 kings in the deck. Once the first card is drawn and not replaced, there are only 51 cards left to draw from, but all the kings are still there.

(c) $P(\text{king, ace}) = \left(\dfrac{4}{52}\right)\left(\dfrac{4}{51}\right) = \dfrac{16}{2652} = \dfrac{4}{663}$

There are 4 kings and 4 aces in the deck. Once the first card is drawn and not replaced, there are only 51 cards left to draw from, but all the aces are still there.

(d) $P(\text{ace } and \text{ king in either order})$
$= P[(\text{ace, king}) \ or \ (\text{king, ace})]$
$= P(\text{ace, king}) + P(\text{king, ace})$ because these two outcomes are mutually exclusive
$= \dfrac{16}{2652} + \dfrac{16}{2652} = \dfrac{32}{2652} = \dfrac{8}{663}$

11. **(a)** Yes; the key idea here is "with replacement." When the first card drawn is replaced, the sample space is the same when the second card is drawn as it was when the first card was drawn and the second card is in no way influenced by the outcome of the first draw; in fact, it is possible to draw the same card twice. Let the card draws be represented by an (x, y) ordered pair; for example $(K, 6)$ means a king was drawn first, replaced, and then the second card, a "6," was drawn independently of the first.

(b) $P(A, K) = P(A) \cdot P(K)$ because they are independent
$= \left(\dfrac{4}{52}\right)\left(\dfrac{4}{52}\right) = \dfrac{16}{2704} = \dfrac{1}{169}$

(c) $P(K, A) = P(K) \cdot P(A)$ because they are independent
$= \left(\dfrac{4}{52}\right)\left(\dfrac{4}{52}\right) = \dfrac{16}{2704} = \dfrac{1}{169}$

(d) $P[(A, K) \ or \ (K, A)] = P(A, K) + P(K, A)$ since the 2 outcomes are mutually exclusive when we consider the order
$= \dfrac{1}{169} + \dfrac{1}{169} = \dfrac{2}{169}$

13. **(a)** $P(6 \ or \ \text{older}) = P[(6 \text{ to } 9) \ or \ (10 \text{ to } 12) \ or \ (13 \text{ and over})]$
$= P(6-9) + P(10-12) + P(13+)$ because they are mutually exclusive age groups-no child is both 7 and 11 years old.
$= 27\% + 14\% + 22\% = 63\% = 0.63$

(b) $P(12 \text{ or younger}) = 1 - P(13 \text{ and over}) = 1 - 0.22 = 0.78$

(c) $P(\text{between 6 and 12}) = P[(6 \text{ to } 9) \ or \ (10 \text{ to } 12)]$
$= P(6 \text{ to } 9) + P(10 \text{ to } 12)$ because the age groups are mutually exclusive
$= 27\% + 14\% = 41\% = 0.41$

(d) $P(\text{between 3 and 9}) = P[(3 \text{ to } 5) \ or \ (6 \text{ to } 9)]$
$= P(3 \text{ to } 5) + P(6 \text{ to } 9)$ because age categories are mutually exclusive
$= 22\% + 27\% = 49\% = 0.49$

Answers vary; however, category 10–12 years covers only 3 years while 13 and over covers many more years and many more people, including adults who buy toys for themselves.

15. What we know: $P(\text{polygraph says "lying" when person is lying}) = 72\%$
$P(\text{polygraph says "lying" when person is not lying}) = 7\%$
Let L denote that the polygraph results show lying and *not* L denote that the polygraph results show the person is not lying. Let T denote that the person is telling the truth and let *not* T denote that the person is not telling the truth, so

$P(\text{L, } given \ not \ \text{T}) = 72\%$
$P(\text{L, } given \ \text{T}) = 7\%.$

We are told whether the person is telling the truth or not; what we know is what the polygraph results are, given the case where the person tells the truth, and given the situation where the person is not telling the truth.

(a) $P(T) = 0.90$ so $P(not\ T) = 0.10$

     P(polygraph says lying and person tells truth)

         $= P(L\ and\ T) = P(T) \cdot P(L,\ given\ T)$

         $= (0.90)(0.07) = 0.063 = 6.3\%$

(b) $P(not\ T) = 0.10$ so $P(T) = 0.90$

     P(polygraph says lying and person is not telling the truth)

         $= P(L\ and\ not\ T) = P(not\ T) \cdot P(L,\ given\ not\ T)$

         $= (0.10)(0.72) = 0.072 = 7.2\%$

(c) $P(T) = P(not\ T) = 0.50$

     (a) $P(L\ and\ T) = P(T) \cdot P(L,\ given\ T)$

           $= (0.50)(0.07) = 0.035 = 3.5\%$

     (b) $P(L\ and\ not\ T) = P(not\ T) \cdot P(L,\ given\ not\ T)$

           $= (0.50)(0.72) = 0.36 = 36\%$

(d) $P(T) = 0.15$ so $P(not\ T) = 1 - P(T) = 1 - 0.15 = 0.85$

     (a) $P(L\ and\ T) = P(T) \cdot P(L,\ given\ T)$

           $= (0.15)(0.07) = 0.0105 = 1.05\%$

     (b) $P(L\ and\ not\ T) = P(not\ T) \cdot P(L,\ given\ not\ T)$

           $= (0.85)(0.72) = 0.612 = 61.2\%$

17. Let C denote the condition is present, and *not* C denote the condition is absent.

     (a) $P(+,\ given\ C) = \dfrac{72}{154}$ (stay in C column)

     (b) $P(-,\ given\ C) = \dfrac{82}{154}$ (stay in C column)

     (c) $P(-,\ given\ not\ C) = \dfrac{79}{116}$ (stay in *not* C column)

     (d) $P(+,\ given\ not\ C) = \dfrac{37}{116}$ (stay in *not* C column)

     (e) $P(C\ and\ +) = P(C) \cdot P(+,\ given\ C) = \left(\dfrac{154}{270}\right)\left(\dfrac{72}{154}\right) = \dfrac{72}{270}$

     (f) $P(C\ and\ -) = P(C) \cdot P(-,\ given\ C) = \left(\dfrac{154}{270}\right)\left(\dfrac{82}{154}\right) = \dfrac{82}{270}$

19. First determine the denominator. If it is a row or column total, the numerator will be in the body (inside) of the table in that same row or column. If the denominator is the grand total, the numerator can be one or more row totals, one or more column totals, or a body-of-the-table cell entry. A cell entry is usually indicated when the problem mentions both a row category and a column category, in which case the desired cell is the one where the row and column intersect.

     (a) $P(2+) = 1 - P(<2) = 1 - P(1\ visit) = 1 - \dfrac{962}{1894} = \dfrac{932}{1894}$

     There is no additional information about the customer, so the denominator is the grand total.

     (b) $P(2+,\ given\ 25\text{–}39\ years\ old) = 1 - P(<2,\ given\ 25\text{–}39) = 1 - \dfrac{386}{739} = \dfrac{353}{739}$

     The customer's age is given, so the denominator is the 25–39 row total, and the numerator is determined by the numbers in that row, using the complimentary rule for probabilities.

(c) $P(> 3 \text{ visits}) = P(4 \text{ or } 5 \text{ or } 6 \text{ or more visits})$

$$= P(4) + P(5) + P(6+)$$

$$= \frac{66}{1894} + \frac{44}{1894} + \frac{32}{1894} = \frac{142}{1894}$$

There is no qualifier on the customer, so we use the grand total, 1894, as the denominator.

(d) $P(> 3, \text{ given age } 65+) = 1 - P(\le 3, \text{ given } 65+)$

$$= 1 - P[(1, 2, \text{ or } 3 \text{ visits}), \text{ given } 65+]$$

$$= 1 - [P(1 \text{ visit, given } 65+) + P(2 \text{ visits, given } 65+) + P(3 \text{ visits, given } 65+)]$$

$$= 1 - \left(\frac{115}{224} + \frac{69}{224} + \frac{18}{224} \right) = 1 - \frac{202}{224} = \frac{22}{224}$$

Alternately, this can be solved without the complementary event rule:

$P(> 3 \text{ visits, given } 65 \text{ or older}) = P(4 \text{ or } 5 \text{ or } 6 \text{ or more visits, given } 65+)$

$$= P(4, \text{ given } 65+) + P(5, \text{ given } 65+) + P(6 \text{ or more, given } 65+)$$

$$= \frac{12}{224} + \frac{7}{224} + \frac{3}{224} = \frac{22}{224}$$

Here, the complementary event rule has no advantage, work-wise, over the regular method.

(e) $P(40 \text{ or older}) = P(40{-}49 \text{ or } 50{-}64 \text{ or } 65+)$

$$= P(40{-}49) + P(50{-}64) + P(65+)$$

$$= \frac{434}{1894} + \frac{349}{1894} + \frac{224}{1894} = \frac{1007}{1894}$$

(f) $P(40 \text{ or older, given 4 visits}) = P(40{-}49 \text{ or } 50{-}64 \text{ or } 65+ \text{ or over, given 4 visits})$

$$= P(40{-}49, \text{ given } 4) + P(50{-}64, \text{ given } 4) + P(65+, \text{ given } 4)$$

$$= \frac{13}{66} + \frac{14}{66} + \frac{12}{66} = \frac{39}{66}$$

The given 4 visits means the denominator is the 4 visit column total, and the numerator is composed from numbers in that column.

(g) $P(25{-}39 \text{ years old}) = \dfrac{739}{1894} \approx 0.3902$

$P(\text{visits more than once a week}) = 1 - P(\text{visits once}) = 1 - \dfrac{962}{1894} = \dfrac{932}{1894} \approx 0.4921$

$P(\text{visits} > 1, \text{ given } 25{-}39) = 1 - P(1 \text{ visit, given } 25{-}39) = 1 - \dfrac{386}{739} = \dfrac{353}{739} \approx 0.4777$

25–39 years old is independent of more than 1 visit if $P(> 1 \text{ visit}) = P(> 1 \text{ visit, given age } 25{-}39)$ but $0.4921 \ne 0.4777$ so they are not independent.

Section 5.3

1. (a) Outcomes for Tossing a Coin Three Times

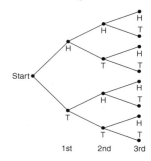

(b) HHT, HTH, THH: 3

(c) 8 possible outcomes, 3 with exactly 2 Hs: $\dfrac{3}{8}$

3. (a) Outcomes for Drawing Two Balls (without replacement)

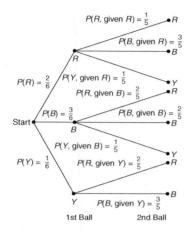

1st Ball   2nd Ball

Because we drew without replacement the number of available balls drops to 5 and one of the colors drops by 1. Note that if the yellow ball is drawn first, there are only two possibilities for the second draw: red and blue; the yellow balls are exhausted.

(b)
$$P(R, R) = \left(\frac{2}{6}\right)\left(\frac{1}{5}\right) = \frac{2}{30} = \frac{1}{15}$$
$$P(R, B) = \left(\frac{2}{6}\right)\left(\frac{3}{5}\right) = \frac{6}{30} = \frac{1}{5}$$
$$P(R, Y) = \left(\frac{2}{6}\right)\left(\frac{1}{5}\right) = \frac{2}{30} = \frac{1}{15}$$
$$P(B, R) = \left(\frac{3}{6}\right)\left(\frac{2}{5}\right) = \frac{6}{30} = \frac{1}{5}$$
$$P(B, B) = \left(\frac{3}{6}\right)\left(\frac{2}{5}\right) = \frac{6}{30} = \frac{1}{5}$$
$$P(B, Y) = \left(\frac{3}{6}\right)\left(\frac{1}{5}\right) = \frac{3}{30} = \frac{1}{10}$$
$$P(Y, R) = \left(\frac{1}{6}\right)\left(\frac{2}{5}\right) = \frac{2}{30} = \frac{1}{15}$$
$$P(Y, B) = \left(\frac{1}{6}\right)\left(\frac{3}{5}\right) = \frac{3}{30} = \frac{1}{10}$$

where $P(x, y)$ is the probability the first ball is color x, and the second ball is color y. Multiply the branch probability values along each branch from start to finish. Observe the sum of the probabilities is 1.

5. 4 wire choices for the first leaves 3 wire choices for the second, 2 for the third, and only 1 wire choice for the fourth wire connection: $4 \cdot 3 \cdot 2 \cdot 1 = 4! = 24.$

7. There are 4 fertilizers to choose from, 3 temperature zones to choose from for each fertilizer, and 3 possible water treatments for every fertilizer-temperature zone combination: $4 \cdot 3 \cdot 3 = 36.$

Problems 9 and 11 deal with permutations, $P_{n,r} = \dfrac{n!}{(n-r)!}$. This counts the number of ways r objects can be selected from n when the order of the result is important. For example, if we choose two people from a group, the first of which is to be the group's chair, and the second, the assistant chair, then (John, Mary) is distinct from (Mary, John).

9. $P_{5,2} : n = 5, r = 2$

$$P_{5,2} = \frac{5!}{(5-2)!} = \frac{5 \cdot 4 \cdot 3 \cdot 2 \cdot 1}{3!} = 20$$

11. $P_{7,7} : n = r = 7$

$$P_{7,7} = \frac{7!}{(7-7)!} = \frac{7!}{0!} = 7! = 5040 \text{ (recall } 0! = 1)$$

In general, $P_{n,n} = \dfrac{n!}{(n-n)!} = \dfrac{n!}{0!} = \dfrac{n!}{1} = n!$.

Problems 13 and 15 deal with combinations, $C_{n,r} = \dfrac{n!}{r!(n-r)!}$. This counts the number of ways r items can be selected from among n items when the order of the result doesn't matter. For example, when choosing two people from an office to pick up coffee and doughnuts, (John, Mary) is the same as (Mary, John) – both get to carry the goodies back to the office.

13. $C_{5,2} : n = 5, r = 2$

$$C_{5,2} = \frac{5!}{2!(5-2)!} = \frac{5!}{2!3!} = \frac{5 \cdot 4 \cdot 3 \cdot 2 \cdot 1}{2 \cdot 1 \cdot 3 \cdot 2 \cdot 1} = \frac{20}{2} = 10$$

15. $C_{7,7} : n = r = 7$

$$C_{7,7} = \frac{7!}{7!(7-7)!} = \frac{7!}{7!0!} = \frac{7!}{7!(1)} = 1 \text{ (recall } 0! = 1)$$

In general, $C_{n,n} = \dfrac{n!}{n!(n-n)!} = \dfrac{n!}{n!0!} = \dfrac{n!}{n!(1)} = 1$. There is only 1 way to choose all n objects without regard to order.

17. Since the order matters (first is day supervisor, second is night supervisor, and third is coordinator), this is a permutation of 15 nurse candidates to fill 3 positions.

$$P_{15,3} = \frac{15!}{(15-3)!} = \frac{15!}{12!} = \frac{15 \cdot 14 \cdot 13 \cdot 12!}{12!} = 2730$$

19. The order of trainee selection doesn't matter, since they are all going to be trained the same.

$$C_{15,5} = \frac{15!}{5!(15-5)!} = \frac{15!}{5!10!} = \frac{15 \cdot 14 \cdot 13 \cdot 12 \cdot 11 \cdot 10!}{5!10!} = \frac{15 \cdot 14 \cdot 13 \cdot 12 \cdot 11}{5 \cdot 4 \cdot 3 \cdot 2 \cdot 1} = 3003$$

21. (a) Six applicants are selected from twelve without regard to order.

$$C_{12,6} = \frac{12!}{6!6!} = \frac{479,001,600}{(720)^2} = 924$$

(b) There are 7 women and 5 men. This problem really asks, in how many ways can 6 women be selected from among 7, and zero men be selected from 5?

$$(C_{7,6})(C_{5,0}) = \left(\frac{7!}{6!(7-6)!}\right)\left(\frac{5!}{0!(5-0)!}\right) = \frac{7!}{6!1!} \cdot \frac{5!}{0!5!} = 7$$

Since the zero men are "selected" be default, all positions being filled. This problem reduces to, in how many ways can 6 applicants be selected from 7 women?

(c) $P(\text{event A}) = \dfrac{\text{number of favorable outcomes}}{\text{total number of outcomes}}$

$P(\text{all hired are women}) = \dfrac{7}{924} = \dfrac{1}{132} \approx 0.008$

Chapter 5 Review

1. $P(\text{asked}) = 24\% = 0.24$
$P(\text{received}, \textit{given} \text{ asked}) = 45\% = 0.45$
$P(\text{asked } \textit{and} \text{ received}) = P(\text{asked}) \cdot P(\text{received}, \textit{given} \text{ asked}) = (0.24)(0.45) = 0.108 = 10.8\%$

3. (a) If the first card is replaced before the second is chosen (sampling with replacement), they are independent. If the sampling is without replacements they are dependent.

(b) $P(\text{heart}) = \dfrac{13}{52} = \dfrac{1}{4}$

with replacement, independent

$P(\text{H on both}) = \left(\dfrac{1}{4}\right)\left(\dfrac{1}{4}\right) = \dfrac{1}{16} = 0.0625 \approx 0.063$

(c) without replacement, dependent

$P(\text{H on first } \textit{and} \text{ H on second}) = \dfrac{13}{52} \cdot \dfrac{12}{51} = \dfrac{156}{2652} \approx 0.059$

5. (a) Throw a large number of similar thumbtacks, or one thumbtack a large number of times, and record the frequency of occurrence of the various outcomes. Assume the thumbtack falls either flat side down (i.e., point up), or tilted (with the point down, resting on the edge of the flat side). (We will assume these are the only two ways the tack can land.)

To estimate the probability the tack lands on its flat side with the point up, find the relative frequency of this occurrence by dividing the number of times this occurred by the total number of thumbtack tosses.

(b) The sample space is the two outcomes flat side down (point up) and tilted (point down).

(c) $P(\text{flat side down, point up}) = \dfrac{340}{500} = 0.68$

$P(\text{tilted, point down}) = 1 - 0.68 = 0.32$

7. (a) possible values for x, the sum of the two dice faces, is 2, 3, 4, 5, 6, 7, 8, 9, 10, 11, and 12

(b) 2:1 and 1
   3:1 and 2, or 2 and 1
   4:1 and 3, 2 and 2, 3 and 1
   5:1 and 4, 2 and 3, 3 and 2, 4 and 1
   6:1 and 5, 2 and 4, 3 and 3, 4 and 2, 5 and 1
   7:1 and 6, 2 and 5, 3 and 4, 4 and 3, 5 and 2, 6 and 1
   8:2 and 6, 3 and 5, 4 and 4, 5 and 3, 6 and 2
   9:3 and 6, 4 and 5, 5 and 4, 6 and 3
   10:4 and 6, 5 and 5, 6 and 4
   11:5 and 6, 6 and 5
   12:6 and 6

x	$P(x)$
2	$\frac{1}{36} \approx 0.028$
3	$\frac{2}{36} \approx 0.056$
4	$\frac{3}{36} \approx 0.083$
5	$\frac{4}{36} \approx 0.111$
6	$\frac{5}{36} \approx 0.139$
7	$\frac{6}{36} \approx 0.167$
8	$\frac{5}{36} \approx 0.139$
9	$\frac{4}{36} \approx 0.111$
10	$\frac{3}{36} \approx 0.083$
11	$\frac{2}{36} \approx 0.056$
12	$\frac{1}{36} \approx 0.028$

Where there are $(6)(6) = 36$ possible, equally likely outcomes (the sums, however, are not equally likely).

9. $C_{8,2} = \dfrac{8!}{2!6!} = \dfrac{8 \cdot 7 \cdot 6!}{(2 \cdot 1)6!} = \dfrac{56}{2} = 28$

11. $3 \cdot 2 \cdot 1 = 6$

13. 5 multiple choice questions, each with 4 possible answers (A, B, C, or D), so 4 answers for first question; and for each of those, 4 answers for the second question; and for each of those, 4 answers for the third question; and for each of those, 4 answers for the fifth question. There are $4 \cdot 4 \cdot 4 \cdot 4 \cdot 4 = 4^5 = 1024$ possible sequences, such as A, D, B, B, C or C, B, A, D, D, etc.

$P(\text{getting the correct sequence}) = \dfrac{1}{1024} \approx 0.00098$

Chapter 6   The Binomial Probability Distribution and Related Topics

Section 6.1

1. **(a)** The number of traffic fatalities can be only a whole number. This is a discrete random variable.

   (b) Distance can assume any value, so this is a continuous random variable.

   (c) Time can take on any value, so this is a continuous random variable.

   (d) The number of ships can be only a whole number. This is a discrete random variable.

   (e) Weight can assume any value, so this is a continuous random variable.

3. **(a)** $\sum P(x) = 0.25 + 0.60 + 0.15 = 1.00$

   Yes, this is a valid probability distribution because a probability is assigned to each distinct value of the random variable and the sum of these probabilities is 1.

   (b) $\sum P(x) = 0.25 + 0.60 + 0.20 = 1.05$

   No, this is not a probability distribution because the probabilities total to more than 1.

5. **(a)** $\sum P(x) = 0.21 + 0.14 + 0.22 + 0.15 + 0.20 + 0.08 = 1.00$

   Yes, this is a valid probability distribution because the events are distinct and the probabilities total to 1.

   (b) Income Distribution ($1000)

   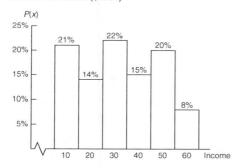

   (c) $\mu = \sum x P(x)$

   $$= 10(0.21) + 20(0.14) + 30(0.22) + 40(0.15) + 50(0.20) + 60(0.08)$$

   $$= 32.3$$

   (d) $\sigma = \sqrt{\sum (x - \mu)^2 \, P(x)}$

   $$= \sqrt{(-22.3)^2 \, (0.21) + (-12.3)^2 \, (0.14) + (-2.3)^2 \, (0.22) + (7.7)^2 \, (0.15) + (17.7)^2 \, (0.20) + (27.7)^2 \, (0.08)}$$

   $$= \sqrt{259.71}$$

   $$\approx 16.12$$

7. $\sum P(x) \neq 1.000$ due to rounding

   (a) $P(1 \text{ or more}) = 1 - P(0)$
   $$= 1 - 0.237$$
   $$= 0.763$$
   This is the complement of the probability that none of the parolees will be repeat offenders.

   (b) $P(2 \text{ or more}) = P(2) + P(3) + P(4) + P(5)$
   $$= 0.264 + 0.088 + 0.015 + 0.001$$
   $$= 0.368$$

   (c) $P(4 \text{ or more}) = P(4) + P(5)$
   $$= 0.015 + 0.001$$
   $$= 0.016$$

   (d) $\mu = \sum xP(x)$
   $$= 0(0.237) + 1(0.396) + 2(0.264) + 3(0.088) + 4(0.015) + 5(0.001)$$
   $$= 1.253$$

   (e) $\sigma = \sqrt{\sum (x - \mu)^2 \, P(x)}$
   $$= \sqrt{\begin{array}{l}(-1.253)^2 (0.237) + (-0.253)^2 (0.396) + (0.747)^2 (0.264) + (1.747)^2 (0.088) \\ + (2.747)^2 (0.015) + (3.747)^2 (0.001)\end{array}}$$
   $$= \sqrt{0.941}$$
   $$\approx 0.97$$

9. **(a)** $P(60 \text{ years}) = 0.01191$
   Expected loss $= \$50,000(0.01191) = \$595.50$
   The expected loss for Big Rock Insurance is $595.50.

   (b)

Probability	Expected Loss
$P(61) = 0.01292$	$\$50,000(0.01292) = \$646$
$P(62) = 0.01396$	$\$50,000(0.01396) = \$698$
$P(63) = 0.01503$	$\$50,000(0.01503) = \$751.50$
$P(64) = 0.01613$	$\$50,000(0.01613) = \$806.50$

   Expected loss $= \$595.50 + \$646 + \$698 + \$751.50 + \$806.50$
   $$= \$3497.50$$
   The total expected loss is $3497.50.

   (c) $\$3497.50 + \$700 = \$4197.50$
   They should charge $4197.50.

   (d) $\$5000 - \$3497.50 = \$1502.50$
   They can expect to make $1502.50.

   Comment: losses are usually denoted by negative numbers such as –$50,000.

Section 6.2

1. A trial is one flip of a fair quarter. Success = head. Failure = tail.
   $n = 3$, $p = 0.5$, $q = 1 - 0.5 = 0.5$

   (a) $P(3) = C_{3,3}(0.5)^3(0.5)^{3-3}$

   $\qquad = 1(0.5)^3(0.5)^0$

   $\qquad = 0.125$

   To find this value in Table 3 of Appendix II, use the group in which $n = 3$, the column headed by $p = 0.5$, and the row headed by $r = 3$.

   (b) $P(2) = C_{3,2}(0.5)^2(0.5)^{3-2}$

   $\qquad = 3(0.5)^2(0.5)^1$

   $\qquad = 0.375$

   To find this value in Table 3 of Appendix II, use the group in which $n = 3$, the column headed by $p = 0.5$, and the row headed by $r = 2$.

   (c) $P(r \geq 2) = P(2) + P(3)$

   $\qquad = 0.125 + 0.375$

   $\qquad = 0.5$

   (d) The probability of getting exactly three tails is the same as getting exactly zero heads.

   $\quad P(0) = C_{3,0}(0.5)^0(0.5)^{3-0}$

   $\qquad = 1(0.5)^0(0.5)^3$

   $\qquad = 0.125$

   To find this value in Table 3 of Appendix II, use the group in which $n = 3$, the column headed by $p = 0.5$, and the row headed by $r = 0$.

   The results from Table 3 of Appendix II are the same.

In the problems that follow, there are often other ways the solve the problems than those shown. As long as you get the same answer, your method is probably correct.

3. **(a)** A trial is a man's response to the question, "Would you marry the same woman again?"
   Success = a positive response. Failure = a negative response.
   $n = 10$, $p = 0.80$, $q = 1 - 0.80 = 0.20$

   Using values in Table 3 of Appendix II:

   $P(r \geq 7) = P(7) + P(8) + P(9) + P(10)$

   $\qquad = 0.201 + 0.302 + 0.268 + 0.107$

   $\qquad = 0.878$

   $P(r \text{ is less than half of } 10) = P(r < 5)$

   $\qquad = P(0) + P(1) + P(2) + P(3) + P(4)$

   $\qquad = 0.000 + 0.000 + 0.000 + 0.001 + 0.006$

   $\qquad = 0.007$

(b) A trial is a woman's response to the question, "Would you marry the same man again?"
Success = a positive response. Failure = a negative response.

$n = 10$, $p = 0.5$, $q = 1 - 0.5 = 0.5$

Using values in Table 3 of Appendix II:

$$P(r \geq 7) = P(7) + P(8) + P(9) + P(10)$$
$$= 0.117 + 0.044 + 0.010 + 0.001$$
$$= 0.172$$
$$P(r < 5) = P(0) + P(1) + P(2) + P(3) + P(4)$$
$$= 0.001 + 0.010 + 0.044 + 0.117 + 0.205$$
$$= 0.377$$

5. A trial consists of a woman's response regarding her mother-in-law. Success = dislike. Failure = like.

$n = 6$, $p = 0.90$, $q = 1 - 0.90 = 0.10$

(a) $P(6) = C_{6,6} (0.90)^6 (0.10)^{6-6}$

$$= 1(0.90)^6 (0.10)^0$$
$$= 0.531$$

(b) $P(0) = C_{6,0} (0.90)^0 (0.10)^{6-0}$

$$= 1(0.90)^0 (0.10)^6$$
$$\approx 0.000 \text{ (to 3 digits)}$$

(c) $P(r \geq 4) = P(4) + P(5) + P(6)$

$$= 0.098 + 0.354 + 0.531$$
$$= 0.983$$

(d) $P(r \leq 3) = 1 - P(r \geq 4)$

$$\approx 1 - 0.983$$
$$= 0.017$$

From the table:

$$P(r \leq 3) = P(0) + P(1) + P(2) + P(3)$$
$$= 0.000 + 0.000 + 0.001 + 0.015$$
$$= 0.016$$

7. A trial consists of taking a polygraph examination. Success = pass. Failure = fail.

$n = 9$, $p = 0.85$, $q = 1 - 0.85 = 0.15$

(a) $P(9) = 0.232$

(b) $P(r \geq 5) = P(5) + P(6) + P(7) + P(8) + P(9)$

$$= 0.028 + 0.107 + 0.260 + 0.368 + 0.232$$
$$= 0.995$$

(c) $P(r \leq 4) = 1 - P(r \geq 5)$

$$= 1 - 0.995$$
$$= 0.005$$

From the table:

$$P(r \leq 4) = P(0) + P(1) + P(2) + P(3) + P(4)$$
$$= 0.000 + 0.000 + 0.000 + 0.001 + 0.005$$
$$= 0.006$$

The two results should be equal, but because of rounding error, they differ slightly.

(d) All students fail is the same as no students pass.

$$P(0) = 0.000 \quad \text{(to 3 digits)}$$

9. A trial is catching and releasing a pike. Success = pike dies. Failure = pike lives.

$$n = 16, \ p = 0.05, \ q = 1 - 0.05 = 0.95$$

(a) $P(0) = 0.440$

(b) $P(r < 3) = P(0) + P(1) + P(2)$
$$= 0.440 + 0.371 + 0.146$$
$$= 0.957$$

(c) All of the fish lived is the same as none of the fish died.

$$P(0) = 0.440$$

(d) More than 14 fish lived is the same as less than 2 fish died.

$$P(r < 2) = P(0) + P(1)$$
$$= 0.440 + 0.371$$
$$= 0.811$$

11. (a) A trial consists of using the Myers-Briggs instrument to determine if a person in marketing is an extrovert. Success = extrovert. Failure = not extrovert.

$$n = 15, \ p = 0.75, \ q = 1 - 0.75 = 0.25$$

$$P(r \geq 10) = P(10) + P(11) + P(12) + P(13) + P(14) + P(15)$$
$$= 0.165 + 0.225 + 0.225 + 0.156 + 0.067 + 0.013$$
$$= 0.851$$

$$P(r \geq 5) = P(5) + P(6) + P(7) + P(8) + P(9) + P(r \geq 10)$$
$$= 0.001 + 0.003 + 0.013 + 0.039 + 0.092 + 0.851$$
$$= 0.999$$

$$P(15) = 0.013$$

(b) A trial consists of using the Myers-Briggs instrument to determine if a computer programmer is an introvert. Success = introvert. Failure = not introvert.

$$n = 5, \ p = 0.60, \ q = 1 - 0.60 = 0.40$$

$$P(0) = 0.010$$

$$P(r \geq 3) = P(3) + P(4) + P(5)$$
$$= 0.346 + 0.259 + 0.078$$
$$= 0.683$$

$$P(5) = 0.078$$

13. A trial is checking the development of hypertension in patients with diabetes. Success = yes. Failure = no.

$n = 10$, $p = 0.40$, $q = 1 - 0.40 = 0.60$

(a) $P(0) = 0.006$

(b) $P(r < 5) = P(0) + P(1) + P(2) + P(3) + P(4)$

$= 0.006 + 0.040 + 0.121 + 0.215 + 0.251$

$= 0.633$

A trial is checking the development of an eye disease in patients with diabetes. Success = yes. Failure = no.

$n = 10$, $p = 0.30$, $q = 1 - 0.30 = 0.70$

(c) $P(r \leq 2) = P(0) + P(1) + P(2)$

$= 0.028 + 0.121 + 0.233$

$= 0.382$

(d) At least 6 will never develop a related eye disease is the same as at most 4 will never develop a related eye disease.

$P(r \leq 4) = P(0) + P(1) + P(2) + P(3) + P(4)$

$= 0.028 + 0.121 + 0.233 + 0.267 + 0.200$

$= 0.849$

15. A trial consists of the response of adults regarding their concern that Social Security numbers are used for general identification. Success = concerned that SS numbers are being used for identification. Failure = not concerned that SS numbers are being used for identification.

$n = 8$, $p = 0.53$, $q = 1 - 0.53 = 0.47$

(a) $P(r \leq 5) = P(0) + P(1) + P(2) + P(3) + P(4) + P(5)$

$= 0.002381 + 0.021481 + 0.084781 + 0.191208 + 0.269521 + 0.243143$

$= 0.812515$

$P(r \leq 5) = 0.81251$ from the cumulative probability is the same, truncated to 5 digits.

(b) $P(r > 5) = P(6) + P(7) + P(8)$

$= 0.137091 + 0.044169 + 0.006726$

$= 0.187486$

$P(r > 5) = 1 - P(r \leq 5)$

$= 1 - 0.81251$

$= 0.18749$

Yes, this is the same result rounded to 5 digits.

Section 6.3

1. (a) Binomial Distribution
   The distribution is symmetrical.

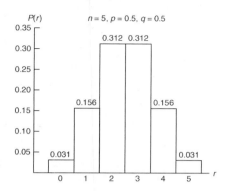

(b) Binomial Distribution
   The distribution is skewed right.

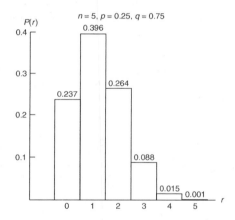

(c) Binomial Distribution
The distribution is skewed left.

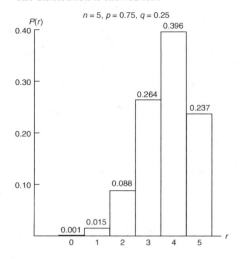

(d) The distributions are mirror images of one another.

(e) The distribution would be skewed left for $p = 0.73$ because the more likely number of successes are to the right of the middle.

3. **(a)** $n = 8$, $p = 0.25$

The probabilities can be taken directly from Table 3 in Appendix II.

(b) $\mu = np = 8(0.25) = 2$

$$\sigma = \sqrt{npq} = \sqrt{8(0.25)(0.75)} \approx 1.225$$

The expected number of people in this sample who believe the product is improved is 1.4.

(c) Find n such that
$$P(r \geq 1) = 0.99.$$
Try $n = 16$.
$$P(r \geq 1) = 1 - P(0)$$
$$= 1 - 0.01$$
$$= 0.99$$

Sixteen people are needed in the marketing study to be 99% sure that at least one person believes the product to be improved.

5. (a) Since success = not a repeat offender, then $p = 0.75$.

From Table 3 in Appendix II and $n = 4$, $p = 0.75$.

r	0	1	2	3	4
$P(r)$	0.004	0.047	0.211	0.422	0.316

(b) Binomial Distribution for Number of Parolees Who Do Not Become Repeat Offenders

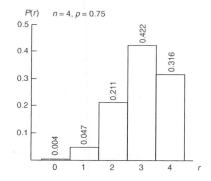

(c) $\mu = np = 4(0.75) = 3$

The expected number of parolees in Alice's group who will not be repeat offenders is 3.
$$\sigma = \sqrt{npq} = \sqrt{4(0.75)(0.25)} \approx 0.866$$

7. (a) Let success = available, then $p = 0.75$, $n = 12$.
$$P(12) = 0.032$$

(b) Let success = not available, then $p = 0.25$, $n = 12$.
$$P(r \geq 6) = P(6) + P(7) + P(8) + P(9) + P(10) + P(11) + P(12)$$
$$= 0.040 + 0.011 + 0.002 + 0.000 + 0.000 + 0.000 + 0.000$$
$$= 0.053$$

(c) $n = 12$, $p = 0.75$
$$\mu = np = 12(0.75) = 9$$

The expected number of those available to serve on the jury is 9.
$$\sigma = \sqrt{npq} = \sqrt{12(0.75)(0.25)} = 1.5$$

9. **(a)** Japan: $n = 7, p = 0.95$

$$P(7) = 0.698$$

United States: $n = 7, p = 0.60$

$$P(7) = 0.028$$

(b) Japan: $n = 7, p = 0.95$

$$\mu = np = 7(0.95) = 6.65$$

$$\sigma = \sqrt{npq} = \sqrt{7(0.95)(0.05)} \approx 0.58$$

United States: $n = 7, p = 0.60$

$$\mu = np = 7(0.60) = 4.2$$

$$\sigma = \sqrt{npq} = \sqrt{7(0.60)(0.40)} \approx 1.30$$

The expected number of verdicts in Japan is 6.65 and in the United States is 4.2.

Chapter 6 Review

1. **(a)** $\mu = \sum xP(x)$

$$= 18.5(0.127) + 30.5(0.371) + 42.5(0.285) + 54.5(0.215) + 66.5(0.002)$$

$$= 37.628$$

$$\approx 37.63$$

The expected lease term is about 38 months.

$$\sigma = \sqrt{\sum (x - \mu)^2 P(x)}$$

$$= \sqrt{(-19.13)^2 (0.127) + (-7.13)^2 (0.371) + (4.87)^2 (0.285) + (16.87)^2 (0.215) + (28.87)^2 (0.002)}$$

$$\approx \sqrt{134.95}$$

$$\approx 11.6 \text{ (using } \mu = 37.63 \text{ in the calculations)}$$

(b) Leases in Months

3. This is a binomial experiment with 10 trials. A trial consists of a claim.

Success = submitted by a male under 25 years of age.
Failure = not submitted by a male under 25 years of age.

(a) The probabilities can be taken directly from Table 3 in Appendix II, $n = 10, p = 0.55$.

Claimants Under 25

(b) $P(r \geq 6) = P(6) + P(7) + P(8) + P(9) + P(10)$
$$= 0.238 + 0.166 + 0.076 + 0.021 + 0.003$$
$$= 0.504$$

(c) $\mu = np = 10(0.55) = 5.5$

The expected number of claims made by males under age 25 is 5.5.

$$\sigma = \sqrt{npq} = \sqrt{10(0.55)(0.45)} \approx 1.57$$

5. $n = 16, p = 0.50$

   (a) $P(r \geq 12) = P(12) + P(13) + P(14) + P(15) + P(16)$
$$= 0.028 + 0.009 + 0.002 + 0.000 + 0.000$$
$$= 0.039$$

   (b) $P(r \leq 7) = P(0) + P(1) + P(2) + P(3) + P(4) + P(5) + P(6) + P(7)$
$$= 0.000 + 0.000 + 0.002 + 0.009 + 0.028 + 0.067 + 0.122 + 0.175$$
$$= 0.403$$

   (c) $\mu = np = 16(0.50) = 8$

The expected number of inmates serving time for drug dealing is 8.

7. $n = 10, p = 0.75$

   (a) The probabilities can be obtained directed from Table 3 in Appendix II.

Number of Good Grapefruit

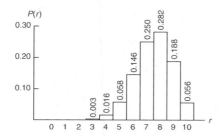

(b) No more than one bad is the same as at least nine good.

$$P(r \geq 9) = P(9) + P(10)$$
$$= 0.188 + 0.056$$
$$= 0.244$$

$$P(r \geq 1) = P(1) + P(2) + P(3) + P(4) + P(5) + P(6) + P(7) + P(8) + P(9) + P(10)$$
$$= 0.000 + 0.000 + 0.003 + 0.016 + 0.058 + 0.146 + 0.250 + 0.282 + 0.188 + 0.056$$
$$= 0.999$$

(c) $\mu = np = 10(0.75) = 7.5$

The expected number of good grapefruit in a sack is 7.5.

(d) $\sigma = \sqrt{npq} = \sqrt{10(0.75)(0.25)} \approx 1.37$

9. $p = 0.85$, $n = 12$

$$P(r \leq 2) = P(0) + P(1) + P(2)$$
$$= 0.000 + 0.000 + 0.000$$
$$= 0.000 \quad \text{(to 3 digits)}$$

The data seem to indicate that the percent favoring the increase in fees is less than 85%.

Chapter 7   Normal Curves and Sampling Distributions

Section 7.1

1. **(a)** not normal; left skewed instead of symmetric

   (b) not normal; curve touches and goes below x-axis instead of always being above the x-axis and being asymptotic to the x-axis in the tails

   (c) not normal; not bell-shaped, not unimodal

   (d) not normal; not a smooth curve

3. The mean is the x-value directly below the peak; in Figure 7-9, $\mu = 10$; in Figure 7-10, $\mu = 4$. Assuming the two figures are drawn on the same scale, Figure 7-9, being shorter and more spread out, has the larger standard deviation.

5. **(a)** 50%; the normal curve is symmetric about μ.

   (b) 68%

   (c) 99.7%

7. **(a)** $\mu = 65$, so 50% are taller than 65 in.

   (b) $\mu = 65$, so 50% are shorter than 65 in.

   (c) $\mu - \sigma = 65 - 2.5 = 62.5$ in. and $\mu + \sigma = 65 + 2.5 = 67.5$ in. so 68% of college women are between 62.5 in. and 67.5 in. tall.

   (d) $\mu - 2\sigma = 65 - 2(2.5) = 65 - 5 = 60$ in. and $\mu - 2\sigma = 65 + 2(2.5) = 65 + 5 = 70$ in. so 95% of college women are between 60 in. and 70 in. tall.

9. **(a)** $\mu - \sigma = 1243 - 36 = 1207$ and $\mu + \sigma = 1243 + 36 = 1279$ so about 68% of the tree rings will date between 1207 and 1279 AD.

   (b) $\mu - 2\sigma = 1243 - 2(36) = 1171$ and $\mu + 2\sigma = 1243 + 2(36) = 1315$ so about 95% of the tree rings will date between 1171 and 1315 AD.

   (c) $\mu - 3\sigma = 1243 - 3(36) = 1135$ and $\mu + 3\sigma = 1243 + 3(36) = 1351$ so 99.7% (almost all) of the tree rings will date between 1135 and 1351 AD.

11. **(a)** $\mu - \sigma = 3.15 - 1.45 = 1.70$ and $\mu + \sigma = 3.15 + 1.45 = 4.60$ so 68% of the experimental group will have pain thresholds between 1.70 and 4.60 mA.

    (b) $\mu - 2\sigma = 3.15 - 2(1.45) = 0.25$ and $\mu + 2\sigma = 3.15 + 2(1.45) = 6.05$ so 95% of the experimental group will have pain thresholds between 0.25 and 6.05 mA.

Section 7.2

1. **(a)** z-scores > 0 indicate the student scored above the mean: Robert, Jan, and Linda

   (b) z-scores $= 0$ indicates the student scored at the mean: Joel

   (c) z-scores < 0 indicate the student scored below the mean: Juan and Susan

(d) $z = \dfrac{x - \mu}{\sigma}$ so $x = \mu + z\sigma$

In this case, if the student's score is x, $x = 150 + z(20)$.

Robert: $x = 150 + 1.10(20) = 172$

Joel: $x = 150 + 0(20) = 150$

Jan: $x = 150 + 1.70(20) = 184$

Juan: $x = 150 - 0.80(20) = 134$

Susan: $x = 150 - 2.00(20) = 110$

Linda: $x = 150 + 1.60(20) = 182$

3. Use $z = \dfrac{x - \mu}{\sigma}$. In this case, $z = \dfrac{x - 73}{5}$.

(a) $53°F < x < 93°F$

$\dfrac{53 - 73}{5} < \dfrac{x - 73}{5} < \dfrac{93 - 73}{5}$ Subtract $\mu = 73°F$ from each piece; divide result by $\sigma = 5°F$.

$-\dfrac{20}{5} < z < \dfrac{20}{5}$

$-4.00 < z < 4.00$

(b) $x < 65°F$

$x - 73 < 65 - 73$ Subtract $\mu = 73°F$.

$\dfrac{x - 73}{5} < \dfrac{65 - 73}{5}$ Divide both sides by $\sigma = 5°F$.

$z < -1.6$

(c) $78°F < x$

$\dfrac{78 - 73}{5} < \dfrac{x - 73}{5}$ Subtract $\mu = 73°F$ from each side; divide by $\sigma = 5°F$.

$\dfrac{5}{5} < z$

$1.00 < z$ (or $z > 1.00$)

For (d)–(f): Since $z = \dfrac{x - 73}{5}$, $x = 73 + 5z$.

(d) $1.75 < z$

$5(1.75) < 5z$ Multiply both sides by $\sigma = 5°F$.

$73 + 5(1.75) < 73 + 5z$ Add $\mu = 73°F$ to both sides.

$81.75°F < x$ (or $x > 81.75$)

(e) $z < -1.90$

$5z < 5(-1.90)$ Multiply both sides by $\sigma = 5°F$.

$73 + 5z < 73 + 5(-1.90)$ Add $\mu = 73°F$ to both sides.

$x < 63.5°F$

(f) $-1.80 < z < 1.65$

$5(-1.80) < 5z < 5(1.65)$ Multiply each part by $\sigma = 5°F$.

$73 + 5(-1.80) < 73 + 5z < 73 + 5(1.65)$ Add $\mu = 73°F$ to each part of the inequality.

$64°F < x < 81.25°F$

5. $z = \dfrac{x - \mu}{\sigma}$, here $z = \dfrac{x - 4400}{620}$

(a)
$$3300 < x$$
$$3300 - 4400 < x - 4400 \quad \text{Subtract } \mu = 4400 \text{ deer.}$$
$$\frac{3300 - 4400}{620} < \frac{x - 4400}{620} \quad \text{Divide by } \sigma = 620 \text{ deer.}$$
$$-1.77 < z$$

(b)
$$x < 5400$$
$$x - 4400 < 5400 - 4400 \quad \text{Subtract } \mu = 4400 \text{ deer.}$$
$$\frac{x - 4400}{620} < \frac{5400 - 4400}{620} \quad \text{Divide by } \sigma = 620 \text{ deer.}$$
$$z < 1.61$$

(c)
$$3500 < x < 5300$$
$$3500 - 4400 < x - 4400 < 5300 - 4400 \quad \text{Subtract } \mu = 4400.$$
$$\frac{3500 - 4400}{620} < \frac{x - 4400}{620} < \frac{5300 - 4400}{620} \quad \text{Divide by } \sigma = 620.$$
$$-1.45 < z < 1.45$$

For (d)–(f): Since $z = \dfrac{x - 4400}{620}$, $x = 4400 + 620z$ deer.

(d)
$$-1.12 < z < 2.43$$
$$620(-1.12) < 620z < 620(2.43) \qquad\qquad \text{Multiply by } \sigma = 620.$$
$$4400 + 620(-1.12) < 4400 + 620z < 4400 + 620(2.43) \quad \text{Add } \mu = 4400 \text{ to each part.}$$
$$3706 \text{ deer } < x < 5907 \text{ deer (rounded)}$$

(e)
$$z < 1.96$$
$$620z < 620(1.96) \qquad \text{Multiply by } \sigma.$$
$$4400 + 620z < 4400 + 620(1.96) \quad \text{Add } \mu.$$
$$x < 5615 \text{ deer}$$

(f)
$$2.58 < z$$
$$620(2.58) < 620z \qquad \text{Multiply by } \sigma.$$
$$4400 + 620(2.58) < 4400 + 620z \quad \text{Add } \mu.$$
$$6000 \text{ deer } < x$$

(g) If $x = 2800$ deer, $z = \dfrac{2800 - 4400}{620} = -2.58$.

This is a small z-value, so 2800 deer is quite low for the fall deer population.

If $x = 6300$ deer, $z = \dfrac{6300 - 4400}{620} = 3.06$.

This is a very large z-value, so 6300 deer would be an unusually large fall population size.

7. $z = \dfrac{x - \mu}{\sigma}$, so in this case $z = \dfrac{x - 4.8}{0.3}$.

(a) $4.5 < x$

$\dfrac{4.5 - 4.8}{0.3} < \dfrac{x - 4.8}{0.3}$ Subtract μ; divide by σ.

$-1.00 < z$

(b) $x < 4.2$

$\dfrac{x - 4.8}{0.3} < \dfrac{4.2 - 4.8}{0.3}$ Subtract μ; divide by σ.

$z < -2.00$

(c) $4.0 < x < 5.5$

$\dfrac{4.0 - 4.8}{0.3} < \dfrac{x - 4.8}{0.3} < \dfrac{5.5 - 4.8}{0.3}$ Subtract μ; divide by σ.

$-2.67 < z < 2.33$

For (d)–(f): Since $z = \dfrac{x - 4.8}{0.3}$, $x = 4.8 + 0.3z$.

(d) $z < -1.44$

$0.3z < 0.3(-1.44)$ Multiply by σ.

$4.8 + 0.3z < 4.8 + 0.3(-1.44)$ Add μ.

$x < 4.4$

(e) $1.28 < z$

$0.3(1.28) < 0.3z$ Multiply by σ.

$4.8 + 0.3(1.28) < 4.8 + 0.3z$ Add μ.

$5.2 < x$

(f) $-2.25 < z < -1.00$

$0.3(-2.25) < 0.3z < 0.3(-1.00)$ Multiply by σ.

$4.8 + 0.3(-2.25) < 4.8 + 0.3z < 4.8 + 0.3(-1.00)$ Add μ.

$4.1 < x < 4.5$

(g) If the RBC was 5.9 or higher, that would be an unusually high red blood cell count.

$x \geq 5.9$

$\dfrac{x - 4.8}{0.3} \geq \dfrac{5.9 - 4.8}{0.3}$

$z \geq 3.67$ (a very large z-value)

For problems 9–47, refer to the following sketch patterns for guidance in calculations

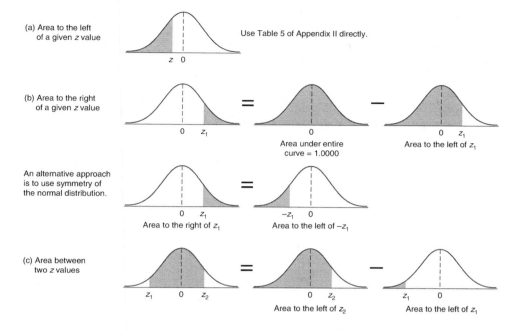

Using the left-tail style standard normal distribution table (see figures above)

   (a) For areas to the *left* of a specified z value, use the table entry directly.

   (b) For areas to the *right* of a specified z value, look up the table entry for z and subtract the table value from 1. (This is the complementary event rule as applied to area as probability.)

   OR: Use the fact that the normal curve is symmetric about the mean, 0. The area in the right tail above a z-value is the same as the area in the left tail below the value of $-z$. To find the area to the right of z, look up the table value for $-z$.

   (c) For areas *between* two z-values, z_1 and z_2, where $z_1 < z_2$, subtract the tabled value for z_1, from the tabled value for z_2.

These sketches and rules for finding the area for probability from the standard normal table apply for *any* z: $-\infty < z < +\infty$.

Student sketches should resemble those indicated with negative z-values to left of 0 and positive z-values to the right of zero.

   9. Refer to figure (b).
   The area to the right of $z = 0$ is 1 – area to left of $z = 0$, or $1 - 0.5000 = 0.5000$.

   11. Refer to figure (a).
   The area to the left of $z = -1.32$ is 0.0934.

13. Refer to figure (a).
The area to left of $z = 0.45$ is 0.6736.

15. Refer to figure (b).
The area to right of $z = 1.52$ is $1 - 0.9357 = 0.0643$.

17. Refer to figure (b).
The area to right of $z = -1.22$ is $1 - 0.1112 = 0.8888$.

19. Refer to figure (c).
The area between $z = 0$ and $z = 3.18$ is $0.9993 - 0.5000 = 0.4993$.

21. Refer to figure (c).
The area between $z = 0$ and $z = -2.01$ is $0.5000 - 0.0222 = 0.4778$.

23. Refer to figure (c).
The area between $z = -2.18$ and $z = 1.34$ is $0.9099 - 0.0146 = 0.8953$.

25. Refer to figure (c).
The area between $z = 0.32$ and $z = 1.92$ is $0.9726 - 0.6255 = 0.3471$.

27. Refer to figure (c).
The area between $z = -2.42$ and $z = -1.77$ is $0.0384 - 0.0078 = 0.0306$.

29. Refer to figure (a).
$P(z \leq 0) = 0.5000$

31. Refer to figure (a).
$P(z \leq -0.13) = 0.4483$ (direct read)

33. Refer to figure (a).
$P(z \leq 1.20) = 0.8849$

35. Refer to figure (b).
$P(z \geq 1.35) = 1 - P(z < 1.35) = 1 - 0.9115 = 0.0885$

37. Refer to figure (b).
$P(x \geq -1.20) = 1 - P(z < -1.20) = 1 - 0.1151 = 0.8849$

39. Refer to figure (c).
$P(-1.20 \leq z \leq 2.64) = P(z \leq 2.64) - P(z < -1.20) = 0.9959 - 0.1151 = 0.8808$

41. Refer to figure (c).
$P(-2.18 \leq z \leq -0.42) = P(z \leq -0.42) - P(z < -2.18) = 0.3372 - 0.0146 = 0.3226$

43. Refer to figure (c).
$P(0 \leq z \leq 1.62) = P(z \leq 1.62) - P(z < 0) = 0.9474 - 0.5000 = 0.4474$

45. Refer to figure (c).
$P(-0.82 \leq z \leq 0) = P(z \leq 0) - P(z < -0.82) = 0.5000 - 0.2061 = 0.2939$

47. Refer to figure (c).

$P(-0.45 \leq z \leq 2.73) = P(z \leq 2.73) - P(z < -0.45) = 0.9968 - 0.3264 = 0.6704$

Section 7.3

1. We are given $\mu = 4$ and $\sigma = 2$. Since $z = \dfrac{x - \mu}{\sigma}$, we have $z = \dfrac{x - 4}{2}$.

$P(3 \leq x \leq 6)$

$= P(3 - 4 \leq x - 4 \leq 6 - 4)$ Subtract $\mu = 4$ from each part of the inequality.

$= P\left(\dfrac{3-4}{2} \leq \dfrac{x-4}{2} \leq \dfrac{6-4}{2}\right)$ Divide each part by $\sigma = 2$.

$= P\left(-\dfrac{1}{2} \leq z \leq \dfrac{2}{2}\right)$

$= P(-0.5 \leq z \leq 1)$

$= P(z \leq 1) - P(z < -0.5)$ Refer to sketch (c) in the solutions for Section 6.2.

$= 0.8413 - 0.3085$

$= 0.5328$

3. We are given $\mu = 40$ and $\sigma = 15$. Since $z = \dfrac{x - \mu}{\sigma}$, we have $z = \dfrac{x - 40}{15}$.

$P(50 \leq x \leq 70)$

$= P(50 - 40 \leq x - 40 \leq 70 - 40)$ Subtract $\mu = 40$.

$= P\left(\dfrac{50-40}{15} \leq \dfrac{x-40}{15} \leq \dfrac{70-40}{15}\right)$ Divide by $\sigma = 15$.

$= P(0.67 \leq z \leq 2)$

$= P(z \leq 2) - P(z < 0.67)$

$= 0.9772 - 0.7486 = 0.2286$

5. We are given $\mu = 15$ and $\sigma = 3.2$. Since $z = \dfrac{x - \mu}{\sigma}$, we have $z = \dfrac{x - 15}{3.2}$.

$P(8 \leq x \leq 12)$

$= P(8 - 15 \leq x - 15 \leq 12 - 15)$ Subtract $\mu = 15$.

$= P\left(\dfrac{8-15}{3.2} \leq \dfrac{x-15}{3.2} \leq \dfrac{12-15}{3.2}\right)$ Divide by $\sigma = 3.2$.

$= P(-2.19 \leq z \leq -0.94)$

$= P(z \leq -0.94) - P(z < -2.19)$

$= 0.1736 - 0.0143 = 0.1593$

7. We are given $\mu = 20$ and $\sigma = 3.4$. Since $z = \dfrac{x - \mu}{\sigma}$, we have $z = \dfrac{x - 20}{3.4}$.

$P(x \geq 30)$

$= P(x - 20 \geq 30 - 20)$ Subtract $\mu = 20$.

$= P\left(\dfrac{x-20}{3.4} \geq \dfrac{30-20}{3.4}\right)$ Divide by $\sigma = 3.4$.

$= P(z \geq 2.94)$

$= 1 - P(z < 2.94)$ Refer to sketch (b) in Section 6.2.

$= 1 - 0.9984 = 0.0016$

9. We are given $\mu = 100$ and $\sigma = 15$. Since $z = \dfrac{x - \mu}{\sigma}$, we have $z = \dfrac{x - 100}{15}$.

$P(x \geq 90)$

$= P\left(\dfrac{x - 100}{15} \geq \dfrac{90 - 100}{15}\right)$ Subtract μ; divide by σ.

$= P(z \geq -0.67)$

$= 1 - P(z < -0.67) = 1 - 0.2514 = 0.7486$

For problems 11–19, refer to the following sketch patterns for guidance in calculation.

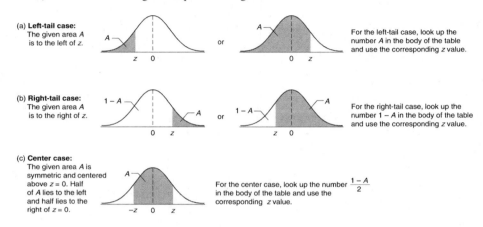

Student sketches should resemble the figures above, with negative z-values to the left of zero and positive z-values to the right of zero, and A written as a decimal.

11. Refer to figure (a).
Find z so that the area A to the left of z is $6\% = 0.06$. Since $A = 0.06$ is less than 0.5000, look for a negative z value. A to left of -1.55 is 0.0606 and A to left of -1.56 is 0.0594. Since 0.06 is in the middle of 0.0606 and 0.0594, for our z-value we will use the average of -1.55 and -1.56:

$$\dfrac{-1.55 + (-1.56)}{2} = -1.555.$$

13. Refer to figure (a).
Find z so that the area A to the left of z is $55\% = 0.55$. Since $A = 0.55 > 0.5000$, look for a positive z-value. The area to the left of 0.13 is 0.5517, so $z = 0.13$.

15. Refer to figure (b).
Find z so that the area A to the right of z is $8\% = 0.08$. Since A to the right of z is 0.08, $1 - A = 1 - 0.08 = 0.92$ is to the left of z-value. The area to the left of 1.41 is 0.9207.

17. Refer to figure (b).
Find z so that the area A to the right of z is $82\% = 0.82$. Since A to the right of z, $1 - A = 1 - 0.82 = 0.18$ is to the left of z. Since $1 - A = 0.18 < 0.5000$, look for a negative z value. The area to the left of $z = -0.92$ is 0.1788.

19. Refer to figure (c).

Find z such that the area A between $-z$ and z is $98\% = 0.98$. Since A is between $-z$ and z, $1 - A = 1 - 0.98$ $= 0.02$ lies in the tails, and since we need $\pm z$, half of $1 - A$ lies in each tail. The area to the left of $-z$ is

$\dfrac{1-A}{2} = \dfrac{0.02}{2} = 0.01.$ The area to the left of -2.33 is 0.0099. Thus $-z = -2.33$ and $z = 2.33$.

21. x is approximately normal with $\mu = 85$ and $\sigma = 25$. Since $z = \dfrac{x - \mu}{\sigma}$, we have $z = \dfrac{x - 85}{25}$.

(a) $P(x > 60)$

$= P\left(\dfrac{x-85}{25} > \dfrac{60-85}{25}\right) = P(z > -1)$

$= 1 - P(z \le -1) = 1 - 0.1587 = 0.8413$

(b) $P(x < 110) = P\left(\dfrac{x-85}{25} < \dfrac{110-85}{25}\right) = P(z < 1) = 0.8413.$

(c) $P(60 < x < 110)$

$= P(-1 < z < 1)$ using (a) and (b)

$= P(z < 1) - P(z \le -1) = 0.8413 - 0.1587 = 0.6826$

(i.e., approximately 68% of the blood glucose measurements lie within $\mu \pm \sigma$)

(d) $P(x > 140)$

$= P\left(\dfrac{x-85}{25} > \dfrac{140-85}{25}\right) = P(z > 2.2)$

$= 1 - P(z \le 2.2) = 1 - 0.9861 = 0.0139$

23. SAT scores, x, are normal with $\mu_x = 500$ and $\sigma_x = 100$. Since $z = \dfrac{x - \mu_x}{\sigma_x}$, we have $x = \dfrac{x - 500}{100}$.

(a) $P(x > 675) = P\left(\dfrac{x-500}{100} > \dfrac{675-500}{100}\right) = P(z > 1.75) = 1 - P(z \le 1.75) = 1 - 0.9599 = 0.0401$

(b) $P(x < 450) = P\left(\dfrac{x-500}{100} < \dfrac{450-500}{100}\right) = P(z < -0.5) = 0.3085$

(c) $P(450 \le x \le 675)$

$= P(-0.5 \le z \le 1.75)$ using (a), (b)

$= P(z \le 1.75) - P(z < -0.5) = 0.9599 - 0.3085$

$= 0.6514$ using work in (a), and (b)

ACT scores, y, are normal with $\mu_y = 18$ and $\sigma_y = 6$. Since $z = \dfrac{y - \mu_y}{\sigma_y}$, we have $z = \dfrac{y - 18}{6}$.

(d) $P(y > 28) = P\left(\dfrac{y-18}{6} > \dfrac{28-18}{6}\right) = P(z > 1.67) = 1 - P(z \le 1.67) = 1 - 0.9525 = 0.0475$

(e) $P(y > 12) = P\left(\dfrac{y-18}{6} > \dfrac{12-18}{6}\right) = P(z > -1) = 1 - P(z \le -1) = 1 - 0.1587 = 0.8413$

(f) $P(12 \le y \le 28)$

$= P(-1 \le z \le 1.67)$ using (a), (b)

$= P(z \le 1.67) - P(z < -1) = 0.9525 - 0.1587 = 0.7938$

25. Lifetime, x, is normally distributed with $\mu = 45$ and $\sigma = 8$ months.

(a) $P(x \le 36) = P\left(\dfrac{x-45}{8} \le \dfrac{36-45}{8}\right) = P(z \le -1.125) \approx P(z \le -1.13) = 0.1292$

The company will have to replace approximately 13% of its batteries.

(b) Find x_0 such that $P(x \le x_0) = 10\% = 0.10$. First, find z_0 such that $P(z \le z_0) = 0.10$.

$P(z \le -1.28) = 0.1003$, so $z_0 = -1.28$. Then $x_0 = \mu + z_0\sigma = 45 + (-1.28)(8) = 34.76 \approx 35$.

The company should guarantee the batteries for 35 months.

27. Age at replacement, x, is approximately normal with $\mu = 8$ and range $= 6$ years.

(a) The empirical rule says that about 95% of the data are between $\mu - 2\sigma$ and $\mu + 2\sigma$, or about 95% of the data are in a $(\mu + 2\sigma) - (\mu - 2\sigma) = 4\sigma$ range (centered around μ). Thus, the range $\approx 4\sigma$, or $\sigma \approx$ range/4. Here, we can approximate σ by $6/4 = 1.5$ years.

(b) $P(x > 5) = P\left(z > \dfrac{5-8}{1.5}\right) = P(z > -2)$ using the estimate of σ from (a)

$= 1 - P(z \le -2) = 1 - 0.0228 = 0.9772$

(c) $P(x < 10) = P\left(z < \dfrac{10-8}{1.5}\right) = P(z < 1.33) = 0.9082$

(d) Find x_0 so that $P(x \le x_0) = 10\% = 0.10$. First, find z_0 such that $P(z \le z_0) = 0.10$.

$P(z \le -1.28) = 0.1003$, so $z_0 = -1.28$. Then $x_0 = \mu + z_0\sigma = 8 + (-1.28)(1.5) = 6.08$.

The company should guarantee their TVs for about 6.1 years.

29. Life expectancy x is normal with $\mu = 90$ and $\sigma = 3.7$ months.

(a) The insurance company wants 99% of the microchips to last <u>longer</u> than x_0. Saying this another way: the insurance company wants to pay the \$50 million at most 1% of the time. So, find x_0 such that $P(x \le x_0) = 1\% = 0.01$. First, find z_0 such that $P(z \le z_0) = 0.01$. $P(z \le -2.33) = 0.0099 \approx 0.01$, so let

$z_0 = -2.33$. Since $z_0 = \dfrac{x_0 - \mu}{\sigma}$, $x_0 = \mu + z_0\sigma = 90 + (-2.33)(3.7) = 81.379 \approx 81$ months.

(b) $P(x \le 84) = P\left(z \le \dfrac{84-90}{3.7}\right) = P(z \le -1.62) = 0.0526 \approx 5\%$.

(c) The "expected loss" is 5.26% [from (b)] of the \$50 million, or $0.0526(50{,}000{,}000) = \$2{,}630{,}000$.

(d) Profit is the difference between the amount of money taken in (here, \$3 million), and the amount paid out (here, \$2.63 million, from (c)). So the company expects to profit $3{,}000{,}000 - 2{,}630{,}000 = \$370{,}000$.

Section 7.4

1. Answers vary. Students should identify the individuals (subjects) and variable involved. Answers may include: A population is a set of measurements or counts either existing or conceptual. For example, the population of all ages of all people in Colorado; the population of weights of all students in your school; the population count of all antelope in Wyoming.

3. A population parameter is a numerical descriptive measure of a population, such as μ, the population mean; σ, the population standard deviation; σ^2, the population variance; p, the population proportion; and ρ (rho) the population correlation coefficient for those who have already studied linear regression from Chapter 10.

5. A statistical inference is a conclusion about the value of a population parameter based on information about the corresponding sample statistic and probability. We will do both estimation and testing.

7. They help us visualize the sampling distribution by using tables and graphs that approximately represent the sampling distribution.

9. We studied the sampling distribution of mean trout lengths based on samples of size 5. Other such sampling distributions abound. Notice that the sample size remains the same for each sample in a sampling distribution.

Section 7.5

Note: Answers may vary slightly depending on the number of digits carried in the standard deviation.

1. (a) $\mu_{\bar{x}} = \mu = 15$

$$\sigma_{\bar{x}} = \frac{\sigma}{\sqrt{n}} = \frac{14}{\sqrt{49}} = 2.0$$

Because $n = 49 \geq 30$, by the central limit theorem, we can assume that the distribution of $\bar{x}$ is approximately normal.

$$z = \frac{\bar{x} - \mu}{\sigma_{\bar{x}}} = \frac{\bar{x} - 15}{2.0}$$

$\bar{x} = 15$ converts to $z = \dfrac{15 - 15}{2.0} = 0$

$\bar{x} = 17$ converts to $z = \dfrac{17 - 15}{2.0} = 1$

$$\begin{aligned} P(15 \leq \bar{x} \leq 17) &= P(0 \leq z \leq 1) \\ &= P(z \leq 1) - P(z \leq 0) \\ &= 0.8413 - 0.5000 \\ &= 0.3413 \end{aligned}$$

(b) $\mu_{\bar{x}} = \mu = 15$

$$\sigma_{\bar{x}} = \frac{\sigma}{\sqrt{n}} = \frac{14}{\sqrt{64}} = 1.75$$

Because $n = 64 \geq 30$, by the central limit theorem, we can assume that the distribution of $\bar{x}$ is approximately normal.

$$z = \frac{\bar{x} - \mu}{\sigma_{\bar{x}}} = \frac{\bar{x} - 15}{1.75}$$

$\bar{x} = 15$ converts to $z = \dfrac{15 - 15}{1.75} = 0$

$\bar{x} = 17$ converts to $z = \dfrac{17 - 15}{1.75} = 1.14$

$$\begin{aligned} P(15 \leq \bar{x} \leq 17) &= P(0 \leq z \leq 1.14) \\ &= P(z \leq 1.14) - P(z \leq 0) \\ &= 0.8729 - 0.5000 \\ &= 0.3729 \end{aligned}$$

(c) The standard deviation of part (b) is smaller because of the larger sample size. Therefore, the distribution about $\mu_{\bar{x}}$ is narrower in part (b).

3. (a) No, we cannot say anything about the distribution of sample means because the sample size is only 9 and so it is too small to apply the central limit theorem.

(b) Yes, now we can say that the $\bar{x}$ distribution will also be normal with

$$\mu_{\bar{x}} = \mu = 25 \text{ and } \sigma_{\bar{x}} = \frac{\sigma}{\sqrt{n}} = \frac{3.5}{\sqrt{9}} = 1.17.$$

$$z = \frac{\bar{x} - \mu}{\sigma_{\bar{x}}} = \frac{\bar{x} - 25}{1.17}$$

$$\begin{aligned}
P(23 \le \bar{x} \le 26) &= P\left(\frac{23 - 25}{1.17} \le z \le \frac{26 - 25}{1.17} \right) \\
&= P(-1.71 \le z \le 0.86) \\
&= P(z \le 0.86) - P(z \le -1.71) \\
&= 0.8051 - 0.0436 \\
&= 0.7615
\end{aligned}$$

5. (a) $\mu = 75, \ \sigma = 0.8$

$$\begin{aligned}
P(x < 74.5) &= P\left(z < \frac{74.5 - 75}{0.8} \right) \\
&= P(z < -0.63) \\
&= 0.2643
\end{aligned}$$

(b) $\mu_{\bar{x}} = 75, \ \sigma_{\bar{x}} = \frac{\sigma}{\sqrt{n}} = \frac{0.8}{\sqrt{20}} = 0.179$

$$\begin{aligned}
P(\bar{x} < 74.5) &= P\left(z < \frac{74.5 - 75}{0.179} \right) \\
&= P(z < -2.79) \\
&= 0.0026
\end{aligned}$$

(c) No. If the weight of only one car were less than 74.5 tons, we cannot conclude that the loader is out of adjustment. If the mean weight for a sample of 20 cars were less than 74.5 tons, we would suspect that the loader is malfunctioning. As we see in part (b), the probability of this happening is very low if the loader is correctly adjusted.

7. (a) $\mu = 85, \ \sigma = 25$

$$\begin{aligned}
P(x < 40) &= P\left(z < \frac{40 - 85}{25} \right) \\
&= P(z < -1.8) \\
&= 0.0359
\end{aligned}$$

(b) The probability distribution of $\bar{x}$ is approximately normal with $\mu_{\bar{x}} = 85$; $\sigma_{\bar{x}} = \dfrac{\sigma}{\sqrt{n}} = \dfrac{25}{\sqrt{2}} = 17.68.$

$$P(\bar{x} < 40) = P\left(z < \frac{40 - 85}{17.68}\right)$$
$$= P(z < -2.55)$$
$$= 0.0054$$

(c) $\mu_{\bar{x}} = 85$, $\sigma_{\bar{x}} = \dfrac{\sigma}{\sqrt{n}} = \dfrac{25}{\sqrt{3}} = 14.43$

$$P(\bar{x} < 40) = P\left(z < \frac{40 - 85}{14.43}\right)$$
$$= P(z < -3.12)$$
$$= 0.0009$$

(d) $\mu_{\bar{x}} = 85$, $\sigma_{\bar{x}} = \dfrac{\sigma}{\sqrt{n}} = \dfrac{25}{\sqrt{5}} = 11.2$

$$P(\bar{x} < 40) = P\left(z < \frac{40 - 85}{11.2}\right)$$
$$= P(z < -4.02)$$
$$< 0.0002$$

(e) Yes; if the average value based on five tests were less than 40, the patient is almost certain to have excess insulin.

9. (a) $\mu = 63.0$, $\sigma = 7.1$

$$P(x < 54) = P\left(z < \frac{54 - 63.0}{7.1}\right)$$
$$= P(z < -1.27)$$
$$= 0.1020$$

(b) The expected number undernourished is $2200(0.1020) = 224.4$, or about 224.

(c) $\mu_{\bar{x}} = 63.0$, $\sigma_{\bar{x}} = \dfrac{\sigma}{\sqrt{n}} = \dfrac{7.1}{\sqrt{50}} = 1.004$

$$P(\bar{x} < 60) = P\left(z < \frac{60 - 63.0}{1.004}\right)$$
$$= P(z < -2.99)$$
$$= 0.0014$$

(d) $\mu_{\bar{x}} = 63.0$, $\sigma_{\bar{x}} = 1.004$

$$P(\bar{x} < 64.2) = P\left(z < \frac{64.2 - 63.0}{1.004}\right)$$
$$= P(z < 1.20)$$
$$= 0.8849$$

Since the sample average is above the mean, it is quite unlikely that the doe population is undernourished.

11. **(a)** The random variable x is itself an average based on the number of stocks or bonds in the fund. Since x itself represents a sample mean return based on a large (random) sample of stocks or bonds, x has a distribution that is approximately normal (Central Limit Theorem).

(b) $\mu_{\bar{x}} = 1.6\%$, $\sigma_{\bar{x}} = \dfrac{\sigma}{\sqrt{n}} = \dfrac{0.9\%}{\sqrt{6}} = 0.367\%$

$$P\left(1\% \leq \bar{x} \leq 2\%\right) = P\left(\frac{1\% - 1.6\%}{0.367\%} \leq z \leq \frac{2\% - 1.6\%}{0.367\%}\right)$$
$$= P\left(-1.63 \leq z \leq 1.09\right)$$
$$= P\left(z \leq 1.09\right) - P\left(z \leq -1.63\right)$$
$$= 0.8621 - 0.0516$$
$$= 0.8105$$

Note: It does not matter whether you solve the problem using percents or their decimal equivalents as long as you are consistent.

(c) Note: 2 years = 24 months; x is <u>monthly</u> percentage return.

$\mu_{\bar{x}} = 1.6\%$, $\sigma_{\bar{x}} = \dfrac{\sigma}{\sqrt{n}} = \dfrac{0.9\%}{\sqrt{24}} = 0.1837\%$

$$P\left(1\% \leq \bar{x} \leq 2\%\right) = P\left(\frac{1\% - 1.6\%}{0.1837\%} \leq z \leq \frac{2\% - 1.6\%}{0.1837\%}\right)$$
$$= P\left(-3.27 \leq z \leq 2.18\right)$$
$$= P\left(z \leq 2.18\right) - P\left(z \leq -3.27\right)$$
$$= 0.9854 - 0.0005$$
$$= 0.9849$$

(d) Yes. The probability increases as the standard deviation decreases. The standard deviation decreases as the sample size increases.

(e) $\mu_{\bar{x}} = 1.6\%$, $\sigma_{\bar{x}} = 0.1837\%$

$$P\left(\bar{x} < 1\%\right) = P\left(z < \frac{1\% - 1.6\%}{0.1837\%}\right)$$
$$= P\left(z < -3.27\right)$$
$$= 0.0005$$

This is very unlikely if $\mu = 1.6\%$. One would suspect that μ has slipped below 1.6%.

13. **(a)** The sample size should be 30 or more.

(b) No. If the distribution of x is normal, the distribution of $\bar{x}$ is also normal, regardless of the sample size.

Section 7.6

Answers may vary slightly due to rounding.

1. Previously, $p = 88\% = 0.88$; now, $p = 9\% = 0.09$; $n = 200$; $r = 50$

   Let a success be defined as a child with a high blood-lead level.

   (a) $P(r \geq 50) = P(50 \leq r) = P(49.5 \leq x)$

   $np = 200(0.88) = 176$; $nq = n(1-p) = 200(0.12) = 24$

   Since both np and nq are greater than 5, we will use the normal approximation to the binomial with

   $\mu = np = 176$ and $\sigma = \sqrt{npq} = \sqrt{200(0.88)(0.12)} = \sqrt{21.12} = 4.60$.

   So, $P(r \geq 50) = P(49.5 \leq x) = P\left(\dfrac{49.5 - 176}{4.6} \leq z\right) = P(-27.5 \leq z)$.

   Almost every z value will be greater than or equal to -27.5, so this probability is approximately 1. It is almost certain that 50 or more children a decade ago had high blood-lead levels.

   (b) $P(r \geq 50) = P(50 \leq r) = P(49.5 \leq x)$

   In this case, $np = 200(0.09) = 18$ and $nq = 200(0.91) = 182$, so both are greater than 5. Use the

   normal approximation with $\mu = np = 18$ and $\sigma = \sqrt{npq} = \sqrt{200(0.09)(0.91)} = \sqrt{16.38} = 4.05$.

   So $P(49.5 \leq x) = P\left(\dfrac{49.5 - 18}{4.05} \leq z\right) = P(7.78 \leq z)$.

   Almost no z values will be larger than 7.78, so this probability is approximately 0. Today, it is almost impossible that a sample of 200 children would include at least 50 with high blood-lead levels.

3. We are given $n = 125$ and $p = 17\% = 0.17$. Let a success be defined as the police receiving enough information to locate and arrest a fugitive within 1 week.

   (a) $P(r \geq 15) = P(15 \leq r) = P(14.5 \leq x)$. 15 is a left endpoint. $np = 125(0.17) = 21.25$ and

   $nq = 125(1 - 0.17) = 125(0.83) = 103.75$, which are both greater than 5, so we can use the normal

   approximation with $\mu = np = 21.25$ and $\sigma = \sqrt{npq} = \sqrt{125(0.17)(0.83)} = \sqrt{17.6375} = 4.20$. So

   $P(14.5 \leq x) = P\left(\dfrac{14.5 - 21.25}{4.2} \leq z\right) = P(-1.61 \leq z) = P(z \geq -1.61) = 1 - P(z < -1.61) = 1 - 0.0537 = 0.9463$.

   (b) $P(r \geq 28) = P(28 \leq r)$ 28 is a left endpoint.

   $= P(27.5 \leq x)$

   $= P\left(\dfrac{27.5 - 21.25}{4.2} \leq z\right)$

   $= P(1.49 \leq z)$

   $= P(z \geq 1.49)$

   $= 1 - P(z < 1.49)$

   $= 1 - 0.9319$

   $= 0.0681$

(c) Remember, r "between" a and b is $a \leq r \leq b$.

$P(15 \leq r \leq 28) = P(14.5 \leq x \leq 28.5)$ 15 is a left endpoint and 28 is a right endpoint.

$$= P\left(\frac{14.5 - 21.25}{4.2} \leq z \leq \frac{28.5 - 21.25}{4.2}\right)$$
$$= P(-1.61 \leq z \leq 1.73)$$
$$= P(z \leq 1.73) - P(z < -1.61)$$
$$= 0.9582 - 0.0537$$
$$= 0.9045$$

(d) $n = 125$, $p = 0.17$, $q = 1 - p = 1 - 0.17 = 0.83$.

np and nq are both greater than 5, so the normal approximation is appropriate.

5. We are given $n = 753$ and $p = 3.5\% = 0.035$; $q = 1 - p = 1 - 0.035 = 0.965$.
Let a success be a person living past age 90.

(a) $P(r \geq 15) = P(15 \leq r) = P(14.5 \leq x)$ 15 is a left endpoint.

Here, $np = 753(0.035) = 26.355$, and $nq = 753(0.965) = 726.645$, both of which are greater than 5; the normal approximation is appropriate, using $\mu = np = 26.355$ and

$$\sigma = \sqrt{npq} = \sqrt{753(0.035)(0.965)} = \sqrt{25.4326} = 5.0431.$$

$$P(14.5 \leq x) = P\left(\frac{14.5 - 26.355}{5.0431} \leq z\right)$$
$$= P(-2.35 \leq z)$$
$$= P(z \geq -2.35)$$
$$= 1 - P(z < -2.35)$$
$$= 1 - 0.0094$$
$$= 0.9906$$

(b) $P(r \geq 30) = P(30 \leq r)$
$$= P(29.5 \leq x)$$
$$= P\left(\frac{29.5 - 26.355}{5.0431} \leq z\right)$$
$$= P(0.62 \leq z)$$
$$= P(z \geq 0.62)$$
$$= 1 - P(z < 0.62)$$
$$= 1 - 0.7324$$
$$= 0.2676$$

(c) $P(25 \leq r \leq 35) = P(24.5 \leq x \leq 35.5)$
$$= P\left(\frac{24.5 - 26.355}{5.0431} \leq z \leq \frac{35.5 - 26.355}{5.0431}\right)$$
$$= P(-0.37 \leq z \leq 1.81)$$
$$= P(z \leq 1.81) - P(z < -0.37)$$
$$= 0.9649 - 0.3557$$
$$= 0.6092$$

(d) $P(r > 40) = P(r \geq 41)$
$$= P(41 \leq r)$$
$$= P(40.5 \leq x)$$
$$= P\left(\frac{40.5 - 26.355}{5.0431} \leq z\right)$$
$$= P(2.80 \leq z)$$
$$= P(z \geq 2.80)$$
$$= 1 - P(z < 2.80)$$
$$= 1 - 0.9974$$
$$= 0.0026$$

7. $n = 66; p = 80\% = 0.80; q = 1 - p = 1 - 0.80 = 0.20$
A success is when a new product fails within 2 years.

(a) $P(r \geq 47) = P(47 \leq r) = P(46.5 \leq x)$

$np = 66(0.80) = 52.8$, and $nq = 66(0.20) = 13.3$. Both exceed 5, so the normal approximation with $\mu = np = 52.8$ and $\sigma = \sqrt{npq} = \sqrt{66(0.8)(0.2)} = \sqrt{10.56} = 3.2496$ is appropriate.

$$P(46.5 \leq x) = P\left(\frac{46.5 - 52.8}{3.2496} \leq z\right)$$
$$= P(-1.94 \leq z)$$
$$= P(z \geq -1.94)$$
$$= 1 - P(z < -1.94)$$
$$= 1 - 0.0262$$
$$= 0.9738$$

(b) $P(r \leq 58) = P(x \leq 58.5) = P\left(z \leq \frac{58.5 - 52.8}{3.2496}\right) = P(z \leq 1.75) = 0.9599$

For (c) and (d), note we are interested now in products succeeding, so a success is redefined to be a new product staying on the market for 2 years. Here, $n = 66$, p is now 0.20 with q is now 0.80 (p and q above have been switched. Now $np = 13.2$ and $nq = 52.8$, $\mu = 13.2$, and σ stays equal to 3.2496.

(c) $P(r \geq 15) = P(15 \leq r)$
$$= P(14.5 \leq x)$$
$$= P\left(\frac{14.5 - 13.2}{3.2496} \leq z\right)$$
$$= P(0.40 \leq z)$$
$$= P(z \geq 0.40)$$
$$= 1 - P(z < 0.40)$$
$$= 1 - 0.6554$$
$$= 0.3446$$

(d) $P(r < 10) = P(r \leq 9) = P(x \leq 9.5) = P\left(z \leq \frac{9.5 - 13.2}{3.2496}\right) = P(z \leq -1.14) = 0.1271$

9. $n = 430; p = 70\% = 0.70; q = 1 - p = 1 - 0.70 = 0.30$
A success is finding the address or lost acquaintances.

(a) $P(r > 280) = P(r \geq 281) = P(281 \leq r) = P(280.5 \leq x)$

$np = 430(0.7) = 301$ and $nq = 430(0.3) = 129$

Since both np and nq are greater than 5, the normal approximation with $\mu = np = 301$ and

$\sigma = \sqrt{npq} = \sqrt{430(0.7)(0.3)} = \sqrt{90.3} = 9.5026$ is appropriate.

$P(280.5 \leq x) = P\left(\dfrac{280.5 - 301}{9.5026} \leq z\right) = P(-2.16 \leq z) = 1 - P(z < -2.16) = 1 - 0.0154 = 0.9846$

(b) $P(r \geq 320) = P(320 \leq r)$
$\qquad\qquad\quad = P(319.5 \leq x)$
$\qquad\qquad\quad = P\left(\dfrac{319.5 - 301}{9.5026} \leq z\right)$
$\qquad\qquad\quad = P(1.95 \leq z)$
$\qquad\qquad\quad = 1 - P(z > 1.95)$
$\qquad\qquad\quad = 1 - 0.9744$
$\qquad\qquad\quad = 0.0256$

(c) $P(280 \leq r \leq 320) = P(279.5 \leq x \leq 320.5)$
$\qquad\qquad\qquad\qquad = P\left(\dfrac{279.5 - 301}{9.5026} \leq z \leq \dfrac{320.5 - 301}{9.5026}\right)$
$\qquad\qquad\qquad\qquad = P(-2.26 \leq z \leq 2.05)$
$\qquad\qquad\qquad\qquad = P(z \leq 2.05) - P(z < -2.26)$
$\qquad\qquad\qquad\qquad = 0.9798 - 0.0119$
$\qquad\qquad\qquad\qquad = 0.9679$

(d) $n = 430, p = 0.7, q = 0.3$
Both np and nq are greater than 5 so the normal approximation is appropriate, See (a).

11. $n = 850, p = 57\% = 0.57, q = 0.43$
Success = pass Ohio bar exam

(a) $P(r \geq 540) = P(540 \leq r) = P(539.5 \leq x)$

$np = 484.5, nq = 365.5, \mu = np = 484.5, \sigma = \sqrt{npq} = \sqrt{208.335} = 14.4338$

Since both np and nq are greater than 5, use normal approximation with μ and σ as above.

$P(539.5 \leq x) = P\left(\dfrac{539.5 - 484.5}{14.4338} \leq z\right) = P(3.81 \leq z) \approx 0$ (to three digits)

(b) $P(r \leq 500) = P(x \leq 500.5) = P\left(z \leq \dfrac{500.5 - 484.5}{14.4338}\right) = P(z \leq 1.11) = 0.8665$

(c) $P(485 \leq r \leq 525) = P(484.5 \leq x \leq 525.5)$
$\qquad\qquad\qquad\qquad = P\left(0 \leq z \leq \dfrac{525.5 - 484.5}{14.4338}\right)$
$\qquad\qquad\qquad\qquad = P(0 \leq z \leq 2.84)$
$\qquad\qquad\qquad\qquad = P(z \leq 2.84) - P(z < 0)$
$\qquad\qquad\qquad\qquad = 0.9977 - 0.5$
$\qquad\qquad\qquad\qquad = 0.4977$

13. $n = 267$ reservations, $P(\text{show}) = 1 - 0.06 = 0.94 = p$ so $q = 0.06$.

   (a) $p = 0.94$

   (b) Success = seat available for all who show up with a reservation, which means the number showing up must be ≤ 255 actual plane seats. Thus, $P(r \leq 255)$.

   (c) $P(r \leq 255) = P(x \leq 255.5)$

     Since $np = 267(0.94) = 250.98 > 5$ and $nq = 267(0.06) = 16.02 > 5$, use normal approximation with $\mu = np$ and $\sigma = \sqrt{npq} = \sqrt{267(0.94)(0.06)} = \sqrt{15.0588} = 3.8806$.

$$P(x \leq 255.5) = P\left(z \leq \frac{255.5 - 250.98}{3.8806}\right) = P(z \leq 1.16) = 0.8770$$

Chapter 7 Review

  1. x is normal with $\mu = 47$ and $\sigma = 6.2$

   (a) $P(x \leq 60) = P\left(z \leq \dfrac{60 - 47}{6.2}\right) = P(z \leq 2.10) = 0.9821$

   (b) $P(x \geq 50) = P\left(z \geq \dfrac{50 - 47}{6.2}\right) = P(z \geq 0.48) = 1 - P(z < 0.48) = 1 - 0.6844 = 0.3156$

   (c) $P(50 \leq x \leq 60) = P(0.48 \leq z \leq 2.10) = P(z \leq 2.10) - P(z < 0.48) = 0.9821 - 0.6844 = 0.2977$

  3. Find z_0 such that $P(z \geq z_0) = 5\% = 0.05$. Same as find z_0 such that $P(z < z_0) = 0.95$

    $P(z < 1.645) = 0.95$, so $z_0 = 1.645$

  5. $\mu = 79$, $\sigma = 9$

   (a) $z = \dfrac{x - \mu}{\sigma} = \dfrac{87 - 79}{9} = 0.89$

   (b) $z = \dfrac{79 - 79}{9} = 0$

   (c) $P(x > 85) = P\left(z > \dfrac{85 - 79}{9}\right) = P(z > 0.67) = 1 - P(z \leq 0.67) = 1 - 0.7486 = 0.2514$

  7. Binomial with $n = 400$, $p = 0.70$, and $q = 0.30$.
    Success = can recycled

   (a) $P(r \geq 300) = P(300 \leq r) = P(299.5 \leq x)$

    $np = 280 > 5$, $nq = 120 > 5$, $\sqrt{npq} = \sqrt{84} = 9.1652$

    Use normal approximation with $\mu = np$ and $\sigma = \sqrt{npq}$.

$$P(299.5 \leq x) = P\left(\frac{299.5 - 280}{9.1652} \leq z\right) = P(2.13 \leq z) = 1 - P(z < 2.13) = 1 - 0.9834 = 0.0166$$

(b) $P(260 \le r \le 300) = P(259.5 \le x \le 300.5)$

$$= P\left(\frac{259.5 - 280}{9.1652} \le z \le \frac{300.5 - 280}{9.1652}\right)$$
$$= P(-2.24 \le z \le 2.24)$$
$$= P(z \le 2.24) - P(z < -2.24)$$
$$= 0.9875 - 0.0125$$
$$= 0.9750$$

9. Delivery time x is normal with $\mu = 14$ and $\sigma = 2$ hours.

(a) $P(x \le 18) = P\left(z \le \dfrac{18 - 14}{2}\right) = P(z \le 2) = 0.9772$

(b) Find x_0 such that $P(x \le x_0) = 0.95$.

Find z_0 so that $P(z \le z_0) = 0.95$.

$P(z \le 1.645) = 0.95$, so $z_0 = 1.645$.

$x_0 = \mu + z_0\sigma = 14 + 1.645(2) = 17.29 \approx 17.3$ hours

11. (a) The $\overline{x}$ distribution approaches a normal distribution.

(b) The mean $\mu_{\overline{x}}$ of the $\overline{x}$ distribution equals the mean μ of the x distribution, regardless of the sample size.

(c) The standard deviation $\sigma_{\overline{x}}$ of the sampling distribution equals $\dfrac{\sigma}{\sqrt{n}}$, where σ is the standard deviation of the x distribution and n is the sample size.

(d) They will both be approximately normal with the same mean, but the standard deviations will be $\dfrac{\sigma}{\sqrt{50}}$ and $\dfrac{\sigma}{\sqrt{100}}$ respectively.

13. $\mu_{\overline{x}} = \mu = 100$, $\sigma_{\overline{x}} = \dfrac{\sigma}{\sqrt{n}} = \dfrac{15}{\sqrt{100}} = 1.5$

$$P(100 - 2 \le \overline{x} \le 100 + 2) = P(98 \le \overline{x} \le 102)$$
$$= P\left(\frac{98 - 100}{1.5} \le z \le \frac{102 - 100}{1.5}\right)$$
$$= P(-1.33 \le z \le 1.33)$$
$$= P(z \le 1.33) - P(z \le -1.33)$$
$$= 0.9082 - 0.0918$$
$$= 0.8164$$

Chapter 8 Estimation

Section 8.1

Answers may vary slightly due to rounding.

1. **(a)** $n = 15$, $\bar{x} = 3.15$, $\sigma = 0.33$, $c = 80\%$, $z_c = 1.28$

    $$E = \frac{z_c \sigma}{\sqrt{n}} = \frac{1.28(0.33)}{\sqrt{15}} \approx 0.11$$

    $$(\bar{x} - E) < \mu < (\bar{x} + E)$$
    $$3.15 - 0.11 < \mu < 3.15 + 0.11$$
    $$3.04 \text{ g} < \mu < 3.26 \text{ g}$$

    The margin of error, E, is 0.11 g.

    (b) The distribution of weights is assumed to be normal and σ is known.

    (c) There is an 80% chance the confidence interval is one of the intervals that contains the population average weight of Allen's hummingbirds in this region.

    (d) $n = \left(\dfrac{z_c \sigma}{E}\right)^2 \approx \left(\dfrac{(1.28)(0.33)}{0.08}\right)^2 = 27.9$

    A sample size of 28 will be large enough to satisfy the specifications.

3. **(a)** $n = 45$, $\bar{x} = 37.5$, $\sigma = 7.50$, $c = 99\%$, $z_c = 2.58$

    $$E = \frac{z_c \sigma}{\sqrt{n}} = \frac{2.58(7.50)}{\sqrt{45}} \approx 2.88$$

    $$(\bar{x} - E) < \mu < (\bar{x} + E)$$
    $$37.5 - 2.88 < \mu < 37.5 + 2.88$$
    $$34.62 \text{ ml/kg} < \mu < 40.38 \text{ ml/kg}$$

    The margin of error, E, is 2.88 ml/kg.

    (b) The sample size is large (30 or more) and σ is known.

    (c) There is a 99% chance the confidence interval is one of the intervals that contains the population average blood plasma level for male firefighters.

    (d) $n = \left(\dfrac{z_c \sigma}{E}\right)^2 \approx \left(\dfrac{(2.58)(7.50)}{2.50}\right)^2 = 59.9$

    A sample size of 60 will be large enough to satisfy the specifications.

5. $n = 30$, $\bar{x} = 138.5$, $\sigma = 42.6$

  (a) $c = 90\%$, $z_c = 1.645$

$$E = \frac{z_c \sigma}{\sqrt{n}} = \frac{1.645(42.6)}{\sqrt{30}} \approx 12.8$$

$$(\bar{x} - E) < \mu < (\bar{x} + E)$$
$$(138.5 - 12.8) < \mu < (138.5 + 12.8)$$

125.7 larceny cases $< \mu < 151.3$ larceny cases

The margin of error, E, is 12.8 larceny cases.

  (b) $c = 95\%$, $z_c = 1.96$

$$E = \frac{z_c \sigma}{\sqrt{n}} = \frac{1.96(42.6)}{\sqrt{30}} \approx 15.2$$

$$(\bar{x} - E) < \mu < (\bar{x} + E)$$
$$(138.5 - 15.2) < \mu < (138.5 + 15.2)$$

123.3 larceny cases $< \mu < 153.7$ larceny cases

The margin of error, E, is 15.2 larceny cases.

  (c) $c = 99\%$, $z_c = 2.58$

$$E = \frac{z_c \sigma}{\sqrt{n}} = \frac{2.58(42.6)}{\sqrt{30}} \approx 20.1$$

$$(\bar{x} - E) < \mu < (\bar{x} + E)$$
$$(138.5 - 20.1) < \mu < (138.5 + 20.1)$$

118.4 larceny cases $< \mu < 158.6$ larceny cases

The margin of error, E, is 20.1 larceny cases.

  (d) Yes.

  (e) Yes.

7. $\bar{x} = 58,940$, $\sigma = 18,490$, $c = 90\%$, $z_c = 1.645$

  (a) $n = 36$

$$E = \frac{z_c \sigma}{\sqrt{n}} = \frac{1.645(18,490)}{\sqrt{36}} \approx 5069$$

$$(\bar{x} - E) < \mu < (\bar{x} + E)$$
$$58,940 - 5069 < \mu < 58,940 + 5069$$
$$\$53,871 < \mu < \$64,009$$

The margin of error, E, is \$5069.

  (b) $n = 64$

$$E = \frac{z_c \sigma}{\sqrt{n}} = \frac{1.645(18,490)}{\sqrt{64}} \approx 3802$$

$$(\bar{x} - E) < \mu < (\bar{x} + E)$$
$$(58,940 - 3802) < \mu < (58,940 + 3802)$$
$$\$55,138 < \mu < \$62,742$$

The margin of error, E, is \$3802.

(c) $n = 121$

$$E = \frac{z_c \sigma}{\sqrt{n}} = \frac{1.645(18,490)}{\sqrt{121}} \approx 2765$$

$$(\bar{x} - E) < \mu < (\bar{x} + E)$$
$$(58,940 - 2765) < \mu < (58,940 + 2765)$$
$$\$56,175 < \mu < \$61,705$$

The margin of error, E, is $2765.

(d) Yes.

(e) Yes.

9. (a) $n = 42, \ \bar{x} = \dfrac{\sum x_i}{n} = \dfrac{1511.8}{42} = 35.9952 \approx 36.0, \text{ as stated.}$

(b) $c = 75\%, \ z_c = 1.15$

$$E \approx \frac{z_c \sigma}{\sqrt{n}} = \frac{1.15(10.2)}{\sqrt{42}} = 1.81$$

$$(\bar{x} - E) < \mu < (\bar{x} + E)$$
$$(36.0 - 1.81) < \mu < (36.0 + 1.81)$$
$$34.19 < \mu < 37.81 \text{ thousand dollars per employee profit}$$

(c) Yes. Since $30 thousand per employee profit is less than the lower limit of the confidence interval (34.19), your bank profits are low compared to other similar financial institutions.

(d) Yes. Since $40 thousand per employee profit exceeds the upper limit of the confidence interval (37.81), your bank profit is higher than other similar financial institutions.

(e) $c = 90\%, \ z_c = 1.645$

$$E \approx \frac{z_c \sigma}{\sqrt{n}} = \frac{1.645(10.2)}{\sqrt{42}} = 2.59$$

$$(\bar{x} - E) < \mu < (\bar{x} + E)$$
$$(36.0 - 2.59) < \mu < (36.0 + 2.59)$$
$$33.41 < \mu < 38.59 \text{ thousand dollars per employee profit}$$

Yes. $30 thousand is less than the lower limit of the confidence interval (33.41), so your bank's profit is less than that of other financial institutions.

Yes. $40 thousand is more than the upper limit of the confidence interval (38.59), so your bank is doing better (profit-wise) than other financial institutions.

Section 8.2

Answers may vary slightly due to rounding.

1. $n = 18$ so $d.f. = n - 1 = 18 - 1 = 17, \ c = 0.95$
$t_c = t_{0.95} = 2.110$

3. $n = 22$ so $d.f. = n - 1 = 22 - 1 = 21, \ c = 0.90$
$t_c = t_{0.90} = 1.721$

5. $n = 9$ so $d.f. = n - 1 = 9 - 1 = 8$

  (a) $\bar{x} = \dfrac{\Sigma x}{n} = \dfrac{11,450}{9} \approx 1272$, as stated

  $$s^2 = \frac{\Sigma x_i^2 - \dfrac{(\Sigma x_i)^2}{n}}{n-1} = \frac{14,577,854 - \dfrac{(11,450)^2}{9}}{8} = 1363.6944$$

  $s = \sqrt{1363.6944} = 36.9282 \approx 37$, as stated

  (b) $c = 90\%$, $t_c = t_{0.90}$ with 8 $d.f. = 1.860$

  $$E = \frac{t_c s}{\sqrt{n}} = \frac{1.86(37)}{\sqrt{9}} = 22.94 \approx 23$$

  $(\bar{x} - E) < \mu < (\bar{x} + E)$

  $(1272 - 23) < \mu < (1272 + 23)$

  1249 A.D. $< \mu < $ 1295 A.D.

7. $n = 6$ so $d.f. = n - 1 = 5$

  (a) $\bar{x} = 91.0$, as stated

  $s = 30.7181 \approx 30.7$, as stated

  (b) $c = 75\%$, so $t_{0.75}$ with 5 $d.f. = 1.301$

  $$E = \frac{t_c s}{\sqrt{n}} = \frac{1.301(30.7)}{\sqrt{6}} \approx 16.3$$

  $(\bar{x} - E) < \mu < (\bar{x} + E)$

  $(91.0 - 16.3) < \mu < (91.0 + 16.3)$

  74.7 pounds $< \mu < $ 107.3 pounds

9. $n = 10$, so $d.f. = n - 1 = 9$

  (a) $\bar{x} = 9.9500 \approx 9.95$, as stated.

  $s \approx 1.0212 \approx 1.02$, as stated.

  (b) $c = 99.9\%$, so $t_{0.999}$ with 9 $d.f. = 4.781$

  $$E = \frac{t_c s}{\sqrt{n}} = \frac{4.781(1.02)}{\sqrt{10}} \approx 1.54$$

  $(\bar{x} - E) < \mu < (x + E)$

  $9.95 - 1.54 < \mu < 9.95 + 1.54$

  8.41 mg/dl $< \mu < $ 11.49 mg/dl

  (c) Since all values in the 99.9% confidence interval are above 6 mg/dl, we can be almost certain that this patient does not have a calcium deficiency.

11. Notice that the four figures are drawn on different scales.

(a) The box plots differ in range (distance between whisker ends), in interquartile range (distance between box ends), in medians (line through boxes), in symmetry (indicated by the placement of the median within the box, and by the placement of the median relative to the whisker endpoints), in whisker lengths, and in the presence/absence of outliers. These differences are to be expected since each box plot represents a different sample of size 20. (Although the data sets were all selected as samples of size $n = 20$ from a normal distribution with $\mu = 68$ and $\sigma = 3$, it is very interesting that Sample 2, figure (b), shows 2 outliers.)

(b)

Sample	Confidence interval width	Includes $\mu = 68$?
1	$69.407 - 66.692 = 2.715$	Yes
2	$69.426 - 66.490 = 2.936$	Yes
3	$69.211 - 66.741 = 2.470$	Yes
4	$68.050 - 65.766 = 2.284$	Yes (barely)

The intervals differ in length; all four enclose $\mu = 68$. If many additional samples of size 20 were generated from this distribution, we would expect about 95% of the confidence intervals created from these samples to enclose the number 68; in approximately 5% of the intervals, 68 would be outside the confidence interval, i.e., 68 would be less than the lower limit or greater than the upper limit. Drawing all these samples (at least conceptually), checking whether or not the confidence intervals include the number 68, and keeping track of the percentage that do, is an illustration of the definition of (95%) confidence intervals.

13. (a) $\bar{x} = 25.176 \approx 25.2$, as stated
$s = 15.472 \approx 15.5$, as stated

(b) $n = 51$, so $d.f. = n - 1 = 50$
$c = 90\%$, $t_{0.90}$ with 50 $d.f. = 1.676$

$$E = \frac{t_c s}{\sqrt{n}} = \frac{1.676(15.5)}{\sqrt{51}} = 3.6$$
$$(\bar{x} - E) < \mu < (\bar{x} + E)$$
$$(25.2 - 3.6) < \mu < (25.2 + 3.6)$$
$$21.6 < \mu < 28.8$$

(c) $c = 99\%$, $t_{0.99}$ with 50 $d.f. = 2.678$

$$E = \frac{t_c s}{\sqrt{n}} = \frac{2.678(15.5)}{\sqrt{51}} \approx 5.8$$
$$(\bar{x} - E) < \mu < (\bar{x} + E)$$
$$(25.2 - 5.8) < \mu < (25.2 + 5.8)$$
$$19.4 < \mu < 31.0$$

(d) Using both confidence intervals, we can say that the P/E for Bank One is well below the population average. The P/E for AT&T Wireless is well above the population average. The P/E for Disney is within both confidence intervals. It appears that the P/E for Disney is close to the population average P/E.

(e) By the central limit theorem, when n is large the $\bar{x}$ distribution is approximately normal. In general, $n \geq 30$ is considered large.

15. (a) $n = 31$, $d.f. = n - 1 = 30$, $\bar{x} = 45.2$, $s = 5.3$

$c = 90\%$, $t_{0.90} = 1.697$, $E = \dfrac{t_c s}{\sqrt{n}} = \dfrac{1.697(5.3)}{\sqrt{31}} \approx 1.62$

$c = 95\%$, $t_{0.95} = 2.042$, $E = \dfrac{t_c s}{\sqrt{n}} = \dfrac{2.042(5.3)}{\sqrt{31}} \approx 1.94$

$c = 99\%$, $t_{0.99} = 2.750$, $E = \dfrac{t_c s}{\sqrt{n}} = \dfrac{2.750(5.3)}{\sqrt{31}} \approx 2.62$

90% C.I.: $(45.2 - 1.62) < \mu < (45.2 + 1.62)$
$43.58 < \mu < 46.82$

95% C.I.: $(45.2 - 1.94) < \mu < (45.2 + 1.94)$
$43.26 < \mu < 47.14$

99% C.I.: $(45.2 - 2.62) < \mu < (45.2 + 2.62)$
$42.58 < \mu < 47.82$

(b) $n = 31$, $\bar{x} = 45.2$, $\sigma = 5.3$

$c = 90\%$, $z_{0.90} = 1.645$, $E = \dfrac{z_c \sigma}{\sqrt{n}} = \dfrac{1.645(5.3)}{\sqrt{31}} \approx 1.57$

$c = 95\%$, $z_{0.95} = 1.96$, $E = \dfrac{z_c \sigma}{\sqrt{n}} = \dfrac{1.96(5.3)}{\sqrt{31}} \approx 1.87$

$c = 99\%$, $z_{0.99} = 2.58$, $E = \dfrac{z_c \sigma}{\sqrt{n}} = \dfrac{2.58(5.3)}{\sqrt{31}} \approx 2.46$

90% C.I.: $(45.2 - 1.57) < \mu < (45.2 + 1.57)$
$43.63 < \mu < 46.77$

95% C.I.: $(45.2 - 1.87) < \mu < (45.2 + 1.87)$
$43.33 < \mu < 47.07$

99% C.I.: $(45.2 - 2.46) < \mu < (45.2 + 2.46)$
$42.74 < \mu < 47.66$

(c) Yes; the respective intervals based on the Student's t distribution are slightly longer.

(d) For Student's t, $n = 81$, $d.f. = n - 1 = 80$, $\bar{x} = 45.2$, $s = 5.3$

$c = 90\%$, $t_{0.90} = 1.664$, $E = \dfrac{t_c s}{\sqrt{n}} = \dfrac{1.664(5.3)}{\sqrt{81}} \approx 0.98$

$c = 95\%$, $t_{0.95} = 1.990$, $E = \dfrac{t_c s}{\sqrt{n}} = \dfrac{1.990(5.3)}{\sqrt{81}} \approx 1.17$

$c = 99\%$, $t_{0.99} = 2.639$, $E = \dfrac{t_c s}{\sqrt{n}} = \dfrac{2.639(5.3)}{\sqrt{81}} \approx 1.55$

90% C.I.: $(45.2 - 0.98) < \mu < (45.2 + 0.98)$
$44.22 < \mu < 46.18$

95% C.I.: $(45.2 - 1.17) < \mu < (45.2 + 1.17)$
$44.03 < \mu < 46.37$

99% C.I.: $(45.2 - 1.55) < \mu < (45.2 + 1.55)$
$43.65 < \mu < 46.75$

For standard normal, $n = 81$, $\bar{x} = 45.2$, $\sigma = 5.3$

$c = 90\%$, $z_{0.90} = 1.645$, $E = \dfrac{z_c \sigma}{\sqrt{n}} = \dfrac{1.645(5.3)}{\sqrt{81}} \approx 0.97$

$c = 95\%$, $z_{0.95} = 1.96$, $E = \dfrac{z_c \sigma}{\sqrt{n}} = \dfrac{1.96(5.3)}{\sqrt{81}} \approx 1.15$

$c = 99\%$, $z_{0.99} = 2.58$, $E = \dfrac{z_c \sigma}{\sqrt{n}} = \dfrac{2.58(5.3)}{\sqrt{81}} \approx 1.52$

90% C.I.: $(45.2 - 0.97) < \mu < (45.2 + 0.97)$
$$44.23 < \mu < 46.17$$

95% C.I.: $(45.2 - 1.15) < \mu < (45.2 + 1.15)$
$$44.05 < \mu < 46.35$$

99% C.I.: $(45.2 - 1.52) < \mu < (45.2 + 1.52)$
$$43.68 < \mu < 46.72$$

The intervals using the t distribution are still slightly longer than corresponding intervals using the standard normal distribution. However, with a larger sample size, the differences between the two methods is less pronounced.

Section 8.3

Answers may vary slightly due to rounding.

1. $r = 39$, $n = 62$, $\hat{p} = \dfrac{r}{n} = \dfrac{39}{62}$, $\hat{q} = 1 - \hat{p} = \dfrac{23}{62}$

    (a) $\hat{p} = \dfrac{39}{62} = 0.6290$

    (b) $c = 95\%, z_c = z_{0.95} = 1.96$

        $E \approx z_c \sqrt{\hat{p}\hat{q}/n} = 1.96\sqrt{(0.6290)(1 - 0.6290)/62} = 0.1202$

        $(\hat{p} - E) < p < (\hat{p} + E)$

        $(0.6290 - 0.1202) < p < (0.6290 + 0.1202)$

        $0.5088 < p < 0.7492$ or approximately 0.51 to 0.75.

    We are 95% confident that the true proportion of actors who are extroverts is between 0.51 and 0.75, approximately. In repeated sampling from the same population, approximately 95% of the samples would generate confidence intervals that would enclose the true value of $\hat{p}$.

    (c) $np \approx n\hat{p} = r = 39$

        $nq \approx n\hat{q} = n - r = 62 - 39 = 23$

    It is quite likely that np and $nq > 5$, since their estimates are much larger than 5. If np and $nq > 5$ then $\hat{p}$ is approximately normal with $\mu = p$ and $\sigma = \sqrt{pq/n}$. This forms the basis for the large sample confidence interval derivation.

3. $n = 5222$, $r = 1619$

    (a) $\hat{p} = \dfrac{r}{n} = \dfrac{1619}{5222} = 0.3100$

        so $\hat{q} = 1 - \hat{p} = 0.6900$

(b) $c = 99\%$, so $z_c = 2.58$

$$E \approx z_c\sqrt{\hat{p}\hat{q}/n} = 2.58\sqrt{(0.3100)(0.6900)/5222} = 0.0165$$
$$(\hat{p}-E) < p < (\hat{p}+E)$$
$$(0.3100-0.0165) < p < (0.3100+0.0165)$$
$0.2935 < p < 0.3265$ or approximately 0.29 and 0.33.

In repeated sampling, approximately 99% of the confidence intervals generated from the samples would include p, the proportion of judges who are hogans.

(c) $np \approx n\hat{p} = r = 1619, nq \approx n\hat{q} = n(1-\hat{p}) = n-r = 3603$

Since the estimates of np and nq are much greater than 5, it is reasonable to assume np and $nq > 5$. Then we can use the normal distribution with $\mu = p$ and $\sigma = \sqrt{pq/n}$ to approximate the distribution of $\hat{p}$.

5. $n = 5792, r = 3139$

(a) $\hat{p} = \dfrac{r}{n} = \dfrac{3139}{5792} = 0.5420$

so $\hat{q} = 1-\hat{p} = 0.4580$

(b) $c = 99\%$, so $z_c = 2.58$

$$E \approx z_c\sqrt{\hat{p}\hat{q}/n} = 2.58\sqrt{(0.5420)(0.4580)/5792} = 0.0169$$
$$(\hat{p}-E) < p < (\hat{p}+E)$$
$$(0.5420-0.0169) < p < (0.5420+0.0169)$$
$0.5251 < p < 0.5589,$ or approximately 0.53 to 0.56.

If we drew many samples of size 5792 physicians from those in Colorado, and generated a confidence interval from each sample, we would expect approximately 99% of the intervals to include the true proportion of Colorado physicians providing at least some charity care.

(c) $np \approx n\hat{p} = r = 3139 > 5; nq \approx n\hat{q} = n-r = 2653 > 5.$

Since the estimates of np and nq are much larger than 5, it is reasonable to assume np and nq are both greater than 5. Under the circumstances, it is appropriate to approximate the distribution of $\hat{p}$ with a normal distribution with $\mu = p$ and $\sigma = \sqrt{pq/n}$.

7. $n = 855, r = 26$

(a) $\hat{p} = \dfrac{r}{n} = \dfrac{26}{855} = 0.0304$

so $\hat{q} = 1-\hat{p} = 0.9696$

(b) $c = 99\%$, so $z_c = 2.58$

$$E \approx z_c\sqrt{\hat{p}\hat{q}/n} = 2.58\sqrt{(0.0304)(0.9696)/855} = 0.0151$$
$$(\hat{p}-E) < p < (\hat{p}+E)$$
$$(0.0304-0.0151) < p < (0.0304+0.0151)$$
$0.0153 < p < 0.0455,$ or approximately 0.02 to 0.05.

If many additional samples of size $n = 855$ were drawn from this fish population, and a confidence interval was created from each such sample, approximately 99% of those confidence intervals would contain p, the catch-and-release mortality rate (barbless hooks removed).

(c) $np \approx n\hat{p} = r = 26 > 5; nq \approx n\hat{q} = n-r = 829 > 5.$

Based on the estimates of np and nq, it is safe to assume both np and $nq > 5$. When np and $nq > 5$, the distribution of $\hat{p}$ can be accurately approximated by a normal distribution with $\mu = p$ and

$$\sigma = \sqrt{pq/n}.$$

9. $n = 730$, $r = 628$, $n - r = 102$; both np and $nq > 5$.

(a) $\hat{p} = \dfrac{r}{n} = \dfrac{628}{730} = 0.8603$, so $\hat{q} = 0.1397$

(b) $c = 95\%$, so $z_c = 1.96$

$E \approx z_c \sqrt{\hat{p}\hat{q}/n} = 1.96\sqrt{(0.8603)(0.1397)/730} = 0.0251$

$(\hat{p} - E) < p < (\hat{p} + E)$

$(0.8603 - 0.0251) < p < (0.8603 + 0.0251)$

$0.8352 < p < 0.8854$, or approximately 0.84 to 0.89.

In repeated sampling, approximately 95% of the intervals created from the samples would include p, the proportion of loyal women shoppers.

(c) Margin of error $= E \approx 2.5\%$

A recent study shows that about 86% of women shoppers remained loyal to their favorite supermarket last year. The study's margin of error is 2.5 percentage points.

11. $n = 1000$, $r = 250$, $n - r = 750$; both np and $nq > 5$.

(a) $\hat{p} = \dfrac{r}{n} = \dfrac{250}{1000} = 0.2500$, so $\hat{q} = 0.7500$

(b) $c = 95\%$, so $z_c = 1.96$

$E \approx z_c \sqrt{\hat{p}\hat{q}/n} = 1.96\sqrt{(0.2500)(0.7500)/1000} = 0.0268$

$(\hat{p} - E) < p < (\hat{p} + E)$

$(0.2500 - 0.0268) < p < (0.2500 + 0.0268)$

$0.2232 < p < 0.2768$, or approximately 0.22 to 0.28.

(c) Margin of error $= E \approx 2.7\%$

In a survey of 1000 large corporations, 25% admitted that, given a choice between equally qualified applicants, they would offer the job to the nonsmoker. The survey's margin of error was 2.7 percentage points.

13. The goal is to estimate the proportion, p, who have blood type B.

Use $n = pq(z_c/E)^2$.

(a) $c = 85\%$, $z_c = 1.44$, $E = 0.05$

With no preliminary estimate of p, we will use $p = q = 0.5$, which maximizes the value of $pq = p(1 - p)$, and, therefore, maximizes the value of n; no other choice of p would give a larger n. The "worst case" scenario, when pq and n are the largest values possible, occurs when

$p = q = \frac{1}{2} = 0.5$.

Then, $n = pq(z_c/E)^2 \approx 0.5 \cdot 0.5(z_c/E)^2 = 0.25(z_c/E)^2 = 0.25(1.44/0.05)^2 = 207.36$, which is rounded up to 208 people.

(b) $\hat{p} = 8/90$ is a preliminary estimate of p; $q = 1 - p$, so $\hat{q} = 1 - \hat{p} = \dfrac{82}{90}$ is a preliminary estimate of q.

Then $n = pq(z_c/E)^2 \approx (8/90)(82/90)(1.44/0.05)^2 \approx 67.2$, or, rounded up, 68 people.

(Note that this sample size is much, much smaller than the sample size of $n = 208$ derived in part (a) where, in the absence of a preliminary estimate of p, we used the worst case estimate of $p, \hat{p} = 1/2$.)

15. The goal is to estimate the proportion of women students; use $n = pq(z_c / E)^2$.

    (a) $c = 99\%, z_c = 2.58, E = 0.05$

        Since there is no preliminary estimate of p, we'll use the "worst case" estimate, $\hat{p} = \frac{1}{2}, \hat{q} = 1 - \hat{p} = \frac{1}{2}$.

          $n \approx 0.5 \cdot 0.5(z_c / E)^2 = 0.25(z_c / E)^2 = 0.25(2.58 / 0.05)^2 = 665.6$, or 666 students.

    (b) Preliminary estimate of p: $\hat{p} = 54\% = 0.54, \hat{q} = 1 - \hat{p} = 0.46$.

          $n \approx (0.54)(0.46)(2.58 / 0.05)^2 = 661.4 \approx 662$ students.

        (There is very little difference between (a) and (b) because (a) uses

        $\hat{p} = \frac{1}{2} = 0.50$ and (b) uses $\hat{p} = 0.54$, and the $\hat{p}$s are approximately the same.)

Chapter 8 Review

1. **point estimate:** a single number used to estimate a population parameter
   critical value: the x-axis values (arguments) of a probability density function (such as the standard normal or Student's t) which cut off an area of c, $0 \le c \le 1$, under the curve between them. Examples: the area under the standard normal curve between $-z_c$ and $+z_c$ is c; the area under the curve of a Student's t distribution between $-t_c$ and $+t_c$ as c. The area is symmetric about the curve's mean, μ.
   maximal margin of error, E: the largest distance ("error") between the point estimate and the parameter it estimates that can be tolerated under certain circumstances; E is the half-width of a confidence interval.
   confidence level, c: A measure of the reliability of an (interval) estimate: c denotes the proportion of all possible confidence interval estimates of a parameter (or difference between 2 parameters) that will include the true value being estimated. It is a statement about the probability the <u>procedure</u> being used will capture the value of interest; it <u>cannot</u> be considered a measure of the reliability of a <u>specific</u> interval, because any specific interval is either right or wrong—either it captures the parameter value, or it does not.
   confidence interval: a procedure designed to give a range of values as an (interval) estimate of an unknown parameter value; compare point estimate. What separates confidence interval estimates from any other interval estimate (such as 4, give or take 2.8) is that the <u>reliability</u> of the procedure can be determined: if $c = 0.90 = 90\%$, for example, a 90% confidence interval (estimate) for μ says that if all possible samples of size n were drawn, and a 90% confidence interval for μ was created for each such sample using the prescribed method (such as $\bar{x} \pm z_c \sigma / \sqrt{n}$), then if the true value of μ became known, 90% of the confidence intervals so created would include the value of μ.

3. $n = 73$, $\bar{x} = 178.70$, $\sigma = 7.81$, $c = 95\%$, $z_c = 1.96$

    $E \approx \dfrac{z_c \sigma}{\sqrt{n}} = \dfrac{1.96(7.81)}{\sqrt{73}} = 1.7916 \approx 1.79$

    $(\bar{x} - E) < \mu < (\bar{x} + E)$

    $(178.70 - 1.79) < \mu < (178.70 + 1.79)$

    $176.91 < \mu < 180.49$

5. **(a)** $\bar{x} = 74.2, s = 18.2530 \approx 18.3$, as indicated

    (b) $c = 95\%, n = 15$, $t_{0.95}$ with $n - 1 = 14$ d.f. $= 2.145$

        $E \approx \dfrac{t_c s}{\sqrt{n}} = \dfrac{2.145(18.3)}{\sqrt{15}} = 10.1352 \approx 10.1$

        $(\bar{x} - E) < \mu < (\bar{x} + E)$

        $(74.2 - 10.1) < \mu < (74.2 + 10.1)$

        64.1 centimeters $< \mu <$ 84.3 centimeters

7. $n = 2958,\ r = 1538,\ \hat{p} = \dfrac{r}{n} = \dfrac{1538}{2958} = 0.5199 \approx 0.52$

$\hat{q} = 1 - \hat{p} = 0.4801,\ n - r = 1420,\ c = 90\%,\ z_c = 1.645$

$np \approx n\hat{p} = r = 1538 > 5,\ nq \approx n\hat{q} = n - r = 1420 > 5$

$E \approx z_c \sqrt{\dfrac{\hat{p}\hat{q}}{n}} = 1.645\sqrt{\dfrac{(0.5199)(0.4801)}{2958}} = 0.0151 \approx 0.02$

$(\hat{p} - E) < p < (\hat{p} + E)$

$(0.52 - 0.02) < p < (0.52 + 0.02)$

$0.50 < p < 0.54$

9. $n = 167,\ r = 68$

(a) $\hat{p} = \dfrac{r}{n} = \dfrac{68}{167} = 0.4072,\ \hat{q} = 0.5928,\ n - r = 99$

(b) $n\hat{p} = r = 68 > 5$ and $n\hat{q} = n - r = 99 > 5$

$c = 95\%,\ z_c = 1.96$

$E \approx z_c \sqrt{\dfrac{\hat{p}\hat{q}}{n}} = 1.96\sqrt{\dfrac{(0.4072)(0.5928)}{167}} = 0.0745$

$(\hat{p} - E) < p < (\hat{p} + E)$

$(0.4072 - 0.0745) < p < (0.4072 + 0.0745)$

$0.3327 < p < 0.4817,$ or approximately 0.333 to 0.482

Chapter 9 Hypothesis Testing

Section 9.1

1. See text for definitions. Essay may include:

   (a) A working hypothesis about the population parameter in question is called the null hypothesis. The value specified in the null hypothesis is often a historical value, a claim, or a production specification.

   (b) Any hypothesis that differs from the null hypothesis is called an alternate hypothesis.

   (c) If we reject the null hypothesis when it is in fact true, we have an error that is called a type I error. On the other hand, if we accept (i.e., fail to reject) the null hypothesis when it is in fact false, we have made an error that is called a type II error.

   (d) The probability with which we are willing to risk a type I error is called the level of significance of a test. The probability of making a type II error is denoted by β.

3. No, if we fail to reject the null hypothesis, we have not proven it to be true beyond all doubt. The evidence is not sufficient to merit rejecting H_0.

5. (a) The claim is $\mu = 60$ kg, so you would use $H_0: \mu = 60$ kg.

   (b) We want to know if the average weight is less than 60 kg, so you would use $H_1: \mu < 60$ kg.

   (c) We want to know if the average weight is greater than 60 kg, so you would use $H_1: \mu > 60$ kg.

   (d) We want to know if the average weight is different from (more or less than) 60 kg, so you would use $H_1: \mu \neq 60$ kg.

   (e) Since part (b) is a left-tailed test, the critical region is on the left. Since part (c) is a right-tailed test, the critical region is on the right. Since part (d) is a two-tailed test, the critical region is on both sides of the mean.

7. (a) The claim is $\mu = 16.4$ ft, so $H_0: \mu = 16.4$ ft.

   (b) You want to know if the average is getting larger, so $H_1: \mu > 16.4$ ft.

   (c) You want to know if the average is getting smaller, so $H_1: \mu < 16.4$ ft.

   (d) You want to know if the average is different from 16.4 ft, so $H_1: \mu \neq 16.4$ ft.

   (e) Since part (b) is a right-tailed test, the area corresponding to the P-value is on the right. Since part (c) is a left-tailed test, the area corresponding to the P-value is on the left. Since part (d) is a two-tailed test, the area corresponding to the P-value is on both sides of the mean.

9. (a) $\alpha = 0.01$
   $H_0: \mu = 4.7\%$
   $H_1: \mu > 4.7\%$
   Since $>$ is in H_1, use a right-tailed test.

(b) Use the standard normal distribution. We assume x has a normal distribution with known standard deviation σ. Note that μ is given in the null hypothesis.

$$z = \frac{\overline{x} - \mu}{\frac{\sigma}{\sqrt{n}}} = \frac{5.38 - 4.7}{\frac{2.4}{\sqrt{10}}} \approx 0.90$$

(c) P-value $= P(z > 0.90) = 0.1841$

P value

$z = 0$ z

$z = 0.90$
or
$\overline{x} = 5.38$
Sample Test Statistic

(d) Since a P-value of $0.1841 > 0.01$ for α, we fail to reject H_0. No

(e) There is insufficient evidence at the 0.01 level to reject the claim that average yield for bank stocks equals average yield for all stocks.

11. (a) $\alpha = 0.01$
$H_0\colon \mu = 4.55$ g
$H_1\colon \mu < 4.55$ g
Since $<$ is in H_1, use a left-tailed test.

(b) Use the standard normal distribution. We assume x has a normal distribution with known standard deviation σ. Note that μ is given in the null hypothesis.

$$z = \frac{\overline{x} - \mu}{\frac{\sigma}{\sqrt{n}}} = \frac{3.75 - 4.55}{\frac{0.70}{\sqrt{6}}} \approx -2.80$$

(c) P-value $= P(z < -2.80) = 0.0026$

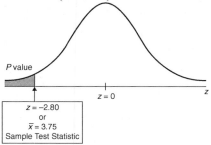

P value

$z = 0$ z

$z = -2.80$
or
$\overline{x} = 3.75$
Sample Test Statistic

(d) Since a P-value of $0.0026 \le 0.01$ for α, we reject H_0. Yes.

(e) The sample evidence is sufficient at the 0.01 level to justify rejecting H_0. It seems the humming birds in the Grand Canyon region have a lower average weight.

13. (a) $\alpha = 0.01$

$H_0: \mu = 11\%$

$H_1: \mu \neq 11\%$

Since $\neq$ is in H_1, use a two-tailed test.

(b) Use the standard normal distribution. We assume x has a normal distribution with known standard deviation σ. Note that μ is given in the null hypothesis.

$$z = \frac{\bar{x} - \mu}{\frac{\sigma}{\sqrt{n}}} = \frac{12.5 - 11}{\frac{5.0}{\sqrt{16}}} = 1.20$$

(c) P-value $= 2P(z > 1.20) = 2(0.1151) = 0.2302$

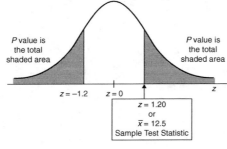

(d) Since a P-value of $0.2302 > 0.01$ for α, we fail to reject H_0. No.

(e) There is insufficient evidence at the 0.01 level of significance to reject H_0. It seems the average hail damage to wheat crops in Weld County matches the national average.

Section 9.2

1. (a) $\alpha = 0.01$

$H_0: \mu = 16.4$ ft

$H_1: \mu > 16.4$ ft

(b) Use the standard normal distribution. The sample size is large, $n \geq 30$, and we know σ.

$$z = \frac{\bar{x} - \mu}{\frac{\sigma}{\sqrt{n}}} = \frac{17.3 - 16.4}{\frac{3.5}{\sqrt{36}}} \approx 1.54$$

(c) P-value $= P(z > 1.54) = 0.0618$

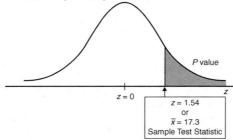

(d) Since a P-value of $0.0618 > 0.01$ for α, we fail to reject H_0. No.

(e) At the 1% level of significance, there is insufficient evidence to say average storm level is increasing.

3. (a) $\alpha = 0.05$
H_0: $\mu = 41.7$
H_1: $\mu \neq 41.7$

(b) Use a standard normal distribution. The sample size is large, $n \geq 30$, and we know σ.
$$z = \frac{\bar{x} - \mu}{\frac{\sigma}{\sqrt{n}}} = \frac{36.2 - 41.7}{\frac{18.5}{\sqrt{45}}} \approx -1.99$$

(c) P-value $= 2P(z < -1.99) = 2(0.0233) = 0.0466$

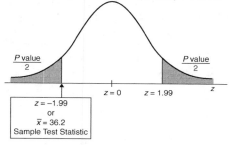

(d) Since a P-value of $0.0466 \leq 0.05$ for α, we reject H_0. Yes.

(e) At the 5% level of significance, there is sufficient evidence to say the average number of e-mails is different with the new priority system.

5. (a) $\alpha = 0.01$
H_0: $\mu = 1.75$ yr
H_1: $\mu > 1.75$ yr

(b) Use the Student's t distribution with $d.f. = n - 1 = 46 - 1 = 45$. The sample size is large, $n \geq 30$, and σ is unknown.
$$t = \frac{\bar{x} - \mu}{\frac{s}{\sqrt{n}}} = \frac{2.05 - 1.75}{\frac{0.82}{\sqrt{46}}} \approx 2.481$$

(c) For $d.f. = 45$, 2.481 falls between entries 2.412 and 2.690. Use one-tailed areas to find that $0.005 < P\text{-value} < 0.010$.

(d) Since the entire P-value interval ≤ 0.01 for α, we reject H_0. Yes.

(e) At the 1% level of significance, sample data indicate the average age of the Minnesota region Coyotes is higher than 1.75 years.

7. **(a)** $\alpha = 0.05$
   $H_0: \mu = 19.4$
   $H_1: \mu \neq 19.4$

(b) Use the Student's t distribution with $d.f. = n - 1 = 36 - 1 = 35$. The sample size is large, $n \geq 30$, and σ is unknown.

$$t = \frac{\bar{x} - \mu}{\frac{s}{\sqrt{n}}} = \frac{17.9 - 19.4}{\frac{5.2}{\sqrt{36}}} \approx -1.731$$

(c) For $d.f. = 35$, 1.731 falls between entries 1.690 and 2.030. Use two-tailed areas to find that $0.05 < P\text{-value} < 0.100$.

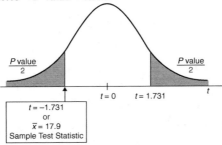

(d) Since the P-value interval > 0.05 for α, we fail to reject H_0. No.

(e) At the 5% level of significance, the sample evidence does not support rejecting the claim that the average P/E for socially responsible funds is different from that of the S&P Stock Index.

9. **(i)** Use a calculator to verify. Rounded values are used in part ii.

(ii) (a) $\alpha = 0.05$
   $H_0: \mu = 4.8$
   $H_1: \mu < 4.8$

(b) Use the Student's t distribution with $d.f. = n - 1 = 6 - 1 = 5$. We assume x has a distribution that is approximately normal and σ is unknown.

$$t = \frac{\bar{x} - \mu}{\frac{s}{\sqrt{n}}} = \frac{4.40 - 4.8}{\frac{0.28}{\sqrt{6}}} \approx -3.499$$

(c) For $d.f. = 5$, 3.499 falls between entries 3.365 and 4.032. Use one-tailed areas to find that $0.005 < P\text{-value} < 0.010$.

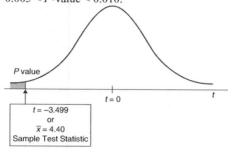

(d) Since the entire P-value interval ≤ 0.05 for α, we reject H_0. Yes.

(e) At the 5% level of significance, sample evidence supports the claim that the average RBC count for this patient is less than 4.8.

11. **(i)** Use a calculator to verify. Rounded values are used in part ii.

    (ii) (a) $\alpha = 0.01$
          $H_0: \mu = 67$
          $H_1: \mu \neq 67$

    (b) Use the Student's t distribution with $d.f. = n - 1 = 16 - 1 = 15$. We assume x has a distribution that is approximately normal and σ is unknown.

$$t = \frac{\bar{x} - \mu}{\frac{s}{\sqrt{n}}} = \frac{61.8 - 67}{\frac{10.6}{\sqrt{16}}} \approx -1.962$$

    (c) For $d.f. = 15$, 1.962 falls between entries 1.753 and 2.131. Use two-tailed areas to find that $0.050 < P\text{-value} < 0.100$.

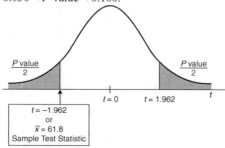

    (d) Since P-value interval > 0.01 for α, we fail to reject H_0. No.

(e) At the 1% level of significance, sample evidence does not support a claim that the average thickness of slab avalanches in Vail is different from those in Canada.

13. (i) Use a calculator to verify. Rounded values are used in part ii.

(ii) (a) $\alpha = 0.05$
H_0: $\mu = 40$ beats per min
H_1: $\mu \neq 40$ beats per min

(b) Use the Student's t distribution with $d.f. = n - 1 = 6 - 1 = 5$. We assume x has a distribution that is approximately normal and σ is unknown.

$$t = \frac{\bar{x} - \mu}{\frac{s}{\sqrt{n}}} = \frac{36.5 - 40}{\frac{4.2}{\sqrt{6}}} \approx -2.041$$

(c) For $d.f. = 5$, 2.041 falls between entries 2.015 and 2.571. Use two-tailed areas to find that $0.050 < P\text{-value} < 0.100$.

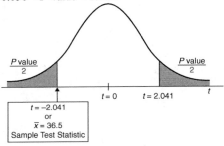

(d) Since the entire P-value interval > 0.05 for α, we fail to reject H_0. No.

(e) At the 5% level of significance, the population average heart rate for the lion is not significantly different.

15. (i) Use a calculator to verify. Rounded values are used in part ii.

(ii) (a) $\alpha = 0.05$
H_0: $\mu = 8.8$
H_1: $\mu \neq 8.8$

(b) Use the Student's t distribution with $d.f. = n - 1 = 14 - 1 = 13$. We assume x has a distribution that is approximately normal and σ is unknown.

$$t = \frac{\bar{x} - \mu}{\frac{s}{\sqrt{n}}} = \frac{7.36 - 8.8}{\frac{4.03}{\sqrt{14}}} \approx -1.337$$

(c) For $d.f. = 13$, 1.337 falls between entries 1.204 and 1.350. Use two-tailed areas to find that $0.200 < P\text{-value} < 0.250$.

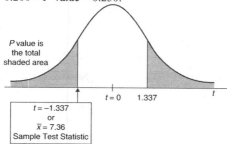

P value is the total shaded area

$t = -1.337$
or
$\bar{x} = 7.36$
Sample Test Statistic

$t = 0$ 1.337

(d) Since P-value interval > 0.05 for α, we fail to reject H_0. No.

(e) At the 5% level of significance, we cannot conclude the catch is different from 8.8 fish per day.

17. **(a)** P-value of a one-tailed test is smaller. For a two-tailed test, the P-value is double because it includes the area in both tails.

   (b) Yes; the P-value of a one-tailed test is smaller, so it might be smaller than α while the P-value of a two-tailed test is larger than α.

   (c) Yes; if the two-tailed P-value is less than α, the smaller one-tail area is also less than α.

   (d) Yes; the conclusions can be different. The conclusion based on the two-tailed test is more conservative in the sense that the sample data must be more extreme (differ more from H_0) in order to reject H_0.

19. **(a)** $H_0 : \mu = 20$
   $H_1 : \mu \neq 20$

   For $\alpha = 0.01$, $c = 1 - 0.01 = 0.99$, $\sigma = 4$, and $z_c = 2.58$.

   $$E \approx z_c \frac{\sigma}{\sqrt{n}} = 2.58 \frac{4}{\sqrt{36}} = 1.72$$

   $$\bar{x} - E < \mu < \bar{x} + E$$
   $$22 - 1.72 < \mu < 22 + 1.72$$
   $$20.28 < \mu < 23.72$$

   The hypothesized mean $\mu = 20$ is not in the interval. Therefore, we reject H_0.

   (b) Because $n = 36$ is large, the sampling distribution of $\bar{x}$ is approximately normal by the central limit theorem, and we know σ.

   $$z = \frac{\bar{x} - \mu}{\sigma / \sqrt{n}} = \frac{22 - 20}{4 / \sqrt{36}} = 3.00$$

   From Table 5, P-value $= 2P(z < -3.00) = 2(0.0013) = 0.0026$. Since $0.0026 \leq 0.01$ for α, we reject H_0. The results are the same.

21. For a right-tailed test and $\alpha = 0.01$, the critical value $z_0 = 2.33$; critical region is values to the right of 2.33. Since the sample statistic $z = 1.54$ is not in the critical region, we fail to reject H_0. At the 1% level, there is insufficient evidence to say the average storm level is increasing. Conclusion is same as with P-value method.

23. For a two-tailed test and $\alpha = 0.05$, the critical value $z_0 = \pm1.96$; critical regions are values to the left of -1.96 together with values to the right of 1.96. Since the sample test statistic $z = -1.99$ is in the critical region, we reject H_0. At the 5% level, there is sufficient evidence to say the average number of e-mails is different with the new priority system. Conclusions is same as with P-value method.

25. For a right-tailed test and $\alpha = 0.01$, critical value is $t_0 = 2.412$ with $d.f. = 45$. Critical region is values to the right of 2.412. Since the sample test statistic $t = 2.481$ is in the critical region, we reject H_0. At the 1% level sample data indicate the average age of Minnesota Region Coyotes is higher than 1.75 yr. Conclusion is same as with P-value method.

Section 9.3

1. (i) (a) $\alpha = 0.01$

$H_0: p = 0.301$
$H_1: p < 0.301$

    (b) Use the standard normal distribution. The $\hat{p}$ distribution is approximately normal when n is sufficiently large, which it is here, since $np = 215(0.301) \approx 647$ and $nq = 215(0.699) \approx 150.3$ are both > 5.

$$\hat{p} = \frac{r}{n} = \frac{46}{215} \approx 0.214$$

$$z = \frac{\hat{p} - p}{\sqrt{\frac{pq}{n}}} = \frac{0.214 - 0.301}{\sqrt{\frac{0.301(0.699)}{215}}} \approx -2.78$$

    (c) P-value $= P(z < -2.78) = 0.0027$

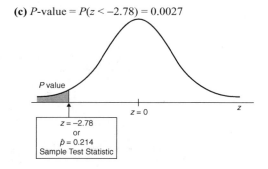

    (d) Since a P-value of $0.0027 \le 0.01$ for α, we reject H_0. Yes.

    (e) At the 1% level of significance, the sample data indicate the population proportion of numbers with a leading "1" in the revenue file is less than the 0.301 predicted by Benford's Law.

    (ii) Yes; the revenue data file seems to include more numbers with higher first non-zero digits than Benford's Law predicts.

(iii) We have not proved H_0 to be false. However, because our sample data leads us to reject H_0, and conclude that there are too few numbers with leading digit "1," more investigation is merited.

3. (a) $\alpha = 0.01$

$H_0: p = 0.70$

$H_1: p \neq 0.70$

(b) Use the standard normal distribution. The $\hat{p}$ distribution is approximately normal when n is sufficiently large, which it is here, since $np = 32(0.7) = 22.4$ and $nq = 32(0.3) = 9.6$ are both > 5.

$$\hat{p} = \frac{r}{n} = \frac{24}{32} \approx 0.75$$

$$z = \frac{\hat{p} - p}{\sqrt{\frac{pq}{n}}} = \frac{0.75 - 0.70}{\sqrt{\frac{0.70(0.30)}{32}}} \approx 0.62$$

(c) $P\text{-value} = 2P(z > 0.62) = 2(0.2676) = 0.5352$

$z = 0.62$
or
$\hat{p} = 0.75$
Sample Test Statistic

(d) Since a P-value of $0.5352 > 0.01$ for α, we fail to reject H_0. No.

(e) At the 1% level of significance, we cannot say that the population proportion of arrests of males aged 15 to 34 in Rock Springs is different from 70%.

5. (a) $\alpha = 0.01$

$H_0: p = 0.77$

$H_1: p < 0.77$

(b) Use the standard normal distribution. The $\hat{p}$ distribution is approximately normal when n is sufficiently large, which it is here, because $np = 27(0.77) = 20.79$ and $nq = 27(0.23) = 6.21$ are both > 5.

$$\hat{p} = \frac{r}{n} = \frac{15}{27} = 0.5556$$

$$z = \frac{\hat{p} - p}{\sqrt{\frac{pq}{n}}} = \frac{0.5556 - 0.77}{\sqrt{\frac{0.77(0.23)}{27}}} = -2.65$$

(c) P-value $= P(z > -2.65) = 0.0004$

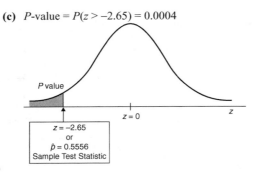

(d) Since a P-value of $0.0004 \le 0.01$ for α, we reject H_0. Yes.

(e) At the 1% level of significance, data show that the population proportion of driver fatalities related to alcohol is less than 77% in Kit Carson County.

7. (a) $\alpha = 0.01$
   $H_0: p = 0.50$
   $H_1: p < 0.50$

(b) Use the standard normal distribution. The $\hat{p}$ distribution is approximately normal when n is sufficiently large, and it is here, because $np = 34(0.50) = 17$ and $nq = 17$ are both > 5.

$$\hat{p} = \frac{r}{n} = \frac{10}{34} = 0.2941$$

$$z = \frac{\hat{p} - p}{\sqrt{\frac{pq}{n}}} = \frac{0.2941 - 0.50}{\sqrt{\frac{0.5(0.5)}{34}}} = -2.40$$

(c) P-value $= P(z < -2.40) = 0.0082$

(d) Since a P-value of $0.0082 \le 0.01$ for α, we reject H_0. Yes.

(e) At the 1% level of significance, the data indicate that the population proportion of female wolves is now less than 50% in the region.

9. (a) $\alpha = 0.01$
   $H_0: p = 0.261$
   $H_1: p \ne 0.261$

(b) Use the standard normal distribution. The $\hat{p}$ distribution is approximately normal when n is sufficiently large, which it is here, because $np = 317(0.261) = 82.737$ and $nq = 317(0.739) = 234.263$ are both > 5.

$$\hat{p} = \frac{r}{n} = \frac{61}{317} = 0.1924$$

$$z = \frac{\hat{p} - p}{\sqrt{\frac{pq}{n}}} = \frac{0.1924 - 0.261}{\sqrt{\frac{0.261(0.739)}{317}}} \approx -2.78$$

(c) P-value $= 2P(z < -2.78) = 2(0.0027) = 0.0054$

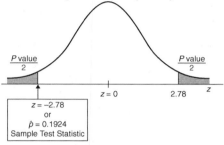

(d) Since a P-value of $0.0054 \le 0.01$ for α, we reject H_0. Yes.

(e) At the 1% level of significance, the sample data indicate that the population proportion of the five-syllable sequence is different from that of the text of Plato's *Republic*.

11. (a) $\alpha = 0.01$
$H_0: p = 0.47$
$H_1: p > 0.47$

(b) Use the standard normal distribution. The $\hat{p}$ distribution is approximately normal when n is sufficiently large, which it is here, because $np = 1006(0.47) = 472.82$ and $nq = 1006(0.53) = 533.18$ are both > 5.

$$\hat{p} = \frac{r}{n} = \frac{490}{1006} = 0.4871$$

$$z = \frac{\hat{p} - p}{\sqrt{\frac{pq}{n}}} = \frac{0.4871 - 0.47}{\sqrt{\frac{0.47(0.53)}{1006}}} = 1.09$$

(c) P-value $= P(z > 1.09) = 0.1379$

(d) Since a P-value of $0.1379 > 0.01$ for α, we fail to reject H_0. No.

(e) At the 1% level of significance, there is insufficient evidence to support the claim that the population proportion of customers loyal to Chevrolet is more than 47%.

13. (a) $\alpha = 0.05$
$H_0: p = 0.092$
$H_1: p > 0.092$

(b) Use the standard normal distribution. The $\hat{p}$ distribution is approximately normal when n is sufficiently large, which it is here, because $np = 196(0.092) = 18.032$ and $nq = 196(0.908) = 177.968$ are both > 5.

$$\hat{p} = \frac{r}{n} = \frac{29}{196} = 0.1480$$

$$z = \frac{\hat{p} - p}{\sqrt{\frac{pq}{n}}} = \frac{0.1480 - 0.092}{\sqrt{\frac{0.092(0.908)}{196}}} = 2.71$$

(c) P-value $= P(z > 2.71) = 0.0034$

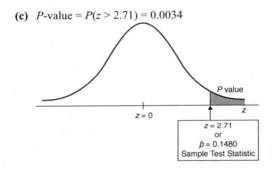

P value

$z = 0$

z

$z = 2.71$
or
$\hat{p} = 0.1480$
Sample Test Statistic

(d) Since a P-value of $0.0034 \leq 0.05$ for α, we reject H_0. Yes.

(e) At the 5% level of significance, the data indicate that the population proportion of students with hypertension during final exams week is higher than 9.2%.

15. (a) $\alpha = 0.01$
$H_0: p = 0.82$
$H_1: p \neq 0.82$

(b) Use the standard normal distribution. The $\hat{p}$ distribution is approximately normal when n is sufficiently large, which it is here, because $np = 73(0.82) = 59.86$ and $nq = 73(0.18) = 13.14$ are both > 5.

$$\hat{p} = \frac{r}{n} = \frac{56}{73} = 0.7671$$

$$z = \frac{\hat{p} - p}{\sqrt{\frac{pq}{n}}} = \frac{0.7671 - 0.82}{\sqrt{\frac{0.82(0.18)}{73}}} = -1.18$$

(c) $P\text{-value} = 2P(z \leq -1.18) = 2(0.1190) = 0.2380$

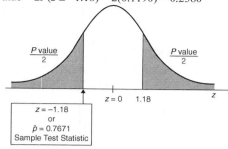

(d) Since a P-value of $0.2380 > 0.01$ for α, we fail to reject H_0. No.

(e) At the 1% level of significance, the evidence is insufficient to indicate that the population proportion of extroverts among college student government leaders is different from 82%.

17. (a) $\alpha = 0.01$
$H_0: p = 0.76$
$H_1: p \neq 0.76$

(b) Use the standard normal distribution. The $\hat{p}$ distribution is approximately normal when n is sufficiently large, which it is here, because $np = 59(0.76) = 44.84$ and $nq = 59(0.24) = 14.16$ are both > 5.

$$\hat{p} = \frac{r}{n} = \frac{47}{59} = 0.7966$$

$$z = \frac{\hat{p} - p}{\sqrt{\frac{pq}{n}}} = \frac{0.7966 - 0.76}{\sqrt{\frac{0.76(0.24)}{59}}} = 0.66$$

(c) $P\text{-value} = 2P(z > 0.66) = 2(0.2546) = 0.5092$

(d) Since a P-value of $0.5092 > 0.01$ for α, we fail to reject H_0. No.

(e) At the 1% level of significance, the evidence is insufficient to conclude that the population proportion of professors in Colorado who would choose the career again is different from the national rate of 76%.

19. For a left-tailed test and $\alpha = 0.01$, critical value is $z_0 = -2.33$. The critical region consists of values less than -2.33. The sample test statistic $z = -2.65$ is in the critical region so we reject H_0. Result is consistent with P-value conclusion.

Chapter 9 Review

1. (a) $\alpha = 0.05$
$H_0: \mu = 11.1$
$H_1: \mu \neq 11.1$
Since $\neq$ is in H_1, use a two-tailed test.

(b) Use the standard normal distribution. We assume x has a normal distribution with known standard deviation σ. Note that μ is given in the null hypothesis.

$$z = \frac{\bar{x} - \mu}{\frac{\sigma}{\sqrt{n}}} = \frac{10.8 - 11.1}{\frac{0.6}{\sqrt{36}}} = -3.00$$

(Note: 600 miles = 0.6 thousand miles)

(c) $P\text{-value} = 2P(z < -3.00) = 2(0.0013) = 0.0026$

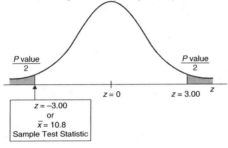

(d) Since a P-value of $0.0026 \leq 0.05$ for α, we reject H_0. Yes.

(e) At the 5% level of significance, the evidence is sufficient to say that the miles driven per vehicle in Chicago is different than the national average.

3. (a) $\alpha = 0.01$
$H_0: \mu = 0.8 \text{ A}$
$H_1: \mu > 0.8 \text{ A}$

(b) Use the Student's t distribution with $d.f. = n - 1 = 9 - 1 = 8$. We assume x has a distribution that is approximately normal and σ is unknown.

$$t = \frac{\bar{x} - \mu}{\frac{s}{\sqrt{n}}} = \frac{1.4 - 0.8}{\frac{0.41}{\sqrt{9}}} \approx 4.390$$

(c) For $d.f. = 8$, 4.390 falls between entries 3.355 and 5.041. Using one-tailed areas, $0.0005 < P\text{-value} < 0.005$.

(d) Since the entire P-value interval ≤ 0.01 for α, we reject H_0. Yes.

(e) At the 5% level of significance, the evidence is sufficient to say the Toylot claim of 0.8 A is too low.

5. (a) $\alpha = 0.01$
$H_0: p = 0.60$
$H_1: p < 0.60$

(b) Use the standard normal distribution. The $\hat{p}$ distribution is approximately normal when n is sufficiently large, which it is here, because $np = 90(0.6) = 54$ and $nq = 90(0.4) = 36$ are both > 5.

$$\hat{p} = \frac{r}{n} = \frac{40}{90} = 0.4444$$

$$z = \frac{\hat{p} - p}{\sqrt{\frac{pq}{n}}} = \frac{0.4444 - 0.60}{\sqrt{\frac{0.60(0.40)}{90}}} = -3.01$$

(c) $P\text{-value} = P(z < -3.01) = 0.0013$

(d) Since a P-value of $0.0013 \leq 0.01$ for α, we reject H_0. Yes.

(e) At the 1% level of significance, the evidence is sufficient to show the mortality rate has dropped.

7. (a) $\alpha = 0.01$
$H_0: p = 0.20$
$H_1: p > 0.20$

(b) Use the standard normal distribution. The $\hat{p}$ distribution is approximately normal when n is sufficiently large, which it is here because $np = 200(0.2) = 40$ and $nq = 200(0.8) = 160$ are both > 5.

$$\hat{p} = \frac{r}{n} = \frac{56}{200} = 0.28$$

$$z = \frac{\hat{p} - p}{\sqrt{\frac{pq}{n}}} = \frac{0.28 - 0.20}{\sqrt{\frac{0.20(0.80)}{200}}} = 2.83$$

(c) $P\text{-value} = P(z > 2.83) = 0.0023$

P value

$z = 0$

z

> $z = 3.18$
> or
> $\hat{p} = 0.29$
> Sample Test Statistic

(d) Since a P-value of $0.0023 \le 0.01$ for α, we reject H_0. Yes.

(e) At the 1% level of significance the evidence is sufficient to show the population proportion of students who read the magazine is larger than 0.20.

9. (a) $\alpha = 0.05$
H_0: $\mu = 7$ oz
H_1: $\mu \ne 7$ oz

(b) Use the Student's t distribution with $d.f. = n - 1 = 8 - 1 = 7$. We assume x has a distribution that is approximately normal and σ is unknown.

$$t = \frac{\bar{x} - \mu}{\frac{s}{\sqrt{n}}} = \frac{7.3 - 7}{\frac{0.5}{\sqrt{8}}} \approx 1.697$$

(c) For $d.f. = 7$, 1.697 falls between entries 1.617 and 1.895. Using two-tailed areas, $0.100 < P\text{-value} < 0.150$.

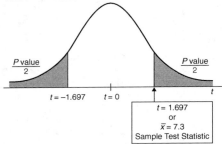

$\frac{P \text{ value}}{2}$

$\frac{P \text{ value}}{2}$

$t = -1.697$ $t = 0$

t

> $t = 1.697$
> or
> $\bar{x} = 7.3$
> Sample Test Statistic

(d) Since the entire P-value interval > 0.05 for α, we fail to reject H_0. No.

(e) At the 5% level of significance, the evidence is insufficient to show that the population mean amount of coffee per cup is different from 7 ounces.

Chapter 10 Inferences About Differences

Section 10.1

1. **(a)** $\alpha = 0.05$
   $H_0: \mu_d = 0$
   $H_1: \mu_d \neq 0$
   Since $\neq$ is in H_1, a two-tailed test is used.

   (b) Use the Student's t distribution. Assume d has a normal distribution or has a mound-shaped symmetric distribution.

Pair	1	2	3	4	5	6	7	8
$d = B - A$	3	−2	5	4	10	−15	6	7

   $\bar{d} = 2.25$, $s_d = 7.78$

   $$t = \frac{\bar{d} - \mu_d}{\frac{s_d}{\sqrt{n}}} = \frac{2.25 - 0}{\frac{7.78}{\sqrt{8}}} = 0.818$$

   (c) $d.f. = n - 1 = 8 - 1 = 7$
   From Table 6, 0.818 falls between entries 0.711 and 1.254. Using two-tailed areas, find that $0.250 < P\text{-value} < 0.500$.

   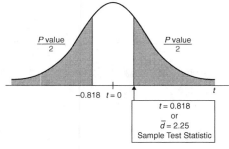

   (d) Since the P-value interval is > 0.05 for α, we fail to reject H_0. No.

   (e) At the 5% level of significance, the evidence is insufficient to claim a difference in population mean percentage increases for corporate revenue and CEO salary.

3. **(a)** $\alpha = 0.01$
   $H_0: \mu_d = 0$
   $H_1: \mu_d > 0$
   Since $>$ is in H_1, a right-tailed test is used.

(b) Use the Student's t distribution. Assume d has a normal distribution or has a mound-shaped symmetric distribution.

Pair	1	2	3	4	5
d = Jan − April	35	9	26	−24	17

$\bar{d} = 12.6$, $s_d = 22.66$

$$t = \frac{\bar{d} - \mu_d}{\frac{s_d}{\sqrt{n}}} = \frac{12.6 - 0}{\frac{22.66}{\sqrt{5}}} = 1.243$$

(c) $d.f. = n - 1 = 5 - 1 = 4$
From Table 6, 1.243 falls between entries 0.741 and 1.344. Using one-tailed areas, find that $0.125 < P$-value < 0.250.

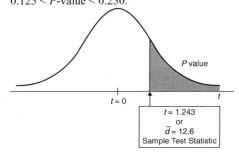

P value

$t = 0$

t

$t = 1.243$
or
$\bar{d} = 12.6$
Sample Test Statistic

(d) Since the P-value interval is > 0.01 for α, we fail to reject H_0. No.

(e) At the 1% level of significance, the evidence is insufficient to claim average peak wind gusts are higher in January.

5. (a) $\alpha = 0.05$
$H_0: \mu_d = 0$
$H_1: \mu_d > 0$
Since $>$ is in H_1, a right-tailed test is used.

(b) Use the Student's t distribution. Assume d has a normal distribution or has a mound-shaped symmetric distribution.

Pair	1	2	3	4	5	6	7	8
d = winter − summer	19	−4	17	7	9	0	−9	10

$\bar{d} = 6.125$, $s_d = 9.83$

$$t = \frac{\bar{d} - \mu_d}{\frac{s_d}{\sqrt{n}}} = \frac{6.125 - 0}{\frac{9.83}{\sqrt{8}}} = 1.76$$

(c) $d.f. = n - 1 = 8 - 1 = 7$

From Table 6, 1.76 falls between entries 1.617 and 1.895. Using one-tailed areas, find that $0.05 < P\text{-value} < 0.075$.

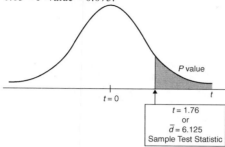

$t = 1.76$
or
$\bar{d} = 6.125$
Sample Test Statistic

(d) Since the P-value interval is > 0.05 for α, we fail to reject H_0. No.

(e) At the 5% level of significance, the evidence is insufficient to indicate the population average percentage of male wolves in winter is higher.

7. (a) $\alpha = 0.05$

$H_0: \mu_d = 0$

$H_1: \mu_d > 0$

Since $>$ is in H_1, a right-tailed test is used.

(b) Use the Student's t distribution. Assume d has a normal distribution or has a mound-shaped symmetric distribution.

Pair	1	2	3	4	5	6	7	8	9
$d = B - A$	7	−2	9	0	6	1	−3	−3	3

$\bar{d} = 2.0,\ s_d = 4.5$

$$t = \frac{\bar{d} - \mu_d}{\frac{s_d}{\sqrt{n}}} = \frac{2.0 - 0}{\frac{4.5}{\sqrt{9}}} = 1.33$$

(c) $d.f. = n - 1 = 9 - 1 = 8$

From Table 6, 1.33 falls between entries 1.240 and 1.397. Use one-tailed areas to find that $0.100 < P\text{-value} < 0.125$.

$t = 1.33$
or
$\bar{d} = 2.0$
Sample Test Statistic

(d) Since the P-value interval is > 0.05 for α, we fail to reject H_0. No.

(e) At the 5% level of significance, the evidence is insufficient to claim that the population score on the
last round is higher than that on the first.

9. (a) $\alpha = 0.05$
$H_0: \mu_d = 0$
$H_1: \mu_d \neq 0$
Since $\neq$ is in H_1, a two-tailed test is used.

(b) Use the Student's t distribution. Assume d has a normal distribution or has a mound-shaped symmetric distribution.

Pair	1	2	3	4	5
$d = 1 - 2$	6	3	−6	−3	5

$\bar{d} = 1.0$, $s_d = 5.24$

$$t = \frac{\bar{d} - \mu_d}{\frac{s_d}{\sqrt{n}}} = \frac{1.0 - 0}{\frac{5.24}{\sqrt{5}}} = 0.427$$

(c) $d.f. = n - 1 = 5 - 1 = 4$
From Table 6, 0.427 falls to the left of (is smaller than) any entry in $d.f. = 4$ row. Use two-tailed areas to find that P-value > 0.500.

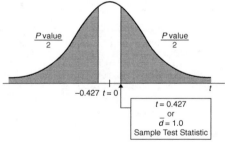

(d) Since the P-value is > 0.05 for α, we fail to reject H_0. No.

(e) At the 5% level of significance, the evidence is insufficient to indicate a difference in the population mean number of service ware sherds in subarea 1 as compared with subarea 2.

11. For a two-tailed test with $\alpha = 0.05$ and $d.f. = 7$, critical values are $\pm t_0 = \pm 2.365$. The sample test statistic
$t = 0.818$ falls between -2.365 and 2.365, so we do not reject H_0. This conclusion is the same as that reached by the P-value method.

Section 10.2

1. (a) (i) $\alpha = 0.01$
$H_0: \mu_1 = \mu_2$
$H_1: \mu_1 > \mu_2$

(ii) Use the standard normal distribution. We assume both population distributions are approximately normal and σ_1 and σ_2 are known.

$$\bar{x}_1 - \bar{x}_2 = 2.8 - 2.1 = 0.7$$

$$z = \frac{(\bar{x}_1 - \bar{x}_2) - (\mu_1 - \mu_2)}{\sqrt{\frac{\sigma_1^2}{n_1} + \frac{\sigma_2^2}{n_2}}} = \frac{0.7 - 0}{\sqrt{\frac{0.5^2}{10} + \frac{0.7^2}{10}}} \approx 2.57$$

(iii) P-value $= P(z > 2.57) = 0.0051$

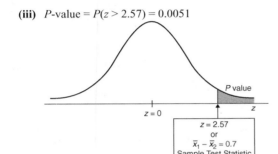

$z = 0$

P value

z

$z = 2.57$
or
$\bar{x}_1 - \bar{x}_2 = 0.7$
Sample Test Statistic

(iv) Since P-value $= 0.0051 \le 0.01$ for α, we reject H_0. Yes.

(v) At the 1% level of significance, the evidence is sufficient to indicate that the population mean REM sleep time for children is more than for adults.

(b) $c = 98\%$, $z_c = 2.33$

$$E = z_c \sqrt{\frac{\sigma_1^2}{n_1} + \frac{\sigma_2^2}{n_2}} = 2.33 \sqrt{\frac{0.5^2}{10} + \frac{0.7^2}{10}} \approx 0.63$$

$$[(\bar{x}_1 - \bar{x}_2) - E] < (\mu_1 - \mu_2) < [(\bar{x}_1 - \bar{x}_2) + E]$$
$$(0.7 - 0.63) < (\mu_1 - \mu_2) < (0.7 + 0.63)$$
$$0.07 < (\mu_1 - \mu_2) < 1.33$$

The confidence interval contains all positive numbers. This indicates that at the 98% confidence level, $\mu_1 > \mu_2$. The evidence is sufficient to indicate that the population mean REM sleep time for children is more than for adults

3. (a) (i) $\alpha = 0.05$
$H_0: \mu_1 = \mu_2$
$H_1: \mu_1 \ne \mu_2$

(ii) Use the standard normal distribution. We assume both population distributions are approximately normal and σ_1 and σ_2 are known.

$$\bar{x}_1 - \bar{x}_2 = 4.9 - 4.3 = 0.6$$

$$z = \frac{(\bar{x}_1 - \bar{x}_2) - (\mu_1 - \mu_2)}{\sqrt{\frac{\sigma_1^2}{n_1} + \frac{\sigma_2^2}{n_2}}} = \frac{0.6 - 0}{\sqrt{\frac{1.5^2}{46} + \frac{1.2^2}{51}}} \approx 2.16$$

(iii) P-value $= 2P(z > 2.16) = 2(0.0154) = 0.0308$

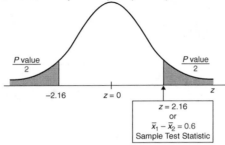

(iv) Since P-value $= 0.0308 \le 0.05$ for α, we reject H_0. Yes.

(v) At the 5% level of significance, the evidence is sufficient to show there is a difference between mean response regarding preference for camping or preference for fishing.

(b) $c = 90\%$, $z_c = 1.645$

$$E = z_c \sqrt{\frac{\sigma_1^2}{n_1} + \frac{\sigma_2^2}{n_2}} = 1.645 \sqrt{\frac{1.5^2}{46} + \frac{1.2^2}{51}} \approx 0.28$$

$$[(\bar{x}_1 - \bar{x}_2) - E] < (\mu_1 - \mu_2) < [(\bar{x}_1 - \bar{x}_2) + E]$$
$$(0.6 - 0.28) < (\mu_1 - \mu_2) < (0.6 + 0.28)$$
$$0.32 < (\mu_1 - \mu_2) < 0.88$$

The confidence interval contains all positive numbers. This indicates that at the 90% confidence level, $\mu_1 > \mu_2$. The evidence is sufficient to indicate that the mean response regarding preference for fishing is greater than that for camping.

5. (a)   **(i)** $\alpha = 0.01$
$$H_0: \mu_1 = \mu_2$$
$$H_1: \mu_1 < \mu_2$$

(ii) Use the Student's t distribution. We assume both population distributions are approximately normal and σ_1 and σ_2 are unknown.

$$\bar{x}_1 - \bar{x}_2 = 3.51 - 3.87 = -0.36$$

$$t = \frac{(\bar{x}_1 - \bar{x}_2) - (\mu_1 - \mu_2)}{\sqrt{\frac{s_1^2}{n_1} + \frac{s_2^2}{n_2}}} = \frac{-0.36 - 0}{\sqrt{\frac{0.81^2}{10} + \frac{0.94^2}{12}}} \approx -0.965$$

(iii) Since $n_1 < n_2$, $d.f. = n_1 - 1 = 10 - 1 = 9$

In Table 6, 0.965 falls between entries 0.703 and 1.230. Use one-tailed areas to find that $0.125 < P\text{-value} < 0.250.$

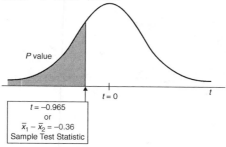

P value

$t = 0$

$t = -0.965$
or
$\bar{x}_1 - \bar{x}_2 = -0.36$
Sample Test Statistic

(iv) Since the P-value interval > 0.01 for α, we fail to reject H_0. No.

(v) At the 1% level of significance, the evidence is insufficient to indicate that violent crime in the Rocky Mountain region is higher than in New England.

(b) $c = 98\%$, $d.f. = 9$, $t_c = 2.821$ (From Table 4)

$$E = t_c\sqrt{\frac{s_1^2}{n_1} + \frac{s_2^2}{n_2}} = 2.821\sqrt{\frac{0.81^2}{10} + \frac{0.94^2}{12}} \approx 1.05$$

$$[(\bar{x}_1 - \bar{x}_2) - E] < (\mu_1 - \mu_2) < [(\bar{x}_1 - \bar{x}_2) + E]$$
$$(-0.36 - 1.05) < (\mu_1 - \mu_2) < (-0.36 + 1.05)$$
$$-1.41 < (\mu_1 - \mu_2) < 0.69$$

Since the confidence interval contains both negative and positive numbers, we cannot conclude there is any difference in the violent crime in the Rocky Mountain region and in New England, at the 98% confidence level.

7. (a) (i) $\alpha = 0.05$
$H_0: \mu_1 = \mu_2$
$H_1: \mu_1 \neq \mu_2$

(ii) Use the Student's t distribution. Both sample sizes are large, $n_i \geq 30$, and σ_1 and σ_2 are unknown.
$$\bar{x}_1 - \bar{x}_2 = 344.5 - 354.2 = -9.7$$
$$t = \frac{(\bar{x}_1 - \bar{x}_2) - (\mu_1 - \mu_2)}{\sqrt{\frac{s_1^2}{n_1} + \frac{s_2^2}{n_2}}} = \frac{-9.7 - 0}{\sqrt{\frac{49.1^2}{30} + \frac{50.9^2}{30}}} \approx -0.751$$

(iii) Since $n_1 = n_2$, $d.f. = n - 1 = 30 - 1 = 29$.

From Table 6, 0.751 falls between entries 0.683 and 1.174. Use two-tailed areas to find $0.250 < P\text{-value} < 0.500$.

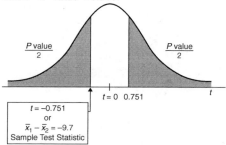

(iv) Since the *P*-value interval > 0.05 for α, we fail to reject H_0. No.

(v) At the 5% level of significance, the evidence is insufficient to indicate there is a difference between the control and experimental group in the mean score on the vocabulary portion of the test.

(b) $c = 95\%$, $d.f. = 29$, $t_c = 2.045$ (From Table 4)

$$E = t_c \sqrt{\frac{s_1^2}{n_1} + \frac{s_2^2}{n_2}} = 2.045 \sqrt{\frac{49.1^2}{30} + \frac{50.9^2}{30}} \approx 26.41$$

$$[(\bar{x}_1 - \bar{x}_2) - E] < (\mu_1 - \mu_2) < [(\bar{x}_1 - \bar{x}_2) + E]$$
$$(-9.7 - 26.41) < (\mu_1 - \mu_2) < (-9.7 + 26.41)$$
$$-36.11 < (\mu_1 - \mu_2) < 16.71$$

Since the confidence interval contains both negative and positive numbers, we cannot conclude there is a difference between the control and experimental group in the mean score on the vocabulary portion of the test, at the 95% confidence level.

9. (a)   **(i)** $\alpha = 0.05$

$H_0: \mu_1 = \mu_2$
$H_1: \mu_1 \neq \mu_2$

(ii) Use the Student's *t* distribution. We assume the population distributions for both are approximately normal and mound shaped, and σ_1 and σ_2 are unknown.

$$\bar{x}_1 - \bar{x}_2 = 4.75 - 3.93 = 0.82$$

$$t = \frac{(\bar{x}_1 - \bar{x}_2) - (\mu_1 - \mu_2)}{\sqrt{\frac{s_1^2}{n_1} + \frac{s_2^2}{n_2}}} = \frac{0.82 - 0}{\sqrt{\frac{2.82^2}{16} + \frac{2.43^2}{15}}} \approx 0.869$$

(iii) Since $n_2 < n_1$, $d.f. = n_2 - 1 = 15 - 1 = 14$.

From Table 6, 0.869 falls between entries 0.692 and 1.200. Use two-tailed areas to find $0.250 < P\text{-value} < 0.500$.

(iv) Since the P-value interval is > 0.05 for α, we fail to reject H_0. No.

(v) At the 5% level of significance, the evidence is insufficient to indicate that there is a difference in the mean number of cases of fox rabies between the two regions.

(b) $c = 95\%$, $d.f. = 14$, $t_c = 2.145$ (From Table 4)

$$E = t_c\sqrt{\frac{s_1^2}{n_1} + \frac{s_2^2}{n_2}} = 2.145\sqrt{\frac{2.82^2}{16} + \frac{2.43^2}{15}} \approx 2.02$$

$$[(\bar{x}_1 - \bar{x}_2) - E] < (\mu_1 - \mu_2) < [(\bar{x}_1 - \bar{x}_2) + E]$$
$$(0.82 - 2.02) < (\mu_1 - \mu_2) < (0.82 + 2.02)$$
$$-1.20 < (\mu_1 - \mu_2) < 2.84$$

Since the confidence interval contains both negative and positive numbers, we cannot conclude there is a difference in the mean number of cases of fox rabies between the two regions, at the 95% confidence level.

11. (a) **(i)** $\alpha = 0.05$

H_0: $\mu_1 = \mu_2$

H_1: $\mu_1 \neq \mu_2$

(ii) Use the Student's t distribution. We assume the population distributions for both are approximately normal and mound shaped, and σ_1 and σ_2 are unknown.

$$\bar{x}_1 - \bar{x}_2 = 4.86 - 6.5 = -1.64$$

$$t = \frac{(\bar{x}_1 - \bar{x}_2) - (\mu_1 - \mu_2)}{\sqrt{\frac{s_1^2}{n_1} + \frac{s_2^2}{n_2}}} = \frac{-1.64 - 0}{\sqrt{\frac{3.18^2}{7} + \frac{2.88^2}{8}}} \approx -1.041$$

(iii) Since $n_1 < n_2$, $d.f. = n_1 - 1 = 7 - 1 = 6$.

From Table 6, 1.041 falls between entries 0.718 and 1.273. Use two-tailed areas to find $0.250 < P\text{-value} < 0.500$.

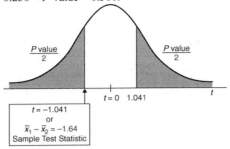

$t = -1.041$
or
$\bar{x}_1 - \bar{x}_2 = -1.64$
Sample Test Statistic

(iv) Since the P-value interval is > 0.05 for α, we fail to reject H_0. No.

(v) At the 5% level of significance, the evidence is insufficient to indicate that the mean time lost due to hot tempers is different from that lost due to technical worker's attitudes.

(b) $c = 95\%$, $d.f. = 6$, $t_c = 2.447$ (From Table 4)

$$E = t_c\sqrt{\frac{s_1^2}{n_1} + \frac{s_2^2}{n_2}} = 2.447\sqrt{\frac{3.18^2}{7} + \frac{2.88^2}{8}} \approx 3.85$$

$$[(\bar{x}_1 - \bar{x}_2) - E] < (\mu_1 - \mu_2) < [(\bar{x}_1 - \bar{x}_2) + E]$$
$$(-1.64 - 3.85) < (\mu_1 - \mu_2) < (-1.64 + 3.85)$$
$$-5.49 < (\mu_1 - \mu_2) < 2.21$$

Since the confidence interval contains both negative and positive numbers, we cannot conclude there is a difference in the mean time lost due to hot tempers and that lost due to technical worker's attitudes, at the 95% confidence level.

13. (a) $d.f. \approx \dfrac{\left(\dfrac{s_1^2}{n_1} + \dfrac{s_2^2}{n_2}\right)^2}{\dfrac{1}{n_1-1}\left(\dfrac{s_1^2}{n_1}\right)^2 + \dfrac{1}{n_2-1}\left(\dfrac{s_2^2}{n_2}\right)^2} = \dfrac{\left(\dfrac{0.81^2}{10} + \dfrac{0.94^2}{12}\right)^2}{\dfrac{1}{9}\left(\dfrac{0.81^2}{10}\right)^2 + \dfrac{1}{11}\left(\dfrac{0.94^2}{12}\right)^2} \approx 19.96$

(Note: Some software will truncate this to 19.)

(b) In Problem 5, $d.f. = n_1 - 1 = 10 - 1 = 9$.

The convention of using the smaller of $n_1 - 1$ and $n_2 - 1$ leads to a $d.f.$ that is always less than or equal to that computed by Satterthwaite's formula.

15. $\alpha = 0.01$
$H_0: \mu_1 = \mu_2$
$H_1: \mu_1 < \mu_2$

From Problem 5, we know that the sample test statistic is $t = -0.965$ and $d.f. = 9$.

In Table 4, find $\alpha = 0.01$ in the one-tail area row, since this is a left-tailed test. The critical value is $t_0 = -2.821$.

Compare the sample test statistic $t = -0.965$ to the critical value. Since $-0.965 > -2.821$, the sample test statistic falls in the 'do not reject H_0" region. We fail to reject H_0.

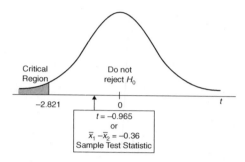

At the 1% level of significance, the evidence is insufficient to indicate that violent crime in the Rocky Mountain region is higher than in New England.

The results are consistent with the result obtained by the P-value method of Problem 5(a).

Section 10.3

1. **(a)** $\alpha = 0.05$
   $H_0: p_1 = p_2$
   $H_1: p_1 \neq p_2$
Since $\neq$ is in H_1, a two-tailed test is used.

(b) Assume two independent binomial experiments and $p_1 = p_2$.

	Sample 1	Sample 2
N	220	175
r	59	56
$\hat{p}$	$59/220 = 0.2682$	$56/175 = 0.3200$

$\hat{p}_1 - \hat{p}_2 = 0.2682 - 0.3200 = -0.0518$

$\bar{p} = \dfrac{r_1 + r_2}{n_1 + n_2} = \dfrac{59 + 56}{220 + 175} = 0.2911$ and $\bar{q} = 1 - \bar{p} = 0.7089$

$n_1\bar{p} = 64$, $n_1\bar{q} = 156$, $n_2\bar{p} = 51$, $n_2\bar{q} = 124$
   All four of these estimates are > 5. Use the standard normal distribution.

$$z = \frac{\hat{p}_1 - \hat{p}_2}{\sqrt{\dfrac{\overline{pq}}{n_1} + \dfrac{\overline{pq}}{n_2}}} = \frac{-0.0518}{\sqrt{\dfrac{(0.2911)(0.7089)}{220} + \dfrac{(0.2911)(0.7089)}{175}}} \approx -1.13$$

(c) From Table 3, P-value $= 2P(z > 1.13) = 2(0.1292) = 0.2584$.

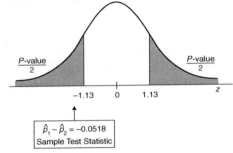

(d) Since the P-value > 0.05 for α, we fail to reject H_0. No.

(e) At the 5% level of significance, the data do not support the claim that there is a difference between the population proportion of women and the population proportion of men who favor spending more federal tax dollars on the arts.

3. **(a)** $\alpha = 0.05$
$H_0: p_1 = p_2$
$H_1: p_1 < p_2$
Since $<$ is in H_1, a one-tailed test is used.

(b) Assume two independent binomial experiments and $p_1 = p_2$.

	Sample 1	Sample 2
N	250	280
r	45	71
$\hat{p}$	$45/250 = 0.1800$	$71/280 = 0.2536$

$\hat{p}_1 - \hat{p}_2 = 0.1800 - 0.2536 = -0.0736$

$$\overline{p} = \frac{r_1 + r_2}{n_1 + n_2} = \frac{45 + 71}{250 + 280} = 0.2189 \text{ and } \overline{q} = 1 - \overline{p} = 0.7811$$

$n_1 \overline{p} = 55, \; n_1 \overline{q} = 195, \; n_2 \overline{p} = 61, \; n_2 \overline{q} = 219$
All four of these estimates are > 5. Use the standard normal distribution.

$$z = \frac{\hat{p}_1 - \hat{p}_2}{\sqrt{\dfrac{\overline{pq}}{n_1} + \dfrac{\overline{pq}}{n_2}}} = \frac{-0.0736}{\sqrt{\dfrac{(0.2189)(0.7811)}{250} + \dfrac{(0.2189)(0.7811)}{280}}} \approx -2.05$$

(c) From Table 3, P-value $= P(z < -2.05) = 0.0202$.

P-value

-2.05 0 z

$\hat{p}_1 - \hat{p}_2 = -0.0736$
Sample Test Statistic

(d) Since the P-value < 0.05 for α, we reject H_0. Yes.

(e) At the 5% level of significance, the data indicate that the population proportion of trusting people in Chicago is higher for the older group.

5. **(a)** $\alpha = 0.01$
$$H_0: p_1 = p_2$$
$$H_1: p_1 < p_2$$
Since $<$ is in H_1, a one-tailed test is used.

(b) Assume two independent binomial experiments and $p_1 = p_2$.

	Sample 1	Sample 2
N	100	100
r	37	47
$\hat{p}$	$37/100 = 0.37$	$47/100 = 0.47$

$$\hat{p}_1 - \hat{p}_2 = 0.37 - 0.47 = -0.10$$

$$\bar{p} = \frac{r_1 + r_2}{n_1 + n_2} = \frac{37 + 47}{100 + 100} = 0.42 \text{ and } \bar{q} = 1 - \bar{p} = 0.58$$

$n_1 \bar{p} = 42$, $n_1 \bar{q} = 58$, $n_2 \bar{p} = 42$, $n_2 \bar{q} = 58$
All four of these estimates are > 5. Use the standard normal distribution.

$$z = \frac{\hat{p}_1 - \hat{p}_2}{\sqrt{\dfrac{\bar{p}\bar{q}}{n_1} + \dfrac{\bar{p}\bar{q}}{n_2}}} = \frac{-0.10}{\sqrt{\dfrac{(0.42)(0.58)}{100} + \dfrac{(0.42)(0.58)}{100}}} \approx -1.43$$

(c) From Table 3, P-value $= P(z < -1.43) = 0.0764$.

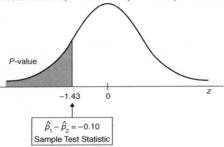

P-value

−1.43   0

z

$\hat{p}_1 - \hat{p}_2 = -0.10$

Sample Test Statistic

(d) Since the P-value > 0.01 for α, we fail to reject H_0. No.

(e) At the 1% level of significance, the data do not support the claim that the proportion of people who attended college and who believe in extraterrestrials is higher than the proportion who did not attend college.

7. **(a)** $\alpha = 0.01$
$H_0: p_1 = p_2$
$H_1: p_1 < p_2$
Since $<$ is in H_1, a one-tailed test is used.

(b) Assume two independent binomial experiments and $p_1 = p_2$.

	Sample 1	Sample 2
N	378	516
r	194	320
$\hat{p}$	194/378 = 0.5132	320/516 = 0.6202

$\hat{p}_1 - \hat{p}_2 = 0.5132 - 0.6202 = -0.1070$

$$\overline{p} = \frac{r_1 + r_2}{n_1 + n_2} = \frac{194 + 320}{378 + 516} = 0.5749 \text{ and } \overline{q} = 1 - \overline{p} = 0.4251$$

$n_1\overline{p} = 217$, $n_1\overline{q} = 161$, $n_2\overline{p} = 297$, $n_2\overline{q} = 219$
All four of these estimates are > 5. Use the standard normal distribution.

$$z = \frac{\hat{p}_1 - \hat{p}_2}{\sqrt{\dfrac{\overline{pq}}{n_1} + \dfrac{\overline{pq}}{n_2}}} = \frac{-0.1070}{\sqrt{\dfrac{(0.5749)(0.4251)}{378} + \dfrac{(0.5749)(0.4251)}{516}}} \approx -3.20$$

(c) From Table 3, P-value $= P(z < -3.20) = 0.0007$.

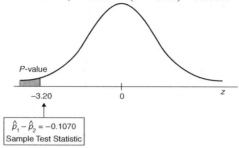

P-value

−3.20

0

z

$\hat{P}_1 - \hat{P}_2 = -0.1070$
Sample Test Statistic

(d) Since the P-value < 0.01 for α, we reject H_0. Yes.

(e) At the 1% level of significance, the data indicate that the population proportion of hotel guests requesting nonsmoking rooms has increased.

9. $\alpha = 0.05$
   $H_0: p_1 = p_2$
   $H_1: p_1 \neq p_2$

From Problem 1, we know that the sample test statistic is $z = -1.13$.

In Table 3(c), see that the critical values are $\pm z_0 = \pm 1.96$ for a two-tailed test with $\alpha = 0.05$.

Compare the sample test statistic $z = -1.13$ to the critical values. Since -1.13 falls between entries -1.96 and 1.96, we fail to reject H_0. The sample test statistic falls in the "do not reject H_0" region.

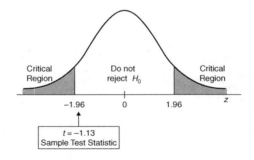

Critical
Region

Do not
reject H_0

Critical
Region

−1.96

0

1.96

z

$t = -1.13$
Sample Test Statistic

At the 5% level of significance, the data do not support the claim that there is a difference between the population proportion of women and the population proportion of men who favor spending more federal tax dollars on the arts.

The results are consistent with the result obtained by the P-value method of Problem 1.

11.

	Sample 1	Sample 2
N	375	571
r	289	23
$\hat{p}$	$289/375 = 0.7707$	$23/571 = 0.0403$

$n_1\hat{p}_1 = 289,\ n_1\hat{q}_1 = 86,\ n_2\hat{p}_2 = 23,\ n_2\hat{q}_2 = 548$
All four of these estimates are > 5.

(a) $c = 99\%, z_c = 2.58$

$$E \approx z_c\sqrt{\frac{\hat{p}_1\hat{q}_1}{n_1} + \frac{\hat{p}_2\hat{q}_2}{n_2}} = 2.58\sqrt{\frac{(0.7707)(0.2293)}{375} + \frac{(0.0403)(0.9597)}{571}} = 2.58(0.0232) = 0.0599 \approx 0.06$$

$[(\hat{p}_1 - \hat{p}_2) - E] < (p_1 - p_2) < [(\hat{p}_1 - \hat{p}_2) + E]$
$[(0.7707 - 0.0403) - 0.0599] < (p_1 - p_2) < [(0.7707 - 0.0403) + 0.0599]$
$0.6705 < (p_1 - p_2) < 0.7903$, or approximately 0.67 and 0.79

(b) Because the confidence interval contains only positive values, $p_1 > p_2$ at the 99% level.

13. $n_1 = 210, r_1 = 65, \hat{p}_1 = 65/210 = 0.3095, \hat{q}_1 = \dfrac{145}{210} = 0.6905$

$n_2 = 152, r_2 = 18, \hat{p}_2 = 18/152 = 0.1184, \hat{q}_2 = \dfrac{134}{152} = 0.8816.$

$n_1\hat{p}_1 = 65, n_1\hat{q}_1 = 145, n_2\hat{p}_2 = 18,$ and $n_2\hat{q}_2 = 134$ are all > 5.

(a) $c = 99\%, z_c = 2.58$

$$E \approx z_c\sqrt{\frac{\hat{p}_1\hat{q}_1}{n_1} + \frac{\hat{p}_2\hat{q}_2}{n_2}} = 2.58\sqrt{\frac{0.3095(0.6905)}{210} + \frac{(0.1184)(0.8816)}{152}} = 2.58(0.0413) = 0.1065$$

$[(\hat{p}_1 - \hat{p}_2) - E] < (p_1 - p_2) < [(\hat{p}_1 - \hat{p}_2) + E]$
$[(0.3095 - 0.1184) - 0.1065] < (p_1 - p_2) < [(0.3095 - 0.1184) + 0.1065]$
$0.0846 < (p_1 - p_2) < 0.2976$, or approximately 0.085 to 0.298.

(b) The interval consists only of positive values, indicating $p_1 > p_2$. At the 99% confidence level, the difference in the percentage of traditional Navajo hogans is between 0.085 and 0.298, i.e., there are between 8.5% and 29.8% more hogans in the Fort Defiance Region than in the Indian Wells Region. If it is true that traditional Navajo tend to live in hogans, then, percentage-wise, there are more traditional Navajo at Fort Defiance than at Indian Hills.

15. (a) $[(\bar{x}_1 - \bar{x}_2) - E] < \mu_1 - \mu_2 < [(\bar{x}_1 - \bar{x}_2) + E]$

where $E \approx z_c \sqrt{\dfrac{s_1^2}{n_1} + \dfrac{s_2^2}{n_2}}$

$z_{0.90} = 1.645, z_{0.95} = 1.96, z_{0.99} = 2.58$

As we change from one c confidence interval to another, the only number that changes is z_c. The interval width is $2E$, and it depends on z_c; if c increases, z_c increases, and the interval gets wider; if c decreases, z_c decreases, and the interval gets narrower. The larger interval (larger z_c) always includes all the points that were in a smaller interval created from a smaller z_c. All intervals are centered at $(\bar{x}_1 - \bar{x}_2)$. Therefore, if a 95% confidence interval includes both positive and negative numbers, the 99% confidence interval must include both positive and negative numbers. However, in going from 95% to 90%, the width of the interval decreases evenly from both sides. If $(\bar{x}_1 - \bar{x}_2)$ is near 0, the 90% confidence interval could have both positive and negative values, just like the 95% confidence interval did, and all values in the 90% confidence interval would also have been in the 95% confidence interval. The farther $(\bar{x}_1 - \bar{x}_2)$ is from zero, however, the more likely it is that the narrower 90% confidence interval will contain only positive or only negative numbers.

(b) $[(\hat{p}_1 - \hat{p}_2) - E] < (p_1 - p_2) < [(\hat{p}_1 - \hat{p}_2) + E]$

where $E \approx z_c \sqrt{\dfrac{\hat{p}_1\hat{q}_1}{n_1} + \dfrac{\hat{p}_2\hat{q}_2}{n_2}}$

As in (a), the only number that changes (and, therefore, affects the width) is z_c, and all the intervals are centered at $(\hat{p}_1 - \hat{p}_2)$. If a 95% confidence interval contains only positive values, a 99% confidence interval could contain all positive numbers, or both positive and negative numbers, depending on how close $(\hat{p}_1 - \hat{p}_2)$ is to zero. However, with a narrower 90% confidence interval, if the 95% confidence interval had only positive values, the 90% interval will; every value in the 90% interval would also have been in the 95% confidence interval.

Note: the principle is the same whether it is a confidence interval for $\mu, \mu_1 - \mu_2, p, p_1 - p_2$, etc. One can make statements paralleling those of (b) for the 95% confidence interval having only negative values.

Chapter 10 Review

1.   **(a)** Using a calculator, the means and standard deviations round to the values given.

    (b) $c = 95\%$, $d.f.$ is smaller of $n_1 - 1$ and $n_2 - 1$, $d.f. \approx n_1 - 1 = 72 - 1 = 71$

      (round down to 70 for Table 6), $t_c = 1.994$

$$E = t_c \sqrt{\frac{s_1^2}{n_1} + \frac{s_2^2}{n_2}} = 1.994 \sqrt{\frac{2.08^2}{72} + \frac{3.03^2}{80}} \approx 0.83$$

$$[(\bar{x}_1 - \bar{x}_2) - E] < (\mu_1 - \mu_2) < [(\bar{x}_1 - \bar{x}_2) + E]$$
$$[(11.42 - 10.65) - 0.83] < (\mu_1 - \mu_2) < [(11.42 - 10.65) + 0.83]$$
$$-0.06 < (\mu_1 - \mu_2) < 1.6$$

    (c) Because the interval contains both positive and negative values, we cannot conclude there is any difference in soil water content in the two fields at the 95% confidence level.

    (d) Student's t distribution because σ_1 and σ_2 are not known. Both samples are large, so no assumptions about the original distribution are needed.

    (e) **(i)** $\alpha = 0.01$

$$H_0: \mu_1 = \mu_2$$
$$H_1: \mu_1 > \mu_2$$

        (ii) Use the Student's t distribution. Both sample sizes are large, $n_i \geq 30$, and σ_1 and σ_2 are unknown.

$$\bar{x}_1 - \bar{x}_2 = 11.42 - 10.65 = 0.77$$

$$t = \frac{(\bar{x}_1 - \bar{x}_2) - (\mu_1 - \mu_2)}{\sqrt{\frac{s_1^2}{n_1} + \frac{s_2^2}{n_2}}} = \frac{0.77 - 0}{\sqrt{\frac{2.08^2}{72} + \frac{3.03^2}{80}}} \approx 1.84$$

        (iii) Since $n_1 < n_2$, $d.f. = n_1 - 1 = 72 - 1 = 71$

            In Table 4, 1.84 falls between entries 1.667 and 1.994 (approximated by $d.f. = 70$). Use one-tailed areas to find that $0.025 < P\text{-value} < 0.050$.

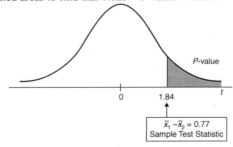

        (iv) Since the P-value interval > 0.01 for α, we fail to reject H_0.

        (v) At the 1% level of significance, the evidence is insufficient to indicate that the population mean soil water content of the first field is higher than that of the second.

3. $n_1 = 18$, $\bar{x}_1 = 98$, $s_1 = 6.5$, $n_2 = 24$, $\bar{x}_2 = 90$, $s_2 = 7.3$

(a) $c = 75\%$, $d.f. \approx 18 - 1 = 17$ (smaller of $n_1 - 1$ and $n_2 - 1$),
$t_c = 1.191$

$$E = t_c \sqrt{\frac{s_1^2}{n_1} + \frac{s_2^2}{n_2}} = 1.191 \sqrt{\frac{6.5^2}{18} + \frac{7.3^2}{24}} \approx 2.5$$

$[(\bar{x}_1 - \bar{x}_2) - E] < (\mu_1 - \mu_2) < [(\bar{x}_1 - \bar{x}_2) + E]$
$[(98 - 90) - 2.5] < (\mu_1 - \mu_2) < [(98 - 90) + 2.5]$
5.5 pounds $< (\mu_1 - \mu_2) < 10.5$ pounds

(b) Since the interval contains only positive values, we can say that $\mu_1 > \mu_2$ at the 75% level, i.e., Canadian wolves weigh more than Alaska wolves, and that the difference is approximately 5.5 to 10.5 pounds.

(c) **(i)** $\alpha = 0.01$
         $H_0: \mu_1 = \mu_2$
         $H_1: \mu_1 \neq \mu_2$

     (ii)   Use the Student's t distribution. We assume the population distributions for both are approximately normal and mound shaped, and σ_1 and σ_2 are unknown.

$$\bar{x}_1 - \bar{x}_2 = 98 - 90 = 8$$

$$t = \frac{(\bar{x}_1 - \bar{x}_2) - (\mu_1 - \mu_2)}{\sqrt{\frac{s_1^2}{n_1} + \frac{s_2^2}{n_2}}} = \frac{8 - 0}{\sqrt{\frac{6.5^2}{18} + \frac{7.3^2}{24}}} \approx 3.74$$

     (iii)   Since $n_1 < n_2$, $d.f. = n_1 - 1 = 18 - 1 = 17$.
         From Table 4, 3.74 falls between entries 2.898 and 3.965. Use two-tailed areas to find $0.001 < P\text{-value} < 0.010$.

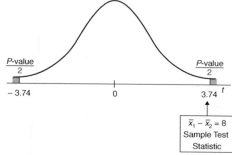

P-value/2   P-value/2

-3.74   0   3.74 t

$\bar{x}_1 - \bar{x}_2 = 8$
Sample Test Statistic

     (iv)   Since the P-value interval is < 0.01 for α, we reject H_0.

     (v)   At the 1% level of significance, there is evidence that the average weight of adult male wolves from the Northwest Territories is different from that of Alaska wolves.

5. $n_1 = 93$, $r_1 = 79$, $\hat{p}_1 = \dfrac{79}{93} = 0.8495$, $\hat{q}_1 = 0.1505$, $n_1 - r_1 = 14$

$n_2 = 83$, $r_2 = 74$, $\hat{p}_2 = \dfrac{74}{83} = 0.8916$, $\hat{q}_2 = 0.1084$, $n_2 - r_2 = 9$

$n_i \hat{p}_i$ and $n_i \hat{q}_i$ are all > 5

(a) $c = 95\%$, $z_c = 1.96$

$$E \approx z_c \sqrt{\dfrac{\hat{p}_1 \hat{q}_1}{n_1} + \dfrac{\hat{p}_2 \hat{q}_2}{n_2}} = 1.96 \sqrt{\dfrac{(0.8495)(0.1505)}{93} + \dfrac{(0.8916)(0.1084)}{83}} = 0.0988$$

$[(\hat{p}_1 - \hat{p}_2) - E] < (p_1 - p_2) < [(\hat{p}_1 - \hat{p}_2) + E]$
$[(0.8495 - 0.8916) - 0.0988] < (p_1 - p_2) < [(0.8495 - 0.8916) + 0.0988]$
$-0.1409 < (p_1 - p_2) < 0.0567$

(b) Since the interval contains positive and negative values, we can say that at the 95% level, there is no significant difference between the proportion of accurate responses to face-to-face interviews and that of accurate responses to telephone interviews.

(c) (i) $\alpha = 0.05$
$H_0: p_1 = p_2$
$H_1: p_1 \neq p_2$

(ii)   Since $\neq$ is in H_1, a two-tailed test is used.

$\hat{p}_1 - \hat{p}_2 = 0.8495 - 0.8916 = -0.0421$

$$\bar{p} = \dfrac{r_1 + r_2}{n_1 + n_2} = \dfrac{79 + 74}{93 + 83} = 0.8693 \text{ and } \bar{q} = 1 - \bar{p} = 0.1307$$

$n_1 \bar{p} = 81$, $n_1 \bar{q} = 12$, $n_2 \bar{p} = 72$, $n_2 \bar{q} = 11$

(iii)   All four of these estimates are > 5. Use the standard normal distribution.

$$z = \dfrac{\hat{p}_1 - \hat{p}_2}{\sqrt{\dfrac{\bar{p}\bar{q}}{n_1} + \dfrac{\bar{p}\bar{q}}{n_2}}} = \dfrac{-0.0421}{\sqrt{\dfrac{(0.8693)(0.1307)}{93} + \dfrac{(0.8693)(0.1307)}{83}}} = -0.83$$

From Table 3, P-value $= 2P(z > 0.83) = 2(0.2033) = 0.4066$.

(iv)   Since the P-value > 0.05 for α, we fail to reject H_0.

(v) At the 5% level of significance, the data do not support the claim that there is a difference in the proportion of accurate responses from face-to-face interviews compared with telephone interviews.

7. (i) $\alpha = 0.05$
$H_0: \mu_d = 0$
$H_1: \mu_d > 0$

(ii) Use the Student's t distribution. Assume d has a normal distribution or has a mound-shaped symmetric distribution.

Pair	1	2	3	4	5
d = After − Before	6.4	7.2	8.6	3.8	−1.3

$\bar{d} = 4.94$, $s_d = 3.90$

$$t = \frac{\bar{d} - \mu_d}{\frac{s_d}{\sqrt{n}}} = \frac{4.94 - 0}{\frac{3.90}{\sqrt{5}}} = 2.832$$

(iii) $d.f. = n - 1 = 5 - 1 = 4$
From Table 4, 2.832 falls between entries 2.776 and 3.747. Use one-tailed areas to find that $0.010 < P\text{-value} < 0.025$.

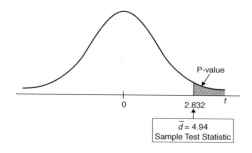

(iv) Since the P-value interval is ≤ 0.05 for α, we reject H_0. Yes.

(v) At the 5% level of significance, there is sufficient evidence to claim that the average net sales improved.

Chapter 11 Additional Topics Using Inference

Section 11.1

1. **(a)** $\alpha = 0.05$
   H_0: Myers-Briggs preference and profession are independent.

   H_1: Myers-Briggs preference and profession are not independent.

   (b) $\chi^2 = \sum \dfrac{(O-E)^2}{E}$

   $= \dfrac{(62-49.02)^2}{49.02} + \dfrac{(45-57.98)^2}{57.98} + \dfrac{(68-74.22)^2}{74.22} + \dfrac{(94-87.78)^2}{87.78} + \dfrac{(56-62.76)^2}{62.76} + \dfrac{(81-74.24)^2}{74.24}$

   $= 8.649$

   All expected frequencies are greater than 5. Use the chi-square distribution.
   Since there are 3 rows and 2 columns, $d.f. = (3-1)(2-1) = 2$.

   (c) In Table 5, with $d.f. = 2$, $\chi^2 = 8.649$ falls between entries 7.38 and 9.21. Therefore, $0.010 < P\text{-value} < 0.025$.

   (d) Since the P-value is less than the level of significance $\alpha = 0.05$, we reject the null hypothesis.

   (e) At the 5% level of significance, there is sufficient evidence to conclude that Myers-Briggs preference and the profession are not independent.

3. **(a)** $\alpha = 0.01$
   H_0: Site type and pottery type are independent.

   H_1: Site type and pottery type are not independent.

   (b) $\chi^2 = \sum \dfrac{(O-E)^2}{E}$

   $= \dfrac{(75-74.64)^2}{74.64} + \dfrac{(61-59.89)^2}{59.89} + \dfrac{(53-54.47)^2}{54.47} + \dfrac{(81-84.11)^2}{84.11} + \dfrac{(70-67.5)^2}{67.5}$

   $+ \dfrac{(62-61.39)^2}{61.39} + \dfrac{(92-89.25)^2}{89.25} + \dfrac{(68-71.61)^2}{71.61} + \dfrac{(66-65.14)^2}{65.14}$

   $= 0.5552$

   All expected frequencies are greater than 5. Use the chi-square distribution.
   Since there are 3 rows and 3 columns, $d.f. = (3-1)(3-1) = 4$.

   (c) In Table 5, with $d.f. = 4$, $\chi^2 = 0.5552$ falls between entries 0.484 and 0.711.
   Therefore, $0.950 < P\text{-value} < 0.975$.

   (d) Since the P-value is greater than the level of significance $\alpha = 0.01$, we do not reject the null hypothesis.

   (e) At the 1% level of significance, there is insufficient evidence to conclude that site and pottery type are not independent.

5. (a) $\alpha = 0.05$

H_0: Age distribution and location are independent.

H_1: Age distribution and location are not independent.

(b) $\chi^2 = \sum \dfrac{(O-E)^2}{E}$

$$= \dfrac{(13-14.08)^2}{14.08} + \dfrac{(13-12.84)^2}{12.84} + \dfrac{(15-14.08)^2}{14.08} + \dfrac{(10-11.33)^2}{11.33} + \dfrac{(11-10.34)^2}{10.34}$$

$$+ \dfrac{(12-11.33)^2}{11.33} + \dfrac{(34-31.59)^2}{31.59} + \dfrac{(28-28.82)^2}{28.82} + \dfrac{(30-31.59)^2}{31.59}$$

$$= 0.67$$

All expected frequencies are greater than 5. Use the chi-square distribution.
Since there are 3 rows and 3 columns, $d.f. = (3-1)(3-1) = 4$.

(c) In Table 5, with $d.f. = 4$, $\chi^2 = 0.67$ falls between entries 0.484 and 0.711.
Therefore, $0.950 < P\text{-value} < 0.975$.

(d) Since the P-value is greater than the level of significance $\alpha = 0.05$, we do not reject the null hypothesis.

(e) At the 5% level of significance, there is insufficient evidence to conclude that age distribution and location are not independent.

7. (a) $\alpha = 0.05$

H_0: Ages of young adult and movie preference are independent.

H_1: Ages of young adult and movie preference are not independent.

(b) $\chi^2 = \sum \dfrac{(O-E)^2}{E}$

$$= \dfrac{(8-10.60)^2}{10.60} + \dfrac{(15-12.06)^2}{12.06} + \dfrac{(11-11.33)^2}{11.33} + \dfrac{(12-9.35)^2}{9.35} + \dfrac{(10-10.65)^2}{10.65}$$

$$+ \dfrac{(8-10.00)^2}{10.00} + \dfrac{(9-9.04)^2}{9.04} + \dfrac{(8-10.29)^2}{10.29} + \dfrac{(12-9.67)^2}{9.67}$$

$$= 3.623$$

All expected frequencies are greater than 5. Use the chi-square distribution.
Since there are 3 rows and 3 columns, $d.f. = (3-1)(3-1) = 4$.

(c) In Table 5, with $d.f. = 4$, $\chi^2 = 3.623$ falls between entries 1.064 and 7.78.
Therefore, $0.100 < P\text{-value} < 0.900$.

(d) Since the P-value is greater than the level of significance $\alpha = 0.05$, we do not reject the null hypothesis.

(e) At the 5% level of significance, there is insufficient evidence to conclude that age of young adult and movie preference are not independent.

9. **(a)** $\alpha = 0.05$

H_0: Stone tool construction material and site are independent.

H_1: Stone tool construction material and site are not independent.

(b) $\chi^2 = \sum \dfrac{(O - E)^2}{E}$

$$= \frac{(731 - 689.36)^2}{689.36} + \frac{(584 - 625.64)^2}{625.64} + \frac{(102 - 102.22)^2}{102.22} + \frac{(93 - 92.78)^2}{92.78}$$

$$+ \frac{(510 - 542.58)^2}{542.58} + \frac{(525 - 492.42)^2}{492.42} + \frac{(85 - 93.84)^2}{93.84} + \frac{(94 - 85.16)^2}{85.16}$$

$$= 11.15$$

All expected frequencies are greater than 5. Use the chi-square distribution. Since there are 4 rows and 2 columns, $d.f. = (4 - 1)(2 - 1) = 3$.

(c) In Table 5, with $d.f. = 3$, $\chi^2 = 11.15$ falls between entries 9.35 and 11.34. Therefore, $0.010 < P\text{-value} < 0.025$.

(d) Since the P-value is less than the level of significance $\alpha = 0.05$, we reject the null hypothesis.

(e) At the 5% level of significance, there is sufficient evidence to conclude that stone tool construction material and site are not independent.

Section 11.2

1. **(a)** $\alpha = 0.05$

H_0: The distributions are the same.

H_1: The distributions are different.

(b) $\chi^2 = \sum \dfrac{(O - E)^2}{E}$

$$= \frac{(47 - 32.76)^2}{32.76} + \frac{(75 - 61.88)^2}{61.88} + \frac{(288 - 305.31)^2}{305.31} + \frac{(45 - 55.06)^2}{55.06}$$

$$= 11.79$$

All expected frequencies are greater than 5. Use the chi-square distribution. $d.f. = k - 1 = 4 - 1 = 3$.

(c) In Table 5, with $d.f. = 3$, $\chi^2 = 11.79$ falls between entries 11.34 and 12.84. Therefore, $0.005 < P\text{-value} < 0.010$.

(d) Since the P-value is less than the level of significance $\alpha = 0.05$, we reject the null hypothesis.

(e) At the 5% level of significance, the evidence is sufficient to conclude that the Red Lake Village population does not fit the general Canadian population.